The Cream of *Irish* Industry, Commerce & Government

A Directory of 5000 of the Largest Businesses, Organisations and Government bodies in the Republic of Ireland

Published by

IDS Publishing
3 Sandyford Office Park
Blackthorn Avenue
Dublin 18
☎ +353 1-2604818 (1800 927 100)
Fax +353 1-2604816

Email: CreamofIrishIndustry@IDSMediaGroup.com
Web: http://www.IDSMediaGroup.com

This publication and the data in it, is also available in electronic format at www.IDSMediaGroup.com

ISBN 186180-030-4

The Cream of
Irish
Industry, Commerce & Government

...is the most comprehensive and current collection of business information on Ireland's largest companies, organisations and government bodies. It is the essential marketing tool and reference guide to Business in the Republic of Ireland.

The directory provides full contact details and information on the Cream of Ireland's manufacturing, service and government sectors. As well as 5000 business records, over 14,000 senior managers /directors, 1000s of emails and web addresses, the Directory also provides a market profile of the Irish Market and a 23 page alphabetical company index.

The directory gives you direct access to current and complete commercial information on prospective suppliers and customers for every type of product and service.

Entry into the directory was based on selecting the top 1% of employers in Ireland (based on number of staff employed). This information was "Creamed" from the Irish Business Masterfiles, the most comprehensive marketing databases for Ireland. These databases contain over 400,000 business records on every business and organisation on the Island of Ireland. These databases hold every size and type of business, organisation and commercial entity though out the Island, from Manufacturers, Retailers, Distributors, Services, and Professionals to Importers/Exporters.

The Directory, as well as the information from the Irish Business Masterfile, is available electronically on CD, and can be accessed on-line at our web site.

Contents

The Directory is divided into 3 Sections;

Section 1
Profiles of the Irish business market by
- Business Size (based on employees)
- Town & County
- Business Sector

Section 2
Listing of Individual Company Details

Section 3
Alphabetical index of Companies

Business Sector Index

How to use the Directory

Business Sector Index

The Business Sector Index provides reference to the start of each particular business classification.

Business Classifications

The business classifications are displayed on the top of each page, providing quick & easy access to a particular section.

Company Index

The company index provides an alphabetical listing of all companies and their location within the directory.

1992 SIC Classification System

All records in the directory are classified using the 1992 Standard Industrial Classification (SIC) coding system. The system is *Hierarchical*, thus allowing you quick access to each business section and sub-section.

Example, the wholesale & distribution section begins with the two digit classification code 51. This general section is further broken down into more specific sub sections which have a 5 digit code eg 51300 relates to Food & Drink Distribution while 51320 relates to the Fruit & Vegetable Distribution sector etc.

The first 4 digits of the 1992 system correlate to the EU NACE classification system.

Sample Business Record Layout

ABC Products Ltd	← Company Name
Company House, 22 High Street	← Business Address
Cork, Co. Cork	← Postal Town & Postcode
Phone: 021-223456 Fax: 021-223456	← Phone & Fax Number
SIC: 24303 Employees: 27	← SIC Classification & Number of Employees
Email: info@abc.co.uk	← Email Address
Web: http://www.abc.co.uk	← Web Address
Chemical Sealant Manufacturer	← Company Business Activity
Mr Sam Johnson Managing Director	← Primary Manager/Director
Mr Peter McPeters Finance Director	← Primary Finance Manager/Director
Ms Sue McFall Personnel Manager	← Primary Personnel & Training Manager/Director
Mr Bill Brady Sales & Marketing Manager	← Primary Sales & Marketing Manager/Director
Mr Gerry McEvoy Production Manager	← Primary Production/Operations Manager/Director
Ms Julie Connelly IT Manager	← Primary IT/Telecoms Manager/Director

Section 1

Profile of the Republic of Ireland Business Market by

- **Business Size (based on employees)**
- **Town & County**
- **Business Sector**

Republic of Ireland - Business Size Profile

SIC2	DESC	TOTAL	Employee Numbers <5	5 - 9	10 - 24	25 - 49	50 - 99	100-249	250+
0	Unclassified	2254	2028	143	10	2	1	1	3
1	Agriculture, hunting & services	5590	5110	267	131	43	23	12	4
2	Forestry, logging & service	237	218	3	11	2	3	0	0
5	Fishing, fish hatcheries & Farms	165	129	20	7	4	3	2	0
10	Mining of coal, lignite & peat	37	31	3	0	0	2	1	0
11	Petroleum and natural gas extraction	11	4	3	2	0	0	2	0
14	Other mining and quarrying	435	317	50	40	17	7	3	1
15	Manufacture of food products & beverages	2122	1312	237	209	121	102	90	50
16	Manufacture of tobacco products	20	10	1	0	3	2	3	1
17	Manufacture of textiles	1308	1020	114	80	35	30	20	8
18	Manufacture of wearing apparel & fur	1178	971	82	45	40	23	14	3
19	Leather manufacture	223	183	24	6	3	4	3	0
20	Wood products manufacture	1168	927	99	87	31	17	4	3
21	Pulp, paper & paper products Manufacture	451	246	70	50	42	24	17	2
22	Publishing, printing & production media	1975	1291	269	224	102	50	29	10
23	Petroleum processing & products	12	7	1	2	0	1	1	0
24	Chemicals Manufacture	1179	869	137	69	39	29	19	17
25	Rubber and plastics Manufacture	558	334	57	69	52	20	21	5
26	Non-metallic products Manufacture	2313	1849	191	147	66	34	16	10
27	Metals Manufacturing	992	782	66	87	38	9	8	2
28	Fabricated metal products Manufacture	1723	1296	157	146	67	29	25	3
29	Machinery & equipment Manufacture	3862	2748	460	362	160	63	45	24
30	Office machinery & computers Manufacture	324	188	56	35	9	20	8	8
31	Electrical machinery Manufacture	1514	1063	165	134	54	39	37	22
32	Radio, TV & communication equip Manuf	435	314	69	30	5	7	6	3
33	Medical, precision & optical Manufacture	574	354	62	60	36	18	23	20
34	Motor vehicles, trailers Manufacture	844	675	91	48	13	12	2	3
35	Transport Equipment Manufacture	258	174	36	22	10	4	6	6
36	Furniture & Other Manufacturing	2561	2040	247	164	61	23	16	10
37	Recycling	135	105	9	13	5	3	0	0
40	Electricity & gas supply	145	92	14	12	6	7	7	7
41	Water distribution	72	57	8	5	1	0	1	0
45	Construction	13847	8019	5156	373	153	78	39	28
50	Cars/Cycles sale, maint & repair	7103	5762	644	541	116	31	9	0
51	Wholesale & commission trade	6385	5142	480	396	171	97	79	20
52	Retail & Repair	25934	23479	983	1004	187	141	97	43
55	Hospitality	21183	13495	6080	925	382	204	77	18
60	Land transport	3695	1758	1723	131	42	23	10	7
61	Water transport	120	65	35	5	5	6	1	3
62	Air transport	182	89	62	11	4	3	2	10
63	Transport supporting services	1997	959	753	174	57	32	13	8
64	Post & telecommunications	4239	1939	2058	117	52	39	15	18
65	Financial intermediation	3308	1271	701	1119	109	33	32	43
66	Insurance and pension funding	1658	688	754	126	34	27	10	19
67	Financial Services	156	33	80	15	8	10	6	4
70	Real estate activities	1820	953	771	75	10	4	5	1
71	Hiring of Equipment	3890	2230	1451	133	49	14	9	4
72	Computer & related activities	2754	1485	472	449	160	94	52	38
73	Research and development	181	151	10	12	1	1	5	1
74	Business activities	15361	9515	4535	867	229	107	64	40
75	Public administration & service	7588	6156	743	350	127	65	73	74
80	Education	7297	5922	251	374	398	299	31	21
85	Health and social work	11325	10288	299	487	101	56	53	40
90	Sewage, refuse & sanitation	403	368	9	14	6	1	4	1
91	Membership organisations	12638	12290	154	147	22	11	8	5
92	Recreational, cultural & sporting	6243	5748	233	158	63	26	12	3
93	Service activities Other	7356	7018	239	73	14	3	5	4
99	Extra-territorial organisations	66	17	13	31	3	2	0	0
	TOTALS	**201404**	**151584**	**31900**	**10414**	**3570**	**2016**	**1153**	**678**

Republic of Ireland - Business Size Profile

Counties Breakdown

COUNTY	TOTALS	NAMED	PHONES	FAXES	EMAILS	URLS
Co. Carlow	2531	1048	2076	446	113	39
Co. Cavan	2520	1459	2129	492	80	28
Co. Clare	5073	2049	4335	868	238	150
Co. Cork	24090	9595	20235	4470	1224	538
Co. Donegal	6580	2894	5648	1204	188	97
Co. Dublin (Exc City)	9036	4298	8023	2555	900	397
Co. Galway	11106	4423	9337	2058	509	270
Co. Kerry	8530	3843	7050	1408	254	127
Co. Kildare	7562	3307	6609	1582	335	112
Co. Kilkenny	3494	1490	2878	527	112	48
Co. Laois	2754	1247	2194	385	80	32
Co. Leitrim	1144	575	910	165	30	14
Co. Limerick	9001	3695	7489	1601	382	210
Co. Longford	2004	1132	1637	350	54	22
Co. Louth	6141	2951	4984	1405	304	118
Co. Mayo	6515	2575	5262	949	234	97
Co. Meath	6663	3415	5675	1321	246	100
Co. Monaghan	3324	2006	2870	637	106	35
Co. Offaly	3106	1456	2444	454	84	32
Co. Roscommon	2427	1229	2050	376	58	31
Co. Sligo	3229	1437	2595	566	109	52
Co. Tipperary	8215	3677	6854	1040	175	82
Co. Waterford	5799	2479	4886	1046	242	117
Co. Westmeath	4231	2146	3628	749	145	60
Co. Wexford	6285	2831	5678	1098	164	92
Co. Wicklow	5056	2625	4578	1253	355	125
TOTALS	**156416**	**69882**	**132054**	**29005**	**6721**	**3025**

Dublin City Breakdown

TOWN	TOTALS	NAMED	PHONES	FAXES	EMAILS	URLS
Dublin 1	3940	1838	3248	1501	551	313
Dublin 2	7979	4548	6964	3993	1879	1069
Dublin 3	1701	824	1555	526	168	75
Dublin 4	2922	1749	2636	1287	578	320
Dublin 5	1250	606	1140	261	67	32
Dublin 6	2330	1170	2055	732	274	134
Dublin 6w	833	366	785	247	99	39
Dublin 7	2103	888	1922	595	166	69
Dublin 8	2422	1135	2274	835	303	137
Dublin 9	1849	865	1684	532	183	90
Dublin 10	622	291	587	218	69	21
Dublin 11	1704	845	1610	542	149	61
Dublin 12	3074	1667	2948	1347	444	161
Dublin 13	1362	686	1238	372	127	50
Dublin 14	1953	972	1708	585	249	105
Dublin 15	1921	836	1742	448	129	50
Dublin 16	1214	557	1101	252	74	24
Dublin 17	435	263	415	224	79	42
Dublin 18	1746	854	1606	550	246	121
Dublin 20	373	197	342	118	44	7
Dublin 22	1572	627	1363	458	144	56
Dublin 24	3079	1332	2684	884	290	127
Totals	**46618**	**23138**	**41813**	**16553**	**6327**	**3112**

Business Sector Profile

SIC	Business Description	Totals	Named	Phone	Fax	Email	URL
1	**Agriculture, Hunting & Services**	**5729**	**2586**	**5255**	**831**	**89**	**32**
1000	Agriculture	1043	397	1028	108	15	10
1120	Garden Centres/Nurseries	1514	411	1479	185	27	5
1121	Mushroom Growers	659	526	558	44	8	0
1221	Studs	1248	754	944	277	15	2
1410	Agricultural Services	687	283	678	109	18	11
1411	Agri Co-Ops	94	59	91	54	5	2
1421	Livestock Marts	333	117	329	49	1	2
1422	Boarding Kennels/Cattery	139	37	137	4	0	0
1423	Horse Farriers	6	2	6	1	0	0
1500	Hunting, Trapping & Game Activities	1	1	1	0	0	0
2000	Forestry	201	50	199	40	12	4
2021	Forest Parks	41	6	35	2	0	0
5000	Fishing	174	110	165	73	11	2
10	**Mining of Coal, Lignite & Peat**	**38**	**18**	**28**	**8**	**1**	**1**
10000	Coalmines (Deep)	1	1	1	1	1	1
10103	Solid Fuels (Manufacture)	37	17	27	7	0	0
11	**Petroleum & Natural Gas Extract**	**11**	**7**	**11**	**7**	**2**	**1**
11100	Crude Oil & Gas (Extraction)	10	6	10	6	1	1
11200	Mineral Oil/Gas Refining	1	1	1	1	1	0
14	**Other Mining & Quarrying**	**436**	**257**	**403**	**137**	**12**	**3**
14100	Quarries	402	238	373	122	5	0
14400	Salt Production	6	2	5	1	0	0
14500	Mineral's Extraction (Other)	27	17	24	14	7	3
15	**Manufacture of Food & Beverages**	**2140**	**1250**	**1976**	**941**	**183**	**75**
15000	Food & Drink	127	76	119	58	10	6
15110	Slaughterhouses/Meat Plants	51	29	43	35	8	3
15112	Animal By-Product Processing	83	37	78	29	3	2
15130	Meat Pork Lamb Processing	244	157	221	113	13	3
15132	Poultry Slaughter/Processing	153	82	143	50	10	0
15200	Fish Processing	151	93	139	69	10	1
15330	Processing Fruit/Vegetables	27	26	24	22	3	1
15400	Processing Organic Oils/Fats	5	3	4	3	0	0
15410	Chemical Treatment (Fats/Oils)	1	1	1	1	0	0
15430	Margarine/Fat Cooking Compound	3	2	3	1	0	0
15510	Milk Preparation & Products	333	244	300	142	23	20
15520	Ice Cream	81	45	72	33	5	0
15600	Grain Milling	99	61	86	41	5	3
15700	Compound Animal Feeds	229	112	221	90	17	6
15720	Pet Foods	46	26	44	19	3	2
15800	Miscellaneous Foods	186	73	180	70	24	9
15820	Biscuits & Crispbreads	3	2	3	2	1	0
15830	Sugar/Sugar By Products	17	8	16	6	1	0
15840	Chocolate/Sugar Confectionery	56	37	52	29	10	5
15860	Processing of Tea & Coffee	3	3	3	3	2	0
15890	Flavouring Materials	1	1	1	1	0	0
15910	Spirit Compounding/Distilling	10	8	10	8	2	1
15940	Wines Cider & Perry	114	42	108	43	14	4
15950	Brewing & Malting	60	31	52	24	9	5
15980	Soft Drinks	57	50	53	48	9	4
16000	Tobacco Industry	21	13	19	12	5	4
17	**Manufacture of Textiles**	**1308**	**687**	**1200**	**460**	**79**	**27**
17150	Polypropylene Yarns/Fabrics	20	12	19	12	2	0
17170	Spinning/Weaving Flax/Hemp	16	7	16	3	0	1
17210	Weaving Cotton/Silk/Man-Made	25	18	21	14	4	1
17220	Wollen/Worsted Industry	67	39	55	25	2	1
17300	Textile Finishing	21	17	16	11	2	0
17400	Adhesive Cloth/Film/Oil	30	12	30	13	7	2
17402	Soft Furnishings	242	77	238	48	5	1
17403	Household Textiles	51	46	45	22	2	0
17404	Blinds (Window)	283	127	263	101	5	0
17500	Textiles	155	97	135	68	15	5
17510	Carpets/Rugs/Matting (Other)	104	59	100	32	5	3
17520	Rope/Twine/Net	9	2	9	2	0	0
17540	Textiles (Other Made Up)	60	43	55	34	8	1
17541	Lace	9	6	8	1	2	2
17542	Narrow Fabrics	15	15	14	11	5	1
17600	Knitted Goods/Fabrics	171	88	151	49	12	7
17710	Hosiery Goods/Fabrics	30	22	25	15	3	2
18	**Manufacture of Wearing Apparel**	**1181**	**488**	**1113**	**269**	**71**	**18**
18200	Clothing & Furnishings	177	75	166	53	15	3
18210	Work Clothing	164	75	161	69	24	8
18220	Weatherproof Outerwear	23	10	23	11	4	3
18221	Mens/Boys Clothes	51	47	47	23	2	2
18222	Womens/Girls Outerwear	35	31	29	21	7	1
18232	Women's Underwear	53	9	53	8	2	1
18240	Dress Industry (Other)	387	84	386	36	9	0
18241	Hats Caps Gloves Millinery	62	14	62	8	2	0
18242	Infants Wear	23	13	16	8	1	0
18243	Tailoring/Alterations	203	127	168	29	5	0
18300	Fur Goods	4	4	4	4	0	0
19	**Leather Manufacture**	**225**	**113**	**194**	**63**	**14**	**3**
19000	Leather Goods	131	58	111	31	5	2
19300	Footwear	93	55	82	32	9	1
20	**Wood Products Manufacture**	**1171**	**555**	**1074**	**352**	**48**	**9**
20100	Wood (Sawmilling/Planing)	147	100	134	61	6	1
20301	Window Frame etc Manufacture	446	119	433	102	16	2
20400	Wooden Containers	16	14	15	8	2	0
20500	Wood Products	248	123	229	86	11	4
20511	Wood Products (Semi-Finished)	92	81	68	27	4	2
20512	Wooden Articles (Other)	140	49	133	42	8	0
20513	Wooden/Upholstered Furniture	74	61	54	24	1	0
20520	Wickerwork, Cork, Straw Manuf	10	9	10	1	0	0
21	**Pulp, & Paper Manufacture**	**441**	**275**	**412**	**251**	**71**	**26**
21110	Paper/Pulp Packaging Products	94	75	90	76	27	9
21120	Pulp/Paper/Board	17	12	16	12	2	0
21210	Board Packaging Products	24	18	20	18	4	2
21220	Paper Hygiene Products	33	13	30	10	1	0
21230	Stationery – Manufacture	81	64	72	56	18	8
21240	Wallpaper & Coverings	125	50	120	34	4	3
21250	Paper/Board Products(other)	79	55	76	55	16	5
22	**Publishing, Printing & Media**	**1969**	**1177**	**1819**	**1115**	**554**	**238**
22110	Books Publishing	123	110	110	93	55	36
22120	Newspapers Publishing	203	112	189	136	102	52
22130	Periodicals Publishing	353	260	279	243	147	72
22150	Publishing (Other)	223	61	220	54	30	16
22220	Printers	986	617	940	574	212	57
22300	Recorded Media Reproduction	77	14	77	12	8	5
22311	Pre-Recorded Tapes	6	3	5	2	1	0
23200	Petroleum Products (Treatment)	11	7	11	4	2	2
24	**Chemical Manufacture**	**1224**	**538**	**1187**	**480**	**118**	**52**
24000	Chemical Products	131	66	127	65	23	11
24100	Industrial Chemicals (Miscellaneous)	11	9	9	8	4	1
24110	Industrial Gases	2	1	2	2	0	0
24120	Dyestuffs & Pigments	4	4	2	2	0	0
24140	Basic Organic Chemicals	1	1	1	1	0	0
24150	Fertilisers	40	28	35	20	3	2
24170	Synthetic Rubber	3	3	3	3	1	0
24200	Pesticides (Formulated)	19	15	17	10	0	0
24301	Varnishes	125	62	125	58	11	3
24302	Printing Ink	12	6	12	6	1	0
24303	Sealants (Formulated)	16	6	14	7	1	0
24400	Pharmaceutical Products	642	223	628	190	49	25
24500	Synthetic Detergents	2	2	2	2	0	0
24510	Disinfectants/Cleaning Agents	15	15	15	14	3	1
24520	Perfumes & Cosmetics	86	29	83	27	6	3
24600	Chemical Products (Other)	62	26	61	24	10	4
24610	Explosives	5	0	5	0	0	0
24620	Adhesives (Formulated)	7	5	7	7	2	1
24650	Photographic Materials	8	4	6	5	1	0
24700	Man-Made Fibres (Production)	3	3	3	3	0	0
25	**Rubber & Plastics Manufacture**	**554**	**330**	**523**	**294**	**98**	**29**
25100	Rubber & Plastic Products	52	20	51	16	6	1
25110	Rubber Tyres/Inner Tubes	20	5	20	4	1	0
25120	Retreading/Repairing Tyres	3	3	3	2	0	0
25130	Rubber Products (Other)	26	18	25	17	5	2
25220	Plastic Coated Textile Fabric	71	53	64	53	14	4
25231	Plastics Floor-Covering	5	4	3	3	0	0
25239	Plastic Building Products	83	37	82	26	5	1
25240	Plastics Products (Other)	295	191	276	175	69	22
26	**Non-Metallic Products Manuf**	**2330**	**1322**	**2152**	**764**	**127**	**45**
26110	Flat Glass	2	2	2	2	1	1
26120	Conservatory Manufacture/Sales	136	45	136	46	7	2
26150	Glass Products (Other)	355	164	342	123	27	15
26200	Ceramic Goods	661	361	598	181	34	12
26400	Bricks, Tiles (Structural Products)	9	9	9	5	3	2
26601	Plaster (Building Products)	54	39	49	18	2	2
26602	Fireplaces	295	176	265	97	14	3
26610	Concrete Products for Construction	94	27	94	27	11	1
26630	Concrete (Ready Mixed)	80	49	74	35	3	1
26660	Cement (Building Products)	252	200	221	112	10	4
26700	Gravestones/Monuments/Sculptors	373	238	343	104	9	0
26810	Abrasive Products	17	10	17	11	3	1
26820	Asbestos Goods	7	5	7	5	3	1
27	**Metals Manufacture**	**986**	**345**	**936**	**265**	**66**	**14**
27100	Ferrous Metal Foundries	31	27	26	15	5	1
27400	Non-Ferrous Metal	4	4	3	3	1	1
27420	Aluminium	210	135	181	100	16	6
27440	Copper	27	4	27	7	1	0
27450	Metals (Non Ferrous)	7	6	5	4	3	2
27451	Brass	47	25	41	13	0	0
27452	Alloys (Non Ferrous)	2	1	2	1	1	0
27500	Forging & Casting of Steel/Iron	140	29	136	15	3	0
27520	Steel Industry	514	114	511	108	36	4
28	**Manufacture of Metal Products**	**1733**	**728**	**1631**	**537**	**137**	**36**
28000	Finished Metal Products	43	30	41	23	6	2
28100	Engineered Products	254	217	232	180	63	20

28110	Fabricated Steelwork	175	152	151	105	16	5
28400	Process Plant Fabrications	6	4	6	3	2	0
28510	Metals Heat & Surface Treated	37	21	32	16	5	0
28520	General Mechanical Engineering	183	13	183	5	1	0
28600	Cutlery/Tableware/Razors	10	8	10	8	3	0
28601	Domestic Utensils (Metal)	37	15	36	11	1	0
28620	Hand Tools/Implements	39	14	38	17	6	1
28701	Metal Doors/Windows/etc	581	75	560	49	4	0
28702	Metal Furniture	22	21	17	7	1	0
28709	Metal Products (Other)	232	108	216	78	17	7
28710	Metal Storage Vessels	35	24	32	14	3	0
28720	Metal (Packaging Products)	8	8	7	7	5	2
28730	Wire Products Manufacture	4	2	4	1	1	1
28740	Bolts, Rivets, Springs, Chains,	63	18	62	15	4	0
29	**Machinery & Equip Manufacture**	**3833**	**2069**	**3589**	**1638**	**479**	**137**
29000	Filtration & Purification Equipment	45	18	43	17	6	1
29100	Commercial Machinery (Other)	79	42	75	35	16	3
29101	Mech/Marine/Precision Engineering	813	473	727	363	138	32
29120	Pumps	119	76	116	53	11	6
29130	Industrial Valves	34	20	28	17	10	6
29140	Ball/Needle/Roller Bearings	34	15	34	13	1	0
29200	General Machinery Manufacture	108	43	107	38	14	3
29220	Lifting/Handling Equipment	183	70	181	71	27	10
29230	Heat/Vent/Refridge/Air Cond Equip	638	296	618	272	88	30
29300	Agricultural/Construction Machinery	672	424	619	319	38	14
29310	Agricultural Tractors Manufacture	63	14	63	10	0	0
29401	Metal-Working Machine Tools	20	14	19	14	4	0
29402	Engineers Small Tools	112	82	98	49	19	5
29409	Fire Prevention Equipment Manuf	203	101	196	89	29	5
29501	Chemical/Waste Treatment Plant	62	38	55	30	14	3
29502	Gas/Water Treatment Plant	60	15	59	18	3	2
29503	Furnaces & Kilns	6	6	6	4	0	0
29504	Transmission Equipment	6	6	5	6	2	0
29520	Mining Machinery	42	25	35	15	5	2
29532	Food Pack/Processing Machines	21	16	18	16	9	2
29533	Tobacco Packaging/Processing Mach	6	6	6	6	2	1
29540	Textile Machinery	6	5	5	4	3	1
29550	Printing etc Machinery Manufacture	72	44	70	39	22	4
29560	Portable Power Tools	110	76	98	42	6	0
29600	Ordnance/Small Arms/Ammunition	40	18	39	10	1	0
29710	Electrical Appliances (Home)	276	123	266	87	11	6
30	**Office Equip & Computers Manuf**	**322**	**206**	**310**	**202**	**109**	**49**
30010	Office Equipment Manufacture	276	163	266	159	73	23
30020	Computer Manufacture	47	44	45	44	37	27
31	**Electrical Machinery Manufacture**	**1529**	**708**	**1476**	**633**	**266**	**127**
31000	Electrical Products	137	77	134	72	38	24
31100	Electronic Sub-Assemblies	87	44	82	40	19	13
31101	Compact Discs (CD) Equipment Mfr	9	9	8	7	4	2
31300	Insulated Wires/Cables	61	44	52	38	11	5
31400	Batteries & Accumulators	57	21	57	19	5	1
31500	Electric Lamps/Lighting Equipment	68	41	64	33	13	6
31600	Basic Electricity Equipment	20	8	19	9	3	2
31601	Electronic Equipment (Other)	271	143	265	141	81	42
31620	Electrical Installation Equipment	9	6	9	3	1	0
31621	Alarms/Signalling Equipment	431	118	426	98	27	6
31622	Electrical Equipment (Industrial)	84	47	78	47	16	8
31629	Electrical Equipment (Other)	296	150	281	126	49	18
32	**Radio, TV Communication Equip**	**438**	**209**	**417**	**214**	**94**	**30**
32100	Control Systems	158	60	155	58	22	8
32201	Telephone Equipment	223	122	207	131	66	21
32202	Radio & Electronic Capital Goods	26	16	24	10	3	1
32300	Non Active Components	30	10	30	15	3	0
33	**Medical Precision Optical Manuf**	**578**	**336**	**547**	**306**	**118**	**57**
33000	Precision Instruments	36	33	34	31	14	6
33100	Medical/Surgical Equipment	148	116	127	89	40	26
33200	Measuring/Checking Apparatus	130	67	125	68	22	9
33201	Medical Diagnostic Equipment	163	66	162	66	31	12
33401	Spectacles/Un-Mounted Lenses	14	12	13	11	0	0
33402	Optical Precision Instruments	40	29	39	23	4	1
33403	Photographic & Cinematographic Equ	20	5	20	7	3	0
33500	Watches & Clocks Manufacture	23	4	23	7	2	2
34	**Motor Vehicles Manufacture**	**849**	**539**	**784**	**306**	**44**	**10**
34100	Motor Vehicles/Engines	25	20	22	14	2	0
34101	Internal Combustion Engines	23	15	21	9	4	1
34200	Motor Vehicle Bodies	265	217	234	79	5	1
34202	Trailers/Semi-Trailers	106	74	95	44	9	2
34203	Caravans Manufacture & Sales	84	30	82	14	3	0
34300	Motor Vehicle Parts	242	131	230	102	12	5
34301	Hydraulic Equipment	103	50	99	43	9	1
35	**Transport Equipment Manufacture**	**260**	**170**	**225**	**122**	**30**	**8**
35100	Shipbuilding/Repairing	144	76	128	63	19	6
35200	Railway/Tramway Vehicles	2	1	1	1	1	1
35300	Aerospace Repairs/Manufacture	23	23	22	20	6	1
35400	Motorcycles & Parts	7	6	7	4	0	0
35420	Pedal Cycles & Parts	40	34	30	12	3	0
35500	Vehicles (Other)	44	31	37	22	1	0

36	**Furniture Manufacture**	**2564**	**1415**	**2340**	**865**	**160**	**55**
36130	Kitchen Manufacture	636	311	589	196	11	2
36140	Furniture Manufacture	1120	587	1020	361	46	13
36200	Jewellery etc Manufacture	133	114	114	52	17	6
36300	Musical Instruments	158	98	146	56	13	6
36400	Sports Goods	220	98	211	71	24	8
36500	Toys & Games Manufacture	65	54	48	23	5	2
36600	Miscellaneous Manufacture	147	125	131	82	32	11
36620	Brushes/Brooms	2	1	2	1	0	0
36630	Manufactured Products (Other)	80	26	77	21	11	6
37	**Recycling**	**133**	**84**	**124**	**45**	**7**	**1**
37100	Scrap Dealers	78	62	72	27	2	1
37200	Recycling Non-Metal Waste & Scrap	56	22	53	18	5	0
40	**Electricity & Gas Supply**	**143**	**67**	**138**	**60**	**20**	**13**
40101	Electricity Production	10	9	10	9	4	4
40102	Energy Distribution	70	11	70	11	4	2
40103	Electricity Distribution	31	26	30	23	5	4
40200	Public Gas Supply	18	13	14	9	2	2
40210	Energy Production	12	8	12	8	5	1
41	**Water Distribution**	**70**	**43**	**64**	**26**	**5**	**1**
41000	Water Supply Industry	70	43	64	26	5	1
45	**Construction**	**13889**	**6834**	**12214**	**1929**	**317**	**66**
45100	Site Preparation	124	18	124	22	2	0
45110	Demolition Companies	33	15	33	9	2	1
45210	Construction/Building Companies	5768	2579	4258	624	100	28
45211	Building Maintenance & Repairs	59	28	59	21	2	1
45213	Civil Engineering	234	127	226	93	23	3
45215	Chimney Builders	2	1	2	1	0	0
45216	Prefabricated Buildings	31	11	31	12	2	1
45217	Timber Frame Buildings	52	17	51	20	5	2
45218	Loft Conversions	14	11	14	2	0	0
45220	Roofing Contractors	520	188	515	65	12	4
45230	Roads, Airfields & Sports Facilities	31	6	31	4	2	1
45240	Construction of Water Projects	1	1	1	1	0	0
45310	Electrical Contractors	2210	1458	2120	349	64	6
45311	Electrical Engineers	56	33	53	23	6	2
45330	Plumbers	731	637	716	69	2	0
45331	Heating Engineers	536	214	529	65	10	4
45400	Building Completion Work	470	92	470	64	23	2
45410	Plasterers	386	190	383	13	1	0
45420	Joiners & Carpenters	840	394	822	98	7	0
45421	Joinery Companies	41	35	41	31	1	0
45431	Flooring Contractors	403	94	401	77	6	1
45432	Cladding	19	11	18	7	2	0
45441	Painters & Decorators	551	398	550	60	5	0
45442	Glazing	340	168	333	101	14	2
45451	Fencing	143	28	143	16	2	0
45452	Shopfitting & Officefitting	286	99	283	75	25	7
45453	Installation Fixtures/Fittings	46	13	45	12	3	2
50	**Cars/Cycles Sale & Repair**	**7160**	**3134**	**6313**	**1474**	**147**	**48**
50101	Car Sales/Dealers	819	291	817	261	49	20
50102	Car Sales (Used Cars)	1257	1115	1192	542	29	9
50103	Commercial Vehicle Sales	186	91	184	51	5	2
50200	Motor Vehicle Repairs/Services	1611	512	1602	218	20	4
50300	Car Parts/Accessories	673	217	596	170	24	8
50301	Tyre Exhaust Centres	536	201	532	104	8	3
50302	Car Radio Dealers	50	14	50	10	4	0
50400	Motorbike Retailers	131	38	131	27	4	0
50500	Petrol Filling Stations	1894	658	1206	93	4	2
51	**Wholesale & Commission Trade**	**6375**	**2844**	**6293**	**1971**	**322**	**127**
51200	Agricultural Supplies Distribution	148	78	148	50	8	3
51230	Live Animals Distribution	301	217	300	42	2	2
51300	Food/Drink Distribution	276	163	272	125	20	10
51310	Fruit & Vegetable Wholesale	113	19	111	14	2	0
51380	Fish Wholesale	215	107	214	73	11	4
51390	Cash & Carry	179	73	171	65	8	3
51420	Clothing & Textiles Distribution	202	88	198	75	7	1
51430	Electrical Products Distribution	295	154	291	148	24	12
51460	Pharmaceutical Distribution	68	61	66	58	18	12
51510	Coal/Gas Retail/Distribution	441	180	437	37	5	3
51511	Heating Oil Distribution	642	335	622	216	28	11
51520	Metals/Ores Distribution	11	10	9	4	0	0
51530	Building Supplies/Distribution	991	482	985	386	44	16
51540	Hardware & Household Goods Distrib	332	78	328	58	8	3
51541	Bathroom Equipment Suppliers	100	40	99	43	7	5
51542	Plumbers Supplies/Merchants	652	129	652	57	10	2
51610	Machinery & Equipment Distribution	292	115	291	95	26	7
51611	Motor Vehicles/Part Distribution	136	125	126	108	22	10
51651	Catering Equipment	167	97	160	78	15	4
51652	Catering Suppliers	189	83	188	59	9	0
51700	Distribution/General Wholesalers	631	211	630	186	52	21
52	**Retail & Repair**	**26292**	**7755**	**20877**	**3399**	**485**	**172**
52121	Shopping Centres	133	38	102	17	2	1
52122	Catalogue Stores	276	245	269	33	1	1
52123	Department Stores	209	63	145	61	6	6
52210	Fruit & Vegetable Shops	618	189	537	36	3	0
52220	Butchers	1758	646	1407	49	2	0

Code	Activity						
52230	Fish Mongers	274	111	247	42	6	3
52240	Bakers	831	245	668	99	17	5
52250	Off Licences	303	57	241	44	9	3
52260	Tobacconists	12	1	7	0	0	0
52271	Supermarkets	1418	492	1227	263	13	7
52272	Grocers	1168	235	1053	18	2	0
52273	Frozen Food Shops	103	47	97	28	2	0
52274	Confectionery Shops	202	20	87	10	3	1
52275	Delicatessens	416	68	382	26	6	1
52276	Multiple Food Stores	19	5	17	2	0	0
52277	Health Food Shops	307	69	243	44	6	3
52278	Florists	1069	226	949	88	18	5
52310	Chemists	703	429	703	151	15	5
52330	Cosmetics & Perfume Retailers	14	5	9	5	2	1
52411	Fabric Retailers	197	40	147	31	4	0
52412	Carpet Sales	359	95	323	72	3	1
52420	Clothes Retailers (Mixed)	567	176	273	56	11	6
52422	Clothes Retailers (Children)	262	26	185	14	1	1
52423	Clothes Retailers (Women)	1777	185	1162	67	5	1
52424	Clothes Retailers (Men)	623	164	415	34	2	1
52425	Baby Goods Retailers	92	12	68	10	2	0
52426	Knitwear Retailers	145	30	96	21	3	2
52431	Shoe Shops	763	206	501	62	8	1
52432	Leather Goods Retailers	51	5	17	0	0	0
52441	Furniture Retailers	1240	521	1135	176	9	5
52442	Lighting Goods Retailers	155	41	134	42	9	3
52443	Soft Furnishing Retailers	156	15	40	9	0	0
52451	Electrical Retailers	305	281	295	227	26	9
52452	Hi Fi Dealers	7	1	6	1	0	0
52461	Hardware Stores	599	265	474	135	11	2
52462	DIY Stores	289	65	226	72	4	5
52471	Bookshops	442	210	346	153	31	13
52472	Newsagents	1594	440	1220	76	9	1
52473	Stationery - Suppliers/Retailers	434	262	386	233	51	11
52474	Greeting Card Shops	155	24	122	20	1	0
52482	Photographic Equipment	95	45	87	27	9	3
52483	Music Shops	153	45	139	28	7	1
52484	Jewellers, Clocks & Coins	956	215	667	91	15	7
52485	Sport Shops	411	79	293	45	9	3
52486	Camping/Hiking Shops	117	12	105	9	2	1
52487	Angling/Fishing Shops	117	28	104	11	1	0
52488	Cycle Shops	283	78	223	31	1	0
52489	Toy Shops	189	40	139	43	6	3
52490	Picture Shops/Framers/Restorers	241	62	227	26	6	1
52491	Art & Craft Shops	396	66	278	41	5	2
52492	Record Shops	237	25	145	28	11	3
52493	Trophies & Medals	39	22	36	19	3	1
52494	Gift Shops	1005	201	799	84	17	6
52495	Mobile Phone Retailers	467	298	461	296	75	30
52496	Pet Shops	207	83	192	19	3	2
52497	Model Shops	32	8	32	1	0	0
52498	Glass & China Retailers	30	10	10	7	0	1
52499	Discount Stores	283	9	128	7	1	1
52510	Charity & Trift Shops	82	5	47	0	0	0
52520	Antiques	395	71	341	28	6	2
52610	Mail Order Companies	24	8	24	5	2	1
52710	Shoe & Leather Goods Repairs	132	22	84	2	0	0
52720	Repair - Consumer Goods	375	89	372	38	5	0
55	**Hospitality**	**21281**	**10214**	**16484**	**2529**	**677**	**566**
55110	Hotels	1295	953	1052	808	402	245
55121	Guesthouses	2016	1722	1840	234	43	140
55122	Bed & Breakfasts	1587	359	1581	157	63	18
55210	Self Catering & Hostels	567	53	563	90	21	29
55220	Caravan & Camping Sites	258	52	253	25	6	12
55231	Holiday Centres & Holiday Villages	13	2	13	2	1	1
55232	Farmhouse Accommodation	523	449	523	45	0	50
55301	Restaurants	3644	779	3160	429	81	44
55302	Cafes	493	44	49	8	4	4
55303	Take-Away Food Shops	1177	93	835	22	2	1
55304	Pizza Parlours	61	6	11	2	0	0
55401	Private Licensed Social Clubs	80	27	5	0	0	0
55402	Public Houses	9017	5478	6080	566	34	14
55403	Public Houses - Late & Food Licence	31	16	28	9	1	1
55404	Night Clubs	130	18	122	21	4	1
55520	Catering	390	161	369	107	16	6
60	**Land Transport**	**3718**	**1694**	**3641**	**500**	**93**	**36**
60100	Urban Railways	36	10	35	8	3	2
60210	Bus Stations/Depots	64	27	63	22	6	5
60220	Taxi Firms	1109	339	1079	44	5	1
60231	Coach Operators	647	261	639	125	17	9
60240	Road Haulage Companies	1685	994	1649	243	38	10
60241	Furniture Removal	26	15	25	15	6	4
60249	Road Transport (Other)	151	47	151	42	18	5
61	**Water Transport**	**126**	**54**	**122**	**57**	**19**	**9**
61100	Sea Transport	126	54	122	57	19	9
62	**Air Transport**	**188**	**49**	**180**	**50**	**15**	**8**
62101	Air Transport - Passenger Airlines	166	46	158	48	12	7
62109	Airline Services	21	3	21	2	3	1
63	**Transport Supporting Services**	**2034**	**963**	**1859**	**1003**	**296**	**161**

Code	Activity						
63110	Cargo Storage, Handling & Warehse	150	18	150	31	7	2
63210	Transport Services (Other)	262	90	257	76	14	4
63220	Support Services/Sea Transport	103	85	94	84	19	9
63221	Freight Forwarders	377	238	365	239	84	43
63230	Support Services/Air Transport	31	15	30	14	7	5
63301	Travel Agent & Tour Operators	800	462	653	490	138	78
63309	Tourist Offices/Services	302	54	302	67	26	19
63400	Transport Agencies – Other	1	1	1	1	1	1
64	**Post & Telecommunications**	**4288**	**576**	**2565**	**409**	**138**	**85**
64111	Post Offices	3363	88	1698	25	2	2
64112	Sorting Offices	110	87	102	51	1	1
64120	Courier/Parcel Delivery Services	606	240	578	169	27	8
64201	Telecommunications	196	152	175	154	101	68
64202	Mobile Phone Service Providers	6	5	5	5	5	4
65	**Financial Intermediaries**	**3217**	**2120**	**3101**	**2010**	**884**	**762**
65111	Bank Head Offices	46	45	46	46	29	24
65112	Building Society Head Offices	3	3	3	3	2	2
65121	Bank Branches	1147	871	1128	863	580	585
65122	Building Society Branches	473	391	410	378	42	25
65128	Bureau de Change	20	7	20	9	1	1
65129	Banking Services (Other)	145	93	141	92	27	23
65200	Financial Institutions – Other	813	499	788	433	179	96
65210	Money Lending Services	13	2	12	4	1	1
65220	Credit Unions	401	157	399	134	13	0
65239	Banking/Finance – Other	150	44	148	42	9	4
66	**Insurance & Pension Funding**	**1646**	**1028**	**1604**	**978**	**232**	**95**
66001	Insurance Companies	297	153	293	180	42	27
66002	Insurance Brokers	1203	836	1165	753	167	60
66003	Insurance Loss Adjusters	149	40	149	47	23	8
67	**Financial Services**	**154**	**137**	**144**	**92**	**35**	**17**
67120	Stock Brokers	81	70	71	57	25	14
67200	Insurance – Other	74	68	74	36	10	3
70	**Real Estate Activities**	**1823**	**895**	**1710**	**717**	**263**	**137**
70120	Owning/Dealing Real Estate	2	0	2	0	0	0
70201	Conference Centres/Organisers	205	91	193	81	41	15
70310	Estate Agents	907	580	815	435	146	86
70320	Auctioneers Practices	711	226	702	203	77	37
71	**Hiring of Equipment**	**3996**	**1586**	**3762**	**621**	**113**	**47**
71000	Hiring & Leasing	97	49	96	39	10	7
71110	Car Hire	403	181	392	137	21	15
71210	Commercial Vehicle Hire	40	16	40	15	4	1
71230	Aircraft Leasing	32	10	32	12	5	4
71310	Hiring Agricultural Equipment	4	3	4	2	0	0
71320	Hiring Construction Equipment	1351	929	1317	202	24	3
71340	Hiring Machinery & Equipment Other	803	197	800	108	22	5
71401	Hire of Sport &	51	9	51	13	5	1
71403	TV/Video Rental	413	65	348	43	9	2
71405	Video Shops	606	77	510	30	7	4
71406	Catering Equipment Hire	21	3	21	8	2	1
71407	Dress Hire/Wedding Hire	169	44	144	10	2	3
71408	Hiring Consumer Goods	11	4	11	4	1	0
72	**Computer & Related Activities**	**2834**	**1730**	**2719**	**1796**	**1300**	**877**
72100	Computer Consultancy	267	148	254	142	110	68
72200	Software/Information Products	923	656	881	655	507	374
72400	Database Activities	1	1	1	1	1	1
72500	Repair of Office & Computing Equip	62	33	59	35	26	8
72601	Computer Services	539	316	504	348	213	131
72602	Network & Data Communications	95	46	93	49	38	26
72603	Computer Sales	268	146	264	158	126	66
72604	Computer Supplies	343	227	334	235	135	76
72605	Internet Providers/Services	230	101	224	105	110	99
72609	Computer Related Activities – Other	105	54	104	66	32	27
73	**Research & Development**	**183**	**63**	**181**	**53**	**30**	**15**
73000	Research & Development Labs	183	63	181	53	30	15
74	**Business Activities**	**15503**	**8215**	**14970**	**6766**	**2399**	**763**
74111	Patent & Copyright Agents	17	2	17	7	1	1
74112	Solicitors Firms	2413	2007	2312	1764	339	70
74113	Solicitors (Individual)	6	5	6	6	0	0
74119	Legal Services (Other)	32	20	28	21	8	6
74121	Accountancy Firms	2063	1356	2009	1174	304	74
74123	Tax Consultancy	112	18	112	11	4	1
74124	Accountants (Individual)	60	5	59	4	1	1
74130	Market Research Firms	42	32	38	31	24	13
74141	Public Relations Companies	68	30	68	30	23	8
74143	Management Consultancy	399	217	378	191	110	43
74144	Marketing Consultancy	283	187	263	170	101	35
74145	Professional/Technical Help	81	45	73	42	19	7
74146	Environmental Consultants	106	27	102	22	17	6
74147	Other Consultancy	352	49	352	54	34	7
74148	Business Advice (Other)	119	22	119	20	7	5
74149	Other Consultancy	349	274	312	240	119	56
74150	Central Offices/Holding Companies	6	6	6	6	2	0
74201	Architect Practices	911	643	888	567	269	54
74202	Landscape Architect Firms	118	65	105	24	10	1
74203	Quantity Surveyors Practices	372	147	367	92	53	10

74204	Consulting Engineers	352	196	343	170	70	18
74207	Building Estimators	12	2	12	1	1	0
74208	Interior Designers	1156	337	1152	186	32	11
74209	Building Consultants	47	22	47	15	2	1
74402	Advertising Companies	310	195	278	186	116	51
74403	Promotional Products	365	155	355	145	50	16
74404	Advertising Signs	351	149	345	132	37	16
74405	Direct Marketing Companies	111	78	98	71	49	28
74406	Call Centres	17	17	16	17	12	12
74500	Employment Agencies	460	230	451	244	182	87
74602	Security Companies	592	234	571	214	45	14
74603	Locksmiths	106	24	95	15	1	0
74701	Cleaning Services	1197	259	1196	148	30	9
74702	Chimney Sweeps	39	21	39	1	0	0
74703	Cleaning Suppliers	173	33	173	41	15	3
74811	Photographers	829	492	739	192	62	15
74812	Photographic Processing Labs	136	46	135	36	5	3
74813	Photographic Services	121	49	119	33	17	6
74820	Packaging Activities	162	50	161	60	25	8
74830	Secretarial & Translation Services	230	42	230	50	36	5
74840	Graphic Designers	717	396	689	323	159	60
74841	Credit Reporting & Collection Agency	29	4	29	4	4	0
74843	Exhibition & Fair Organisers	49	9	49	9	2	1
75	**Public Administration & Service**	**7675**	**3594**	**6679**	**1289**	**336**	**239**
75100	Government (General)	597	62	590	57	32	26
75101	Permanent Secretaries	1	1	0	1	0	0
75103	Members of Parliament	163	163	160	0	0	0
75104	Irish Senators/NI Assembly Members	224	222	221	3	2	3
75105	Member of European Parliament	15	15	15	15	3	1
75106	District/County Councillors	964	962	556	35	13	11
75107	Urban District Councillors	438	438	122	2	0	0
75108	Town Commissioners	151	151	45	1	1	0
75111	District/County Councils	701	61	700	48	23	18
75112	Corporation/Authorities	23	20	22	21	13	12
75113	Urban District Council (UDC)	48	39	47	44	16	9
75114	Town Commissions	25	13	19	9	0	1
75119	Council Services	27	22	25	23	3	2
75120	Health Boards	687	37	687	35	8	4
75131	Econ Dev/Statistics/Enterprise	90	87	85	88	27	22
75132	Fobairt Offices	11	10	11	11	2	2
75133	IDA	12	11	12	12	1	0
75134	FAS/T&EA Employment Offices	55	23	55	53	9	9
75135	Enterprise Agencies	123	87	123	84	54	29
75136	Business Development Service	17	8	17	12	7	5
75141	Heritage/Information/NI Office	134	40	132	30	11	11
75142	Inland Revenue/Tax Commissoner	116	71	80	62	2	3
75143	Finance & Personnel/Civil Services	23	21	22	17	5	5
75144	Customs & Excise/VAT	6	2	6	2	0	0
75145	Information System Directorate	5	3	5	5	2	2
75161	Dept of Agriculture/Fishery/Marine	202	74	199	63	7	5
75162	Agricultural Development Offices	202	35	202	16	0	0
75163	Animal Health Offices	37	32	6	1	0	0
75164	Research Centres	48	32	47	36	19	19
75165	Watercourse Management	2	0	2	0	0	0
75171	Education	793	71	789	57	24	9
75172	Education Board Supplies Pool	46	15	44	13	2	0
75181	Environment/Valuation	81	50	79	48	16	9
75182	Vehicle Test Centres (MOT)	21	8	21	6	0	0
75183	Housing Executives	1	1	1	1	0	0
75210	Foreign Affairs Departments	14	11	13	5	2	1
75221	Defence-Army/Navy/Air/Rescue	139	24	137	19	3	0
75222	Lighthouses	31	1	31	1	0	1
75230	Justice/Attorney General/DPP/Law	119	94	93	20	4	2
75241	Police Stations/Depots	932	430	921	234	2	1
75242	Prisons	14	12	12	12	0	0
75250	Fire Stations	103	54	95	12	3	0
75301	Health & Social Services/Welfare	122	69	118	69	18	16
75302	Social Security Offices	117	8	117	4	0	1
80	**Education**	**7306**	**2114**	**4436**	**1490**	**693**	**257**
80101	Creche/Nursery Schools	554	162	525	23	5	3
80102	Primary Schools	2953	132	174	31	12	9
80103	Special Schools	52	24	51	15	3	0
80211	Secondary Schools (Intermediate)	1002	735	982	626	313	57
80212	Secondary Schools (Grammar)	15	15	15	12	5	0
80220	Further Education/VEC	562	113	554	103	52	37
80301	Agricultural Colleges	38	28	38	11	5	2
80302	University & University Faculty	73	65	73	66	29	21
80400	Government Training Centres	39	21	37	33	3	3
80410	Driving Schools	474	101	472	16	3	1
80421	Training Companies	705	446	689	359	152	68
80422	Language/Language Schools	432	81	429	87	51	28
80429	Education (Other)	400	194	390	110	62	28
85	**Health & Social work**	**11339**	**7290**	**9110**	**1792**	**279**	**87**
85111	Hospitals (Public Sector)	316	140	265	114	15	9
85112	Hospitals (Private)	7	7	7	7	3	1
85113	Nursing Homes	434	216	383	60	4	0
85116	Hospitals (Geriatric)	31	30	31	27	0	0
85117	Hospitals (Mental)	15	11	15	10	1	1
85118	NHS Trusts	2	1	2	1	1	0
85119	Childminders/Day Nurseries	33	8	33	4	1	0
85121	Health Centre/Clinics	304	119	296	59	16	7
85122	Medical Institution (Other)	113	66	110	63	17	7
85123	Day Care Centres	26	11	26	8	2	1
85124	Doctors (GP)	2171	1650	2147	750	39	4
85130	Dentists	2108	1614	1016	111	23	1
85141	Opticians	509	407	387	158	9	3
85142	Chiropodists	341	219	340	19	8	0
85143	Nurses/Midwives	28	7	26	3	0	0
85144	Physiotherapists	264	115	264	27	13	2
85145	Psychologists	237	195	228	12	5	4
85149	Other Human Health Activities	734	117	733	41	9	1
85200	Veterinary Surgeons	2382	1987	1545	62	10	0
85201	Veterinary Clinics	31	13	29	4	1	0
85313	Care Homes (Children's)	11	0	10	0	0	0
85314	Care Homes Hostel/Shelter/Resident	74	16	73	23	2	4
85320	Social Welfare	356	157	339	92	32	12
85321	Charities	697	171	688	128	65	30
85322	Citizens Advice Bureau	121	13	121	10	3	0
90	**Sewage, Refuse & Sanitation**	**414**	**123**	**411**	**84**	**13**	**5**
90001	Sewage Disposal	56	26	56	14	2	1
90002	Refuse Disposal Fumigation	321	85	318	61	10	3
90003	Sanitation & Similar Activities	15	1	15	4	1	1
90004	Skip Hire	22	11	22	5	0	0
91	**Membership Organisations**	**12695**	**8857**	**9753**	**1310**	**418**	**200**
91111	Business Chamber/Trade Federation	73	55	73	48	8	3
91112	Business Clubs	2	0	2	1	0	0
91120	Professional Associations	520	467	477	307	125	82
91200	Trade Unions/Employee Groups	444	372	381	228	98	50
91310	Religious/Similar Groups	1795	854	1759	217	22	4
91311	Roman Catholic Presbyteries	3448	2352	2566	94	1	1
91312	Presbyterian Religion	83	83	82	0	0	0
91313	Church of Ireland Religion	389	388	370	37	3	1
91314	Orthodox Religion	2	1	1	1	0	0
91315	Methodist Religion	33	33	32	2	0	0
91316	Independent Religions	2	1	2	0	0	0
91317	Baptist Religion	15	15	15	0	0	0
91319	Places of Worship (Other)	15	4	14	4	1	0
91320	Political Party/Group	25	6	25	5	4	2
91331	Clubs & Associations – Governing	115	103	109	26	14	12
91332	Clubs & Associations	3529	2366	2577	122	32	16
91333	Housing Associations	9	8	9	7	4	1
91334	Youth Centres/Clubs	1410	1104	714	50	17	9
91335	Community Service/Centres/Groups	787	644	546	160	88	19
92	**Recreational, Cultural & Sporting**	**6523**	**1986**	**5953**	**997**	**261**	**126**
92110	Film Production/Distribution	485	255	472	200	61	24
92130	Cinemas	164	12	159	12	1	0
92201	Radio Broadcasting Companies	109	67	99	61	36	20
92202	Television Broadcasting Companies	37	12	37	12	6	5
92311	Theatres	128	27	124	27	10	7
92312	Music Composers	112	30	112	13	8	4
92313	Authors/Journalists	19	12	16	6	1	1
92320	Art Galleries/Museums	380	116	374	68	15	8
92349	Entertainment (Other)	416	56	414	37	21	8
92510	Libraries	358	33	224	20	9	7
92521	Museums	34	3	34	4	2	0
92530	Zoos, Gardens & Nature Reserves	16	0	16	1	0	0
92610	Sports Arenas & Stadiums	26	6	26	5	0	0
92612	Bowling Alleys	20	7	19	3	0	1
92613	Pitch & Putt Clubs	76	49	50	1	0	0
92614	Horse Riding Stables/Schools	430	215	427	101	12	5
92615	Golf Courses	590	234	574	137	16	7
92616	Leisure Swimming & Sport Centres	474	165	419	90	24	14
92617	Outdoor Education/Pursuits Centres	34	19	30	15	6	2
92620	Sports/Recreational Services	497	138	481	74	18	8
92621	National Hunts	10	10	9	1	0	0
92622	Horse Trainers	600	173	591	64	8	2
92623	Horse Jockeys	754	128	714	7	0	0
92710	Betting Shops	656	197	475	31	3	2
92720	Amusement Arcades	95	20	54	5	1	0
93	**Service Activities Other**	**7451**	**1763**	**6739**	**343**	**62**	**22**
93011	Dry Cleaning/Allied Services	548	88	489	7	0	0
93012	Launderettes	174	19	168	3	0	1
93013	Laundries	174	19	127	4	1	0
93021	Hairdressers (Ladies)	1466	150	1457	17	0	1
93022	Hairdressers (Mixed)	1301	371	935	17	1	0
93023	Hairdressers (Mens)	335	45	243	0	0	0
93024	Beauty Salons	1172	292	1097	41	6	1
93030	Funeral Parlours/Directors	795	430	754	92	6	1
93041	Health Studios/Gyms	310	110	300	51	13	6
93048	Detective & Investigations Agencies	73	10	71	17	5	1
93049	Personal Services (Other)	697	149	693	46	17	6
93051	Domestic Services	27	14	25	10	6	2
93052	Wedding Services	372	66	371	38	7	3
99	**Embassies**	**65**	**41**	**64**	**40**	**16**	**7**
99000	Embassy	65	41	64	40	16	7
0	**Unclassified**	**2327**	**674**	**1636**	**560**	**179**	**97**
Total		203091	93042	173823	45580	13054	6140

Section 2

The Cream of Irish Industry Commerce & Government

5000 Businesses, Organisations and Government bodies in the Republic of Ireland

Agriculture

Agriculture

SIC	Sector Description
1	**Agriculture, Hunting & Services**
1000	Agriculture
1120	Garden Centres/Nurseries
1121	Mushroom Growers
1221	Studs
1410	Agricultural Services
1411	Agri co-op's
1421	Livestock Marts
1422	Boarding Kennel/Cattery
1500	Hunting,Trapping & Game Activities
	Farmers
2	**Forestry, Logging & Service**
2000	Forestry
2021	Forest Parks
5	**Fishing, Fish Hatchery & Farms**
5000	Fishing

Erin Group Ltd
Erin Horticulture
Derrinlough
Birr Co. Offaly
Phone: 0509-20161 Fax: 0509-33007
Email: eringroup@eircom.net
SIC: 1000 Employees: 70
Horticultural Specialists
Mr John Malloy Managing Director
Mr Daryl Hooper Finance Manager
Mr Paddy Duffy Sales & Marketing Manager
Mr Tom Flynn Production Director

Harte Peat
Leonards Island, Clones
Monaghan Co. Monaghan
Phone: 047-51557 Fax: 047-51827
Email: kay@iol.ie
SIC: 1000 Employees: 40
Mushroom Casing
Ms Kay O'Harte Joint Managing Director
Mr Thomas O'Harte Joint Managing Director
Mr Frank Cassidy Office Manager
Ms Una McPhilips Sales Manager
Mr Maurice O'Shea Production Manager

Darrers Stores
14 Mary Street
Dungarvan Co. Waterford
Phone: 058-41581 Fax: 058-45052
SIC: 1120 Employees: 80
Garden Centre/Nurseries
Mr Brendan Darrer Chief Executive
Mr Michael Darrer Financial Controller

Fountains & Decor Aquarium Centre
Kingswood Cross, Naas Road
Clondalkin
Dublin 22
Phone: 01-4591724 Fax: 01-4592613
Email: info@fountains.net
Web: http://www.fountains.net
SIC: 1120 Employees: 23
Garden Centre
Mr Albert Crowley Managing Director

Newlands Garden Centre
New Road
Clondalkin
Dublin 22
Phone: 01-4592013 Fax: 01-4593658
Email: info@newlands.ie
SIC: 1120 Employees: 30
Garden Centre
Mr Michael Devitt Proprietor

Sap Holdings & Landscapers Ltd
Garnavilla
Cahir Co. Tipperary
Phone: 052-42222 Fax: 052-42215
Email: sap@iol.ie
Web: http://www.sapgroup.com
SIC: 1120 Employees: 170
Garden Centre/Nurseries
Mr Niall Grogan Managing Director
Mr Tom McInerney Accountant
Mr John Murphy Sales & Marketing Manager
Ms Grainne Murphy Production Manager

Carbury Mushrooms
Carbury
Naas Co. Kildare
Phone: 0405-53222 Fax: 0405-53225
SIC: 1121 Employees: 70
Mushroom Growers
Mr Cahal MacCanna Managing Director
Mr Michael Garry Finance Manager
Mr Michael Cusack Personnel Manager

Connaught Mushrooms
Claremount
Claremorris Co. Mayo
Phone: 094-62106 Fax: 094-62110
Email: connaught@eircom.net
SIC: 1121 Employees: 100
Mushroom Growers
Mr John Whittle Proprietor
Mr Terry Hayes Financial Controller

Foxfield Mushrooms
Foxfield
Kilnaleck
Cavan Co. Cavan
Phone: 049-4336611 Fax: 049-4336622
Email: foxfield@monaghanmiddlebrook.co.uk
SIC: 1121 Employees: 102
Mushroom Production/Marketing
Mr John Kiernan Managing Director
Mr Patrick Moran Finance Manager

Goldshield Products
Cortown
Kells Co. Meath
Phone: 046-40670 Fax: 046-41593
Email: goldshieldfood@eircom.net
SIC: 1121 Employees: 50
Mushrooms
Mr John Kerrigan Managing Director

Kingdom Mushrooms
Duagh
Listowel Co. Kerry
Phone: 068-45279 Fax: 068-45222
SIC: 1121 Employees: 30
Mushroom Growers
Mr Mark Ahern Manager

Airlie Stud
Grangewilliam
Maynooth Co. Kildare
Phone: 01-6286336 Fax: 01-6286674
Email: info@airlie-stud.com
Web: http://www.airlie-stud.ie
SIC: 1221 Employees: 30
Stud Farm
Ms Sonia Rogers Manager

Coolmore Stud Farm
Coolmore
Fethard
Clonmel Co. Tipperary
Phone: 052-31298 Fax: 052-31382
Email: info@coolmore.com
Web: http://www.coolmore.com
SIC: 1221 Employees: 150
Stud Farm
Mr Chrissy Grassick General Manager
Mr Jerome Casey Financial Advisor
Mr Richard Henry Sales Manager
Mr Gerry McEvoy IT Manager

Grange Stud
Fermoy Co. Cork
Phone: 025-33006 Fax: 025-32247
SIC: 1221 Employees: 50
Stud Farm
Mr Albert Sherwood Manager

Irish Equine Centre
Johnstown
Naas Co. Kildare
Phone: 045-866266 Fax: 045-866273
Email: iecentre@equine-centre.ie
SIC: 1221 Employees: 25
Diagnosis / Research into Horses
Mr Mark Sherry Manager

Irish National Stud
Tully
Kildare Co. Kildare
Phone: 045-521251 Fax: 045-522129
Email: stud@irish-national-stud.ie
Web: http://www.irish-national-stud.ie
SIC: 1221 Employees: 55
Stud Farm
Mr John Clarke Chief Executive
Mr John McStay Financial Controller
Ms Eileen Kavanagh Office Manager

Thomastown Castle Stud
Golden
Cashel Co. Tipperary
Phone: 062-54129 Fax: 062-54399
SIC: 1221 Employees: 24
Racehorse Training
Mr Tommy Stack Proprietor

AW Ennis Dublin Ltd
Maghera Mills
Virginia
Cavan Co. Cavan
Phone: 049-8547588 Fax: 049-8547598
Email: awennis@eircom.net
SIC: 1410 Employees: 25
Feed Manufacturing
Mr Victor Ennis Managing Director
Mr Martin Sheridan Accountant
Ms Mildred Morton Sales Manager

Bride & Blackwater Farm Relief Service
55 McCurtain Street
Fermoy Co. Cork
Phone: 025-32643 Fax: 025-33303
Email: b~bfrs@eircom.net
SIC: 1410 Employees: 50
Farm Relief Services
Ms Patricia Coughlian Manager
Ms Lourdes Ryan Secretary

Cow Comforts Ltd
Tallaght, Belmullet
Ballina Co. Mayo
Phone: 097-82057 Fax: 097-82376
SIC: 1410 Employees: 25
Manufacture Mating For Agricultural Sector
Mr Tom Duffy Proprietor
Mr John McGrath Production & Training Officer

Curragh Bloodstock Agency
Main Street
Newbridge Co. Kildare
Phone: 045-431402 Fax: 045-432720
Email: enquiries@curraghbloodstock.ie
Web: http://www.curraghbloodstock.ie
SIC: 1410 Employees: 70
Bloodstock Agency
Mr Harry McCalmont Chairman
Mr Geoff Miller Finance Manager
Mr John Anderson Sales Director
Mr Eugene O'Rourke DP Manager

Agriculture

Dairygold AI & Farm Services
Ballyvorisheen
Mallow Co. Cork
Phone: 022-21585 Fax: 022-42527
Email: farmsevices@dairygold.ie
Web: http://www.mitchelstown.ie
SIC: 1410 Employees: 30
AI Services - Cattle Breeding
Ms Doreen Corridan Proprietor

Dairygold Co-Op Society Ltd
Fermoy Road
Mitchelstown Co. Cork
Phone: 025-24411 Fax: 025-84227
Email: info@dairygold.ie
Web: http://www.dairygold.ie
SIC: 1410 Employees: 2500
Dairy Products & Agri Retailing
Mr Denis Lucey Chief Executive
Mr Maurice Roche Financial Controller
Mr James Woulfe Head of Human Resources
Mr John O'Brien Sales & Marketing Manager
Mr Michael Walsh Data Processing Manager

Grove Turkeys Ltd
Jamestown
Ballybrittas
Portlaoise Co. Laois
Phone: 0502-26109 Fax: 0502-26260
SIC: 1410 Employees: 44
Turkey Breeding
Mr Colin MacDougal Director

Marley Compost
Crush
Carrickroe
Monaghan Co. Monaghan
Phone: 047-87542 Fax: 047-87738
SIC: 1410 Employees: 23
Mushroom Compost
Mr Bernard Connolly Manager

Murphy Brothers
Mount Bolton
Portlaw
Waterford Co. Waterford
Phone: 051-387396 Fax: 051-387455
Email: murphybrothersagri@iol.ie
SIC: 1410 Employees: 30
Agricultural Contractors
Mr John Murphy Proprietor

North Eastern Cattle Breeding Society
Head Office
Ballyhaise
Cavan Co. Cavan
Phone: 049-4338152 Fax: 049-4338442
SIC: 1410 Employees: 40
Agriculture
Mr John Joe McKarney General Manager

North Western Cattle Breeding Society
Doonally House
Sligo Co. Sligo
Phone: 071-45314 Fax: 071-43288
Email: info@nwcbs.ie
Web: http://www.nwcbs.ie
SIC: 1410 Employees: 100
Agriculture
Mr Seamus Bergin Manager
Mr Cormac Monaghan Laboratory Manager

Tinsley Wire Ltd
Jamestown Business Park
Finglas
Dublin 11
Phone: 01-8342533 Fax: 01-8362773
Email: tinsleywire@eircom.net
Web: http://www.bekaert.com
SIC: 1410 Employees: 45
Agricultural Services
Mr Fran Brennan General Manager
Ms Una Kennedy Financial Controller
Mr John Atkinson Sales Administrator
Mr Charles Healy Production Manager
Mr Paul Horan Computer Manager

Bandon Co-Op Dairy Society Ltd
Watergate StreetBandon Co. Cork
Phone: 023-41409 Fax: 023-44931
Email: admin@bandoncoop.ie
Web: http://www.bandoncoop.ie
SIC: 1411 Employees: 45
Agricultural Co-Op
Mr William Sheehan General Manager
Mr John Looney Accountant

Barryroe Co-op Ltd
Lislevane
Bandon Co. Cork
Phone: 023-40142 Fax: 023-40148
SIC: 1411 Employees: 66
Agricultural Co-Op
Mr Peter Dineen General Manager
Mr Stephen O'Leary Financial Controller
Mr John Keohane Sales & Marketing Manager
Mr Dennis O'Mahony Production Manager

Castleisland Co-Op & Livestock Mart
Convent Street
Castleisland
Tralee Co. Kerry
Phone: 066-7141247 Fax: 066-7141881
SIC: 1411 Employees: 23
Agricultural Co-Ops
Mr Richard Harnett Chief Executive
Mr G Carmody Company Secretary
Mr J Roche Chairman

Centenary Co-Op Creamery Ltd
Ballyduff
Thurles Co. Tipperary
Phone: 0504-45216 Fax: 0504-45277
Email: info@centenaryco-op.com
Web: http://www.centenarycoop.com
SIC: 1411 Employees: 60
Agricultural Co-Op
Mr Tom Commins Managing Director
Mr Joe Kerrigan Finance Manager
Mr Eamon Healy Marketing Manager
Mr John Ryan Production Director

Connacht Gold Co-Op Society
Ballina Road
Tubbercurry
Sligo Co. Sligo
Phone: 071-86500 Fax: 071-85239
Email: info@cgold.ie
Web: http://www.connachtgold.ie
SIC: 1411 Employees: 500
Agricultural Co-op
Mr Michael Farrell Chief Executive
Mr Michael Morley Financial Controller
Mr Michael Guilfoyle Personnel Manager
Mr Peadar Kivlehan Sales & Marketing Manager
Mr Noel Farry IT Manager

Cork Co-Operative Marts Ltd
Cork Farm Centre, Dennehy's Cross
Wilton Co. Cork
Phone: 021-4545733 Fax: 021-4545325
Email: corkmart@eircom.net
Web: http://www.ccmproperty.com
SIC: 1411 Employees: 150
Agricultural Co-Operative
Mr Sean O'Sullivan General Manager
Mr John Stanley Chairman

ICOS Ltd
The Plunkett House
84 Merrion Square
Dublin 2
Phone: 01-6764783 Fax: 01-6624502
SIC: 1411 Employees: 23
Agricultural Co-Ops
Mr John Tyrrell Director General
Mr Shane Dolan Finance Manager
Ms Frances Russell Personnel Manager
Ms Alison Mugan Computer Manager

Inishowen Co-op
Moville Road
Carndonagh
Lifford Co. Donegal
Phone: 077-74178 Fax: 077-74654
Email: inishowen@eircom.net
SIC: 1411 Employees: 27
Agricultural Co-op
Mr Paddy Gallen Proprietor
Mr Seamus Gorman Finance Manager

Mayo-Sligo Co-Op Mart
Crossmolina Road
Ballina Co. Mayo
Phone: 096-22555 Fax: 096-22555
SIC: 1411 Employees: 28
Agricultural Co-Op
Mr Mark Breslin General Manager
Mr Jerry O'Mara Accountant

Mid Tipperary Co-op
Ballycurrane
Thurles Co. Tipperary
Phone: 0504-21499 Fax: 0504-21714
SIC: 1411 Employees: 27
Agricultural Co-Op
Mr Joe O'Connell General Manager
Mr Seamus Ryan Secretary

Midwest Farmers Co-Op
Kilconnell
Ballinasloe Co. Galway
Phone: 0905-86618 Fax: 0905-86705
SIC: 1411 Employees: 100
Agricultural Co-Op / Dairy Processors
Mr Joseph Rabbitte General Manager
Mr Tom Dolan Financial Controller
Mr John Slattery Sales Manager
Mr Eamon Donoghue DP Manager

Nenagh Co Op Livestock Sales Mart
Staford Street
Nenagh Co. Tipperary
Phone: 067-31380 Fax: 067-31849
SIC: 1411 Employees: 30
Agri Co-Ops
Mr Matt Malone Managing Director
Mr Christy Griffin IT Manager

Newmarket Co-Op Ltd
Newmarket
Co. Cork
Phone: 029-60005 Fax: 029-60024
Email: nmkcoop@iol.ie
SIC: 1411 Employees: 64
Agricultural Co-Op
Mr Michael Cronin Chief Executive
Mr Gerard Ryan Financial Controller
Ms Josephine Angland Assistant Production Manager
Mr Pat Buckley Production Director

Roscommon Co-Op Livestock Marts Ltd
Circular Road
Roscommon Co. Roscommon
Phone: 0903-26352 Fax: 0903-25689
Email: rosmart@eircom.net
SIC: 1411 Employees: 26
Agricultural Co-Op
Mr Owen Morgan General Manager

Thurles Co-Op Creamery Ltd
Templemore Road
Thurles Co. Tipperary
Phone: 0504-21522 Fax: 0504-22657
Email: thurlescoop@eircom.net
SIC: 1411 Employees: 65
Agricultural Co-Ops
Mr Michael Lanigan Managing Director
Mr Patrick Ryan Financial Controller
Mr Tom Aherne Sales & Marketing Manager

Tuam Co-Op Livestock Mart Ltd
Vicar Street
Tuam Co. Galway
Phone: 093-24353 Fax: 093-24601
SIC: 1411 Employees: 25
Agricultural Co-Op
Mr Michael Mannion Managing Director
Ms Marion Devane Accounts Manager

Wexford Farmers Co-Op
Dublin Road
Enniscorthy Co. Wexford
Phone: 054-33606 Fax: 054-34386
Email: wexfarm@iol.ie
SIC: 1411 Employees: 180
Livestock Auctioneers & Co-Op
Mr PJ Darcy Chief Executive
Mr Frank Devoy Financial Controller
Mr Toddy O'Brian Sales Manager
Mr John Commins Computer Manager

Associated Livestock Marts
Ellenborough House
Dublin Road
Naas Co. Kildare
Phone: 045-879529 Fax: 045-874082
SIC: 1421 Employees: 30
Livestock Mart
Mr Gus Egan Chairman

Ballyjamesduff Co-op
Ramonan
Ballyjamesduff Co. Cavan
Phone: 049-8544485 Fax: 049-8544748
Email: ballyjamesdufflivestock@eircom.net
SIC: 1421 Employees: 50
Livestock Auctions
Mr Danny Reilly Chief Executive

Camlough Livestock Agency Ltd
46 Quarter Road, Camlouch
Dundalk Co. Louth
Phone: 041-9254555 Fax: 041-9254575
SIC: 1421 Employees: 26
Livestock Mart
Mr Richard Ryan General Manager

Clare Marts Ltd
Quinn Road
Ennis Co. Clare
Phone: 065-6824411 Fax: 065-6829978
Email: claremartsltd@eircom.net
SIC: 1421 Employees: 40
Livestock Mart
Mr Donal Ryan General Manager
Ms Moira Green Company Secretary
Mr Pat Garrihy Sales Manager

East Donegal Co-Op Mart
Raphoe
Lifford Co. Donegal
Phone: 074-45250 Fax: 074-45385
SIC: 1421 Employees: 27
Livestock Mart
Mr John Vance President
Ms Ann Harkin Financial Controller

Kilkenny Cattle Mart Ltd
Barrack Street
Kilkenny Co. Kilkenny
Phone: 056-21407 Fax: 056-21509
SIC: 1421 Employees: 50
Livestock Mart
Mr Michael Harty Manager

Mullingar Livestock Agency
Patrick Street
Mullingar Co. Westmeath
Phone: 044-48224 Fax: 044-48895
Email: livestock@mullingarmart.com
SIC: 1421 Employees: 30
Livestock Mart
Mr David Gibson Brabazon Chairman

Wexford Farmers Co-op
Dublin Road
Enniscorthy Co. Wexford
Phone: 054-33606 Fax: 054-34386
Email: info@wfc.ie
Web: http://www.wfc.ie
SIC: 1421 Employees: 50
Livestock Mart
Mr Toddy O'Brien Manager
Mr Frank Devoy Finance Manager

Coillte - Irish Forestry Board
Leeson Lane
Dublin 2
Phone: 01-6615666 Fax: 01-6789527
Email: info@coillte.ie
Web: http://www.coillte.ie
SIC: 2000 Employees: 5000
Forestry Service
Mr Martin Lowery Chief Executive
Mr John Dwyer Finance Manager
Mr Eamon Magee Personnel Manager
Mr Kevin Collins Systems Manager

Forestry Services Ltd
Lower Main Street
Glin
Limerick Co. Limerick
Phone: 068-34533 Fax: 068-34066
SIC: 2000 Employees: 31
Forestry
Mr Michael Sweeney Forester

Glenasack Tree Service
Block Road
Portlaoise Co. Laois
Phone: 0502-21669 Fax: 0502-21669
SIC: 2000 Employees: 31
Forestry
Mr John O'Connell Manager

Greenbelt Ltd
Virginia Co. Cavan
Phone: 049-8548000 Fax: 049-8547509
Email: info@greenbelt.ie
SIC: 2000 Employees: 32
Private Forestry Investment & Development
Mr Maurice Ryan Director
Mr Tim O'Brien Director

Dundalk Bay Seafoods Ltd
Drogheda Road
Clogherhead
Drogheda Co. Louth
Phone: 041-9822736 Fax: 041-9822428
SIC: 5000 Employees: 24
Fish Sales
Mr Paddy Lynch Managing Director
Mr Emmet Moore Production Manager

Rapire Teoanta
Inverin
Galway Co. Galway
Phone: 091-593211 Fax: 091-593078
Web: http://www.rapire.iol.ie
SIC: 5000 Employees: 95
Manufacture Fishing Lures
Mr Juhani Pahkonen Chief Executive
Mr Gerry O'Neill Finance Manager
Mr Martin Lavin Personnel Manager
Mr Martin Lyden Production Manager

Mining

10	**Mining of Coal, Lignite & Peat**
10102	Coal Working (Opencast)
10103	Solid Fuels (Manufacture)
11	**Petroleum & Natural Gas**
11100	Crude Oil & Gas (Extraction)
11200	Mineral Oil/Gas Refining
14	**Other Mining & Quarrying**
14100	Quarries
14400	Salt Production
14500	Mineral's Extraction (Other)

Bord Na Mona
Main Street
Newbridge Co. Kildare
Phone: 045-439000 Fax: 045-439001
Email: info@bnm.ie
Web: http://www.bnm.ie
SIC: 10103 Employees: 1980
Peat Processor
Mr John Hourican Chief Executive
Mr Gordon Murphy Finance Manager
Mr Kevin Gavin Personnel Manager
Mr Ronny Coffey Marketing Manager
Mr Paddy O'Brien Production Manager
Mr John Holmes Head of MIS

Denis McClair
Portlester
Ballivor
Navan Co. Meath
Phone: 0405-46458 Fax: 0405-46458
SIC: 10103 Employees: 23
Turf & Turf Products
Mr Denis McClure Proprietor

Standard Brands (Ireland) Ltd
Castlebellingham
Dundalk Co. Louth
Phone: 042-9372140 Fax: 042-9372218
Email: info@standardbrands.net
SIC: 10103 Employees: 70
Fire Lighters Manufacturing
Mr Pat Mulroy General Manager
Mr Denis McCourt Finance Manager
Mr George McDonald Production Manager
Mr Pat Finnegan Computer Manager

Irish National Petroleum Corporation
Warrington House
Mount Street Crescent
Dublin 2
Phone: 01-6607966 Fax: 01-6607952
SIC: 11200 Employees: 220
Oil Import/Refining
Mr Paddy Power Chief Executive
Mr Rory O'Shea Finance Manager

Irish Refining Plc
Whitegate
Midleton Co. Cork
Phone: 021-4622200 Fax: 021-4622222
SIC: 11200 Employees: 150
Crude Oil Refining
Mr Neill O'Carroll Refinery Manager
Mr Richard Healy Company Secretary
Mr Michael Biggane Personnel Manager
Mr William Joyce Operation Manager
Mr Chris Amos Technical Manager

Marathon International Petroleum
Mahon Industrial Estate
Blackrock Co. Cork
Phone: 021-4357301 Fax: 021-4357696
SIC: 11200 Employees: 90
Oil/Gas Exploration/Natural Gas
Mr Marvin Rainsdon Chief Executive
Mr Kevin Diver Finance/Admin Manager
Ms Jackie Mann Personnel Manager
Mr Tom O'Shea Engineering Manager
Mr Jim Lordan Supervisor - IT Services

Mining

Tullow Oil
Airfield House, Airfield Park
Donnybrook
Dublin 4
Phone: 01-2602611 Fax: 01-2602672
Email: ops@tullowoil.ie
Web: http://www.tullowoil.ie
SIC: 11200 Employees: 140
Oil & Gas Exploration Company
Mr Aidan Heavey Chief Executive
Mr Michael Hickey Finance Manager
Mr Jack Scott Engineering Manager

Casey's
Coolishal
Gorey Co. Wexford
Phone: 055-21261 Fax: 055-22982
SIC: 14100 Employees: 35
Quarries
Mr James Casey Managing Director
Mr Ronan Hopkins Finance Manager
Mr Paddy Casey Personnel Manager
Mr John Jordan Sales Manager

Clogrennane Lime Ltd
Clogrennane
Carlow Co. Carlow
Phone: 0503-31811 Fax: 0503-31607
Email: clogren@iol.ie
SIC: 14100 Employees: 34
Quarries
Mr Leo Groghan Managing Director
Mr Derry Ryan Accounts Manager
Mr Larry Kelly Production Manager

Dan McMonagle & Sons Ltd
Mountcharles
Donegal Co. Donegal
Phone: 073-35061 Fax: 073-35408
Email: monagle@iol.ie
SIC: 14100 Employees: 50
Quarries
Mr Dan McMonagle Managing Director
Mr Michael McMonagle Sales & Marketing Manager

Handly Brothers Ltd
Laragan Quarries
Elphin
Castlerea Co. Roscommon
Phone: 078-35049 Fax: 078-35292
Email: info@hbl.ie
SIC: 14100 Employees: 72
Quarries
Mr Joseph Hanley Managing Director
Mr Colum Hyden Finance Manager
Mr Alan Tiernan Sales & Marketing Manager
Ms Martina Feehily Computer Manager

Hillstreet Quarries Ltd
Hillstreet Village
Roscommon Co. Roscommon
Phone: 078-37205 Fax: 078-37085
SIC: 14100 Employees: 60
Quarries
Mr Denis Flynn Manager

Hudson Brothers
Redbog
Blessington
Naas Co. Kildare
Phone: 045-865880 Fax: 045-891908
SIC: 14100 Employees: 30
Sand & Gravel
Mr Peter Hudson Managing Director
Ms Celine Lipsett Accounts Manager

JJ Owens & Sons
Knockdrin
Mullingar Co. Westmeath
Phone: 044-72187 Fax: 044-72329
Email: owensgrp@iol.ie
SIC: 14100 Employees: 50
Sand, Gravel & Concrete
Mr John Owens Proprietor
Ms Ineke Owens Accountant
Mr Martin Owens Sales Manager

Keegan Quarries
Longwood Road
Trim
Navan Co. Meath
Phone: 046-31324 Fax: 046-36851
SIC: 14100 Employees: 25
Quarries
Mr John Keegan Managing Director

Kilkenny Limestone Ltd
Killymount Quarries
Paulstown
Kilkenny Co. Kilkenny
Phone: 0503-26191 Fax: 0503-26276
Email: info@feelystonekk.ie
Web: http://www.feelystone.com
SIC: 14100 Employees: 200
Quarries
Mr Michael Meaney Managing Director
Mr Brendan Allen Finance Manager
Mr Richard Dunne Sales & Marketing Manager
Mr Gerard Hennessy Accountant

Lackagh Quarry
Hardiman House
Eyre Square
Galway Co. Galway
Phone: 091-562862 Fax: 091-565646
SIC: 14100 Employees: 120
Quarry
Mr John Dempsey Managing Director
Mr Paul Dempsey Joint Managing Director

McKeown Stone Ltd
Brockley Park
Stradbally
Portlaoise Co. Laois
Phone: 0502-25151 Fax: 0502-25301
Email: info@mckeownstone.ie
SIC: 14100 Employees: 55
Natural Stone
Mr Niall Kavanagh Managing Director
Ms Helen McKeown Financial Controller
Mr Mick Renehan Sales & Marketing Manager
Mr Charles Mullane General Manager

McSweeney Brothers
Manch
Balineen
Cork Co. Cork
Phone: 023-45285 Fax: 023-45190
Email: midcorkgroup@eircom.net
SIC: 14100 Employees: 41
Quarries
Mr Pat McSweeney Proprietor
Ms Mary Topp Accounts Manager
Mr Eugene Daly Production Manager

Quirke Sand & Gravel
Rangue
Killorgan
Killarney Co. Kerry
Phone: 066-9761279 Fax: 066-9761415
SIC: 14100 Employees: 80
Quarries
Mr Tom Quirke Proprietor
Mr Michael O'Donoghue Financial Accountant

Whelans Quarry
Fountain Cross
Ennis Co. Clare
Phone: 065-6829470 Fax: 065-6828316
SIC: 14100 Employees: 100
Sand & Gravel Suppliers
Mr Patrick Whelan Manager
Mr John McKeogh Financial Controller

Cementation Skanska
Lisheen Mine
Moyne
Thurles Co. Tipperary
Phone: 0504-45481 Fax: 0504-45484
SIC: 14500 Employees: 40
Mining Company
Mr Steve Barber Managing Director
Mr Steve Early Accountant

Ivernia West Plc
97 Henry Street Upper
Limerick Co. Limerick
Phone: 061-319922 Fax: 061-310210
Email: info@ivernia.com
Web: http://www.ivernia.com
SIC: 14500 Employees: 42
Mining Company
Mr David Hough Managing Director

Lisheen Mine
Killoran
Thurles Co. Tipperary
Phone: 0504-45369 Fax: 0504-45700
SIC: 14500 Employees: 300
Mining Company
Mr Don Cunningham General Manager
Mr Leo Shaughnessey Finance Director
Mr Martin Prendiville Administration Manager
Mr Bill Cash Sales Manager
Mr Gordan Graham IS Manager

Navan Resources
Kennedy Road
Navan Co. Meath
Phone: 046-22363 Fax: 046-22372
Email: navanr@iol.ie
Web: http://www.navanminingplc.co.uk
SIC: 14500 Employees: 850
Mining & Mineral Extraction
Mr Brian Calver Chief Executive
Ms Valerie Prall Accountant
Mr Vaughan Williams Explorations Manager
Mr Philip Nelson IT Manager

Tara Mines Ltd
Knockumber
Navan Co. Meath
Phone: 046-79800 Fax: 046-79899
SIC: 14500 Employees: 700
Zinc & Lead Mining
Mr Eero Laatio Managing Director
Mr Tadgh Farrell Financial Controller
Mr John Kelly Human Resources Manager
Mr Rauno Pitkanen Production Manager
Mr Gerry Harte IT Manager

Food & Beverage Manufacturing

15 Manufacture of Food & Beverages
15000 General Food & Drink
15110 Slaughterhouses/Meat Plants
15112 Animal By-Product Processing
15130 Meat Pork Lamb Processing
15132 Poultry Slaughter/Processing
15200 Fish Processing
15330 Processing Fruit/Vegetables
15400 Processing Organic Oils/Fats
15410 Chemical Treatment (Fats/Oils)
15430 Margarine/Fat Cooking Compound
15510 Milk Preparation & Products
15520 Ice Cream
15600 Grain Milling
15700 Compound Animal Feeds
15720 Pet Foods
15800 Miscellaneous Foods
15820 Biscuits & Crispbreads
15830 Sugar/Sugar By products
15840 Chocolate/Sugar Confectionery
15860 Processing of Tea & Coffee
15910 Spirit Compounding/Distilling
15940 Wines Cider & Perry
15950 Brewing & Malting
15980 Soft Drinks

16 Manufacture of Tobacco Products
16000 Tobacco Industry

Blenders Ltd
Unit 4 The IDA Centre
Newmarket
Dublin 8
Phone: 01-4536960 Fax: 01-4537607
SIC: 15000 Employees: 60
Food Manufacture
Mr David Simpson Director
Mr Robin Simpson Finance Manager
Mr David Chandler Sales Director

Cow & Gate (Ireland) Ltd
Unit 1B Sandyford Business Centre
Burton Hall Road
Dublin 18
Phone: 01-2954744 Fax: 01-2061950
Email: info@nutrita-ireland.ie
SIC: 15000 Employees: 80
Baby Food Products
Ms Niamh Rice General Manager
Ms Valerie Plant Finance Manager
Ms Geraldine Bolton Sales Manager
Mr Kevin Therubini Computer Manager

DD Williamson Ireland Ltd
Little Island Industrial Estate
Little Island
Cork Co. Cork
Phone: 021-4353821 Fax: 021-4354328
SIC: 15000 Employees: 30
Manufacture Food Additives
Mr Ted Nixon Proprietor
Mr Martin Corbett Financial Controller
Ms Geraldine Ahern Personnel Manager
Mr David Barrett Sales Manager

Doyles Quality Products
Unit 2 Cookstown Industrial Estate
Tallaght
Dublin 24
Phone: 01-4517177 Fax: 01-4517456
Email: charlotte@doyles.iol.ie
SIC: 15000 Employees: 56
Foods Manufacturing
Mr Pat Maguire Managing Director

Drogheda Concentrates
Industrial Estate
Drogheda Co. Louth
Phone: 041-9849472 Fax: 041-9846435
SIC: 15000 Employees: 272
Manufactures Soft Drink Concentrates
Mr Evan Taylor General Manager

E K Foods Ltd
Bliary Industrial Estate
Athlone Co. Westmeath
Phone: 0902-72019 Fax: 0902-73420
SIC: 15000 Employees: 75
Food Products
Mr Edward Kelly Managing Director

George Richmond Co Ltd
Annaville Avenue
Blackrock Co. Dublin
Phone: 01-2883177 Fax: 01-2885849
SIC: 15000 Employees: 35
Baker Supplies
Mr Joseph Brennan General Manager

Golden Bake Ltd
Unit 4 Malahide Road Industrial Park
Coolock
Dublin 17
Phone: 01-8470857 Fax: 01-8486077
Email: goldenbake@eircom.net
SIC: 15000 Employees: 70
Frozen Pastry
Mr Brian Manning Managing Director
Mr Cecil Manning Finance Manager
Mr Michael O'Carroll General Manager
Mr Martin Connaughton Production Manager
Mr Derek O'Brien Technical Director

Green Isle Food Group
IDA Industrial Estate
Monread Road
Naas Co. Kildare
Phone: 045-876511 Fax: 045-897001
SIC: 15000 Employees: 900
Frozen Food Manufacturers
Mr Billy O'Regan Managing Director

Greencore Group Plc
St Stephen's Green House
Earlsfort Terrace
Dublin 2
Phone: 01-6051000 Fax: 01-6051100
Email: mail@greencore.ie
Web: http://www.greencore.ie
SIC: 15000 Employees: 40
Food Manufacture
Mr David Dilger Chief Executive Officer
Mr Kevin O'Sullivan Finance Manager
Mr Pat Lunney Chief Human Resources Officer
Ms Joan Ryan Computer Manager

Grove Farms
Smithborough
Monaghan Co. Monaghan
Phone: 047-57003 Fax: 047-57253
SIC: 15000 Employees: 243
Food Products - Manufacturing & Distribution
Mr Tom O'Driscoll General Manager
Mr Brendan Maguire Factory Manager

Icon Foods Ltd
Unit 5 Finisklin Industrial Park
Sligo Co. Sligo
Phone: 071-51220 Fax: 071-51221
SIC: 15000 Employees: 75
Food Products
Mr Tony Heath Managing Director

Lime & Lemongrass
2/3 Mary Abbey
Dublin 7
Phone: 01-8722965 Fax: 01-8722993
SIC: 15000 Employees: 23
Manufacture Salad Dressings & Sauces
Mr Richard Baker Manager

Food Manufacturing

Milish Foods
Unit 55 Cookstown Industrial Estate
Tallaght
Dublin 24
Phone: 01-4514433 Fax: 01-4518485
Email: lrowe@indigo.ie
SIC: 15000 Employees: 50
Food Processing
Mr Liam Coughlan Managing Director
Mr Leonard Rowe Financial Controller
Mr Mike Conway Sales & Marketing Manager

Natures Best Ltd
Greenvale Park
Donore Road
Drogheda Co. Louth
Phone: 041-9823546 Fax: 041-9846045
SIC: 15000 Employees: 210
Fresh Food Manufacturer
Mr Paddy Callaghan Managing Director
Mr Hugh O'Brien Finance Manager
Ms Helen Carney Personnel Manager
Mr Shea Coleman Sales Manager

Nestle Ireland
Whitestown Industrial Estate, Blessington Road
Dublin 24
Phone: 01-4512244 Fax: 01-4512823
Email: postmaster@ienestle.com
SIC: 15000 Employees: 430
Food Manufacturing
Mr Eddie Humpreys Chief Executive
Mr Simon Smith Finance Manager
Mr Tony Mullett Human Resources Manager
Mr John Redmond Operations Director
Mr Tom Rossiter IT Manager

Newbridge Foods
Newbridge Industrial Estate
Newbridge Co. Kildare
Phone: 045-434620 Fax: 045-433996
Email: newfoods@indigo.ie
SIC: 15000 Employees: 70
Food Products Manufacturing
Mr David Kitchen Managing Director
Ms Mary Lawlor Accounts Manager
Mr Sean Ryan Personnel Manager

O'Brien Ingredients
Ballymoss Road
Sandyford Industrial Estate
Dublin 18
Phone: 01-2952511 Fax: 01-2952265
Email: sales@obrien-ingredients.ie
SIC: 15000 Employees: 40
Food Products
Mr Bruce O'Brien Partner
Mr Paul O'Brien Finance Manager
Mr Declan Hassett Human Resources Manager
Mr Stanley Lew Sales Manager
Mr Chris Furlong Computer Manager

Pasta Concepts Ltd
Maudlins Industrial Estate
Naas Co. Kildare
Phone: 045-894174 Fax: 045-894175
Email: info@pastaconcepts.ie
SIC: 15000 Employees: 50
Food Products
Mr Olivier Bazin General Manager
Ms Claire Ryan Finance Manager
Mr Brian Cullinane Sales Manager

Walsh Family Foods Ltd
IDA Poppintree Industrial Estate
Finglas
Dublin 11
Phone: 01-8348033 Fax: 01-8348078
Web: http://www.walshfamilyfood.ie
SIC: 15000 Employees: 70
Food Products Manufacturing & Distributors
Mr Patrick McCaughy Managing Director
Mr Joe Bergin Finance Manager
Mr Tony Cahill Production Manager

Windmill Farm Ltd
Main Street
Elphin
Castlerea Co. Roscommon
Phone: 078-35744 Fax: 078-35761
Email: sauce@gofree.indigo.ie
SIC: 15000 Employees: 75
Food Products
Ms Kathleen Brady Proprietor

Zed Gum
Tyrellstown Way
Damastown Ind Pk
Dublin
Phone: 01-8219166 Fax: 01-8219167
Email: info@zedgum.com
Web: http://www.zedgum.com
SIC: 15000 Employees: 60
Manufacture Bubble Gum
Mr Brendan Roantree Proprietor
Ms Audrey Mitton Accounts Manager
Mr Donal Kavanagh Sales & Marketing Director

Blanchvac
Blessington Industrial Estate
Blessington
Naas Co. Kildare
Phone: 045-865273 Fax: 045-865293
SIC: 15110 Employees: 25
Meat Plant
Mr Derek Montgomery Managing Director
Mr Martin McDonagh Sales & Marketing Manager

Carrickmacross Meats
Clough Valley Upper
Industrial Estate
Carrickmacross Co. Monaghan
Phone: 042-9662113 Fax: 042-9662115
SIC: 15110 Employees: 70
Meat Factory
Mr Seamus McCrink Managing Director
Mr Eugene McGinn Financial Director
Ms Marie Donaghy Personnel Manager
Mr John Hannah Sales & Marketing Manager
Mr Declan McMahon Production Manager
Mr Peter Donaghy Computer Manager

Dew Valley Foods Ltd
Holycross Road
Thurles Co. Tipperary
Phone: 0504-46110 Fax: 0504-23405
Email: info@dewvalley.com
Web: http://www.dewvalley.com
SIC: 15110 Employees: 122
Meat Plant
Mr Jack Blake Managing Director
Mr Gerard Cross Finance Manager
Mr Thomas Brennan Personnel Manager
Mr Paul Vince Sales & Marketing Manager

Dublin Products Ltd
Dunlavin
Naas Co. Kildare
Phone: 045-401381 Fax: 045-401313
Email: dproduct@iol.ie
SIC: 15110 Employees: 50
Meat Rendering
Mr Gerry Tierney Managing Director
Mr Nicholas Tierney Finance Manager
Mr Martin Byrne Sales Manager

Greenval Ltd
Ashbury Industrial Estate
Roscrea Co. Tipperary
Phone: 0505-22237 Fax: 0505-22122
SIC: 15110 Employees: 30
Meat Plant
Mr Barry O'Loughlin General Manager
Ms Joanne Turner Secretary

Greenvale (Carlow) Ltd
Montgomery Street
Carlow Co. Carlow
Phone: 0503-41166 Fax: 0503-41681
Email: sales@greenvale.net
Web: http://www.greenvale.net
SIC: 15110 Employees: 75
Meat Plant
Mr Tom O'Loughlin Managing Director
Ms Sheila Fitzpatrick Finance Manager
Mr Laurence Phelan General Manager
Mr Tommy Gorman Production Manager

Honeyclover (Freshford) Ltd
Bridge Street
Freshford
Kilkenny Co. Kilkenny
Phone: 056-32333 Fax: 056-32435
Email: honeyclover@indigo.ie
SIC: 15110 Employees: 150
Meat Plant
Mr Richard Blake Managing Director
Mr Gerard Foskin Group Financial Controller
Mr John Fitzpatrick General Manager
Mr Paul Lanigan Sales Manager

McCarthy Meats Ltd
Clane
Naas Co. Kildare
Phone: 045-868165 Fax: 045-861122
SIC: 15110 Employees: 42
Abbatoir
Mr Jim McCarthy Managing Director
Mr Jim O'Brien Sales & Marketing Manager

MJ Bergin & Sons Ltd
Tandragee
Broadford
Naas Co. Kildare
Phone: 0405-51422 Fax: 0405-51043
SIC: 15110 Employees: 70
Meat Plant
Mr John Bergin Managing Director
Mr Russell Brennan Accountant

O'Herlihys (Bacon) Ltd
Unit 22 Ballincollig Commercial Park
Ballincollig
Cork Co. Cork
Phone: 021-4874077 Fax: 021-4874071
Email: ohbacon@eircom.net
SIC: 15110 Employees: 230
Meat Plant
Mr Noel O'Herlihy Managing Director
Ms Noreen Cronin Finance Manager
Ms Geraldine Daly Personnel Manager
Ms Adrienne McGeough IT Manager

Quin Lok Ltd
Kilcruttin Business Park
Tullamore Co. Offaly
Phone: 0506-23022 Fax: 0506-23022
Email: quinlok@eircom.net
SIC: 15110 Employees: 50
Supply Wood Work
Mr Pat Quinn Proprietor

Slaney Cooked Meats Group
PO Box 8, Ryland
Bunclody
Enniscorthy Co. Wexford
Phone: 054-77477 Fax: 054-77788
Email: sales@slaney.com
Web: http://www.slaney.com
SIC: 15110 Employees: 500
Meat Factory
Mr Bert Allen Managing Director
Mr Pat Aspel Finance Manager
Mr Frank Walshe Personnel Officer
Mr Rory Fanning Sales & Marketing Manager
Mr Brendan Dunne Production Manager
Mr Lesley Warren Computer Manager

Food Manufacturing

Tralee Beef & Lamb Ltd
Monavalley Industrial Estate
Tralee Co. Kerry
Phone: 066-7126411 Fax: 066-7126016
Email: info@traleebl.com
Web: http://www.traleebl.com
SIC: 15110 Employees: 105
Slaughterhouse
Mr John Delaney Managing Director
Mr Alan O'Connell Financial Controller
Ms Valerie O'Leary Receptionist
Mr John O'Dowd Sales Manager

Charles Wynne Ltd
Belan Moone
Athy Co. Kildare
Phone: 0507-24106 Fax: 0507-24236
Email: crwynne@eircom.net
SIC: 15112 Employees: 35
Animal Feed Suppliers
Mr Charles Wynne Managing Director

Corby Rock Eggs Ltd
Ballybay Road
Monaghan Co. Monaghan
Phone: 047-30066 Fax: 047-83104
Email: info@corbyrock.ie
SIC: 15112 Employees: 60
Egg Supplier
Mr Seamus Kelly Managing Director
Ms Bonnie Murphy Finance Manager
Mr Mick Johnston Computer Manager

John Ronan & Sons
Oldbawn Road
Tallaght
Dublin 24
Phone: 01-4511709 Fax: 01-4511186
SIC: 15112 Employees: 100
Skin & Hides
Mr Eddie Fox Manager

Monery By-Products
Monery
Crossdoney
Cavan Co. Cavan
Phone: 049-4337107 Fax: 049-4337555
Email: info@iaws.ie
SIC: 15112 Employees: 26
Animal By Products
Ms Ita Brady General Manager
Mr John Gormley Production Manager

Munster Proteins
Cahir
Tipperary Co. Tipperary
Phone: 052-41088 Fax: 052-42101
Email: munsterproteins@eircom.net
SIC: 15112 Employees: 50
Meat By-Product Processing
Mr Edward Lowry General Manager
Mr Conal Murphy Financial Controller
Mr Noel Brophy Plant Manager

National By-Products Ltd
Castleblake
Rosegreen
Cashel Co. Tipperary
Phone: 052-35104 Fax: 052-35282
SIC: 15112 Employees: 50
Renderers of Bonemeal
Mr Louis Ronan Managing Director
Mr Martin Crowley Financial Controller
Mr Michael Fitzgerald General Manager
Mr Sean Walsh Production Manager

Premier Proteins 2000
Poolboy
Ballinasloe Co. Galway
Phone: 0905-42305 Fax: 0905-42738
SIC: 15112 Employees: 120
Rendering Plant
Mr Noel Ryan Director

Food Manufacturing

AIBP Ltd
Kilcommon
Cahir Co. Tipperary
Phone: 052-41444 Fax: 052-41221
Email: aibpcahir@eircom.net
SIC: 15130 Employees: 280
Beef Processing
Mr Peter Maguire General Manager
Mr Pat Looram Finance Manager
Mr Alan Harris Sales & Marketing Manager

Anglo Irish Beef Packers Ltd
Grange
Nenagh Co. Tipperary
Phone: 067-31199 Fax: 067-33431
SIC: 15130 Employees: 150
Meat Products
Mr Don O'Brien General Manager
Mr Tim Gleeson Finance Manager
Mr Liam White Personnel Officer

Ashbourne Foods Ltd
Castleholding
Roscrea Co. Tipperary
Phone: 0505-21411 Fax: 0505-21910
SIC: 15130 Employees: 37
Meat Processors
Mr Gerry Mehan Manager

Ashgrove Meats Ltd
Dually
Newcastle West
Limerick Co. Limerick
Phone: 069-62865 Fax: 069-62079
Email: ashgrove@iol.ie
SIC: 15130 Employees: 37
Meat Processors
Mr Frank Burke Plant Manager
Mr James Kinnane Finance Director

Baltinglass Meats Ltd
Baltinglass
Wicklow Co. Wicklow
Phone: 0508-81366 Fax: 0508-81013
SIC: 15130 Employees: 40
Meat Processing Plant
Mr Seamus O'Farrell Managing Director
Ms Marian English Financial Controller
Mr Alan Gray Personnel Manager

Barford Meats Ltd
Cloughvalley
Carrickmacross Co. Monaghan
Phone: 042-9661939 Fax: 042-9661940
Email: office@barford.iol.ie
Web: http://www.office.barford.iol.ie
SIC: 15130 Employees: 100
Meat Processors
Mr Seamus McCrink Managing Director
Mr Eugene McGinn Finance Manager
Ms Sharon Stoney Personnel Manager
Mr John Hanna Marketing Director
Mr Joe O'Sullivan Operation Manager

Barry Bros Carrigmore Meats Ltd
Conna
Cork Co. Cork
Phone: 058-59171 Fax: 058-59405
SIC: 15130 Employees: 32
Meat Pork Chicken & Processing
Mr John Barry Managing Director

Callan Bacon Co
Westcourt
Callan
Kilkenny Co. Kilkenny
Phone: 056-25144 Fax: 056-25337
Email: callanb@indigo.ie
SIC: 15130 Employees: 85
Bacon & Pork Processing
Mr John Walshe Managing Director
Ms Geraldine Curran Finance Manager
Ms Caroline Holmes Personnel Manager
Mr Thomas McCluskey Production Manager

Carroll Meats Manufacturing Ltd
Church Road
Tullamore Co. Offaly
Phone: 0506-51183 Fax: 0506-51385
Email: carrollmeatsltd@eircom.net
SIC: 15130 Employees: 75
Meat Processing Plant
Mr Seamus Carroll Managing Director
Mr John Carroll Sales & Marketing Manager
Mr Michael Gonserowski Production Manager
Ms Anna Daly IT Manager

Dawn Meats
Knockgriffin
Midleton Co. Cork
Phone: 021-4631521 Fax: 021-4632055
SIC: 15130 Employees: 300
Meat Products
Mr Niall Brown Manager
Mr Anthony English Financial Controller
Mr Philip Tallon Sales & Marketing Manager
Mr Dan Galvin Production Manager

Dehymeats
Ballast Quay
Sligo Co. Sligo
Phone: 071-61316 Fax: 071-61435
Email: dehymeat@iol.ie
Web: http://www.dehymeats.ie
SIC: 15130 Employees: 40
Meat Products
Mr Patrick Murphy Managing Director
Mr Eugene O'Connell Financial Controller
Mr Brendan Maguire Operations Manager

Fair Oak Foods
Upper Irishtown
Clonmel Co. Tipperary
Phone: 052-21811 Fax: 052-29600
Email: info@fairoakfoods.ie
Web: http://www.fairoakfoods.ie
SIC: 15130 Employees: 280
Meat Processing/Packaging
Mr Michael Behan Managing Director
Ms Marie Lane Financial Controller
Mr John O'Connor General Manager
Mr John Brennan Sales Manager
Mr Richard Dilton Production Manager
Mr John Lewis Computer Manager

Feldhues
Monaghan Road
Clones
Monaghan Co. Monaghan
Phone: 047-51605 Fax: 047-51759
SIC: 15130 Employees: 80
Meat Processors
Mr Joe O'Connell Managing Director
Mr Sean North Production Manager
Mr Mike Hamill Technical Director

Galtee Meats (Charleville) Ltd
Charleville
Cork Co. Cork
Phone: 063-81521 Fax: 063-89613
Email: info@dairygold.ie
Web: http://www.dairygold.ie
SIC: 15130 Employees: 220
Meat Processors
Mr Colm O'Keefe Managing Director
Mr Kevin Keane Accounts Manager
Mr Kenneth Kingston Production Manager

Goldstar Meats
Moyle Road, Dublin Industrial Estate
Glasnevin
Dublin 11
Phone: 01-8309255 Fax: 01-8307322
Email: info@goldstarmeats.ie
Web: http://www.bigals.ie
SIC: 15130 Employees: 190
Meat Processors
Mr Ray Moylan Director
Mr Brendan Cleary Financial Controller
Mr Simon Walker Sales Manager
Mr Ray O'Brien Production Manager

Granby Ltd
38-40 Granby Place
Dublin 1
Phone: 01-8722366 Fax: 01-8722179
Email: granby@indigo.ie
SIC: 15130 Employees: 70
Meat Processors
Mr Patrick Kavanagh Managing Director
Mr Daragh Kavanagh Finance Manager
Mr Maurice Kavanagh Personnel Manager
Mr Owen Kavanagh Computer Manager

Iman Casing & Foods Ltd
Clare Road
Ballyhaunis Co. Mayo
Phone: 0907-30647 Fax: 0907-30895
SIC: 15130 Employees: 37
Sausage Casings
Mr Mohammed Kezze Managing Director

Irish Country Meats
Baylands
Camolin
Enniscorthy Co. Wexford
Phone: 054-66300 Fax: 054-66396
Email: irishcountrymeatscamolin@iol.ie
SIC: 15130 Employees: 120
Meat Processing
Mr Joe Hyland Managing Director
Mr James Geoghegan Financial Controller
Mr Liam Walsh Sales & Marketing Manager

Irish Food Processors
14 Castle Street
Ardee Co. Louth
Phone: 041-6853754 Fax: 041-6853064
Email: info@ardee.aibp.ie
SIC: 15130 Employees: 30
Meat Processing - Export
Mr Laurence Goodman Chief Executive
Mr John O'Donnell Finance Manager
Mr Eamonn Hanley Personnel Manager
Mr Mike Tarrant Marketing Manager
Mr Alan Scanlan DP Manager

Jas Farrell & Sons Ltd
Pipe Street
Thomastown
Kilkenny Co. Kilkenny
Phone: 056-24158 Fax: 056-24349
SIC: 15130 Employees: 37
Meats
Mr Jas Farrell Proprietor
Mr Seamus Farrell Sales Director

Kepak Ltd
Rathmore
Ballymahon
Longford Co. Longford
Phone: 0902-32411 Fax: 0902-32402
Email: postmaster@kepak.com
SIC: 15130 Employees: 750
Beef Products Processing
Mr Martin Finucane Managing Director
Mr John O'Toole Financial Controller
Mr Brian Donoghue Personnel Director
Mr Brian Finnegan Sales & Marketing Manager
Mr Dermot Milner Production Manager

Kiely Meats
Grannagh
Waterford Co. Waterford
Phone: 051-878195 Fax: 051-858977
SIC: 15130 Employees: 36
Meat Processing
Mr Stan Kiely Proprietor
Ms Aileen Doherty Accounts Manager

Kieran Hartnett
Ballinorig West
Tralee Co. Kerry
Phone: 066-7126513 Fax: 066-7129753
SIC: 15130 Employees: 37
Meat Pork Chicken Processing
Mr Kieran Hartnett Managing Director

Food Manufacturing

Kildare Chilling Company
Kildare Co. Kildare
Phone: 045-521200 Fax: 045-522061
Email: kcc@eircom.net
SIC: 15130 Employees: 400
Meat Processor & Exporter
Mr Thomas McParland Managing Director
Mr George Ryan Finance Manager
Mr PJ Whelan Personnel Manager
Mr Joe Bourke Sales & Marketing Manager
Mr David Wright Production Manager
Mr Jim Kennedy Computer Manager

Liffey Meats Ltd
Ballyjamesduff Co. Cavan
Phone: 049-8544377 Fax: 049-8544378
Email: info@liffeymeats.ie
Web: http://www.liffeymeats.ie
SIC: 15130 Employees: 300
Meat Processors
Mr Francis Mallon Managing Director
Mr John Murphy Finance Manager
Mr Christie Kett Personnel Manager
Mr Sean MacNamara Sales & Marketing Manager

M & M Walshe & Company Ltd
Unit 7 Raheen Food Centre
Raheen Industrial Estate
Limerick Co. Limerick
Phone: 061-304166 Fax: 061-303595
SIC: 15130 Employees: 30
Vacuum Packed Bacon/Pork
Ms Geraldine Clohessy Managing Director
Mr Seamus O'Donoghue Sales & Marketing Manager

McCorren & Company
Farnaham Road
Cavan Co. Cavan
Phone: 049-4331500 Fax: 049-4361275
SIC: 15130 Employees: 103
Bacon and Pork Processors
Mr Andrew McCorren Managing Director
Mr Jim Ward Finance Manager
Mr Christopher McCorren Production Manager
Mr Pat McEnroe Computer Manager

Michael Staunton & Sons Ltd
Spital Cross
Timoleague
Bandon Co. Cork
Phone: 023-46128 Fax: 023-46066
Email: staun@esatclear.ie
SIC: 15130 Employees: 40
Pork & Bacon Products
Mr Peadar Murphy Managing Director
Ms Therese Staunton Finance Manager

Moyvalley Meats
Tanderagee
Broadford
Naas Co. Kildare
Phone: 0405-51041 Fax: 0405-51043
SIC: 15130 Employees: 120
Meat Processing
Mr Padraig Melvin Managing Director

O'Farrell Meats Ltd
Knockgriffin
Midleton Co. Cork
Phone: 021-4632131 Fax: 021-4632003
SIC: 15130 Employees: 37
Meat Processors
Mr Keith Bitesse Managing Director
Mr Edward O'Farrell Sales Manager

Oakpark Foods Ltd
Clogheen Road
Cahir Co. Tipperary
Phone: 052-41600 Fax: 052-41490
Email: info@oakparkfoods.ie
SIC: 15130 Employees: 50
Meat Processing
Mr James Brett Managing Director
Ms Helen Morrissey Finance Manager
Mr William O'Sullivan Sales Manager
Mr Philip Harte Production Manager

Olhausens Ltd
Unit 3 Malahide Road Industrial Park
Coolock
Dublin 17
Phone: 01-8472708 Fax: 01-8671999
Email: sales@olhausens.com
Web: http://www.olhausens.com
SIC: 15130 Employees: 180
Meat Processing Plant
Mr Denis Murphy Managing Director
Mr Niall Redmond Finance Manager
Mr Brian Geoghegan Personnel Director
Mr Des Hurley Sales & Marketing Manager
Mr Declan Williamson Production Director

Parkview Pork Products
2 JFK Industrial Estate, Naas Road
Dublin 12
Phone: 01-4500762 Fax: 01-4505529
Email: parkpro@indigo.ie
SIC: 15130 Employees: 40
Meat Processing
Mr Damian Ryan Managing Director
Ms Carmel Ryan Finance Manager
Mr Gary Ryan Sales Manager

Rangeland Meats Ltd
Tullynamalra
Castleblayney Co. Monaghan
Phone: 042-9745132 Fax: 042-9745030
Email: sales@rangelandmeats.iol.ie
Web: http://www.rangelandmeats.iol.ie
SIC: 15130 Employees: 79
Meat Processing Plant
Mr Jim Lucey Managing Director
Ms Sheila McShane Financial Accountant
Mr John Ward Production Manager
Mr Paul Hughes Plant Manager

Real Food Company Tallow Ltd
Barrack Street
Tallow
Waterford Co. Waterford
Phone: 058-56796 Fax: 058-56068
Email: realfood@gofree.indigo.ie
SIC: 15130 Employees: 37
Meat Processors
Mr John Delaney Manager

Sean Duffy & Company
The Square
Gort
Galway Co. Galway
Phone: 091-631126 Fax: 091-631968
Email: seanduffyexportsltd@eircom.net
SIC: 15130 Employees: 150
Meat
Mr Sean Duffy Proprietor

Silvercrest Foods
Corkeeran
Ballybay
Castleblayney Co. Monaghan
Phone: 042-9748400 Fax: 042-9748499
Email: info@silvercrest.ie
Web: http://www.silvercrest.ie
SIC: 15130 Employees: 50
Meat Processors
Mr Paul McBride General Manager
Ms Mary Hanlan Accountant
Mr John McGinnity Personnel Manager
Mr Dermot McArdle Sales Director

Tendermeats Ltd
17B Canal Turn
Clondalkin Industrial Estate
Dublin 22
Phone: 01-4575300 Fax: 01-4575277
SIC: 15130 Employees: 60
Meat Processing
Mr Terence Ryan Managing Director
Mr Joe Roddy Accounts Manager
Mr Kevin Murphy Sales Manager
Mr Paddy Farrelly Production Manager

Cappoquinn Chickens
Lefanta
Cappoquin
Waterford Co. Waterford
Phone: 058-54402 Fax: 058-54668
Email: cappo@iol.ie
SIC: 15132 Employees: 300
Poultry Processors
Mr Michael O'Connor Managing Director
Mr Tom Vaughan Accountant
Mr Eoin Russell Production Manager

Castlemahon Food Products
Castlemahon
Limerick Co. Limerick
Phone: 069-72344 Fax: 069-72211
SIC: 15132 Employees: 330
Chicken Processing
Mr Gerry O'Dwyer Chief Executive
Mr Sean Coke Human Resources Manager
Mr Jim Woulse Sales Manager

Co-Operative Poultry Products Ltd
Dyan
Cootehill Co. Cavan
Phone: 049-5552200 Fax: 049-5552728
SIC: 15132 Employees: 50
Poultry Slaughter/Processing
Mr JackScot Gormley Managing Director
Ms Annie Gallagher Personnel Manager
Mr Eddie Dawson Sales Manager

Cobb Ireland Ltd
New Road
Straffan
Naas Co. Kildare
Phone: 01-6288358 Fax: 01-6273150
Email: cobbchic@indigo.ie
SIC: 15132 Employees: 50
Hatchery
Mr Daniel Lenihan Managing Director
Ms Margaret Green Company Accountant

Glenhaven Foods
Kilbride Industrial Estate
Arklow Co. Wicklow
Phone: 0402-39000 Fax: 0402-39100
SIC: 15132 Employees: 70
Manufacture Frozen Poultry Products
Mr David Cahill Managing Director
Mr Paul Sheedy Finance Manager
Mr Hugh McLoughlin Sales & Marketing Manager
Mr Paul Doran Production Director
Ms Mary McGrath Personal Assistant

Greenfields Foods Ltd
Smithborough
Monaghan Co. Monaghan
Phone: 047-57014 Fax: 047-57335
Email: postmaster@greenfieldfoods.com
Web: http://www.greenfieldfoods.com
SIC: 15132 Employees: 30
Poultry Slaughter/Processing
Mr John Mohan Manager
Mr Martin Donohue Sales Manager
Ms Marie Mohan Computer Manager

Grove Farm
Robinhood Industrial Estate
Ballymount
Dublin 12
Phone: 01-4564755 Fax: 01-4507866
SIC: 15132 Employees: 96
Poultry
Mr Paul Traynor Office Manager

Food Manufacturing

Kellistown Chickens Ltd
Pollerton Industrial Estate
Carlow Co. Carlow
Phone: 0503-31612 Fax: 0503-42875
Email: postmaster@cartongroup.ie
SIC: 15132 Employees: 36
Poultry Processing
Ms Susan Carey Managing Director
Mr Gerard Foley Sales Manager

Monaghan Poultry Products
Gallinagh
Monaghan Co. Monaghan
Phone: 047-30200 Fax: 047-30252
Email:
SIC: 15132 Employees: 300
Poultry Processing
Mr Barry McEntee Chief Executive
Mr B O'Driscoll Financial Controller
Mr Brendan McBride Sales Manager

Pallas Foods Ltd
Station Road
Newcastle West
Limerick Co. Limerick
Phone: 069-20200 Fax: 069-20201
Email: info@pallasfoods.com
SIC: 15132 Employees: 170
Poultry Processing & Food Service Distribution
Mr Tim Geary Managing Director
Mr David Geary Finance Manager
Mr Jim Herlihy Sales Manager
Mr Damien Dowling Computer Manager

Shalvey Poultry Ltd
Corragarry
Canningstown
Cootehill Co. Cavan
Phone: 042-9660555 Fax: 042-9660572
Email: gshalv@eircom.net
SIC: 15132 Employees: 30
Poultry Processing
Mr Gabriel Shalvey Proprietor
Ms Carmel O'Reilly Finance Manager
Ms Carmel Shalvey Human Resources Manager
Ms Lisa McCabe Sales Manager
Ms Mary Moore Production Manager

Shannon Vale Foods Ltd
Gullane
Clonakilty Co. Cork
Phone: 023-33608 Fax: 023-34482
Email: shfoods@iol.ie
SIC: 15132 Employees: 80
Poultry Processing
Ms Phil O'Regan Managing Director
Mr Liam Santry Finance Manager
Mr Noel O'Callaghan Sales & Marketing Manager
Mr Kieran O'Regan Production Manager

Springvale Poultry Products Ltd
Limerick Road
Kildorry
Mallow Co. Cork
Phone: 022-25145 Fax: 022-25402
SIC: 15132 Employees: 30
Poultry Slaughter/Processing
Mr Joe Carney Proprietor
Mr Kieran Carney Sales & Marketing Manager
Mr Geoff Whales Production Manager

Western Brand Chickens Ltd
Knock Road
Ballyhaunis Co. Mayo
Phone: 0907-30069 Fax: 0907-30834
SIC: 15132 ,Employees: 120
Poultry Processing
Mr Eugene Lannon Managing Director
Mr Michael O'Keefe Financial Controller
Mr George McGrath Materials Manager
Mr Michael Jordon Computer Manager

Atlanfish (Ireland) Ltd
Malin Road
Carndonagh
Lifford Co. Donegal
Phone: 077-74285 Fax: 077-74685
Email: atlan@iol.ie
SIC: 15200 Employees: 38
Fish Processing
Mr Gareth Gallagher Managing Director
Mr Declan McCarty Accountant

Atlantic Dawn Ltd
Elmwood Terrace
Killybegs
Donegal Co. Donegal
Phone: 073-31644 Fax: 073-31646
Email: info@atlanticdawn.com
Web: http://www.atlanticdawn.com
SIC: 15200 Employees: 100
Frozen Food Processing
Mr Kevin McHugh Managing Director
Mr Niall O'Gorman Financial Controller
Mr Pat Rowan Office Manager
Mr Patrick O'Reilly Production Manager

Bantry Bay Seafoods
Gortalassa
Bantry Co. Cork
Phone: 027-50977 Fax: 027-50943
Email: info@bantrybayseafoods.ie
Web: http://www.bantrybayseafoods.ie
SIC: 15200 Employees: 55
Shellfish Processing
Mr Denis O'Driscoll Managing Director
Mr Paul Connolly Financial Controller
Mr Denis Minihane Sales & Marketing Director
Mr Ian Corkery Production Manager

Burtonport Fishermans Co-Op
Burtonport
Letterkenny Co. Donegal
Phone: 075-42046 Fax: 075-42166
Email: bportfishsales@eircom.net
SIC: 15200 Employees: 95
Fish Processing
Mr Connor Boyce General Manager
Mr Conor McBride Finance Manager

Carokeel Seafoods
Station House
Shankill
Dublin 18
Phone: 01-2823688 Fax: 01-2826592
SIC: 15200 Employees: 220
Fish Processing
Mr Brendan Chambers Managing Director
Mr Ciaran Cronin Financial Controller

Castletownbere Fishermans Co-Op
The Pier
Castletownbere
Bantry Co. Cork
Phone: 027-70045 Fax: 027-70194
SIC: 15200 Employees: 85
Export Fish
Mr John Nolan Chief Executive
Mr Brendan Finch Accountant
Mr Donal O'Sullivan Sales & Marketing Manager

Clare Island Sea Farm
Clogmore
Achill
Westport Co. Mayo
Phone: 098-45375 Fax: 098-45378
Email: efish@emerarldfisheries.ie
Web: http://www.emerarldfisheries.ie
SIC: 15200 Employees: 25
Organic Salmon Farm
Mr David Baird Managing Director

Eiranova Fisheries Ltd
Dinish Island
Castletownbere
Bantry Co. Cork
Phone: 027-70249 Fax: 027-70085
SIC: 15200 Employees: 45
Fish Catching and Processing
Mr Brendan Minehane Managing Director

Errigal Fish Ltd
Meenaneary
Carrick
Donegal Co. Donegal
Phone: 073-39023 Fax: 073-39114
Email: errigal@iol.ie
SIC: 15200 Employees: 150
Fish Processing
Mr Hugh O'Donnell Managing Director
Mr John Shannon Finance Manager
Mr Tom Glynn Sales Manager
Ms Teresa McLoughlin Secretary

Gaelic Seafood Ireland Ltd
Unit 9 Glornamar
New Docks Street
Galway Co. Galway
Phone: 091-565522 Fax: 091-565371
SIC: 15200 Employees: 60
Fish Farm
Mr Robert Forman Managing Director
Mr Thomas O'Griofa Financial Controller
Ms Breda Kenna Personnel Manager
Mr Michael O'Malley Production Manager

Gallagher Bros Ltd
Killybegs
Donegal Co. Donegal
Phone: 073-31004 Fax: 073-31509
Email: fish@gallagherbros.ie
Web: http://www.gallagherbros.ie
SIC: 15200 Employees: 240
Fish Processing
Mr Tadhg Gallagher General Manager
Ms Ann Gallagher Finance Manager
Ms Tina McFadden Office Manager
Mr Donal Campbell Production Manager

HJ Nolan Ltd
Rathdown Road
Dublin 7
Phone: 01-8680066 Fax: 01-8680260
Email: nolanhj@iol.ie
SIC: 15200 Employees: 60
Fish Processing
Mr George Nolan Managing Director
Mr James Lawlor Financial Controller
Mr Matthew Farrell Sales Manager
Mr Alan Bellemy Production Manager
Mr Kevin Brady Computer Manager

Irfish Ltd
The Harbour
Dunmore East
Waterford Co. Waterford
Phone: 051-383233 Fax: 051-383767
SIC: 15200 Employees: 45
Fish Processing
Mr Andrew Verwijs Director

Island Seafoods Ltd
Carricknamohill
Killybegs
Donegal Co. Donegal
Phone: 073-31216 Fax: 073-31633
SIC: 15200 Employees: 35
Fish Processing
Mr Bobby Cunningham Joint Managing Director
Mr Mick O'Donnell Joint Managing Director

Food Manufacturing

Kenmare Salmon Co
Kilmurry, Kenmare
Killarney Co. Kerry
Phone: 064-41422 Fax: 064-41414
SIC: 15200 Employees: 24
Fish Processing
Mr Remi Benoit Managing Director
Mr Ronan Cullen Sales & Marketing Manager
Mr Sean Jones Factory Manager

Killary Salmon Ltd
Rosroe
Renvyle
Galway Co. Galway
Phone: 095-43523 Fax: 095-43403
Email: killarysalmon@eircom.net
SIC: 15200 Employees: 45
Salmon Farms
Mr James Ryan Manager
Ms Leslie Sammon Administrator

Killybegs Seafoods Ltd
Conlin Road
Killybegs
Donegal Co. Donegal
Phone: 073-31028 Fax: 073-31597
Email: jmg@killybegsseafoods.com
Web: http://www.killybegsseafoods.com
SIC: 15200 Employees: 150
Fish Processors
Mr Sean McGuinness Managing Director
Mr Hugh McFadden Foreman
Mr John McGuinness Sales & Marketing Manager

Kilmore Fish Company Ltd
Kilmore Quay
Wexford Co. Wexford
Phone: 053-29755 Fax: 053-29700
Email: info@cki.ie
SIC: 15200 Employees: 45
Fish Processing
Mr Paul Younger Manager
Mr Eamon O'Hanlon Finance Manager

Lett Group
Batt Street
Wexford Co. Wexford
Phone: 053-22811 Fax: 053-22678
Email: lettgrp@iol.ie
SIC: 15200 Employees: 350
Fish Processing
Mr James Lett Chief Executive
Mr Desmond Lett General Manager

Marine Harvest Ireland
Kindrum
Fanad
Letterkenny Co. Donegal
Phone: 074-59071 Fax: 074-59077
Web: http://www.marineharvest.com
SIC: 15200 Employees: 160
Salmon Farm
Mr Jan Feenstran General Manager
Mr Damian O'Toole Financial Controller
Mr Pat Connors Production Manager

Padraig Mulloy Shellfish Ltd
Carrowbeg
Kilmeena
Westport Co. Mayo
Phone: 098-41328 Fax: 098-41666
Email: csf@iol.ie
SIC: 15200 Employees: 24
Shellfish Purification and Processing Plant
Mr Andy Molloy Managing Director
Ms Ann-Marie Molloy Sales Manager

Polar Fish
Killybegs
Donegal Co. Donegal
Phone: 073-31114 Fax: 073-31512
Email: polarfish@eircom.net
SIC: 15200 Employees: 120
Fish Processing
Mr John Ward General Manager
Mr John Brennan Financial Controller
Mr Pauraic Breslin Sales Manager
Mr Jim O'Donnell IT Manager

Proiseail Teoranta
Meenmore
Dungloe
Letterkenny Co. Donegal
Phone: 075-21100 Fax: 075-21287
Email: proiseail@eircom.net
SIC: 15200 Employees: 50
Fish Smokers, Curers & Packers
Mr Donal Johnston Manager

Red Sail Kilmore Ltd
Kilmore Quay
Wexford Co. Wexford
Phone: 053-29627 Fax: 053-29668
Email: edsailk@indigo.ie
SIC: 15200 Employees: 50
Fish Processing
Mr Derek Younger Managing Director
Mr Denis Murphy Financial Controller

Sofrimar
Kilmore Quay
Wexford Co. Wexford
Phone: 053-29660 Fax: 053-29699
Email: sofrimar@tinet.ie
SIC: 15200 Employees: 90
Fish Processing
Mr Leslie Bates Managing Director
Mr Lorcan Barden Financial Controller

Batchelors Ltd
Rathstewart Mills
Athy Co. Kildare
Phone: 0507-31589 Fax: 0507-32149
SIC: 15330 Employees: 250
Vegetable Canning
Mr Brendan Curley Manager

Gem Pack Foods Ltd
Cherry Orchard Industrial Estate
Ballyfermot
Dublin 10
Phone: 01-6267756 Fax: 01-6263890
Email: info@gempackfoods.ie
SIC: 15330 Employees: 40
Manufacture Dried Fruit & Cereal
Mr Paddy Mulligan Managing Director
Mr Oliver Cronin Finance Manager
Mr Bobby Mulligan Sales Manager

Grennan Mills
Rath
Birr Co. Offaly
Phone: 0509-33002 Fax: 0509-33054
SIC: 15330 Employees: 24
Field Bean Processing
Mr John Grennan Managing Director
Mr Michael Burke Finance Manager
Mr Frank Pey Personnel Director
Mr Tim Guinan Sales Representative

Hugh McNulty Wholesalers
13/17 Little Britain Street
Dublin 7
Phone: 01-8721100 Fax: 01-8730018
Email: info@fyffes.com
SIC: 15330 Employees: 25
Fruit Importers
Mr Liam King Joint Managing Director
Ms Breda Temple Financial Controller
Mr Tony O'Hara Sales Manager
Mr Ben O'Sullivan Joint Managing Director

John Dockrell Market Gardener
Burrow Road
Portrane
Swords Co. Dublin
Phone: 01-8436067 Fax: 01-8436996
SIC: 15330 Employees: 35
Vegetable Growing
Mr Tony Doyle Manager
Mr John Dockrell Proprietor

Pierres Food Services
Bond Road
Dublin 3
Phone: 01-8557200 Fax: 01-8556671
SIC: 15330 Employees: 30
Frozen Vegetables & Meat
Mr Kieran O'Donoghan General Manager
Mr Brian O'Keith Sales & Marketing Manager

Dromkeen Food Ingredients
Dromkeen
Limerick Co. Limerick
Phone: 061-384533 Fax: 061-384534
SIC: 15430 Employees: 30
Manufacturers of Edible Proteins Fats & Phosphates
Mr Noel Nicholas Managing Director

James Daly & Sons Ltd
John F Connolly Road
Churchfield
Cork Co. Cork
Phone: 021-4301363 Fax: 021-4393384
Email: info@jamesdaly.ie
Web: http://www.jamesdaly.ie
SIC: 15430 Employees: 28
Manufacture Margarine & Bakery Sundries
Mr Charlie Fleury Managing Director
Mr Connor Foley Finance Manager
Mr Neil White Sales Manager
Mr Philip Murphy Production Manager

Arrabawn Co-Operative Society Ltd
Nenagh Co. Tipperary
Phone: 067-33204 Fax: 067-32232
Email: info@nenaghcoop.ie
Web: http://www.nenaghcoop.ie
SIC: 15510 Employees: 36
Creamery
Mr James Murphy Chief Executive

Bailey Foods Ltd
Old Cheese Factory
Bailieborough Co. Cavan
Phone: 042-9694234 Fax: 042-9665534
Email: info@goldenvale.com
Web: http://www.goldenvalen.com
SIC: 15510 Employees: 60
Make Butter & Milk Powder
Mr Gerry Carlon General Manager
Mr Liam Carlon Finance Manager
Ms Anne Tierney Customer Services
Mr Martin Nulty Production Manager

Carbery Group
Ballineen
Cork Co. Cork
Phone: 023-47222 Fax: 023-47541
Email: info@carbery.com
Web: http://www.carbery.com
SIC: 15510 Employees: 160
Dairy Processing Group
Mr Dan MacSweeney Chief Executive
Mr Colm Leen Finance Director
Mr Michael McCarthy Office Manager
Mr Noel Corcoran Sales Manager
Mr Pat Calnan IT Manager

Clare Dairies Golden Vale Ltd
Quinn Road
Ennis Co. Clare
Phone: 065-6824586 Fax: 065-6820233
Email: info@goldenvale.ie
Web: http://www.goldenvale.ie
SIC: 15510 Employees: 100
Dairies
Ms Pat Falbey Manager

Food Manufacturing

Clona Dairy Products
Sand Quay
Clonakilty Co. Cork
Phone: 023-33324 Fax: 023-33530
Email: clona@indigo.ie
SIC: 15510 Employees: 63
Dairy Products
Mr Tony O'Driscoll General Manager
Mr Martin Long Financial Controller
Mr Brian Whelton Production Manager

CMP Dairy
Kinsale Road
Cork Co. Cork
Phone: 021-4964000 Fax: 021-4313201
Email: cmpmkt@dairygold.ie
Web: http://www.dairygold.ie
SIC: 15510 Employees: 86
Dairies
Mr Tom Garraghy Manager

Compsey Creamery Society Ltd
Mullinahone
Tipperary Co. Tipperary
Phone: 052-53357 Fax: 052-53289
Email: info@mull-coop.ie
Web: http://www.mull-coop.ie
SIC: 15510 Employees: 70
Dairy Products
Mr Michael Dwyer Managing Director
Mr Gerard Flynn Financial Director
Mr Nigel Whittaker Sales & Marketing Manager
Mr Donal O'Mahony Production & Purchasing Manage
Mr Keith Bowden Computer Manager

Coolea Farmhouse Cheese
Milleens
Coolea
Macroom Co. Cork
Phone: 026-45204 Fax: 026-45732
SIC: 15510 Employees: 40
Cheese Manufacturing
Mr Dick Williams Proprietor

Dairymaster
Causeway
Tralee Co. Kerry
Phone: 066-7131124 Fax: 066-7131670
Email: info@dairymaster.com
Web: http://www.dairymaster.com
SIC: 15510 Employees: 60
Dairy Products
Mr Edmund Hardy Managing Director
Ms Mary Hardy Accounts Manager
Mr Stephen Pierse Production Manager

Dawn Dairies Ltd
Dublin Road
Tuam Co. Galway
Phone: 091-770580 Fax: 091-755725
SIC: 15510 Employees: 120
Milk Creameries
Mr Paul Keyes Manager
Mr Padraig Fitzmaurice Financial Controller
Ms Grainne Murphy Personnel Officer
Ms Patricia Murphy Sales Manager

Donegal Creameries Plc
Killygordan
Lifford Co. Donegal
Phone: 074-49127 Fax: 074-49560
Email: info@donegal-creameries.ie
Web: http://www.donegal-creameries.ie
SIC: 15510 Employees: 144
Milk Products
Mr Michael Murphy General Manager
Mr Dominic Kelly Accountant
Mr Donal Reid Sales & Marketing Director

Glanbia Plc
Glanbia House
Kilkenny Co. Kilkenny
Phone: 056-72200 Fax: 056-72222
Email: info@glanbia.ie
Web: http://www.glanbia.ie
SIC: 15510 Employees: 7300
Milk & Milk Products
Mr John Moloney Group Managing Director
Mr Geoff Meagher Group Financial Director
Mr Tony Plunkett Group Director of HS
Mr Jim Bergin Business Process Director

Golden Vale Plc
Kilmallock Road
Charleville
Cork Co. Cork
Phone: 063-81501 Fax: 063-35001
Email: headoffice@goldenvale.com
SIC: 15510 Employees: 2640
Dairy Products
Mr James Murphy Group Managing Director
Mr Liam Irvine Group Finance Director
Mr Sexton Cahill Human Resource Director
Ms Denise O'Riordan Sales Manager
Mr Martin Dullea Production Manager
Mr Ray Lavery IT Director

Irish Dairy Board
Gratten House, Lower Mount Street
Dublin 2
Phone: 01-6022372 Fax: 01-6622941
Email: idb@idb.ie
Web: http://www.idb.ie
SIC: 15510 Employees: 200
Dairy Products
Mr Noel Cawley Managing Director
Mr Frank O'Reilly Financial Director
Ms Eva Hanley Human Resources Manager
Mr Ivan Hayes International Sales Director
Mr Dan O'Callaghan IT Manager

Irish Yogurts Ltd
Scartagh
Clonakilty Co. Cork
Phone: 023-34745 Fax: 023-35791
Email: irishyogarts@oceanfree.net
Web: http://www.irish/yogarts.com
SIC: 15510 Employees: 60
Dairy Products
Mr Diarmuid O'Sullivan Managing Director
Ms Marion Herriott Office Manager

Kerry Group Plc
Prince's Street
Tralee Co. Kerry
Phone: 066-7182000 Fax: 066-7182961
Email: info@kerrygroup.com
Web: http://www.kerrygroup.com
SIC: 15510 Employees: 12650
Consumer Foods & Ingredients
Dr Denis Brosnan Group Managing Director
Mr Michael Ryan Financial Controller
Mr Adrian Grey Personnel Director
Mr Conor Kavanagh Computer Manager

Killarney Dairies
Kilcoolaght
Killarney Co. Kerry
Phone: 064-31135 Fax: 064-31804
Email: dawn.killarney@kerry.ie
SIC: 15510 Employees: 50
Milk Preparation & Products
Mr Gerard Coughlan General Manager
Mr Denis Calnan Financial Controller
Mr Michael Murphy Sales Manager
Mr Donal O'Mahony Production Manager
Ms Kathleen Chambers Computer Manager

Lakeland Dairies
Killeshandra
Cavan Co. Cavan
Phone: 049-4364200 Fax: 049-4364201
Email: info@lakelanddairies.ie
Web: http://www.lakeland.ie
SIC: 15510 Employees: 100
Dairy Processing
Mr Desmond Boyla Chairman
Mr Patrick Smith Finance Director
Ms Halinna Mc Evoy Human Resources Manager

Lee Strand Co-Operative
Ballymullen
Tralee Co. Kerry
Phone: 066-7121084 Fax: 066-7125698
SIC: 15510 Employees: 40
Dairy Products
Mr William Kennedy Managing Director
Mr Tim O'Keeffe Financial Controller
Mr Gerry Dwyer Production Manager
Mr Michael Mangan Computer Manager

Lisavaird Co-Op
Lisavaird
Clonakilty Co. Cork
Phone: 023-33334 Fax: 023-34379
Email: admin@lisavairdcoop.ie
Web: http://www.lisavairdcoop.ie
SIC: 15510 Employees: 83
Milk Preparation & Products
Mr Patrick Dineen Chief Executive
Mr Dermot Coakley Accountant
Mr Anthony O'Brien Sales & Marketing Manager
Mr Edward Draper Computer Manager

Newtownsandes Co-op
Moyvane
Listowel Co. Kerry
Phone: 068-49354 Fax: 068-49431
SIC: 15510 Employees: 36
Creameries
Mr Michael Liston Managing Director

North Cork Co-Op Creameries Ltd
Strand Street
Kanturk
Mallow Co. Cork
Phone: 029-50003 Fax: 029-50860
Email: info@northcorkco-op.com
SIC: 15510 Employees: 54
Co-Op Creameries
Mr Sean McAuliffe Manager
Mr Gerard Meehan Finance Manager
Mr Gerry James Personnel Manager
Mr Tim Murphy Sales Manager
Mr Tom Griffin Operations Manager

Oranmore Dairies
Oranmore
Galway Co. Galway
Phone: 091-794162 Fax: 091-794509
SIC: 15510 Employees: 50
Milk Production
Mr Pat Kenironn Proprietor
Mr Damian Feeney Finance Manager
Mr Brian Kennedy Marketing Manager
Mr Jim Finn Production Manager

Pure-Fresh Dairies Ltd
Castle Road
Ballina Co. Mayo
Phone: 096-72488 Fax: 096-70610
SIC: 15510 Employees: 25
Milk Preparation & Products
Mr Martin Dervin Manager
Mr Damien Devaney Finance Manager

Food Manufacturing

Shannonside Milk Products Co-Op Ltd
Dublin Road
Ballaghadereen
Castlerea Co. Roscommon
Phone: 0907-60114 Fax: 0907-60157
Email: shannons@iol.ie
SIC: 15510 Employees: 70
Export & Manufacture Dairy Foods
Mr Tom Farrell Managing Director
Mr Willie Murphy Production Manager
Mr David Hickey Marketing Sales Manager

Sligo Dairies Ltd
Barnasraghy
Sligo Co. Sligo
Phone: 071-60883 Fax: 071-69722
SIC: 15510 Employees: 30
Dairy Products
Mr Frank McKiernan Managing Director
Mr Joe Wilson Office Manager
Mr Peadar Kivlehan Sales & Marketing Manager
Mr Gerry O'Rourke Production Manager

Tipperary Co-op Creamery Ltd
Station Road
Tipperary Co. Tipperary
Phone: 062-33111 Fax: 062-51963
SIC: 15510 Employees: 250
Creameries
Mr Sean Murray Chairman
Mr J Horgan General Manager
Mr Patrick O'Dwyer Vice Chairman

Town of Monaghan Co-op
Coolshannagh
Monaghan Co. Monaghan
Phone: 047-81400 Fax: 047-82940
Email:
SIC: 15510 Employees: 124
Dairy Produce Manufacturers
Mr Vincent Gilhawley Chief Executive
Mr Tommy McLoughlin Financial Controller

Traditional Cheese Co Ltd
224 Holly Road Western Ind Estate
Dublin 12
Phone: 01-4509494 Fax: 01-4506261
Email: tcctelesales@eircom.net
SIC: 15510 Employees: 30
Cheese Production
Mr Eugene Carr Managing Director
Ms Grainne Whalley Marketing Manager

West Cork Natural Cheese Ltd
Dereenatra
Schull
Skibbereen Co. Cork
Phone: 028-28593 Fax: 028-28593
Email: dh@wcnc.ie
Web: http://www.wcnc.ie
SIC: 15510 Employees: 60
Farmhouse Cheese
Mr B Hogan Managing Director
Mr Sean Ferry Sales & Marketing Manager

Wexford Creamery Ltd
Rocklands
Wexford Co. Wexford
Phone: 053-42088 Fax: 053-43321
SIC: 15510 Employees: 100
Creamery
Dr Seamus O'Beirne Managing Director
Mr Eamon Murphy Finance Manager
Mr Bernard Rutdlege Production Manager

Silver Pail Dairy
Dublin Road
Fermoy Co. Cork
Phone: 025-31466 Fax: 025-32126
SIC: 15520 Employees: 80
Ice Cream Manufacturers
Mr Michael Murphy Managing Director
Mr Stephen O'Sullivan Financial Controller
Mr John Murphy Production Manager

Bolands Mills
33 Barrow Street
Dublin 4
Phone: 01-6680794 Fax: 01-6680334
Web: http://www.iaws.ie
SIC: 15600 Employees: 50
Flour Milling
Mr John McInerney Managing Director
Mr Ronan Hughes Finance Manager
Mr Noel Hayden Sales Manager
Mr Mark Robinson Operations Manager

NC FCo-Operative
Ballaghaderreen
Castlerea Co. Roscommon
Phone: 0907-60234 Fax: 0907-60234
SIC: 15600 Employees: 23
Provender Milling
Mr Gabriel Lavin Managing Director
Mr Michael McGowan Marketing Manager
Mr Tony Gilligen Production Manager

Odlums Group Ltd
Alexandra Road
Dublin 1
Phone: 01-8887500 Fax: 01-8741866
Email: odlums@iol.ie
Web: http://www.odlums.ie
SIC: 15600 Employees: 500
Flour Millers
Mr Jim Henry Chief Executive
Ms Suzanne Dickenson Financial Controller
Mr Brian Poland Sales & Marketing Manager

Wicklow Corn Company Ltd
Tinakilly
Rathnew
Wicklow Co. Wicklow
Phone: 0404-67027 Fax: 0404-69748
Email: wickcorn@eircom.net
SIC: 15600 Employees: 40
Grain/Solid Fuel/Oil Company
Mr John McCairn Managing Director
Mr Patrick Brady Finance Manager
Mr James Wilkinson Sales Manager
Mr Orville Roache Production Manager
Mr Tom Ferguson Computer Manager

Brownes Cash Stores
Castleisland
Tralee Co. Kerry
Phone: 066-7141216 Fax: 066-7142270
SIC: 15700 Employees: 32
Animal Feeds Hardware & Steel
Mr Noel Browne General Manager
Ms Kathleen Browne Director

Dan O'Connor Feeds
Ballysimon Road
Limerick Co. Limerick
Phone: 061-414988 Fax: 061-410961
Email: docfeeds@indigo.ie
SIC: 15700 Employees: 30
Compound Animal Feeds
Mr Gerry Clifford General Manager
Mr Michael Fahey Financial Controller
Mr Eddie Ryan Production Manager

David Patton Feeds
Milltown Mills
Monaghan Co. Monaghan
Phone: 047-82099 Fax: 047-83577
SIC: 15700 Employees: 30
Animal Feed Manufacturer
Mr John Bole Managing Director
Ms Geraldine Smith Finance Manager
Mr Trevor Pollock Production Manager
Mr George White DP Manager

Drinagh Co Op Ltd
Drinagh
Dunmanway Co. Cork
Phone: 028-30116 Fax: 028-30266
SIC: 15700 Employees: 158
Animal Feed Producers/Suppliers
Mr Joe O'Sullivan Managing Director
Mr Tom Ryan Finance Manager
Mr Teddy O'Regan Personnel Manager

Henry Good Ltd
Waterlands
Kinsale Co. Cork
Phone: 021-4772300 Fax: 021-4772548
Email: hgood@iol.ie
SIC: 15700 Employees: 40
Animal Feed Suppliers
Mr Courtney Good Managing Director
Ms Linda Reynolds Accounts Manager
Mr Cameron Good Sales & Marketing Manager
Mr Francis Kelly Production Manager

HKM Milling Co
Granardkille
Granard
Longford Co. Longford
Phone: 043-86166 Fax: 043-86073
Web: http://www.kiernanmilling.ie
SIC: 15700 Employees: 30
Compound Animal Feeds
Mr Ciaran Nally Chief Executive
Mr Tadhg O'Leary Sales Manager
Mr Tom Lynam Production Manager

James Grennan & Sons
Rath
Birr Co. Offaly
Phone: 0509-33102 Fax: 0509-33054
SIC: 15700 Employees: 35
Animal Feeds Production
Mr John Grennan Managing Director
Mr Michael Burke Marketing Manager
Mr Sean Guinan Production Manager

JH Roche & Sons Ltd
Dock Road
Limerick Co. Limerick
Phone: 061-308111 Fax: 061-308211
Email: roches@eircom.net
SIC: 15700 Employees: 40
Animal Feed Suppliers
Mr Bobby Roche Managing Director
Mr Paul Hennessy Sales Manager
Mr Peter Roche Production Manager

Kerry Farm Supplies Ltd
Farranfore
Killarney Co. Kerry
Phone: 066-9764466 Fax: 066-9764971
SIC: 15700 Employees: 30
Compound Animal Feeds
Mr Raymond Moynihan Managing Director
Mr Joe Sheehy Sales Manager

Macroom Mills Ltd
Ardnacrushy
Macroom Co. Cork
Phone: 026-41111 Fax: 026-41116
Email: mcrmills@iol.ie
SIC: 15700 Employees: 50
Animal Feeds
Mr John Quinn Managing Director
Mr Jim Kennedy Financial Controller
Mr Con Drew Sales & Marketing Manager

Food Manufacturing

Maghera Mills
Maghera Mills
Virginia Co. Cavan
Phone: 049-8547588 Fax: 049-8547598
Email: awennis@eircom.net
SIC: 15700 Employees: 55
Animal Feed Manufacturer
Mr Victor Ennis Chief Executive
Mr Martin Sheridan Credit Controller
Mr Arthur Ennis Sales Manager
Mr Breccene Ennis Technical Manager

NUTEC
Greenhills Centre, Greenhills Road
Tallaght
Dublin 24
Phone: 01-4524555 Fax: 01-4524007
SIC: 15700 Employees: 90
Manufacture of Animal Nutrition
Mr Padraig Ryan Managing Director
Ms Rachel Byrne Personal Assistant
Ms Michelle Burke Sales & Marketing Manager

Paul & Vincents
Longford Road
Edgeworthstown
Longford Co. Longford
Phone: 043-71149 Fax: 043-71331
SIC: 15700 Employees: 60
Compound Animal Feeds
Mr John Cahill General Manager
Ms Geraldine Smith Company Accountant

Premier Proteins
151 Thomas Street
Dublin 8
Phone: 01-6121212 Fax: 01-6121210
Web: http://www.iaws.ie
SIC: 15700 Employees: 40
Animal Feedstuffs & Supplements
Mr Noel Rynn Director

Quinns of Baltinglass Ltd
Main Street
Baltinglass
Wicklow Co. Wicklow
Phone: 0508-81266 Fax: 0508-81080
Email: quinnsb@indigo.ie
SIC: 15700 Employees: 100
Animal Feed Suppliers
Mr Liam Quinn Managing Director
Mr Dan O'Leary Accountant
Ms Pauline Murray Office Manager

Robert Smyth & Sons Ltd
Ballindrait
Lifford Co. Donegal
Phone: 074-41011 Fax: 074-41011
SIC: 15700 Employees: 38
Preparation of Compound Foods
Mr Ronnie Barratt Managing Director
Ms Yvonne Toner Financial Controller
Mr Jeremy McGonigal Sales Manager
Mr Simon Smyth Production Manager

Southern Milling Ltd
Marina Mills
Marina Walk
Cork Co. Cork
Phone: 021-4317321 Fax: 021-4317015
Email: info@southernmilling.ie
SIC: 15700 Employees: 65
Animal Feed Suppliers
Mr Richard O'Brien Managing Director
Mr Norman Singleton Finance Manager
Mr Richard Riordan Sales & Marketing Manager

Stonearch
Abbeyleix
Portlaoise Co. Laois
Phone: 0502-31285 Fax: 0502-31406
Email: stonearch@iol.ie
SIC: 15700 Employees: 56
Manufacture Animal Feed Additives
Ms Lynn Gallery Managing Director

Tommie Howley Ltd
Barracks Street
Dunmore
Tuam Co. Galway
Phone: 093-38159 Fax: 093-38632
SIC: 15700 Employees: 25
Compound Animal Feeds & Supermarket
Mr Tommie Howley Proprietor

C & D Foods
Edgeworthstown
Longford Co. Longford
Phone: 043-71067 Fax: 043-71388
Email: info@cdfoods.ie
Web: http://www.cdfoods.ie
SIC: 15720 Employees: 225
Manufacture Pet Food
Mr Philip Reynolds Chief Executive
Mr Terry Carr Financial Director
Mr Jimmy Dalton Administration Manager
Mr John McNamee Marketing Sales Manager
Mr Adrian Glover Production Director

Connolly's Red Mill
Goresbridge
Kilkenny Co. Kilkenny
Phone: 0503-75800 Fax: 0503-75378
Email: redmills@indigo.ie
Web: http://www.redmills.ie
SIC: 15720 Employees: 100
Pet Foods
Mr Joe Connolly Chief Executive
Mr Michael Dunden Financial Controller
Mr Michael Feelan Sales & Marketing Manager

Manor Products Co Ltd
Carrigeen Industrial Estate
Clonmel Co. Tipperary
Phone: 052-21211 Fax: 052-21752
SIC: 15720 Employees: 30
Pet Food Manfacture
Mr Barry Deasy Proprietor
Ms Mary Cahill Financial Controller
Mr Anthony Wall Production Manager

Master Foods Ltd
Burton Court, Burton Hall Road
Sandyford
Dublin 18
Phone: 01-4185400 Fax: 01-4783687
Web: http://www.masterfoods.ie
SIC: 15720 Employees: 130
Pet Foods
Ms Fiona Dawson Managing Director
Mr Noel Kinsella Sales Manager

Merops (Nutrition) Ltd
Lower Ballymount Road
Walkinstown
Dublin 12
Phone: 01-4602777 Fax: 01-4602697
Email: info@meropsnutrition.ie
Web: http://www.meropsnutrition.ie
SIC: 15720 Employees: 80
Pet Foods Manufacture
Ms Barbara Breen Managing Director
Mr John Hammond Personnel Manager
Mr Bob Powell Sales & Marketing Manager
Ms Marie Hammond Company Secretary

Convenience Foods Ltd
Unit 5a Cookstown Industrial Estate
Tallaght
Dublin 24
Phone: 01-4520300 Fax: 01-4524290
Email: sales@cfoods.iol.ie
SIC: 15800 Employees: 80
Food Processing
Mr Eamonn Prenderville General Manager
Mr Paul Magee Financial Controller

Curley Quality Foods
Carrowbrowne
Castlegar
Galway Co. Galway
Phone: 091-771717 Fax: 091-757989
Email: info@eircom.net
SIC: 15800 Employees: 70
Food Processing
Mr John Curley Proprietor
Mr Cyril Curley Sales Manager

Heinz Custom Foods Ltd
Finnabair Industrial Park
Dundalk Co. Louth
Phone: 042-9385200 Fax: 042-9385293
Email: postmaster@heinz.co.uk
SIC: 15800 Employees: 400
Food Manufacture
Mr Mike Parsons Managing Director
Mr Eugene O'Neill Financial Controller
Ms Eilish Rattigan Human Resources Director
Mr Phil Connell Sales & Marketing Manager

International Meat Ingredients Ltd
Maudlins Industrial Estate
Naas Co. Kildare
Phone: 045-871111 Fax: 045-871120
Email: info@iminaas.ie
Web: http://www.iminaas.ie
SIC: 15800 Employees: 70
Pizza Toppings
Mr John Donnelly Manager
Mr Martin Denby Financial Controller
Ms Laura Gilchrist Sales & Marketing Manager
Mr Enda Giles Production Manager
Mr Enda Martin Computer Manager

Kelkin Natural Products
Unit 1 Crosslands Industrial Park
Ballymount Cross
Dublin 12
Phone: 01-4600400 Fax: 01-4600411
Email: info@kelkin.ie
SIC: 15800 Employees: 43
Manufacture & Distribution of Health Foods
Mr Bernard Rooney Managing Director
Ms Sally Byrne Financial Controller
Mr Charles Sothern Sales Director
Mr Michael McDonagh Operations Manager

Knorr Best Foods Ireland Ltd
Goldenbridge
Inchicore
Dublin 12
Phone: 01-4557638 Fax: 01-4553292
Email: cpcfoods@indigo.ie
SIC: 15800 Employees: 240
Food Manufacture
Mr Jules Noten Chief Executive
Ms Sharon Bennett Finance Manager
Ms Catherine Byrne Personnel Manager
Mr Brendan Smart Sales & Marketing Manager
Mr Gerry Keane Operations Manager
Mr Michael Weldon IT Manager

Largo Foods
Kilbrew
Ashbourne Co. Meath
Phone: 01-8350611 Fax: 01-8351832
Email: info@perri.ie
SIC: 15800 Employees: 200
Snackfood Manufacturers
Mr Raymond Coyle Managing Director
Mr Sean Francis General Manager
Mr Seamus McGowan Operations Manager
Mr Francis Lyons Sales Manager
Mr Sean Clinton Production Manager

Nutricia Manufacturing Ireland Ltd
Rocklands
Wexford Co. Wexford
Phone: 053-42277 Fax: 053-45273
Email: nutwex@iol.ie
SIC: 15800 Employees: 100
Babyfood Manufacturers
Mr Pat Caulfield Managing Director
Mr Sean Cullen Financial Controller
Mr Dave Elwood Production Manager
Mr Tony Kelly IT Manager

Platters Food Co Ltd
Finisklin Industrial Estate
Sligo Co. Sligo
Phone: 071-42640 Fax: 071-42655
Email: platt@eircom.net
SIC: 15800 Employees: 60
Salads & Cheesecake Manufacturer
Ms Bernadette Butler Managing Director
Mr Michael McGlone Finance Manager

Quest International (Ireland) Ltd
Kilnageary
Carrigaline
Cork Co. Cork
Phone: 021-4372541 Fax: 021-4372652
Web: http://www.questintl.com
SIC: 15800 Employees: 100
Manufacture Food Enzymes
Mr Tom Noonan Manager
Mr Anthony Noonan Accountant
Ms Elma Gilligan Personnel Manager
Mr Dennis Coffey Production Manager
Mr Ger O'Connor Computer Manager

Rye Valley Foods Ltd
IDA Industrial Estate
Carrickmacross Co. Monaghan
Phone: 042-9690400 Fax: 042-9690401
SIC: 15800 Employees: 700
Produce Convenience Ready Made Foods
Mr Pat Doyle Managing Director
Mr Eddie Fitzgerald Finance Manager
Ms Carla McQuade Personnel Director
Mr Pat O'Leary Operation Manager
Mr Ben Kelly Computer Manager

Sona Ltd
Unit 27 Tallaght Business Centre
Tallaght Industrial Estate
Dublin 24
Phone: 01-4515087 Fax: 01-4515737
Email: sona@iol.ie
SIC: 15800 Employees: 25
Manufacture Nutritional Products
Mr Ohan Yergainharsian Managing Director
Ms Valerie Madden Finance Manager
Ms Breda Hickey Sales Manager

Swissco Ltd
Little Island Industrial Estate
Little Island
Cork Co. Cork
Phone: 021-4354288 Fax: 021-4354201
Email: swissco@swissco.techex.co.uk
SIC: 15800 Employees: 90
Food Processing
Mr Donnacha Casey Managing Director
Mr Liam Madigan Manufacturing Manager
Mr Tony Power Operation Service Manager

Tayto Ltd
Green Castle Road
Coolock
Dublin 17
Phone: 01-8037510 Fax: 01-8037500
Email: info@taytocrisps.ie
Web: http://www.taytocrisps.ie
SIC: 15800 Employees: 200
Crisps & Snacks
Mr Vincent O'Sullivan Managing Director

Wyeth Nutritionals Ireland
Askeaton
Limerick Co. Limerick
Phone: 061-392168 Fax: 061-392440
Web: http://www.ahp.com
SIC: 15800 Employees: 500
Baby Foods Manufacturing
Mr Tom Mulqueen Chief Executive
Mr John Minihan Financial Director
Mr Michael Cusack Personnel Manager
Mr John Killowry Production Manager
Mr John Holmes MIS Manager

Yeats Country Cheese
Convoy
Lifford Co. Donegal
Phone: 074-47463 Fax: 074-47523
Email: yeatscheese@eircom.net
Web: http://www.yeatscheese.com
SIC: 15800 Employees: 25
Cheese-Manufacturing
Mr John Malloy Managing Director
Mr Tommy Kilcoyne Finance Manager
Mr Richard Burke Sales & Marketing Manager

Biscuit Makers
Ballyboughal Co. Dublin
Phone: 01-8433500 Fax: 01-8433547
Email: chocchip@eircom.net
SIC: 15820 Employees: 30
Biscuit Makers
Mr Paul Kelly Managing Director

Eurosnax International
Mount Tallant Avenue
Terenure
Dublin 6w
Phone: 01-4904691 Fax: 01-4904693
SIC: 15820 Employees: 200
Snack Food Manufacturers
Mr Vincent O'Sullivan Managing Director
Mr Des Watchorne Accountant
Mr Connor Kinsella Personnel Manager
Mr Kevin Masterson Sales & Marketing Manager

Harrisons Food Co Ltd
Unit 77 Broomhill Industrial Estate
Tallaght
Dublin 24
Phone: 01-4598461 Fax: 01-4526412
SIC: 15820 Employees: 35
Preserves - Jam Marmalade & Biscuits
Mr Michael Horgan General Manager
Mr Edward Hardy Finance Manager
Ms Nora Gahon Accountant

King Foods
Merrywell Industiral Estate
Ballymount Road
Dublin 12
Phone: 01-4050154 Fax: 01-4090530
SIC: 15820 Employees: 160
Potato Crisps Manufacturer
Mr Sean Kelly General Manager
Mr Anthony Donnelly Accountant
Mr Connor Kinsella Personnel Manager
Mr Peter Smith Sales Manager
Mr Michael Ronan Production Manager

W & R Jacob Plc
Belgard Road
Tallaght
Dublin 24
Phone: 01-4141111 Fax: 01-4511898
SIC: 15820 Employees: 800
Biscuit Manufacturing Packaging & Distribution
Mr Neil Murphy Managing Director
Mr Tom Hope Finance Manager
Mr John Keogh Head of Human Resources
Mr Rory Burke Production Manager
Mr Pat O'Malley IT Manager

Food Manufacturing

Chivers Ireland Ltd
Coolock Drive, Box 2489
Coolock
Dublin 5
Phone: 01-8484044 Fax: 01-8484053
Email: info@chivers.ie
Web: http://www.chivers.ie
SIC: 15830 Employees: 140
Jams/Jellies/Non-Alcoholic Beverages
Mr Liam O'Rourke Chief Executive
Mr Cathal Drohan Financial Director
Mr Francis Killeen Sales & Marketing Director
Mr Maurice Horgan Operations Director
Mr David Brady Computer Manager

Irish Sugar Plc
Athy Road
Carlow Co. Carlow
Phone: 0503-31651 Fax: 0503-43087
Email: info@irish-sugar.ie
Web: http://www.irish-sugar.ie
SIC: 15830 Employees: 550
Sugar Production
Mr Tony Heaphy Managing Director
Mr Paddy Withrow Finance Manager
Mr Gerry Lynch Personnel Manager
Ms Deirdre Keogh Marketing Manager
Mr Tom Tracey Computer Manager

Cadbury Ireland Ltd
Malahide Road
Coolock
Dublin 5
Phone: 01-8480000 Fax: 01-8472905
Email: info@csplc.com
Web: http://www.cadbury.ie
SIC: 15840 Employees: 1600
Confectionery Manufacture
Mr Liam Murnane Managing Director
Mr Chris Orchard Finance Manager
Mr Aidan Flaherty Human Resources Director
Mr Michael Smith Sales & Marketing Director
Mr Martin West Operations Director
Mr Kieran O'Connell IT Manager

Caffrey's Confectionery
Mulcahy Industrial Estate
Greenhills Road Walkinstown
Dublin 12
Phone: 01-4503844 Fax: 01-4509602
Email: caffrey@eircom.net
SIC: 15840 Employees: 31
Sweets Manufacturing
Mr Neville Caffrey Managing Director
Ms Elizabeth Phillips Sales Manager

Dunhills Confectionery Production
McKee Avenue
Finglas
Dublin 11
Phone: 01-8343668 Fax: 01-8342487
Email: haribo@uk.haribo.com
Web: http://www.haribo.com
SIC: 15840 Employees: 55
Confectionery Manufacture
Mr Robert Wilkins Director
Mr Frank Windmann Director

Gallaghers Irish Chocolates
Finglas Business Centre
Jamestown Road
Dublin 11
Phone: 01-8646840 Fax: 01-8646841
SIC: 15840 Employees: 40
Manufacture Chocolate
Ms Carol Kinsella Managing Director

Irish Chocolate Company Ltd
77 Sir John Rogersons Quay
Dublin 2
Phone: 01-6710599 Fax: 01-6710480
Email: chocolate@butlers.ie
Web: http://www.butlers.ie
SIC: 15840 Employees: 160
Chocolate & Confectionery Manufacture
Mr Colm Sorensen Joint Managing Director
Ms Susan Connolly Financial Controller
Ms Suzanne Dunne Personnel Manager
Ms Aisling Walsh Marketing Director
Mr Michael Cooney Production Manager
Mr Owen Sorensen Production Director

Leaf Ireland
Church Street
Kilcock
Naas Co. Kildare
Phone: 01-6287361 Fax: 01-6287661
Email: reception@leaf.ie
Web: http://www.leaf.ie
SIC: 15840 Employees: 135
Bubble Gum & Cool Pops Manufacturing
Mr Charles Sproat Managing Director
Ms Sarah Duffy Financial Controller
Ms Maureen Harte Personnel Secretary
Mr Ian Gillard Sales & Marketing Manager
Mr Sean O'Keefe Operations Controller
Mr Roy McBride IT Administrator

Lily O'Briens
IDA Business Centre
The Green Road
Newbridge Co. Kildare
Phone: 045-486800 Fax: 045-486865
Email: sales@lilyobrien.iol.ie
Web: http://www.lilyobriens.ie
SIC: 15840 Employees: 40
Manufacture Chocolates
Ms Lily O'Brien Proprietor
Ms Mary Anne O'Brien Sales Manager

Lir Chocolates Ltd
Unit 1-2 Dockland Innovation Park
East Wall Road
Dublin 3
Phone: 01-8740365 Fax: 01-8749341
Email: info@lirchocolate.com
Web: http://www.lirchocolates.ie
SIC: 15840 Employees: 50
Manufacture Chocolates
Mr Stephen Cope Managing Director
Ms Lorraine Madden Financial Controller
Ms Mary White Sales & Marketing Manager
Ms Grace Shaughnessy Production Manager

Lyons Tea Ltd
Goldenbridge
Inchicore
Dublin 12
Phone: 01-4556423 Fax: 01-4556353
SIC: 15840 Employees: 200
Tea Manufacturers
Mr Jules Norton General Manager
Mr Andy Smith Finance Manager
Mr Robert McKeran Sales Manager
Mr Tony Talbot Site Manager

Manhattan Peanuts Ltd
McKee Avenue
Finglas
Dublin 11
Phone: 01-8344411 Fax: 01-8362264
Email: sales@manhattan.ie
Web: http://www.manhattan.ie
SIC: 15840 Employees: 25
Peanuts & Popcorn Manufacture
Mr George Hogan General Manager
Mr Donal O'Neill Finance Manager

Mannings Bakery Ltd
Greencastle Parade
Coolock
Dublin 17
Phone: 01-8477236 Fax: 01-8477922
Email: manningsoffice@eircom.net
SIC: 15840 Employees: 150
Bread & Confectionery Manufacture
Mr Cecil Manning Managing Director
Mr Damien Manning Financial Controller
Mr Brian Manning Marketing Manager
Mr Eamon Manning Production Manager
Ms Carol Heffernan DP Manager

Rose Confectionery
Unit 23a Robinhood Industrial Estate
Clondalkin
Dublin 22
Phone: 01-4568064 Fax: 01-4565522
SIC: 15840 Employees: 50
Confectionery Manufacture
Mr William Grant Managing Director
Ms Fidelma Mallon Finance Manager
Mr Richard Kennedy Sales & Marketing Manager

William McKinney & Sons
Oatfield Confectionery Works
Letterkenny Co. Donegal
Phone: 074-22011 Fax: 074-24796
Email: oatfield@eircom.net
SIC: 15840 Employees: 90
Confectionery Manufacture
Mr Robert Davidson Chief Executive
Mr Harold Jacob Company Secretary
Mr Robert Murphy Sales & Marketing Manager
Mr Niall O'Donnell Production Manager
Mr Tim Ryan IT Manager

Wilton Candy
Cutlery Road
Newbridge Co. Kildare
Phone: 045-434699 Fax: 045-431318
SIC: 15840 Employees: 40
Manufacture Confectionery
Mr John Stanley Managing Director

Barry's Tea Ltd
Kinsale Road
Cork Co. Cork
Phone: 021-4966644 Fax: 021-4313606
Email: info@barrystea.ie
Web: http://www.barrystea.ie
SIC: 15860 Employees: 75
Blending & Packaging of Tea
Mr Tony Barry Managing Director
Mr Greg Butler Financial Controller
Mr Michael Hourihan Computer Manager

Bewleys Ltd
Northern Cross
Malahide Road
Dublin 17
Phone: 01-8160606 Fax: 01-8160681
Email: info@bewleys.ie
Web: http://www.bewleys.ie
SIC: 15860 Employees: 1500
Tea & Coffee Manufacture
Mr Patrick Bewley Managing Director
Mr Jerry Murphy Financial Controller
Mr Brendan McDonald Sales & Marketing Manager
Ms Jacqueline McCarthy Production Manager
Ms Catherine Costello IT Manager

Athy International Concentrates
Town Parks Industrial Estate
Athy Co. Kildare
Phone: 0507-31516 Fax: 0507-38356
SIC: 15890 Employees: 70
Concentration Manufacturing
Mr Hugo Reidy Operations Director
Mr Eamon O'Connor Financial Controller
Mr John Nolan IT Manager

Food Manufacturing

Christian Hansen Ltd
Rohen Industrial Estate
Little Island
Cork Co. Cork
Phone: 021-4353500 Fax: 021-4353912
Email: info@chr.com
Web: http://www.chr.com
SIC: 15890 Employees: 30
Food Colourings & Flavours Manufacture
Mr Mark Hurley General Manager
Mr Sean Lyons Finance Manager
Mr Tony Barry Sales & Marketing Manager
Mr John Conroy IT Manager

Cooley Distillery Plc
Riverstown
Dundalk Co. Louth
Phone: 042-9376102 Fax: 042-9376484
Email: cooleydistillery@eircom.net
Web: http://www.cooleywhiskey.com
SIC: 15910 Employees: 45
Irish Whiskey/Bottling
Mr David Hynes Managing Director
Mr Jim Finn Financial Controller
Mr John Harte Marketing Manager

Irish Distillers Wines & Spirits Ltd
Bow Street Distillery
Smithfield
Dublin 7
Phone: 01-8725566 Fax: 01-8723109
Email: info@idl.ie
Web: http://www.irishdistillers.ie
SIC: 15910 Employees: 2000
Distillers
Mr Philip Savinel Chief Executive
Mr John Purcell Key Accounts Director
Mr Denis O'Flynn Human Resources Director
Mr Peter Gallogly Field Sales Director
Mr Maurice Smyth Production Director
Mr John Kenny IT Director

Grants of Ireland Ltd
St Lawrence Road
Chapelizod
Dublin 20
Phone: 01-6264455 Fax: 01-6264680
SIC: 15940 Employees: 400
Sprits and Wines
Mr Philip Robinson Commercial Director
Mr Michael Howley Finance Manager
Mr Barry Fuller Personnel Director
Mr Andrew Healy Production Manager
Mr Donal Ahern Computer Manager

Madigan Group
32 Merrion Road
Ballsbridge
Dublin 4
Phone: 01-6604199 Fax: 01-6680984
SIC: 15940 Employees: 119
Licenced Drink Industry
Mr Patrick Madigan Managing Director
Mr David Madigan Financial Director
Mr Edmund Ryan Personnel Manager

Beamish & Crawford Ltd
South Main Street
Cork Co. Cork
Phone: 021-4911100 Fax: 021-4911111
Email: info@beamish.ie
Web: http://www.beamish.ie
SIC: 15950 Employees: 190
Ale, Lager & stout
Mr Alf Smiddy Managing Director
Mr Stephen Murphy Finance Director
Mr Fergus O'Connor Personnel Director
Mr Jim Darcy Production Director
Mr John Buckley MIS Manager

Food Manufacturing

Carlow Brewing Co
Station Road
Carlow Co. Carlow
Phone: 0503-34356 Fax: 0503-40038
Email: ccb@iol.ie
Web: http://www.carlowbrewing.com
SIC: 15950 Employees: 85
Brewers
Mr Seamus O'Hara Managing Director
Mr Brendan Flanagan General Manager

Dundalk Packaging
Ardee Road
Dundalk Co. Louth
Phone: 042-9335441 Fax: 042-9388252
Email: reception@guinness.com
SIC: 15950 Employees: 190
Brewing & Packaging
Mr Frank Crowley Operations Manager
Mr Tom Mahon Accountant
Ms Catrina Murphy Personnel Manager
Mr Terry Redmond Sales & Marketing Manager
Mr Jason Magee IT Controller

Gilbey Group
Nangor House
Western Estate
Dublin 12
Phone: 01-4194000 Fax: 01-4194001
Web: http://www.gilbeys.com
SIC: 15950 Employees: 400
Alco Beverages Prod/Sales/Dist
Mr Pat Given Chief Executive
Mr Shane Clarke Finance Director
Mr John Gilmore Sales Director
Ms Catherine Harris IT Director

Grants Of Ireland
Annervale
Clonmel Co. Tipperary
Phone: 052-25222 Fax: 052-72256
SIC: 15950 Employees: 1200
Alcoholic Beverages/Non-Alcoholic
Mr Brendan McGuinness Managing Director
Mr Michael Howley Finance Manager
Mr Barry Fuller Personnel Manager
Mr John Costigan Sales Director
Mr Peter Chambers Production Director

Great Northern Brewery
Carrick Road
Dundalk Co. Louth
Phone: 042-9334793 Fax: 042-9339624
Email: info@guinness.com
SIC: 15950 Employees: 165
Lager Brewery
Mr Steve Topliss Operations Manager
Mr Frank Manning Finance Manager
Mr Tom Clarke Personnel/Admin Manager
Mr Seamus Lennon Head Brewer
Mr Michael Morgan Computer Manager

Guinness Ireland Group
St James's Gate
James Street
Dublin 8
Phone: 01-4536700 Fax: 01-4533631
Email: sales@guinness.com
Web: http://www.guinness.com
SIC: 15950 Employees: 4500
Brewing
Mr Brian Duffy Managing Director
Mr Michael Whelan Personnel Manager
Mr Steve Langan Marketing Director
Mr Tim Buckler European Operations Director
Ms Mary Donovan IT Manager

J Donohoe Ltd
Templeshannon
Enniscorthy Co. Wexford
Phone: 054-33801 Fax: 054-33186
SIC: 15950 Employees: 450
Brewing and Malting
Mr Dan Kickham Managing Director
Mr John Kickham Finance Manager
Mr John O'Dwyer Sales & Marketing Manager

Minch Norton & Company Ltd
The Maltings
Athy Co. Kildare
Phone: 0507-31716 Fax: 0507-31046
Email: minch@iol.ie
SIC: 15950 Employees: 133
Malting Company
Mr Sean Brady Managing Director
Mr Michael McCarthy Finance Manager
Mr PJ Murphy Sales & Marketing Director
Mr John McNamara Production Manager
Mr James Mann Computer Manager

Murphy Brewery Ireland Ltd
57 Leitrim Street
Cork Co. Cork
Phone: 021-4503371 Fax: 021-4503926
Email: info@heineken.ie
Web: http://www.heineken.ie
SIC: 15950 Employees: 470
Brewing
Mr Padraic Liston Chief Executive
Mr Steven Siemer Financial Controller
Mr Ken O'Connor Human Resources Manager
Mr Patrick Conway Commercial Manager
Mr Derek Orford Technical Operations Manager
Mr Donal Manning IT Manager

Tennents Ireland Ltd
Finisklin Road
Sligo Co. Sligo
Phone: 071-69055 Fax: 071-60789
Email: sligo@brewers.bass.com
SIC: 15950 Employees: 85
Brewers
Mr Joe Manning Managing Director

Waterford Brewery
9 Mary Street
Waterford Co. Waterford
Phone: 051-874963 Fax: 051-850227
SIC: 15950 Employees: 40
Brewery
Mr Willie Murphy Manager

Ballygowan Spring Water Co Ltd
Castle Demesne
Newcastle West
Limerick Co. Limerick
Phone: 069-61226 Fax: 069-61242
SIC: 15980 Employees: 60
Bottled Water Manufacturer
Mr Brendan McGuinness Managing Director
Mr Michael Howley Finance Manager
Ms Deirdre Deasy Personnel Officer
Mr John Costigan Sales Director
Mr Donal O'Sullivan Operations Manager
Mr Donal Ahern Computer Manager

Cantrell & Cochrane Ltd
Kylemore Park
Dublin 10
Phone: 01-6266371 Fax: 01-6161125
Email: info@cantrell.ie
Web: http://www.cantrellandcochrane.ie
SIC: 15980 Employees: 1490
Soft Drinks Manufacture
Mr Tony O'Brien Managing Director
Mr Brendan Dwan Finance Director
Mr Pat Rowan IT Manager

Coca Cola Bottlers Ireland
Western Industrial Estate
Naas Road
Dublin 12
Phone: 01-4565377 Fax: 01-4602169
Email: info@cchbc.com
SIC: 15980 Employees: 560
Soft Drinks Manufacturer & Distributor
Mr Alfie Lydon Managing Director
Ms Eamonn O'Leary Finance Manager
Ms Libby McKnight Human Resources Manager

Coman's Wholesale Ltd
Belgard Road
Tallaght
Dublin 24
Phone: 01-4519146 Fax: 01-4519772
Email: comans@indigo.ie
SIC: 15980 Employees: 40
Soft Drinks Manufacturers & Suppliers
Mr Jeff Cuman Managing Director
Mr Frank Costello Financial Controller
Mr John Reynolds Sales Manager

Deasy & Co Ltd
Lamb Street
Clonakilty Co. Cork
Phone: 023-33204 Fax: 023-34675
SIC: 15980 Employees: 25
Soft Drinks
Mr Michael O'Donovan Managing Director
Mr Michael Lynch Sales Manager

Glenpatrick Spring Water
Powerstown
Clonmel Co. Tipperary
Phone: 052-26622 Fax: 052-22330
Email: sales@glenpatrick.com
SIC: 15980 Employees: 75
Manufacture of Natural Spring Water
Mr Kieran Hynes Managing Director
Mr Sean Griffin Finance Manager
Ms Orla Fortune Sales Manager
Ms Aishling Hyde IT Manager

MJ Gleeson & Co Ltd
Borrisoleigh
Thurles Co. Tipperary
Phone: 0504-51113 Fax: 0504-51480
Email: info@tipperary-water.ie
Web: http://www.tipperary-water.ie
SIC: 15980 Employees: 180
Food and Drink Manufacturing & Distribution
Mr Patrick Cooney Managing Director
Mr PJ Nugent Finance Manager
Mr Pat Tynes Personnel Manager
Mr Paul Kelly Marketing Manager
Mr Gerard McInerney Production Manager
Mr Pat Phillips Computer Manager

P Mulrine & Sons (Sales) Ltd
Donegal Road
Ballybofey
Lifford Co. Donegal
Phone: 074-31009 Fax: 074-31892
SIC: 15980 Employees: 70
Soft Drink Manufacturers & Distributors
Mr Peter Mulrine Managing Director
Mr Barry McFadden Financial Controller
Mr John Boner Sales & Marketing Manager

Pepsi Cola International
PO Box 111
Little Island Industrial Estate
Cork Co. Cork
Phone: 021-4353921 Fax: 021-4353926
Email: info@inpl.pepsi.com
Web: http://www.inpl.pepsi.com
SIC: 15980 Employees: 150
Manufacture Concentrates
Mr Frank O'Mahony Chief Executive
Mr John Burke Financial Director
Ms Marie Sweeney Personnel Director
Mr Martin McDonald Production Manager
Mr Paul O'Callaghan IT Director

Richard Nash & Co Ltd
The Square
Newcastle West
Limerick Co. Limerick
Phone: 069-62022 Fax: 069-62218
Email: info@nashswater.com
Web: http://www.nashswater.com
SIC: 15980 Employees: 30
Soft drinks and mineral water
Mr Richard Nash General Manager
Mr James Stewart Finance Manager
Ms Kathleen O' Dwyer Marketing Manager
Mr Robert Gardner Production Manager

Shannon Mineral Waters
Upper Clare Street
Limerick Co. Limerick
Phone: 061-418068 Fax: 061-418179
SIC: 15980 Employees: 24
Soft Drinks
Mr Brendan O'Mara General Manager

Tipperary Irish Natural Mineral Water
Pallas Street
Barrisolagh
Tipperary Co. Tipperary
Phone: 0504-51677 Fax: 0504-51418
Web: http://www.tipperary/water.ie
SIC: 15980 Employees: 1200
Water Coolers
Mr Alfe Harnett Manager
Mr PJ Nugent Finance Manager
Mr Muirne Hurley Sales Manager

Douwe Egberts Ireland
Dublin Road
Mullingar Co. Westmeath
Phone: 044-48691 Fax: 044-48652
SIC: 16000 Employees: 130
Tabacco Manufacturer
Mr Thyes Van Hout Managing Director
Mr Kieran Dardis Financial Controller
Mr John Mills Production Manager
Ms Marie Bardon IT Manager

Gallaher (Dublin) Ltd
Airton Road
Tallaght
Dublin 24
Phone: 01-4040200 Fax: 01-4040266
Email: info@gallaher.ie
Web: http://www.gallaher.ie
SIC: 16000 Employees: 246
Tobacco Company
Mr Adrian Goodrich Managing Director
Mr Sam Mulholland Financial Director
Mr Nick Robinson Sales & Marketing Director
Mr Tom Clark Operations Director
Ms Deirdre Mooney IT Manager

John Player & Sons
South Circular Road
Dublin 8
Phone: 01-4537900 Fax: 01-4114601
Email: info@johnplayer.ie
Web: http://www.johnplayer.ie
SIC: 16000 Employees: 200
Tobacco Manufacture
Mr Liam Peters Chief Executive
Mr Peter Daly Finance Manager
Mr Martin Devlin Personnel/Admin Manager
Mr Andrew Meagher Marketing Manager
Mr Brian Connell Production Director
Mr Peter DeCourcey IT Manager

Kapp & Peterson Ltd
Peterson House
Sallynoggin
Dun Laoghaire Co. Dublin
Phone: 01-2851011 Fax: 01-2856593
Email: sales@peterson.indigo.ie
SIC: 16000 Employees: 44
Smoking Pipes Manufacture
Mr Tom Palmer Managing Director
Mr Michael Davis Financial Controller
Mr Harry Phelan Sales Director
Mr Joe Kenny Production Manager

PJ Carroll & Co
Burton Hall Park
Sandyford Industrial Estate
Dublin 18
Phone: 01-2052300 Fax: 01-2958107
SIC: 16000 Employees: 120
Tobacco Manufacture & Distribution
Mr Alister Ross Chief Executive
Mr Pat Carroll Public Affairs Manager
Ms Penny Lilley Human Resources Manager
Mr Paul Hollingsworth Sales Director
Mr Paul Ogborn Operations Manager

Villiger (Ireland) Ltd
Charlestown Road
Ballaghadereen
Castlerea Co. Roscommon
Phone: 0907-60220 Fax: 0907-60503
Web: http://www.villiger.ie
SIC: 16000 Employees: 75
Manufacture Cigar Wrappers & Cigars
Mr Gerry O'Dowd Managing Director
Mr James Donney Finance Manager
Mr William O'Hara Office Manager
Ms Aoife O'Dowd Sales & Marketing Manager

Textiles

17	Manufacture of Textiles
17150	Polypropylene Yarns/Fabrics
17170	Spinning/Weaving Flax/Hemp
17210	Weaving Cotton/Silk/Man-Made
17220	Woollen/Worsted Industry
17250	Spinning/Doubling Cotton
17300	Textile Finishing
17400	Adhesive Cloth/Film/Oil
17402	Soft Furnishings
17403	Household Textiles
17404	Blinds (Window)
17500	Textiles
17510	Carpets/Rugs/Matting (Other)
17520	Rope/Twine/Net
17540	Textiles (Other Made Up)
17541	Lace
17600	Knitted Goods/Fabrics
17710	Hosiery Goods /Fabrics

Boran Packaging Ltd
Johnstown
Naas Co. Kildare
Phone: 045-876601 Fax: 045-875710
Email: postmaster@boran.ie
Web: http://www.boran.ie
SIC: 17150 Employees: 30
Manufacture Packaging Products
Mr Martin Boran Managing Director
Mr Martin Boran Jnr Personnel Manager
Mr Brendan Togher Production Manager

Chemfab Europe
Sales & Marketing Head Office
Clonroad
Ennis Co. Clare
Phone: 065-6820988 Fax: 065-6820993
Email: sales@chemfab.ie
Web: http://www.chemfab.com
SIC: 17150 Employees: 300
Coated Fabrics Manufacturers
Mr Eric Kevorkian Managing Director
Mr Chris Vaughan Financial Controller
Ms Margaret O'Sullivan Personnel Manager
Ms Tanya Coady Sales Manager
Mr Tom Keane Operation Manager
Ms Noelle Keating IT Support

Comerama Ltd
Castlecomer
Kilkenny Co. Kilkenny
Phone: 056-41291 Fax: 056-41430
Email: info@comerama.net
Web: http://www.comerama.net
SIC: 17150 Employees: 480
Yarn Spinning
Mr Michael Brooke Managing Director
Ms Maura McInerney Financial Controller
Mr Paddy Dowling Personnel Manager
Ms Cathy Crowley Sales & Marketing Manager
Mr Bill Nelan Production Manager
Mr Anil Abrol Computer Manager

Kilcarra Yarns Ltd
Kilcar
Donegal Co. Donegal
Phone: 073-38055 Fax: 073-38193
Email: kilcarra@eircom.net
SIC: 17150 Employees: 34
Yarns
Mr Brendan McShane General Manager
Ms Maureen Cannon Credit Controller

Unifi Textured Yarns Europe Ltd
Letterkenny Co. Donegal
Phone: 074-24455 Fax: 074-24265
Email: info@unifi-inc.com
Web: http://www.unifi-inc.com
SIC: 17150 Employees: 850
Polyester Yarn Manufacture
Mr Edward Wicks General Manager
Mr Fintan McGrath Financial Controller
Mr Jim Kelly Personnel Director
Mr Denis McCaffrey Data Processing Manager

Herdmans Holdings
Ballybofey
Lifford Co. Donegal
Phone: 074-31126 Fax: 074-32165
Email: info@herdmans.com
SIC: 17170 Employees: 115
Linen Yarn
Mr Neville Orr Managing Director
Mr Moore Hamillton Financial Controller
Ms Shauna Mitchell Personnel Manager
Mr Sidney Spence Sales/Marketing Director
Mr Mark Stuart Production Director

Seafield Technical Textiles Ltd
Seafield
Cork Road
Youghal Co. Cork
Phone: 024-92001 Fax: 024-92004
Email: info@seafieldtextiles.ie
Web: http://www.seafieldtextiles.ie
SIC: 17170 Employees: 70
Weaver Dye & Finish Fabrics
Mr John Parker Managing Director
Mr Brian McCutcheon Finance Manager
Ms Linda McKeaveney Sales & Marketing Manager
Mr Stephan Schmeitez Operation Manager

Botany Weaving Mill
Vauxhall Avenue
Cork Street
Dublin 8
Phone: 01-4532278 Fax: 01-4544428
Email: info@botanyweaving.iol.ie
Web: http://www.botany.iol.ie
SIC: 17210 Employees: 110
Woollen Fabric Manufacture
Mr Jonathan Hackett Managing Director
Mr Paul Cahill Financial Controller
Mr David Lawson Sales & Marketing Manager
Mr Jason Quarnby Production Manager

Emblem Weavers Ltd
Whitemill Industrial Estate
Wexford Co. Wexford
Phone: 053-24173 Fax: 053-24383
Email: emblem@emblemweavers.com
Web: http://www.emblemweavers.com
SIC: 17210 Employees: 30
Weaving
Mr Jim Conway Managing Director
Mr Ivor Murphy Financial Controller
Mr Dominic Dunphy Sales & Marketing Manager
Mr Martin Newport Production Manager

Irish Breeze Ltd
Donore Road Industrial Estate
Drogheda Co. Louth
Phone: 041-9870389 Fax: 041-9870349
SIC: 17210 Employees: 30
Manufacture Cotton Wool Products
Mr Edward McCloskey Managing Director
Mr Michael Power Finance Manager
Mr Ed Fawcett Production Manager

Textiles

Swiss Wire Ireland
Clash Industrial Estate
Tralee Co. Kerry
Phone: 066-7126544 Fax: 066-7120488
SIC: 17210 Employees: 150
Manufacture Polyester Fibre
Mr Michael Crowe Managing Director
Mr Pat Maloney Sales Manager

Blarney Woollen Mills Ltd
Blarney
Cork Co. Cork
Phone: 021-4385280 Fax: 021-4381111
Email: blarney@blarney.ie
Web: http://www.blarney.ie
SIC: 17220 Employees: 811
Wool Manufacture
Ms Freda Hayes Chief Executive
Mr Robert Riordan Financial Director
Mr Tony Jackson Computer Manager

Brendan Gilligan
Abbey
Trinity
Tuam Co. Galway
Phone: 093-24378 Fax:
SIC: 17220 Employees: 23
Wollen/Worsted Industry
Mr Brendan Gilligan

Foxford Woollen Mills
Foxford
Westport Co. Mayo
Phone: 094-56104 Fax: 094-56415
SIC: 17220 Employees: 30
Manufacturing Woollen Products
Mr Joe Queenan Managing Director
Mr Ivor Zaures Sales & Marketing Manager

J Babington Wollen/Worsted Industry
95 Main Street
Carrick On Suir Co. Tipperary
Phone: 051-640418 Fax:
SIC: 17220 Employees: 23
Wollen/Worsted Industry
Mr J Babington

Quills Woollen Market
107 Patrick Street
Cork Co. Cork
Phone: 021-4271717 Fax: 021-4270773
SIC: 17220 Employees: 250
Woollen/Worsted Industry & Drapers
Mr John Quill Manager
Ms Gillian Higgins Accounts Manager

O'Neills Sportswear
The Diamond
Lifford Co. Donegal
Phone: 074-42008 Fax: 074-42063
SIC: 17300 Employees: 30
Printing Logos
Mr Paul Houston General Manager

Coating & Technical Tapes Ltd
Unit 10 Ind Estate Purcell Inch
Dublin Road
Kilkenny Co. Kilkenny
Phone: 056-23677 Fax: 056-23724
Email: techtape@gofree.indigo.ie
SIC: 17400 Employees: 34
Adhesive Tapes
Mr Andrew Kirby Manager
Mr Des McDonough Sales Manager

Dynea Ireland Ltd
Marino Point
Cobh Co. Cork
Phone: 021-4855100 Fax: 021-4855156
Email: info@dynea.com
Web: http://www.dynea.com
SIC: 17400 Employees: 32
Adhesives
Mr Liam Moynihan Operations Manager
Mr Con Carroll Sales Manager

Loctite Ireland Ltd
Tallaght Business Park
Tallaght
Dublin 24
Phone: 01-4519466 Fax: 01-4519494
Email: loctitelreland@henkel.ie
SIC: 17400 Employees: 590
Chemical/Adhesive Manufacturer
Mr Liam Murphy Managing Director

PPI Adhesive Products
Unit 5-6 Waterford Industrial Estate
Waterford Co. Waterford
Phone: 051-373555 Fax: 051-377687
Email: info@ppi.ie
Web: http://www.ppi.ie
SIC: 17400 Employees: 130
Manufacture Adhesives
Mr Lutz Weinhold Managing Director
Mr Donal Costigan Finance Manager
Mr Paddy Gallagher Personnel Manager
Mr Paul Brazil Sales Manager
Mr Aidan Hackett Computer Manager

RS Group Ltd
8 Hanover Quay
Dublin 2
Phone: 01-6731300 Fax: 01-6731301
Email: rssales@rsgroup.ie
Web: http://www.rsgroup.ie
SIC: 17400 Employees: 50
Adhesives
Mr James Coffey Managing Director
Mr David Hughes Finance Manager
Ms Christina Goss Personnel Manager
Mr Robert Massey Sales Manager
Mr Niall Hanlon Production Supervisor
Ms Michelle Pemberton IT Manager

Jodi Manufacturing Co
Abbeylands
Duleek
Drogheda Co. Louth
Phone: 041-9823404 Fax: 041-9823266
Email: jodiman@gofree.indigo.ie
SIC: 17402 Employees: 70
Soft Furnishings Manufacture
Mr Anthony O'Connell Group Managing Director
Mr Richard Duffy Accountant
Mr Gerry Fitzgerald Sales & Marketing Manager
Mr Owen Power Production Manager

Kayfoam Woolfson Ltd
Sitecast Industrial Estate
Little Island
Cork Co. Cork
Phone: 021-4354044 Fax: 021-4354072
SIC: 17402 Employees: 41
Bed Manufacturer
Mr Owen O'Donavan Manager
Mr John Sexton Finance Manager
Mr Saul Woolfson Personnel Manager
Mr Declan Brady Marketing Manager
Ms Nora Friel Production Manager
Mr James Notley Computer Manager

Kelletts Oldcastle Ltd
Cavan Road
Oldcastle
Kells Co. Meath
Phone: 049-8541488 Fax: 049-8541260
Email: kelletts@iol.ie
Web: http://www.kelletts.ie
SIC: 17402 Employees: 128
Bedding Manufacture
Mr Thomas Kellett Managing Director
Mr Seamus Mullan Financial Controller
Ms Nicole Kellett Personnel Manager
Mr Gerry Connolly Sales Manager
Mr Darren Kellett Production Manager

Northern Feather Ltd
The Demesne
Westport Co. Mayo
Phone: 098-25411 Fax: 098-25743
Email: nf_ltd@anu.ie
SIC: 17402 Employees: 50
Continental Quilts & Textiles
Mr Vincent Coakley Managing Director
Mr Brendan O'Malley Finance Manager
Mr Robert Coakley Personnel Manager
Mr John Hyland Sales Manager
Mr John Roland Computer Manager

Tabetex Ltd
Shercock
Cavan Co. Cavan
Phone: 042-9669125 Fax: 042-9669576
Email: vergnano@iol.ie
SIC: 17402 Employees: 25
Furnishing Fabrics
Mr Mark Vergnano Partner
Mr Richard Vergnano Finance Manager
Mr Richard Vergnano Partner

Kayfoam Woolfson
Bluebell Industrial Estate
Naas Road
Dublin 12
Phone: 01-4509055 Fax: 01-4602574
SIC: 17403 Employees: 250
Foam & Bedding Manufacturer
Mr Solomon Woolfson Chief Executive
Mr John Sexton Financial Director
Mr Michael Power Marketing Manager
Mr Neill Willis Operations Manager
Mr Sean O'Reilly IT Manager

Lissadell Towels
Aclint Bridge
Carrickmacross Co. Monaghan
Phone: 041-6855134 Fax: 041-6855105
Email: info@lissadell.com
Web: http://www.lissadell.com
SIC: 17403 Employees: 103
Towel Manufacture
Mr Tom O'Neill Managing Director
Mr Pat Nolan Financial Controller
Ms Philemena Flannagan Personnel Manager
Mr Bobby Rusk Sales Manager

Poplar Linens Trading Co
Altamount Street
Westport Co. Mayo
Phone: 098-25633 Fax: 098-26133
Email: poplar@poplarlinen.com
SIC: 17403 Employees: 40
Export & Manufacture Household Textiles
Mr Sean Walsh Managing Director
Ms Bridie Hughes Accounts
Mr Ben Walsh Sales Manager
Mr Liam Walsh Jnr Production Manager

Pownall & Hampson (Irl) Ltd
Greencastle Parade
Coolock
Dublin 17
Phone: 01-8477311 Fax: 01-8477264
SIC: 17403 Employees: 50
Quilt Manufacture
Mr Trevor Stevenson Chairman
Ms Andrea Stevenson Manager
Mr Noel Costello Sales & Marketing Manager
Mr Gary Stevenson Production Manager

Acme Blinds
Old Mallow Road
Cork Co. Cork
Phone: 021-4502358 Fax: 021-4502295
Email: sales@acmeblinds.com
Web: http://www.acmeblinds.com
SIC: 17404 Employees: 50
Manufacture Blinds
Mr Nicholas Walsh Managing Director
Mr Colm Fenton Finance Manager
Mr Gerard Murphy Sales Manager
Ms Lillian Ronayne Computer Manager

Textiles

Charles Bell Ireland
Unit 76 Cherry Orchard Ind Estate
Ballyfermot Road
Dublin 10
Phone: 01-6268721 Fax: 01-6268149
Email: info@charlesbell.ie
SIC: 17404 Employees: 175
Manufacture Blinds
Mr Don Tallon Managing Director
Mr Gerard Kelly Financial Controller
Mr John Murray Sales Manager

Ringsun Blinds
10A Coolock Industrial Estate
Coolock
Dublin 17
Phone: 01-8482888 Fax: 01-8482006
Email: ringsun@eircom.net
SIC: 17404 Employees: 25
Manufacture Blinds
Mr Alf Mahood Managing Director
Mr Peter Smyth Finance Manager
Mr Gabriel Ring Sales Manager
Mr David Ring Production Manager

Amann Industries Corporation
Clash Industrial Estate
Tralee Co. Kerry
Phone: 066-7183300 Fax: 066-7183350
Email: info@amann-online.de
Web: http://www.amann-online.de
SIC: 17500 Employees: 320
Hi tech textiles
Mr Frank O'Reilly General Manager
Mr Eamon Moynihan Finance & Admin Manager
Ms Katja Maiserger Personnel Officer

Inishowen Clothing
Mullins
Carndonagh
Lifford Co. Donegal
Phone: 077-74533 Fax: 077-74533
Email: info@raydoherty.com
Web: http://www.raydoherty.com
SIC: 17500 Employees: 35
Clothing & Textiles
Mr Raymond Doherty Managing Director

Linen Supplies Ireland
Rosmedda Business Park
Ballysimon Road
Limerick Co. Limerick
Phone: 061-419911 Fax: 061-415373
SIC: 17500 Employees: 25
Linen Suppliers
Mr Tom Burke Manager
Ms Elaine Decourcy Credit Officer

Moville Clothing Manufacturing
Foyle Street
Moville
Lifford Co. Donegal
Phone: 077-85882 Fax: 077-82564
Email: movilleclothing@eircom.net
Web: http://www.movilleclothing.com
SIC: 17500 Employees: 40
Clothing & Textiles
Mr Harry Doherty General Manager
Mr Joe Doherty Finance Manager
Ms Hillary Doherty Production Manager

Tex Tech Industries (Irl) Ltd
IDA Industrial & Business Park
Purcellinch
Kilkenny Co. Kilkenny
Phone: 056-61426 Fax: 056-61520
Email: info@textech.ie
Web: http://www.textech.ie
SIC: 17500 Employees: 70
Textiles - Industrial Tennis Felts
Mr Michael Power Managing Director
Mr John McEvoy Financial Controller
Mr John Martin Sales Manager

Couristan Carpets (Irl) Ltd
Store Street
Youghal Co. Cork
Phone: 024-93454 Fax: 024-92959
Email: info@couristanyoughal.com
Web: http://www.couristanyoughal.com
SIC: 17510 Employees: 160
Carpet Manufacturers
Mr Barry McCarthy General Manager
Ms Eileen Linehan Accountant
Mr Michael Lenehan Sales & Marketing Manager
Mr John Ahern Production Manager
Mr David O'Sullivan Computer Manager

Curragh Carpet Ltd
Newbridge
Kildare Co. Kildare
Phone: 045-431304 Fax: 045-431310
SIC: 17510 Employees: 80
Carpet Manufacturer
Mr John Hudson Managing Director
Mr Larry Donoghue Accounts Manager
Ms Jo Coy Personnel Manager
Mr Keith Hammond Sales & Marketing Director
Mr Frank Meehan Production Manager
Mr Pat Doyle Computer Manager

Joyce V'Soske
Oughterard
Galway Co. Galway
Phone: 091-552113 Fax: 091-552301
Email: tonyvsos@iol.ie
Web: http://www.failte.com/vsoske/
SIC: 17510 Employees: 35
Carpet Manufacturer
Mr Tony Dixon Managing Director
Ms Rose O'Neill Accountant
Mr Gerry Dixon Production Director

Navan Carpets Ltd
Kells Road
Navan Co. Meath
Phone: 046-21653 Fax: 046-29367
Email: carpets@iol.ie
SIC: 17510 Employees: 237
Carpet Manufacture
Mr John Ryan Managing Director
Mr Luke Bowden Financial Controller
Mr Robert Dier Personnel Manager
Mr Terry Harper Production Director

Peerless Rug Europe
Townparks Industrial Estate
Athy Co. Kildare
Phone: 0507-31416 Fax: 0507-38195
Email: sales@peerless.ie
SIC: 17510 Employees: 100
Bathroom Sets Manufacturer
Mr Noel McEvoy Managing Director
Ms Violet Powell Finance Manager
Ms Kathleen Gray Office Manager
Ms Lenore Maleady Marketing Manager
Mr Seamus Mageean Plant Manager
Mr Derek Tighe Computer Manager

Schmidt Industries International
Unit 64-65 Cherry Orchard Ind Estate
Ballyfermot
Dublin 10
Phone: 01-6260299 Fax: 01-6260910
Email: info@schmidt.ie
SIC: 17510 Employees: 54
Matting Manufacturers
Mr James Donnelly Managing Director
Ms Rachel Lewellyn Finance Manager
Ms Nicola Gernon Personnel Manager
Ms Dara Donnelly Production Manager

Waterford Carpets Ltd
Unit 201 Industrial Park
Waterford Co. Waterford
Phone: 051-375941 Fax: 051-379607
Email: info@tretford.com
Web: http://www.tretford.com
SIC: 17510 Employees: 50
Manufactured Products (Other)
Mr Eamon Piercy Managing Director
Mr Irwin Navan Financial Controller
Mr Bill Lyons Production Manager

Gundry (Irl) Ltd
Roshine Road
Killybegs
Donegal Co. Donegal
Phone: 073-31100 Fax: 073-31486
SIC: 17520 Employees: 95
Manufacture & Supply of Fishing Nets
Mr Michael Gallagher Managing Director
Ms Evelyn Cassidy Human Resources Manager
Mr Jim Cunningham Sales Manager
Mr Danny Gallagher Production Manager
Mr James McLeod Technical Director

Gundrys Ltd
Skibbereen Co. Cork
Phone: 028-22388 Fax: 028-22390
Email: sales@gundrys.ie
Web: http://www.gundrys.ie
SIC: 17520 Employees: 45
Nets & Netting
Mr Michael Gallagher Manager

Swan Net Ltd
Kellys Quay
Killybegs
Donegal Co. Donegal
Phone: 073-31180 Fax: 073-31574
Email: info@swannet.ie
SIC: 17520 Employees: 60
Manufacture of Fishing Nets
Mr Martin Howley Managing Director
Mr Declan Kennedy Finance Manager
Ms Noelle Campbell Office Manager

Chris Kay Ltd
Farm Lane
Kinsale Co. Cork
Phone: 021-4772050 Fax: 021-4772900
Email: irishsales@chriskay.ie
Web: http://www.chriskay.ie
SIC: 17540 Employees: 95
Manufacture Press On Labels
Mr Christopher Kay Managing Director
Ms Patricia McCarthy Company Accountant
Mr Alan Barret Operations Manager
Mr John O'Sullivan Supervisor of Art Department

Wellman International Ltd
Mullagh
Kells Co. Meath
Phone: 046-80200 Fax: 046-80300
Email: info@wellman-intl.com
Web: http://www.wellman-intl.com
SIC: 17540 Employees: 400
Produce Fibres & Textiles
Mr Richard Budden Managing Director
Mr Eamon Hodge Finance Manager
Mr Michael Lynch Human Resources Director
Mr Peter Walsh Marketing Director
Mr Paddy Ward Production Manager
Mr Joe Hanley Department Manager

BA Dhun na Gall Teo
Ballymoon
Kilcar
Donegal Co. Donegal
Phone: 073-38233 Fax: 073-38236
Email: fisherman@eircom.net
SIC: 17600 Employees: 35
Manufacture Knitwear
Mr Des Daly General Manager
Ms Mary Finegan Sales & Marketing Manager
Mr Sean Byrne Production Manager

Textiles

Carraig Donn
Lodge Road
Westport Co. Mayo
Phone: 098-25566 Fax: 098-25229
Email: cdi@anu.ie
SIC: 17600 Employees: 55
Aran Knitwear
Mr Vincent Hughes Managing Director
Mr Frank Gillan Financial Controller
Ms Anne Harrison Personnel Manager
Mr Ciaran Costello Marketing Manager
Mr Pierce Staunton Production Manager

Castle of Ireland
Castle House
2001 Citywest Business Campus
Dublin 24
Phone: 01-4660363 Fax: 01-4660375
Email: sales@castle-of-ireland.ie
Web: http://www.castle-of-ireland.ie
SIC: 17600 Employees: 35
Knitwear
Mr Peter Gleeson Managing Director
Mr Michael Kelly Accounts Manager
Mr Des Kennerney Sales Manager
Mr John O'Driscoll Productions Manager

Cladyknit of Donegal
Derrybeg
Letterkenny Co. Donegal
Phone: 075-32450 Fax: 075-31270
Email: sweatersofireland@eircom.net
SIC: 17600 Employees: 42
Knitwear
Mr John O'Gallchoir General Manager
Ms Sarah O'Gallchoir Finance Manager
Ms Bernie Duffy Personnel Manager
Ms Mary Sweeney Sales & Marketing Manager
Ms Sandra Cannon Production Manager

Ireland Eye Knitwear
Unit 118 Baldoyle Industrial Estate
Baldoyle
Dublin 13
Phone: 01-8393145 Fax: 01-8393227
Email: info@ieknit.com
Web: http://www.ieknit.com
SIC: 17600 Employees: 28
Knitwear
Mr Paul O'Sullivan Managing Director
Mr Brendan O'Sullivan Production Manager

John Molloy (Ardara) Ltd
Killybegs Road
Ardara
Donegal Co. Donegal
Phone: 075-41133 Fax: 075-41336
Email: info@iol.ie
Web: http://www.johnmolloy.com
SIC: 17600 Employees: 90
Manufacture Knitwear & Tweed
Mr Michael Molloy Managing Director
Mr Jeff Molloy Financial Director
Mr Ronan Molloy Production Director

Little Chic Knitwear
Distillery Lane
Dundalk Co. Louth
Phone: 042-9331271 Fax: 042-9331273
SIC: 17600 Employees: 30
Knitwear & Outerwear
Mr Dermot Coburn Proprietor

Mountmellick Textiles
Mountmellick
Kells Co. Meath
Phone: 0502-24230 Fax: 0502-24377
SIC: 17600 Employees: 50
Mohair Yarn
Mr John Hennessey General Manager
Mr Martin Buckley Finance Manager
Ms Mary Fitzpatrick Personnel Manager

Ridgeview Ltd
Monavalley Industrial Estate
Tralee Co. Kerry
Phone: 066-7126711 Fax: 066-7126912
Email: info@ridgeview.ie
SIC: 17600 Employees: 150
Sport Socks
Mr Bernard Collins General Manager
Mr Richard Knight Sales & Marketing Manager
Mr Vincent O'Reagan Production Manager
Mr John O'Connor Office Administrator

Rossan Knitwear
Malinmore
Glencolmcille
Donegal Co. Donegal
Phone: 073-30069 Fax: 073-30183
SIC: 17600 Employees: 23
Knitted Goods/Fabrics Manufacturer
Mr John McNelis General Manager

Tyna International Ltd
Whelan Street
Monasterevin
Kildare Co. Kildare
Phone: 045-525336 Fax: 045-525634
SIC: 17600 Employees: 35
Knitwear Manufacture
Mr Robert Hunt Managing Director
Mr Richard Duffy Sales Director

West End Knitwear
Main Street
Monasterevin
Kildare Co. Kildare
Phone: 045-525319 Fax: 045-525244
Email: weknit@iol.ie
Web: http://http://www.sweaters.org
SIC: 17600 Employees: 70
Knitwear Manufacturing
Mr John Cullen Managing Director
Ms Angela McCormack Accounts Manager
Ms Catriona Harrison Sales & Marketing Manager
Mr Owen Cullen Computer Manager

Arthur Dagg Ltd
Crossbeg Industrial Estate
Ballymount Road Upper
Dublin 24
Phone: 01-4505022 Fax: 01-4503694
Email: info@adagg.ie
Web: http://www.adagg.ie
SIC: 17710 Employees: 50
Woven Elastic
Mr Michael Dagg Proprietor
Mr Michael McCarthy Financial Controller

Glenross Hosiery Ltd
Unit 2 Poppintree Industrial Estate
Finglas
Dublin 11
Phone: 01-8361573 Fax: 01-8361578
Email: glenross@iol.ie
SIC: 17710 Employees: 90
Manufacture Socks & Tights
Mr Ken Bale Managing Director
Mr John Burke Sales Manager
Mr David O'Toole Production Manager

Healy Hosiery
Killarney Road
Bray Co. Wicklow
Phone: 01-2863666 Fax: 01-2863957
SIC: 17710 Employees: 60
Hosiery Products
Mr Timothy Healy Managing Director
Mr Peter Morrisey Finance Manager
Ms Sheila Farrell Personnel Manager
Mr Richard Mooney Sales & Marketing Manager

Clothing Manufacture

18 Manufacture of Wearing Apparel
18200 Clothing & Furnishings
18210 Work Clothing
18220 Weatherproof Outerwear
18221 Mens/Boys Clothes
18222 Womens/Girls Outerwear
18231 Men's Underwear
18232 Women's Underwear
18240 Dress Industry (Other)
18241 Hats Caps Gloves Millinery
18242 Infants Wear
18243 Tailoring/Alterations

Deerpark Knitwear Ltd
Moore Abbey
Monasterevin
Kildare Co. Kildare
Phone: 045-525584 Fax: 045-525597
Email: deerpark@iol.ie
SIC: 18200 Employees: 36
Manufacture of Childrens & Menswear
Mr Michael Mahon Managing Director
Mr Paul Mahon IT Manager

Eurostyle Ltd
Fitz's Boreen
Mallow Road
Cork Co. Cork
Phone: 021-4211155 Fax: 021-4211166
Email: sales@greenlamb.ie
Web: http://www.greenlamb.ie
SIC: 18200 Employees: 40
Leisurewear Manufacturer
Mr Alan Dwyer Managing Director
Ms Gillian Rice Finance Manager
Mr Tony Taylor Sales Manager
Ms Catherine Cronin Production Director

Fruit of the Loom International Ltd
Ballymacarry
Buncrana
Lifford Co. Donegal
Phone: 077-62222 Fax: 077-62333
Email: info@fruit.com
Web: http://www.fruit.com
SIC: 18200 Employees: 600
Clothing Manufacture
Mr Joe Mullan Director of Manufacturing
Mr Frank Gallagher Finance Director
Mr Eugene McElroy Personnel Manager
Ms Kathleen Gill Marketing Manager
Mr Austin Cutlisse Computer Manager

Galvia Clothing Ltd
13 Riverside Commercial Estate
Tuam Road
Galway Co. Galway
Phone: 091-755105 Fax: 091-758032
SIC: 18200 Employees: 25
Manufacture Clothing
Mr Fergal Cavanagh Managing Director
Ms Helena Gordon Sales Manager

Glen Prince Textiles
Newtowngore
Carrick On Shannon Co. Leitrim
Phone: 049-4333593 Fax: 049-4333036
SIC: 18200 Employees: 45
Clothing Manufacturing
Mr Patrick Mitchel Manager
Mr Sean Donegan Sales Manager
Ms Evelyn Smith Computer Manager

Clothing Manufacturing

Libra Designs Ltd
8-9 Great Strand Street
Dublin 1
Phone: 01-8726000 Fax: 01-8735284
Email: librades@iol.ie
Web: http://www.libra-design.com
SIC: 18200 Employees: 100
Ladies Clothing Wholesale & Manufacture
Mr Michael Nally General Manager
Ms Bridget Flattery Credit Controller
Mr Dermot O'Sullivan Personnel Manager
Mr Brian Beggan Sales & Marketing Manager

Magee & Company Ltd
New Row
Donegal Co. Donegal
Phone: 073-21100 Fax: 073-21283
Email: clothing@magee.iol.ie
SIC: 18200 Employees: 340
Cloth & Clothing Manufacture
Ms Lynn Temple Managing Director
Mr Jim Nixon Finance Manager
Mr Sean Magee Personnel Manager
Mr Peter Carrington Group Marketing Director
Mr Oswald Perry Factory Manager
Mr Vincent Harrison DP Manager

Mamselle Ltd
54 Merchants Road
East Wall Road
Dublin 3
Phone: 01-8556837 Fax: 01-8550093
SIC: 18200 Employees: 60
Clothing Manufacturing
Ms Marie McKenna Managing Director
Mr Michael Jordan Finance Manager
Ms Eileen Foran Personnel Manager

Montex Holdings Ltd
Mall Road
Monaghan Co. Monaghan
Phone: 047-82111 Fax: 047-84877
Email: mel@montex.iol.ie
SIC: 18200 Employees: 75
Denim Wear
Mr Aonghus McGuinness Marketing Manager
Mr Mel McMorrow Finance Manager
Mr Peadar Black Personnel Manager

O'Neill of Dublin
Music Bar, Copper Alley
Temple Bar
Dublin 8
Phone: 01-6714310 Fax: 01-6714598
Email: info@ond.ie
SIC: 18200 Employees: 34
Manufacture Tartan Kilts & Skirts
Mr Dermot Sexton Managing Director
Mr James Sexton Accounts Manager

Purrfect Clothing Ltd
Unit 6, 45 Marrowbone Lane
Dublin 8
Phone: 01-4545944 Fax: 01-4545944
SIC: 18200 Employees: 30
Clothing Manufacturing
Mr Kevin O'Hara Proprietor

Riverside Manufacturing Co
Industrial Estate
Coes Road
Dundalk Co. Louth
Phone: 042-9331235 Fax: 042-9339184
Email: info@riverside-mfg.com
SIC: 18200 Employees: 120
Clothing Manufacture
Mr Ronnie Lawlor Managing Director
Ms Olivia O'Callaghan Financial Controller
Ms Pauline Monahan Customer Service Manager
Mr John Baird Production Manager
Mr Martin McAnallen IT Manager

Sable Outerwear Co Ltd
Stradavoher Industrial Estate
Thurles Co. Tipperary
Phone: 0504-22277 Fax: 0504-22392
Email: sable@indigo.ie
SIC: 18200 Employees: 35
Clothing Manufacturer
Mr John Murtagh Managing Director
Ms Marian Murtagh Finance Manager
Ms Christine O'Brien Production Manager

Shannon Clothing Ltd
Watchouse Lane
Off Patrick Street
Limerick Co. Limerick
Phone: 061-410333 Fax: 061-412929
Email: info@shannonclothing.ie
SIC: 18200 Employees: 45
Clothing Related Products
Mr Liam McNamara General Manager
Mr George Ryan Administration Director

Sweaters of Ireland
Derrybeg
Letterkenny Co. Donegal
Phone: 075-32175 Fax: 075-31270
Email: sweatersofireland@tinet.ie
SIC: 18200 Employees: 47
Manufacture Clothing
Ms Mary Sweeney Director
Ms Sara Gallagher Office Manager

TJT Manufacturing Ltd
Ashe Road
Shantalla
Galway Co. Galway
Phone: 091-521033 Fax: 091-521842
SIC: 18200 Employees: 80
Manufacture Casual Clothing
Mr Tom Tuohy General Manager
Ms Maria Murphy Accountant
Mr Anthony Meehan Personnel Officer
Ms Maura Duignan Sales & Marketing Manager

Acorn Fashions Ltd
Whitemill Industrial Estate
Wexford Co. Wexford
Phone: 053-42560 Fax: 053-23242
Email: sales@acornfashions.ie
Web: http://www.acornfashions.ie
SIC: 18210 Employees: 42
Manufacture Uniforms
Mr James Wallace Manager
Ms Siobhan Doyle Credit Controller

Anderco Safety
Little Island Industrial Estate
Little Island
Cork Co. Cork
Phone: 021-4355355 Fax: 021-4355007
Email: anderco@anderco.ie
Web: http://www.anderco.ie
SIC: 18210 Employees: 27
Protective Clothing Equipment
Mr Alan Bruce Manager
Ms Catherine Lyons Finance Manager
Mr Douglas Guilfoyle Sales Manager

BSN Medical Ltd
Archerstown Industrial Estate
Thurles Co. Tipperary
Phone: 0504-22007 Fax: 0504-22735
Email: orders@jobst.ie
SIC: 18210 Employees: 150
Medical Garments
Mr Jeff Phipps Managing Director
Mr Andrew Fogarty Financial Controller
Ms Margaret Dwyer Production Manager
Mr John Nolan IT Manager

Corporate Apparel
Green Street
Roscrea Co. Tipperary
Phone: 0505-21399 Fax: 0505-22044
Email: info@corporate-apparel.ie
Web: http://www.corporate-apparel.ie
SIC: 18210 Employees: 50
Manufacture & Distribution of Corporate Clothing & Workwear
Mr Edward Condon Managing Director
Mr Maurice Murphy Finance Manager

Irema Ireland
Kilmallock Industrial Estate
Bruree Road
Kilmallock Co. Limerick
Phone: 063-98544 Fax: 063-98799
Email: irema@iol.ie
Web: http://www.irema.ie
SIC: 18210 Employees: 68
Industrial Surgical Masks & Filter Materials
Mr Diarmuid Herbert Managing Director
Ms Geraldine Murphy Accounts Manager
Mr William Harvey Sales & Marketing Manager
Mr Maurice Lynch Production Manager

LCC Clothing Ltd
Summerhills Enterprise Centre
Summerhill
Navan Co. Meath
Phone: 0405-57788 Fax: 0405-57900
Email: info@lcceurotex.com
SIC: 18210 Employees: 30
Protective Clothing
Mr Paul Beddy Managing Director
Ms Eileen Palmer Accounts Manager

Orrwear Ltd
40-42 Hill Street
Dublin 1
Phone: 01-8743382 Fax: 01-6616643
Email: orrwear@iol.ie
SIC: 18210 Employees: 40
Work Wear Manufacture & Sales
Mr Andrew Orr Managing Director
Mr John Ward Finance Manager
Mr Philip Orr Marketing Manager

Portwest Ltd
Castlebar Road
Westport Co. Mayo
Phone: 098-26411 Fax: 098-26161
Email: info@portwest.com
SIC: 18210 Employees: 128
Manufactures Protective Clothing
Mr Harry Hughes Managing Director
Mr Tony Kirby Financial Controller
Mr Paul Smith Sales & Marketing Manager

Sioen Ireland
Industrial Estate
Derrybeg
Letterkenny Co. Donegal
Phone: 075-31169 Fax: 075-31591
Email: sales@sioen.ie
SIC: 18210 Employees: 150
Protective Clothing & Equipment
Mr Gaetan Frys General Manager
Mr Pat McNickle Financial Controller
Mr Adrian Towey Sales Manager
Mr Danny Gillespie Production Manager
Mr Christian Barsch Computer Manager

Slivergate Ltd
Creation House
59 Botanic Road
Dublin 9
Phone: 01-8302912 Fax: 01-8306189
Web: http://www.silvergate.ie
SIC: 18210 Employees: 30
Uniforms
Mr Michael Jacobs Managing Director
Ms Brigid O'Donal Sales Director

Clothing Manufacturing

Snickers Production Ltd
Sragh Industrial Estate
Tullamore Co. Offaly
Phone: 0506-41404 Fax: 0506-21271
Email: specialss@plprod.ie
SIC: 18210 Employees: 400
Workwear Jackets
Ms Breffni MacNamara Managing Director
Mr Andy O'Grady Financial Controller
Ms Rose O'Toole Production Manager
Ms Elaine Westman IT Manager

T O'Gorman & Sons
Churchfield Business Park
Churchfield
Cork Co. Cork
Phone: 021-4302257 Fax: 021-4305415
Email: togshandon@eircom.net
SIC: 18210 Employees: 35
Protective Clothing
Mr Gregory O'Gorman Managing Director
Mr John Tobin Financial Controller
Mr John O'Gorman Director
Mr Vincent Daly Sales Manager

Total Safety Ltd
Newmarket
Dublin 8
Phone: 01-4544955 Fax: 01-4536648
Email: tsafety@indigo.ie
Web: http://www.totalsafety.ie
SIC: 18210 Employees: 46
Protective Clothing & Equipment
Mr Noel McVeigh General Manager
Mr Bill Goulding Finance Manager
Mr Eddie Doyle Commercial Manager

Cunningham Covers Ltd
Unit 4 Maudlins Industrial Estate
Monread Road
Naas Co. Kildare
Phone: 045-895951 Fax: 045-895952
SIC: 18220 Employees: 42
Waterproof Covers
Mr Paul Cunningham Director

Lowe Alpine Systems International Ltd
Sragh Industrial Estate
Tullamore Co. Offaly
Phone: 0506-41124 Fax: 0506-21944
Email: lowe@iol.ie
Web: http://www.lowealpine.com
SIC: 18220 Employees: 260
Outdoor Clothing
Mr Owen Smith Director & General Manager
Mr Michael Robbins Financial Controller
Ms Ann-Marie Cunniffe Customer Services Manager
Mr Owen McCall Production Manager
Mr Kevin Murphy Computer Supervisor

Mizen Head Enterprises
Bantry Enterprise Centre
Seafield
Bantry Co. Cork
Phone: 027-50999 Fax: 027-51984
Email: info@mizenhead.com
Web: http://www.mizenhead.com
SIC: 18220 Employees: 25
Manufacturing Wax Jackets & Hats
Mr Tim Deasy General Manager
Mr Richard Deasy Accounts Manager
Mr Ron Lehane Sales Manager
Mr Gerald Walsh Production Manager

Trimproof Ltd
Wellington Place
Trim Co. Meath
Phone: 046-31396 Fax: 046-31756
Email: customerservices@trimproof.ie
Web: http://www.iol.ie/trimproof
SIC: 18220 Employees: 75
PVC Coated Fabrics
Mr Donal Kinsella Acting Managing Director
Mr Tom Wallace Financial Controller
Ms Joanna Cunningham Marketing Manager
Mr Tom Colser Production Manager

Henry White Ltd
15 South Summer Street
Dublin 8
Phone: 01-4533611 Fax: 01-4543950
Web: http://www.henrywhite.ie
SIC: 18222 Employees: 40
Ladies Outerwear Manufacturers
Mr Bernard White Managing Director
Ms Penny White Sales & Marketing Manager

MA International Ltd
Unit 6-7 IDA Centre
Newmarket
Dublin 8
Phone: 01-4544361 Fax: 01-4544363
Email: info@michelambers.ie
SIC: 18222 Employees: 35
Ladies Fashions
Mr Peter Catterson Managing Director
Mr Dennis Ryan Financial Controller
Mr Ben Catterson Sales Manager

Maidenform International Ltd
6/7 Distribution Centre
Shannon Industrial Estate
Shannon Co. Clare
Phone: 061-474435 Fax: 061-475460
Email: info@mfwweoc.com
SIC: 18222 Employees: 32
Ladies Apparel
Mr Tony O'Sullivan General Manager
Mr George Kierans Financial Controller
Mr Vincent Purcell Systems Manager

Nena Models Ltd
Letterkenny Road
Stranorlar
Lifford Co. Donegal
Phone: 074-31511 Fax: 074-31169
Email: sales@nena.ie
SIC: 18222 Employees: 475
Ladies Clothes Manufacturer
Mr Paul Sharma Managing Director
Mr Cyril Gilhawley Company Secretary
Ms Frances Callaghan Personnel Officer
Mr Danny Cullin Production Manager

Swamp Ltd
37 Patrick Street
Cork Co. Cork
Phone: 021-4275789 Fax: 021-4274802
Email: info@swamp.ie
Web: http://www.swamp.ie
SIC: 18222 Employees: 70
Casual Womens Wear
Mr Kieran Coogan Managing Director
Ms Margaret Good Financial Controller
Ms Marie Mackey Personnel Director
Mr Paul Williams Data Processing Manager

Traffic Clothing Ltd
Unit 1 IDA Centre
Prussia Street
Dublin 7
Phone: 01-8386266 Fax: 01-8386502
Email: traffic@eircom.net
SIC: 18222 Employees: 25
Ladies Outerwear
Mr Denis Booth Chairman
Mr Gerard Burke Sales Manager
Ms Una O'Connor Production Manager

Sapphire Lingerie Ltd
St Margaret's Road
Finglas
Dublin 11
Phone: 01-8362203 Fax: 01-8344588
Email: sapphire1@eircom.net
SIC: 18232 Employees: 60
Ladies Fashions
Mr James Power Managing Director
Mr Peter Lynott Sales & Marketing Manager
Ms Lisa Power Computer Manager

Blarney Castle Knitwear Ltd
Blarney
Cork Co. Cork
Phone: 021-4383400 Fax: 021-4516187
SIC: 18240 Employees: 45
Manufacture Knitwear/ Menswear Wholesale
Ms Fiona McKenna Managing Director
Mr Jeremy Murphy Financial Controller
Ms Liz Fitzgerald Customer Services Manager
Mr William Fitzgerald Production Manager

Hanna Hats of Donegal
Tirconaills Street
Donegal Co. Donegal
Phone: 073-21084 Fax: 073-22349
Email: sales@hannahats.com
Web: www.hannahats.com
SIC: 18241 Employees: 30
Manufacture Hats
Mr John Hanna Managing Director
Ms Angela Gillespie Finance Manager
Ms Anne Marie Meehan Sales Manager

Hats of Ireland Ltd
Breaffy Road
Castlebar Co. Mayo
Phone: 094-21144 Fax: 094-23972
Email: hatsofireland@gandonenterprise.ie
Web: http://www.hatsofireland.ie
SIC: 18241 Employees: 34
Hat Manufacturer
Mr Padraic Shaughnessy General Manager
Ms Briege Walsh Accountant
Ms Pamela Burke Sales & Marketing Manager

O'K Irish Gloves
Lisnamult
Roscommon Co. Roscommon
Phone: 0903-26182 Fax: 0903-30081
SIC: 18241 Employees: 25
Gloves - Manufacturing
Mr Eddie Shanahan Manager

Tinywear Ltd
Cavan Road
Oldcastle
Kells Co. Meath
Phone: 049-8541233 Fax: 049-8541181
SIC: 18242 Employees: 75
Clothing Manufacturer
Mr Paddy Mullen Managing Director

Leather Manufacture

19 Leather Manufacture
19000 Leather Goods
19300 Footwear

Michell Ireland
Killowen
Portlaw
Waterford Co. Waterford
Phone: 051-387177 Fax: 051-387199
Email: michell@eircom.net
SIC: 19000 Employees: 110
Bovine Tannery
Mr Graham Oades Chief Executive
Mr Sean Donnelly Company Secretary
Ms June Power Administration Supervisor

Monarc Leather Co Ltd
The Ramparts
Dundalk Co. Louth
Phone: 042-9331751 Fax: 042-9334881
Email: info@monarcleather.com
Web: http://www.monarcleather.com
SIC: 19000 Employees: 32
Leather Handbags
Mr Neil O'Donoghue Joint Managing Director
Mr David Mulholland Financial Controller
Mr Eddie Wall Personnel Manager

Ronan Group
Dudleys Mill
Coleville Road
Clonmel Co. Tipperary
Phone: 052-22599 Fax: 052-22892
SIC: 19000 Employees: 150
Industrial Tanners
Mr Thomas Ronan Managing Director
Mr Pat Farrell Financial Controller
Mr Paul Ronan Marketing Manager
Mr Paul O'Dwyer Production Manager

Blackthorn Shoes
Coes Road
Dundalk Co. Louth
Phone: 042-9334741 Fax: 042-9333371
SIC: 19300 Employees: 50
Mens/Ladies Footwear
Mr Kenneth Connolly Managing Director
Mr Anthony Langan Finance Manager
Mr Patsy Sheridan Personnel Manager

Dubarry Shoes Ltd
Glentaun
Ballinasloe Co. Galway
Phone: 0905-42348 Fax: 0905-43147
Email: info@dubarry.ie
Web: http://www.dubarry.ie
SIC: 19300 Employees: 200
Shoe Manufacturers
Mr Eamonn Fagan Managing Director
Mr Michael Larkin Finance Manager
Mr Sean Hurley Personnel Manager
Mr Dermott Kelly Sales Manager
Mr Johnny Campbell Production Manager
Mr Michael Flynn DP Manager

Wood Products Manufacture

20 Wood Products Manufacture
20100 Wood (Sawmilling/Planing)
20301 Window Frame etc Manufacture
20400 Wooden Containers
20500 Wood Products
20511 Wood Products (Semi-Finished)
20512 Wooden Articles (Other)
20513 Wooden/Upholstered Furniture
20524 Wickerwork, Cork, Straw Manufacture

AS Richardson & Co Ltd
Newtowngore
Carrick On Shannon Co. Leitrim
Phone: 049-4333208 Fax: 049-4333043
SIC: 20100 Employees: 70
Sawmills
Mr Andrew Kidney Managing Director
Mr Brian Murphy Financial Controller
Ms Angela McGovern Office Manager
Mr Richard Kavanagh Sales Manager
Mr Seamus Walsh Production Manager
Mr Noel Boyle Computer Manager

Coolrain Sawmills
Coolrain
Portlaoise Co. Laois
Phone: 0502-35152 Fax: 0502-35093
Email: coolrainsawmills@hotmail.com
SIC: 20100 Employees: 37
Timber Producer & Sawmiller
Mr Declan Hutchinson Manager
Ms Antoinette Connolly Personnel Manager
Mr Damien Connolly Sales Manager
Ms Sue Leonard Computer Manager

Glennon Bros Timber
The Sawmills
Longford Co. Longford
Phone: 043-46223 Fax: 043-46262
SIC: 20100 Employees: 200
Timber Processors
Mr Patrick Glennon Managing Director
Mr Ron Corry Financial Controller
Mr Mike Glennon Marketing Manager
Mr Joe Durkan Computer Manager

Grainger Sawmills
Enniskeane
Cork Co. Cork
Phone: 023-47377 Fax: 023-47698
Email: info@graingersawmills.ie
Web: http://www.graingersawmills.ie
SIC: 20100 Employees: 300
Sawmill
Mr William Grainger Managing Director
Mr Pat Twomey Finance Manager
Ms Carol Crean Personnel Officer
Mr Maurice Cullen Marketing Manager
Mr Michael Russell Production Director

Irish Forest Products Ltd
Mountrath
Portlaoise Co. Laois
Phone: 0502-32108 Fax: 0502-32419
Email: ifpinfo@esatclear.ie
SIC: 20100 Employees: 35
Sawmilling
Mr John Brady Managing Director
Mr Michael Rice Sales Manager

James McMahon Dublin Ltd
U 200 North West Bus Pk, Ratoath Rd
Blanchardstown
Dublin 15
Phone: 01-8477644 Fax: 01-8476651
SIC: 20100 Employees: 295
Timber Importers & Providers
Mr Victor Byrne General Manager
Ms Carol Cormack Credit Controller
Ms Marie McAuley Personnel Manager
Mr Philip Reilly Sales Manager

Laois Sawmills Ltd
Ballymacken
Portlaoise Co. Laois
Phone: 0502-21075 Fax: 0502-22892
SIC: 20100 Employees: 30
Timber Producer/Sawmiller
Mr Jim McNamara Managing Director
Ms Sara Deegan Finance Manager
Mr Rory Roberts Sales Manager

McMahon Timber Ltd
Corcanree
Dock Road
Limerick Co. Limerick
Phone: 061-315388 Fax: 061-315781
SIC: 20100 Employees: 400
Sawmill Products
Mr Mark McMahon General Manager
Mr Steven Mulhall Financial Controller

Murphy & O'Connor
The Quay
Bantry Co. Cork
Phone: 027-50024 Fax: 027-50120
SIC: 20100 Employees: 30
Sawmilling
Mr Stephen Hourihane General Manager

Murray Timber Products Ltd
Hermitage
Ballygar
Ballinasloe Co. Galway
Phone: 0903-24688 Fax: 0903-24735
Email: ballygar@murraytimber.iol.ie
SIC: 20100 Employees: 120
Sawmill/Timber Processing
Mr Patrick Murray Chief Executive
Mr Sean Brandon Finance Manager
Mr Derek McGrath Sales & Marketing Manager
Mr John Murray Production Manager
Mr Tony Hanlon Computer Manager

Palfab Ltd
Doonisky
Lissarda
Cork Co. Cork
Phone: 021-7336198 Fax: 021-7336306
Email: palfab@iol.ie
SIC: 20100 Employees: 50
Sawmillers
Mr Donal O'Callaghan Managing Director
Mr Jim Prendergast Financial Controller
Mr William Hendy Sales Manager
Mr Gerald O'Callaghan Works Director

Patrick Kelly Timbers
Kilshane Cross
North Road, Finglas
Dublin 11
Phone: 01-8342511 Fax: 01-8343661
SIC: 20100 Employees: 60
Timber Processing
Mr Michael McDonald Chief Executive
Mr Dermot Fitzpatrick Financial Controller
Mr Liam O'Brien Production Manager
Mr Damien Taheny Company Secretary

PDM Ltd
Old Milltown
Kill
Naas Co. Kildare
Phone: 045-877165 Fax: 045-877467
Email: pdmltd@iol.ie
Web: http://www.pdm.ie
SIC: 20100 Employees: 37
Timber Processors
Mr Brendan Gibbons Managing Director
Mr Patrick Sneyd Finance Manager
Mr Michael Grogan Sales & Marketing Manager

Wood Industries Rathdrum Ltd
Corballis
Rathdrum
Wicklow Co. Wicklow
Phone: 0404-46390 Fax: 0404-46621
Email: rathdrum@eircom.net
SIC: 20100 Employees: 25
Timber Producer/Sawmiller
Mr John O'Halloran Managing Director
Mr Joe Ivors Finance Manager
Mr Michael Cunningham Sales Manager
Mr Michael Byrne Production Manager
Ms Anne-Marie Smyth Computer Manager

Woodfab Timber Ltd
Aughrim
Arklow Co. Wicklow
Phone: 0402-36228 Fax: 0402-36293
Email: info@woodfabtimber.ie
Web: http://www.woodfabtimber.ie
SIC: 20100 Employees: 50
Sawmillers
Mr John Brady Managing Director
Mr Michael Lynn Financial Director
Mr Sean Condren Sales & Marketing Manager
Mr Lorcan Doyle Production Manager
Ms Mary O'Connell Computer Manager

Modular Cold Store Manufacturers
Mohill
Carrick on Shannon Co. Leitrim
Phone: 078-31162 Fax: 078-31519
Email: modular@indigo.ie
SIC: 20301 Employees: 150
Manufacture insulation panels & doors
Mr Charlie Ward General Manager
Ms Kathleen Fox Credit Controller
Mr Timothy Beirne Sales Manager

Royal Windows Ltd
Seatown Road
Swords Co. Dublin
Phone: 01-8404481 Fax: 01-8901007
Email: royalwindows@iol.ie
SIC: 20301 Employees: 25
Windows & Doors -Trade
Mr Paul O'Quigley Managing Director

Star Alliance Ltd
Ballinagore
Mullingar Co. Westmeath
Phone: 0506-32747 Fax: 0506-32079
Email: starline@eircom.net
SIC: 20301 Employees: 25
Manufacture Window Handles
Ms Anne Daly General Manager

W & J Bolger
18 Ardee Street
Dublin 8
Phone: 01-4542544 Fax: 01-4540005
Email: info@wjbolger.ie
Web: http://www.wjbolger.ie
SIC: 20301 Employees: 40
Manufacture Sash Windows
Mr John Bolger Managing Director
Mr Sean Richards Finance Manager
Mr Paul Bolger Sales Manager

W & J Bolger Ltd / Ventrolla
18 Ardee Street
Dublin 8
Phone: 01-4530377 Fax: 01-4540005
Email: info@wjbolger.ie
Web: http://www.wjbolger.ie
SIC: 20301 Employees: 60
Window Refurbishment
Mr John Bolger Managing Director
Mr Paul Bolger Sales Manager

Weatherglaze Systems Ltd
Clonattin Road
Gorey Co. Wexford
Phone: 055-21557 Fax: 055-20443
Email: info@weatherglaze.ie
Web: http://www.weatherglaze.ie
SIC: 20301 Employees: 90
PVC Windows/Doors
Mr James Dempsey Managing Director
Mr Nick Cosgrave Financial Controller
Mr Nicholas Cosgrave Personnel Manager
Mr Ian Tyrell Sales Manager
Mr Chris Smith Production Manager
Mr Gerard Shields Computer Manager

Windows & Doors Store
Sitecast Industrial Estate
Little Island
Cork Co. Cork
Phone: 021-4354177 Fax: 021-4353950
Email: info@marinagroup.ie
SIC: 20301 Employees: 120
Manufacture Windows & Doors
Mr Gerard O'Halloran General Manager
Ms Caroline O'Halloran Finance Manager
Ms Rita Ryan Personnel Manager
Mr Simon McAuliffe Sales Manager
Mr John Heaphy Purchasing Manager

Wright Window Systems
Milltownpass
Mullingar Co. Westmeath
Phone: 044-22118 Fax: 044-22352
Email: info@wrightwindowsystems.ie
Web: http://www.wrightwindowsystems.ie
SIC: 20301 Employees: 185
Manufacture & Supply of Windows
Ms Rose Wright Managing Director
Mr Sean Luskin Financial Director
Ms Caroline Finn Personnel Manager
Mr Frank Wright Sales & Marketing Director
Mr Tom Fitzgerald Production Manager

Long Richard Ltd
Goresbridge
Kilkenny Co. Kilkenny
Phone: 0503-73201 Fax: 0503-73526
SIC: 20400 Employees: 25
Manufacture Coffins
Mr Richard Long Manager
Mr Michael Long Personnel Manager

Brooks Thomas Ltd
Bluebell
Naas Road
Dublin 12
Phone: 01-4190000 Fax: 01-4190050
Email: brooks.thomas@upm-kymmene.com
Web: http://www.brooksgroup.ie
SIC: 20500 Employees: 60
Timber-Builder Providers
Mr John Walsh Chief Executive
Mr Jerry Swarbrigg Finance Manager
Mr Eugene Gilmore Sales Director

Chep Ireland
Jamestown Business Park
Dublin 11
Phone: 01-8362655 Fax: 01-8362855
Email: info@europe.chep.com
SIC: 20500 Employees: 105
Wood Products - Pallet Repair
Mr Patrick Ryan Director/General Manager
Mr Gearoid Lavin Finance Manager
Ms Kathy Kelly Administration
Mr Colin Reid Business Development Manager
Mr Gerry Gavin Depot Manager

Finsa Forest Products Ltd
Scariff
Ennis Co. Clare
Phone: 061-921038 Fax: 0619-21129
SIC: 20500 Employees: 50
Timber Products
Mr Liam Moloney Managing Director
Mr Gonzalo Frey Chief Executive

GEM Construction Company
Athlone Road
Longford Co. Longford
Phone: 043-45217 Fax: 043-41854
Email: info@gemgroup.ie
Web: http://www.gemgroup.net
SIC: 20500 Employees: 95
Manufacture & Construction of Wooden Products
Mr Pat Fay Managing Director
Mr Kevin Hughes Financial Controller
Mr Vincent Fay Director
Mr Jim O'Reilly Sales Manager

Kingspan Group Plc
Dublin Road
Kingcourt
Cavan Co. Cavan
Phone: 042-9698000 Fax: 042-9667501
Email: admin@kingspan.ie
Web: http://www.kingspan.com
SIC: 20500 Employees: 2300
Manufacture of Construction Products
Mr Eugene Murtagh Chief Executive
Mr Dermot Mulvihill Finance Director
Mr Sean Hickey IT Manager

Louisiana Pacific Europe
Belview
Slieverue
Waterford Co. Waterford
Phone: 051-851233 Fax: 051-851130
Email: lpeurope@lpcorp.com
Web: http://www.lp-europe.com
SIC: 20500 Employees: 180
Manufacture Engineered Wood Products
Mr Lou Hess Managing Director
Mr Pat Trihy Financial Controller
Ms Siobhan McGrath Human Resources Director
Mr Andrew MacDonald Sales & Marketing Manager
Mr Jim McCann Operations Director

Morgan McMahon & Co Ltd
Promenade Road
East Wall
Dublin 3
Phone: 01-8552588 Fax: 01-8557940
Email: timber@morgan.ie
Web: http://www.heitonbuckley.ie
SIC: 20500 Employees: 25
Timber
Mr Jim Sullivan General Manager
Mr Michael Flanagan Sales Manager

Panelling Centre
109 Longmile Road
Dublin 12
Phone: 01-4564899 Fax: 01-4564898
Email: info@panelcentre.ie
Web: http://www.panelcentre.ie
SIC: 20500 Employees: 32
Timber
Mr Eamon Thomas Manager

Protim Abrasives
Tolka Industrial Estate
Ballyboggan Road
Dublin 11
Phone: 01-8305966 Fax: 01-8305126
Email: sales@protim.ie
SIC: 20500 Employees: 140
Wood Preservation & Treatment
Mr Anthony Lynch Chief Executive
Mr Martin Kane Finance Manager
Mr Terry Mullholland Sales Manager
Mr John McCarthy Production Manager

Soft Line Panels Ltd
21-22 Cherry Orchard Industrial Estate
Dublin 10
Phone: 01-6265995 Fax: 01-6235621
Email: slp@indigo.ie
Web: http://www.softlineplanels.com
SIC: 20500 Employees: 25
Cabinet Doors
Mr Brendan Cawley Proprietor
Mr Pat O'Shea Finance Manager

Williamette Europe Ltd
Redmondstown
Clonmel Co. Tipperary
Phone: 052-21166 Fax: 052-21815
Email: info@willamette-europe.com
Web: http://www.willamette-europe.com
SIC: 20500 Employees: 200
Manufacture & Distribution of Medium Density Fibreboard
Mr Duane McDougall Chairman
Mr J O'Brien Finance Director
Mr L O'Reilly Personnel Director
Mr Rory Kirwan Managing Director

Balcas Ltd
Kill
Naas Co. Kildare
Phone: 045-877671 Fax: 045-877073
Email: postmaster@balcas.com
Web: http://www.balcas.com
SIC: 20511 Employees: 75
Manufacture Wooden Mouldings
Mr David Kidney Managing Director
Mr Anthony Casey Accountant

Framanc
Unit 14/17 Ashbourne Industrial Park
Ashbourne
Navan Co. Meath
Phone: 01-8350543 Fax: 01-8352896
Email: framanc@iol.com
SIC: 20511 Employees: 35
Manufacture Picture Frames
Mr Michael Magee Managing Director

Waterford Joinery
Dungarvan
Waterford Co. Waterford
Phone: 058-41399 Fax: 058-42872
SIC: 20511 Employees: 70
Wood Products (Semi-Finished)
Mr John McGrath Managing Director

Dexion Materials Handling
1A Blanchardstown Corporate Park
Blanchardstown
Dublin 15
Phone: 01-8210500 Fax: 01-8219026
Email: info@dexion-mh.ie
Web: http://www.dexion-mh.ie
SIC: 20512 Employees: 35
Partitions Shelving Racking
Mr Sam Evans Managing Director
Ms Mary Madden Financial Controller
Mr Pat Kane Personnel Manager
Mr Marcus Bradshaw IT Manager

SBS Timber Frame Ltd
SIAC Industrial Estate
Portarlington
Portlaoise Co. Laois
Phone: 0502-43470 Fax: 0502-43864
SIC: 20512 Employees: 30
Manufacture of timber frames
Mr Colin Sterling Manager

Pulp,Paper & Paper Manufacture

21	Pulp, Paper & Paper Manufacture
21110	Paper/Pulp Packaging Products
21120	Pulp/ Paper/ Board
21210	Board Packaging Products
21220	Paper Hygiene Products
21230	Stationery – Manufacture
21240	Wallpaper & Coverings
21250	Paper/Board Products (Other)

Aerobord Ltd
Askeaton
Limerick Co. Limerick
Phone: 061-604600 Fax: 061-604601
Email: mail@aerobord.ie
Web: http://www.aerobord.ie
SIC: 21110 Employees: 80
Insulation & Packaging
Mr Des Clinton Managing Director
Mr Gerard Barry Financial Director
Mr John Nash Marketing Director
Mr Joe Condon Production Manager
Mr Richard Woulfe Computer Manager

Alert Packaging Ltd
Southern Cross
Bray Co. Wicklow
Phone: 01-2860300 Fax: 01-2863755
Email: info@alertpackaging.ie
SIC: 21110 Employees: 55
Manufacture Plastic Packaging
Mr Justin Burke Managing Director
Mr Conor Lynch Finance Manager
Ms Sheila Farrell Personnel Officer

Alpaco Foil Ltd
Charvey Lane
Rathnew
Wicklow Co. Wicklow
Phone: 0404-68222 Fax: 0404-69467
SIC: 21110 Employees: 30
Foil Container Manufacturer
Mr Frank McKenzie Managing Director
Mr Richard Murray Production Manager

Amcor Rentschf
33 Botanic Road
Glasnevin
Dublin 9
Phone: 01-8302244 Fax: 01-8309852
SIC: 21110 Employees: 85
Cigarette Cartons
Mr Sandy Robertson Chief Executive
Mr Ian Swanton Finance Manager
Ms Bernie Curtin Sales Administrator
Mr Neville Shekleton Operations Director
Mr Stephen Crooks IT Manager

Barlow Packaging Ltd
Newbridge Business Park
Newbridge Co. Kildare
Phone: 045-431302 Fax: 045-437902
Email: info@barlowpackaging.com
Web: http://www.barlowpackaging.com
SIC: 21110 Employees: 100
Packaging
Mr Christy Howard Managing Director
Mr Ian Menzies Financial Director
Mr Dan Bell Sales Manager
Mr Michael Kenneally Production Manager
Mr Fergal Booth IT Manager

Cavan Box Co
Kilmore
Ballyjamesduff Co. Cavan
Phone: 049-8544788 Fax: 049-8544787
Email: info@cavanbox.ie
Web: http://www.cavanbox.ie
SIC: 21110 Employees: 40
Laminated Cartons
Mr Anselm Lovett Managing Director
Mr David Lovett General Manager

Cork Packaging Ltd
Unit 1 Enterprise Park
Fermoy Co. Cork
Phone: 025-33182 Fax: 025-33107
Email: osheam@indigo.ie
SIC: 21110 Employees: 36
Boxes - Corrugated & Fibre
Mr Micheal O'Shea Managing Director

Dollard Packaging Ltd
6-7 Newtown Industrial Estate
Coolock
Dublin 17
Phone: 01-8470044 Fax: 01-8470614
Email: sales@dollard-packaging.ie
Web: http://www.dollard-packaging.ie
SIC: 21110 Employees: 45
Paper/Pulp Packaging Products
Mr Ken Blake Managing Director
Mr David Hilliard Sales Director
Mr David Kelly Production Director
Mr Kevin Byrne Computer Manager

Dolphin Packaging Ltd
Greenore
Dundalk Co. Louth
Phone: 042-9373222 Fax: 042-9373179
Email: dolpac@gofree.indigo.ie
SIC: 21110 Employees: 50
Packaging Materials
Mr Noel Larkin Manager

Donoghue Packaging
Ballylangley
Bandon Co. Cork
Phone: 023-421111 Fax: 023-412111
Email: donpack@donpack.ie
SIC: 21110 Employees: 30
Manufacture Packaging
Mr Ray Donoghue Managing Director

Fitz-Pack
Galvone Industrial Estate
Limerick Co. Limerick
Phone: 061-413855 Fax: 061-413004
SIC: 21110 Employees: 600
Manufacture Cardboard Boxes & Packaging Software
Mr Ian Gilmore Managing Director
Mr Jerry McGarry Finance Manager
Ms Connie Ryan Sales & Marketing Manager
Mr Paul Meeson Production Manager
Mr Liam Dowling Computer Manager

Paper Manufacturing

Galway Corrugated Cases
Parkmore Industrial Estate
Galway Co. Galway
Phone: 091-753001 Fax: 091-770020
Email: info@galwaycorrugated.com
SIC: 21110 Employees: 40
Cardboard Box Manufacture
Mr Paraic Shaugnessy Managing Director
Mr Alan Croghan Accounts Manager
Mr Michael Earls Sales Manager

International Paper Ireland
Ashbourne
Navan Co. Meath
Phone: 01-8010400 Fax: 01-8351249
SIC: 21110 Employees: 160
Paper/Pulp Packaging Products
Ms Mary Hansell Administration Manager
Mr Ian Baker Financial Controller
Mr Brian Murnane Sales & Marketing Manager
Mr Martin Quinn Technical Manager

Jefferson Smurfit Group Plc
Beechhill
Clonskeagh
Dublin 4
Phone: 01-2027000 Fax: 01-2694481
Email: info@smurfit.ie
Web: http://www.smurfit.ie
SIC: 21110 Employees: 2000
Paper & Paper based packaging products
Dr Michael Smurfit Chief Executive
Mr Ian Curley Financial Controller
Mr Dermot Smurfit Sales & Marketing Manager
Mr Gary McGann Chief Operations Officer

JJ O'Toole Ltd
Raheen Business Park
Limerick Co. Limerick
Phone: 061-229333 Fax: 061-301960
Email: enquiries@jjotoole.ie
SIC: 21110 Employees: 80
Paper & Packaging Supplier
Mr Fergus O'Toole Managing Director
Mr Tony Frawley Finance Manager
Mr John Hayes Sales & Marketing Director

Kartoncraft
84/85 Lagan Road
Dublin Industrial Estate
Dublin 11
Phone: 01-8306222 Fax: 01-8309409
Email: info@kartoncraft.ie
Web: http://www.kartoncraft.ie
SIC: 21110 Employees: 85
Printed folding Cartons for
Mr Frank Whelan Managing Director
Mr Kealan Lennon Finance Director
Mr Fergus Flannagan Commercial Director
Mr Colm Nolan Operations Manager
Mr Kevin Byrne Head of IT

Kempis Group
Jamestown Business Park
Jamestown Road, Finglas
Dublin 11
Phone: 01-8641900 Fax: 01-8641907
Email: kempis@indigo.ie
SIC: 21110 Employees: 32
Manufacturer of Paper
Mr Paul Molloy Managing Director
Mr Francis Byrne Finance Manager
Mr John Cray Sales & Marketing Manager
Mr George Molloy Production Director
Mr Keith Molloy Computer Manager

Lenpak Ltd
Unit 3-4 Stag Industrial Estate
Ballyboggan Road, Glasnevin
Dublin 11
Phone: 01-8307899 Fax: 01-8307762
SIC: 21110 Employees: 70
Manufacture Corrugated Cases
Mr Liam Nolan General Manager
Mr Declan Kenny Financial Controller
Mr Jim McDonald Sales Manager

Marchmont Packaging Ltd
U E40 Cloverhill Industrial Estate
Clondalkin
Dublin 22
Phone: 01-4570126 Fax: 01-4130299
Email: marchmont@printnet.ie
Web: http://www.printnet.ie
SIC: 21110 Employees: 110
Folding Cartons Manufacturing
Mr Patrick Doran Managing Director
Mr Michael Aherne Financial Controller
Ms Vivian McGarry Administration Manager
Mr David Locket Sales & Marketing Director
Mr Brendan Mulqueen Operations Director

Merkel Freudenberg
Unit 48 Cookstown Industrial Estate
Tallaght
Dublin 24
Phone: 01-4514404 Fax: 01-4522028
Email: packings@freudenberg.com
Web: http://www.freudenberg.com
SIC: 21110 Employees: 65
Manufacture Packaging & Seals
Mr Sean Hennessy Managing Director
Mr John Curley Finance Manager
Ms Mary McGowan Computer Manager

P Faulkner & Sons Ltd
Chapelizod Hill Road
Dublin 20
Phone: 01-6260000 Fax: 01-6234747
Email: info@faulkner.ie
Web: http://www.faulkner.ie
SIC: 21110 Employees: 68
Packing - Bubble Wrap
Mr Denis O'Donovan Managing Director
Ms Jackie Connolly Personnel Manager
Mr Pat Furlong Sales & Marketing Manager

Packaging Industries Ltd
Fox & Geese House
Naas Road
Dublin 12
Phone: 01-4565384 Fax: 01-4507567
Email: info@packagingindustries.ie
Web: http://www.packagingindustries.ie
SIC: 21110 Employees: 30
Plastic Packaging Sales
Mr Richard Powell Managing Director
Ms Linda Daniels Finance Manager
Mr Torren Gale DP Manager

Smurfit Corrugated Cases
Ballymount Road
Walkinstown
Dublin 12
Phone: 01-4090000 Fax: 01-4506764
SIC: 21110 Employees: 200
Manufacture Corrugated Boxes
Mr John O'Loughlin Manager
Mr Shane Quinn Computer Manager

Smurfit Packaging Systems
Kileen Road
Dublin 10
Phone: 01-6160030 Fax: 01-6265740
SIC: 21110 Employees: 80
Manufacture of Packaging Systems
Mr Colm O'Raghallaigh General Manager
Mr Oliver Larkin Financial Controller
Mr Mark Russell Production Manager

Tetra Pak Ltd
Arkle Road
Sandyford Industrial Estate
Dublin 18
Phone: 01-2942370 Fax: 01-2942402
SIC: 21110 Employees: 40
Packaging & Processing Milk Cartons
Mr Brian McGuinness Managing Director
Ms Deirdre Ryan Finance Manager
Mr Donal Buckley Sales Director
Mr Derek Nugent Technical Manager

Time Packaging Ltd
29 Cookstown Industrial Estate
Tallaght
Dublin 24
Phone: 01-4511944 Fax: 01-4511567
Email: sales@tpk.ie
SIC: 21110 Employees: 30
Carton Manufacture
Mr Willy Duffy General Manager
Mr Paul Earls Finance Manager
Mr Alan Moody Sales Manager

Clondalkin Group Ltd
SIAC Building, Monastery Road
Clondalkin
Dublin 22
Phone: 01-4591559 Fax: 01-4591550
Email: clondalkin.ifsc@clondalkin.group.com
Web: http://www.clondalkingroup.com
SIC: 21120 Employees: 3100
Manufacture Packaging Products
Mr Norbert McDermot Chief Executive
Mr Colman O'Neill Finance Manager
Mr Liam Bergin Company Secretary

DM Paper Ltd
Unit A Fonthill Industrial Park
Fonthill Road
Dublin 22
Phone: 01-6233788 Fax: 01-6233773
SIC: 21120 Employees: 30
Paper Merchants
Mr Frank Mooney Managing Director
Mr Darren Lawlor Personnel Manager

Mortin Paper Co Ltd
Edward Street
Limerick Co. Limerick
Phone: 061-417188 Fax: 061-417434
SIC: 21120 Employees: 45
Corrugated Paper
Mr Bernard Berkery General Manager

Sensormatic Electronics Corporation Ireland
Melbourne Road
Bishopstown
Cork Co. Cork
Phone: 021-4801000 Fax: 021-4801050
Email: info@sensormatic.com
Web: http://www.sensormatic.com
SIC: 21120 Employees: 350
Security Systems
Mr Michael Corkery Chief Executive
Mr Mark O'Donoghue Financial Controller
Mr John Kinnealy Production Manager
Mr Aidan Lenaghan MIS Manager

Atlas Print & Packaging Ltd
Lower Dargle Road
Bray Co. Wicklow
Phone: 01-2860477 Fax: 01-2828245
Email: atlas@eircom.net
SIC: 21210 Employees: 30
Manufacture Cartons
Mr James Kavanagh Managing Director
Ms Stephanie Kavanagh-Antoun Financial Controller
Mr Ravi Antoun Sales Manager

Connaught Packaging
Unit 6 Merlin Park Industrial Estate
Galway Co. Galway
Phone: 091-755032 Fax: 091-771875
Email: info@cpk.ie
Web: http://www.cpk.ie
SIC: 21210 Employees: 40
Corrugated Cardbox Manufacturer
Mr Martin Clancy General Manager
Mr Brian Leahy Finance Manager
Mr Winston Depinna Sales & Marketing Manager
Mr Jim McHugh Production Manager

Paper Manufacturing

Ire-Tex Group Plc
Collinstown
Leixlip
Naas Co. Kildare
Phone: 01-6246777 Fax: 01-6246001
Email: info@iretex.com
Web: http://www.iretex.com
SIC: 21210 Employees: 200
Foam Packaging & Box Production
Mr Paul McLoughlin General Manager
Mr Kevin Hogan Finance Manager
Mr John Fitzgerald Production Manager
Mr Alan Keegan IT Manager

Irish Co-Op Society
Roxboro Road
Limerick Co. Limerick
Phone: 061-415833 Fax: 061-410633
Email: europaks@irish-co-op.ie
Web: http://www.irish-co-op.ie
SIC: 21210 Employees: 110
Corrugated Board Packaging
Mr Liam Ahern Chief Executive
Mr Barry Kelleher Company Accountant
Mr Gerry Ryan Plant Manager
Mr Denis Crowley Sales & Marketing Manager
Mr Peadar O'Keeffe Production Manager
Mr Graham Prendercast IT Manager

Woodfab Packaging
South Quay
Arklow Co. Wicklow
Phone: 0402-32011 Fax: 0402-39298
SIC: 21210 Employees: 44
Board Packaging Products
Mr Dave Barnes Chief Executive
Mr Paul Earls Financial Controller
Mr Pat Gillis Sales & Marketing Manager

Tara Tissue Ltd
Kilcohan
Waterford Co. Waterford
Phone: 051-854440 Fax: 051-857353
Email: reception@tara-tissues.ie
Web: http://www.tara-msl.ie
SIC: 21220 Employees: 40
Toilet Paper & Tissues
Mr Brendan McGrath Managing Director
Ms Stella Burke Finance Manager
Mr Vladimir Tulik IT Manager

Abbot Labels Ltd
110 Baldoyle Industrial Estate
Dublin 13
Phone: 01-8320220 Fax: 01-8326834
SIC: 21230 Employees: 30
Manufacturers Of Labels
Mr Liam Brady Managing Director

Advanced Labels
Unit 126 Baldoyle Industrial Estate
Dublin 13
Phone: 01-8321335 Fax: 01-8321336
Email: alabel@alabels.ie
Web: http://www.alabels.ie
SIC: 21230 Employees: 27
Label Printers, Labelling Machines
Mr Joe Killion Manager
Ms Pamela Roche Finance Manager

AT Cross Distribution
Ballinasloe Co. Galway
Phone: 0905-31400 Fax: 0905-31497
Email: info@cross.com
Web: http://www.cross.com
SIC: 21230 Employees: 195
Manufacture Writing Instruments
Mr Seamus Cunniffe General Manager
Mr Martin Conroy Head of Personnel
Mr Paul Gibney National Sales Manager
Ms Olive Warde IT Manager

Continuous Business Forms Ltd
Cobh Cross Industrial Estate
Carrigtwohill
Cork Co. Cork
Phone: 021-4883755 Fax: 021-4883814
SIC: 21230 Employees: 25
Business Stationary
Mr John Martin General Manager
Mr Aidan Sellers Accountant
Mr Paul Keegan Sales Director
Mr Robert Healy Production Director
Mr Brian Sweetman Computer Manager

D & A O'Leary
DAOL Business Centre
Tramore Road
Cork Co. Cork
Phone: 021-4271221 Fax: 021-4275421
SIC: 21230 Employees: 36
Printing/Stationery/Office Furniture
Mr Maurice O'Leary Managing Director
Ms Deirdre Walsh Financial Controller

Flight Label Company Ltd
65 Heather Road
Sandyford Industrial Estate
Dublin 18
Phone: 01-2957588 Fax: 01-2957673
Email: info@flightlabel.com
Web: http://www.label.com
SIC: 21230 Employees: 45
Manufacture Labels
Mr John Lawless Chief Executive
Ms Sharon Butler Financial Controller
Mr John McGrillen Customer Service Manager
Mr Jason Dingle Production Manager
Mr Damian Brady Accounts Administrator

General Binding Co Ltd
Unit 12 Naas Road, Business Park
Muir Field Drive
Dublin 12
Phone: 01-4602200 Fax: 01-4602422
Email: info@documentbinding.com
Web: http://www.documemtbinding.com
SIC: 21230 Employees: 50
Binding & Stationery Company
Mr Colin Paul Managing Director
Ms Hazel Balfe Office Manager
Mr Colin Paul Sales & Marketing Manager

John Dickinson (Irl)
Greenhills Industrial Estate
Walkinstown
Dublin 12
Phone: 01-4506771 Fax: 01-4502729
Web: http://www.johndickinson.com
SIC: 21230 Employees: 60
Stationary Converters (Make Envelopes)
Mr Tony Clarke Manager
Mr Michael Nolan Finance Manager

Label Art Ltd
70-74 Broomhill Road
Tallaght Industrial Estate
Dublin 24
Phone: 01-4513555 Fax: 01-4510424
Email: sales@labelart.ie
Web: http://www.labelart.ie
SIC: 21230 Employees: 60
Manufacture Self Adhesive Labels
Mr John Browne Managing Director
Mr Donal Healy Financial Controller
Ms Glenda Duff Sales Manager
Mr Patrick Tully Production Manager
Ms Orla Kelly IT Manager

Lantz Stationery Ltd
PO Box 3077
Dublin 8
Phone: 01-4531311 Fax: 01-4538784
Email: sales@lantz.ie
Web: http://www.lantz.ie
SIC: 21230 Employees: 26
Stationery Manufacturers & Wholesalers
Ms Mary Hughes Managing Director
Ms Audrey Dunne Finance Manager

Multiprint Labels Ltd
Unit 2 Swords Business Park
Swords
Dublin 1
Phone: 01-8300544 Fax: 01-8138950
Web: http://www.multiprint.ie
SIC: 21230 Employees: 60
Self Adhesive/Thermal Labels
Mr David Clarkin Managing Director
Mr Michael Moriarty Financial Controller
Ms Dymphna Bird Personnel Officer
Mr Brian Clarkin Sales & Marketing Director
Mr Bill Smith Production Manager

Serla Print Ltd
Serla House
Greenhills Road, Tallaght
Dublin 24
Phone: 01-4521433 Fax: 01-4526818
Email: sales@serlaprint.com
SIC: 21230 Employees: 50
Computer Stationery Printers
Mr Joe Rodgers Managing Director
Mr Michael Kelly Group Accountant
Mr Muiris DeCogan Production Manager

System Label
Racecourse Road
Roscommon Co. Roscommon
Phone: 0903-30900 Fax: 0903-25815
Email: info@systemlabel.com
Web: http://www.systemlabel.com
SIC: 21230 Employees: 40
Label & Sign Manufacture
Mr Maurice Buckley Managing Director
Mr Niall O'Shea Marketing Manager
Mr Mark Haddock Production Manager
Mr Alan Byrne Computer Manager

Trimfold Ltd
Duggan Industrial Estate, Athboy Road
Trim
Navan Co. Meath
Phone: 046-31497 Fax: 046-36049
Email: envelopes@trimfold.com
Web: http://www.trimfold.com
SIC: 21230 Employees: 75
Stationery - Production of Envelopes
Mr Eugene Healey Director
Mr Kevin Murray Finance Manager
Mr Des Ryan Sales Executive

Turners Printing Co
Earl Street
Longford Co. Longford
Phone: 043-45423 Fax: 043-41430
Email: turner@iol.ie
SIC: 21230 Employees: 65
Printing Stationery
Mr Warren Turner Managing Director
Mr Joe Mitchell Financial Controller

Wigoders
Long Mile Road
Dublin 12
Phone: 01-4500888 Fax: 01-4500889
Email: info@wigoders.ie
Web: http://www.wigoders.ie
SIC: 21240 Employees: 220
Wallpaper & Paint
Mr Chris Wognar
Mr Bernard Wognar

AB Converters Ltd
Blessington Industrial Estate
Blessington
Wicklow Co. Wicklow
Phone: 045-865611 Fax: 045-865026
Email: info@abconverters.ie
Web: http://www.abconverters.ie
SIC: 21250 Employees: 40
Paper Bag Manufacturer
Mr Dermot Brady Managing Director
Mr Tony Leahy Finance Manager
Mr Pat Healy Sales Manager

AC Tape & Packaging
Parkway Business Centre
Dublin 24
Phone: 01-4565027 Fax: 01-4568826
Email: sales@actape.ie
Web: http://www.actape.ie
SIC: 21250 Employees: 30
Manufacture Tape & Packaging
Mr Syl Murphy General Manager
Mr Gerry Griffin Finance Manager
Mr Hugh Fitzsimons Sales Manager

Antalis Ireland
Century Business Park
Finglas
Dublin 11
Phone: 01-8763100 Fax: 01-8567116
SIC: 21250 Employees: 43
Paper Merchant/Envelope Manufacturer
Mr Arthur Vincent Chief Executive
Mr Donal Tierney Finance Director
Mr Michael Callaghan Chief Executive
Mr David Quinn General Manager

Benson Box Co (Irl) Ltd
Killaloe
Ennis Co. Clare
Phone: 061-376119 Fax: 061-376169
Email: bensonbox@eircom.net
SIC: 21250 Employees: 28
Cardboard Boxes & Carton Manufacture
Mr Roy Benson General Manager

Bong Bauwenn Ireland Ltd
Purcellsinch Business Park
Dublin Road
Kilkenny Co. Kilkenny
Phone: 056-70877 Fax: 056-71434
Email: wbire@indigo.ie
SIC: 21250 Employees: 50
Envelope Manufacturers
Mr Michael Breen Managing Director
Mr Robert Twist Financial Controller

Buckeye Technology Ireland Ltd
Barnahely
Ringaskiddy
Cork Co. Cork
Phone: 021-4512700 Fax: 021-4512750
Email: info@buckeye.ie
Web: http://www.bkitech.com
SIC: 21250 Employees: 110
Paper Mill
Mr Gavin O'Neil Managing Director
Mr Eamon O'Riordan Financial Controller
Mr Barry Colgan Personnel Manager
Ms Joan O'Sullivan Sales & Marketing Manager
Mr Michael O'Brien Production Manager
Ms Louise Holland IT Specialist

Fort James Ireland Ltd
McKee Avenue
Finglas
Dublin 11
Phone: 01-8343000 Fax: 01-8068183
Email: info@fortjames.com
Web: http://www.fortjames.com
SIC: 21250 Employees: 169
Disposable Paper Products
Mr Richard Broderick Managing Director
Ms Ruth Lloyd Personnel Manager
Mr Liam Fortune Sales & Marketing Director
Mr Harry Murphy Production Manager
Ms Maura Begley Computer Manager

Industrial Packaging Ltd
IDA Industrial Estate
Killarney Road
Bray Co. Wicklow
Phone: 01-2864010 Fax: 01-2864015
Email: mail@industrialpackaging.ie
Web: http://www.industrialpackaging.ie
SIC: 21250 Employees: 50
Manufacture Cardboard Containers
Mr Michael Lee Managing Director
Ms Jackie Lennon Finance Manager
Mr Padraig Nolan Personnel Manager
Mr Norman Lee Marketing Director

McNaughton Paper Ireland Ltd
Cherry Orchard Industrial Estate
Ballyfermot
Dublin 10
Phone: 01-6261601 Fax: 01-6055318
Email: info@mcnaughton-paper.ie
Web: http://www.mcnaughton-paper.ie
SIC: 21250 Employees: 60
Paper Merchants
Mr John Havel Managing Director
Mr Tony Bell Sales Manager
Mr Luke Short IT Manager

New Era Packaging
Donore Road
Drogheda Co. Louth
Phone: 041-9844398 Fax: 041-9834481
Email: newera@eircom.net
SIC: 21250 Employees: 130
Manufacture Labels
Mr Peter Higgins Managing Director
Mr John Murray Sales Manager

O'Hagan Corrugated Packaging Ltd
Coe's Road
Dundalk Co. Louth
Phone: 042-9328199 Fax: 042-9328236
Email: ohaganz@indigo.ie
SIC: 21250 Employees: 30
Manufacturers of Printed Corrugated Cartons
Mr Eugene O'Hagan Managing Director
Ms Aisling Duffy Accountant
Mr Ken Maverley General Manager
Mr David O'Connor Production Manager

Robert Horne Paper (Irl) Ltd
Huntsman House Ballymount
Cross Industrial Estate
Dublin 24
Phone: 01-4508900 Fax: 01-4505839
Email: sales@roberthorne.ie
Web: http://www.roberthorne.co.uk
SIC: 21250 Employees: 31
Paper Merchants
Mr Brian McCleery Managing Director
Mr Reg Power Finance Director
Mr Eddie Timlin Sales Manager

Publishing, Printing & Media

22	Publishing, Printing & Media
22110	Books Publishing
22120	Newspaper Publishing
22150	Publishing (Other)
22220	Printers
22300	Recorded Media Reproduction
22310	Gramophone Records

Blackwater Press C/O Folens
Hibernian Industrial Estate
Dublin 24
Phone: 01-4515311 Fax: 01-4137282
Web: http://www.folens.ie
SIC: 22110 Employees: 50
Book Publisher
Mr John O'Connor Managing Director
Ms Aoife Geraghty Financial Controller
Ms Joanne Fanning Computer Technician

CJ Fallon & Co
Lucan Road
Palmerstown
Dublin 20
Phone: 01-6265777 Fax: 01-6166499
Email: cjfallon@iol.ie
SIC: 22110 Employees: 40
Publishing Educational Books
Mr Henry McNicholas Managing Director
Mr Patrick Tolan Accounts Manager
Ms Anne Connolly Office Manager

Anglo-Celt Ltd
Station House
Cavan Co. Cavan
Phone: 049-4331100 Fax: 049-4332280
Email: info@akrecruit.ie
Web: http://www.anglocelt.ie
SIC: 22120 Employees: 30
Newspapers
Mr Johnny O'Hanlon Editor
Mr Vincent Walsh Sales & Marketing Manager

Clare Champion Ltd
Barrack Street
Ennis Co. Clare
Phone: 065-6828105 Fax: 065-6820374
Email: editor@clarechampion.ie
Web: http://www.clarechampion.ie
SIC: 22120 Employees: 30
Local Newspaper
Mr John Galvin General Manager
Mr Liam Duggan Financial Controller
Mr Oliver O'Regan Sales & Marketing Manager
Mr Paddy Brennan Production Manager

Connacht Sentinel
15 Market Street
Galway Co. Galway
Phone: 091-567251 Fax: 091-567970
Email: ctribune@iol.ie
SIC: 22120 Employees: 60
Newspaper Printers & Publishers
Mr Gerry Cloherty Managing Director
Mr Iggy Madden Finance Manager
Ms Sabina Shephard Sales & Marketing Manager
Mr John O'Donnell Computer Manager

Drogheda Independent Co Ltd
9 Shop Street
Drogheda Co. Louth
Phone: 041-9838658 Fax: 041-9834271
Email: info@drogheda-independent.ie
Web: http://www.drogheda-independent.ie
SIC: 22120 Employees: 47
Provincial Newspaper
Mr Frank Mulrennan Managing Director
Ms Eleanor Hurley Personnel Manager
Mr Pat Gough Sales & Marketing Manager
Mr Martin Garry Production Manager
Mr Martin Pepper Computer Manager

Echo Newspaper Group
The Echo House
48 Old Bawn Road
Dublin 24
Phone: 01-4620711 Fax: 01-4598514
Email: info@the-echo.ie
Web: http://www.the-echo.ie
SIC: 22120 Employees: 40
Newspaper
Mr David Kennedy Managing Director
Ms Deirdre Doyle Accounts Manager
Ms Maria Moran Production Manager

Galway Advertiser
41-42 Ere Square
Galway Co. Galway
Phone: 091-567077 Fax: 091-567079
Email: reception@galwayadvertiser.ie
Web: http://www.galwayadvertiser.ie
SIC: 22120 Employees: 45
Newspaper Publishing
Mr Peter Timmins Managing Director
Mr Kevin Devane Finance Manager
Mr Ronnie O'Gorman Chairman

Imokilly People
57 Main Street
Midleton Co. Cork
Phone: 021-4613333 Fax: 021-4632500
Email: news@imokillypeople.ie
Web: http://www.imokillypeople.ie
SIC: 22120 Employees: 32
Newspaper
Ms Margaret England Advertising Executive
Mr Patrick O'Connor Editor

Independent News & Media Plc
2023 Binconi Avenue
City West Bus Campus Nass Road
Dublin 24
Phone: 01-4663200 Fax: 01-4663222
Email: mail@inplc.com
Web: http://www.independentnews.media.com
SIC: 22120 Employees: 8750
Media Group
Sir Anthony O'Reilly Executive Chairman
Mr James P Parkinson Finance Manager
Mr Alf McGrath Human Resources Director
Mr Barry Brennan Sales & Marketing Director
Mr Harry McCarthy IT Processing Manager

Ireland On Sunday
50 City Quay
Dublin 2
Phone: 01-6718255 Fax: 01-4179830
Email: info@irelandonsundaycom
Web: http://www.irelandonsunday.com
SIC: 22120 Employees: 50
Sunday Newspaper
Mr Colm Coghlan Managing Director
Mr Howard Walshe Marketing Manager
Mr Ciaran O'Tuama Production Manager

Irish Farmers Journal
Irish Farm Centre
Bluebell
Dublin 12
Phone: 01-4501166 Fax: 01-4520876
Email: info@farmersjournal.ie
Web: http://www.farmersjournal.ie
SIC: 22120 Employees: 50
Farming Newspaper
Mr Matt Dempsey Editor
Mr John Gill Sales Manager
Mr Pat O'Keeffe Operation Manager
Mr Brian Morrissey Computer Manager

Irish Times
PO Box 74
10-16 D'Olier Street
Dublin 2
Phone: 01-6792022 Fax: 01-6773241
Email: postmaster@irish-times.ie
Web: http://www.irish-times.ie
SIC: 22120 Employees: 700
Newspaper Publishing
Mr Nicholas Chapman Managing Director
Mr Richard Gee Financial Controller
Mr John McCormac Human Resources Manager
Ms Maeve Donovan Director of Sales & Marketing
Mr Seamus McCague Director of Technology

Kerryman Group Ltd
Clash Industrial Estate
Tralee Co. Kerry
Phone: 066-7121666 Fax: 066-7145572
Email: kerryman@indigo.ie
Web: http://www.kerryman.ie
SIC: 22120 Employees: 85
Newspapers
Ms Donna O'Doherty Managing Director
Ms Barbara Lynch Accountant
Mr Bernard O'Keeffe Advertising Manager
Mr Gerald Kearey Production Manager
Mr Tom King Computer Manager

Kilkenny People
34 High Street
Kilkenny Co. Kilkenny
Phone: 056-21015 Fax: 056-21414
Email: info@kilkennypeople.ie
Web: http://www.kilkennypeople.ie
SIC: 22120 Employees: 120
Newspapers Printing/Publishing
Mr Joe Hayes Managing Director
Ms Lillian Beattie Sales & Marketing Manager
Mr Peter Seaver Advertising Manager

Leinster Express
Dublin Road
Portlaoise Co. Laois
Phone: 0502-21666 Fax: 0502-20491
Email: lexpress@indigo.ie
Web: http://www.leinsterexpress.ie
SIC: 22120 Employees: 30
Newspaper
Mr Derek Quinn Managing Director
Mr Ray McGowan Advertising Director

Leinster Leader Ltd
19 South Main Street
Naas Co. Kildare
Phone: 045-897302 Fax: 045-875388
Email: tomh@leinster-leader.ie
Web: http://www.rmbi.ie
SIC: 22120 Employees: 60
Newspaper
Mr Ian Stewart Managing Director
Mr Tom Hanlon Financial Controller
Mr Seamus Morahan Sales & Marketing Manager
Mr Tony Ryan Production Manager

Limerick Post
Town Hall Centre
Rutland Street
Limerick Co. Limerick
Phone: 061-413322 Fax: 061-417684
Email: news@limerickpost.ie
Web: http://www.limerickpost.ie
SIC: 22120 Employees: 30
Local Newspaper
Mr Billy Ryan Editor
Mr Johnny Ryan Financial Controller
Mr Gerry O'Malley Advertising Manager
Ms Ann-Marie Quinn Production Manager

Meath Chronicle Group
Market Square
Navan Co. Meath
Phone: 046-79600 Fax: 046-23565
Email: info@meath-chronicle.ie
Web: http://www.meath/chronicle.ie
SIC: 22120 Employees: 100
Newspaper Publishers & Contract Printers
Mr Ken Davis Editor
Mr Peter Quigley Finance Manager
Ms Mary Smyth Company Secretary
Mr Gene Hennessy Advertisement Manager
Ms Georgina Davis Production Manager
Mr Paul Davies Computer Manager

Midland Tribune
Syngefield
Birr Co. Offaly
Phone: 0509-20003 Fax: 0509-20588
Email: midtrib@iol.ie
SIC: 22120 Employees: 80
Newspapers
Mr Arnold Fanning Managing Director
Ms Kay Crerar Financial Controller
Ms Phyllis Byrne Advertising Manager
Mr Noel McDermott Manager

Munster Express
37-38 The Quay
Waterford Co. Waterford
Phone: 051-872141 Fax: 051-873452
Email: munster@iol.ie
Web: http://www.munster-express.ie
SIC: 22120 Employees: 25
Newspaper
Mr Kieran Walsh Managing Director
Mr Chris Walsh Accounts Manager
Mr Liz McGough
Mr Michael Brophy Production Manager

Nationalist & Leinster Times Ltd
42 Tullow Street
Carlow Co. Carlow
Phone: 0503-31731 Fax: 0503-31442
Email: nltnews@eircom.net
SIC: 22120 Employees: 51
Newspaper
Mr Tom Geoghegan Managing Director
Mr Adrian Dunleavey Accounts Manager
Mr Willie Cremin Advertising Manager

Nationalist Newspaper
Queen Street
Clonmel Co. Tipperary
Phone: 052-22211 Fax: 052-25248
Email: info@nationalist.ie
Web: http://www.nationalist.ie
SIC: 22120 Employees: 29
Newspaper
Mr Arthur O'Leary Managing Director
Mr Phil Corby Advertising Manager

News International Plc
Huguenot House
35-38 St Stephen's Green
Dublin 2
Phone: 01-6028878 Fax: 01-6028880
Email: info@newsint.co.uk
SIC: 22120 Employees: 50
Newspapers
Ms Deborah Walsh Manager

Publishing, Printing & Media

Northern Standard
The Diamond
Monaghan Co. Monaghan
Phone: 047-82188 Fax: 047-84070
Email: garysmyth@eircom.net
SIC: 22120 Employees: 40
Newspapers Printing/Publishing
Mr Tommy Smith Manager

People Newspapers
Channing House, Rowe Street
Wexford Co. Wexford
Phone: 053-22155 Fax: 053-40100
Email: info@peoplenews.ie
Web: http://www.peoplenews.ie
SIC: 22120 Employees: 200
Local Newspaper
Mr Ger Walsh Managing Director
Ms Imelda Sinnott Credit Controller
Ms Ann Jones Advertising Manager
Mr Toddy Walsh Production Editor
Mr Paddy Winter Computer Manager

Southern Star
Ilen Street
Skibbereen Co. Cork
Phone: 028-21200 Fax: 028-21071
Email: advertising@southernstar.ie
Web: http://www.southernstar.ie
SIC: 22120 Employees: 25
Local Newspaper
Mr Liam O'Regan Managing Director
Mr John Hamilton Office Manager

Southside People (East)
85-86 Omni Park Shopping Centre
Santry
Dublin 9
Phone: 01-8621611 Fax: 01-8621626
Email: northnews@dublinpeople.com
Web: http://www.northsidepeople.ie
SIC: 22120 Employees: 50
Newspaper
Mr Robin Webb Managing Director
Mr Neil Boland Finance Manager
Mr Ray O'Neill Personnel Manager
Ms Maria Nulty Classified Manager
Mr Simon Archer Computer Manager

Star Newspaper
62A Terenure Road North
Dublin 6
Phone: 01-4901228 Fax: 01-4902193
Email: news@the-star.ie
SIC: 22120 Employees: 100
Newspaper
Mr Paul Cooke Managing Director
Mr Colin Davitt Financial Controller
Ms Margaret Mariarty Personnel Manager
Mr Ken Grace Advertising Manager
Mr James Clifford Head of Computers

Sunday Business Post
80 Harcourt Street
Dublin 2
Phone: 01-6026000 Fax: 01-6796498
Email: sbpost@iol.ie
Web: http://www.thepost.ie
SIC: 22120 Employees: 100
Newspaper
Mr Fiachra O'Riordan General Manager
Mr Kieran Moloney Financial Controller
Ms Deirdre Gilmartin Personnel Manager
Mr Finton Swanton IT Manager

Roscommon Herald
Patrick Street
Boyle Co. Roscommon
Phone: 079-62004 Fax: 079-62926
Email: roherald@indigo.ie
SIC: 29550 Employees: 23
Newspaper & Printing
Mr Brian Nerney Managing Director
Ms Christina McHugh Editor
Ms Claire Morgan Sales & Marketing Manager
Mr Raymond Latimer Production Director

Sunday Tribune
15 Lower Baggot Street
Dublin 2
Phone: 01-6314300 Fax: 01-6314390
Email: sales@tribune.ie
Web: http://www.tribune.ie
SIC: 22120 Employees: 120
Newspaper
Mr Jim Farrelly Managing Director
Mr John Scanlon Financial Controller
Mr Dave Kelly Personnel Manager
Mr John Holland Advertising Manager
Mr Paul Howe IT Manager

Tallaght Publishing Ltd
Old Bawn Road
Tallaght
Dublin 24
Phone: 01-4598513 Fax: 01-4620710
Email: studio@the-echo.ie
Web: http://www.the-echo.ie/
SIC: 22120 Employees: 35
Newpaper Publishing
Mr David Kennedy Editor
Ms Genevieve Murray Sales & Marketing Manager
Ms Liz Kennedy Computer Manager

Tipperary Star
Friar Street
Thurles Co. Tipperary
Phone: 0504-21122 Fax: 0504-21110
SIC: 22120 Employees: 23
Newspaper
Mr Arthur O'Leary Managing Director
Ms Paula St John Sales & Marketing Manager

Tribune Newspapers - Sunday Tribune
15 Lower Baggot Street
Dublin 2
Phone: 01-6615555 Fax: 01-6615302
Email: editorial@tribune.ie
SIC: 22120 Employees: 170
Publish Newspapers
Mr Jim Farrelly Managing Director
Mr John Stanlon Financial Controller
Mr John Holland Advertising Manager
Mr Paul Howe Production Manager

Trinity News
House 6
Trinity College
Dublin 2
Phone: 01-6082335 Fax: 01-6082656
Email: info@trinitynews.com
Web: http://www.trinitynews.com
SIC: 22120 Employees: 67
University Newspaper
Mr Karl White Editor

Vale Mallow Star & Observer
Broad Street
Charleville
Cork Co. Cork
Phone: 063-89682 Fax: 022-22959
Email: wob@vso.iol.ie
SIC: 22120 Employees: 32
Newspapers
Mr Michael Bigane Managing Director

Western People
Francis Street
Ballina Co. Mayo
Phone: 096-21188 Fax: 096-70208
Email: info@westernpeople.ie
Web: http://www.westernpeople.ie
SIC: 22120 Employees: 43
Newspaper Publishers
Mr Terry Reilly Manager
Mr David O'Sullivan Finance Manager
Mr David Dwane Sales Manager

Westmeath Examiner Ltd
19 Dominic Street
Mullingar Co. Westmeath
Phone: 044-48426 Fax: 044-40640
Email: company@westmeathexaminer.ie
Web: http://www.westmeathexaminer.ie
SIC: 22120 Employees: 90
Local Newspaper
Mr Martin Nally Director
Ms Julie Egan Personnel Officer
Mr Billy Brown Sales Manager
Mr Nicolas Nally Acting Editor
Mr Joe Tone Computer Manager

Wicklow Times
1 Eglinton Road
Bray Co. Wicklow
Phone: 01-2869111 Fax: 01-2869074
Email: wicklowtimes@tinet.ie
SIC: 22120 Employees: 25
Newspaper
Mr Shay Fitzmaurice Manager
Ms Pauline Carton Finance Manager
Mr Brian Kenny General Sales Manager
Mr Adrian Kelly Computer Manager

Accountancy Ireland
Institute of Chartered Accountants
87-89 Pembroke Road, Ballsbridge
Dublin 4
Phone: 01-6377200 Fax: 01-6685685
Email: ca@icai.ie
Web: http://www.icai.ie/accountancy-ireland
SIC: 22130 Employees: 80
Business Magazine
Ms Daisy Downes Editor
Ms Diredre Morrissey Accounts Manager
Mr John Hayes Personnel Manager
Ms Mairead Walsh Advertisement Manager
Ms Caroline Harte Computer Manager

African Missionary (SMA)
Blackrock Road
Cork Co. Cork
Phone: 021-4292871 Fax: 021-4293876
SIC: 22130 Employees: 30
Religious Periodical
Fr Bernard Cotter Editor

An Bord Altranais News
31-32 Fitzwilliam Square
Dublin 2
Phone: 01-6760226 Fax: 01-6763348
Email: admin@nursingboard.ie
Web: http://www.nursingboard.ie
SIC: 22130 Employees: 39
Nursing Registration Board
Ms Maria Neary Editor
Mr Jim O'Sullivan Finance Manager
Mr Desmond Bell Computer Manager

Business & Finance Media Ltd
Belenos Publications Group
50 Fitzwilliam Square West
Dublin 2
Phone: 01-6764587 Fax: 01-6619781
Email: belenos@eircom.net
Web: http://www.businessandfinance.ie
SIC: 22130 Employees: 50
Weekly Business Publication
Mr John McGee Managing Director
Ms Lisa Cosgrave Financial Controller
Ms Ann Butler Personnel Manager
Ms Maura Maughan Sales & Marketing Manager
Ms Maeve O'Byrne Advertising Manager
Mr Vincent Wall Editor

Publishing, Printing & Media

Eireann Healthcare Publications
25 Windsor Place
Dublin 2
Phone: 01-4753300 Fax: 01-4753311
Web: http://www.eireannpublications.ie
SIC: 22130 Employees: 25
Publish Magazines
Mr Chris Goodey Managing Director
Mr Pat O'Connor Financial Controller
Ms Caoimhe Tierney Production Manager

Hoson Publishing Company
6-7 Camden Place
Dublin 2
Phone: 01-4784322 Fax: 01-4781055
Email: ryanho@iol.ie
Web: http://www.ryanho.ie
SIC: 22130 Employees: 60
Publishing House
Ms Joan Fitzpatrick Chief Executive Officer
Mr Liam Fahy Financial Controller
Ms Laura Quinn Head of Operations

Intuition Publishing Ltd
IFSC House
Custom House Quay
Dublin 1
Phone: 01-6054300 Fax: 01-6054301
Email: info@intuitionpublishing.com
Web: http://www.intuitionpublishing.com
SIC: 22130 Employees: 65
Publishing Web Magazines
Mr Stephen Higgins Joint Managing Director
Mr David Harrison Finance Manager
Mr Denis Cody Sales & Marketing Manager
Ms Cathy Sheridan Operation Manager
Mr John Reddin Computer Manager

Irish Timber & Forestry Magazine
Fivealley
Birr Co. Offaly
Phone: 0509-33119 Fax: 0509-33119
Email: irishtimberforestry@eircom.net
Web: http://www.irishforests.com
SIC: 22130 Employees: 31
Forestry
Mr Brendan Dooley Editor
Ms Roisin Kendrick Publishing Co-Ordinator

Jude Publications
4 Santry Hall
Santry
Dublin 9
Phone: 01-8625063 Fax: 01-8869351
Email: judepublications@clubi.ie
SIC: 22130 Employees: 23
Periodical
Ms Arlene Scanlan Managing Director
Ms Sheila Garvey Finance Manager
Ms Annemarie Moran Head of Administration

Scope Communication
Prospect House 3 Prospect Road
Glasnevin
Dublin 9
Phone: 01-8303455 Fax: 01-8300888
Email: info@scope.ie
Web: http://www.scope.ie
SIC: 22130 Employees: 37
Computer Magazine Company
Mr Mark Egan Managing Director
Ms Ann-Marie Conkey Finance Manager
Mr Paul Byrne Sales Director
Ms Miriam Casey Production Manager
Mr Micheal Rohan Computer Manager

Smurfit Communications
2 Clanwilliam Court
Lower Mount Street
Dublin 2
Phone: 01-2405300 Fax: 01-6619757
Email: info@smurfit-comm.ie
Web: http://www.smurfit.ie/comms
SIC: 22130 Employees: 70
In-Flight Magazine
Mr Paul Whitington Editor
Mr Glen Kilroy Financial Controller
Ms Sorcha Cunningham Sales Manager

Smurfit Publications
2 Clanwilliam Court
Dublin 2
Phone: 01-6623158 Fax: 01-6619757
Email: info@smurfit.ie
Web: http://www.smurfit.ie/comms
SIC: 22130 Employees: 70
Publish Women's Magazines
Ms Nora Casey Chief Executive
Mr Glen Kilroy Finance Manager
Ms Patricia Barry Personnel Manager
Mr Ciaran Havelin Sales/Marketing Manager
Mr Paul Byrne Circulation Manager

Tara Publishing Company Ltd
Poolbeg House
1-2 Poolbeg Street
Dublin 2
Phone: 01-6719244 Fax: 01-2413040
Email: production@tara.iol.ie
SIC: 22130 Employees: 30
Trade Publishers Magazines
Mr Fergus Farrell Managing Director
Ms Niamh Mongey Credit Controller
Ms Kathleen Belton Sales Manager
Ms Valerie Doyle Commercial Manager

Veritas Publications
Veritas House
7-8 Lower Abbey Street
Dublin 1
Phone: 01-8788177 Fax: 01-8786507
Email: sales@veritas.ie
Web: http://www.veritas.ie
SIC: 22130 Employees: 80
Publish Religious Periodicals
Fr Sean Melody Director
Mr Charles Duignan Financial Controller
Ms Brid Healy Sales & Marketing Manager

Alucolor Ltd
Unit C Fonthill Industrial Park
Dublin 22
Phone: 01-6305955 Fax: 01-6305959
Email: alucolor@indigo.ie
SIC: 22150 Employees: 45
Printing/Publishing
Mr Jonathan Inglis Managing Director
Mr Denis O'Connell Financial Controller
Mr Tommy Carr Production Manager

Ashville Media Group Ltd
Apollo House
8th Floor, Tara Street
Dublin 2
Phone: 01-6787222 Fax: 01-6727100
Email: info@ashville.ie
SIC: 22150 Employees: 50
Publishing
Mr Diarmaid Lennon Director
Ms Kim Nyhan Operations Manager

IDS Media Group Ltd
3 Sandyford Business Park
Blackthorn Avenue
Dublin 18
Phone: 01-2604818 Fax: 01-2104816
Email: info@MediaGroup.com
Web: http://www.idsmediagroup.com
SIC: 74141 Employees: 75
Publishing
Mr Martin Crilly Managing Director

CBG.ie Ltd
Unit 6 Lepoardstown Office Park
Sandyford Industrial Park
Dublin 18
Phone: 01-2959222 Fax: 01-2943303
Email: info@cbg.ie
Web: http://www.cbg.ie
SIC: 22150 Employees: 25
Publishing
Mr Ray Egan Managing Director
Ms Sandra Egan Sales & Marketing Manager
Ms Aisling Donnellly Operations Manager

Deerpark Publishing Services Ltd
Kincora Hall
Shannon Town Centre
Shannon Co. Clare
Phone: 061-361211 Fax: 061-361323
Web: http://www.deerpark.ie
SIC: 22150 Employees: 27
Publishing Services
Ms Nora O'Brien Manager

Dublin Institute for Advanced Studies
10 Burlington Road
Dublin 4
Phone: 01-6140100 Fax: 01-6680561
Email: registrar@admin.dias.ie
Web: http://www.dias.ie
SIC: 22150 Employees: 60
Academic Publishers
Mr John Duggan Registrar

Dyflin Publishing
58 North Great Charles Street
Dublin 1
Phone: 01-8550477 Fax: 01-8550473
Email: info@dyflin.ie
SIC: 22150 Employees: 25
Publishing Company
Ms Karen Hesse Managing Director
Mr Finian Fallon Finance Manager
Mr Philip McGaley Sales Director

Educational Company Of Ireland
Ballymount Road
Walkinstown
Dublin 12
Phone: 01-4500611 Fax: 01-4500993
Email: info@edco.ie
Web: http://www.ebs.ie
SIC: 22150 Employees: 40
Publishing
Mr Frank Maguire Chief Executive
Ms Martina Harford Financial Controller
Mr Paul Cullen Production Manager

Elsevier Science Ireland Ltd
Elsevier House Brookvale Plaza
East Park
Shannon Co. Clare
Phone: 061-709600 Fax: 061-709100
Email: info@elsevierscience.ie
Web: http://www.elsevierscience.nl
SIC: 22150 Employees: 100
Scientific Publishers
Ms Niehaus Managing Director
Ms Pauline Carey Financial Controller
Mr Kenneth Buchholtz Personnel Manager
Ms Mary Minogue Administration Manager
Mr Brendan Curtin IT Manager

Examiner Publications Ltd
P.O. Box 21
Academy Street
Cork Co. Cork
Phone: 021-4272722 Fax: 021-4275477
Email: info@examiner.ie
Web: http://www.irishexaminer.ie
SIC: 22150 Employees: 400
Publishers
Mr Padraig Mallon Managing Director
Mr John McKenna IT Manager

Publishing, Printing & Media

Geological Survey of Ireland
Beggars Bush
Haddington Road
Dublin 4
Phone: 01-6707444 Fax: 01-6681782
Email: info@gsi.ie
Web: http://www.gsi.ie
SIC: 22150 Employees: 65
Map Making, Publish Geological Books
Dr Peadar McArdle Director
Dr Ralph Horne Assistant Director
Mr Eddie Mortimer Admin/Marketing Manager
Ms Mary Carter Head of IT

HW Wilson Co Ltd
Wilson House
1-14 Fenian Street
Dublin 2
Phone: 01-6621222 Fax: 01-6621233
Email: hwwilson@indigo.ie
Web: http://www.hwwilson.com
SIC: 22150 Employees: 130
Publishing Company
Mr Michael Heelan Associate Director
Ms Elaine McDonnell Personnel Manager
Mr Alan Boxberger Systems Manager

Mac Communications
Taney Hall
Eglinton Terrace Dundrum
Dublin 14
Phone: 01-2960000 Fax: 01-2960383
Email: info@maccommunication.ie
SIC: 22150 Employees: 40
Publishing Company
Ms Rosemary Delaney Managing Director
Mr Des Deasy Financial Controller
Ms Ann-Marie St John Personnel Administrator
Ms Ciara O'Driscoll Production Manager

Round Hall Ltd
43 Fitzwilliam Place
Dublin 2
Phone: 01-6024800 Fax: 01-6625302
Email: info@roundhall.ie
Web: http://www.roundhall.ie
SIC: 22150 Employees: 23
Legal Publishing
Ms Eleanor McGarry Managing Director

Advantage Printers
Newtown Industrial Estate
Dublin 17
Phone: 01-8476711 Fax: 01-8484433
Email: info@advantageprinters.ie
Web: http://www.advantageprinters.ie
SIC: 22220 Employees: 25
Screen Printing
Mr Aidan McGlynn Managing Director
Ms Marie Glabby Accounts Manager

AGI Media Packaging Dublin Ltd
Broomhill Road
Tallaght
Dublin 24
Phone: 01-4623522 Fax: 01-4623507
Email: info@agimedia.com
Web: http://www.agimedia.com
SIC: 22220 Employees: 55
Printing for Multi Media Industry
Mr Donal Forsythe General Manager
Mr Martin Hammond Financial Controller
Mr Michael Molloy Sales Manager
Mr Dave Flynn Operations Manager
Mr Brian Morley IT Manager

Alpha Bookbinding Co Ltd
Unit 115
Baldoyle Industrial Estate
Dublin 13
Phone: 01-8320222 Fax: 01-8326562
SIC: 22220 Employees: 40
Print Finishers
Mr John Harold Managing Director
Mr Damien Quinn Finance Manager
Ms Susan Dillon Personnel Manager
Mr Paul Bissett Production Manager

Aluset Group Ltd
Broomsbridge House Lagan Road
Dublin Industrial Estate
Dublin 11
Phone: 01-8307533 Fax: 01-8307230
Email: sales@aluset.ie
Web: http://www.aluset.ie
SIC: 22220 Employees: 127
Printing Company
Mr Michael Brady Chief Executive
Mr Liam Lyons Finance Manager
Mr Pat Slane Sales Director
Mr Martin Cashel Production Manager
Mr Tim Rafferty Computer Director

Berry Print Group
Golf Road
Westport Co. Mayo
Phone: 098-28500 Fax: 098-25752
Email: info@berryprint.com
Web: http://www.berryprint.com
SIC: 22220 Employees: 140
Commercial Printing
Mr David Lennon Managing Director
Mr Dermot Berry Sales & Marketing Manager
Mr Larry Sage Production Manager
Mr John Rowlands IT Manager

Blackthorn Print & Design
Blackthorn Close
Stillorgan Industrial Park
Blackrock Co. Dublin
Phone: 01-2957235 Fax: 01-2957236
Email: info@blackthorn.com
Web: http://www.blackthorn.com
SIC: 22220 Employees: 40
Printing Company
Mr Graeme Sedgewick Managing Director
Ms Zoe Gash Finance Manager
Mr John Hick Sales Director

Boylans
South Bank Industrial Estate
Marsh Road
Drogheda Co. Louth
Phone: 041-9839905 Fax: 041-9834827
SIC: 22220 Employees: 30
Printing Labels
Mr Micheal Boylan Managing Director

BP Colour
Unit 3-4 Fonthill Industrial Park
Fonthill Road
Dublin 22
Phone: 01-6239311 Fax: 01-6239320
Email: bpcolour@bp-colour.ie
Web: http://www.bp-colour.ie
SIC: 22220 Employees: 30
Printing
Mr Brian Reilly Managing Director
Mr Al Reilly Director

Brookfield Printing Company Ltd
Blackthorn Close
Stillorgan Industrial Park
Blackrock Co. Dublin
Phone: 01-2957088 Fax: 01-2957236
Web: http://www.brookfieldprint.com
SIC: 22220 Employees: 40
Colour Printing
Mr Graham Sedgwick Managing Director

Brunswick Press Ltd
Unit B2 Bluebell Industrial Estate
Dublin 12
Phone: 01-4569555 Fax: 01-4569599
Email: brunpres@indigo.ie
SIC: 22220 Employees: 45
Printers
Mr Peter Allman Manager
Mr Dermot Langanbach Finance Manager
Mr Brendan McKenna Sales & Marketing
Mr Peter Behan Production Manager

Cahill Printers Ltd
East Wall Road
Dublin 3
Phone: 01-2412000 Fax: 01-8365346
Email: info@cahill-printers.ie
Web: http://www.cahill-printers.ie
SIC: 22220 Employees: 170
Printing
Mr Lorcan O'Hobain Managing Director

Cara Craftwear
79 Lagan Road
Dublin Industrial Estate
Dublin 11
Phone: 01-8372155 Fax: 01-8309617
Email: info@fashionclothes.ie
Web: http://www.fashionclothes.ie
SIC: 22220 Employees: 100
Printing T-Shirts
Mr Frank Murphy Managing Director
Mr John Green Finance Manager
Ms Margaret Murphy Personnel Manager
Mr Dermot Kelly Sales Director
Mr Shay Kennedy Productions Manager
Ms Audrey Farrell Office Manager

Castletown Press Ltd
Maynooth Road
Cellbridge
Naas Co. Kildare
Phone: 01-6271170 Fax: 01-6272345
Email: sales@castlestowenpress.ie
SIC: 22220 Employees: 27
Law Printers & Maunufacture Stationery
Mr Michael Keating Managing Director
Mr Patrick Shaw General Manager

Claymon Laboratories Ltd
Three Rock Road
Sandyford Industrial Estate
Dublin 18
Phone: 01-2958545 Fax: 01-2955399
Email: info@claymon.ie
Web: http://www.claymon.com
SIC: 22220 Employees: 30
Laboratory
Ms Carmel Fitzpatrick Manager
Mr Aaron Keegan Financial Controller
Mr Connor Hoey Sales Director

Codex Print Ltd
89 Lagan Road, Dublin Industrial Est
Glasnevin
Dublin 11
Phone: 01-8303580 Fax: 01-8307180
Email: sales@codexltd.com
Web: http://www.codexltd.com
SIC: 22220 Employees: 56
Printing
Mr Brendan Murphy Managing Director
Mr Traolach O'Sullivan Finance Manager
Mr Michael Yates Sales Manager

Coleridge Fine Arts
Broomhill Road
Tallaght
Dublin 24
Phone: 01-4515144 Fax: 01-4527752
Email: fineart@indigo.ie
Web: http://www.coleridgefineart.ie
SIC: 22220 Employees: 100
Printers
Mr Kevin Walsh Managing Director
Mr Tom Lawlor Financial Controller
Mr Tony Little Operations Manager
Mr Eugene Reynolds IT Manager

Color Communications
IDA Industrial Estate
Station Road
Castlerea Co. Roscommon
Phone: 0907-21000 Fax: 0907-21007
Email: ccebv@iol.ie
SIC: 22220 Employees: 35
Colour Cards
Mr John Winstanley General Manager
Ms Maureen McKervey Personnel Manager

Colorman Ireland Ltd
Broombridge Industrial Estate
Dublin 11
Phone: 01-8301566 Fax: 01-8301171
Email: info@colorman.ie
Web: http://www.colorman.ie
SIC: 22220 Employees: 180
Print Computer Manuals
Ms Claire Nixen Managing Director
Mr David Clancy Financial Controller
Ms Claire Herbert Personnel Manager
Mr Gary Clarke Sales & Marketing Manager
Mr Derek Geelon General Manager
Mr David Nixen Computer Manager

Colorprint Ltd
Chapelizod Industrial Estate
Dublin 20
Phone: 01-6265066 Fax: 01-6264579
Email: colorprint@info.ie
SIC: 22220 Employees: 50
Computer Manuals
Mr Paul Walshe Managing Director
Mr Pat Dunne Company Accountant
Ms Francis Walshe Company Secretary
Mr Niall Healy Production Director

Colour House
U3a Ballyboggan Industrial Estate
Cabra
Dublin 11
Phone: 01-8308177 Fax: 01-8303023
Email: colourhs@eircom.net
SIC: 22220 Employees: 25
Lithographic Printers
Mr Tony O'Hanlon Manager
Mr Brendan Byrne Finance Manager

Colourbooks Ltd
Unit 105 Baldoyle Industrial Estate
Baldoyle
Dublin 13
Phone: 01-8325812 Fax: 01-8325825
Email: colorbk@indigo.ie
Web: http://www.colourbook.ie
SIC: 22220 Employees: 100
Printers
Mr John Harold Managing Director
Ms Marie Doran Financial Controller
Ms Adrienne Foran Sales Manager
Mr Ray Buckley Production Manager

Craftprint Ltd
86 Jamestown Road
Inchicore
Dublin 8
Phone: 01-4532288 Fax: 01-4536221
Email: info@craftprint.ie
Web: http://www.craftprint.ie
SIC: 22220 Employees: 50
Printing & Design
Mr Laurence Caulfield Managing Director

Criterion Press Ltd
74 The Industrial Estate
Glasnevin
Dublin 11
Phone: 01-8307011 Fax: 01-8306017
SIC: 22220 Employees: 24
Printing
Mr Colm Handley Managing Director
Mr Al Somani Financial Controller
Mr Tom Fay Production Director

Cuspal Ltd
27-28 Long Lane
Dublin 8
Phone: 01-4731322 Fax: 01-4731873
Email: sales@cuspal.com
Web: http://www.cuspal.com
SIC: 22220 Employees: 36
Printing
Mr Kevin Williams Managing Director
Ms Vicky Christiansen Finance Manager
Mr Derek McDonnell Sales Director
Mr Paul Dunne Production Manager

Data Page International Ltd
U18 IDA Enterprise Centre
East Wall
Dublin 3
Phone: 01-8552577 Fax: 01-8552579
Email: info@datapage.ie
Web: http://www.datapage.ie
SIC: 22220 Employees: 100
Typesetters
Mr Dave Keenan Managing Director
Mr Tony Donnelly Financial Controller
Mr Oliver Smith Sales Manager
Mr Graham Kelly IT Manager

De La Rue Smurfit Ltd
Pinewood Close Bray Industrial Est
Boghall Road
Bray Co. Wicklow
Phone: 01-2867724 Fax: 01-2768666
SIC: 22220 Employees: 135
Security Printers
Mr Noel Reilly Managing Director
Mr Tom O'Mahony Financial Controller
Ms Jackie Simpson Personnel Director
Mr Gary Breslin Production Manager
Ms Patsy McCarthy DP Manager

Fergus Kelly & Company Ltd
Jamestown Business Park
Finglas
Dublin 11
Phone: 01-8343468 Fax: 01-8362229
Email: kevin60@gofree.indigo.ie
SIC: 22220 Employees: 30
Print Finishers
Mr Kevin Kelly Managing Director

Fodhla Printing Company Ltd
The Print Works
Brookfield Road, Kilmainham
Dublin 8
Phone: 01-4537785 Fax: 01-4537074
Email: fodhla@iol.ie
SIC: 22220 Employees: 35
Printing Company
Mr Ken Rue Managing Director
Mr Tim May Financial Controller
Mr Sean Mooney Sales & Marketing Manager

Future Print Ltd
Grangeway
Baldoyle Industrial Estate
Dublin 13
Phone: 01-8392070 Fax: 01-8392591
SIC: 22220 Employees: 95
Printers
Mr Chris Johnson Managing Director
Mr Noel Lane Sales & Marketing Manager

Gallagher Printers Ltd
Unit 69 IDA Industrial Park
Old Kilmeaden Road
Waterford Co. Waterford
Phone: 051-376484 Fax: 051-378407
Email: sales@galprint.ie
SIC: 22220 Employees: 30
Computer Stationery & Print Packaging
Mr Michael Gallagher Managing Director
Mr Declan Dower Financial Controller
Mr Ray Gallagher Operations Manager

Gillespie Screen Print
20a St Josephs Parade
Dorset Street
Dublin 7
Phone: 01-8601000 Fax: 01-8302843
SIC: 22220 Employees: 25
Screen Printing
Mr Kevin Gillespie Managing Director
Ms Debra Hurley Accounts Manager
Mr Joseph Gillespie Computer Manager

GMI
Unit C2 Weatherwell Business Park
Clondalkin
Dublin 22
Phone: 01-4574006 Fax: 01-4574112
Email: info@global-mark.com
SIC: 22220 Employees: 30
Screen Printing
Mr Paul Young Managing Director
Mr Ian Donohue Account Manager
Mr Dermot Somers Production Manager

Grafton Litho Ltd
19 Hanover Street East
Dublin 2
Phone: 01-6772900 Fax: 01-6772906
Email: sales@graftonlitho.ie
Web: http://www.graftonlitho.ie
SIC: 22220 Employees: 30
Printing
Mr Brian Rowantree Sales Director

Groprint Ltd
U1 Beechlawn Industrial Complex
Greenhills Road
Dublin 12
Phone: 01-4566755 Fax: 01-4567343
Email: info@groprint.ie
Web: http://www.groprint.ie
SIC: 22220 Employees: 32
Printing
Mr Paul Gallagher Joint Managing Director
Ms Anne McDermott Smith Financial Controller

Harvey Printers Ltd
Unit 122 Industrial Estate
Cork Road
Waterford Co. Waterford
Phone: 051-372106 Fax: 051-378907
Email: enquiries@harvey-printers.ie
SIC: 22220 Employees: 46
Printing Company
Mr Anthony Malone Managing Director
Mr Peter Callender Finance Manager
Mr Ray Tyndle Personnel Manager
Mr John Kelly Works Manager

Horizon Graphics
U2A Phoenix Industrial Estate
Navan Road
Dublin 15
Phone: 01-8681257 Fax: 01-8686194
Email: salesup@horizongraphics.ie
SIC: 22220 Employees: 35
Printing Company
Mr Ken Kavanagh Manager
Ms Breda Kavanagh Finance Manager
Mr Tony Gillen Sales Manager

Publishing, Printing & Media

Hudson Killeen Ltd
130 Slaney Road
Dublin Industrial Estate
Dublin 11
Phone: 01-8306128 Fax: 01-8306993
Email: print@hudsonkilleen.ie
Web: http://www.hudsonkilleen.ie
SIC: 22220 Employees: 70
Lithographic Printers
Mr Jim Hudson Joint Managing Director
Ms Anne McGrath Financial Controller
Mr Don Ross Production Manager

IMEC Technologies Ltd
19/20 York Road
Dun Laoghaire Co. Dublin
Phone: 01-2054200 Fax: 01-2054201
Email: sales@imec.ie
Web: http://www.imec.ie
SIC: 22220 Employees: 65
Labels/Printers/Scanners
Mr Simon Burke Managing Director

Industrial Print Group Ltd
Pinewood Close, Boghall Road
Bray Co. Wicklow
Phone: 01-2860965 Fax: 01-2828481
Web: http://www.industrialprint.ie
SIC: 22220 Employees: 110
Industrial Printers
Mr Alan Squires Managing Director
Ms Grainne Kennedy Personnel Manager
Mr Noel Boyle Sales & Marketing Director
Ms Trisha O'Halloran Operation Manager

International Screen Ltd
Unit E1 Ballymont Industrial Estate
Walkingstown
Dublin 12
Phone: 01-4196700 Fax: 01-4599929
SIC: 22220 Employees: 45
Screen Printers
Mr Gerry Andrew Managing Director
Mr John Quinn Accountant
Mr John Moylan Sales Director

Irish International Print Corporation
146 Harmonstown Road
Dublin 5
Phone: 01-8318631 Fax: 01-8058801
Email: sales@directmailsolutions.net
Web: http://www.iipcprint.com
SIC: 22220 Employees: 64
Printing
Mr Paul Keegan Managing Director
Mr Alan Colt Finance Manager
Mr John O'Loughlin Sales Manager

Jaycee Printers
Liosbaun Industrial Estate
Galway Co. Galway
Phone: 091-758777 Fax: 091-758758
Email: info@jcprint.ie
Web: http://www.jcprint.ie
SIC: 22220 Employees: 40
Printers
Mr Jack Cunningham Manager
Mr Mervin Kerr Finance Manager
Mr John Cunningham Sales & Marketing Manager
Mr Tom Cunningham Production Manager

JF Walsh Roscrea Ltd
Main Street
Roscrea Co. Tipperary
Phone: 0505-21322 Fax: 0505-21976
SIC: 22220 Employees: 39
Printing & Bag Manufacturers
Mr Desmond Walsh Managing Director
Ms Shauna Walsh Factory Manager

JJ Lalor Ltd
60-61 Middle Abbey Street
Dublin 1
Phone: 01-8730032 Fax: 01-8730588
SIC: 22220 Employees: 25
Printers
Mr Francis Ennis Manager

Kelly's Printing Works
Poolboy Industrial Estate
Ballinasloe Co. Galway
Phone: 0905-42297 Fax: 0905-43225
Email: office@kpw.ie
Web: http://www.kpwbf.ie
SIC: 22220 Employees: 45
Printing
Mr Brendan Kelly Managing Director
Mr Alan McGonnagh Finance Manager
Mr Tony Killeen Personnel Manager
Ms Neasa O'Connor Marketing Manager
Mr Larry Rohan Production Director

Kenilworth Products Ltd
59 Nore Road, Dublin Industrial Esta
Glasnevin
Dublin 11
Phone: 01-8062200 Fax: 01-8062299
Email: info@kenilworth.ie
Web: http://www.kenilworth.ie
SIC: 22220 Employees: 120
Printers
Mr Gary Saul Managing Director
Mr Philip Ennis Financial Controller
Mr Paul Thompson Sales & Marketing Manager
Mr Larry Byrne Production Manager

Lettertec
Springhill
Carrigtwohill
Cork Co. Cork
Phone: 021-4883370 Fax: 021-4883423
Email: info@lettertec.com
Web: http://www.lettertec.com
SIC: 22220 Employees: 30
Printers
Mr Frank Kelly Managing Director
Ms Patricia Coughlan Financial Controller
Ms Olga Delaney Personnel Manager
Mr Liam Lester Sales Manager

Limerick Leader
54 O'Connell Street
Limerick Co. Limerick
Phone: 061-315233 Fax: 061-314804
Email: admin@limerick-leader.ie
Web: http://www.limerick-leader.ie
SIC: 22220 Employees: 70
Print & Publishing
Mr Joseph Gleeson Managing Director
Ms Breda McAuliffe Financial Director
Mr Gerard Kennedy Personnel Manager
Mr Jim Marks Production Manager

Litho Studios
Kylemore Road
Ballyfermot
Dublin 10
Phone: 01-6266123 Fax: 01-6262514
Email: mail@lithostudios.ie
Web: http://www.lithostudios.ie
SIC: 22220 Employees: 40
Reproduction Plates & Films
Mr Paul Leamy Managing Director
Mr Andrew Scanlan Financial Controller
Mr John McIntyre Operations Manager
Mr Michael Fleming IT Manager

Lithographic Group
Bray Business Park
Southern Cross
Bray Co. Wicklow
Phone: 01-2861936 Fax: 01-2867723
Email: info@lul.ie
SIC: 22220 Employees: 130
Printers
Mr John O'Connell Group Chief Executive
Mr Ian Delany Group Financial Director
Mr Brian Fortune Sales & Marketing Director
Ms Sandra Colgan Operations Manager
Mr Thomas O'Neill Computer Manager

Lithographic Plate Plan
Greenville Place
21 Blackpitts
Dublin 8
Phone: 01-4548711 Fax: 01-4548717
Email: lppl@indigo.ie
SIC: 22220 Employees: 50
Printing Plates
Mr Tony Bennett Managing Director
Mr Eddie Byrne Sales & Marketing Manager

Marksell Hobson Morris Ltd
Malahide Road Industrial Park
Newtown
Dublin 17
Phone: 01-8471043 Fax: 01-8479302
Email: marksell@eircom.net
SIC: 22220 Employees: 50
Printing Company
Mr Christopher McCormack Production Director
Mr David Tevlin Personnel Manager
Mr Niall Smith Sales & Marketing Director

Miller Group Ltd
Davitt Road
Inchicore
Dublin 12
Phone: 01-4550066 Fax: 01-4557037
Web: http://www.millerg.ie
SIC: 22220 Employees: 60
Print Engineers/Suppliers
Mr John Quinn Managing Director
Mr Eddie Gallen Financial Director
Mr John Birmigham Sales & Marketing Manager

Mount Salus Press
Long Mile Road
Dublin 12
Phone: 01-4780500 Fax: 01-4567195
Email: print@mountsalus.ie
Web: http://www.mountsalus.ie
SIC: 22220 Employees: 50
General Printing
Mr Eugene McGrath Manager
Mr Peter Calendar Finance Manager
Ms Imelda Coughlan Personnel Manager
Mr Peter Delaney Sales Director

Ormond Printing Company Ltd
Reilly's Bridge
Ratoath Road
Dublin 11
Phone: 01-8822719 Fax: 01-8304195
SIC: 22220 Employees: 60
Printing
Mr Brendan Mowles Proprietor

Phillip Warwick Co
Warwick House, Ballymount Road
Walkinstown
Dublin 12
Phone: 01-4507163 Fax: 01-4507673
Email: sales@pwl.ie
Web: http://www.pwl.ie
SIC: 22220 Employees: 65
Printers
Mr Tony Murphy Managing Director
Ms Eileen Murray Finance Manager
Mr Damien Warwick Production Manager

Playprint Ltd
80 Saint Ignatius Road
Drumcondra
Dublin 7
Phone: 01-8300433 Fax: 01-8309524
Email: sales@playprint.com
Web: http://www.playprint.com
SIC: 22220 Employees: 100
Printing
Mr Manus MacCrosain Managing Director
Mr Eamonn Harkin Financial Controller
Mr Joe Walsh Personnel Manager
Mr Seamus MacCrosain Sales & Marketing Manager
Mr Joe Lynch Production Manager
Mr Paul Roe Technical Manager

Publishing, Printing & Media

Print & Display Digital Ltd
U80 Cookstown Industrial Estate
Tallaght
Dublin 24
Phone: 01-4131444 Fax: 01-4513624
Web: http://www.printanddisplay.ie
SIC: 22220 Employees: 30
Printing
Ms Cliona Conway Managing Director
Mr Mark Edwards Financial Controller

Print Finishers Ltd
Unit 6 Cherry Orchard Industrial Estate
Dublin 10
Phone: 01-6235678 Fax: 01-6235679
SIC: 22220 Employees: 25
Print Finishing Company
Mr Thomas Browne Managing Director

Print Set & Design
Damastown Industrial Park
Mulhuddart
Dublin 15
Phone: 01-8260500 Fax: 01-8260525
Email: info@printset.ie
Web: http://www.printset.ie
SIC: 22220 Employees: 25
Printing
Mr Colm Hanley Managing Director

Printcraft Ltd
32 Malahide Road Industrial Park
Malahide Road
Dublin 17
Phone: 01-8478866 Fax: 01-8478734
Email: info@wpg.ie
Web: http://www.wpg.ie
SIC: 22220 Employees: 120
Printers
Mr Colin Ring Managing Director
Mr Gerard Daly Financial Controller
Mr Kieran Clancy Marketing Manager
Mr John Purcell Production Director
Mr Liam McIntyre Computer Manager

Reprocentre Group Ltd
Graphic House
Nangor Road Business Park
Dublin 12
Phone: 01-4093100 Fax: 01-4093150
Email: sales@reprocentre.ie
Web: http://www.reprocentre.ie
SIC: 22220 Employees: 60
Printing Equipment & Supplies
Mr Chris Williams Chief Executive
Mr Richard Noble Finance Director
Mr Brian Crawford Sales Director
Mr Damien Mullen Transport Manager
Mr Shane Price Director of Technology

Shamrock Printers Ltd
Ramparts Road
Dundalk Co. Louth
Phone: 042-9334652 Fax: 042-9334653
SIC: 22220 Employees: 30
Printing Cartons
Mr Pat Brannigan Manager
Ms Marie Kelly Accountant

Smurfit Web Press
Botanic Road
Glasnevin
Dublin 9
Phone: 01-8303511 Fax: 01-8303706
Email: print@smurfitwebpress.ie
Web: http://www.smurfit.ie
SIC: 22220 Employees: 100
Printers
Mr Tom Mooney Chief Executive
Ms Lynne Adams Finance Manager
Mr Tony Amoroso Sales & Marketing Director
Mr Cecil Whitty Operations Manager

SNAP Printing
33/34 Dame Street
Dublin 2
Phone: 01-6791333 Fax: 01-6794842
Email: info@dame.snapprinting.ie
SIC: 22220 Employees: 30
Print & Design
Mr Michael Carney Managing Director
Mr John Wallnut Sales Manager

Speciality Print & Design Ltd
69D Donore Avenue
South Circular Road
Dublin 8
Phone: 01-4536077 Fax: 01-4543164
Email: speciality@iol.ie
SIC: 22220 Employees: 35
Printers
Mr David Altman Managing Director
Mr Gay O'Brien Finance Manager
Mr Harry Crean Sales Manager

Standard Printers Ltd
Ballybrit Upper Industrial Estate
Galway Co. Galway
Phone: 091-751619 Fax: 091-755984
Email: sales@standardprinters.com
Web: http://www.standardprinters.com
SIC: 22220 Employees: 60
Commercial Printing
Mr Michael Cunningham Managing Director
Mr Jarlath Hanly Financial Controller
Ms Margo Cunningham Marketing Director
Mr Peter Cunningham Computer Manager

Techman Ltd
13B Cherry Orchard Industrial Estate
Ballyfermot
Dublin 10
Phone: 01-6260100 Fax: 01-6260246
Email: sales@techman.ie
Web: http://www.techman.ie
SIC: 22220 Employees: 48
Printers
Mr John McKinney Managing Director
Mr Joe Stewart Financial Controller
Mr Sean Eagan Sales & Marketing Manager
Mr John Perry Production Director
Mr Chris O'Brien Computer Manager

The Kerryman
Clash Industrial Estate
Tralee Co. Kerry
Phone: 066-7145500 Fax: 066-7145570
SIC: 22220 Employees: 100
Print Newspapers
Ms Maria Carroll Managing Director

Thermo Foil Colour Print Ltd
Unit 12-13 Gort Road Industrial Estate
Ennis Co. Clare
Phone: 065-6829144 Fax: 065-6821370
Email: hughfox@eircom.net
SIC: 22220 Employees: 31
Printing Publishing
Mr Hugh Fox Managing Director
Mr Martin Fox Accounts Manager
Mr David Bradley Production Manager

Total Print & Design
12-17 Mark Street
Dublin 2
Phone: 01-6727510 Fax: 01-6727520
Email: totalpd@iol.ie
SIC: 22220 Employees: 30
Printing
Mr Patrick Myers Manager
Mr PJ Watson Financial Controller

Treaty Press
Unit D Eastway Business Park
Ballysimon Road
Limerick Co. Limerick
Phone: 061-311188 Fax: 061-310760
Email: treatypress@eircom.net
SIC: 22220 Employees: 26
Printing
Mr Jim O'Connor Proprietor
Mr Pat Moriarty Sales Manager

Turners Printing Co
Convent Road
Longford Co. Longford
Phone: 043-46275 Fax: 043-41194
Email: info@turnersprinting.com
SIC: 22220 Employees: 40
Printing
Mr Warren Turner Managing Director
Ms Marie Prunty Accounts Manager
Mr Frank Quinn Sales Manager
Mr Brian Johnston Production Manager

Vujitsu Isotec Ireland
Snogborough Industrial Estate
Blanchardstown
Dublin 15
Phone: 01-8118598 Fax: 01-8205906
Email: info@fir.ie
Web: http://www.fir.ie
SIC: 22220 Employees: 200
Printer Components
Mr Kuyzo San Managing Director

Wilkes-Cerdac Ltd
110 Bann Road
Dublin Industrial Estate
Dublin 11
Phone: 01-8303644 Fax: 01-8303452
Email: wilkcer@indigo.ie
SIC: 22220 Employees: 40
Printing/Publishing
Mr Terry Martin Managing Director
Mr Jim Hickey Finance Manager
Mr Brian Thornton Production Manager

Winston Print
Brookfield Terrace
Carrysfort Avenue
Blackrock Co. Dublin
Phone: 01-2834875 Fax: 01-2836970
SIC: 22220 Employees: 25
Printing & Mailing
Mr Paul Healy Manager

Ainm Records
5-6 Lombard Street
Dublin 2
Phone: 01-6778701 Fax: 01-6778701
Email: info@anim-music.com
Web: http://www.anim-music.com
SIC: 22300 Employees: 25
Record Company
Mr Frank Stubbs Manager

Sun Recording Studios
8 Crow Street
Temple Bar
Dublin 2
Phone: 01-6777255 Fax: 01-6791968
Email: info@tbmc.ie
Web: http://www.tbmc.ie
SIC: 22300 Employees: 25
Recording & Rehearsal Studios
Mr Patrick Dunning Managing Director
Ms Liz Alao Personnel Director

Chemical Manufacture

Chemical Manufacture

24	Chemicals Manufacture
24000	Chemical Products
24100	Industrial Chemicals (Misc)
24110	Industrial Gases
24120	Dyestuffs & Pigments
24130	Inorganic Goods
24150	Fertilisers
24160	Synthetic Plastic Materials
24200	Pesticides (Formulated)
24301	Varnishes
24302	Printing Ink
24303	Sealants (Formulated)
24400	Pharmaceutical Products
24500	Synthetic Detergents
24510	Disinfectants/Cleaning Agents
24520	Perfumes & Cosmetics
24600	Chemical Products (Other)
24610	Explosives
24620	Adhesives (Formulated)
24650	Photographic Materials
24700	Man-Made Fibres (Production)

ARCH Chemicals BV
Watery Lane
Swords Co. Dublin
Phone: 01-8407744 Fax: 01-8404043
Email: info@archcemicals.com
Web: http://www.archcemicals.com
SIC: 24000 Employees: 65
Fine Chemical Manufacturers
Mr Michael Devlin Managing Director
Mr Michael O'Donoghue Financial Controller
Mr Kevin Whelan Plant Manager

Bandon Agricultural Products
5 Bridge Street
Bandon Co. Cork
Phone: 023-41115 Fax: 023-44750
SIC: 24000 Employees: 30
Agrochemical Products
Mr John McLoughlin Director

Barclay Chemicals Manufacturing Ltd
Damastown Industrial Park
Mulhuddart
Dublin 15
Phone: 01-8224555 Fax: 01-8224678
Email: info@barclay.ie
Web: http://www.barclay.ie
SIC: 24000 Employees: 35
Manufacture Chemicals
Mr Philip Sheridan Managing Director
Ms Lisa Sheeran Financial Controller
Ms Ursula Wilson Sales & Marketing Manager
Mr Jim Deeniffe Operation Manager
Ms Martine Denihan IT Manager

Carbon Chemicals Group Ltd
Ringaskiddy
Cork Co. Cork
Phone: 021-4378839 Fax: 021-4378950
Email: info@carbon.ie
Web: http://www.carbon.ie
SIC: 24000 Employees: 50
Chemical Manufacture
Mr Ronan Walsh Managing Director
Mr Aidan Brady Financial Controller
Mr Pat Gallagher Production Manager

Cognis Ireland Ltd
Little Island
Cork Co. Cork
Phone: 021-4354277 Fax: 021-4353559
Web: http://www.cognis.com
SIC: 24000 Employees: 125
Manufacture of Fine Chemicals
Mr Enda Quigley Managing Director
Mr Liam Keirns Finance Manager
Ms Maura Long Human Resources Manager
Ms Anne Moore Sales & Marketing Manager
Mr Patrick Vaughan Manufacturing Manager
Mr Liam Hourigan Computer Manager

Ellis & Everard Ireland Ltd
Grange Mills, Newcastle Road
Lucan Co. Dublin
Phone: 01-6282888 Fax: 01-6280769
Email: info@elliseverard.ie
Web: http://www.elliseverard.ie
SIC: 24000 Employees: 85
Chemicals & Food Ingredients
Mr Neil Blackburn Chief Executive
Ms Bernie Latimer Financial Controller
Mr Tadhg Moriarty Sales & Commercial Director
Mr Charles Baker Production Manager

Hygeia Chemicals Ltd
Carrowmoneash
Oranmore
Galway Co. Galway
Phone: 091-794722 Fax: 091-794738
Email: info@hygeia.ie
Web: http://www.hygeia.ie
SIC: 24000 Employees: 32
Chemicals Manufacturing
Mr Eugene McCartan Managing Director
Mr Peter Moore Finance Director
Mr Joe Jennings Market Development Manager
Mr Chris Pearson Production Manager Director

Micro-Bio (Ireland)
Industrial Estate
Fermoy Co. Cork
Phone: 025-31388 Fax: 025-32458
Email: info@micro-bio.ie
Web: http://www.micro-bio.com
SIC: 24000 Employees: 27
Hydrochloric Acid (Chemicals)
Mr Liam Tracey Managing Director
Mr Patrick Royce Finance Manager
Mr Peter McNamara Sales & Marketing Manager

Mitsui Denman Ireland Ltd
Little Island
Cork Co. Cork
Phone: 021-4354001 Fax: 021-4354002
Email: info@mitsui.ie
Web: http://www.mitsui.ie
SIC: 24000 Employees: 100
Chemicals Manufacturing
Mr Robin Gill Managing Director
Mr Len McLoughlin Financial Controller

T.E. Laboratories Ltd
Tullow Industrial Estate
Tullow
Carlow Co. Carlow
Phone: 0503-52881 Fax: 0503-52882
Email: tellab@indigo.ie
SIC: 24000 Employees: 90
Manufactures Chemicals
Mr Mark Bowkett Managing Director
Mr James Leone General Manager
Mr John McGrath Sales Director

GE Superabrasives
Clonshaugh Industrial Estate
Clonshaugh
Dublin 17
Phone: 01-8037700 Fax: 01-8037888
Email: info@geinfo.ge.com
Web: http://www.geinfo.ge.com
SIC: 24100 Employees: 255
Industrial Diamonds
Ms Rita Clare Proprietor

Schlotter Ireland
Newbridge Industrial Estate
Newbridge Co. Kildare
Phone: 045-432128 Fax: 045-447477
Email: schlotter@schlotter.ie
SIC: 24100 Employees: 49
Electroplating Chemicals
Mr Michael Habenicht Managing Director
Ms Mary Malcolm Material Manager
Mr Fergus McGee Sales/Marketing Manager
Mr Damian Carey Operations Manager

Air Products Ireland Ltd
Unit 950 Western Industrial Estate
Killeen Road
Dublin 12
Phone: 01-4566526 Fax: 01-4500860
Email: postmaster@airproducts.com
Web: http://www.airproducts.com
SIC: 24110 Employees: 41
Industrial Gases
Mr Patrick Flynn Managing Director
Mr Tony Morris Customer Service Manager

Truform Laserdyes Ireland Ltd
60a Park Street
Dundalk Co. Louth
Phone: 042-9334452 Fax: 042-9339355
Email: truform@iol.ie
SIC: 24120 Employees: 35
Dye Makers
Ms Ann Tumilty Managing Director
Ms Caroline Tumilty Financial Controller
Mr Brendan Tumilty Sales & Marketing Manager

Goulding Chemicals Ltd
151 Thomas Street
Dublin 8
Phone: 01-6121314 Fax: 01-6121216
Email: sales@gouldings.ie
Web: http://www.gouldings.ie
SIC: 24150 Employees: 110
Fertilizer Manufacturer
Mr JC Maloney Chairman
Mr Brendan Kent Finance Manager
Mr Tim O'Mahony Sales Director
Mr Sean Prendeville Production Manager
Mr Denis Moran Computer Manager

Irish Fertiliser Industries Ltd
2-5 Warrington Place
Dublin 2
Phone: 01-6764081 Fax: 01-6762318
Web: http://www.ifi.ie
SIC: 24150 Employees: 625
Manufacture of Bulk Chemical/Agricultural Fertilizer
Mr Brendan Cummins Managing Director
Mr William O'Brien Secretary & Financial Director
Mr Frank Brennan Personnel Director
Mr Jim McNamara Production Manager
Mr John O'Toole Computer Manager

McDonnell Bros
Coolagowan
Fermoy Co. Cork
Phone: 025-36477 Fax: 025-36899
Email: mcdbros@indigo.ie
SIC: 24150 Employees: 30
Agrochemical Products/Animal Feeds & Fertilisers
Mr Dennis McDonnell Managing Director
Ms Marie Barry Accounts Manager
Mr Colm Griffen Sales Manager

Akzo Nobel Car Refinishes
Longmile Road
Dublin 12
Phone: 01-4501392 Fax: 01-4501397
SIC: 24301 Employees: 26
Paint, Varnish & Lacquer Manufacturers & Supplier
Mr Mike Young Managing Director

Chemical Manufacture

Dulux Paints Ireland Ltd
Shandon Works, Commons Road
PO Box 45
Cork Co. Cork
Phone: 021-4302381 Fax: 021-4302563
Email: dulux@dulux.ie
Web: http://www.dulux.ie
SIC: 24301 Employees: 170
Manufacture Paint
Mr Gus Delaney IT Manager
Mr Finbar Harrington Finance Manager
Ms Anita Power Personnel Manager
Mr Colin Whitley Sales Manager
Mr Michael O'Reagan Computer Manager

FSW Coatings Ltd
Molesworth House
Molesworth Street
Dublin 2
Phone: 01-6710176 Fax: 01-6717854
Email: info@fsw.iol.ie
Web: http://www.fsw.ie
SIC: 24301 Employees: 80
Paint & Varnish Manufacturers
Mr Conor Doyle Managing Director
Mr Stanley Buckley Financial Controller
Mr Stephen McQuillan Sales & Marketing Manager
Mr Liam Hughes Production Director

Manders Coatings & Inks Ltd
Dunsinea Works
Ashtown
Dublin 15
Phone: 01-8387300 Fax: 01-8387382
SIC: 24301 Employees: 40
Paint Varnish & Lacquer Manufacture & Supplies
Mr Sandy Smith Managing Director
Mr Tony Mooney Finance Manager
Ms Maura Darcy Sales Manager

Pat McDonnell Paint Sales Ltd
Centrepoint Centre, Centre Park Road
Cork Co. Cork
Phone: 021-4320200 Fax: 021-4320194
SIC: 24301 Employees: 25
Painters Supplies
Mr Pat McDonnell Proprietor
Mr Richard Bradfield Accountant

SPL Paints Ireland Ltd
Blessington Industrial Estate
Blessington
Wicklow Co. Wicklow
Phone: 045-865163 Fax: 045-865331
Email: postmaster.spl@indigo.ie
SIC: 24301 Employees: 30
Paint Varnish & Lacquer Manufacturers & Suppliers
Mr Cormac O'Bric Managing Director
Ms Ann Meehan Finance Manager
Ms Nicole Healey Marketing Manager

Trimite True Coat Ltd
Naas Industrial Estate
Kildare Co. Kildare
Phone: 045-876714 Fax: 045-876798
SIC: 24301 Employees: 34
Paint Manufacturing
Mr Robert McLlorum Managing Director
Mr Harry Hannigan Sales Manager
Ms Jennifer Harrington IT Manager

Coates Lorilleux
Glenside Works Mill Lane
Palmerstown
Dublin 20
Phone: 01-6264477 Fax: 01-6262573
Email: coateslorilleux@iol.ie
SIC: 24302 Employees: 40
Manufacturing Printing Inks
Mr Greg Harris Managing Director
Mr John O'Brien Finance Manager
Mr Harry Conway Marketing Manager

Hewlett-Packard (Manufacturing)
Liffey Park Technology Campus
Leixlip
Naas Co. Kildare
Phone: 01-6150000 Fax: 01-6150975
Email: info@hp.com
Web: http://www.hp.com
SIC: 24302 Employees: 2150
Manufacture Ink Jet Cartridges
Mr Lionel Alexander Managing Director
Mr Des Thornton Financial Controller
Mr Brian Cannon Personnel Director
Mr John Holohan IT Manager

Shackell Edwards & Co
Naas Industrial Estate
Kildare Co. Kildare
Phone: 045-876714 Fax: 045-876798
SIC: 24302 Employees: 34
Printing Ink
Mr Robert McIlorum Manager
Mr Kevin Callaghan Sales Manager

Abbot Labratories
1 Broomhill Business Park
Broomhill Road Tallaght
Dublin 24
Phone: 01-4651500 Fax: 01-4651501
SIC: 24400 Employees: 90
Pharmaceutical Health care company
Ms Bonnie Fhul Managing Director
Mr Basil Blakeney Finance Director
Ms Francis Finnerty IT Manager

Allegro Ltd
Jamestown House
Jamestown Road
Dublin 11
Phone: 01-8341381 Fax: 01-8580610
SIC: 24400 Employees: 50
Pharmaceutical Products
Mr David Fox Managing Director
Ms Grace Cashen Financial Controller
Mr Tony Pacitti Marketing Manager

Allergan Pharmaceuticals (Irl) Ltd
Castlebar Road
Westport Co. Mayo
Phone: 098-25222 Fax: 098-25791
Email: info@allergan.com
Web: http://www.allergan.com
SIC: 24400 Employees: 1000
Pharmaceuticals Manufacture
Mr Colm O'Neill Vice President
Mr Steve Goggins Financial Controller
Mr Martin Gillen Personnel Manager

Athlone Laboratories Ltd
Ballymurray
Roscommon Co. Roscommon
Phone: 0903-61109 Fax: 0903-61921
Web: http://www.athlone-laboratories.com
SIC: 24400 Employees: 65
Manufacture Pharmaceuticals
Mr Louis Flannery General Manager
Mr Peter Mayes Sales & Marketing Manager

Aventis Pharma Ltd
Lisbunny Industrial Estate
Nenagh Co. Tipperary
Phone: 067-50500 Fax: 067-32249
Email: info@aventis.com
Web: http://www.aventis.com
SIC: 24400 Employees: 240
Pharmaceuticall Company
Mr Alain Le Duc Managing Director
Mr Vincent O'Brien Finance Director
Mr John Driver Human Resources Director
Mr John Howell Production Director
Ms Liz Duggan Information Technologies Direc

B Braun Hospicare
Collooney
Sligo Co. Sligo
Phone: 071-67491 Fax: 071-67054
SIC: 24400 Employees: 75
Healthcare Products
Dr Lawrence Storey Managing Director
Mr Paul Mullaly Finance Manager
Mr Daire Lynch Technical Manager

B Braun Medical Ltd
3 Naas Road Industrial Park
Dublin 12
Phone: 01-4553111 Fax: 01-4553115
Email: postmaster@bbraun.com
Web: http://www.bbraun.com
SIC: 24400 Employees: 46
Medical Supplies
Mr Paul Mullaly General Manager
Mr Peter McGahren Marketing Manager
Ms Mary Murphy Production Manager

Bee Line Healthcare
Unit 3 Crag Crescent
Clondalkin Industrial Estate
Dublin 22
Phone: 01-4575011 Fax: 01-4575015
Email: beeline@eircom.net
SIC: 24400 Employees: 35
Vitamins & Supplements
Mr Gerry Finn Managing Director
Mr John O'Shea Finance Director
Ms Carmel Connolly Operations Manager

Bioglan Generics Ltd
Unit 5, 151 Baldoyle Industrial Estate
Dublin 13
Phone: 01-8392355 Fax: 01-8392616
Email: admin@bioglan.ie
Web: http://www.bioglan.com
SIC: 24400 Employees: 35
Chemists & Pharmaceutical Products
Mr Andy Haggerty Operations Manager
Ms Alva Baxter Financial Controller

Biotrin International
93 The Rise
Mount Merrion
Blackrock Co. Dublin
Phone: 01-2831166 Fax: 01-2831232
Email: info@biotrin.ie
Web: http://www.biotrin.ie
SIC: 24400 Employees: 45
Pharmaceuticals Manufacture & Distribution
Dr Cormac Kilty Managing Director
Mr Jonathan Bishop Financial Controller
Ms Sandra Murphy Human Resources Manager
Mr Des O'Leary Production Manager
Mr Ross Eccles IT Manager

Bristol-Myers Squibb Pharmaceuticals
Watery Lane
Swords Co. Dublin
Phone: 01-8406244 Fax: 01-8139112
Email: info@bms.com
Web: http://www.bms.com
SIC: 24400 Employees: 30
Bulk Pharmaceutical Manufacturing
Mr Michael Dempsey Managing Director
Mr Anthony Feighan Accounts Manager
Mr Eugene Conlan Sales Manager

C & M (Vet Distributors) Ltd
Unit 2 Docklands Business Park
Dock Road
Limerick Co. Limerick
Phone: 061-314933 Fax: 061-314937
Email: cmvet@iol.ie
Web: http://www.cmvet.ie
SIC: 24400 Employees: 25
Veterinary Supplies
Mr Edmund Wall Managing Director
Mr Gerry Hayes Financial Controller

Chemical Manufacture

Chanelle Veterinary Ltd
Athenry Road
Loughrea
Galway Co. Galway
Phone: 091-841788 Fax: 091-841303
Email: chanellesales@eircom.net
SIC: 24400 Employees: 100
Veterinary Supplies
Mr Michael Burke Managing Director
Ms Geraldine Roane Financial Controller
Ms Breda Byrne Sales Manager

Clonmel Healthcare
Unit 28 Parkwest Business Park
Beckett Way
Dublin 12
Phone: 01-6204000 Fax: 01-6204099
SIC: 24400 Employees: 200
Pharmaceutical Manufacturer
Mr Rory O'Riordan Chief Executive

Cross Vetpharm Group
Broomhill Road
Tallaght
Dublin 24
Phone: 01-4515522 Fax: 01-4515803
Email: info@bimeda.com
Web: http://www.bimeda.com
SIC: 24400 Employees: 300
Pharmaceutical Products
Mr Randall Tierney Managing Director
Mr Vincent O'Reilly Finance Manager
Mr Raoul Masterson Sales & Marketing Manager
Mr Noel Godfrey Computer Manager

Elan Pharmaceutical Technology
Monksland Industrial Estate
Athlone Co. Westmeath
Phone: 0902-95000 Fax: 0902-95800
Email: info@elancorp.com
Web: http://www.elancorp.com
SIC: 24400 Employees: 750
Pharmaceutical Manufacture
Mr Mick O'Connor Operations Manager

Eli Lilly SA Irish Branch
Dunderrow
Kinsale Co. Cork
Phone: 021-4772699 Fax: 021-4775152
Email: kinsale@lilly.com
SIC: 24400 Employees: 326
Pharmaceutical Manufacturer
Mr David Broker Chief Executive

Elisa Partnership
Ringaskiddy
Cork Co. Cork
Phone: 021-4379257 Fax: 021-4379250
SIC: 24400 Employees: 40
Manufacture Pharmacueticals
Mr Alan McKnight Managing Director
Ms Lisa Cahalane Financial Controller

Fiacla Ltd
Unit 7 Industrial Yarns
Dublin Road
Bray Co. Wicklow
Phone: 01-2828257 Fax: 01-2861710
SIC: 24400 Employees: 45
Toothpaste Manufacturer
Mr Cillian Molloy General Manager
Mr Christy Dodd Commercial Sales Manager

FMC International
Wallingstown
Little Island
Cork Co. Cork
Phone: 021-4354133 Fax: 021-4353057
SIC: 24400 Employees: 100
Food & Pharmaceutical Products Manufacturers
Mr Brendan Keane General Manager
Mr Michael Murphy Financial Controller
Ms Jacqui O'Regan Human Resources Manager
Ms Ann Butler Materials & Customer Service
Mr David Murray Information System Accountant

Forest Laboratories Ltd
Clonshaugh Industrial Estate
Dublin 17
Phone: 01-8670047 Fax: 01-8670530
Email: forest@forest-labs.ie
SIC: 24400 Employees: 110
Manufacture Pharmaceuticals
Mr Raymond Stafford Managing Director
Mr Dermot Burke Financial Controller

Fort Dodge Laboratories Ireland
Finisklin Industrial Estate
Sligo Co. Sligo
Phone: 071-70005 Fax: 071-70009
SIC: 24400 Employees: 100
Maunfacture Animal Vaccines
Mr Patrick Glynn Managing Director
Mr Leo Logan Financial Controller
Mr Bill Collins Computer Manager

Gerard Laboratories
Baldoyle Industrial Estate
Grange Road
Dublin 13
Phone: 01-8393788 Fax: 01-8395621
SIC: 24400 Employees: 160
Pharmaceutical Manufacture
Dr Anna Power European Operations Director
Mr Patrick White Financial Controller

Glaxo SmithKline Ireland
Corrig Avenue
Dun Laoghaire Co. Dublin
Phone: 01-2147777 Fax: 01-2147670
Email: info@gsk.ie
Web: http://www.gsk.ie
SIC: 24400 Employees: 100
Healthcare Products
Mr Joe Lecouillaird Chief Executive

Helsinn Birex
Damastown
Mulhuddart
Dublin 15
Phone: 01-8225404 Fax: 01-8225410
Email: info@helsinn.com
Web: http://www.helsinn.com
SIC: 24400 Employees: 100
Pharmaceutical & Chemists Manufacture
Mr Padraig Summers Proprietor
Mr Tony Grannell Financial Controller
Ms Ursula Darcy Personnel Manager
Mr Jim O'Leary Sales Manager

Honeywell Iropharm
Vale Road
Arklow Co. Wicklow
Phone: 0402-39756 Fax: 0402-31147
SIC: 24400 Employees: 3500
Pharmaceutical & Chemists - Manufacture
Mr Wolfgang Dannenberg Plant Manager
Ms Dorothy Breslin Accounts Administrator
Ms Mary McGrew Personnel Manager
Mr Philip Kavanagh Sales & Marketing Manager
Mr Owen Quinn Head of Computers/Purchasing

Kinerton Ltd
Blanchardstown Industrial Park
Blanchardstown
Dublin 15
Phone: 01-8203899 Fax: 01-8201538
Email: info@beaufour-ipsen.co
Web: http://www.beaufour-ipsen.co
SIC: 24400 Employees: 43
Pharmaceutical Products
Mr Finbar Larkin General Manager
Ms Sarah Kinsella Financial Controller
Mr Aidan Murphy Production Manager
Mr Mark Kavanagh Computer Manager

Merck Sharp & Dohme Ireland Ltd
Ballydine
Kilsheelan
Clonmel Co. Tipperary
Phone: 051-601000 Fax: 051-601241
Email: msdireland@merck.com
Web: http://www.msdireland.ie
SIC: 24400 Employees: 400
Pharmaceuticals Manufacturer
Mr Declan Buckley Chief Executive
Mr Patrick O'Keefe Financial Controller
Mr John Condon Personnel Manager
Mr Dermott Walsh IT Director

Newport Synthesis
Baldoyle Industrial Estate
Baldoyle
Dublin 13
Phone: 01-8320020 Fax: 01-8320026
Email: info@newportsynthesis.com
SIC: 24400 Employees: 70
Manufacturing Pharmaceuticals
Mr Jim O'Daly Managing Director
Mr Paul Dempsey Financial Controller

Norton Waterford
Unit 301 Industrial Estate
Waterford Co. Waterford
Phone: 051-372016 Fax: 051-331398
Email: info@nortonhc.co.uk
Web: http://www.ivax.com
SIC: 24400 Employees: 400
Pharmaceuticals
Mr John Perrem Managing Director
Mr Donal McBride Finance Manager
Ms Mary Hanson Personnel Manager

Novartis Ringaskiddy Ltd
Ringaskiddy
Co. Cork
Phone: 021-4862000 Fax: 021-4862358
Web: http://www.pharma.novartis.com
SIC: 24400 Employees: 400
Bulk Pharmaceutical Manufacturer
Mr Franz Sutter Managing Director
Mr Martin Farrell Human Resources Manager

Chemical Manufacture

Ovelle Pharmaceuticals
Industrial Estate
Coe's Road
Dundalk Co. Louth
Phone: 042-9332304 Fax: 042-9332008
Email: ovelle@eircom.net
Web: http://www.ovelle.com
SIC: 24400 Employees: 50
Pharmaceutical Manufacturers
Mr Sean Gardiner Managing Director

Pfizer Pharmaceuticals Ireland
Pottery Road
Dun Laoghaire Co. Dublin
Phone: 01-2853277 Fax: 01-2856108
Email: info@pfizer.com
Web: http://www.pfizer.com
SIC: 24400 Employees: 700
Pharmaceutical Manufacturers
Mr Kurt Weiditz Operations Manager
Mr Peter Duffy Finance Director
Mr Paul Logue Production Manager
Mr Frank Kenny IT Manager

Pharmacia Cork Ltd
Little Island
Cork Co. Cork
Phone: 021-4510200 Fax: 021-4510291
Email: postmaster@pmu.com
Web: http://www.pharmacia.com
SIC: 24400 Employees: 250
Pharmaceuticals
Mr Gerry Cathal Managing Director
Mr Michael Stokes Finance Manager
Ms Teresa O'Sullivan Personnel Officer
Ms Deirdre Sinnott Computer Manager

Pinewood Laboratories Ltd
Unit 1 M50 Road Industrial Estate
Dublin 12
Phone: 01-4569123 Fax: 01-4569125
Web: http://www.pinewood.ie
SIC: 24400 Employees: 161
Pharmaceutical Manufacturing
Mr Michael Costello Managing Director
Mr Damien Martin Financial Controller
Mr Chris O'Brien Personnel Officer
Ms Mairead English-Maher Marketing Executive
Mr Tony Hynes Production Manager
Mr David Costello IT Director

Schering Plough Animal Health Ireland
Boghall Road
Bray Co. Wicklow
Phone: 01-2050900 Fax: 01-2867312
Email: schering.plough@spcorp.com
SIC: 24400 Employees: 650
Veterinary Supplies
Mr Michael Buckley General Manager
Mr John Howard Finance Manager
Ms Susan Murphy Personnel Officer
Mr Shane Maguire Sales Manager
Mr Michael Clery Production Manager
Mr Padraig O'Regan IT Manager

Servier (Irl) Industries Ltd
Gorey Road
Arklow Co. Wicklow
Phone: 0402-31111 Fax: 0402-20888
Email: info@ie.metgrs.com
Web: http://www.servier.com
SIC: 24400 Employees: 110
Pharmaceuticals
Mr Antoine Potie General Manager
Mr Jim Sullivan Accounts Manager
Ms Joan Casey Personnel Officer
Mr Francoise Dumontet Production Manager
Ms Marie Louis Marshall IT Manager

Smithkline Beecham (Cork) Ltd
Currabinny
Carigaline Co. Cork
Phone: 021-4378800 Fax: 021-4378983
Web: http://www.gsk.com
SIC: 24400 Employees: 230
Pharmaceutical Manufacture
Mr Finbar Whyte Director & Vice President
Mr Brian Callan Quality Assurance Team Leader

Stiefel Laboratories Ireland
Finisklin Industrial Estate
Sligo Co. Sligo
Phone: 071-61626 Fax: 071-61950
Email: info@stiefel.ie
Web: http://www.stiefel.ie
SIC: 24400 Employees: 225
Pharmaceutical Manufacture
Mr Jim Kernan Managing Director
Mr Jim McGrath Finance Manager
Mr Charlie Culhane Operations Manager
Mr John Sharkey IT Manager

Swords Laboratories
Administration Buildings
Watery Lane
Swords Co. Dublin
Phone: 01-8139000 Fax: 01-8139160
Web: http://www.bms.com
SIC: 24400 Employees: 600
Manufacturing Pharmaceutical Products
Mr Kieran Brady Managing Director
Mr Anthony Feighan Financial Controller
Mr Michael Dempsey Sales Manager
Mr Chris Farrell IT Manager

Takeda Ireland Ltd
Bray Business Park
Kilruddery
Bray Co. Wicklow
Phone: 01-2050600 Fax: 01-2050601
Email: info@takeda.ie
Web: http://www.takeda.ie
SIC: 24400 Employees: 74
Pharmaceutical Manufacture
Mr Greg Timmons General Manager
Mr Ted Okimoto Finance Manager
Ms Kathleen Lane Personnel Manager
Mr Paul Murtagh Production Manager

Tosara Products
Unit 146 Baldoyle Industrial Estate
Baldoyle
Dublin 13
Phone: 01-8321199 Fax: 01-8321200
Email: tosara@forest-labs.ie
SIC: 24400 Employees: 50
Pharmaceuticals
Mr Ray Stafford Chief Executive
Mr Diarmuid Burke Financial Controller
Mr Damien Browne Production Manager

Univet Ltd
Tullyvin
Cootehill Co. Cavan
Phone: 049-5553203 Fax: 049-5553266
SIC: 24400 Employees: 30
Veterinary Supplies
Mr George Crowe Managing Director
Mr Brendan Crowe Sales & Marketing Manager

Warner Lambert Ltd
Pottery Road
Dun Laoghaire Co. Dublin
Phone: 01-2049100 Fax: 01-2856108
SIC: 24400 Employees: 700
Manufacture Pharmaceutical & Confectionery Products
Mr Paul Breen General Manager
Mr Peter Duffy Director of Finance

Yamanouchi Ireland Ltd
Damastown
Mulhuddart
Dublin 15
Phone: 01-8030800 Fax: 01-8030801
SIC: 24400 Employees: 69
Pharmaceutical Manufacture
Mr Joe Harford President
Mr Dev Bergin IT Manager

Burgess Galvin & Co Ltd
Jamestown Road
Finglas
Dublin 11
Phone: 01-8342255 Fax: 01-8361399
Email: mail@burgessgalvin.ie
Web: http://www.burgessgalvin.ie
SIC: 24510 Employees: 40
Industrial Detergents Distribution
Mr Michael Galvin Managing Director

Diversey Lever (Ireland) Ltd
Jamestown Road
Finglas
Dublin 11
Phone: 01-8361966 Fax: 01-8081850
Email: info@diverseylever.com
Web: http://www.diverseylever.com
SIC: 24510 Employees: 50
Hygiene Product Manufacturers
Mr Bill Austin Managing Director
Mr Paul Byrne Financial Controller
Ms Susan Morgan Computer Manager

Kilco Chemicals Ltd
5 Harrington Street
Dublin 8
Phone: 01-4780335 Fax: 01-4780113
SIC: 24510 Employees: 30
Chemicals & Detergents Distribution
Mr Peter Donaldson Managing Director
Mr Jim Henry Sales & Marketing Manager
Mr Martin Burke Production Manager

Killarney Enterprise
Kilbride Industrial Estate
Arklow Co. Wicklow
Phone: 0402-31166 Fax: 0402-31194
SIC: 24510 Employees: 60
Soap Manufacturing
Mr Eddie McGrath Managing Director
Mr Kevin Kavanagh Accountant
Mr Thomas Halpin Production Manager

Cambridge Diagnostics Ireland Ltd
Mervue Business Park Industrial Estate
Mervue
Galway Co. Galway
Phone: 091-755699 Fax: 091-758576
Email: cambdiag@aol.ie
SIC: 24520 Employees: 100
Manufacturer of Healthcare Products
Mr Brian Mitchel General Manager
Mr Conor O'Shea Accounts Manager
Ms Michelle Walshe Personnel Manager

Colgate Palmolive
U3054 Lake Drive, City West
Naas Road
Dublin 24
Phone: 01-4039800 Fax: 01-4039801
Web: http://www.colgate.com
SIC: 24520 Employees: 45
Hygiene Products
Mr Donal Graham Chief Executive
Mr Gerry Delahunt Sales & Marketing Director
Mr Gerry Stephens Product Programme Manager

Chemical Manufacture

Irish Flavours & Fragrances
Industrial Estate
Donore Road
Drogheda Co. Louth
Phone: 041-9831031 Fax: 041-9835119
SIC: 24520 Employees: 70
Manufacture Essential Oils
Mr Charles Collier Managing Director
Mr Martin Tolan Company Accountant

Proctor & Gamble Manufacturing Ireland
Gortlandroe Industrial Estate
Nenagh Co. Tipperary
Phone: 067-50100 Fax: 067-32740
Email: info@pg.com
Web: http://www.pg.com
SIC: 24520 Employees: 620
Beauty Care Product Manufacture
Mr Graham Keast Chief Executive
Mr Donal Leahy Financial Controller
Mr Eamon Duggan Human Resources Manager
Mr Gerry Farnell Production Manager
Mr Oliver Grace IT Manager

Revlon Professional
Harmonstown Road
Atha Leathan
Dublin 5
Phone: 01-8311411 Fax: 01-8311994
SIC: 24520 Employees: 70
Hair Products
Mr Chris Threadgold Managing Director
Mr Donald Moore Finance Manager
Mr Xavier Berrell Sales Manager
Mr Joe McMunn MIS Manager

Yves Rocher Manufacturing (Ireland)
Kilbarry Industrial Park, Dublin Hill
Cork Co. Cork
Phone: 021-4395101 Fax: 021-4395550
Email:
SIC: 24520 Employees: 270
Manufacture Cosmetic Products
Mr John G Barry General Manager
Mr Matt Carter Head of Finance

Biocel Ltd
Rockgrove
Little Island
Cork Co. Cork
Phone: 021-4353516 Fax: 021-4354358
Email: biocel@indigo.ie
SIC: 24600 Employees: 31
Chemical Manufacturers
Mr Luke McCarthy Managing Director
Ms Maura O'Sullivan Sales Manager

Chemecon
Shannon Free Zone
Shannon Co. Clare
Phone: 061-475333 Fax: 061-472303
Email: sale@reagecon.ie
Web: http://www.reagecon.com
SIC: 24600 Employees: 45
Chemical Manufacturer
Mr John Barron Managing Director
Mr John O'Keeffe Operations Director

Chemsab
Kilrush Co. Clare
Phone: 065-9051421 Fax: 065-9051423
SIC: 24600 Employees: 500
PTFE Coat Fibreglass Fabrics
Mr Eric Kevorkian Managing Director

Colet International
140/141 Slaney Close
Dublin Industrial Estate
Dublin 11
Phone: 01-8309444 Fax: 01-8309798
Email: coletdublin@eircom.net
SIC: 24600 Employees: 30
Manufacture Hair Care Products
Mr Niall Sweeney Managing Director
Ms Lorraine O'Connor Financial Controller

FHW Coating Ltd
Browns Grove
Tuam Co. Galway
Phone: 093-38043 Fax: 093-38043
Email: info@fhw.ie
Web: http://www.fleetwood.ie
SIC: 24600 Employees: 150
Paint Supplier
Mr Aiden Corless Area Manager
Mr Tom O'Connell Sales Manager
Mr Connor O'Doyle IT Manager

Labscan Ltd
Unit T26 Stillorgan Industrial Park
Stillorgan
Blackrock Co. Dublin
Phone: 01-2952684 Fax: 01-2952685
Email: info@labscan.ie
Web: http://www.labscan.ie
SIC: 24600 Employees: 34
Chemical Solvents
Mr Gerry Kenny Managing Director
Mr Steve Pritchard Financial Controller
Mr Ray Traynor General Manager
Ms Anja Wouters Sales Director
Mr David Bearny Production Manager
Mr John Campbell Computer Manager

Premier Periclase Ltd
Boyne Road
Drogheda Co. Louth
Phone: 041-9870700 Fax: 041-9870707
Email: ppl@eircom.net
SIC: 24600 Employees: 150
Produce Seawater Magnesia
Mr Leo Grogan Managing Director
Ms Noeleen O'Reilly Financial Director
Mr Bill Trodden Human Resources Director

Reheis Ireland
Kilbarrock Road
Dublin 5
Phone: 01-8322621 Fax: 01-8392205
SIC: 24600 Employees: 75
Fine Chemical Producers
Mr Gary Wickham General Manager
Mr David Sutton Financial Controller

Adhesive Tape & Diecutters
Dunboyne Industrial Estate
Dunboyne Co. Meath
Phone: 01-8251500 Fax: 01-8251360
Email: info@diecuttape.com
SIC: 24620 Employees: 40
Specialist Converters
Mr Michael Rochford Materials Manager
Mr Declan Hickey Finance Manager
Mr John Ryan Personnel Director
Mr Edward Gaynor Sales Manager
Mr Michael Rochford Production Director

Cold Chon (Galway)
Oranmore
Galway Co. Galway
Phone: 091-794650 Fax: 091-794675
Email: info@coldchon.ie
SIC: 24620 Employees: 60
Manufacture Tar (Bitumen)
Mr John O'Shaughnessy General Manager
Ms Marjorie Collins Accountant
Mr PJ Naughton Sales Manager

Devcon
Bay 150 Shannon Free Zone
Shannon Industrial Estate
Shannon Co. Clare
Phone: 061-471299 Fax: 061-471285
SIC: 24620 Employees: 47
Manufacturers of Adhesive Chalking & Compounds
Mr Chris O'Herlihy Managing Director
Mr Dennis Ryan Financial Controller

Sealing Products Adhesive Tapes
Dunboyne Industrial Estate
Dunboyne Co. Meath
Phone: 01-8251237 Fax: 01-8251360
Email: info@diecuttape.com
Web: http://www.mfm.com
SIC: 24620 Employees: 40
Adhesive Products
Mr John Ryan Managing Director
Mr Gerard Donnelly Financial Controller
Mr Ned Gaynor Sales & Marketing Manager
Mr Michael Rochford Production Manager

Agfa Ltd
John F Kennedy Drive
Naas Road
Dublin 12
Phone: 01-4506733 Fax: 01-4565267
Email: info@agfa.com
Web: http://www.agfa.com
SIC: 24650 Employees: 30
Photographic Goods
Mr Robert Vervoort Chief Executive

JJ Fields & Company
26 Main Street
Skibbereen Co. Cork
Phone: 028-21400 Fax: 028-22050
SIC: 24700 Employees: 85
Candle Manufacturer
Mr John Field Managing Director
Ms Mary McCarthy Finance Manager
Mr Chris Dempsey Sales Director
Ms Clara French General Supervisor

John G Rathbourne Ltd
132 East Wall Road
Dublin 3
Phone: 01-8743515 Fax: 01-8365987
Email: info@rathbourne.ie
Web: http://www.rathbourne.ie
SIC: 24700 Employees: 35
Candles Manufacturer
Mr Peadar Lennon Managing Director
Mr Vincent Armstrong Office Manager
Mr Michael Duffy Sales Manager
Mr Joe Brennan Production Manager
Mr Colin O' Carroll Computer Manager

Killarney Plastics
Ballyspillane Industrial Estate
Killarney Co. Kerry
Phone: 064-32421 Fax: 064-32777
Email: sales@killarneyplastics.com
Web: http://www.killarneyplastics.com
SIC: 24700 Employees: 70
Fibreglass Tanks
Mr Con Stack General Manager
Mr Leo Murphy Finance Manager
Ms Peggy Lynch Sales & Marketing Manager
Mr Con Stack Jnr Production Manager

Rubber & Plastics Manufacture

25	Rubber & Plastics Manufacture
25100	Rubber & Plastic Products
25110	Rubber Tyres/Inner Tubes
25120	Retreading/Repairing Tyres
25130	Rubber Products (Other)
25220	Plastic Packaging Products
25231	Plastics Floorcovering
25239	Plastic Building Products
25240	Plastics Products (Other)

Caideil MP Teoranta
Claremorris Co. Mayo
Phone: 092-44074 Fax: 092-44204
SIC: 25100 Employees: 200
Produce Minature Pumps for Lotions & Perfumes
Mr Brian Sproll Managing Director
Ms Jacqueline Prendergast Finance Manager
Ms Theresa Costello Sales & Marketing Manager

Consort Case Company Ltd
Mooncoin
Kilkenny Co. Kilkenny
Phone: 051-895191 Fax: 051-895488
Email: info@consortcases.ie
Web: http://www.consortcases.ie
SIC: 25100 Employees: 30
Case Manufacturing
Mr John Kimpton Managing Director
Ms Joan Kelly Accounts Manager
Mr Michael Lusby Production Manager

G Bruss GMBH
Finisklin Road
Sligo Co. Sligo
Phone: 071-61720 Fax: 071-69352
Email: bruss@iol.ie
Web: http://www.iol.ie/~bruss
SIC: 25100 Employees: 415
Rubber Seals
Mr Ernst Pawlowski Chief Executive
Ms Breda Milmoe Accounts Manager
Mr Bernard Geoghegan Personnel Officer
Ms Andrea Pawlowski Sales & Marketing Manager
Mr Pat Doddy Production Manager
Mr Eamonn Reddin IT Manager

GMT Ireland Ltd
Galway Road
Clifden
Galway Co. Galway
Phone: 095-21382 Fax: 095-21704
SIC: 25100 Employees: 25
Rubber to Metal Bonded Products
Mr Ivor Duane General Manager

McLaughlin Components
Portnason
Ballyshannon
Donegal Co. Donegal
Phone: 072-52393 Fax: 072-52396
Email: mlcltd@eircom.net
SIC: 25100 Employees: 40
Rubber Products
Mr Seamus McLaughlin Managing Director

Ophardt Ireland GMBH & Co
Tubbercurry Road
Ballymote
Sligo Co. Sligo
Phone: 071-83347 Fax: 071-83286
Email: info@ophardt.iol.ie
SIC: 25100 Employees: 56
Manufacture Hygiene Equipment
Mr Douglas Colvin General Manager

Q Flex Ltd
Beechmount Industrial Estate
Navan Co. Meath
Phone: 046-28611 Fax: 046-28710
Email: qflex@iol.ie
SIC: 25100 Employees: 50
Foam Products
Mr Colin Moran Managing Director
Ms Majella Ryan Financial Controller
Ms Irene O'Reilly Sales Manager

Schlegel Ireland
Dublin Road
Loughrea
Galway Co. Galway
Phone: 091-841000 Fax: 091-841860
Email: info@maps-eu.com
SIC: 25100 Employees: 48
Automotive Seal Manufacturing
Mr Pat McWeeney Managing Director
Mr Dermot Graham Financial Controller
Mr Eric Hannagan Manufacturing Manager
Mr Liam Farrell IT Manager

Swagematic Ltd
Dungourney
Midleton Co. Cork
Phone: 021-4668341 Fax: 021-4668474
SIC: 25100 Employees: 40
Manufacture & Distribute Hoses
Mr Brendan Ottman Managing Director
Ms Eileen Ottman Company Secretary
Mr Tom Llewellyn Sales & Marketing Manager

Tubex Ltd
Gortland Row Industrial Estate
Nenagh Co. Tipperary
Phone: 067-32777 Fax: 067-33862
Email: tubex@tubex.ie
SIC: 25100 Employees: 110
Tubes & Tube Fittings
Mr Michael Gaffney Managing Director

Hanover Tyres Ltd
166 Bohermore Road
Galway Co. Galway
Phone: 091-565642 Fax: 091-562798
SIC: 25110 Employees: 42
Tyre Manufacturers
Mr Pat Tierney Manager

Pat Coyne Senior Ltd
Ballina Road
Swinford
Claremorris Co. Mayo
Phone: 094-51247 Fax: 094-52753
SIC: 25120 Employees: 25
Re-Conditioning Heavy Duty Tyres
Mr Pat Coyne Proprietor

Cavan MacLellan Hose Manufacturers
Cavan Road
Cootehill Co. Cavan
Phone: 049-5552340 Fax: 049-5552312
SIC: 25130 Employees: 25
Hose Manufacturer
Mr Aidan O'Connor Managing Director
Ms Katherine Freeman Finance Manager

DIS Enbi Seals Ltd
Clonminan Industrial Estate
Portlaoise Co. Laois
Phone: 0502-21992 Fax: 0502-22322
Email: enbi104@iol.ie
SIC: 25130 Employees: 150
Rubber Sealing Products
Mr Arthur Hendricks Managing Director
Mr Tony Connolly Financial Controller
Mr Brian O'Neill Production Manager

Rubber & Plastics

Elastometall Ireland Ltd
IDA Industrial Estate
Manorhamilton Co. Leitrim
Phone: 072-55590 Fax: 072-55591
Email: elastometall@eircom.net
SIC: 25130 Employees: 40
Manufacture Rubber to Metal Bonded Products
Mr Patrick Doherty Plant Manager

Durapak International Ltd
Unit 120 Broombridge Close
Dublin Industrial Estate
Dublin 11
Phone: 01-8305722 Fax: 01-8305660
Email: sales@durapak.ie
Web: http://www.durapak.ie
SIC: 25220 Employees: 40
Plastic Packaging
Mr Alan Dunne Office Manager
Ms Marie Kelly-Taylor Finance Manager
Mr David Fitzgerald Sales Director

EPI
Derrybeg Industrial Estate
Letterkenny Co. Donegal
Phone: 075-32666 Fax: 075-32677
Email: epi@iol.ie
SIC: 25220 Employees: 30
Plastic Bag Manufacturer
Mr Tziano Terperesson General Manager
Mr John Diver Production Manager

Hytherm Packaging
Hollymount Industrial Estate
Hollyhill
Cork Co. Cork
Phone: 021-4392622 Fax: 021-4393515
SIC: 25220 Employees: 25
Polystyrene Packaging Products
Mr Brian Marshall General Manager
Ms Bernadette Shannon Finance Manager
Mr Ken Steenson Sales Manager

Kwik Lok (Ireland) Ltd
Bay R72 Shannon Free Zone
Shannon Co. Clare
Phone: 061-471193 Fax: 061-472683
Email: kwiklok@iol.ie
Web: http://www.kwiklok.com
SIC: 25220 Employees: 25
Plastic Bag Closures
Mr Gerard Storan Managing Director
Mr Jim Conerty Finance Manager

Limerick Blow Moulding Ltd
Parteen
Limerick Co. Limerick
Phone: 061-346490 Fax: 061-340324
SIC: 25220 Employees: 30
Containers - Plastic
Mr Seamus Madden Managing Director

Panpak
Greenore
Dundalk Co. Louth
Phone: 042-9373184 Fax: 042-9373274
SIC: 25220 Employees: 90
Plastic Bottle Manufacturer
Mr Brendan Ryan Managing Director
Mr Patrick Keenan Financial Controller
Mr Bernard O'Rourke Plant Co-Ordinator
Ms Deirdre Brennan Officer Manager

Shabra
Ardee Road
Carrickmacross Co. Monaghan
Phone: 042-9663002 Fax: 042-9662099
SIC: 25220 Employees: 45
Plastics & Packaging
Mr Oliver Brady Managing Director
Ms Rita Shah Sales Director
Mr Brian Finnegan Production Director

Rubber & Plastics

Storsack Ltd
Little Island Industrial Estate
Little Island
Cork Co. Cork
Phone: 021-4353017 Fax: 021-4354074
Email: ireland@storsack.ie
Web: http://www.storsack.ie
SIC: 25220 Employees: 25
Plastics Packaging Products
Mr Christopher Cuddy Managing Director
Ms Karen Caplis Finance Manager
Mr Padraig Hartnett Sales Manager

National Tile Company
Coes Road Industrial Estate
Dundalk Co. Louth
Phone: 042-9337678 Fax: 042-9335424
Email: info@national.tile.com
SIC: 25231 Employees: 23
Tiles
Mr Ian Purcell Managing Director

Carson Industries Ltd
Racecourse Road
Roscommon Co. Roscommon
Phone: 0903-25922 Fax: 0903-25921
Email: carson@iol.ie
Web: http://www.carsonind.com
SIC: 25239 Employees: 30
Structural Foam Manufacturers
Mr Michael Kelly General Manager
Mr Anthony Troy Finance Manager
Mr Keith Pallett Sales & Marketing Manager
Mr Charlie Dunn Production Manager

Hytherm Ireland Ltd
Liscarton Industrial Estate
Navan Co. Meath
Phone: 046-66000 Fax: 046-66090
Email: office@hytherm.com
Web: http://www.hytherm.com
SIC: 25239 Employees: 80
Polystyrene Insulation
Mr Eoghan Hynes Managing Director
Ms Thelma Hynes Financial Controller
Mr Ken Steenson Sales Manager
Mr Kevin Rennicks Transport Manager

Abbey Vac Ltd
Millbrook Road
Oldcastle Co Meath
Phone: 049-8541188 Fax: 049-8541651
Email: abbeyvac@eircom.net
Web: http://www.kol.ie/abbeyvacforming
SIC: 25240 Employees: 48
Manufacture Plastic Injection Moulding/Vac Forms/Corrugates Boxes
Mr Padraig Shine Managing Director
Ms Marie Wallace Finance Manager
Mr Sean Daly Production Director
Mr Christy Kelly Technical Manager

Aclare Plastics Ltd
Aclare
Sligo Co. Sligo
Phone: 071-81144 Fax: 071-81458
Email: info@clare.iol.ie
Web: http://www.iol.ie/~aclare
SIC: 25240 Employees: 27
Technical Blow Moulding & Injection Moulding
Mr Neil Egan Managing Director

AJ Precision Components Ltd
Tuamgraney Industrial Estate
Scariff
Ennis Co. Clare
Phone: 061-921355 Fax: 061-921477
Email: admin@ajpc.com
SIC: 25240 Employees: 45
Injection Moulded Plastic
Mr Tony Lang Managing Director
Mr Matthew Quirke Financial Controller
Mr Raymond McArdle Computer Manager

Allsop Europe
Industrial Park
Waterford Co. Waterford
Phone: 051-355091 Fax: 051-377717
Email: info@allsop.ie
Web: http://www.allsop.com
SIC: 25240 Employees: 35
Audio, Video, Computer Accessories, Trade Moulding
Mr Luke Cody Chief Executive Officer
Ms Anne McGovern Financial Controller
Mr Kjell Olsson Sales & Marketing Manager
Mr Tom Douglas Research & Development

Associated Plastics of Ireland
Ballycumber Road
Clara
Tullamore Co. Offaly
Phone: 0506-31351 Fax: 0506-31151
Email: sales@api.ie
Web: http://www.api.ie
SIC: 25240 Employees: 26
PVC Compounding
Mr Lars Bjork Chief Executive
Ms Mary Scully Senior Accounts Manager
Mr Joe Birmingham Manufacturing Manager
Mr Colm Mulvihill Sales & Administration Manager

Athlone Extrusions Ltd
Grace Road
Athlone Co. Westmeath
Phone: 0902-92679 Fax: 0902-94086
Email: info@athloneextrusions.ie
Web: http://www.athloneextrusions.ie
SIC: 25240 Employees: 165
Plastic Sheet & Film Manufacturer
Mr James McGee Chief Executive
Mr Enda Cunningham Financial Controller
Mr Jackie Brown Sales Director
Mr Joe Lawless Production Manager

Automatic Plastics Ltd
School Road
Tinahely
Arklow Co. Wicklow
Phone: 0402-38231 Fax: 0402-38169
Email: info@autoplas.iol.ie
Web: http://www.automaticplastics.com
SIC: 25240 Employees: 65
Plastic Injecting Moulding
Mr Alfred Lawless Engineering Manager
Ms Mary Nolan Accounts Manager
Mr Kevin Fitzgerald Personnel Manager

Avenue Mouldmaking Ltd
Finisklin Industrial Estate
Finisklin
Sligo Co. Sligo
Phone: 071-69510 Fax: 071-69511
Email: sales@avenuemould.com
Web: http://www.avenuemould.com
SIC: 25240 Employees: 39
Mould & Toolmaking
Mr Phelim McNeela Managing Director
Mr Des Forde Sales Manager
Mr Joe Hunt Sales Director
Mr Noel Garrity Production Manager
Mr Billy Gaffney Technical Director

Avoncourt Packaging
U2 Ballycurreen Industrial Estate
Frankfield
Cork Co. Cork
Phone: 021-4965161 Fax: 021-4965501
Email: info@avoncourt.com
Web: http://www.avoncourt.com
SIC: 25240 Employees: 41
Plastic Trays Manufacturing
Mr William Bateman Managing Director
Mr Jonathan Bateman Finance Manager
Ms Mary Conroy Personnel Manager
Ms Rebecca Sharpe Sales Co-ordinator

Barlo Group Plc
Alexandra House, Sweepstakes
Ballsbridge
Dublin 4
Phone: 01-2310700 Fax: 01-2310744
Email: info@barlogroup.ie
Web: http://www.barlogroup.ie
SIC: 25240 Employees: 1500
Manufacture of Radiators & Plastic Products
Mr N Carroll Chairman
Mr A Barlow Deputy Chairman

Bellco Sports Ltd
Corroy
Ballina Co. Mayo
Phone: 096-22344 Fax: 096-70377
Email: bellco@eircom.net
SIC: 25240 Employees: 45
Plastic Footballs & Road Cones
Mr Vincent Dempsey General Manager
Ms Marie Timlin Financial Controller
Mr Padraig Hughes Production Manager

BIC (Ireland) Ltd
PO Box 872, Park House
North Circular Road
Dublin 7
Phone: 01-8102800 Fax: 01-8684246
Email: info@bicworld.com
Web: http://www.bicworld.com
SIC: 25240 Employees: 30
Manufacture Pens Lighters & Tippex
Mr Connor Murphy Manager
Mr Tony Kelly Finance Manager
Mr Conor Murphy General Manager
Mr Joe McGrath Sales & Marketing Manager

Boxmore Plastics Ltd
Annagh Industrial Park
Ballyconnell
Belturbet Co. Cavan
Phone: 049-9526219 Fax: 049-9526423
Email: enquiries@cavan.plastics.boxmore.com
Web: http://www.boxmore.com
SIC: 25240 Employees: 250
Plastics Manufacturer
Mr Dermot Gates Managing Director
Mr Michael Smith Financial Controller
Mr Chris Gaffney Sales Director
Mr Michael O'Reilly Plant Manager
Ms Paula O'Hara Computer Manager

Carbery Plastics Ltd
Enterprise Park
Clonakilty Co. Cork
Phone: 023-33531 Fax: 023-34368
Email: carbery@iol.ie
SIC: 25240 Employees: 50
Plastic Mouldings
Mr Michael McCarthy Managing Director
Mr Rory Walsh Financial Controller
Mr Jim Clarkin Sales & Marketing Manager
Mr Jim Hunt Production Manager

Connabride Plastics Export Ltd
Conna
Mallow Co. Cork
Phone: 058-59255 Fax: 058-59110
SIC: 25240 Employees: 40
Plastic Manufacturers
Mr Robert Collinwerg Managing Director
Mr John Cusack Financial Controller
Mr Darren Peterson Production Manager

Cork Plastic Manufacturers
Little Island Industrial Estate
Little Island
Cork Co. Cork
Phone: 021-4510600 Fax: 021-4510670
SIC: 25240 Employees: 172
Plastic Pipes
Mr Timothy O'Brien Managing Director
Ms Mary Cortin Human Resources Manager
Mr Richard Lynch Sales Director
Mr Pat O'Brien Computer Manager

Rubber & Plastics

Cregg Mouldings Ltd
Block L4
Smithstown Industrial Estate
Shannon Co. Clare
Phone: 061-363318 Fax: 061-363329
SIC: 25240 Employees: 80
Outsourcing Manufacturing
Mr Edmund Jennings Managing Director
Ms Rosemary Loughran Personnel Manager
Ms Aideen Byrne Sales & Marketing Manager
Mr Neil Gillespie Production Manager

CVP Ltd
Kylemore Road
Ballyfermot
Dublin 10
Phone: 01-6264888 Fax: 01-6266228
SIC: 25240 Employees: 70
Plastics Manufacture
Mr Steve Moss Manager
Mr John Brennan Financial Controller
Mr Gerry O'Brien Sales Manager
Mr Trevor Kearney Production Manager
Mr Robert Gardiner Computer Manager

Daret Manufacturing Ltd
Finisklin Industrial Estate
Sligo Co. Sligo
Phone: 071-69092 Fax: 071-69120
Email: daret-ireland@daret.ie
SIC: 25240 Employees: 60
Cosmetic Displays
Mr John Cox Manager
Ms Margaret Leonard Accounts Manager
Mr John Whitehead Sales Manager
Mr Richard Lially Administration Manager

Data Packaging
Mullingar Business Park
Mullingar Co. Westmeath
Phone: 044-41954 Fax: 044-41448
Email: info@datapackaging.com
Web: http://www.datapackaging.com
SIC: 25240 Employees: 200
Contract Injection Moulding
Mr Paul Walsh Managing Director
Mr Donal Lawlor Financial Controller
Ms Teresa O'Connell Personnel Assistant
Mr Leo Lawless Business Manager
Mr Brendan Murtagh Manufacturing Manager
Ms Carmel Martin IT Manager

Embankment Plastics Ltd
Rosedale, Saggart
Dublin 24
Phone: 01-4582128 Fax: 01-4582604
Email: sales-account@embankment.ie
Web: http://www.embankment.ie
SIC: 25240 Employees: 38
Plastics Manufacture
Mr Hugh Armstrong Managing Director
Ms Irene Ellis-Casey Accounts Manager
Mr Barry Armstrong Personnel Manager

Engineered Plastic Components
Finnabair Industrial Estate
Dundalk Co. Louth
Phone: 042-9328735 Fax: 042-9328736
Email: info@epceurope.com
Web: http://www.epceurope.com
SIC: 25240 Employees: 70
Manufacture Plastic Components for the Automotive Industry
Mr George Eigenheer General Manager
Ms Carol Thornton Office Manager
Mr Ian Hazard IT Manager

Ezy Koter Ltd
Virginia Co. Cavan
Phone: 049-8547017 Fax: 049-8547320
Email: ezykoter@ezykoter.ie
SIC: 25240 Employees: 50
Paint Roller Manufacturer
Mr Des McClelland Managing Director
Mr Raymond Coey Financial Controller
Ms Katherine Gordon Personnel Manager
Mr Sebastian James Sales & Marketing Manager
Mr Seamus Brady Production Manager

Form Grinders Ltd
Unit 1 Enterprise Centre
Drumcollogher
Kilmallock Co. Limerick
Phone: 063-83118 Fax: 063-83244
Email: info@formgrinder.com
Web: http://www.formgrinder.com
SIC: 25240 Employees: 70
Injection Mouldings
Mr Don Hipgrave Managing Director
Mr Michael Wallace Financial Controller
Mr Liam Quaid General Manager

Gernord
Ballybay Road
Carrickmacross Co. Monaghan
Phone: 042-9661060 Fax: 042-9662370
SIC: 25240 Employees: 137
PVC Tiles/Rolls
Mr Ciaran Daly General Manager
Ms Geraldine O'Reilly Finance Manager
Mr Brian Murray Sales & Marketing Manager
Mr Eugene Winters Computer Manager

Holfeld Plastics Ltd
Kilmacanogue
Bray Co. Wicklow
Phone: 01-2860922 Fax: 01-2860546
Web: http://www.holfeld-plastics.com
SIC: 25240 Employees: 145
Manufacture Plastic Packaging
Mr Edmond Holfield Managing Director
Mr Brian Keely Finance Manager
Mr Michael Dodd Sales Manager
Mr Frank Coleman Production Manager

Hostaglas
Unit 7 Westgate Business Park
Ballymount
Dublin 24
Phone: 01-4569266 Fax: 01-4569269
Email: emerof@hostaglas.ie
Web: http://www.hagedorn.de
SIC: 25240 Employees: 30
Manufacture Plastic
Mr David Brophy Managing Director
Mr Mark Canty Finance Manager
Mr Philip Jones Production Manager

Intesys
Lurganboy
Donegal Co. Donegal
Phone: 073-22477 Fax: 073-22490
Email: ireland@intesys.com
Web: http://www.irelandintesys.com
SIC: 25240 Employees: 30
Plastic Injection Moulding
Mr Tom Cummings Managing Director
Ms Geraldine McCawley Financial Controller

IP Europe
IDA Industrial Estate
Courtown Road
Gorey Co. Wexford
Phone: 055-22990 Fax: 055-22994
Email: ipeurope@iol.ie
SIC: 25240 Employees: 130
Manufacture Agricultural Plastic
Mr Peter Norbstern Managing Director
Ms Deidre Ryan Financial Controller
Ms Betty Murphy Personnel Director
Ms Ann-Marie Brennan Sales Director
Mr Ben Campbell IT Director

Irish Custom Extruders Ltd
Poppintree Industrial Estate
Finglas
Dublin 11
Phone: 01-8643494 Fax: 01-8643502
Email: icext@iol.ie
Web: http://www.irishcustomextruders.com
SIC: 25240 Employees: 34
Plastic Extrusions
Mr Anthony Dunne Managing Director
Mr Eamonn Howlin Operations Director
Mr Martin McElligott Production Director

Irish Tube & Fittings Supply Ltd
Kilcohan
Waterford Co. Waterford
Phone: 051-875577 Fax: 051-878001
Email: itfs@eircom.net
Web: http://www.eircom.net
SIC: 25240 Employees: 35
Plastics & Steel Products
Mr Richard Passberger Managing Director
Mr Micheal Staunton Sales Manager

JFC Manufacturing Ltd
Weir Road
Tuam Co. Galway
Phone: 093-24066 Fax: 093-24923
Email: info@jfc.ie
Web: http://www.jfc.ie
SIC: 25240 Employees: 50
Manufacture Plastic Products
Mr John Concannon Managing Director
Ms Patricia Concannon Finance Manager
Mr Brendan Morrin Sales & Marketing Manager
Mr Joe Moran Production Manager
Mr Colm Concannon Computer Manager

Kelly Hunter Ltd
Molesworth House
Molesworh Street
Dublin 2
Phone: 01-6710210 Fax: 01-6712697
Email: kellyhunter@oceanfree.net
Web: http://www.kellyhunter.com
SIC: 25240 Employees: 80
Plastics - Manufacturing Processes
Mr Brian Doyle Managing Director
Mr Padraig Campbell Finance Manager
Mr Ray Hunt Manager

Key Plastics Ltd
Kilarney Road, Business Park
Bray Co. Wicklow
Phone: 01-2869231 Fax: 01-2760205
Email: keyplast@iol.ie
SIC: 25240 Employees: 30
Produce Plastic Injection Moulds
Mr Alan Downes Manager

Lawter International BV
Grannagh
Waterford Co. Waterford
Phone: 051-876616 Fax: 051-879399
Email: info@lawterint.ie
Web: http://www.lawterint.ie
SIC: 25240 Employees: 35
Resin Manufacture
Mr Maurice Parker Plant Manager
Mr William O'Reilly Financial Controller
Mr Peter Cody Personnel Manager

Rubber & Plastics

Listal
Cleveragh Industrial Estate
Listowel Co. Kerry
Phone: 068-22838 Fax: 068-22874
Email: lisirl@aol.com
SIC: 25240 Employees: 50
Plastic Injection Moulding
Mr Pat Casey Managing Director
Ms Noreen Meade Finance Manager

M & Q Packaging Ltd
Po Box 283
Roxboro Enterprise Centre
Limerick Co. Limerick
Phone: 061-318505 Fax: 061-318507
Email: sales@mqpackaging.com
Web: http://www.mqpackaging.com
SIC: 25240 Employees: 25
Heat resistant film
Mr James Upton Managing Director

MacFarlane Plastics Ltd
Kilmacullagh
Newtownmountkennedy
Greystones Co. Wicklow
Phone: 01-2810234 Fax: 01-2810133
Email: admin@macfarlaneplastics.ie
SIC: 25240 Employees: 110
Injection Moulders
Mr Noel Mullen Managing Director
Ms Allison Cooney Finance Manager
Mr Jim Crawford Manufacturing Manager Manager
Ms Maxine Bonus Production Manager

Master Plast Ltd
Monread Industrial Estate
Naas Co. Kildare
Phone: 045-866565 Fax: 045-875765
Email: masterplast@clariant.com
SIC: 25240 Employees: 45
Plastic Additives
Mr Brian O'Neill Deputy General Manager
Mr Billy McKeown Accounts Manager
Mr Brian O'Neill Sales Manager
Mr Leo Fleming-Farrell Manufacturing Manager
Mr Nigel Tyrrell Technical Manager

Mentec International Ltd
Pottery Road
Dun Laoghaire Co. Dublin
Phone: 01-2059797 Fax: 01-2059798
Email: sales@mentec.ie
Web: http://www.mentec.ie
SIC: 25240 Employees: 164
Micro Processor Chips
Mr Michael Peirce Chief Executive
Mr Mark Horgan Group Financial Director
Mr Kevin Haverty Managing Director
Mr Dermot O'Connor Production Manager
Mr Liam Butler Computer Manager

Mergon International
Water Street
Castlepollard
Mullingar Co. Westmeath
Phone: 044-62000 Fax: 044-61397
Email: mergon@mergon.ie
Web: http://www.mergon.com
SIC: 25240 Employees: 200
Plastic Mouldings
Mr Patrick Byrne Managing Director
Mr Paul Fahey Financial Controller
Ms Ashling Duffy Personnel Officer
Mr Tom Mullan Sales & Marketing Manager
Mr John Burke Production Manager
Mr David Power IT Manager

MFP Plastics
Laraghcon
Lucan Co. Dublin
Phone: 01-6280691 Fax: 01-6280318
Email: info@mfp.ie
Web: http://www.mfp.ie
SIC: 25240 Employees: 48
Manufacture Drainage Systems
Mr Fergus Malone Managing Director
Ms Breda Dunne Accounts Manager
Mr Damian Sallon Production Manager

Munekata Ireland Ltd
Jamestown Road
Finglas
Dublin 11
Phone: 01-8346333 Fax: 01-8346586
Email: postmaster@munekata.ie
Web: http://www.munekata.ie
SIC: 25240 Employees: 329
Plastics Moulding
Mr Yasuda San Managing Director
Mr Peter Reilly Financial Controller
Ms Orla Hanley Personnel Manager
Mr Don Kenny Marketing Manager
Mr Ronan Gibbons Operations Manager

Nelipak Thermoforming Ireland Ltd
Unit 6d Mervue Industrial Estate
Galway Co. Galway
Phone: 091-757175 Fax: 091-757151
Email: admin@nelipak.ie
Web: http://www.nelipak.ie
SIC: 25240 Employees: 80
Manufacture Plastic Packaging
Mr Joe Holland Managing Director
Ms Evelyn Hannon Finance Manager
Ms Elaine Boyle Personnel Manager
Mr David McAndrew Sales & Marketing Manager
Ms Stella Glavin Computer Manager

Nypro
Cork Abbey
Bray Co. Wicklow
Phone: 01-2043300 Fax: 01-2822331
Email: postmaster@nypro.ie
Web: http://www.nypro.com
SIC: 25240 Employees: 350
Injection Moulding Company
Mr Sean Lenaghan Production Manager
Mr Michael Delahunty Finance Manager
Ms Helena Nolan Human Resources Manager
Mr Jack Hennessy Sales & Marketing Manager
Mr David Whelan Computer Manager

Profile Development Ltd
Kilfergus
Glin
Limerick Co. Limerick
Phone: 068-34312 Fax: 068-34492
Email: profiledevelop@eircom.net
Web:
http://www.profiledevelopments.sagenet.co.uk
SIC: 25240 Employees: 30
PVC Door Panels
Mr Tim Costello General Manager
Ms Catherine Scanlon Financial Controller
Ms Joan Costello Director
Mr Joe Barry Sales Manager
Mr Declan Barrett Production Manager

Punch Holdings Ltd
SIAC Building, Ballycurreen Cross
Airport Road
Cork Co. Cork
Phone: 021-4310622 Fax: 021-4311098
SIC: 25240 Employees: 400
Candles & Plastic Manufacture & Grocery
Wholesale
Mr John F Punch Chairman
Mr John R Punch Group Financial Controller
Mr Martin J Punch Group Secretary
Mr Conal Boyle Group Director

Pyco Electronics
100-109 Shannon Industrial Estate
Shannon Co. Clare
Phone: 061-472855 Fax: 061-472676
Email: info@raychem.com
Web: http://www.raychem.com
SIC: 25240 Employees: 280
Plastic Products
Mr Paul O'Brien Managing Director
Mr Don Foynes Financial Controller
Ms Fiona O'Carroll Personnel Manager
Mr Joe Lane Production Manager
Mr Aidan Grace MIS Manager

Quality Plastics Ltd
PO Box 29
Whites Cross
Cork Co. Cork
Phone: 021-4884700 Fax: 021-4884701
Email: qpl@qpl.ie
SIC: 25240 Employees: 130
Manufacture Plastic Pipes & Sheeting
Mr Gary Horgan Managing Director
Mr Liam Ahern Financial Director
Mr Adrian Sheady Human Resources Manager
Mr Brendan O'Brien Sales & Marketing Manager
Mr Ian Murphy Accountant

Richard Barrett Moulds Ltd
Old Court Industrial Estate
Boghall Road
Bray Co. Wicklow
Phone: 01-2829842 Fax: 01-2868011
Email: rbm@indigo.ie
Web: http://www.indigo.ie/~rbm
SIC: 25240 Employees: 50
Manufacturers of Tools & Dies for Injection
Moulding
Mr Richard Barrett Managing Director
Ms Maeve Miller Accounts Manager
Mr Warren Doyle General Manager
Mr John Kearney Production Manager

ROM Plastics Ltd
Dunmore Road
Glenmaddy
Galway Co. Galway
Phone: 0907-59110 Fax: 0907-59189
Email: rom@tinet.ie
Web: http://www.romplastics.ie
SIC: 25240 Employees: 55
Rotation Moulded Products
Mr Kevin McPartlan General Manager
Ms Breda O'Mally Finance Manager
Mr Tony Lettis Sales Manager
Mr Mike Egan Production Manager

Rotofab Ltd
Blyry Industrial Estate
Athlone Co. Westmeath
Phone: 0902-79000 Fax: 0902-79004
Email: sales@rotofab.com
Web: http://www.rotofab.com
SIC: 25240 Employees: 25
Manufacture Plastic Products
Mr Michael Cleary Manager
Mr Catherine Lafferty Finance Manager
Mr Michael Cleary Sales Manager
Mr Terry McCaul Production Manager
Ms Jean Shine Computer Manager

Smallwares Dormer Ltd
Castlebellingham
Dundalk Co. Louth
Phone: 042-9372106 Fax: 042-9372757
SIC: 25240 Employees: 41
Contract Injection Mouldings
Mr Paul Jevens General Manager
Ms Anne Jevens Personnel Director

Steiner Ltd
Carnmore
Oranmore
Galway Co. Galway
Phone: 091-755444 Fax: 091-757722
Email: steiner@eircom.net
SIC: 25240 Employees: 95
Metallising Plastics
Mr Pat Crehan Managing Director
Mr Frank McDonagh Financial Controller
Mr Padraig Lohan Production Manager
Mr Michael Casserly IT Manager

Tank Engineering Ltd
Blessington Industrial Estate
Blessington
Wicklow Co. Wicklow
Phone: 045-865044 Fax: 045-865721
Email: tankeng@indigo.ie
Web: http://www.tank-engineering.ie
SIC: 25240 Employees: 50
Manufacture Plastics
Mr John Hanlon Managing Director
Ms Fiona Rowntree Accounts Manager

Technicast Plastic Moulding Ltd
Unit 16-18 Enterprise Centre
Gort Road
Ennis Co. Clare
Phone: 065-6820711 Fax: 065-6829119
Email: technicast@eircom.net
SIC: 25240 Employees: 28
Micro Precision Mouldings
Mr John Power Managing Director
Ms Patricia Casey Accounts Manager

Thormac Engineering Ltd
Shannon Industrial Estate
Shannon Co. Clare
Phone: 061-472030 Fax: 061-475151
Email: thormac@iol.ie
SIC: 25240 Employees: 70
Contract Injection Moulders
Mr Art Thornbury Managing Director
Mr Liam Culhane Finance Manager
Mr Ivan Thornbury Production Director

Thorsman Ireland
Donorer Road
Drogheda Co. Louth
Phone: 041-9871800 Fax: 041-9871810
Web: http://www.thorsman.com
SIC: 25240 Employees: 80
Manufacture Embibe Plastic Pres Lens
Mr Ake Vikander Managing Director
Ms Francis Drew Finance Director
Mr Brian Leech Sales Director
Ms Francis Drew

Tool & Plastic Co Ltd
Townsparks Industrial Estate
Longford Co. Longford
Phone: 043-46133 Fax: 043-46066
Email: tplastic@eircom.net
SIC: 25240 Employees: 50
Plastic Injection Moulding
Mr Declan O'Rourke Managing Director
Mr John Davis Office Manager
Mr Colm Cuffe Partner
Mr John Casey Production Manager

Ultraplastic
Ultra House, Unit 6-10
Baldoyle Industrial Estate
Dublin 13
Phone: 01-8324200 Fax: 01-8323688
Email: sales@ultraframe.iol.ie
SIC: 25240 Employees: 30
Plastics
Mr Bernard Collins Director
Mr John Murphy Personnel Manager
Mr Karl Simpson Sales Manager

Uponor Plastics
Bishopstown
Cork Co. Cork
Phone: 021-4541834 Fax: 021-4543541
SIC: 25240 Employees: 48
Plastic Pipe Manufacturer
Mr John Allcoran Managing Director
Mr Eddie Ahern Marketing Manager
Mr Paul Toole Production Manager
Ms Nuala Harrington Computer Executive

Wavin Ireland Ltd
Dublin Road
Balbriggan Co. Dublin
Phone: 01-8415000 Fax: 01-8415664
Email: info@wavin.com
Web: http://www.wavin.com
SIC: 25240 Employees: 120
Plastic Pipe Systems Manufacturing
Mr Desmond Byrne Chief Executive
Mr Ruairi Magiley Financial Director
Mr Patrick Atkinson Marketing Manager
Mr Fergal McGeogh Production Manager
Mr Paul Norton IT Manager

Wen-Plast Ltd
North Quay
Wicklow Co. Wicklow
Phone: 0404-67101 Fax: 0404-67012
Email: wenplast@eircom.net
SIC: 25240 Employees: 32
Plastics
Mr Alfonsiz O'Mara Managing Director
Mr Lesley Blennerhassett Sales & Marketing Manager
Mr Sean Cassidy Production Manager

Western Plastics Ltd
Ballybrit Industrial Estate
Ballybrit
Galway Co. Galway
Phone: 091-771588 Fax: 091-752877
SIC: 25240 Employees: 30
Manufacturing Plastics
Mr Mike Cunningham Manager
Mr Jarlath Hanley Finance Manager
Mr Tommy McLean Sales Manager

Manufacture of Non Metallic Products

26 Non-Metallic Products Manufacture
26110 Flat Glass Manufacture
26120 Conservatories Manufacture/Sales
26150 Glass Products (Other)
26200 Ceramic Goods
26400 Bricks, Tiles (Structural Products)
26601 Plaster (Building Products)
26602 Fireplaces
26610 Concrete Products for Construction
26620 Plaster Products for Construction
26630 Concrete (Ready Mixed)
26660 Cement (Building Products)
26700 Gravestone/Monument/Sculptors
26810 Abrasive Products
26820 Asbestos Goods

Norman Pratt Conservatories
Carnisle
Ballivor
Navan Co. Meath
Phone: 046-35166 Fax: 046-35290
Email: npc@indigo.ie
SIC: 26120 Employees: 24
Conservatory Manufacture & Sales
Mr Derek Pratt Managing Director

Reynaers Architectural Systems Ltd
Fairfield
Enniscorthy Co. Wexford
Phone: 054-35600 Fax: 054-35812
Email: reynaers@reynaers.com
SIC: 26120 Employees: 45
Sale & Manufacture Conservatories
Mr Frank Hamilton Managing Director
Mr Michael Roche Sales & Marketing Manager

Ardagh Plc
Southbank Road
Ringsend
Dublin 4
Phone: 01-6670844 Fax: 01-6670856
Email: headoffice@ardaghplc.ie
Web: http://www.ardaghplc.ie
SIC: 26150 Employees: 320
Glass Container Manufacturer
Mr Edward Kilty Group Chief Executive

Carey Glass Ltd
Limerick Road
Nenagh Co. Tipperary
Phone: 067-50700 Fax: 067-33233
Email: sales@careybros.ie
Web: http://www.careybros.ie
SIC: 26150 Employees: 370
Manufactures of Double Glazing & Toughened Glass
Mr Denis Carey Managing Director
Mr Martin Dunne Financial Controller
Mr Edward Lillis Personnel Manager
Mr Pat Magher Sales & Marketing Manager
Mr Denis Sherlock Operations Manager
Mr Tony Moran Computer Manager

Cavan Crystal Glass Ltd
Dublin Road
Cavan Co. Cavan
Phone: 049-4331800 Fax: 049-4331198
Email: cavancrystaldesign@eircom.net
Web: http://www.cavancrystaldesign.com
SIC: 26150 Employees: 30
Manufacture of Crystal Ware
Ms Winnie Corr Managing Director
Ms Mary Fay Sales & Marketing Manager

Douglas Glassworks Ltd
Drumacrutten
Dunraymond
Monaghan Co. Monaghan
Phone: 047-82955 Fax: 047-82840
Email: douglasglass@eircom.net
SIC: 26150 Employees: 26
Glass Processing
Mr Raymond Douglas Managing Director
Ms Eva Douglas Director

Francis Studios Pro Signs
Castlebellingham
Dundalk Co. Louth
Phone: 042-9372279 Fax: 042-9372749
SIC: 26150 Employees: 24
Traditional Glass Signs
Mr Francis Wayte Manager
Mr Brian Wayte Finance Manager
Mr Martin Wayte Sales Manager

Galway Irish Crystal Ltd
Merlin Park
Galway Co. Galway
Phone: 091-757311 Fax: 091-757316
Email: info@galwaycrystal.ie
Web: http://www.galwaycrystal.ie
SIC: 26150 Employees: 120
Crystal
Mr John Layde Managing Director
Ms Ann Cathal Personnel Director
Ms Darina MacCrosain Sales & Marketing Manager
Mr Des Sheeran Production Manager
Ms Sinead Cunnane Computer Manager

Non Metalic Manufacture

Heritage Irish Crystal Ltd
Bilberry
Waterford Co. Waterford
Phone: 051-841787 Fax: 051-841792
Email: heritagecrystal@eircom.net
Web: http://www.heritagecrystal.com
SIC: 26150 Employees: 40
Irish Crystal
Mr Joe Williams Managing Director
Mr Sonie Williams Sales Manager

Irish Glass Bottle Company Ltd
South Bank Road
Ringsend
Dublin 4
Phone: 01-6052400 Fax: 01-6683416
Email: sales@irishglass.ie
SIC: 26150 Employees: 375
Container Glass Manufacturing
Mr Brendan Goery Managing Director
Mr Brian Butterly Financial Controller/Secretary
Mr Finbar Duggan Personnel Manager
Mr Paddy Ring Sales & Marketing Director
Ms Laura Bissett Computer Manager

Sark International Ltd
Purcellfinch
Carlow Road
Kilkenny Co. Kilkenny
Phone: 056-23374 Fax: 056-20020
Email: sarkimages@eircom.net
Web: http://www.imageshowers.com
SIC: 26150 Employees: 35
Manufacture of Shower Doors
Mr John Kelly Managing Director

Saronix (Ireland) Ltd
Clonshaugh Industrial Estate
Dublin 17
Phone: 01-8472255 Fax: 01-8472038
Web: http://www.saronix.com
SIC: 26150 Employees: 48
Manufacture Crystal Oscilators
Mr Ben Healy General Manager
Mr George Munnelly Financial Controller
Ms Carmen Muresan Sales & Marketing Manager
Mr Paul O'Rourke Production Manager
Mr Patrick Burke IT Manager

Taylor Made Glass and Systems Ltd
Railway Road
Tipperary Co. Tipperary
Phone: 0504-31411 Fax: 0504-31986
Web: http://www.taylormadegroup.com
SIC: 26150 Employees: 70
Glass Products
Mr Thomas Peters Managing Director
Mr Joseph Ryan Financial Controller
Mr Uwe Roder Sales & Marketing Manager

Tipperary Crystal
Ballynoran
Carrick-On-Suir
Tipperary Co. Tipperary
Phone: 051-641188 Fax: 051-641190
Email: sales@tipperarycrystal.com
Web: http://www.tipperary-crystal.com
SIC: 26150 Employees: 70
Tableware & Crystal
Mr Niall Wall Managing Director
Mr Brian O'Kane Financial Manager
Mr Richard Strapp General Manager
Ms Michelle Power Sales & Marketing Manager
Mr Conal Boyle Chief Operations Manager

Waterford Crystal Ltd
Kilbarry
Waterford Co. Waterford
Phone: 051-373311 Fax: 051-378539
Web: http://www.review.com
SIC: 26150 Employees: 2200
Crystal Manufacturer
Mr John Foley Chief Executive
Mr John Fearon Finance Manager
Mr Brendan O'Donoghue Personnel Manager
Mr Michael Wilcock Manufacturing Director

WMG Group
Churchfield
Cork Co. Cork
Phone: 021-4211666 Fax: 021-4211677
Email: wmg@iol.ie
Web: http://www.wmg.ie
SIC: 26150 Employees: 120
Manufacture Double Glazed Units
Mr Don O'Gorman Managing Director
Mr Brian Neville Financial Controller
Ms Angela O'Brien Personnel Manager
Mr Terry McGrath Marketing Manager
Ms Deirdre Fitzgerald Production Manager

Blarney Stone Enterprise
Unit A7-A8 Calmount Park
Calmount Road
Dublin 12
Phone: 01-4191800 Fax: 01-4600133
Email: info@blarney-stone.com
Web: http://www.finnians.com
SIC: 26200 Employees: 25
Giftware Items
Mr Declan Fearon Managing Director
Mr Niall Geoghegan Finance Manager
Ms Alison Fox Production Manager

Carrigaline Pottery Ireland Ltd
Carrigaline
Cork Co. Cork
Phone: 021-4372305 Fax: 021-4373090
Email: carrigaline.pottery@indigo.ie
Web: http://www.carrigalinepottery.ie
SIC: 26200 Employees: 70
Ceramic Goods
Mr Michael Tattan Managing Director
Mr Ray Cronin Finance Manager
Ms Sinead Enright Sales & Marketing Manager

Dineen Refractories Ltd
Wolfhill
Athy Co. Kildare
Phone: 0507-35557 Fax: 0507-35655
Email: michealdineen@eircom.net
Web: http://www.dineenrefractories.ie
SIC: 26200 Employees: 30
Refractory Products
Mr Michael Dineen Managing Director
Ms Netta Dineen Company Secretary
Ms Stacey Farrell Sales & Marketing Manager
Mr Eamon Doyle Production Director
Ms Niamh Dineen Computer Manager

Dingle Lamps Ltd
Clothar, Baile 'N Fheirtearaigh
Dingle
Tralee Co. Kerry
Phone: 066-9156229 Fax: 066-9156366
Email: clothar@mulcahy-pottery.ie
Web: http://www.mulcahy-pottery.ie
SIC: 26200 Employees: 35
Pottery
Mr Louis O'Maolcatha Managing Director
Mr Clayton Reidy Office Manager
Ms Mary Cotter Sales & Marketing Manager

Gilroy Tile Designs
Grange
Sligo Co. Sligo
Phone: 071-63631 Fax: 071-63702
Email: tiles@gilroy-tiling.ie
Web: http://www.gilroy-tiling.ie
SIC: 26200 Employees: 50
Tile Manufacture
Mr Martin Gilroy Managing Director
Mr Jim Kerigan Financial Controller
Ms Patricia Henry Personnel Manager
Mr Jim Costigan Sales & Marketing Manager
Mr Noel Neary Computer Manager

Gilroy Tiling
29 Castle Street
Sligo Co. Sligo
Phone: 071-61692 Fax: 071-51061
Web: http://www.gilroy-tiling.ie
SIC: 26200 Employees: 50
Tiling Company
Mr John O' Reilly Manager
Mr Jim Kerrigan Financial Controller
Mr Paul Henry Sales Manager

Irish Parian Donegal China Ltd
Unit 1 Industrial Estate
Ballyshannon
Donegal Co. Donegal
Phone: 072-51826 Fax: 072-51122
Email: donchina@indigo.ie
Web: http://www.donegalchina.ie
SIC: 26200 Employees: 80
Manufacture of China & Giftware
Mr Danny Breslin Managing Director
Mr Donal Breslin Finance Manager
Mr Michael Freeburn Marketing Manager
Mr Benny Carty Production Manager

Midland Tile Merchants
Mullingar Business Park
Mullingar Co. Westmeath
Phone: 044-43337 Fax: 044-43338
SIC: 26200 Employees: 40
Tile & Bath Merchants
Mr Matthew Lough Proprietor
Mr Seamus Kincaid Finance Manager
Mr Tommy Lynch Sales & Marketing Manager

Rocca Tiles Ltd
Unit 4 Royal Liver Retail Park
Dublin 12
Phone: 01-4568055 Fax: 01-4568060
SIC: 26200 Employees: 30
Tile Importers & Retailers
Mr Patrick Rocca Managing Director
Mr Declan Doran Financial Controller
Ms Karen Fairbrother Personnel Manager
Mr Gerry Doheny Sales & Marketing Manager

Royal Tara China Ltd
Tara Hall
Mervue
Galway Co. Galway
Phone: 091-751301 Fax: 091-757574
Email: cust.service@royal-tara.com
Web: http://www.royal-tara.com
SIC: 26200 Employees: 110
Bone China Tableware Giftware & Bronze
Mr Michael Kilroy Managing Director
Mr James Phelan Financial Controller
Mr John Kelly Sales Manager
Mr Martin Murphy Production Manager

Stephen Pearce Pottery
Shanagarry
Midleton Co. Cork
Phone: 021-4646807 Fax: 021-4646706
SIC: 26200 Employees: 55
Handmade Earthenware
Mr Stephen Pearce Managing Director
Ms Helen Crotty Office Manager

Tile Style Ltd
89/90 North Wall Quay
Dublin 1
Phone: 01-8742900 Fax: 01-8557471
Email: info@tilestyle.ie
Web: http://www.tilestyle.ie
SIC: 26200 Employees: 45
Tiles Import & Retail
Mr Jim McNaughton Managing Director
Mr Andrew Crotty Financial Advisor
Mr Martin Newell Assistant Contract Manager

Non Metalic Manufacture

Value Tile
Trim High Street
Trim
Navan Co. Meath
Phone: 046-31841 Fax: 046-37674
SIC: 26200 Employees: 35
Tiles
Mr Stewart Penne Managing Director
Ms Paula Cole Secretary
Ms Diane Butterfield Sales Manager
Mr Niall Cunningham Managing Director

Vetra Tiles Ireland Ltd
South Quay
Arklow Co. Wicklow
Phone: 0402-91344 Fax: 0402-91355
Email: info@vetra-tiles.ie
Web: http://www.vetra-tiles.ie
SIC: 26200 Employees: 75
Manufacture & Supply Tiles
Mr Robert Hickson Administrative Director
Ms Catherine Clerkin Financial Controller
Mr Salim Ozen Commerical Manager
Mr Alp Gulder Senior IT Manager

Waterford Wedgwood
Kilbarry
Waterford Co. Waterford
Phone: 051-373311 Fax: 051-378539
Web: http://www.wwreview.com
SIC: 26200 Employees: 6500
Crystal & Ceramic Manufacture
Mr Redmond O'Donoghue President
Mr John Foley Chief Executive
Mr Gerry Conheady IT Director

Building Industries
Unit 143 Baldoyle Industrial Estate
Dublin 13
Phone: 01-8325958 Fax: 01-8393539
Email: ibcltd@indigo.ie
Web: http://www.ibcltd.net
SIC: 26400 Employees: 30
Manufacture of Building Materials
Mr Tim Grace Managing Director
Mr George Keane Finance Manager
Mr Edward Grace Director

Castle Court Bricks & Paviors
Castlemore
Crookstown
Cork Co. Cork
Phone: 021-7336336 Fax: 021-7336374
Email: bricksales@castlemore.ie
Web: http://www.castlemore.ie
SIC: 26400 Employees: 100
Brick & Pavior Manufacturing
Mr Peadar Creedon Managing Director
Mr Pat Fitzgerald Sales Manager

Fleming Fireclays
The Swan
Athy Co. Kildare
Phone: 0507-35513 Fax: 0507-35582
SIC: 26400 Employees: 50
Bricks & Flue Liners for Chimneys
Mr Pat Kavanagh Managing Director
Ms Rosaleen Fitzpatrick Personnel Manager
Mr Matt O Halloran Sales & Marketing Manager
Mr Tom Fleming Production Manager

Kingscourt Brick Ltd
Kingscourt
Cavan Co. Cavan
Phone: 042-9667317 Fax: 042-9667206
Email: info@kingscourtbrick.ie
Web: http://www.kingscourtbrick.ie
SIC: 26400 Employees: 60
Building Bricks
Mr Pat Kavanagh Managing Director
Mr Kevin McCoy Accounts Manager
Mr Matt O'Halloran Sales & Marketing Manager
Mr Ciaran O'Reilly Computer Manager

Stone Developments Ltd
Ballybrew
Enniskerry
Bray Co. Wicklow
Phone: 01-2862981 Fax: 01-2860449
Email: stonebb@indigo.ie
Web: http://www.stone-dev.ie
SIC: 26400 Employees: 100
Tiles
Mr Philip Meaney Chief Executive
Mr Martin Loughman Finance Manager
Mr John O'Neill Sales & Marketing Manager

Zaria Co-Operation Ltd
Blanchardstown Business Park
Ballycoolan Road
Dublin 15
Phone: 01-4530288 Fax: 01-8859650
Email: zaria@zaria.com
SIC: 26400 Employees: 30
Import Tiles from Spain
Mr Manuel Alonso Managing Director
Ms Ann Ellis Accounts Manager

Chadwicks Ltd
Newbridge Road
Naas Co. Kildare
Phone: 045-876711 Fax: 045-876902
Email: info@chadwick.ie
SIC: 26601 Employees: 200
Builders Providers
Mr John Dowling General Manager
Mr Darragh Carr Credit Controller

Gypsum Industries Ltd
Clonskeagh Road
Dublin 14
Phone: 01-2693644 Fax: 01-2694180
Email: info@gypsum.com
Web: http://www.gypsum.com
SIC: 26601 Employees: 315
Manufacture Plaster Boards
Mr Paul Ellis Managing Director
Mr Brian Dolan Finance Manager
Mr Tom Gogarty Personnel Manager
Mr Noel O'Donoghue Marketing Director
Mr John Byrnes Works Manager
Mr Tom Farrell DP Manager

Ardri Marble Mantlepieces Ltd
John Joe Sheehy Road
Tralee Co. Kerry
Phone: 066-7126177 Fax: 066-7127763
SIC: 26602 Employees: 30
Manufacture Marble Fireplaces
Mr John Fitzgibbon Proprietor
Ms Marie Fitzgibbon Finance Manager
Ms Lisa Fitzgibbon Sales Manager
Ms Emma Fitzgibbon Accounts

Kilkenny Mantelpieces Ltd
Ballyhale
Kilkenny Co. Kilkenny
Phone: 056-68730 Fax: 056-68949
Email: info@kilkennymantelpiece.iol.ie
Web: http://www.kilkennymantelpieces.ie
SIC: 26602 Employees: 40
Fireplaces
Mr George Murphy Managing Director
Mr Thomas Bergin Finance Manager
Ms Caroline Murphy Sales Manager

Leinster Foundry (Athy) Ltd
Barrowford Industrial Estate
Athy Co. Kildare
Phone: 0507-31366 Fax: 0507-31637
Email: info@leinsterfoundry.com
Web: http://www.leinsterfoundry.com
SIC: 26602 Employees: 30
Manufacture of Fireplaces
Mr Gerry Crosse Manager
Ms Dolores Myles Financial Controller

Midwest Mantel & Design Ltd
Cork Road
Raheen
Limerick Co. Limerick
Phone: 061-301666 Fax: 061-302233
SIC: 26602 Employees: 38
Manufacture of Fireplaces Surrounds
Mr Brian McMahon Managing Director
Mr John Walker Financial Controller
Mr Jim O'Brien Personnel manager
Mr Mark McMahon Data Processing Manager

Ardfert Quarry Products
Sackville
Ardfert
Tralee Co. Kerry
Phone: 066-7134144 Fax: 066-7134378
SIC: 26610 Employees: 30
Concrete (Building Products)
Mr Joe Doyle Manager
Mr Colm Foley Accountant
Mr Gerard O'Connor Sales Manager

Austin Grogan & Sons Ltd
Cave
Ballyhaunis Co. Mayo
Phone: 0907-30072 Fax: 0907-30707
Email: tpg@iol.ie
SIC: 26610 Employees: 25
Concrete (Building Products)
Mr Tommy Grogan Partner
Mr Michael Grogan Partner

Banagher Concrete Ltd
Queen Street
Banagher
Birr Co. Offaly
Phone: 0509-51417 Fax: 0509-51558
Email: bancon@iol.ie
SIC: 26610 Employees: 260
Precast Concrete Products
Mr Kieran Keenaghan Managing Director
Mr Patrick Mulhare Finance Manager
Mr Willy Mooney Personnel Manager
Mr Brendan Flynn Sales & Marketing Manager
Mr Michael Kelly Production Manager
Mr Barry Keenaghan Computer Manager

Breton Rocrete Tinode
Tinode
Blessington
Bray Co. Wicklow
Phone: 01-4015200 Fax: 01-4015201
Email: mail@breton.ie
Web: http://www.breton.ie
SIC: 26610 Employees: 100
Concrete Products
Mr Tom Sweeney Director/General Manager
Mr Jim Charters Sales & Marketing Manager
Mr Pat Reihill Operation Manager

Carlow Precast Tanks Ltd
Kilnock
Ballon
Carlow Co. Carlow
Phone: 01-8252744 Fax: 0503-59202
Email: cammeray@indigo.ie
SIC: 26610 Employees: 37
Precast Tanks
Mr Bernard Kennedy Proprietor
Ms Ann Rooney Accounts Manager

Cassidy Bros Concrete Products Ltd
Gransha
Buncrana
Lifford Co. Donegal
Phone: 077-61777 Fax: 077-61972
Email: info@cassidybrosltd.eircom.net
Web: http://www.cassidybrosltd.eircom.net
SIC: 26610 Employees: 75
Concrete Products
Mr Seamus Cassidy Manager
Mr Gerard O'Donnell Finance Manager
Mr Jack McElroy Sales & Marketing Manager
Mr Gerard O'Donal Computer Manager

Non Metalic Manufacture

Concrete Pipes Ltd
Maudlins
Naas Co. Kildare
Phone: 045-879354 Fax: 045-875202
SIC: 26610 Employees: 40
Concrete Pipes Manufacture
Mr Eftim Ivanoss Managing Director

Condron Concrete
Arden Road
Tullamore Co. Offaly
Phone: 0506-21220 Fax: 0506-41565
SIC: 26610 Employees: 110
Concrete Products Manufacturing
Mr John Condron Managing Director
Mr Oliver Whelan Financial Controller
Mr Padraig Prendergast Office Manager
Mr John Condron Jnr Sales & Marketing Manager

Cong Concrete Products Ltd
Cregaree Quarries
Claremorris Co. Mayo
Phone: 092-46022 Fax: 092-46467
Email: mcgcong@indigo.ie
SIC: 26610 Employees: 40
Concrete
Mr Michael McGrath Managing Director
Mr Billy McGrath Computer Manager

CPI Ltd
Laraghcon
Lucan Co. Dublin
Phone: 01-6280691 Fax: 01-6280318
Email: webmaster@cpi.ie
Web: http://www.cpi.ie
SIC: 26610 Employees: 70
Concrete Products Manufacturer
Mr Alan Haugh Chief Executive
Mr Ivan Cosgrove Finance Manager
Mr Aidan O'Mara Personnel Manager
Mr Christy Dunne Sales Manager
Mr Bill Good Production Director

Doyle Concrete Ltd
Rathangan
Kildare Co. Kildare
Phone: 045-524307 Fax: 045-524159
Email: steelite@eircom.net
Web: http://www.eircom.net
SIC: 26610 Employees: 60
Concrete Window Sills/Lintels
Mr Phil Doyle Managing Director
Ms Catherine Marshall Company Secretary
Mr Billy Doyle Sales & Marketing Manager
Mr John Nolan Production Manager

Ducon Concrete Ltd
Kanturk
Mallow Co. Cork
Phone: 029-56037 Fax: 029-56245
Email: ducon@iol.ie
SIC: 26610 Employees: 60
Concrete
Mr Frank Healy Managing Director
Mr James O'Connell Finance Manager

Gleeson Quarries Ltd
Laffansbridge
Thurles Co. Tipperary
Phone: 052-56117 Fax: 052-56117
SIC: 26610 Employees: 25
Concrete Products
Mr Peter Gleeson Managing Director
Mr John Kelly Sales Manager

Grangeford Precast Ltd
Grangeford
Carlow Co. Carlow
Phone: 0503-48780 Fax: 0503-48734
Email: info@grangefordprecast.ie
Web: http://www.grangefordprecast.ie
SIC: 26610 Employees: 125
Precast Concrete
Mr Bernard Quinn Managing Director
Mr Liam Daly Finance Manager
Mr Robert Hickey Sales & Marketing Manager
Mr Nicholas Aolimer Production Manager

Healy Brothers
Mile Bush Quarry
Midleton Co. Cork
Phone: 021-4883123 Fax: 021-4883706
Email: healybros@eircom.net
SIC: 26610 Employees: 60
Building Materials (concrete blocks)
Mr Paddy Healy Managing Director
Mr Ray McGrath Financial Controller

Irish Building Chemicals
Unit 143Baldoyle Industrial Estate
Baldoyle
Dublin 13
Phone: 01-8321005 Fax: 01-8393539
Email: ibcltd@indigo.ie
SIC: 26610 Employees: 35
Concrete Products
Mr Timothy Grace Managing Director
Mr George Keane Financial Controller
Mr Eddie Grace General Manager

John A Wood Ltd
Killarney Co. Kerry
Phone: 064-31974 Fax: 064-31802
SIC: 26610 Employees: 40
Concrete (Building Products)
Mr Michael Buckley General Manager

Kelly's of Fantane Concrete Ltd
Fantane
Borrisoleigh
Thurles Co. Tipperary
Phone: 0504-52118 Fax: 0504-52200
SIC: 26610 Employees: 80
Concrete Products
Mr PJ Kelly General Manager
Mr Niall Berry Finance Manager
Mr Martin Flynn Personnel Manager
Mr Gus Maher Sales & Marketing Manager
Mr Michael Tynan Computer Manager

Kilkenny Block Company Ltd
Troyswood Freshford Road
Kilkenny Co. Kilkenny
Phone: 056-21438 Fax: 056-51535
SIC: 26610 Employees: 25
Concrete Blocks & Tarmacadam
Mr Padraic O'Rourke Managing Director
Mr Gerry Curtin Finance Manager
Mr John Wilson Sales Manager
Mr Willie Horgan Production Manager

Killeshal Precast Concrete
Killeshal
Tullamore Co. Offaly
Phone: 0506-53018 Fax: 0506-53272
Email: sales@killeshal.com
Web: http://www.killeshal.com
SIC: 26610 Employees: 90
Precast Concrete
Mr Frank Mulligan Managing Director
Mr Pat Nolan Personnel Manager

Kilsaran Concrete Ltd
Tinnycross
Tullamore Co. Offaly
Phone: 0506-21918 Fax: 0506-51032
SIC: 26610 Employees: 40
Concrete Blocks
Mr Michael O'Rourke Plant Manager
Mr Tom Cossey Sales Manager

Loughnane Concrete
Ballinaguilsha
Birr Co. Offaly
Phone: 0509-20208 Fax: 0509-20584
SIC: 26610 Employees: 40
Concrete Manufacturers
Mr Christy Loughnane Managing Director
Mr Michael Feighery Financial Controller
Ms Onagh Murphy Sales Manager
Mr Sean Loughnane Computer Manager

Maye Concrete Ltd
Wine Street
Sligo Co. Sligo
Phone: 071-62248 Fax: 071-69582
SIC: 26610 Employees: 65
Concrete Products
Mr Sean McQuaid General Manager
Mr Michael Henry Accounts Manager
Mr Peter Deaxy Personnel Manager

McAndrew Aggregates
Pearse Street
Ballina Co. Mayo
Phone: 096-22709 Fax: 096-22709
SIC: 26610 Employees: 25
Ready Mixed Concrete / Gravel
Mr Patrick McAndrew Managing Director
Ms Beatrice Timlin Administration Manager

Mena O'Donnell
Atlantic Industries
Town Park Industrial Estate
Athy Co. Kildare
Phone: 0507-40475 Fax: 0507-40471
SIC: 26610 Employees: 70
Concrete
Mr Tom Brennan Manager

Michael J Cannon
Oranhill
Oranmore
Galway Co. Galway
Phone: 091-794104 Fax: 091-794141
SIC: 26610 Employees: 30
Blocks & Concrete
Mr Michael Cannon Managing Director
Mr Stephen Cullinan Finance Manager
Mr Pat Conacur Sales Manager

Mullafarry Quarry
Killala
Claremorris Co. Mayo
Phone: 096-32055 Fax: 096-32498
SIC: 26610 Employees: 75
Concrete Products
Ms May Smyth Proprietor
Ms Bernie Ward Sales Manager
Ms Bridget Cogger Operations Manager

O'Regan Precast
Classis
Ovens
Cork Co. Cork
Phone: 021-4871756 Fax: 021-4872219
SIC: 26610 Employees: 25
Concrete (Building Products)
Mr Dermot O'Regan Proprietor
Ms Jackie O'Regan Accountant

O'Reilly Bros Ltd
Kingscourt
Cavan Co. Cavan
Phone: 042-9667237 Fax: 042-9667311
Email: orbros@indigo.ie
SIC: 26610 Employees: 58
Concrete Products
Mr Andrew O'Reilly Managing Director
Mr Henry Fitzsimons Financial Controller
Mr Barry O'Reilly Sales Manager
Mr Terence O'Reilly Director

Oldbridge Concrete Products Ltd
Oldbridge
Drogheda Co. Louth
Phone: 041-9833001 Fax: 041-9833003
Email: info@oldbridgeconcrete.ie
SIC: 26610 Employees: 25
Manufacture Concrete Products
Mr Pat McCullough Managing Director
Mr Jim Murphy Finance Manager
Mr Pat Ryan Sales & Marketing Manager

Non Metalic Manufacture

P Corbett Concrete Products
Mooneraha
Cahir Co. Tipperary
Phone: 052-41590 Fax: 052-41590
SIC: 26610 Employees: 30
Concrete Building Products
Mr Pat Corbett Managing Director

P McCaffreys & Sons Ltd
Ballymagroarty Quarries
Ballintra
Donegal Co. Donegal
Phone: 073-34036 Fax: 073-34300
SIC: 26610 Employees: 100
Concrete (Building Products)
Mr Adrian Britton General Manager
Mr Peter McKenna Sales Manager

Precast Products Ltd
Building 18, Airport Business Park
Killowen
Waterford Co. Waterford
Phone: 051-374048 Fax: 051-371077
Email: sales@precast.ie
Web: http://www.precast.ie/pans
SIC: 26610 Employees: 35
Manufacture Stonecast Products for Construction Industry
Mr Niall Griffin Managing Director
Mr Padraig Griffin Finance Manager

Roadstone (Dublin) Ltd
Fortunestown
Tallaght
Dublin 24
Phone: 01-4041200 Fax: 01-4041321
Email: rstone@indigo.ie
Web: http://www.roadstone.ie
SIC: 26610 Employees: 300
Suppliers of Concrete Products
Mr Donal Dempsey Managing Director
Mr Tom Heely Finance Manager
Mr Maurice O'Connor Personnel Manager
Ms Judy Fusco Marketing Manager
Mr Pat Martin Operations Manager
Mr Frank Cox Computer Manager

Sean Quinn Quarries
Williamstown
Castlerea Co. Roscommon
Phone: 0907-43052 Fax: 0907-43145
SIC: 26610 Employees: 300
Concrete (Building Products)
Mr Frank Murray General Manager

Shay Murtagh Ltd
Raharney
Mullingar Co. Westmeath
Phone: 044-74108 Fax: 044-74552
Email: sales@shaymurt.com
Web: http://www.shaymurt.com
SIC: 26610 Employees: 80
Ready Mixed Concrete & Other Concrete Products
Mr Shay Murtagh Managing Director
Mr Jim Buckley Finance Manager
Mr Liam McGovern Sales & Marketing Manager
Mr Ciaran Murtagh Computer Manager

Structural Concrete Bonding (SCB)
Cill Dara Industrial Estate
Newbridge Co. Kildare
Phone: 045-435270 Fax: 045-435272
Email: scb@indigo.ie
SIC: 26610 Employees: 55
Concrete Repair Work
Mr Tony Gahan Managing Director
Ms Christine Twomey Personnel Manager

Treacy Enterprises Ltd
Ballinascorney
Upper Brittas
Blackrock Co. Dublin
Phone: 01-4582237 Fax: 01-4582430
SIC: 26610 Employees: 50
Sand/Gravel/Stone/Macadam
Mr Patsy Monaghan Manager
Mr Gerry Fitzpatrick Sales Director

Concrete Manufacturing Co Ltd
Ballygabdy Road
Tuam Co. Galway
Phone: 093-24315 Fax: 093-25447
SIC: 26630 Employees: 30
Concrete Manufacturing
Mr Jim Farragher Manager Director

Concrete Pumping Ltd
Greenhills Road
Walkinstown
Dublin 12
Phone: 01-4600744 Fax: 01-4600478
SIC: 26630 Employees: 30
Concrete- Ready Mixed
Mr Martin Banbrick Manager

Dan Morrisey Ireland Ltd
Bennekerry
Carlow Co. Carlow
Phone: 0503-31464 Fax: 0503-32091
Email: dmil@dmil.ie
Web: http://www.dmil.ie
SIC: 26630 Employees: 150
Ready Mixed Concrete / Blocks
Mr Andrew Morrissey Managing Director
Mr Philip Morrissey Finance Manager
Mr Andy Whitmore Computer Manager

Denis Duggan Ready Mix Ltd
Prospect House
Dunmanway Co. Cork
Phone: 023-55011 Fax: 023-55011
SIC: 26630 Employees: 37
Concrete - Ready Mixed
Mr Denis Duggan Proprietor

Finbarr O'Neill Ltd
Poulavone
Ballincollig
Cork Co. Cork
Phone: 021-4871933 Fax: 021-4873623
Email: foneillltd@eircom.net
SIC: 26630 Employees: 30
Concrete- Ready Mixed
Mr Finbarr O'Neill Proprietor

Flanagan Concrete Ltd
Feighcullen
Rathangan
Kildare Co. Kildare
Phone: 045-524111 Fax: 045-524452
SIC: 26630 Employees: 40
Ready Mixed Concrete & Concrete Blocks
Mr Des Flanagan Managing Director
Ms Marian Stewart Financial Controller
Mr Brendan Fitzsimons Personnel Manager
Ms Fiona Gunning Sales & Marketing Manager

Goode Concrete Ltd
Naas Industrial Estate
Naas Co. Kildare
Phone: 045-897510 Fax: 045-875646
SIC: 26630 Employees: 50
Concrete
Mr Tom Goode Managing Director
Mr Richard Godsil Accountant
Mr Peter Goode Marketing Manager
Mr Dave Murphy Production Manager

Laois Concrete
New Road
Portlaoise Co. Laois
Phone: 0502-21487 Fax: 0502-20323
SIC: 26630 Employees: 35
Ready-Mix Concrete and Blocks
Mr Andy Galvin Manager
Mr Joe Bergin Plant Manager
Mr Billy White Sales Representative

Longford Precast Co Ltd
Cloonaugh
Drumlish
Longford Co. Longford
Phone: 043-24128 Fax: 043-24264
Email: mulleadys@oceanfree.net
SIC: 26630 Employees: 30
Precast Contractors
Mr Anthony Mulleady Managing Director

P Plunkett Ltd
Williamstown
Finea
Mullingar Co. Westmeath
Phone: 043-81240 Fax: 043-81380
SIC: 26630 Employees: 45
Concrete (Ready Mixed) & Blocks
Mr Oliver Plunkett Proprietor

Ready Mix Concrete (Ireland) Ltd
Riverstown
Dundalk Co. Louth
Phone: 042-9376210 Fax: 042-9376186
SIC: 26630 Employees: 30
Ready Mix Concrete
Mr Brian McSloy Manager

Readymix Plc
5-23 East Wall Road
Dublin 3
Phone: 01-8741411 Fax: 01-8558648
Email: readymix@readymix.ie
SIC: 26630 Employees: 2000
Concrete Sales
Mr Brendan Fitzgerald Managing Director
Mr Frank Lynch Finance Manager
Ms Philomena Doherty Personnel Manager
Mr John Newell Sales Director
Mr Mark McNally IT Manager

Wright Quarry Products
Swans Cross
Monaghan Co. Monaghan
Phone: 042-9744811 Fax: 042-9744940
SIC: 26630 Employees: 55
Ready Mixed Concrete & Kerbs
Mr George Hamilton Manager
Mr Clive Grudgings Sales Manager

Irish Cement Ltd
Stillorgan Road
Stillorgan
Blackrock Co. Dublin
Phone: 01-2064000 Fax: 01-2064001
Email: info@irishcement.ie
Web: http://www.irishcement.ie
SIC: 26660 Employees: 400
Cement
Mr Jim Nolan Managing Director
Mr Eddie McDonnell Finance Manager
Mr Brian Aylward Personnel Director
Mr Ken McKnight Sales & Marketing Director

Irish Stoneware & Fireclays Ltd
Kingcourt Road
Carrickmacross Co. Monaghan
Phone: 042-9661256 Fax: 042-9662494
Email: postmaster@stonwarecarrick.ie
SIC: 26660 Employees: 35
Clay Pipe Manufacture
Ms Deirdre Hunt General Manager
Mr Brendan Kelly Sales & Marketing Manager

Oran Pre-Cast Ltd
Deerpark Industrial Estate
Oranmore
Galway Co. Galway
Phone: 091-794537 Fax: 091-794586
Email: info@oranprecast.ie
Web: http://www.oranprecast.ie
SIC: 26660 Employees: 110
Precast Concrete Products
Mr Donal Dooley General Manager
Mr Des Keating Financial Controller
Ms Michelle Melville Personnel Manager
Mr Pat Fahey Sales Manager

Non Metalic Manufacture

Feely & Sons
Greatmeadow
Boyle Co. Roscommon
Phone: 079-62066 Fax: 079-62894
Email: info@feelystone.ie
Web: http://www.feelystone.com
SIC: 26700 Employees: 100
Natural Stone Processors for Monumental & Architectural Sector
Mr Michael Meaney Managing Director
Mr Brendan Allen Financial Controller
Mr Christopher O'Connor Director
Mr James Giblin Building Sales Manager
Ms Matilda Meehan Production Manager
Ms Regina Finn Monumental Sales

Atto Abrasives Ltd
Dunmain
New Ross Co. Wexford
Phone: 051-562700 Fax: 051-562707
Email: info@attoabrasives.com
Web: http://www.attoabrasives.com
SIC: 26810 Employees: 48
Manufacture of Abrasives
Mr Tom Prendergast Managing Director
Mr Michael Prendergast Finance Manager

John Duffy Construction Ltd
The Commons
Navan Co. Meath
Phone: 046-23215 Fax: 046-23976
SIC: 26820 Employees: 30
Asbestos - Surveying & Removals
Mr John Duffy Proprietor

Metals Manufacture

27	**Metals Manufacture**
27100	Ferrous Metal Foundries
27400	Non-Ferrous Metal
27420	Aluminium
27440	Copper
27450	Metals (Non Ferrous)
27451	Brass
27500	Forging & Casting of Steel/Iron
27520	Steel Industry
27530	Casting of Light Metals

Alcast Company Ltd
Clonhaston
Enniscorthy Co. Wexford
Phone: 054-33900 Fax: 054-33872
Email: info@alcastgroup.com
SIC: 27420 Employees: 55
Aluminium Diecasters
Mr Jim McCauley Managing Director
Mr Niall Sunderland Company Accountant
Mr Rory McCauley Sales & Marketing Manager
Mr Michael Quirk Production Manager

Alucraft Ltd
Unit 5 Newtown Park
Malahide Road Industrial Park
Dublin 17
Phone: 01-8470455 Fax: 01-8470036
Email: alucraft@iol.ie
SIC: 27420 Employees: 40
Aluminium Roofs/Windows/Doors
Mr Ben Hyde Managing Director
Mr Rory O'Sullivan Financial Controller

APA Holdings
Parkmore Industrial Estate
Longmile Road
Dublin 12
Phone: 01-4509102 Fax: 01-4509530
Email: contact@apasystems.ie
SIC: 27420 Employees: 70
Aluminium Systems
Mr Fred Trenaman Chief Executive
Mr John Shiedy Finance Director
Mr John Loughney IT Manager

Architectural Aluminium Ltd
Oak Road
Western Buisness Park
Dublin 12
Phone: 01-4568400 Fax: 01-4568480
SIC: 27420 Employees: 180
Aluminium Products
Mr John Hallahan Managing Director
Mr Tom Kenny Finance Director
Mr Anthony Flynn Training Manager
Mr Ken Green Sales & Marketing Manager
Mr Finnian Hyland Director
Mr Tom Ginty Design Director

Atlas Aluminium Ltd
Atlas Enterprise Park
Atlas Avenue
Limerick Co. Limerick
Phone: 061-313777 Fax: 061-313077
Email: postmaster@atlasalu.ie
Web: http://www.atlasalu.ie
SIC: 27420 Employees: 280
Aluminium Die Casting
Mr John Lyons Managing Director
Mr Derek Tuite Financial Controller
Mr Ken Halle Personnel Manager
Mr Sean Lyons Sales & Marketing Manager
Mr John Guerin Shipping Manager
Mr Philip O'Brien IT Manager

Aughinish Alumina Ltd
Aughnish Island
Askeaton
Limerick Co. Limerick
Phone: 061-604000 Fax: 061-604001
Web: http://www.aughinish.com
SIC: 27420 Employees: 450
Extracts Alumnia from Imported Bauxite
Mr I Perkins Chairman
Mr Pat Lynch Public Affairs Manager

Douglas Engineering Ltd
Industrial Estate
Northern Extension
Waterford Co. Waterford
Phone: 051-375381 Fax: 051-370773
Email: info@douglas-engineering.com
Web: http://www.douglas-engineering.com
SIC: 27420 Employees: 40
Manufacture of Aluminium Pullys
Mr John Douglas Managing Director
Ms Mary Byrne Finance Manager
Mr Patrick Douglas Sales Director

Duggan Systems Ltd
Lurriga
Patrickswell
Limerick Co. Limerick
Phone: 061-355377 Fax: 061-355405
Email: sales@duggansystems.ie
SIC: 27420 Employees: 50
Aluminium & PVC Doors / Windows
Mr Bernard Duggan General Manager
Ms Monica Bonar Finance Manager

Kit-Fab (Ireland) Ltd
Kilfergus
Glin
Limerick Co. Limerick
Phone: 068-34171 Fax: 068-34448
Email: tomktsb@gofree.indigo.ie
SIC: 27420 Employees: 200
Aluminium
Mr John Costello Managing Director
Ms Carol Costello Financial Director
Ms Marie Ambrose Computer Manager

MI Metals Ltd
Carrickmacross Road
Ballybay
Castleblayney Co. Monaghan
Phone: 042-9741226 Fax: 042-9741360
Email: info@mimetals.ie
Web: http://www.mimetals.ie
SIC: 27420 Employees: 23
Iodised Aluminium
Mr Joe Brophy Chief Executive
Ms Evanna Cahill Sales & Marketing Manager

Murphy Aluminium Ltd
Ballycurreen Industrial Estate
Airport Road
Cork Co. Cork
Phone: 021-4962000 Fax: 021-4962468
Email: murphyal@iol.ie
SIC: 27420 Employees: 30
Aluminium Windows Manufacture
Mr John Crowley Managing Director
Mr Alan O'Brien Production Manager
Mr Joe O'Connell Technical Director

Sean Doyle & Sons
Circular Road
Roscommon Co. Roscommon
Phone: 0903-26753 Fax: 0903-25438
SIC: 27420 Employees: 45
Manufacture Aluminium & PVC Windows
Mr Sean Doyle Proprietor
Mr Kenny Doyle Sales & Marketing Manager

Shamrock Aluminium Ltd
Grannagh
Waterford Co. Waterford
Phone: 051-855511 Fax: 051-875843
Email: sales@shamrockaluminium.ie
SIC: 27420 Employees: 25
Manufacture Aluminum Paste & Flake Powder
Mr Tom Barry Managing Director
Mr Sean Grace Finance Manager
Mr David Power Sales Manager

Weather Care Window Systems
Mullingar Business Park
Mullingar Co. Westmeath
Phone: 044-42288 Fax: 044-44302
Email: wcare@tinet.ie
SIC: 27420 Employees: 25
Aluminium & PVC Windows
Mr Jim Kenny Managing Director

Westcast Ltd
Baltimore Road
Skibbereen Co. Cork
Phone: 028-22266 Fax: 028-22379
Email: westcast@iol.ie
SIC: 27420 Employees: 30
Aluminium Foundry
Mr Lothar Thoni Director
Mr Jordan McKeown Finance Manager
Ms Kathleen O'Connell Sales Manager

Barbre Construction
652-654 South Circular Road
Ranelagh
Dublin 6
Phone: 01-4967800 Fax: 01-4540603
SIC: 27440 Employees: 30
Coppersmiths
Mr Sean Reynolds Managing Director

Keytech Enclosures Ltd
The Island
Newmarket
Mallow Co. Cork
Phone: 029-60420 Fax: 029-60509
Email: enclosures@keytechglobal.com
Web: http://www.keytechglobal.com
SIC: 27450 Employees: 70
Sheet Metal Fabrication
Mr John Harty General Manager

Metals Manufacture

Metal Processors
Station Road
Clondalkin
Dublin 22
Phone: 01-4573240 Fax: 01-4573253
Email: info@metalproc.ie
Web: http://www.metalproc.ie
SIC: 27450 Employees: 30
Metal Processors
Mr Michael O'Hanlon Managing Director
Mr Gary Smith Financial Controller
Mr Jack Finnot Production Manager

Mining Company of Ireland & Stracham Brothers
PO Box 3726
Clondalkin
Dublin 22
Phone: 01-4570211 Fax: 01-4573832
Email: info@metalproc.ie
SIC: 27450 Employees: 28
Lead Manufacture
Mr Michael O'Hanlon Managing Director
Mr Gary Smyth Finance Manager
Mr Robin Fleming Sales & Marketing Manager

Longford Brassware Ltd
Churchland
Longford Co. Longford
Phone: 043-46195 Fax: 043-45985
Email: info@longfordbrass.com
SIC: 27451 Employees: 45
Architectural Metalwork
Mr Tony Nerney Managing Director
Mr Eamon Reilly Finance Manager
Mr Kevin Campbell Personnel Manager
Mr Paul McDonagh Marketing Executive
Mr Seamus Cullen Computer Manager

Hoskins Manufacturing
Kildare Enterprise Centre
Kildare Co. Kildare
Phone: 045-522027 Fax: 045-522011
Email: sales@hoskinsalloysirl.ie
Web: http://www.hoskinsalloysirl.ie
SIC: 27452 Employees: 30
Manufacture Wire
Mr Padraig Scully Managing Director

Wire Weaver's Ireland
Mountmahon Industrial Estate
Abbeyfeale
Limerick Co. Limerick
Phone: 068-31284 Fax: 068-31377
Email: weaversw@indigo.ie
SIC: 27452 Employees: 33
Fine Wire Weaving
Mr Michael Quigley General Manager
Mr Colm Divilly Finance Manager
Ms Betty O'Reilly Personnel Director

Ardmore Engineering Ltd
Poppintree Industrial Estate
Finglas
Dublin 11
Phone: 01-8640766 Fax: 01-8640830
Email: info@ardmore.iol.ie
SIC: 27500 Employees: 70
Metal Forgings
Mr Dermot O'Brien Managing Director
Mr Brendan O'Brien Finance Manager
Ms Karen Byrne Sales & Marketing Manager

Bailieborough Foundry Ltd
Bailieborough Co. Cavan
Phone: 042-9665275 Fax: 042-9665476
Email: bailfdry@eircom.net
Web: http://www.bailsfdry.iol.ie
SIC: 27500 Employees: 85
Cast Iron Foundry
Mr Eugene Clarke Managing Director
Mr Seamus Kearney Financial Controller
Mr John Dempsey Personnel Manager
Mr Cyril Barnett Sales Director
Mr Raymond Clarke Computer Manager

Hitech Plating Ltd
Ballycoolin Business Park
Blanchardstown
Dublin 15
Phone: 01-8215520 Fax: 01-8215524
Email: hitechpl@iol.ie
SIC: 27500 Employees: 50
Electoless Plating
Mr Sean Boland Managing Director
Ms Rosaleen McMahon Accounts Manager
Mr Paul Mulready Production Manager

Irish ISPAT
Haulbowline
Cobh Co. Cork
Phone: 021-4378011 Fax: 021-4378879
SIC: 27500 Employees: 400
Steel Manufacturer
Mr Jerry Gorman Chief Executive
Mr Harak Banthia Financial Controller
Mr Tony Hewitt Personnel Manager
Mr Kees Snoek Sales & Marketing Manager
Mr Nigel Walker Production Manager
Ms Patricia Verling DP Manager

Murphy Stainless Steel Specialist Ltd
Industrial Estate
Castlebar Co. Mayo
Phone: 094-22457 Fax: 094-23936
Email: murphystainless@eircom.net
SIC: 27500 Employees: 30
Stainless Steel Engineering
Mr Michael Murphy Director
Mr Brendan Murphy Sales Manager
Mr Kieran Murphy Production Manager

Oerlikon Welding (Ireland) Ltd
Jamestown Business Park
Jamestown Road, Finglas
Dublin 11
Phone: 01-6771270 Fax: 01-8342694
Web: http://www.oerlikonweld.com
SIC: 27500 Employees: 60
Welding Electrodes
Mr John McSweeney General Manager
Mr Fred Elliott Finance Manager
Mr Brendan Byrne Sales & Marketing Manager
Mr Brian Barry Computer Manager

Thomas Corry & Sons
1 Mygan Business Park
Jamestown Road Finglas
Dublin 11
Phone: 01-8362828 Fax: 01-8362526
SIC: 27500 Employees: 35
Iron Monger
Mr Paul Dalton Manager
Mr Joe Baker Sales Manager
Mr Noel Sutton Computer Manager

Andrew Mannion Engineering Ltd
Clara Road
Moate
Athlone Co. Westmeath
Phone: 0902-81184 Fax: 0902-81735
Email: info@ameng.ie
Web: http://www.ameng.ie
SIC: 27520 Employees: 45
Structural Steelwork.
Mr Andrew Mannion Managing Director
Mr Charles Ward Financial Controller
Mr Paddy Lambe Workshop Manager

Coolock Engineering Ltd
Grange Works, 68 Grange Close
Baldoyle Industrial Estate
Dublin 13
Phone: 01-8392278 Fax: 01-8392498
Email: ce@iol.ie
SIC: 27520 Employees: 35
Steel Structural Fabricators & Erectors
Mr Des Clark Managing Director
Ms Louise Clark Finance Manager
Mr Paul Clark Sales & Marketing Manager

Duggan Steel (Ire) Ltd
Tullamaine
Callan Road
Kilkenny Co. Kilkenny
Phone: 056-25050 Fax: 056-25055
Email: sales@dugganssteel.com
Web: http://www.dugganssteel.com
SIC: 27520 Employees: 30
Steel Stockholders
Mr Francis Duggan Managing Director
Ms Yvonne Duggan Finance Manager
Mr John Moore Sales Manager
Mr Frank Keoghan Computer Manager

Goggin Buckley
Drumcollogher
Limerick Co. Limerick
Phone: 063-83149 Fax: 063-83170
SIC: 27520 Employees: 80
Manufacture Structural Steel
Mr John Buckley Managing Director
Mr Gerard McAree Financial Controller

Impact Ireland (Metals) Ltd
76 Cookstown Industrial Estate
Tallaght
Dublin 24
Phone: 01-4512144 Fax: 01-4515405
Email: info@impactirl.ie
Web: http://www.impactirl.ie
SIC: 27520 Employees: 42
Steel Stock Holders
Mr Don Clarke Managing Director
Mr John Caroll Finance Manager
Mr Bernard Foley Sales Manager

J Murphy Structural Engineers
Shanowen Road
Santry
Dublin 9
Phone: 01-8423799 Fax: 01-8424868
Email: jmse@iol.ie
SIC: 27520 Employees: 150
Structural Steel
Mr Frank Reynolds Group Managing Director
Mr John Maher Financial Controller
Mr Don Kane Contracts Director
Mr Ken Moore Computer Manager

Kells Stainless Ltd
Oldcastle Road
Kells Co. Meath
Phone: 046-41520 Fax: 046-41528
Email: ksl@iol.ie
Web: http://www.kells/stainless.com
SIC: 27520 Employees: 37
Stainless Steel
Mr Pat O'Connor Managing Director
Ms Ann Clarke Company Secretary

Kerry Die Products Ltd
Fossa
Killarney Co. Kerry
Phone: 064-44233 Fax: 064-44433
Email: sales@kerrydie.iol.ie
SIC: 27520 Employees: 25
Manufacture Pellet Dyes/Steel Products
Mr Liam O'Connor Manager
Mr Sean Keating Financial Controller
Mr Peter Wheelan Electrical Engineer

Leslie Reynolds & Co Ltd
126 East Wall Road
Dublin 3
Phone: 01-8364988 Fax: 01-8364879
Email: info@leslie-reynolds.ie
Web: http://www.leslie-reynolds.ie
SIC: 27520 Employees: 45
Stainless Steel Stockholders
Mr Leslie Reynolds Managing Director
Mr Peter Noctor Finance Manager
Ms Emma Reynolds Personnel Manager
Mr John Griffith Sales Director

Max Mauch GMBH Ireland Ltd
Whitemill Industrial Estate
Wexford Co. Wexford
Phone: 053-60005 Fax: 053-60004
Email: mauchstainless@tinet.ie
Web: http://www.mauchedelstahl.de
SIC: 27520 Employees: 35
Manufacture Stainless Fitting Parts
Mr Seamus Gladney General Manager

McAree's Engineering
Ballinode
Monaghan Co. Monaghan
Phone: 047-89333 Fax: 047-89335
Email: bmcaree@eircom.net
SIC: 27520 Employees: 30
Steel Bulk Bin Silos / Precision Laser Cutting & Specialists
Mr Brendan McAree Managing Director

McArthur Group Ltd
M50 Business Park
Ballymount Avenue
Dublin 12
Phone: 01-4505070 Fax: 01-4507058
Email: sales.dublin@mcarthur-group.com
SIC: 27520 Employees: 25
Steel Stockholders
Mr Edward Sarratt Managing Director
Mr Pat O'Shea Sales Manager

OMC Engineering Ltd
Ballysimon Road
Limerick Co. Limerick
Phone: 061-419333 Fax: 061-418644
SIC: 27520 Employees: 120
Stainless Steel Specialists
Mr Tom Comerford Managing Director
Mr Tom Griffin Finance Director
Mr Neil Casey Sales Director

PJ Murphy Engineering
Monahan Road
Cork Co. Cork
Phone: 021-4962494 Fax: 021-4315979
Email: pjmurphyeng@eircom.net
SIC: 27520 Employees: 25
Steel Fabrications
Mr Martin Lane Proprietor

Shortt Steel Fabrications Ltd
Robin Hill
Drombanna
Limerick Co. Limerick
Phone: 061-351544 Fax: 061-351566
Email: info@shorttstainless.ie
Web: http://www.shorttstainless.ie
SIC: 27520 Employees: 45
Stainless Steel
Mr Brendan Shortt General Manager
Mr Sean O'Sullivan Finance Manager
Mr Dermot Shortt Personnel Manager
Mr Pat McNamara Sales & Marketing Manager
Mr Noel Manion Production Manager

Steel & Roofing Systems
Kilkenny Road
Castlecomer
Kilkenny Co. Kilkenny
Phone: 056-41855 Fax: 056-41860
SIC: 27520 Employees: 30
Steel & Roofing Systems
Mr Michael Whelan Managing Director

Steel Company of Ireland Ltd
Ballymount Road
Clondalkin
Dublin 22
Phone: 01-4050390 Fax: 01-4508924
Email: ray.garry@corusgroup.com
SIC: 27520 Employees: 70
Steel Stockholders
Mr John Troup General Manager
Mr Mike Lowe Commercial Services Manager
Mr John Sheehan Sales Manager

Stephen Dolan
Ard-Na-Sool
Ballindrait
Lifford Co. Donegal
Phone: 074-45244 Fax: 074-45244
SIC: 27520 Employees: 25
Scaffolding & Formwork
Mr Stephen Dolan Proprietor

Fabricated Metal Manufacture

28	**Fabricated Metal Manufacture**
28000	Finished Metal Products
28100	Engineered Products
28110	Fabricated Steelwork
28400	Process Plant Fabrications
28510	Metals Heat & Surface Treated
28520	General Mechanical Engineering
28600	Cutlery/Tableware/ Razors
28601	Domestic Utensils (Metal)
28620	Hand Tools/ Implements
28701	Metal Doors/ Windows/etc
28702	Metal Furniture
28709	Metal Products (Other)
28710	Metal Storage Vessels
28720	Metal (Packaging Products)
28730	Wire Products Manufacture
28740	Bolts Rivets Springs Chains

Amari Dublin Ltd
Amari House, Font Hale Business Park
Clondalkin
Dublin 22
Phone: 01-4505300 Fax: 01-4602530
Email: dublin@amari-dublin.com
SIC: 28000 Employees: 36
Metal & Plastic Stockholders
Mr Robin Malcolm Managing Director
Mr Adam Thompson Financial Director
Mr Declan Kearns Sales & Marketing Manager
Mr Robert Billings Quality Assurance Manager

Baco Metal Centres Dublin
Unit 500, Beech Road
Western Industrial Estate
Dublin 12
Phone: 01-4562511 Fax: 01-4602150
Email: bacodublin@hotmail.com
SIC: 28000 Employees: 33
Metal Stockholders
Mr Dennis Mitchell Managing Director
Mr Michael Beatty Sales Manager

Diesenvale Engineering Ltd
Killmallock Road
Charleville
Cork Co. Cork
Phone: 063-89795 Fax: 063-89862
Email: dve@eircom.net
SIC: 28000 Employees: 28
Stainless Steel Vessels
Mr Eddie Biggane Managing Director
Ms Mary Guiney Finance Manager
Ms Irene White Personnel Manager
Mr Denis Biggane Production Manager

Flexi Fabrication Ltd
U 2B Knockmitten Industrial Estate
Naas Road
Dublin 12
Phone: 01-4568182 Fax: 01-4564553
Email: flexifab@indigo.ie
SIC: 28000 Employees: 45
Metal Fabrication
Ms Susan Maguire Managing Director
Ms Belinda McDermott Personnel Manager
Mr Tony Keating Sales Manager
Mr Vincent Cahill Production Manager

HNK
Cherry Orchard Industrial Estate
Dublin 10
Phone: 01-6055403 Fax: 01-6055466
Web: http://www.hki.com
SIC: 28000 Employees: 100
Manufacturing Stainless Steel
Mr David Bobbett Managing Director
Ms Anne-Marie Miskella Personnel Director
Mr Keith Cassidy Sales & Marketing Manager
Mr Michael Reidy Computer Manager

MI Flues
U 5/6 Summerhill Enterprise Centre
Summerhill
Navan Co. Meath
Phone: 0405-58030 Fax: 0405-58034
Email: miflues@eircom.net
Web: http://www.miflues.net
SIC: 28000 Employees: 34
Manufacture Flues
Mr Jim McNally Manager
Ms Ann-Marie McCooey Financial Controller
Mr Vincent Kavanagh Sales Manager

Taras Manufacturing Ltd
Finisklin Industrial Estate
Sligo Co. Sligo
Phone: 071-61101 Fax: 071-61105
SIC: 28000 Employees: 40
Tubular Steel Products
Mr Michael McGoldrick Manager
Mr Padraic McGowan Finance Manager
Ms Kathleen Harte Company Secretary

ATA Tools & Abrasives
Clones Road
Belturbet Co. Cavan
Phone: 049-9522860 Fax: 049-9522861
Email: ata@eircom.net
Web: http://www.atatools.ie
SIC: 28100 Employees: 30
Rotary Disks, Belts & Bands
Mr Barry Smyth Managing Director
Ms Annette Smyth Office Manager
Mr Paul Gilsenan Production Manager

BCD Engineering & Trading Ltd
Railway Road
Charleville
Cork Co. Cork
Phone: 063-81414 Fax: 063-89879
Email: engineering@bcd.iol.ie
SIC: 28100 Employees: 230
Manufacture Metal Products & Engineering
Mr John McMahon Managing Director
Mr Seamus Lynam Financial Controller
Mr Eoghan O'Donnell Business Development Manager
Mr Tom Walsh Operations Manager

Bellurgan Precision Engineering Ltd
Bellurgan Point
Dundalk Co. Louth
Phone: 042-9380171 Fax: 042-9371761
Email: info@bellurgan.com
SIC: 28100 Employees: 40
Engineering Company Manufacturer of Precision Machine Parts
Ms Suzanne Carroll Managing Director
Ms Alison Carroll Finance Manager
Mr Derek Roddy Sales Manager
Mr Andrew Carroll Production Manager

CL Precision Engineering Ltd
Racecourse Road
Roscommon Co. Roscommon
Phone: 0903-26280 Fax: 0903-30970
Web: http://www.clprecisionengineering.com
SIC: 28100 Employees: 25
Injection Moulds
Mr Louis Conlon Managing Director
Ms MaryJo Conlon Finance Director
Mr Brian Murphy Engineering Manager

Metals Manufacture

Dickson Bearings & Transmitions Ltd
Unit 7 Northern Cross Business Park
North Road
Dublin 11
Phone: 01-8443000 Fax: 01-8443050
Email: sales@dicksonbearings.ie
Web: http://www.dicksonbearings.ie
SIC: 28100 Employees: 25
Engineering
Mr Derek Dickson Managing Director

Ellickson Engineering Ltd
Kilmurry
Waterford Co. Waterford
Phone: 051-832316 Fax: 051-832907
Email: servicewat@ellickson.ie
Web: http://www.ellickson.ie
SIC: 28100 Employees: 80
Engineered Products
Mr John Brennan Managing Director
Mr Steve Hennessey Accounts Department
Mr Michael Keane Personnel Manager
Mr Paul Carol Sales Co-ordinator

Europlex Technologies
Clonshaugh Industrial Estate
Clonshaugh
Dublin 17
Phone: 01-2500500 Fax: 01-2500590
Email: info@europlex.ie
Web: http://www.europlex.ie
SIC: 28100 Employees: 120
Manufacture Building Control Systems
Mr Mike Brosnan Managing Director
Mr Adrian Kelehan Finance Director
Mr Giles Callan International Sales
Mr Sean Carroll Production Manager

Glanmire Precision Co Ltd
Glanmire Business Park
Cork Co. Cork
Phone: 021-4866290 Fax: 021-4866002
Email: glanmireprecision@eircom.net
SIC: 28100 Employees: 30
Engineered Products
Mr Gerry O'Connell Managing Director

Graepel Perforators & Weavers Ltd
Barrack Green
Kinsale Co. Cork
Phone: 021-4772105 Fax: 021-4772005
Email: graepel@indigo.ie
SIC: 28100 Employees: 50
Engineering Contractors
Ms Annette Graepel Managing Director

HR Holfeld Group
2-4 Merville Road
Stillorgan
Blackrock Co. Dublin
Phone: 01-2887361 Fax: 01-2887380
SIC: 28100 Employees: 30
Engineered Products/Pumps/Spares
Mr Richard Holfeld Managing Director
Mr Frank Guilfoyle Operations Director

Kilkenny Cooling Systems Ltd
Hebron Industrial Estate
Hebron Road
Kilkenny Co. Kilkenny
Phone: 056-22913 Fax: 056-62772
SIC: 28100 Employees: 55
Engineering Company
Mr William Smee Managing Director
Mr Stephen O'Connor Finance Manager
Ms Anne Smee Sales & Marketing Manager

Killala Precision Components Ltd
Woodlands Industrial Estate
Killala
Ballina Co. Mayo
Phone: 096-32255 Fax: 096-32306
Email: kpc@iol.ie
Web: http://www.killala.precision.com
SIC: 28100 Employees: 62
Engineering Parts
Mr Sean Hannick Managing Director
Ms Deirdre Irwin Financial Controller
Mr Noel McCabe Sales Manager

Lenehan Engineering Ltd
Old Cork Road
Mallow Co. Cork
Phone: 022-21268 Fax: 022-21855
Email: lenchem@eircom.net
SIC: 28100 Employees: 24
General Engineering
Mr Paddy Lenehan Managing Director

Newtowngore Engineering Ltd
Newtowngore
Carrick On Shannon Co. Leitrim
Phone: 049-4333232 Fax: 049-4333262
SIC: 28100 Employees: 24
Engineering Products
Mr PJ Duignan Proprietor

Oldenberg Engineering Ltd
Unit 2005 Orchard Avenue
City West Business Park
Dublin 24
Phone: 01-4136200 Fax: 01-4571325
SIC: 28100 Employees: 100
Engineered Products
Mr Maurice Moynihan Managing Director
Mr Michael Broderick Sales & Marketing Manager

Perenco Ltd
Unit F Croke Park Industrial Estate
Russell Street
Dublin 1
Phone: 01-8363377 Fax: 01-8363608
Email: info@perenco.ie
Web: http://www.perenco.ie
SIC: 28100 Employees: 30
Industrial Engineering & Safety Supplies
Mr James Stowe Joint Managing Director
Ms Adrienne Thornton Accounts Manager
Ms Imelda Dempsey Personnel Manager
Mr Derek Murphy Sales Manager
Mr Paul Casserly IT Manager

Prism Engineering Ltd
19 Ballymount Road
Walkinstown
Dublin 12
Phone: 01-6273332 Fax: 01-4565426
Email: prismeng@indigo.ie
SIC: 28100 Employees: 40
Engineering Sheet Metal
Mr Pat Garvey Managing Director
Ms Liza Alldritt Accounts Manager

Proscon Ltd
Rushbrooke Park
Cobh Co. Cork
Phone: 021-4811802 Fax: 021-4811804
Email: info@proscon.com
Web: http://www.proscon.com
SIC: 28100 Employees: 175
Engineered Products
Mr Niall Foley Managing Director
Ms Roisin O'Sullivan Financial Controller
Mr Declan O'Grady Sales & Marketing Manager
Mr Don Shane Computer Manager

Radley Engineering Ltd
PO Box 22 Killadangan
Dungarvan Co. Waterford
Phone: 058-41181 Fax: 058-42169
Email: info@radleyeng.ie
Web: http://www.radleyeng.ie
SIC: 28100 Employees: 220
Engineering Company
Mr Brendan Moloney General Manager

Snapon Equipment
Unit B1, Boland Industrial Estate
Mallow Road
Cork Co. Cork
Phone: 021-4211600 Fax: 021-4211601
Email: info@snapon.ie
SIC: 28100 Employees: 50
Engineering Company
Mr John Brennan Managing Director

Speedline Engineering
Unit 1& 2 Enterprise Centre
Moyross
Limerick Co. Limerick
Phone: 061-452102 Fax: 061-452016
Email: speedline@tinet.ie
Web: http://www.speedline.ie
SIC: 28100 Employees: 23
General Engineering
Mr Bart O'Halloran Manager
Mr Ray O'Halloran Sales Manager

Tara Stainless Engineering Ltd
Durhanstown
Bohermeen
Navan Co. Meath
Phone: 046-27599 Fax: 046-28228
Email: tarastain@eircom.ie
SIC: 28100 Employees: 23
Engineering
Mr Tom O'Reilly Managing Director

Tucks Ltd
Unit 9 Hume Avenue
Park West Industrial Park
Dublin 12
Phone: 01-6215555 Fax: 01-6215566
Email: info@tucks.ie
Web: http://www.tucks.ie
SIC: 28100 Employees: 40
Engineering Products
Mr Eamon O'Daly Managing Director
Mr Tony Gavagan IT Manager

Wavemaster Ltd
Rathcairn
Athboy
Navan Co. Meath
Phone: 046-32243 Fax: 046-32226
Email: info@wavemaster.ie
Web: http://www.wavemaster.ie
SIC: 28100 Employees: 70
Engineering
Mr Joe Coffey Managing Director
Mr Terry Nolan Director

Cashel's Engineering Ltd
Aghamore
Ballyhaunis Co. Mayo
Phone: 0907-30517 Fax: 0907-30214
Email: cashels@iol.ie
SIC: 28110 Employees: 40
Fabricated Steelwork
Mr Peter Cunnane General Manager
Mr Matt Basin Accountant

Metals Manufacture

Cisco Ltd
Industrial Estate
Donore Road
Drogheda Co. Louth
Phone: 041-9831445 Fax: 041-9833182
Email: info@cisco.ie
Web: http://www.cisco.ie
SIC: 28110 Employees: 25
Fabricated Steelwork
Mr Patrick Carolan Managing Director

Cronin Buckley Fabrications
Killumney
Ovens
Cork Co. Cork
Phone: 021-4870017 Fax: 021-4872890
SIC: 28110 Employees: 100
Fabricated Steelwork
Mr Dan Buckley Managing Director
Ms Margaret O'Sullivan Finance Manager
Mr Gerard Tangney Production Manager
Mr Aidan Murphy IT Manager

F & S Engineering
Liscarton Industrial Estate
Kells Road
Navan Co. Meath
Phone: 046-23043 Fax: 046-23046
Email: fandsengineering@eircom.net
SIC: 28110 Employees: 38
Structural Steel Engineers - Manufacture & Installation
Mr Noel Fitzsimons Managing Director
Ms Noreen Varley Financial Controller
Mr James Tully General Manager

FDK Engineering Services Ltd
Ballaghaderreen
Castlerea Co. Roscommon
Phone: 0907-60175 Fax: 0907-60326
Email: fdk@iol.ie
SIC: 28110 Employees: 32
Stainless Steel Fabrication
Mr Peter Cassidy General Manager
Mr Michael Kenny Sales Manager

Irish Fencing Ltd
Kylemore Park South
Ballyfermot
Dublin 10
Phone: 01-6268363 Fax: 01-6262309
Email: irfen@indigo.ie
Web: http://www.irishfencing.com
SIC: 28110 Employees: 45
Steel Fencing Manufacturing
Mr Terry Hobdell Managing Director
Mr John Behan Finance Manager
Mr Shane Winters General Manager

Kiernan Structural Steel Ltd
Carrigglas
Longford Co. Longford
Phone: 043-41445 Fax: 043-45904
Email: fkll@tinet.ie
SIC: 28110 Employees: 34
Fabricated Steelwork
Mr Frank Kiernan Managing Director
Ms Dolores Kiernan Company Secretary
Ms Caroline Kilcoine Sales Manager

Lister Tubes Ltd
Ballymount Road
Clondalkin
Dublin 22
Phone: 01-4050300 Fax: 01-4567084
SIC: 28110 Employees: 75
Steel Piping
Mr John Troup Managing Director
Mr Leonard Brown Financial Controller
Mr Michael Lowe Marketing Manager
Mr John Sheridan Production Manager

Master Engineering Ltd
Unit 9 Little Island Industrial Est
Cork Co. Cork
Phone: 021-4354026 Fax: 021-4354486
Email: masterengineering@tinet.ie
SIC: 28110 Employees: 23
Stainless Steel Fabrication
Mr John O'Flynn Joint Managing Director
Ms Cathy Steele Office Manager
Mr Michael O'Flynn Production Manager

Noone Engineering Ltd
Old Convent Building
Rathangan
Kildare Co. Kildare
Phone: 045-524469 Fax: 045-524275
Email: nooneengineering@eircom.net
Web: http://www.nooneeng.com
SIC: 28110 Employees: 32
Fabricated Steelwork
Mr Paul Noone Managing Director
Ms Juile Noonan Accounts Manager
Mr Gerry England Sales & Marketing Manager

O'Dwyer Steel
Dundrum
Tipperary Co. Tipperary
Phone: 062-71102 Fax: 062-71412
Email: info@odwyersteel.ie
SIC: 28110 Employees: 90
Fabricated Steelwork
Mr John Hunt Managing Director
Mr Sean Dalton Company Accountant
Mr Pat Ryan Production Manager
Ms Breda Ryan Creditors Clerk

PSV Fabrication Ltd
Long Mile Road
Drimnagh
Dublin 12
Phone: 01-4503566 Fax: 01-4508662
Email: psv@psv.ie
Web: http://www.psv.ie
SIC: 28110 Employees: 40
Metal Fabrications
Mr Paul Darmody Director
Ms Alice Blanchfield Financial Controller
Mr David Duffy Sales Engineer
Mr Noel Maguire Deputy Manager

SF Engineering
Grange
Sligo Co. Sligo
Phone: 071-63334 Fax: 071-63553
Email: sfeng@eircom.net
Web: http://www.sfeng.ie
SIC: 28110 Employees: 25
Fabricated Metal Products
Mr Seamus Farrell Managing Director
Mr Gary Reynolds Financial Controller
Ms Jane Staunton Sales & Marketing Manager

Steelforms Ltd
Oranmore
Galway Co. Galway
Phone: 091-794672 Fax: 091-794866
Email: steelforms@iol.ie
Web: http://www.steelforms.ie
SIC: 28110 Employees: 30
Fabricated Steelwork
Mr Owen McConn Managing Director
Mr Sean Connors Financial Controller

Tuam Engineering Hynes Ltd
Airglooney
Tuam Co. Galway
Phone: 093-24770 Fax: 093-24750
Email: info@tuamengineering.com
Web: http://www.tuamengineering.com
SIC: 28110 Employees: 25
Fabricated Steelwork
Ms Sinead Hynes Managing Director

Valley Forge Ltd
Drumnasilla
Ravensdale
Dundalk Co. Louth
Phone: 042-9371586 Fax: 042-9371285
Email: valleyforge@eircom.net
SIC: 28110 Employees: 25
Sheet Metal & Brass Fabrication
Mr Ken Stewart Managing Director
Mr Frank McQuaid Personnel Director
Mr John Stewart Production Manager

Velox Ltd
Grattan Hill
Lower Glanmire Road
Cork Co. Cork
Phone: 021-4501279 Fax: 021-4501004
Email: velox@eircom.net
SIC: 28110 Employees: 25
Fabricated Steelwork
Mr Dermot Casey Managing Director

WI Ltd
Jamestown Road
Finglas
Dublin 11
Phone: 01-8342222 Fax: 01-8343471
Email: wil@iol.ie
SIC: 28110 Employees: 30
Fabricated Steelwork
Mr Martin McEvoy Managing Director
Mr Tim O'Neill Marketing Manager
Mr Sam Griffiths Production Manager

Irish Chrome Industries Ltd
Unit 1B Cookstown Industrial Estate
Tallaght
Dublin 24
Phone: 01-4624477 Fax: 01-4624495
Email: status@indigo.ie
Web: http://www.ststua.ire.ie
SIC: 28510 Employees: 40
Electroplating
Mr Hugh Hannigan Managing Director
Mr Derek Byrne Sales Director

Irish Finishing Technologies
35/38 Ballybane Ind Estate
Galway Co. Galway
Phone: 091-756360 Fax: 091-773363
Email: ift@indigo.ie
SIC: 28510 Employees: 40
Metals Heat & Surface Treated
Mr Ollie Burgin General Manager
Ms Lorraine Harrison Finance Manager
Mr James Allison Operation Manager

Irish Pioneer Works
Kinsale Road
Cork Co. Cork
Phone: 021-4964299 Fax: 021-4964110
Email: pioneerw@iol.ie
SIC: 28510 Employees: 50
Galvanising & Fabricators
Mr Michael Roche Managing Director
Mr Matt Twomey Sales Manager

Whyte & Son Ltd
Dromiskin Road
Castlebellingham
Dundalk Co. Louth
Phone: 042-9372365 Fax: 042-9372464
Email: vwhyte@iol.ie
SIC: 28510 Employees: 23
Galvanised Gutters
Mr Victor Whyte Managing Director
Ms Georgina Whyte Finance Director
Mr Kevin Magee Sales Manager
Ms Sandra Byrne Computing

Metals Manufacture

Automation & Tooling Specialist Ltd
Unit 11a Westlink Park
Wilton
Cork Co. Cork
Phone: 021-4345598 Fax: 021-4345605
Email: info@a.t.sltd.com
Web: http://www.a.t.sltd.com
SIC: 28520 Employees: 25
Toolmakers
Mr David Coleman Managing Director
Mr John Mullins Finance Manager
Mr Ann McKeown Personnel Manager
Mr Kieran Redican Sales Manager
Mr Paddy Troy Computer Manager

Carrig Engineering
68 Dames Street
Dublin 2
Phone: 01-6715777 Fax: 01-6715544
Web: http://www.carrig.ie
SIC: 28520 Employees: 39
Building & Energy Conservation
Mr Peter Cox Managing Director
Ms Vera Cox Sales Manager

Overland Bolling
Showgrounds Road
Ennis Co. Clare
Phone: 065-6820497 Fax: 065-6820879
SIC: 28520 Employees: 55
Integrated Manufacturer
Mr Seamus Bowe Plant Manager
Mr Seamus Foley European General Manager

Smithstown Light Engineering
Bay H1A Smithstown Industrial Estate
Shannon Co. Clare
Phone: 061-362111 Fax: 061-364303
Email: sle@iol.ie
SIC: 28520 Employees: 59
Tool Jig Fixtures
Mr Brian King Managing Director
Ms Marie Mulrennan Financial Controller
Mr P J Phillips Production Director
Ms Colette Murphy Process Engineer

Newbridge Cutlery Company
Cutlery Road
Newbridge Co. Kildare
Phone: 045-431301 Fax: 045-432759
Email: newbrcut@indigo.ie
SIC: 28600 Employees: 60
Cutlery
Mr William Doyle Managing Director
Ms Mary Cahir Finance Manager
Ms Noelle Graham Sales Manager
Mr Dominic Doody Production Manager

Ace Tool Supplies Ltd
114 Boyne Road
Glasnevin
Dublin 11
Phone: 01-8308766 Fax: 01-8308640
SIC: 28620 Employees: 50
Manufacture Tools
Mr Kevin Smith Manager

Heycowerk Ltd
Bonree Road
Ballina Co. Mayo
Phone: 096-70444 Fax: 096-70259
Email: info@heycowerkireland.ie
Web: http://www.heyco.ie
SIC: 28620 Employees: 60
Manufactures Tools
Mr Dieter Losleben Managing Director
Mr Kieran Finn Accounts/Commerical Manager
Mr Wolfgang Kurtz Production Manager
Mr Burkhard Killian Computer Supervisor

Imperial Schrade (Europe) Ltd
Imperialstag
Listowel Co. Kerry
Phone: 068-21066 Fax: 068-22155
Email: info@imperialschcrade.ie
Web: http://www.imperialschcrade.ie
SIC: 28620 Employees: 110
Pocket Knives
Mr Henrick Weber General Manager
Ms Hannah Mulvihill Accounts Manager
Ms Joan Horgan Commerical Manager
Mr Matt Wolf Sales Manager

True Temper
6 Coole East
White Cross
Cork Co. Cork
Phone: 021-4302433 Fax: 021-4304621
Email: info@truetemper.ie
Web: http://www.truetemper.ie
SIC: 28620 Employees: 60
Manufacturing Tools Company
Mr Domnall MacDomhmaill Managing Director
Mr Sean O'Mahony Finance Manager
Mr Dermot O'Brien Plant Engineer

Carrabine Joinery
Sligo Road
Ballina Co. Mayo
Phone: 096-22147 Fax: 096-70366
Email: carjoin@eircom.net
SIC: 28701 Employees: 30
Manufacture Metal Doors & Windows
Mr Joe Carrabine Proprietor

Door Fix Ltd
Unit 11 Hume Avenue
Park West Industrial Park
Dublin 12
Phone: 01-6207000 Fax: 01-6207060
Email: doorfix@eolais.ie
SIC: 28701 Employees: 28
Industrial Doors & Shutters
Mr Miceal Beatty Managing Director
Ms Margaret McDonald Accounts Manager
Mr Richard Garrigan Sales Manager
Mr Tom Bealin Production Manager

Futura Frames
Lauragh
Bandon Co. Cork
Phone: 023-43870 Fax: 023-43876
Email: info@futuraframes.iol.ie
Web: http://www.futuraframes.iol.ie
SIC: 28701 Employees: 60
Manufacturing Windows
Mr John Crowley Proprietor

Marine Terminals Ltd
South Bank Quay
Pigeon House Road
Dublin 4
Phone: 01-6670588 Fax: 01-6670620
Email: info@mtl.ie
Web: http://www.mtl.ie
SIC: 28701 Employees: 38
Container Steel Doors
Mr John Forrester Managing Director
Mr Michael Malone Finance Manager
Mr Gerry Lucan Marketing Manager

Ring Gard Roller Shutters & Doors
Ring Gard House
Baldoyle Industrial Estate
Dublin 13
Phone: 01-8322731 Fax: 01-8391274
Email: info@ring-gard.ie
SIC: 28701 Employees: 160
Manufacture of Roller Shutters
Mr Brian Woodford Managing Director
Mr Gerard Newe Finance Manager
Ms Aileen Dowdall Sales & Marketing Manager

Senator Windows
Seaview Industrial Estate
Wexford Co. Wexford
Phone: 053-41522 Fax: 053-41526
Email: info@senatorwindows.com
Web: http://www.senatorwindows.com
SIC: 28701 Employees: 1500
Manufacture Windows/Doors/Conservatories
Mr Noel McSweeney Managing Director
Mr John Doran Finance Manager
Mr Michael Ward Sales & Marketing Manager
Mr Peter Lambert Production Manager

Skelly Doors
U3 Ballymount Drive Industrial Est
Ballymount
Dublin 24
Phone: 01-4502829 Fax: 01-4502799
Web: http://www.skellydoors.ie
SIC: 28701 Employees: 36
Steel Door Manufacturers
Mr David Skelly Managing Director
Mr Alan Flynn Sales Director

Walsh Aluminium (Sales) Ltd
Crossagalla
Ballysimon Road
Limerick Co. Limerick
Phone: 061-412823 Fax: 061-414626
SIC: 28701 Employees: 35
Window Sashes Frames Metal
Mr James Walsh Managing Director
Ms Ann Walsh Finance Manager
Mr John Walsh Sales Manager

Alfrank Design Ltd
Brickfields Lane
Cork Street
Dublin 8
Phone: 01-4540209 Fax: 01-4539099
SIC: 28702 Employees: 52
Manufacture of Metal Furniture
Mr Frank Carroll Managing Director
Mr Patrick O'Connell Finance Manager
Ms Kate Byrne Customer Services Manager
Ms Clodagh Whelan Projects Manager
Mr Dave Neacy Production Manager

Castleblayney Steel Products Ltd
Muckno Street
Castleblayney Co. Monaghan
Phone: 042-9740106 Fax: 042-9740982
SIC: 28702 Employees: 40
Steel Furniture Manufacturer
Mr Michael Byrne Proprietor
Mr Gerry Aiken Sales & Marketing Manager

Ringshield
Greenhills Industrial Estate
Walkinstown
Dublin 12
Phone: 01-4601133 Fax: 01-4601727
Email: rinshld@indigo.ie
SIC: 28702 Employees: 25
Lockers
Mr Gerard Newell Managing Director

Fabricated Products Shannon
Smithstown Industrial Estate
Shannon Co. Clare
Phone: 061-362744 Fax: 061-362267
Email: systemsadministrator@fabricated-products.com
Web: http://www.fabricated-products.com
SIC: 28709 Employees: 120
Fabricated Metal Products
Mr Michael MacDonagh Managing Director
Mr Kieran Keating Financial Controller
Ms Pauline Hayes Personnel Manager
Mr Mike Brown Sales & Marketing Manager
Mr Gerry Crossan Computer Manager

Metals Manufacture

Farran Technology Ltd
Ballincollig
Cork Co. Cork
Phone: 021-4872814 Fax: 021-4873892
Email: sales@farran.com
Web: http://www.farran.com
SIC: 28709 Employees: 25
Millimetre-Wave Components & Subsystems
Mr Tony McEnroe General Manager
Dr David Vizard Sales & Marketing Manager

John Davis Design
Wallingstown
Little Island
Cork Co. Cork
Phone: 021-4353903 Fax: 021-4354445
Email: jdd@eircom.net
Web: http://www.johndavisdesign.ie
SIC: 28709 Employees: 120
Manufacture of Aluminium Profiles for Shower Enclosures
Mr Michael Scannell General Manager
Ms Susan Lennon Sales Manager

Lynfar Company
Kylemore Park North
Ballyfermot
Dublin 10
Phone: 01-6260633 Fax: 01-6260973
Email: info@lynfar.iol.ie
SIC: 28709 Employees: 65
Sheet Metal Fabrication
Mr Frank Lynch Managing Director
Mr Barry Connell Finance Manager

Offian Ltd
Ballyvourney Industrial Park
Ballyvourney
Macroom Co. Cork
Phone: 026-45333 Fax: 026-45358
SIC: 28709 Employees: 44
Metals
Mr Tomas Lagerqvist Managing Director
Ms Niamh Murphy Sales & Marketing Manager
Mr Steven Sels Production Manager

Ohshima Ireland Ltd
Clonshaugh Industrial Estate
Coolock
Dublin 17
Phone: 01-8484666 Fax: 01-8036158
Email: info@ohshima.ie
Web: http://www.ohshima.ie
SIC: 28709 Employees: 85
Manufacture Stainless Steel Components
Mr Ted Hurley Managing Director
Mr Kevin Carroll Finance Manager
Mr Maurice Devlin Purchasing Manager
Mr Steven Tormey Engineering Manager

P Carney Ltd
Crossakiel
Kells Co. Meath
Phone: 046-43634 Fax: 046-43916
Email: pcarneyltd@eircom.net
SIC: 28709 Employees: 55
Metal Manufacturer
Mr Jim McCabe Managing Director

PGM Ballscrews Ireland Ltd
Tallaght Business Park, Whitestown Indust E
Tallaght
Dublin 24
Phone: 01-4628101 Fax: 01-4629080
Email: info@pgm-irl.ie
Web: http://www.pgm-irl.ie
SIC: 28709 Employees: 25
Manufacture Ballscrews
Ms Anne Madsen Managing Director

R R Elliott Engineering Ltd
Denhu Complex
Walkinstown Avenue
Dublin 12
Phone: 01-4505954 Fax: 01-4503890
SIC: 28709 Employees: 27
Sheet Metal Manufacturers & Air Conditioning
Mr Ray Elliott Managing Director

Rexan Bebarate Can Ireland Ltd
Industrial Park
Cork Road
Waterford Co. Waterford
Phone: 051-372137 Fax: 051-378892
SIC: 28709 Employees: 144
Can End Manufacture
Mr Bernard Brown Plant Manager
Mr Fergal O'Brien Financial Controller

Sheet Metal Industries Ltd
Monavalley Industrial Estate
Monavalley
Tralee Co. Kerry
Phone: 066-7121466 Fax: 066-7122133
SIC: 28709 Employees: 25
Metal Products Manufacturing
Mr William Fealy Managing Director
Mr Edward Stack Accountant

Tente Ltd
Balymote
Sligo Co. Sligo
Phone: 071-83414 Fax: 071-83147
Email: tir@tenete.ie
Web: http://www.tente.com
SIC: 28709 Employees: 100
Manufacture Castors & Wheels
Mr Robert Wallace Managing Director
Mr John Stewart Financial Controller
Mr Liam King Sales & Marketing Manager
Mr Peter Leonard Production Manager

Container & Pressure Vessels
Clones
Monaghan Co. Monaghan
Phone: 047-51090 Fax: 047-51616
Email: sales@cpv.ie
Web: http://www.cpv.ie
SIC: 28710 Employees: 120
Stainless Steel
Mr Martin Laverty Managing Director
Ms Maureen Redmond Financial Controller
Mr Vincent McKenna Production Manager
Ms Breige Cooper Sales Co-Ordinator
Mr Seamus Murchan Factory Manager
Mr Thomas Quigley Technical Director

Corrugated Containers Ireland Ltd
Beechmount Industrial Estate
Navan Co. Meath
Phone: 046-27726 Fax: 046-22380
Email: cti@eircom.net
SIC: 28720 Employees: 150
Corrugated Containers & Packaging
Mr Pat O'Reilly General Manager
Mr Sean Brennan Finance Manager
Mr Fra Nolan Sales & Marketing Manager

Killeen Corrugated Products Ltd
Killeen Road
Dublin 12
Phone: 01-4503011 Fax: 01-4508479
Email: postmaster@kcp.ie
Web: http://www.kcp.ie
SIC: 28720 Employees: 125
Corrugated Packaging Manufacturer
Mr Tony O'Connor Chief Executive
Mr John O'Callaghan Financial Director
Mr Seamus Walsh Sales Manager
Ms Josephine Campion Systems Manager

Multi Storage
Donabate
Swords Co. Dublin
Phone: 01-8435123 Fax: 01-8436055
Email: racking@iol.ie
SIC: 28720 Employees: 25
Storage Equipment & Mezzanine Floors
Mr Chris Murtagh Managing Director
Mr Keith Murtagh Finance Director
Mr Rory Murtagh Sales Director

Alida Systems Ltd
IDA Industrial Estate
Coolcower
Macroom Co. Cork
Phone: 026-41329 Fax: 026-41851
Email: alida@iol.ie
Web: http://www.foundmark.com/alida.hpml
SIC: 28730 Employees: 35
Wire & Cable Processing
Ms Pauline Kearns Managing Director
Ms Liz McSweeney Accounts Manager
Ms Margaret O'Shea Production Supervisor
Mr Dennis McCarthy Marketing Manager
Ms Margaret O'Shea Production Supervisor

Printing Wire Supplies/GBC
IDA Business Park, Poppintree
Finglas
Dublin 11
Phone: 01-8361744 Fax: 01-8361559
Email: info@gbcie.com
SIC: 28730 Employees: 50
Double loop binding Wire Specialists
Mr Richard Morris General Manager
Ms Margaret Deegan Sales & Marketing Manager
Mr Denis Morris Production Manager

Basta Hardware Ltd
Tubbercurry
Sligo Co. Sligo
Phone: 071-85032 Fax: 071-85439
Email: basta@indigo.ie
SIC: 28740 Employees: 108
Lock Manufacturing
Mr Kevin Norton Chief Executive
Ms Patricia Holton Finance Manager
Ms Susan Kelly Sales & Marketing Manager
Mr Pauric Morrin Production Manager

Ireland Woco Components
Tullyleague
Carrick On Shannon Co. Leitrim
Phone: 078-20385 Fax: 078-20922
Email: irishrubber.irc@wocr.de
SIC: 28740 Employees: 75
Industrial Components
Mr James Cooke Acting Plant Manager
Mr Cormac McCormack Financial Controller

MacB Ltd
Unit 3-4 Glanmire Industrial Estate
Glanmire
Cork Co. Cork
Phone: 021-4866733 Fax: 021-4866742
Email: macb@macb.ie
Web: http://www.macb.ie
SIC: 28740 Employees: 40
Fasteners & Electronic Hardware
Mr Domhnall Mac A'Bhaird Managing Director
Mr Kevin O'Donovan Finance Manager
Mr Peter Fitzgerald General Manager
Mr Mervyn Judge Operation Manager
Mr Anthony O'Brien IT Manager

NN Euroball Ireland Ltd
Unit 4, IDA Industrial Estate
Purcellsinch
Kilkenny Co. Kilkenny
Phone: 056-71000 Fax: 056-71007
Email: info@nneuroball.com
SIC: 28740 Employees: 80
Making Provision Balls for Bearings
Mr Gearoid McDermot Financial Controller
Mr Andy Power Manager

Precision Steel Components Ltd
Mervue Industrial Estate
Galway Co. Galway
Phone: 091-751714 Fax: 091-753541
SIC: 28740 Employees: 90
Manufacture Specialised Components
Mr Charles Coughlan Managing Director
Mr Patrick Gilligan Company Accountant
Ms Mary-Ann Fergus Commercial Manager
Mr Tom Byrne Production Manager
Mr James Tiviney Technical Manager

Shannon Coiled Springs Ltd
Crossagalla Industrial Estate
Ballysimon Road
Limerick Co. Limerick
Phone: 061-311666 Fax: 061-310830
Email: scspring@iol.ie
SIC: 28740 Employees: 35
Springs & Wire Shapes
Mr John Walsh Managing Director
Ms Shirley Mullane Finance Manager
Mr Eammon Barrett Sales & Marketing Manager

Machinery & Equipment Manufacture

29 Machinery & Equipment Manufacture
29000 Filtration & Purification Equipment
29100 Commercial Machinery (Other)
29101 Mech/Marine/Precision Engineering
29120 Pumps
29130 Industrial Valves
29140 Ball/Needle/Roller Bearings
29200 General Machinery Manufacture
29220 Lifting/Handling Equipment
29230 Heat/Vent/Refridge/Air Cond Equipment
29300 Agri/Construction Machinery
29310 Agricultural Tractors Manufacture
29401 Metal-Working Machine Tools
29402 Engineers Small Tools
29409 Fire Prevention Equipment Manufacture
29501 Chemical/Waste Treatment Plant
29502 Gas/Water Treatment Plant
29504 Transmission Equipment
29520 Mining Machinery
29532 Food Pack/Processing Machines
29533 Tobacco Packaging/Processing Machines
29540 Textile Machinery
29550 Printing etc Machinery Manufacture
29560 Portable Power Tools
29600 Ordnance/Small Arms/Ammunition
29710 Electrical Appliances (Home)

All Water Systems Ltd
Unit 2018 Citywest Business Campus
Saggart
Dublin 24
Phone: 01-4660133 Fax: 01-4660134
Web: http://www.aws.ie
SIC: 29000 Employees: 35
Water Cooler Systems
Mr Brian Clooney Managing Director
Mr Ciaran McKenna Sales Manager
Ms Hazel O'Doherty Customer Service Manager

Favourable Trading
19-20, Royal Rock Building
Ballybane Industrial Estate
Galway Co. Galway
Phone: 091-741000 Fax: 091-750041
SIC: 29000 Employees: 60
Water Purification Company
Mr Joseph Guthrie General Manager
Mr Fergus Curley Sales Manager

Filtertek BV
Industrial Estate
Newcastlewest
Limerick Co. Limerick
Phone: 069-62666 Fax: 069-62575
Email: info@filtertek.ie
Web: http://www.filtertek.ie
SIC: 29000 Employees: 100
Filtration for Medical Supplies
Mr John Humphreys General Manager
Mr Jim Burke Financial Controller
Ms Margaret Doherty Sales Manager
Mr Noel Kane Supervisor

Gilroy Automation Ltd
Shanbally
Ringaskiddy
Cork Co. Cork
Phone: 021-4372711 Fax: 021-4378089
Email: custserv@gilroy.com
Web: http://www.gilroys.com
SIC: 29000 Employees: 50
Supply of Filtration Equipment
Mr Fred Gilroy Executive Director
Ms Denise O'Connell Financial Controller
Mr Ronnie Hurley Personnel Officer
Ms Susan Chisholm Sales & Marketing Manager
Mr Martin Hurley Computer Manager

Kinetics Ireland Ltd
Mountrath
Portlaoise Co. Laois
Phone: 0502-56225 Fax: 0502-56222
Email: aramsbottom@kinetics.iol.ie
Web: http://www.kineticsgroup.com
SIC: 29000 Employees: 25
High Purity Piping
Mr Sean Fennell General Manager
Mr Martin Moran Personnel Officer

Medentech
Whitemills Industrial Estate
Wexford Co. Wexford
Phone: 053-60040 Fax: 053-41271
Email: enquiry@medentech.com
SIC: 29000 Employees: 50
Manufacture Water Purification & Disinfectant Tablets
Mr Oliver McAdam Managing Director
Mr Fergus Hilliard Financial Controller
Mr John Hackett Sales Manager

Electronic Cash Registers Ltd
71/73 Cable Street
Dublin 1
Phone: 01-8730577 Fax: 01-8730569
Email: info@ecr-figure.com
Web: http://www.ecr-figure.com
SIC: 29100 Employees: 94
Commercial Machinery
Mr Micheal Dwyer Managing Director

Ingersoll Rand Ltd
Blanchardstown Industrial Park
Dublin 15
Phone: 01-8179487 Fax: 01-8179489
SIC: 29100 Employees: 150
The Sales & Service of Industrial Compressors
Mr David Wolohan Managing Director
Mr Peter Whelan Sales Manager

Looby Bros Ltd
Dublin Road
Johnstown
Kilkenny Co. Kilkenny
Phone: 056-31332 Fax: 056-31410
SIC: 29100 Employees: 30
Commercial Vehicles-Auto Buildings
Mr Liam Looby Managing Director
Mr Pat Looby Sales Director

Mincon International Ltd
Smithstown Industrial Estate
Shannon Co. Clare
Phone: 061-361099 Fax: 061-361808
Email: info@mincon.com
Web: http://www.mincon.com
SIC: 29100 Employees: 50
Rock Drilling Equipment Manufacture
Mr Kevin Barry Managing Director
Ms Mary Tierney Personnel Manager
Mr John O'Dea Production Manager
Mr John Tierney Computer Manager

Pacific Scientific
Gort Road Industrial Estate
Ennis Co. Clare
Phone: 065-6821200 Fax: 065-6829733
Email: info@pacsci.ie
Web: http://www.pacsci.ie
SIC: 29100 Employees: 115
Manufacture of Motors for Machine Industry
Mr Michael Travers Managing Director
Mr Gerry Broderick Financial Controller
Mr Mike Sheehan Production Manager

Pat O'Donnell & Co Ltd
18-20 Richmond Avenue
Fairview
Dublin 3
Phone: 01-8379151 Fax: 01-8372172
Email: info@patodonnell.com
Web: http://www.patodonnell.com
SIC: 29100 Employees: 130
Importers of Heavy Machinery
Mr Patrick O'Donnell Managing Director
Mr Brendan O'Halloran Finance Manager
Mr Christy Cunningham Personnel Manager
Mr Paul Markey Sales Manager
Mr Brian McDonnell IT Manager

Pauwels Trafo Ireland
Dublin Road
Cavan Co. Cavan
Phone: 049-4331588 Fax: 049-4332053
Email: pti@pauwels.com
Web: http://www.pauwels.ie
SIC: 29100 Employees: 350
Transformer Manufacture
Mr James McMahon General Manager
Mr Padraig McCabe Company Accountant
Ms Helen Bennett Human Resources Manager
Mr Rowan O'Reilly Sales Manager
Mr Manu Domen Production Director
Mr John Flanagan Computer Manager

Romaquip Ltd
Singfield
Birr Co. Offaly
Phone: 0509-20836 Fax: 0509-21084
Email: romaquip@eircom.net
SIC: 29100 Employees: 30
Manufacture Machinery
Mr Ray Leonard Managing Director
Ms Fiona Ely Accountant
Mr John McKeown Technical Director

Rothenberger Ireland Ltd
Bay N119
Shannon Industrial Estate
Shannon Co. Clare
Phone: 061-472188 Fax: 061-472436
Email: rothenb@iol.ie
SIC: 29100 Employees: 25
Pipeline Bending Equipment
Mr Christopher Carpenter Managing Director
Mr Gerard Newman Financial Controller
Mr Tom Austin Production Supervisor

Machinery & Equipment

Tucks Fasteners Ltd
East Wall Road
Dublin 3
Phone: 01-8555628 Fax: 01-8555628
SIC: 29100 Employees: 26
Industrial DIY
Mr Michael Haines Managing Director
Mr M Earls General Manager
Mr M McCann Divisional Manager

AGB Scientific
Finnabair Industrial Park
Dundalk Co. Louth
Phone: 042-9339985 Fax: 042-9339987
SIC: 29101 Employees: 400
Precision Tooling - Automotive
Ms Roisin McEntee Managing Director
Mr Connor Berrill Finance Manager
Ms Imelda Matthews Business Administrator
Mr Brendan Baxter IT Manager

Arrowcrest Ltd
221 Holly Road
Western Industrial Estate
Dublin 12
Phone: 01-4503533 Fax: 01-4503561
Email: arrowcrest@indigo.ie
SIC: 29101 Employees: 40
Precision Engineers
Mr Pius Finnegan Proprietor
Mr Raymond Finnegan Sales Manager

Arup Consulting Engineers
10 Wellington Road
Dublin 4
Phone: 01-6144200 Fax: 01-6683169
Email: arup@dublin.com
SIC: 29101 Employees: 300
Engineer Consulting
Mr Donal Hutchinson Proprietor
Mr Noel O'Hara IT Manager

Atlantic Projects Company
18 Longford Terrace
Monkstown
Blackrock Co. Dublin
Phone: 01-2301843 Fax: 01-2301817
Email: postmaster@apc.ie
SIC: 29101 Employees: 100
Mechanical Contractors
Mr William Neenan Managing Director
Mr Paul Seever Financial Controller
Mr David Agnew Personnel Manager
Mr Philip Healey Sales Manager

Auxiliary Chemicals Ltd
Ringaskiddy
Cork Co. Cork
Phone: 021-4311377 Fax: 021-4378950
Email: carbon@iol.ie
SIC: 29101 Employees: 40
Pre-Treatment Chemicals
Mr Brian Walsh Chief Executive
Mr Aidan Brady Finance Manager
Mr Paul Cronin Sales Manager
Mr Pat Gallagher Production Manager

Bolger Engineering Ltd
Smithstown Industrial Estate
Shannon Co. Clare
Phone: 061-362123 Fax: 061-362462
Email: info@bolger-eng.ie
Web: http://www.bolger-eng.ie
SIC: 29101 Employees: 30
Sheet Metal Fabrication
Mr John Bolger Managing Director
Mr Ian Bolger Finance Manager
Mr Graham Bolger Operations Manager

Bonnar Engineering Ltd
Neil T Blaney Road
Letterkenny Co. Donegal
Phone: 074-22256 Fax: 074-24877
Email: enquiries@bonnarengltd.ie
Web: http://www.bonnarengltd.ie
SIC: 29101 Employees: 35
Structural Steelwork & Marine Engineering
Mr Patrick Bonnar Managing Director
Mr Malcolm McCormack Sales Manager
Mr Colm McCormick Production Manager

Byrne Mech Enclosures Systems
Raheen Industrial Estate
Athenry
Galway Co. Galway
Phone: 091-844271 Fax: 091-844677
Email: info@byrnemech.ie
Web: http://www.byrnemech.ie
SIC: 29101 Employees: 90
Modular Enclosure Manu / Data Comm Products / Telecommunications etc
Mr Patrick C Byrne Managing Director
Mr Adrian Tyrell Financial Controller
Mr Seamus Mulkerrins Sales Manager
Mr Malachy Lally Production Manager
Mr Gerry Carroll Engineering Manager

Caragh Tool & Die Ltd
Ballybane Industrial Estate
Galway Co. Galway
Phone: 091-755773 Fax: 091-753832
Email: sales@caragh.ie
Web: http://www.caragh.ie
SIC: 29101 Employees: 50
Precision Engineering
Mr Steven Higgins Managing Director
Mr Edward Kenny Finance Manager
Mr John Farragher Sales & Marketing Manager
Mr Cormac O'Brien Production Manager

Caraher & Ward Ltd
CRV Buildings
Ardee Road
Dundalk Co. Louth
Phone: 042-9339089 Fax: 042-9336784
Email: caraherward@eircom.net
SIC: 29101 Employees: 27
Mechanical/Fabrication/Precision Engineering
Mr Sean Ward Managing Director
Mr Jim Byrne Finance Manager

Clifton Scannell Emerson Association
Seafort Lodge
Castledawson Avenue
Blackrock Co. Dublin
Phone: 01-2885006 Fax: 01-2833466
Email: csea@iol.ie
SIC: 29101 Employees: 32
Consulting Civil Structural Engineers
Mr Geoffrey Emerson Managing Director
Mr Ernie Crean Finance Manager
Mr Aidan Smith Sales Director
Mr Padraic Matthews Computer Manager

Delap & Waller
Bloomfield House
Bloomfield Avenue
Dublin 8
Phone: 01-4534031 Fax: 01-4535975
Email: mail@ewmi.ie
SIC: 29101 Employees: 90
Engineer Consulting
Mr Alex O'Riordain Managing Director

Diamond Engineering Ltd
Gotoon
Kilmallock Co. Limerick
Phone: 063-98276 Fax: 063-98173
Email: info@diamond-engineering.com
SIC: 29101 Employees: 200
Mechanical Engineers
Mr Seamus Buckley Managing Director
Mr Michael Kennedy Finance Manager
Mr Michael Hennesy Sales & Marketing Manager
Mr Dara O'Brien Production Manager

Dornan Engineering
Hexagon House
Little Island
Cork Co. Cork
Phone: 021-4354222 Fax: 021-4354226
Email: kentech@hexagon.ie
Web: http://www.hexagon.ie
SIC: 29101 Employees: 300
Mechanical & Electrical Engineering
Mr Michael Healy Managing Director
Mr John Daly Financial Director
Mr John Kavanagh Personnel Manager
Mr Brian Acheson Sales & Marketing Manager

Dromone Engineering
Dromone
Oldcastle
Kells Co. Meath
Phone: 044-66346 Fax: 044-66236
Email: postmaster@dromone.ie
Web: http://www.dromone.ie
SIC: 29101 Employees: 100
Engineering
Mr Pat McCormick Managing Director
Mr Robert Campbell Financial Controller
Mr Gerry Mahon Sales & Marketing Manager
Mr Jess Dooner Production Manager

E-E-L
14 O'Connell Street
Waterford Co. Waterford
Phone: 051-841880 Fax: 051-841944
Email: eel@eircom.net
Web: http://www.eel.ie
SIC: 29101 Employees: 30
Engineer Constructional
Mr Seamus Tully Managing Director
Ms Catherine Flynn Sales Manager

Edward Buttimer & Company Ltd
Carrigeen Industrial Estate
Cahir Co. Tipperary
Phone: 052-41377 Fax: 052-41087
Email: info@buttimer.ie
Web: http://www.buttimer.ie
SIC: 29101 Employees: 105
Mechanical Engineers
Mr Edward Buttimer Managing Director
Mr Jim O'Connor Personnel Director
Mr Larry Hogan Sales & Marketing Manager

Eirfab Engineers Ltd
Slieverue
Waterford Co. Waterford
Phone: 051-832619 Fax: 051-832164
Email: eirfab@iol.ie
SIC: 29101 Employees: 40
Engineering
Mr John Power Managing Director
Ms Julie Hoynes Accounts Manager

Ellickson Laser Cutting Ltd
Unit 22 IDA Industrial Estate
Cork
Waterford Co. Waterford
Phone: 051-358022 Fax: 051-358023
Email: info@elickson.com
Web: http://www.elickson.com
SIC: 29101 Employees: 25
Laser Cutting
Mr Michael Finnegan Managing Director
Ms Susan Grant Finance Manager

Environmental Engineering Ltd
Fluredell University Technical Park
Currahenn Road, Bishopstown
Cork Co. Cork
Phone: 021-4372231 Fax: 021-4372231
Email: eelcork@iol.ie
Web: http://www.eel.ie
SIC: 29101 Employees: 215
Environmental Engineering
Mr Michael Hennessy Managing Director
Mr John Wilmot Business Development Manager

Machinery & Equipment

Fenelon Manufacturing
Townspark Industrial Estate
Longford Co. Longford
Phone: 043-46846 Fax: 043-41751
Email: fenelon@iol.ie
SIC: 29101 Employees: 170
Mechanical Engineers
Mr Michael Fenelon Managing Director
Mr George Ryan Finance Manager
Mr Michael McGann Sales & Marketing Manager
Mr Aidan Kelly Production Manager
Mr Ray Fenelon IT Manager

FKM Group
FKM Group Head Office
Belgard Road
Dublin 24
Phone: 01-4520077 Fax: 01-4521139
Email: office@fkm.ie
SIC: 29101 Employees: 250
Mechanical Engineering Service
Mr T Sullivan Managing Director
Mr Turlough Flynn Financial Accountant
Mr Patrick Delaney Director of Personnel
Mr Matt Mohan Chief Executive

Gibney Steel Products
Moylagh
Dromone Oldcastle
Kells Co. Meath
Phone: 049-8541302 Fax: 049-8541760
SIC: 29101 Employees: 40
Mech/Marine/Precision Engineering
Mr Oliver Gibney Manager
Ms Catrina Gibney Finance Manager
Mr Felix Reilly Production Director

Hanley Controls Ltd
Monknewtown
Slane
Navan Co. Meath
Phone: 041-9824500 Fax: 041-9824503
Email: sales@hanleycontrols.com
Web: http://www.hanleycontrols.com
SIC: 29101 Employees: 120
Measurement Engineers
Mr Malachy Hanley Chief Executive
Mr Conor Murphy Financial Controller
Mr Padraig Troy Sales Engineer
Mr Noel Killeen Sales Manager

Hitol Ltd
Bay 9 Industrial Estate
Cork Road
Waterford Co. Waterford
Phone: 051-355735 Fax: 051-379394
Email: sales@hitol.com
Web: http://www.hitol.com
SIC: 29101 Employees: 48
Precision Engineering
Mr John Lyons Managing Director
Mr Liam Mernagh Finance Manager
Mr Sean Lyons Sales & Marketing Manager

John Bisset Ltd
South Bank Road
Ringsend
Dublin 4
Phone: 01-6683168 Fax: 01-6683860
SIC: 29101 Employees: 28
Engineering
Mr Tom Joyce General Manager

John F Dunne Engineering Ltd
Jamestown Business Park
Finglas
Dublin 11
Phone: 01-8642496 Fax: 01-8642499
Email: info@jfdeng.com
SIC: 29101 Employees: 28
Engineering
Mr Jack Dunne Managing Director
Ms Orla Dunne Personnel Officer

Kel-Tech Engineering Ltd
IDA Industrial Estate
Waterford Co. Waterford
Phone: 051-377900 Fax: 051-378551
Email: keltech@eircom.net
SIC: 29101 Employees: 60
Precision Sheet Metal Engineering
Mr Ray Breen Managing Director
Ms Ann Walsh Accounts Manager
Mr Pat Goldrick Customer Service Manager
Mr Declan Walsh Production Manager

Kelly Coachbuilding
St John's
Castledermot
Athy Co. Kildare
Phone: 0503-44120 Fax: 0503-44307
Email: kelbo@eircom.net
SIC: 29101 Employees: 40
Engineering Body Building Service
Mr John Kelly Managing Director
Mr Martin Kirwin Accounts Manager

Kent Stainless
Ardcavan Works
Wexford Co. Wexford
Phone: 053-46333 Fax: 053-41802
Email: info@kentstainless.com
Web: http://www.kentstainless.com
SIC: 29101 Employees: 100
Stainless Steel Manufacture
Mr Tony Donegan Managing Director
Mr Michael Clarke Financial Controller
Ms Ann O'Brien Personnel Manager
Mr Peter Edwards Production Manager

Kentz Group
Gortnafluir
Clonmel Co. Tipperary
Phone: 052-22811 Fax: 052-26021
Email: contact@kentz.ie
Web: http://www.kentz.com
SIC: 29101 Employees: 350
Mechanical Electrical Engineering Contractors
Mr Hugh O'Donnell Group Managing Director
Mr Peter Doyle Finance Manager
Ms Mary McGrath Personnel Officer
Mr Bob Greaney Engineering Director

Lapple Ireland Ltd
Dublin Road
Carlow Co. Carlow
Phone: 0503-76100 Fax: 0503-76181
Email: info@laepple.ie
Web: http://www.laepple.ie
SIC: 29101 Employees: 300
Press Tool & Die Manufacture
Mr John Slattery Managing Director
Mr Frank Donnelly Human Resources Manager
Mr John Fleming Estimates Manager
Ms Grainne Kelly IT Manager

Lazer Engineering Ltd
Stamullen
Navan Co. Meath
Phone: 01-8412690 Fax: 01-8412002
Email: lazer@eircom.net
SIC: 29101 Employees: 50
Mech/Marine/Precision Engineering
Mr John Sullivan Manager
Mr David Kierans Sales Manager

LMH Engineering
Croghan Industrial Estate
Arklow Co. Wicklow
Phone: 0402-32719 Fax: 0402-39981
Email: lmheng@eircom.net
SIC: 29101 Employees: 40
Mechanical & Structural Engineering
Mr Myles Fenlon Managing Director
Mr Sean O'Neill Sales Director

Loredo Ltd
Unit 120 Ashbourne Industrial Estate
Ashbourne
Navan Co. Meath
Phone: 01-8351784 Fax: 01-8351982
Web: http://www.loredo.ie
SIC: 29101 Employees: 47
Engineering
Mr Colm O'Farrell Managing Director
Mr Ray O'Farrell Finance Manager
Mr Bosco O'Farrell Sales & Marketing Manager

M & K Engineering Ltd
Unit 53 Baldoyle Industrial Estate
Dublin 13
Phone: 01-8390478 Fax: 01-8326896
Email: mkengineering@eircom.net
SIC: 29101 Employees: 50
Engineering Company
Mr Frank Kavanagh Managing Director
Ms Kay Murphy Office Manager

Marine Technical & Development Services Ltd
Parkmore Business Park West
Galway Co. Galway
Phone: 091-773980 Fax: 091-773982
Email: martech@indigo.ie
SIC: 29101 Employees: 24
Marine Engineering
Mr John O'Sullivan Managing Director

McSharry Bros Plant Sales
Four Mile House
Roscommon Co. Roscommon
Phone: 0903-29529 Fax: 0903-29666
Email: mcsbrosplant@eircom.net
Web: http://www.mcsharrybrosplant.com
SIC: 29101 Employees: 30
Heavy Engineering
Mr Cyril McSharry Proprietor
Mr Ronan McSharry Sales Director

Mercury Engineering Ltd
Mercury House
Sandyford Industrial Estate
Dublin 18
Phone: 01-2163000 Fax: 01-2163005
Email: info@mercury.plc
Web: http://www.mercury.plc
SIC: 29101 Employees: 1500
Engineering Contractors
Mr Frank O'Kane Managing Director
Mr Gerry Morrissey Finance Manager
Mr John Davis Personnel Manager
Mr Alex Murphy Sales Manager
Mr Seamus Noonan Management Accountant

Metallocraft
Kill Avenue
Dun Laoghaire Co. Dublin
Phone: 01-2801988 Fax: 01-2844852
Email: info@metallocraft.com
Web: http://www.metallocraft.com
SIC: 29101 Employees: 25
Precision Engineering
Mr Simon Miller Managing Director

MFH Contract Engineering Services
500 Charlottes Road
Chefield
Dublin 2
Phone: 01-4752111 Fax: 01-2795501
Email: enq@mhsgroup.co.uk
SIC: 29101 Employees: 65
Mechanical Engineers
Mr Mike Hobson Managing Director
Mr Michael Bugg Admin & Computer Manager

Machinery & Equipment

MSL Engineering
Kilbarry Enterprise Centre
Dublin Hill
Cork Co. Cork
Phone: 021-4300559 Fax: 021-4393276
Email: msl99@iol.ie
SIC: 29101 Employees: 300
Mechanical Engineers
Mr Maurice McGrath Managing Director
Mr Adrian White Accountant

Noreside Conveyors & Elevators
Hebron Industrial Estate
Kilkenny Co. Kilkenny
Phone: 056-63966 Fax: 056-63977
Email: info@noreside.ie
Web: http://www.noreside.ie
SIC: 29101 Employees: 40
Conveyors & Elevators Manufacturers
Mr Joe Riordan Managing Director
Ms Dolores Dolling Financial Controller
Mr William Murphy Sales & Marketing Manager
Mr Tom Cleere Production Manager

Pat Rynn Engineering Ltd
New Docks
Galway Co. Galway
Phone: 091-567804 Fax: 091-567070
Email: rynnengineering@eircom.net
SIC: 29101 Employees: 50
Mechanical & Marine Engineering
Mr Pat Rynn Managing Director
Mr John Higgins Finance Manager

Patrick Engineering
Unit 26/27 Southern Cross Bus Park
Bray Co. Wicklow
Phone: 01-2762077 Fax: 01-2762088
Email: pateng@iol.ie
SIC: 29101 Employees: 60
Mechanical Engingeering
Mr Patrick Gormley Managing Director
Mr Donal McMenamin Director

Patrick J Tobin & Co Ltd
Hynes Building
St Augustine Street
Galway Co. Galway
Phone: 091-565211 Fax: 091-565398
Email: pjt@iol.ie
SIC: 29101 Employees: 50
Consulting Engineers
Mr Eamonn Waldron Managing Director
Mr Eamonn Harrigan Finance Manager
Mr Adrian Downes Project Engineer

PB Machine Tech Ltd
Royal Oak Road
Bagenalstown Co. Carlow
Phone: 0503-21729 Fax: 0503-21670
Email: pbmach@eircom.net
SIC: 29101 Employees: 65
Engineering
Ms Lily Holmes Director
Ms Annie Byrne Accounts Manager
Mr Raymond Kehoe Sales Manager

Pederson Engineering Ltd
Combermere House
Glounthaune
Cork Co. Cork
Phone: 021-4353051 Fax: 021-4354275
Email: pederson@pederson-eng.ie
Web: http://www.pederson-eng.ie
SIC: 29101 Employees: 25
Specialised Conveyor Systems
Mr Freddie Pederson Managing Director

PH McCarthy & Partners
Rosemount Hall
Dundrum Road
Dublin 14
Phone: 01-2989377 Fax: 01-2989521
Email: info@phmcc.com
Web: http://www.phmcc.com
SIC: 29101 Employees: 80
Consulting Engineers
Mr Michael Hand Senior Partner
Mr David Dinn Financial Controller
Mr Ciaran McIntyre Personnel Manager
Ms Dee Kehoe Sales Manager
Mr John Kelly Computer Manager

PJ Clonan & Co Ltd
214 Clonliffe Road
Dublin 3
Phone: 01-8373637 Fax: 01-8376576
Email: pjclonan@iol.ie
SIC: 29101 Employees: 55
Mechanical Service Contractors
Mr Noel Memery Managing Director
Mr Damien Clonan Sales & Marketing Manager

Precision Parts & Products
Sandyhill
Charlestown
Claremorris Co. Mayo
Phone: 094-54420 Fax: 094-54631
Email: pduffy@eircom.net
Web: http://www.pppireland.com
SIC: 29101 Employees: 25
Precision Engineering
Mr Patrick Duffy Managing Director
Ms Wendy Dowler Finance Manager
Mr Michael Fleming Computer Manager

Prodieco Ltd
Unit 30 Cookstown Industrial Estate
Tallaght
Dublin 24
Phone: 01-4513411 Fax: 01-4521479
Email: sales@prodieco.ie
Web: http://www.prodieco.ie
SIC: 29101 Employees: 57
Tool Making & Pharmaceuticals
Mr David Barker Managing Director
Ms Rhonda Clarke Finance Manager
Mr Graham Clark Director of Operations
Mr Tommy Kelly Production Manager
Mr Joseph Higgins Design Director

Radiac Sales Europe Ltd
Tralee Road
Castleisland
Tralee Co. Kerry
Phone: 066-7141188 Fax: 066-7141234
Email: radiac@iol.ie
SIC: 29101 Employees: 50
Precision Abrasives Engineering
Mr Tony Cronin Managing Director
Mr Michael Prendergast Financial Controller

Roughan & O'Donovan
Arena House, Arena Road
Sandyford
Dublin 18
Phone: 01-2940800 Fax: 01-2940820
Email: info@rod.ie
Web: http://www.roughanodonovan.com
SIC: 29101 Employees: 70
Consulting Engineers
Mr Joe O'Donovan Managing Director
Mr John Harkin Sales & Marketing Manager
Mr Colm McCratt Computer Manager

Rynn Engineering Ltd
Galway Harbour Enterprise Park
New Docks
Galway Co. Galway
Phone: 091-562568 Fax: 091-567070
Email: rynnengineering@eircom.net
SIC: 29101 Employees: 54
Mechanical Engineering
Mr Pat Rynn Proprietor
Mr John Higgins Financial Controller
Mr Morgan Rynn Sales & Marketing Manager

Sanmina Ireland
Blanchardstown Industrial Park
Dublin 15
Phone: 01-8222363 Fax: 01-8222365
Web: http://www.sanmina.com
SIC: 29101 Employees: 280
Assembly Plant
Mr Seamus Grady Plant Manager

Sapphire Engineering Company Ltd
Ballybricken Grange
Ballybricken
Limerick Co. Limerick
Phone: 061-351444 Fax: 061-351395
Email: sapphireeng@eircom.net
SIC: 29101 Employees: 35
Manufacture Stainless Steel Vessels
Mr David Keating Managing Director
Ms Imelda O'Connor Accounts Manager
Mr Pat Morrisey Production Manager
Mr Kevin Quain Computer Manager

Senator Engineering
Millmount
Kilmallock Co. Limerick
Phone: 063-20190 Fax: 063-20191
Email: seneng@eircom.net
SIC: 29101 Employees: 40
Mechanical Engineering
Mr Donal Daly Managing Director
Ms Caroline Boles Personnel Director

SFL Engineering Ltd
The Industrial Estate
Callan
Kilkenny Co. Kilkenny
Phone: 056-25111 Fax: 056-25506
Email: info@sfleng.com
Web: http://www.sfleng.com
SIC: 29101 Employees: 70
Mech/Marine/Precision Engineering
Mr Norman Leeper Managing Director
Mr Pat Tynan Finance Manager
Mr Tony Deegan Personnel Manager
Mr Michael Comerford Sales & Marketing Manager
Mr Norman Fulton Projection Manufacturer

Siac Butler Steel Ltd
Lea Road
Portarlington
Portlaoise Co. Laois
Phone: 0502-23305 Fax: 0502-23207
Email: butlers.steel@siac.ie
Web: http://www.siac.ie
SIC: 29101 Employees: 130
Steel Fabricators
Mr Peter O'Shea General Manager
Mr Peter Kelleher Financial Controller
Mr Aidan Mullins Personnel Manager
Mr Brian Fennell Sales Executive
Mr John Patterson Production Manager
Mr John Curry IT Manager

Steele & Co Ltd
The Quay
New Ross Co. Wexford
Phone: 051-421401 Fax: 051-421094
Email: sales@steeleandco.com
Web: http://www.steeleandco.com
SIC: 29101 Employees: 33
Engineered Products
Mr Eoin Minihan Partner
Mr Mark Minihan Financial Controller
Mr Billy O'Connor Sales Manager

Machinery & Equipment

T Bourke & Co Ltd
Unit 22 Stillorgan Industrial Park
Blackrock Co. Dublin
Phone: 01-2952721 Fax: 01-2954063
SIC: 29101 Employees: 48
Mechanical Engineering
Mr Edward Bourke Managing Director
Mr Liam Bryan Finance Manager
Mr John Lavelle Personnel Manager

Taltech Engineering
U4 Jamestown Road Industrial Estate
Inchicore
Dublin 8
Phone: 01-4536600 Fax: 01-4783069
Email: taltech@iol.ie
SIC: 29101 Employees: 38
Sheet Metal Fabrication
Mr James Conway Managing Director
Mr Sean Corrigan Finance Manager
Mr Peter Kiernan Sales & Marketing Manager

Tegral Metal Forming
Athy Co. Kildare
Phone: 0507-31619 Fax: 0507-38156
Email: metalinfo@tegral.ie
Web: http://www.tegral.ie
SIC: 29101 Employees: 600
Metal Cladding
Mr Michael Fenlan Managing Director
Mr Vincent O'Brien Financial Controller
Mr Michael McEntee Human Resources Director
Mr Ron McWilliams Sales Manager
Mr Edward Winn Operations Manager

Thompson Group
84 Cherry Orchard Industrial Estate
Ballyfermot
Dublin 10
Phone: 01-6261211 Fax: 01-6263635
Email: info@thompsongroup.ie
SIC: 29101 Employees: 50
Engineering Services
Mr Denis Power Managing Director
Mr Martin Coady Financial Controller
Mr Alan Green Technical Director

Tim Crowley Ltd
Upper Glanmire Bridge
Glanmire
Cork Co. Cork
Phone: 021-4396666 Fax: 021-4396665
Email: tclsales@eircom.net
SIC: 29101 Employees: 50
Mechanical Engineering
Mr Tim Crowley Managing Director
Mr Seamus O'Dugain Finance Manager

Tolka Structural Engineers Ltd
Unit 1- 4 Tolka Industrial Estate
Ballyboggan Road, Finglas
Dublin 11
Phone: 01-8306365 Fax: 01-8306904
Email: tolkaengineers@eircom.net
Web:
http://www.cudigital.com/tolkastructuralengineerin
g
SIC: 29101 Employees: 35
Structural Engineer
Mr Brendan Heavey Managing Director
Mr Shay Byrne Financial Director
Mr Tony Kelly Sales & Marketing Director
Mr Jimmy Kealey Production Manager

Tool & Mould Steel Ireland Ltd
Beechpark
Ennis Co. Clare
Phone: 065-6824144 Fax: 065-6828509
SIC: 29101 Employees: 28
Precision Mould & Die Components
Mr Rudolph Berndt General Manager

Trend Technology Europe
Knockmitten Lane
Western Industrial Estate
Dublin 12
Phone: 01-4505633 Fax: 01-4505065
Web: http://www.trendtechnology.com
SIC: 29101 Employees: 300
Precision Engineering
Mr Martin Mooney Director
Mr Ciaran Harris Finance Manager
Ms Lorraine Lawlor Head of Human Resources
Mr Henry Cahill Operations Director
Mr Chris Spring IT Manager

Tube Rollers Ltd
Callan
Kilkenny Co. Kilkenny
Phone: 056-25245 Fax: 056-25383
SIC: 29101 Employees: 25
Engineering Products
Mr Eamon Kealy Director
Mr Michael Lewis Finance Manager
Mr Brendan Finnelly Production Manager

ABS Pumps Ltd
Clonard Road
Wexford Co. Wexford
Phone: 053-63200 Fax: 053-42335
Web: http://www.abspumps.com
SIC: 29120 Employees: 325
Pumps
Mr Svante Berner Managing Director
Mr Patrick Butler Finance Manager
Ms Bernadette Malone Personnel Manager
Mr James Meyler Marketing Director
Mr Eddie Whelan Production Manager
Mr Paul Kelly Information Systems Manager

Bijur Lubricating Ireland
Industrial Estate
Gort Road
Ennis Co. Clare
Phone: 065-6821543 Fax: 065-6820327
Email: bijur@iol.ie
Web: http://www.bijur.com
SIC: 29120 Employees: 70
Pumps & Pump Parts
Mr Martin Egan Managing Director
Mr Michael Cahill Financial Controller
Mr Mike Daffy Sales Manager

Pneumatics Ltd
Old Naas Road
Bluebell
Dublin 12
Phone: 01-4568111 Fax: 01-4568108
Email: sales@pneumatics.ie
Web: http://www.pneumatics.ie
SIC: 29120 Employees: 30
Distribution Of Engineering Components
Mr Donal O'Reilly Managing Director
Mr Philip Honer Financial Controller
Mr Michael O'Reilly General Manager
Mr D J O'Reilly Sales & Marketing Manager

Cameron Willis Ireland Ltd
Aghafad
Longford Co. Longford
Phone: 043-45301 Fax: 043-41560
SIC: 29130 Employees: 111
Valves for Oil Wells
Mr Bob Walker Managing Director
Ms Carmel Strange Financial Controller
Mr Tom McKeown Manufacturing Manager
Mr Martin O'Reilly IT Co-ordinator

Carten Controls Ltd
Unit 609 Northern Extension
Waterford Co. Waterford
Phone: 051-355436 Fax: 051-378054
Web: http://www.carten.net
SIC: 29130 Employees: 35
Stainless Steel Valves
Mr Brendan Grogan Managing Director
Ms Jean Grogan Finance Manager
Mr Martin Malloy Personnel Manager
Mr Seamus Sweeney Sales & Marketing Manager

Induchem Components Ltd
Unit 53 Southern Cross Bus Park
Boghall Road
Bray Co. Wicklow
Phone: 01-2763177 Fax: 01-2763178
Email: rward@dublin.induchem.ie
Web: http://www.dublin.induchem.ie
SIC: 29130 Employees: 35
Valves Process & Ancillary Equipment
Mr Arthur Carroll Managing Director
Ms Cathal O'Mahony Finance Manager
Mr Stephen Keogh Sales Manager

Schuf Valve Technology Gmbh
Lehenaghmore
Togher
Cork Co. Cork
Phone: 021-4312027 Fax: 021-4310342
Email: info@schuf.ie
Web: http://www.schuf.ie
SIC: 29130 Employees: 35
Manufacture Valves
Mr Wolfgang Frank Managing Director
Ms Ethna O'Flynn Accounts Manager
Mr Pat Walsh Production Manager
Mr John Cremin IT Manager

Snap-Tite Europe BV
Whitemills Industrial Estate
Wexford Co. Wexford
Phone: 053-41566 Fax: 053-41582
Email: snaptite@snap-tite.iol.ie
Web: http://www.snap-tite.iol.ie
SIC: 29130 Employees: 97
Hydraulic Valves/Couplings
Mr Arthur Robb Managing Director
Ms Emer Kirwan Finance Manager
Ms Sarah Cassidy Sales Manager
Mr Nick Steel Operations Manager
Mr William Davis IT Manager

Star Ball Linear Systems
Baltimore Road
Skibbereen Co. Cork
Phone: 028-21399 Fax: 028-22095
SIC: 29140 Employees: 38
Linear Motion Parts
Mr Leo Werner General Manager

Atlas Copco Ireland Ltd
Kylemore Road
Bluebell
Dublin 12
Phone: 01-4505978 Fax: 01-4567686
Email: info.ireland@atlascopco.com
Web: http://www.atlascopco.com
SIC: 29200 Employees: 30
Manufacture Air Compressors
Mr Ricardo Tinperi Managing Director
Mr Peter Webb Finance Manager
Ms Geri Mangan Administrator
Mr Joe Newman Sales Manager

Carlow Warehousing
Kilcarry
Bagenalstown Co. Carlow
Phone: 0503-22307 Fax: 0503-23094
Email: cwh@eircom.net
Web: http://www.carlowwarehousing.ie
SIC: 29200 Employees: 40
Machinery Manufacturing
Mr Edward Nolan Managing Director

Machinery & Equipment

Dennison Trailers Ltd
Maudins Cross
Naas Co. Kildare
Phone: 045-866468 Fax: 045-876244
Email: info@dennisontrailers.com
Web: http://www.dennisontrailers.com
SIC: 29200 Employees: 80
Trailers - Utility - Manufacturing
Mr George Dennison Managing Director
Mr Philip Murphy Financial Controller
Mr Jonathan Dennison Sales Manager

H & K Dublin Ltd
Cherry Orchard Industrial Estate
Ballyfermot Road
Dublin 10
Phone: 01-6267416 Fax: 01-6055466
Email: info@hki.com
Web: http://www.hki.com
SIC: 29200 Employees: 120
Manufacture Catering Equipment
Mr David Bobbit Managing Director
Mr Nick Scannon Finance Director
Ms Karen Molloy Administrative Office
Ms Keith Cassidy Sales Director

Hencliff Holdings Ltd
Sligo Road
Ballyhaunis Co. Mayo
Phone: 0907-31375 Fax: 0907-30788
Email: hencliffholdings@eircom.net
SIC: 29200 Employees: 40
Manufacture Grass Cutting Equipment
Mr John Murphy Manager
Ms Josephine Gallagher Finance Manager
Mr Martin Keane Sales Manager

Mac-Fab Systems Ltd
Magheracloone
Carrickmacross Co. Monaghan
Phone: 042-9667193 Fax: 042-9667846
Email: sales@macfab.com
Web: http://www.macfab.com
SIC: 29200 Employees: 30
Manufacture Machines & Moulds for Concrete Industry
Mr Gene McMahon Managing Director
Ms Mary McMahon Financial Administrator
Mr Gene McConnon Sales & Marketing Manager

SHS Conveyors Ltd
2/3 Finglas Business Centre
Jamestown
Dublin 11
Phone: 01-8567051 Fax: 01-8567058
Email: info@shsconveyors.ie
SIC: 29200 Employees: 60
Conveyors & Conveyor Systems Manufacturers
Mr Paul Hardy Managing Director
Ms Yvonne Crapton Financial Controller

Standex Ireland Ltd
Irishtown
Mountmellick
Portlaoise Co. Laois
Phone: 0502-24350 Fax: 0502-24744
Email: info@standex.iol.ie
SIC: 29200 Employees: 65
Manufacture & Assembly of Pumps for Vending Machines
Mr Patrick McCormack Managing Director
Ms Angela Dunphy Financial Controller
Mr Kevin Egan Sales Manager

Carraigbui Engineering
Durrus
Bantry Co. Cork
Phone: 027-61103 Fax: 027-61227
SIC: 29220 Employees: 45
Manufacture Cable & Harness Equipment
Mr Wils Stock General Manager
Ms Noreen Moynihan Finance Manager
Mr Paul Stock Production Manager

Castle Mechanical Handling Co Ltd
Quarry Road
Cabra
Dublin 7
Phone: 01-8383564 Fax: 01-8382588
Email: info@castlemh.ie
Web: http://www.castlemh.ie
SIC: 29220 Employees: 40
Hire & Sell Forklift Trucks
Mr Val Murray Managing Director
Mr Dermot Kane Financial Controller
Mr Damian Murray Marketing Director
Mr Ken Murray Production Manager

Conveyors & Packaging
Industrial Estate
Dunmore Road, Tuam
Galway Co. Galway
Phone: 093-25732 Fax: 093-25731
Web: http://www.caps.ie
SIC: 29220 Employees: 25
Manufacture Conveyor Systems
Mr John Byrne Managing Director
Mr Gerry McDonagh Financial Controller
Mr Martin Mullins Engineering Manager

Crown Equipment
Monivea Road
Galway Co. Galway
Phone: 091-706100 Fax: 091-751125
Web: http://www.crown.com
SIC: 29220 Employees: 300
Lifting Equipment
Mr John McGinley Managing Director
Mr Kieran Jordan Financial Controller
Ms Michelle Kenny Human Resources Manager

Handling & Storage Equipment Ireland
Greenhills Industrial Estate
Dublin 12
Phone: 01-4566626 Fax: 01-4566518
Email: sales@lansing.com
Web: http://www.lansing.com
SIC: 29220 Employees: 25
Fork Lift Trucks
Mr Tony Cooke General Manager

Industrial Logistics Ltd
City Link Business Park
Old Naas Road
Dublin 12
Phone: 01-4500069 Fax: 01-4500374
Email: info@industriallogistics.ie
SIC: 29220 Employees: 55
Lifts
Mr John Coughlan Proprietor
Mr Barry Woods Computer Manager

Irish Crane & Lifting Ltd
Unit 2 Lissivigeen
Killarney Co. Kerry
Phone: 064-33722 Fax: 064-34233
Email: icl@iol.ie
Web: http://www.irishcrane.com
SIC: 29220 Employees: 30
Lifting/Handling Equipment
Mr Gerry Cossey Proprietor
Ms Maureen Coffey Financial Controller
Ms Donna Murphy Internal Sales

Irish Lift Services
6 Clyde la Herbert Park
Ballsbridge
Dublin 4
Phone: 01-6600901 Fax: 01-6688114
Email: queries@irishliftservices.ie
SIC: 29220 Employees: 30
Lifts
Mr Paul Kelly Managing Director

Liebherr Container Cranes Ltd
Fossa
Killarney Co. Kerry
Phone: 064-31511 Fax: 061-34041
Email: sales@lcc.liebherr.com
Web: http://www.liebherr.com
SIC: 29220 Employees: 400
Manufacture Cranes
Mr Klaus Noelke Manufacturing Director
Mr Hans Brunner Finance Manager
Mr Tom Foley Personnel Manager
Mr Reiner Geiler Sales Director
Mr John Coffey Production Manager
Mr John McCarthy IT Manager

Newage Storage Systems Ltd
Unit36, Rosemount Business Park
Ballycoolin Road
Dublin 15
Phone: 01-8128616 Fax: 01-8128620
Email: storage@newageservices.ie
Web: http://www.newageservices.ie
SIC: 29220 Employees: 25
Storage Equipment & Office Furniture
Mr Jack Phelan Managing Director
Mr Brian Grehan Finance Manager
Ms Mary Bueno Sales Manager
Ms Michelle Davitt Operations Manager

OTIS
21, Nass Road Business Park
Dublin 12
Phone: 01-4199812 Fax: 01-4199801
Email: info@otis.com
Web: http://www.otis.com
SIC: 29220 Employees: 151
Lift & Escalator Installation & Maintenance
Mr James McGarry Managing Director
Mr Richard O'Dwyer Finance Manager

Pickering Lifts
Unit 7 Dunboyne Industrial Estate
Dunboyne Co. Meath
Phone: 01-8252333 Fax: 01-8252339
SIC: 29220 Employees: 40
Lift Installation & Manufacture
Mr Connor Brennan Managing Director
Ms Shauna Whelan Financial Controller
Ms Mary Kerby Personnel Manager

Shuttleworth Europe Ltd
Woodstock Industrial Estate
Athy Co. Kildare
Phone: 0507-31001 Fax: 0507-38329
Email: sel@shuttleworth.com
Web: http://www.shuttleworth.ie
SIC: 29220 Employees: 60
Roller Conveyors
Mr Ted Mooney Managing Director
Mr Michael Barnes Financial Controller
Mr David Murray Sales & Marketing Manager
Mr John Ryan Engineering Manager

Technical Support Services Ltd
Jamestown Road
Inchicore
Dublin 8
Phone: 01-6264349 Fax: 01-6264320
Email: info@tsslimited.ie
SIC: 29220 Employees: 36
Tail Lifts & Refrigeration Units
Mr Noel Lacey Managing Director
Mr Ross Martin Accounts Manager
Mr Des Farrell Sales Manager

Air-Con Engineering Ltd
Spring Valley
Enniscorthy Co. Wexford
Phone: 054-38888 Fax: 054-38891
Email: info@airconengineering.com
SIC: 29230 Employees: 50
Heating & Ventilation Contractors
Mr John Dempsey Director
Mr Ted Flannelly Finance Manager
Mr Jim Mullett Director

Machinery & Equipment

Anglo Irish Refrigeration Co Ltd
Unit 1 Ashbourne Industrial Estate
Ashbourne
Navan Co. Meath
Phone: 01-8350866 Fax: 01-8351379
SIC: 29230 Employees: 30
Heat/Vent/Refridge/Air Cond Equipment
Mr Jack Fitzsimons Managing Director
Mr John Gogan Finance Manager

Ballinlough Electrical & Refrigeration Company
Ballyhaunis Road
Ballinlough
Castlerea Co. Roscommon
Phone: 0907-40045 Fax: 0907-40230
Email: info@brtks.iol.ie
Web: http://www.brtks.iol.ie
SIC: 29230 Employees: 68
Heat/Vent/Refridge/Air Conditioning Equipment
Mr Joe Jordan Managing Director
Mr Michael Crowe Finance Manager
Ms Sandra Jordan Personnel Officer
Mr Bernard McHugh Sales & Marketing Manager

C & F Quadrant
Quadrant House
Chapelizod
Dublin 20
Phone: 01-6265711 Fax: 01-6305715
Email: sales@cfquadrant.ie
Web: http://www.cfquadrant.ie
SIC: 29230 Employees: 40
Supply boilers Domestic & Leisure
Mr John Duignan Chief Executive
Ms Fiona Millane Financial Controller
Mr Michael Melligan Sales Manager
Mr Killian Duignan IT Manager

Camfil (Ireland) Ltd
Clonshaugh Industrial Estate
Clonshaugh
Dublin 17
Phone: 01-8484977 Fax: 01-8484969
Web: http://www.camfilfarr.com
SIC: 29230 Employees: 50
Air Filters Dust Collection
Mr Don Donovan Managing Director
Mr Brian Reddin Financial Director
Mr Paul Flannagan Sales Manager
Mr Mark Kavanagh Production Manager

Ceramicx Ireland
Gortnagrough
Ballydehob
Skibbereen Co. Cork
Phone: 028-37510 Fax: 028-37509
Email: sales@ceramicx.ie
Web: http://www.ceramicx.com
SIC: 29230 Employees: 50
Manufacture of Infra Red Heating Elements
Mr Frank Wilson Managing Director
Ms Cynthia Corcoran Human Resources Manager
Ms Joanne Hickey Sales & Production Scheduler
Mr John White General Manager

Chambers Refrigeration Service
Unit 7 Port View Industrail Estate
Cullion Road
Letterkenny Co. Donegal
Phone: 074-23089 Fax: 074-26173
Email: info@chambers-crs.com
SIC: 29230 Employees: 120
Heat/Vent/Refridge/Air Conditioning Equipment
Mr Jim Chambers Proprietor
Ms Margaret Chambers Finance Manager

Clancy Radiators Ltd
Crossagalla
Ballysimon Road
Limerick Co. Limerick
Phone: 061-419497 Fax: 061-411104
Email: clancyrad@indigo.ie
SIC: 29230 Employees: 35
Radiator Manufacture
Mr Gerry Clancy Managing Director
Mr Niall Fay Finance Manager

Cross Refrigeration Ltd
25 Cookstown Industrial Estate
Tallaght
Dublin 24
Phone: 01-4511915 Fax: 01-4511565
Email: info@cross-refrig.ie
Web: http://www.cross-refrig.ie
SIC: 29230 Employees: 100
Refrigeration Units
Mr Ken Keating Manager
Ms Linda Wiste Finance Manager
Mr John Goggin Sales & Marketing Manager

Davenham Engineering Ltd
10-13 Weatherwell Industrial Estate
Clondalkin
Dublin 22
Phone: 01-4570739 Fax: 01-4570934
Email: reception@davenham.iol.ie
Web: http://www.davenham.com
SIC: 29230 Employees: 70
Manufacture Electrical Switch Gears
Mr John Corcoran Managing Director
Mr Gary O'Shaughnessy Finance Manager
Mr Shay Doyle Sales Manager

EDPAC International Ltd
Carrigaline Industrial Estate
Carrigaline
Cork Co. Cork
Phone: 021-4372850 Fax: 021-4373975
Email: info@edpac.com
Web: http://www.edpac.com
SIC: 29230 Employees: 33
Manu Close control air condition equipment & air handling equipment
Mr Noel Lynch General Manager
Ms Ann Harding Accounts Manager
Mr Ciaran Coughlan Sales & Marketing Director
Mr Aidan Madden Production Manager
Mr Gerry Kelleher Quality & Engineering Manager

Energy Action Ltd
Unit 14 IDA Enterprise Park
Newmarket
Dublin 8
Phone: 01-4545464 Fax: 01-4549797
Email: info@energyaction.ie
Web: http://www.energyaction.ie
SIC: 29230 Employees: 60
Draught Proofing Insulation & Energy Awareness
Mr David McCarthy Chairman
Mr Connor Moore Finance Manager

Erba Engineering Co Ltd
Unit 8 Ballymount Cross
Business Park
Dublin 24
Phone: 01-4568777 Fax: 01-4568441
Email: erba@eircom.net
SIC: 29230 Employees: 39
Air Conditioning Contractors
Mr John White Managing Director
Mr Dermot Crumley Finance Manager
Mr Gerard Hutchinson Sales Manager
Mr Dean Mulvaney Computer Manager

GB Metals Ltd
Doughcloyne Industrial Estate
Wilton
Cork Co. Cork
Phone: 021-4545577 Fax: 021-4542432
Email: gbmetalsltd@gbgroup.ie
Web: http://www.gbgroup.ie
SIC: 29230 Employees: 120
Insulation
Mr Gerry Byrne Manager
Ms Maureen O'Donovan Finance Manager
Ms Nora Murphy Personnel Officer
Mr Pat Kavanagh Sales/General Manager

Grant Engineering
Crinkle
Birr Co. Offaly
Phone: 0509-20089 Fax: 0509-21060
Email: grantengineering@eircom.net
SIC: 29230 Employees: 140
Manufacture Boilers
Mr John Say Managing Director
Ms Phyllis Grant Finance Manager
Mr Gary O'Mara Sales Manager
Mr Peter Darcy Computer Manager

HDS Energy Ltd
Celbridge Industrial Estate
Celbridge
Naas Co. Kildare
Phone: 01-6271011 Fax: 01-6271015
Email: info@hds-energy.com
Web: http://www.hds-energy.com
SIC: 29230 Employees: 37
Industrial Boilers
Mr Alan Fox Managing Director

Hi-Tech Refrigeration Ltd
Unit 1 Industrial Centre
Ballyinagh Road
Cavan Co. Cavan
Phone: 049-4361588 Fax: 049-4361590
Email: hitech@iol.ie
SIC: 29230 Employees: 26
Industrial Refrigeration
Mr David Keith Managing Director
Ms Mary Reilly Finance Manager
Mr John Lynch Computer Manager

John Horgan & Son Ltd
70 Beaumount Drive
Blackrock
Cork Co. Cork
Phone: 021-4294801 Fax: 021-4292554
Email: info@horgan-mechanical.com
SIC: 29230 Employees: 50
Mechanical Servicing Contractor
Mr Noel Horgan Managing Director
Ms Ann Dromey Finance Manager
Mr John O'Driscoll Sales & Marketing Manager
Mr Brian Power IT Manager

Liberty Air Technology
6C Ballymount Drive
Walkinstown
Dublin 12
Phone: 01-4564064 Fax: 01-4564071
Email: liberty@indigo.ie
SIC: 29230 Employees: 45
Manufacture Air-Conditioning & Heating Systems
Mr Pat Gough Managing Director
Mr Sean Brady Sales Director
Mr Luke Gough Computer Manager

Machinery & Equipment

Mark Eire BV
Coolea
Macroom Co. Cork
Phone: 026-45334 Fax: 026-45383
Email: sales@markeire.com
Web: http://www.markeire.nl
SIC: 29230 Employees: 60
Industrial and Heating Equipment - Manufacturing
Mr Michael O'Donoghue Managing Director
Ms Brid Calanan Financial Controller
Mr Mike O'Donaghan Personnel Manager
Mr Michael Keane Sales Manager
Mr Paric O'Conaola Computer Manager

Masterair Sales Ltd
John F Kennedy Park
Kileen Road
Dublin 12
Phone: 01-4602188 Fax: 01-4602193
Email: info@masterair.ie
Web: http://www.masterair.ie
SIC: 29230 Employees: 75
Air Conditioning Equipment Manufacturing
Mr Patrick Thundle Managing Director
Mr Liam Dowling Financial Controller
Mr Michael Lynch Sales Director
Mr Naois Wilson Production Manager
Mr Alan Monaghan Computer Manager

Michael Williams Cork Ltd
Granary House
Rutland Street
Cork Co. Cork
Phone: 021-4272329 Fax: 021-4507259
Email: mwcorkltd@eircom.net
SIC: 29230 Employees: 35
Heating, Plumbing & Ventilation
Mr Liam Curtin Manager
Mr Dermot Spillane Personnel Manager

MK Refrigeration
180 Oak Road Western Indust Estate
Naas Road
Dublin 12
Phone: 01-4566411 Fax: 01-4566414
Email: swalsh@imicornelius.ie
Web: http://www.imicornelius.ie
SIC: 29230 Employees: 23
Refrigeration
Mr Mahon Devereux Managing Director
Mr Stephen Walsh Accountant

Myson Heating Control
Newcastle West
Limerick Co. Limerick
Phone: 069-62277 Fax: 069-62448
Email: enquiries@mysonheatingcontrols.com
Web: http://www.myson.ie
SIC: 29230 Employees: 100
Heating Controls Manufacturers
Mr Sean Hanratty Managing Director
Mr John Moloney Finance Manager
Mr Donal O'Grady Sales Manager

NCS Group
Knockgriffin
Midleton Co. Cork
Phone: 021-4631111 Fax: 021-4631335
Email: enquiries@norcold.ie
Web: http://www.norcold.ie
SIC: 29230 Employees: 45
Cold Storage
Mr Dermot Conroy Manager
Mr Liam Spring Finance Manager
Mr Martin Hackett Personnel Director
Ms Elizabeth Kelleher Computer Manager

Norcool Ltd
Whitemill Industrial Estate
Wexford Co. Wexford
Phone: 053-23655 Fax: 053-41564
Email: norcool@iol.ie
SIC: 29230 Employees: 60
Manufacture Fridge Coolers
Mr Joe Hore Managing Director
Mr Ultin Ryan Finance Manager
Mr Noel Breslin Sales Manager

O'Reilly & Co Ltd
Unit 16 Greenhills Business Park
Tallaght
Dublin 24
Phone: 01-4511133 Fax: 01-4512617
Email: oreillyandco@indigo.ie
SIC: 29230 Employees: 35
Heating Equipment & Supplies
Mr Ciaran Casey Director
Mr Seamus O'Reilly Finance Director
Mr Denis Brown Sales Director

Oasis
Bunree Industrial Estate
Ballina Co. Mayo
Phone: 096-71222 Fax: 096-71433
Email: info@oasis.ie
Web: http://www.oasis.ie
SIC: 29230 Employees: 200
Drinking Water Coolers & Dehumidifiers
Mr James Preston General Manager
Mr Gordon Ryan Financial Controller
Mr Gus McMenaman Personnel Manager
Mr Donal Garrihy Sales Manager
Mr Paul Gallagher Production Manager

Prince O'Burren Ltd
Unit 23 Cookstown Industrial Estate
Tallaght
Dublin 24
Phone: 01-4599901 Fax: 01-4599905
Email: poburren@iol.ie
Web: http://www.poburren.com
SIC: 29230 Employees: 100
Panel Manufacturing for Cold Rooms
Mr Danny Glynn Managing Director
Ms Grainne Kyne Finance Manager
Mr Gerry Byrne Production Manager

QK Cold Stores Ltd
The Maudlins
Naas Co. Kildare
Phone: 045-894100 Fax: 045-876204
Email: qkcoldstores@qkcs.ie
SIC: 29230 Employees: 150
Cold Store
Mr Martin Barrett General Manager
Mr John Kearns Financial Controller

Reconair Services Ltd
307 Swords Road
Santry
Dublin 9
Phone: 01-8425200 Fax: 01-8425880
Email: havac@reconair.ie
Web: http://www.reconair.ie
SIC: 29230 Employees: 25
Supply & Install Air Conditioning & Heating
Mr Mark Cooney Joint Managing Director
Ms Lorraine McGrath Personnel Manager

Refrigeration Engineering Ltd
Hebron Industrial Estate
Kilkenny Co. Kilkenny
Phone: 056-21310 Fax: 056-65046
Email: rel@eircom.net
Web: http://www.rel.ie
SIC: 29230 Employees: 30
Refridgeration Equip for Commercial & Home
Mr David McDonald Managing Director
Mr John Ryan Finance Manager
Mr Chris Rainey Sales Manager
Mr Niall Rhatigan Computer Manager

Rockwell Holdings
Millstreet Road
Macroom Co. Cork
Phone: 026-41490 Fax: 026-41117
Email: mailbox@rockwell.eircom.com
SIC: 29230 Employees: 60
Air Conditioning Systems
Mr Harry Kaiser Managing Director
Ms Mary Hickey Financial Controller
Mr Jim Devaney Sales Manager
Mr Leslie Edwards Chief Projects Manager
Mr Dave Mulcahy Systems Supervisor

Ryan Insulations Ltd
Chapel Street
Borrisoleigh
Thurles Co. Tipperary
Phone: 0504-51444 Fax: 0504-51515
SIC: 29230 Employees: 23
Manufacture Beer Cooling Equipment
Mr Don Ryan Managing Director
Mrs Mary O'Connell Finance Manager
Ms Anna Egan Sales Director
Mr Mick Ryan Production Manager

Satchwell Grant Ltd
Unit 2, Coolmine Industrial Estate
Clonsilla
Dublin 15
Phone: 01-8200163 Fax: 01-8200167
Email: info@thegrantgroup.com
SIC: 29230 Employees: 60
Heating & Ventilation
Mr Niall Grant Manager
Ms Muire Grant Financial Controller

Season Control
Unit 2b Nangor Road, Business Park
Nangor Road
Dublin 12
Phone: 01-4568200 Fax: 01-4568210
Email: season@clubi.ie
SIC: 29230 Employees: 68
Manufacture and Supply Air Condition and Ventilation
Mr John Kennedy Managing Director
Mr Turlough Flinn Financial Controller
Mr Carl Dumbellton Sales Manager
Mr Eamon McEntee Production Manager

Thermo Dial Ltd
Unit A Centre Point Business Park
Oak Road
Dublin 12
Phone: 01-4546885 Fax: 01-4546887
Email: info@thermodial.ie
Web: http://www.thermodial.ie
SIC: 29230 Employees: 25
Air Conditioning Heating & Ventilation Enginee
Mr Willy Carney Managing Director
Ms Imelda Sherry Finance Manager
Mr Barry Brennan Sales Manager

Thermo King Europe
Monivea Road
Mervue
Galway Co. Galway
Phone: 091-751231 Fax: 091-751911
Email: postmaster@thermoking.com
Web: http://www.thermoking.com
SIC: 29230 Employees: 1000
Temperature Control Units
Mr Christy Hayes Chief Executive
Ms Mary Kenny Human Resources Manager
Mr Pat Howard Sales & Marketing Manager
Mr Vincent Comer IT Manager

Machinery & Equipment

Thompsons Air Systems
Shortcastle
Mallow Co. Cork
Phone: 022-21521 Fax: 022-42067
Email: thomair@iol.ie
SIC: 29230 Employees: 50
Ventilating Systems Manufacturers
Mr Laurence Thompson Managing Director
Mr Denis Eherne Financial Controller
Ms Una O'Connor Personnel Manager
Mr Joe Mulligan Sales Manager
Mr Malachy Downey Production Manager

Uchiya Ireland Ltd
Tallaght Business Park
Whitestown Industrial Estate
Dublin 24
Phone: 01-4620192 Fax: 01-4620288
Email: sales@uchiya.ie
SIC: 29230 Employees: 65
Thermal Protectors
Mr Sean Shimitzu Chief Executive
Mr Eamon Clint Sales & Marketing Manager
Mr Berni Ruana Production Manager

Veha Ltd
The Murrough
Wicklow Co. Wicklow
Phone: 0404-67278 Fax: 0404-67731
Email: veha@indigo.ie
SIC: 29230 Employees: 125
Radiators
Mr Hugh O'Byrne Managing Director
Mr Kieran Doyle Sales & Marketing Manager
Ms Breda Murphy Head of Computers

Waterford Stanley Ltd
Bilberry
Waterford Co. Waterford
Phone: 051-302300 Fax: 051-302375
Email: info@waterfordstanley.com
Web: http://www.waterfordstanley.com
SIC: 29230 Employees: 450
Cast Iron Cookers
Mr Gerry Currid Partner
Mr Sean McGowan Financial Controller
Mr Tom Kennedy Personnel Director
Mr Michael Lassan Partner
Ms Laura Borla Production Manager
Mr Robb Vandervelt IT Manager

Abbey Farm Machinery Ltd
Well Road
Nenagh Co. Tipperary
Phone: 067-31278 Fax: 067-33229
Email: abbeyfe@iol.ie
Web: http://www.ie.euro-tradelink.com
SIC: 29300 Employees: 80
Farm Machinery
Mr Charles Kavanagh Managing Director
Mr Declan Tiernan Financial Controller
Mr Dermot Gallagher General Manager
Mr Tom Kirby Sales Manager
Mr John O'Brien Computer Manager

Advanced Industries Ltd
Causeway
Tralee Co. Kerry
Phone: 066-7131215 Fax: 066-7131670
Email: info@diarymaster.com
SIC: 29300 Employees: 50
Farm Machinery
Mr Edmond Harty Managing Director
Ms Mary Harty Finance Manager
Mr Diarmuid Cronin Personnel Manager
Mr Stephen Pearse Production Manager

Aughey Screens Ltd
Killyconnigan
Monaghan Co. Monaghan
Phone: 047-82055 Fax: 047-30734
Email: info@augheyscreens.com
Web: http://www.augheyscreens.com
SIC: 29300 Employees: 30
Suppliers to Quarries
Mr Barry Aughey Managing Director
Ms Orla McKenna Finance Manager
Ms Kulli Partel Personnel Manager
Mr Ray Mangan Sales Person
Mr Eamon McKernan Production Manager
Mr Alistair Craig Computer Manager

Blackwater Engineering Ltd
Quartertown Industrial Estate
Mallow Co. Cork
Phone: 022-21795 Fax: 022-42051
Email: reception@blackwaterengineering.ie
SIC: 29300 Employees: 50
Road Tankers
Mr Dermot Doyle Managing Director
Mr Derry O'Gorman Financial Controller
Mr Sean Sheehan Production/Purchasing Manager

Burnside Hydracyl Ballymoon Ltd
Ballymoon
Bagenalstown Co. Carlow
Phone: 0503-21364 Fax: 0503-21830
Email: burnside@eircom.net
Web: http://www.burnside/eng.com
SIC: 29300 Employees: 113
Agricultural Machinery
Mr James Byrne Managing Director
Mr Mark O'Sullivan Financial Controller
Mr Jimmy Byrne Personnel Manager
Mr PJ Byrne Sales & Marketing Director
Mr Gerard Byrne IT Manager

Cavanaghs Fermoy Ltd
Cork Road
Fermoy Co. Cork
Phone: 025-31211 Fax: 025-32345
Email: sales@cavanagh.sgi.ie
SIC: 29300 Employees: 30
Agriculture/Construction Machinery
Mr Sean Barry Managing Director

Cork Farm Machinery Ltd
Carrigrohane Road
Cork Co. Cork
Phone: 021-4543801 Fax: 021-4541861
Email: corkfarmmachinery@eircom.net
Web: http://www.corkfarmmachinery.ie
SIC: 29300 Employees: 31
Agricultural Machinery
Mr Frank Crowley Managing Director
Mr Gerard O'Donoghue Accountant
Mr Gerry Lehane Sales Manager

Flynn Machinery Ltd
The Downs
Mullingar Co. Westmeath
Phone: 044-74148 Fax: 044-74588
SIC: 29300 Employees: 25
Farm Machinery Dealers
Mr Thomas Flynn Managing Director
Mr John Flynn Director

Flynns Garage Ltd
Dublin Road
Tullow
Carlow Co. Carlow
Phone: 0503-51205 Fax: 0503-51425
Email: info@nissan.ie
Web: http://www.flynnsoftullow.ie
SIC: 29300 Employees: 35
Car & Farm Machinery Dealers
Mr Brian Flynn Managing Director
Mr Ray Flynn Sales Director

Fox Brothers Engineering
Ballycanew
Gorey Co. Wexford
Phone: 055-21677 Fax: 055-21733
Email: foxbros@eircom.net
SIC: 29300 Employees: 60
Agricultural Machinery & Buildings/ Structural Steel
Mr Christopher Fox Managing Director
Ms Bernie Casey Financial Controller
Mr Liam Fox Sales Manager
Mr John O'Hara Production Manager
Mr PJ Fox Office Manager

Grascare Machinery Ltd
Coolnaha
Ballyhaunis Co. Mayo
Phone: 0907-30572 Fax: 0907-30788
Email: grascare@eircom.net
Web: http://www.major-grascare.com
SIC: 29300 Employees: 45
Manufacture Agricultural/Construction Machinery
Mr John Murphy Managing Director
Ms Josephine Gallagher Accountant
Mr Martin Keane Sales Director

HI-SPEC Engineering Ltd
Station Road
Bagenalstown Co. Carlow
Phone: 0503-21929 Fax: 0503-21980
Email: sales@hispec.net
Web: http://www.hispec.net
SIC: 29300 Employees: 40
Manufacture Farm Machinery & Industrial Tankers
Mr John J Nolan Director
Mr Nicholas Byrne Accountant
Mr Mike Nolan Personnel Director
Mr Tom Nolan Sales Manager
Mr Henry Nolan Production Director
Mr James Nolan Computer Manager

IAM Agricultural Machinery Ltd
Hebron Industrial Estate
Kilkenny Co. Kilkenny
Phone: 056-65826 Fax: 056-62207
Email: info@keerneland.com
Web: http://www.keernelandgroup.com
SIC: 29300 Employees: 40
Farm Machinery Dealers
Mr David Jones Managing Director
Mr Nicholas Dunne Sales Manager
Mr Michael Reiley IT Manager

IAWS Group
151 Thomas Street
Dublin 8
Phone: 01-6121200 Fax: 01-6121321
Email: sales@gouldings.ie
Web: http://www.iaws.ie
SIC: 29300 Employees: 950
Agricultural Supplier
Mr Philip Lynch Chief Executive
Mr David Martin Finance Manager
Mr John Phelan Company Secretary
Mr Tom Tynan Marketing Manager
Mr Alan Lowther Development Manager
Mr Dennis Moran Computer Manager

Lund International BV
Business & Technology Park
Garrycastle
Athlone Co. Westmeath
Phone: 0902-75311 Fax: 0902-74935
Email: info@lundonline.com
Web: http://www.lundonline.com
SIC: 29300 Employees: 90
Agricultural Machinery Blades
Mr Sean Daly Acting Managing Director
Mr Gerry McManus Financial Controller
Mr Arthur Fultz Marketing Manager Worldwide

Machinery & Equipment

McHale's Engineering Ltd
Castlebar Road
Ballinrobe
Claremorris Co. Mayo
Phone: 093-33326 Fax: 092-20356
Email: info@mchale.net
Web: http://www.mchale.net
SIC: 29300 Employees: 100
Farm Machinery Dealers
Mr Padraic McHale Managing Director
Mr Brian Moran Finance Manager
Mr John Biggins Sales & Marketing Manager
Mr Kieran Tendergast Production Manager

Michael Tighe Engineering Ltd
Nobber Road
Drumconrath
Navan Co. Meath
Phone: 041-6854187 Fax: 041-6854222
Email: mtigheeng@eircom.net
SIC: 29300 Employees: 50
Agricultural Equipment - Heavy Duty Attachment
Mr Michael Tighe Managing Director
Mr Stephen Byrne Production Manager

Pearson & Co Ltd
Woodstock Street
Athy Co. Kildare
Phone: 0507-31842 Fax: 0507-31909
Email: pearson@oceanfree.net
Web: http://www.pearson-international.com
SIC: 29300 Employees: 25
Milking Machine Manufacturers
Mr Alan Pearson Manager
Ms Ruth Carter Finance Manager

Richard Keenan & Co Ltd
Borris
Carlow Co. Carlow
Phone: 0503-71200 Fax: 0503-71227
Email: info@keenantmr.com
Web: http://www.keenantmr.com
SIC: 29300 Employees: 150
Farm Machinery Dealers
Mr Gerard Keenan Managing Director
Mr Jim Green Finance Manager
Mr Mark Simpson Marketing Manager
Mr Ollie O'Neill Production Manager
Mr Conan Condon IT Manager

Ruscon Engineering Works
Townley Hall
Drogheda Co. Louth
Phone: 041-9824437 Fax: 041-9824698
Email: ruscon@iol.ie
SIC: 29300 Employees: 25
Manu Agricultural Machinery
Mr Noel Mackin Manager
Mr Louis Kelly Sales Manager
Mr Anthony Ruffle Production Manager

Tanco Engineering Company
Royal Oak Road
Bagenalstown Co. Carlow
Phone: 0503-21336 Fax: 0503-21737
Email: info@tanco.ie
Web: http://www.tanco.ie
SIC: 29300 Employees: 50
Agricultural Machinery
Mr Lee Choo Managing Director
Mr Joe O'Brien Finance Manager
Mr Brian McArdle Export Sales Manager

Trouw Aquaculture Ltd
Roman Island
Westport Co. Mayo
Phone: 098-26677 Fax: 098-25873
Email: info@trouw.iol.ie
Web: http://www.trouw.iol.ie
SIC: 29300 Employees: 35
Fish Feed Manufacturer
Mr Sean Murphy Managing Director
Ms Grainne O'Mahony Finance Manager
Mr Anthony Murphy Marketing Manager
Ms Joan Jennings Plant Manager

William J Carroll Ltd
Coolanga
Clonoulgy
Cashel Co. Tipperary
Phone: 0504-42235 Fax: 0504-42313
Email: rossmore@eircom.net
SIC: 29300 Employees: 30
Agricultural & Construction Machinery Manufacturing
Mr William Carroll Managing Director
Ms Mary Ryan Office Manager
Mr Michael Ryan Sales Representative

Mohawk Europe Ltd
Bays Q86/87
Shannon Industrial Estate
Shannon Co. Clare
Phone: 061-471400 Fax: 061-472970
Email: sales@mohawkeuropa.com
Web: http://www.mohawkeuropa.com
SIC: 29401 Employees: 140
Cutting Tools
Mr Leonard Kiely Managing Director
Mr Neil O'Dwyer Financial Controller
Mr Con Egan Plant Manager
Mr Dan Leonard Commercial Manager
Mr Seamus O'Callaghan Production Manager
Mr Tom Golden Computer Manager

Reliance Precision
Parnell Street
Bandon Co. Cork
Phone: 023-41642 Fax: 023-41913
Email: relianceprecision@eircom.net
SIC: 29401 Employees: 24
Machine Tool Accessories
Mr Lesley Borsew General Manager
Ms Monica O'Reagan Accounts Manager

APV Ireland Ltd
Unit 5 Red Cow Business Park
Naas Road
Dublin 22
Phone: 01-4033008 Fax: 01-4593399
Email: apv@dublin.com
SIC: 29402 Employees: 45
Engineering Expertise
Mr Steven Davies Managing Director
Mr Terry Gilham Engineering Manager
Mr Michael Maquire Sales Manager
Mr Sam Giltrap IT Manager

Calmark Ireland Ltd
Cappoquin Industrial Estate
Cappoquin
Dungarvan Co. Waterford
Phone: 058-54205 Fax: 058-54197
Email: info@calmark-irl.ie
Web: http://www.calmark-irl.ie
SIC: 29402 Employees: 55
Precision Metal
Mr Colm Morrissey Managing Director
Ms Mary Hale Accounts Manager
Mr Kieran Walsh Personnel Manager
Mr Brendan Quinn Sales Manager
Mr Martin McGrath Production Manager

Harris Calorific Ireland
Harris House
Rathnew
Wicklow Co. Wicklow
Phone: 0404-68404 Fax: 0404-66282
SIC: 29402 Employees: 120
Welding Equipment Manufacture
Mr Brendan McCullough General Manager
Mr Brendan Mulholland Financial Controller
Mr Gerry Doyle Services Manager
Ms Brigid Marrigan Computer Manager

Inmo-Tech Ltd
Cloona
Enniscrone
Sligo Co. Sligo
Phone: 096-36213 Fax: 096-36236
Email: inmotech@eircom.net
SIC: 29402 Employees: 35
Contract Injection Moulders & Tool Makers
Mr Brendan Cunningham Managing Director
Ms Frances Kilroy Administration Manager
Mr James Ginty Production Manager

Maysteel CME Teo
Coillrua
Inverin
Galway Co. Galway
Phone: 091-593132 Fax: 091-593019
Email: info@maysteel.ie
Web: http://www.maysteel.com
SIC: 29402 Employees: 130
Engineering Precision Products
Mr Michael Clifford Managing Director
Mr Rick Lajeuneuse Financial Controller
Mr John Fox Production Manager
Mr Peter Gleeson Senior Buyer

MPI Metal Powders International
Main Road
Tallaght
Dublin 24
Phone: 01-4515833 Fax: 01-4515197
Email: info@mpi.ie
Web: http://www.castolin.com
SIC: 29402 Employees: 85
Manufacture Welding Materials
Mr Ken Sullivan General Manager
Mr Tadhg Donovan Financial Controller
Ms Coliene McKenna Customer Services Manager
Mr Garry Morton Production Manager
Mr Joseph Ledreidge IT Manager

Prior Tool & Die Ltd
Keenaghan Industrial Estate
Carrick On Shannon Co. Leitrim
Phone: 078-20980 Fax: 078-21149
Email: info@priors.com
Web: http://www.priors.com
SIC: 29402 Employees: 36
Toolmaking
Mr John Prior Proprietor

Procut Engineering Processes Ltd
Bailieborough Road
Virginia
Cavan Co. Cavan
Phone: 049-8547266 Fax: 049-8547567
Email: sales@procut.ie
SIC: 29402 Employees: 30
Manufacture Tungsten Carbide Burs
Ms Carmel Lynch Managing Director
Mr Barry Smith Sales Manager

Ridge Tool Co
Bessboro Road
Blackrock
Cork Co. Cork
Phone: 021-4515400 Fax: 021-4515401
Web: http://www.ridgid.com
SIC: 29402 Employees: 100
Pipe Tool Manufacture
Mr Tom Fannon Managing Director
Mr Carl Levis Financial Controller
Mr Frank Mullane Business Support Specialist

Shannon Precision Engineering Ltd
Unit D6 Shannon Industrial Estate
Shannon Co. Clare
Phone: 061-472841 Fax: 061-475240
Email: spe@indigo.ie
SIC: 29402 Employees: 35
Engineering
Mr Dominic Murphy Managing Director
Mr Kevin Geaney General Manager

Machinery & Equipment

Stet Engineering Ltd
Finisklin Industrial Estate
Sligo Co. Sligo
Phone: 071-61040 Fax: 071-62560
Email: cam@stet.iol.ie
Web: http://www.stet.ie
SIC: 29402 Employees: 37
Tool Making
Mr Andrew Cullen Managing Director
Mr Gerard Mallon Personnel Manager
Mr Noel Sexton Production Manager
Mr John Sheridan Computer Manager

Tool & Gauge Co
Tubbercurry
Sligo Co. Sligo
Phone: 071-85063 Fax: 071-85134
Email: info@toolgauge.iol.ie
Web: http://www.homepage.tinet.ie/~toolandgauge/
SIC: 29402 Employees: 50
Tool Makers
Mr John O'Donnell Managing Director
Mr Joe Brennan Personnel Manager
Mr Gerry Hunt Sales Director
Mr John Joe Brennan Production Manager

Antifyre Ireland Ltd
New Road
Thomondgate
Limerick Co. Limerick
Phone: 061-455288 Fax: 061-326756
Email: sales@antifyre.ie
Web: http://www.antifyre.com
SIC: 29409 Employees: 33
Fire Extinguishers Manufacture Sales & Service
Mr Michael Riordan Managing Director
Ms Sandra Keady Finance Manager
Mr Harry Reid Sales Manager
Ms Cathy Bannon Quality Manager

Apex Fire Ltd
Apex House, Greenmount Industrial Estate
Harolds Cross Road
Dublin 12
Phone: 01-4533177 Fax: 01-4533173
Email: info@apexfire.ie
Web: http://www.apexfire.ie
SIC: 29409 Employees: 200
Fire Protection Equipment
Mr Chris Lundy Managing Director
Mr Michael Phillips Finance Manager
Mr Steven O'Connell President

Custodian Security Systems
16 Forster Street
Galway Co. Galway
Phone: 091-562212 Fax: 091-562212
Email: custodian@indigo.ie
SIC: 29409 Employees: 45
Security/Alarm Systems
Mr Jack Mulveen Managing Director

DDH Sprinklers Ltd
31 Cherry Orchard Industrial Estate
Ballyfermot
Dublin 10
Phone: 01-6267563 Fax: 01-6265873
Email: ddh@indigo.ie
SIC: 29409 Employees: 40
Fire Protection Engineers
Mr Mervin Dunn Proprietor
Ms Beth Dunn Computer Manager

EI Electronics
Shannon Industrial Estate
Shannon Co. Clare
Phone: 061-471277 Fax: 061-471053
Email: ei.electronics@eiltd.ie
SIC: 29409 Employees: 350
Manufacture Smoke Alarms
Mr Michael Guinee Chief Executive
Mr Tom O'Loughlin Financial Controller
Ms Kay McCormack Personnel Manager
Mr John Crampton Marketing Manager
Mr Jim Duignan Operations Director
Mr Gerard Hogan Computer Manager

Fondermann & Company (Irl) Ltd
Park Road
Longford Co. Longford
Phone: 043-46209 Fax: 043-46914
Email: info@protector.com
Web: http://www.protector/tech.com
SIC: 29409 Employees: 30
Industrial Safety Equipment
Mr James Finn Managing Director
Ms Kathleen Farrell Office Manager
Mr PJ Bennett Sales Manager
Mr Tom Cochrane Production Manager

GD Group
Whitestown Industrial Estate
Tallaght
Dublin 24
Phone: 01-4511433 Fax: 01-4524294
SIC: 29409 Employees: 30
Fire Extinguishers/Fire Protective Clothing
Mr Declan Bradbury Manager
Ms Fiona Young Finance Manager
Mr Tony Reynolds Sales Manager

Irish Superior Safety Systems Ltd
Rasseen House
Ringaskiddy
Cork Co. Cork
Phone: 021-4373839 Fax: 021-4852316
Email: isss@eircom.net
Web: http://www.isss.ie
SIC: 29409 Employees: 50
Fire Prevention
Mr Tony Scott Manager
Ms Susan Barratt Finance Manager

Mather & Platt (Irl)
7 Ardee Road
Rathmines
Dublin 6
Phone: 01-4966077 Fax: 01-4966858
Email: mpsales@tycoint.com
Web: http://www.tycoint.com
SIC: 29409 Employees: 47
Sprinkler Systems
Mr Ray Bingham Managing Director
Mr Paul Burke Financial Controller
Mr Barry Shearman Sales & Operations Director

Moyne Engineering Ltd
Moynehall
Cavan Co. Cavan
Phone: 049-4332685 Fax: 049-4361159
Email: moyne@eircom.net
SIC: 29409 Employees: 30
Fire Hose Reels
Mr Pat Cosgrove Manager
Mr Adrian McCabe Finance Manager
Mr Declan Kelly Factory Manager
Ms Ann Cosgrove Sales Manager
Mr Brendan Morgan Production Manager

Preussag Champion Fire Defence Ltd
Unit 2C Avonbeg Industrial Estate
Longmile Road
Dublin 12
Phone: 01-4508920 Fax: 01-4508862
Email: info@preussag.ie
Web: http://www.preussag.ie
SIC: 29409 Employees: 130
Fire Detection Safety Equipment
Mr Vincent Carrigy Managing Director
Mr Michael Phillips Financial Controller
Mr Jim Valentine Personnel Manager
Ms Martina Connolly IT Manager

Seamus Byrne Electrical Ltd
Tullow Road
Carlow Co. Carlow
Phone: 0503-31890 Fax: 0503-41483
Email: sbelec@eircom.net
SIC: 29409 Employees: 70
Fire Prevention & Electrical Contractors
Mr Seamus Byrne Managing Director
Ms Mary Doody Accounts Manager
Mr Tom Tracey Production Manager
Ms Marcella Kelly IT Manager

Shirley Engineering
Handel House
Western Industrial Estate
Dublin 12
Phone: 01-4502922 Fax: 01-4502976
Email: sel@iol.ie
SIC: 29409 Employees: 27
Fire Escapes
Mr George Shirley Managing Director
Mr John Shirley Sales Director

Allied Waste Systems
Unit 2B Feltrim Business Park
Drynam Road
Swords Co. Dublin
Phone: 01-8900919 Fax: 01-8900932
Email: building@abmconstruction.ie
SIC: 29501 Employees: 30
Waste Disposal Equipment & Supplies
Mr Aidan Crimmins Manager

Atlas Ireland
Clonminan Industrial Estate
Portlaoise Co. Laois
Phone: 0502-74747 Fax: 0502-74757
Email: garageservices@atlasoil.iol.ie
SIC: 29501 Employees: 50
Tank Cleaning & Waste Oil Management
Mr Declan Ryan Managing Director
Mr Vincent Grady Financial Controller
Ms Anne Fitzpatrick Personnel Manager
Mr Michael Nolan Director

Biocycle Ltd
Unit 107 Baldoyle Industrial Estate
Dublin 13
Phone: 01-8391000 Fax: 01-8391998
Email: biocycle@indigo.ie
Web: http://www.biocycle.ie
SIC: 29501 Employees: 40
Effluent Treatment Plant
Mr Frank Kavanagh Managing Director
Ms Sandra Elmes Financial Director
Ms Michelle Dean Sales Manager

BMS Ltd
Strokestown Road
Longford Co. Longford
Phone: 043-26100 Fax: 043-26258
Email: butler@iol.ie
Web: http://www.waste-watertreatment.com
SIC: 29501 Employees: 30
Manufacture of Sewage Treatment
Mr Seamus Butler Managing Director
Mr John Lee Finance Manager
Mr Thomas Mooney Production Manager

Irwin Cobbe Products Ltd
Kilbride
Portarlington
Portlaoise Co. Laois
Phone: 0502-23018 Fax: 0502-43649
Email: lynne.cobbe@oceanfree.net
SIC: 29501 Employees: 40
Waste Disposal
Mr Irwin Cobbe Managing Director
Mr John Gorman Finance Manager
Mr Raymond Little Sales Manager
Ms Breda Mortin Computer Manager

Solids Technology International
14 Holly Avenue
Stillorgan Industrial Park
Blackrock Co. Dublin
Phone: 01-2952229 Fax: 01-2953874
Email: solids@iol.ie
Web: http://www.solidstechnology.com
SIC: 29501 Employees: 50
Sludge Treatment
Mr Pat Torpey Managing Director
Mr Paul Philips Financial Controller
Mr Terry Gillespie Sales & Marketing Director

Machinery & Equipment

USS Bowen Water Technology Ltd
Kilkenny Industrial & Business Park
Purcellsinch
Kilkenny Co. Kilkenny
Phone: 056-63950 Fax: 056-22900
Email: admin@bwt.ie
Web: http://www.bowen.ie
SIC: 29502 Employees: 80
Water Technology
Mr Fergus Cronin Managing Director
Mr John Molloy Company Secretary
Mr Lionel Hatt Marketing Director
Mr Gerry Power Technical Director

Terex Aerials
Courtstown Industrial Park
Little Island
Cork Co. Cork
Phone: 021-4353011 Fax: 021-4353368
Web: http://www.terex.com
SIC: 29504 Employees: 65
Aerial Platform Manufacturing
Mr Tim Lenahan Managing Director
Ms Orla McDermot Accountant
Ms Margaret Moore Personnel Officer
Ms Kathleen Walshe Sales & Marketing Director
Mr Gerry Coleman Production Director

Boart Longyear Ltd
Shannon Industrial Estate
Shannon Co. Clare
Phone: 061-471422 Fax: 061-715777
Email: info@boartlongyear.ie
Web: http://www.boartlongyear.com
SIC: 29520 Employees: 212
Manufacture Mining Machinery
Mr Jim McEnerney General Manager
Mr Bill Gorman Financial Controller
Mr Frank Owens Personnel/Training Manager
Ms Mary Woods Systems Analyst

Concrete & Quarry Engineering Services Ltd
Church Road
Tullamore Co. Offaly
Phone: 0506-52124 Fax: 0506-52135
Email: cqems@iol.ie
SIC: 29520 Employees: 85
Concrete & Quarry Engineering Equipment
Mr Gerald Fogarty Partner
Ms Mary Houlihan Financial Controller
Mr Matthew Corgan Personnel Manager
Mr Pat Fleming Sales & Marketing Director
Mr Brendan Feighery Partner

De Beers Industrial Diamond
Block A, Shannon Free Zone
Shannon Co. Clare
Phone: 061-471655 Fax: 061-471201
Email: dbshannon@esatlink.com
Web: http://www.debidcom
SIC: 29520 Employees: 525
Industrial Diamonds
Mr Christian Haultner Managing Director
Ms Carmel Sexton Financial Controller
Mr John Green Personnel Manager
Mr Gerry O'Rourke IT Manager

Geith International
Grangegeeth
Slane
Navan Co. Meath
Phone: 041-9824143 Fax: 041-9824478
Email: sales@geith.com
Web: http://www.geith.com
SIC: 29520 Employees: 110
Manufacture Excavator Attachments
Mr Bart Cunningham Managing Director
Ms Paula Coughlan Financial Controller
Mr Anthony Price Sales Manager
Mr Jim Barron Production Director

Powerscreen Ltd (Ireland)
Mineska Lane, Main Street
Kilbeggan
Mullingar Co. Westmeath
Phone: 0506-32178 Fax: 0506-32443
Email: mail@powerscreen.ie
Web: http://www.powerscreen.com
SIC: 29520 Employees: 130
Screening Units
Mr John Coffey Managing Director
Ms Rita Graham Finance Manager
Mr Tony Maher Personnel Officer
Mr Rory Walsh Production Manager
Mr John Conor Computer Manager

GM Steel Fabrication Ltd
Coe's Road Industrial Estate
Dundalk Co. Louth
Phone: 042-9331877 Fax: 042-9334131
Email: gmsteel@iol.ie
SIC: 29532 Employees: 40
Meat Processing Equipment
Mr Diarmuid Heussass General Manager
Ms Briege Rooney Accountant
Mr Ken Curtis Sales Manager

Little Island Engineering Ltd
Little Island
Cork Co. Cork
Phone: 021-4353026 Fax: 021-4353109
Email: lieng@rbj.ie
SIC: 29532 Employees: 23
Manufacture & Sale Of Machines For Food Industry
Mr Martin Bond General Manager
Ms Patricia Carr Finance Manager
Mr Derry O'Leary Production Manager

Marco Manufacturing Ltd
Heather Road, Sandyford Ind Estate
Foxrock
Dublin 18
Phone: 01-2952674 Fax: 01-2953715
Email: info@marcoboilers.com
Web: http://www.marcoboilers.com
SIC: 29532 Employees: 25
Manuf & Service Water Boilers & Coffee Brewers
Mr Drew Pearson Managing Director
Mr Eugene Ryan Sales Manager

Masser Hammond
Unit 6a Broomhill Business Complex
Broomhill Road, Tallaght
Dublin 24
Phone: 01-4505795 Fax: 01-4031650
SIC: 29532 Employees: 50
Commercial & Industrial Catering Equipment
Mr Brian O'Keeffe Chief Executive
Mr Colum Dunne Financial Controller

Packo Ireland
Ballymaquirke
Kanturk
Mallow Co. Cork
Phone: 029-56097 Fax: 029-56123
Email: reception@packo.ie
Web: http://www.packo.ie
SIC: 29532 Employees: 35
Manufacture refrigerated milk cooling tanks
Mr William Walsh Managing Director
Mr Joe Higgins Finance Manager
Mr Andy Buckley Sales Manager
Ms Margaret McAuliffe Computer Manager

Digital Solutions Ltd
Knockmitten Lane
Naas Road
Dublin 12
Phone: 01-4564839 Fax: 01-4507072
Email: sales@dos.iol.ie
Web: http://www.digitalsolutions.ie
SIC: 29550 Employees: 50
Printing Suppliers
Mr Gerard O'Sullivan Managing Director
Mr David Hughes Finance Manager
Ms Marie Poole Personnel Manager
Mr John White Sales & Marketing Manager
Mr Bill Ryan Computer Manager

Euroscreen Ltd
Unit E1 Ballymount Drive
Ballymount Road
Dublin 12
Phone: 01-4196700 Fax: 01-4509929
Email: info@es-group.ie
Web: http://www.es-group.ie
SIC: 29550 Employees: 104
Printing
Mr Gerry Andrews Managing Director
Mr John Quinn Finance Manager
Mr John Moylan Marketing Director

Herald Works
Patrick Street
Boyle Co. Roscommon
Phone: 079-62004 Fax: 079-62926
Email: advertising@roscommonherald.ie
Web: http://www.roscommonherald.ie
SIC: 29550 Employees: 35
Newspaper & Printing
Mr Brian Nerney Managing Director
Mr Paul Connolly Finance Manager
Ms Clare Morgan Sales Manager

Image Machine
Image House, Clonattin Road
Gorey Co. Wexford
Phone: 055-20194 Fax: 055-20195
Email: info@imagemachine.ie
Web: http://www.imagemachine.ie
SIC: 29550 Employees: 35
Printing
Mr John Quinn Managing Director
Ms Evelyn Quinn Accountant
Mr George Wilson Production Manager
Mr Chris Gleasure Sales Director

Ko-Rec-Type Ltd
Syngefield Industrial Estate
Birr Co. Offaly
Phone: 0509-20506 Fax: 0509-21212
Email: sales@korectype.ie
SIC: 29550 Employees: 52
Produce Typewriter Ribbons
Mr Paul Hudson Managing Director
Mr Anthony Young Financial Controller
Mr Pat Seery Sales Manager

Lexmark
Eastpoint Business Park
Freeman House
Dublin 3
Phone: 01-8049393 Fax: 01-8099058
Email: irecurit@lexmark.ie
Web: http://www.lexmark.ie
SIC: 29550 Employees: 100
Call Centre for Lexmark Printers
Mr Phillip Bourdeous Managing Director
Ms Karen Cook Accounts Manager
Mr Ray Byrne Sales Manager
Mr Patrick Lubin Computer Manager

Machinery & Equipment

McGowans
Unit 2, 107 Cork Street
Dublin 8
Phone: 01-4106700 Fax: 01-4106701
Email: info@mcgdigital.com
Web: http://www.mcgdigital.com
SIC: 29550 Employees: 40
Digital Printing
Mr Mal McGowan Proprietor
Mr Adrienne Kelly Finance Manager
Mr Mal McGowan Personnel Director
Mr Dave Murphy Sales Manager
Mr Mark Cassidy Production Manager
Mr Brendan Devitt Computer Manager

Rexam Medical Packaging Ltd
Finisklin Business Park
Sligo Co. Sligo
Phone: 071-61354 Fax: 071-61343
Email: info@rexam.co.uk
SIC: 29550 Employees: 36
Printing & Packaging
Mr Ciaran Donnellan General Manager
Ms Karen Neary Office Manager

Screentech Ltd
Bray Business Park, Southern Cross Road
Bray Co. Wicklow
Phone: 01-2869555 Fax: 01-2869597
Email: info@screentech.ie
Web: http://www.screentech.ie
SIC: 29550 Employees: 140
Injection Moulding Silk Screen Tampo Printing & Sub Assembly
Mr Derek Kelly Managing Director
Mr Paul Cullen Finance Manager
Ms Leslie Kelly Personnel Officer
Mr Niall Kelly Sales Director
Mr Gerard Dunne Production Manager

Smurfit Display
IDA Tallaght Business Park
Whitestown Tallaght
Dublin 24
Phone: 01-4524333 Fax: 01-4524646
Email: sales@smurfitgroup.iol.ie
SIC: 29550 Employees: 30
Screen Print Displays
Mr Dermot Hughes General Manager
Mr Brian Allen Accounts Manager
Mr Morgan Webster Production Manager

CPM Europe Ltd
Industrial Estate
Whitemill
Wexford Co. Wexford
Phone: 053-23633 Fax: 053-24646
Email: info@cpm-europe.ie
SIC: 29560 Employees: 34
Portable Power Tools
Mr Brendan Wallace General Manager
Mr Greg Ryan Financial Controller
Mr Liam McCann Production Controller

Oglesby and Butler Ltd
O'Brien Road Industrial Estate
Carlow Co. Carlow
Phone: 0503-43333 Fax: 0503-43577
Email: info@portasol.com
Web: http://www.portasol.com
SIC: 29560 Employees: 110
Portable Gas Power Tools
Mr Peter Oglesby Managing Director
Mr Michael Boran Financial Controller
Mr Corry O'Regan General Manager

Waterford Tool Co Ltd
IDA Industrial Park, Western Park
Waterford Co. Waterford
Phone: 051-372010 Fax: 051-372524
Email: info@waterfordtool.com
Web: http://www.waterfordtool.com
SIC: 29560 Employees: 60
Portable Power Tools
Mr Bill Curtin Managing Director
Mr Martin Lynch General Manager
Mr Jim Bell Personnel Manager

Electrolux Group
Long Mile Road
Dublin 12
Phone: 01-4565222 Fax: 01-4565097
Email: info@electrolux.ie
Web: http://www.electrolux.ie
SIC: 29710 Employees: 80
Domestic Appliances
Mr Paul O'Connor Managing Director
Mr Michael Forde Financial Controller
Ms Gemma Rafferty Personnel Manager
Mr Thomas Lee Services Manager
Ms Mary Hannaghan DP Manager

Glen Dimplex
Ardee Road
Dunleer
Drogheda Co. Louth
Phone: 041-6851700 Fax: 041-6851807
Email: postmaster@glendimplex.com
Web: http://www.glendimplex.com
SIC: 29710 Employees: 1000
Heating and other Electrical Equipment
Mr Martin Naughton Group Chairman
Mr Michael Maher Chief Financial Officer
Mr Michael Murphy Personnel Manager
Mr Neil Naughton Group Export Director
Mr Mark Kirk Computer Manager

Goblin Ireland
Clash Industrial Estate
Tralee Co. Kerry
Phone: 066-7121444 Fax: 066-7121460
Email: goblinir@iol.ie
SIC: 29710 Employees: 170
Vacuum Cleaner Manufacturers
Mr Conor Stack Managing Director
Mr Joe Clifford Finance Manager
Ms Margaret Howard Personnel Manager
Mr John Kelliher Materials Manager

Krups Engineering Ltd
Roxboro Road
Limerick Co. Limerick
Phone: 061-204500 Fax: 061-419464
SIC: 29710 Employees: 500
Electrical Appliances
Mr Liam McElligott Industrial Director
Mr Pat O'Neill Financial Manager
Mr John O'Connor Human Resources Director
Mr Seamus Seery MIS Manager

Sennheiser Ireland
Spollanstown Industrial Estate
Tullamore Co. Offaly
Phone: 0506-41122 Fax: 0506-21726
Email: info@sennheiser.ie
Web: http://www.sennheiser.ie
SIC: 29710 Employees: 150
Mini Hi-Fi Headphones (German)
Mr Peter Callan Site General Manager
Mr Peter Kiefer Financial Controller
Ms Veronica Divine Personnel Clerk
Mr Philip Fagan Production Director
Mr Frank Concannon Computer Manager

Sony Ireland
82 Broomhill Road
Tallaght
Dublin 24
Phone: 01-4131700 Fax: 01-4510045
Email: sony.ireland@eu.sony.com
Web: http://www.sony.com
SIC: 29710 Employees: 35
Entertainment Products
Mr Sushil Teji General Manager
Mr Kevin Maguire National Sales Manager
Mr Pat Farrell Operations Manager

Telford Group Ltd
Main Street
Mountrath
Portlaoise Co. Laois
Phone: 0502-32208 Fax: 0502-32735
Email: mountrath@telford.net
SIC: 29710 Employees: 120
Hardware/Building Material
Mr William Telford Group Managing Director
Mr Stephen Maguire Finance Director

The Salmor Group Ltd
26 Bannbridge Rd
Dromore, Lis-burn
Clones Co. Monaghan
Phone: 1800-928555 Fax: 01-2586732
SIC: 29710 Employees: 120
Portable Power Tools
Mr Martin Salmor Managing Director
Ms Gemma Rafferty Personnel Manager
Mr Sean Maguire Sales Manager
Mr Patrick Farrell Operations Manager
Mr Joe Clifford IT Manager

Whirlpool Ireland
Font Hill Industrial Park
Font Hill Road
Dublin 22
Phone: 01-6231013 Fax: 01-6231020
Email: info@whirlpool.ie
Web: http://www.whirlpool.ie
SIC: 29710 Employees: 70
Electrical Appliances
Mr Desmond McCormack Managing Director
Ms Patricia Foster Finance Manager
Ms Imelda O'Sullivan Personnel Manager
Mr Michael Shaw Sales Manager
Mr Ray Wilson IT Manager

IDS Electric Seed Company Ltd
Cream of Irish 2002 Directory
15 Merchants Quay
Newry, Co. Down, NI
SIC: 29710 Employees: 70
Electrical Appliances
Mr Martin Rrilly Managing Director
Ms Patricia Foster Finance Manager
Ms Patricia Allen Sales Manager
Mr Sean Smith IT Manager

Office & IT Equipment

Office Equipment &Computer Manufacture

30 Office Equip & Computer Manufacture
30010 Office Equipment Manufacture
30020 Computer Manufacture

Albany Office Supplies Ltd
Unit 8-9 Phase, 2 Knockmitten Close
Western Industrial Estate, Naas Road
Dublin 12
Phone: 01-4501200 Fax: 01-4501182
Email: albany@eircom.net
SIC: 30010 Employees: 45
Office Furniture Equipment & Stationery
Mr John Power Managing Director
Ms Breda McKeown Accounts Manager
Mr Brian O'Donoghue Sales Director

Alpha Office Furniture
Unit 12 Hibernian Industrial Estate
Greenhills Road
Dublin 24
Phone: 01-4599299 Fax: 01-4599383
Email: aoftallaght@msn.com
Web: http://www.aoftallaght.msn.com
SIC: 30010 Employees: 50
Manufacture Office Furniture
Mr Kieran Malone General Manager
Mr John Reid Accountant

Brahler Electronics
6 Portside Business Centre
Eastwall Road
Dublin 3
Phone: 01-8053080 Fax: 01-8366900
Email: info@brahler.com
Web: http://www.brahler.com
SIC: 30010 Employees: 25
Conference Equipment Manufacture
Ms Winifred Bockmann Managing Director

Capco
Mount Tallant Avenue
Dublin 6w
Phone: 01-4901002 Fax: 01-4920203
Web: http://www.capco.ie
SIC: 30010 Employees: 180
Office Furniture & Equipment Sales
Mr George Appleton Managing Director
Mr John Keaveney Financial Controller
Ms Patricia Nolan Personnel Manager
Ms Frances Coogan Computer Manager

Castle T Furniture Ltd
Crossagalla Industrial Estate
Ballysimon Road
Limerick Co. Limerick
Phone: 061-419077 Fax: 061-419398
Email: sales@castlet.ie
Web: http://www.castlet.ie
SIC: 30010 Employees: 70
Manufacture Office Equipment
Mr Clement McInerney General Manager
Mr Mark Kerton Financial Controller
Mr John McInerney Production Director

Europlan Furniture Ltd
Unit 54 Le Brocquy Avenue
Parkway Industrial Estate
Dublin 20
Phone: 01-6232622 Fax: 01-6232132
Email: info@europlanfurniture.com
Web: http://www.europlanfurniture.com
SIC: 30010 Employees: 55
Office Furniture & Equipment
Mr Frans de Ru Managing Director
Ms Maureen Browne Financial Controller
Mr Tony Browne Sales Manager
Mr Seamus Kennedy Computer Manager

Fieldmaster Ltd
Unit 2 Cleaboy Tycor
Waterford Co. Waterford
Phone: 051-876995 Fax: 1800415900
Email: sales@fieldmaster.ie
Web: http://www.fieldmaster.ie
SIC: 30010 Employees: 27
Office Furniture Suppiles
Mr John O'Gorman Managing Director
Ms Maureen O'Gorman Finance Manager
Mr David Cookie Sales & Marketing Manager

Ikon Document Services Ltd
Unit 4
Nangor Road Business Park
Dublin 12
Phone: 01-6239000 Fax: 01-6230166
Email: ikondsleona@eircom.net
Web: http://www.ikon.com
SIC: 30010 Employees: 30
Office Facilities
Mr Rory Kelly General Manager
Mr Gary Owens Sales & Marketing Manager

Keltech
21 Cookstown Industrial Estate
Tallaght
Dublin 24
Phone: 01-4524653 Fax: 01-4525148
Email: info@keltech.ie
Web: http://www.keltech.ie
SIC: 30010 Employees: 50
Office Furniture & Equipment
Mr John Wood General Manager
Ms Fiona Ward Sales & Marketing Manager

Midland Office Equipment
Ken Lew Business Park
Limerick Road
Portlaoise Co. Laois
Phone: 0502-21964 Fax: 0502-22910
Email: sales@the-office-centre.com
Web: www.the-office-centre.com
SIC: 30010 Employees: 75
Stationery & Office Furniture
Mr John Lyons Proprietor
Mr Brian Deering Finance Director
Ms Poilin Hooban Personnel Manager
Mr Mark O'Kane Computer Manager

MJ Flood (Irl)
2024 Citywest Business Camp
Dublin 24
Phone: 01-4663500 Fax: 01-2952254
Email: mjfsys@indigo.ie
SIC: 30010 Employees: 100
Office Equipment Suppliers
Mr Michael Power Managing Director
Mr David Power Financial Controller
Mr Martin Keating Sales & Marketing Manager
Mr Shay Clarke Computer Manager

Oltech-Olivetti Ltd
9 Westway Centre
Ballymount Avenue Ballymount
Dublin 12
Phone: 01-4092999 Fax: 01-4092998
Email: info@oltecholivetti.ie
SIC: 30010 Employees: 26
Office Equipment
Mr Kieran Kavanagh Managing Director
Ms Dolores Launders Personnel Director
Mr Sandy Miller Sales & Marketing Manager
Mr Philip Wallace Computer Manager

Sheelin Office Group
Ballymakenny Road
Drogheda Co. Louth
Phone: 041-9831667 Fax: 041-9836170
Email: info@sheelinoffice.ie
Web: http://www.sheelinoffice.ie
SIC: 30010 Employees: 30
Manufacture Screen Systems/Office Furniture Systems.
Mr Thomas Stanley Managing Director
Ms Frances Stanley Accounts Manager
Mr Raymond Ferguson Sales Manager
Mr Tony McKeown Warehouse Manager

Sheila Moore Ltd
Stillorgan Industrial Park
Blackrock Co. Dublin
Phone: 01-2957077 Fax: 01-2957131
Email: moores@iol.ie
SIC: 30010 Employees: 25
Office Furniture & Equipment
Ms Sheila Moore Managing Director
Mr Keith Brassington Finance Manager

TOS Ireland Ltd
Unit 2 The Square Industrial Complex
Tallaght
Dublin 24
Phone: 01-4623560 Fax: 01-4623569
Email: tosireland@clubi.ie
Web: http://www.tosiba-ireland.com
SIC: 30010 Employees: 30
Toshiba Electronic Office Equipment
Mr Padraig Brady Managing Director
Ms Rosemary McCarthy Finance Manager
Ms Carol Fleming Administration Manager
Mr Martin O'Sullivan Sales Manager
Mr Peter Duggan Computer Manager

American Power Conversion Ireland
Ballybrit Business Park
Galway Co. Galway
Phone: 091-702000 Fax: 091-756909
Email: info@apcc.com
Web: http://www.apcc.com
SIC: 30020 Employees: 900
Continuous Power Supply
Mr Ray Ballard Chief Executive
Mr Donagh Mullins Financial Controller
Mr Andrew Cole Human Resources Director
Mr Peter Bates Director of Order Fulfillment
Mr Pat Bushell Production Manager
Mr Eugene Maxwell Computer Manager

Ashling Microsystems Ltd
National Technological Park
Castletroy
Limerick Co. Limerick
Phone: 061-334466 Fax: 061-334477
Email: info@aisling.com
Web: http://www.ashling.com
SIC: 30020 Employees: 50
Micro Processor Development
Mr John Murphy Managing Director
Mr Michael Conlon Operations Manager
Mr Hugh O'Keefe Research & Development

Beta Electronics Ltd
Ashbourne Industrial Estate
Ashbourne Co. Meath
Phone: 01-8350607 Fax: 01-8350628
Email: info@beta-electronics.com
Web: http://www.beta-electronics.com
SIC: 30020 Employees: 80
Electronic Manufacturer
Mr Phillip O'Rourke Managing Director
Mr Patrick Brophy Financial Controller

Euro 2000 Computer Systems Ltd
Unit 2 Willow Business Park
Western Ind Estate Nangor Road
Dublin 12
Phone: 01-4907366 Fax: 01-4097826
Email: sales@euro2000.ie
Web: http://www.onlineit.com
SIC: 30020 Employees: 23
Computer Manufacturing
Mr Declan O'Beirne Managing Director
Mr Sean Conlon Finance Manager
Ms Jacqueline O'Beirne Personnel Manager
Ms Laura Boland Production Manager
Mr Justin Neeson Computer Manager

Expert Technology
Unit 3 Furze Court, Furze Road
Sandyford Industrial Estate
Dublin 18
Phone: 01-2130144 Fax: 01-2957646
Email: info@expert.ie
SIC: 30020 Employees: 40
Compact Computers
Mr James Delaney General Manager
Mr John Dolan Sales & Marketing Manager

Flex Tronics
Clara Road
Tullamore Co. Offaly
Phone: 0506-24171 Fax: 0506-25977
Email: info@flextronics1.com
Web: http://www.flextronics.com
SIC: 30020 Employees: 450
Computer Plastics
Mr Mark Johnston Managing Director
Ms Martina Whyte Financial Controller
Ms Dympna Gibbons Personnel Manager
Mr John Peavoy Sales & Marketing Manager
Mr Martin Minnock IT Manager

Honeywell Measurex Ireland ltd
Industrial Estate
Cork Road
Waterford Co. Waterford
Phone: 051-372151 Fax: 051-376180
Email: postmaster@hmx.honeywell.com
Web: http://www.hmx.honeywell.com
SIC: 30020 Employees: 60
Manufacture Industrial Computer Systems
Mr Liam Wallace General Manager
Ms Mary Walsh Finance Manager
Mr Brendan Finnott Production Manager
Mr Derek Breslin Computer Manager

IBM International Holdings
Damestown Industrial Estate
Mulhuddart
Dublin 15
Phone: 01-8152119 Fax: 01-8153111
Email: info@ibm.com
Web: http://www.ibm.com
SIC: 30020 Employees: 3000
Manufacture Computer Equipment
Ms Angela Brown Secretary
Mr Patrick O'Reilly Finance Manager
Ms Edith Chu Human Resources Manager

Intel (Ireland) Ltd
Collinstown Industrial Park
Leixlip
Naas Co. Kildare
Phone: 01-6067000 Fax: 01-6067070
Email: info@intel.ie
Web: http://www.intel.ie
SIC: 30020 Employees: 4100
Computer Chip Manufacturer
Mr John McGowan General Manager
Mr Peter Ardale Finance Manager
Ms Ann Parriott Personnel Manager
Mr Diarmuid O'Connor Production Manager
Mr Peter Plunkett Computer Manager

Key Tronic Europe
Finnabair Industrial Park
Dundalk Co. Louth
Phone: 042-9338100 Fax: 042-9338309
Email: info@keytronic.com
Web: http://www.keytronic.com
SIC: 30020 Employees: 55
Computer Keyboard Processing
Mr Tom Fintan Managing Director
Mr Mark Lowth Financial Director
Ms Adrienne Vallely Personnel Manager
Ms Louise O'Callaghan Sales Manager
Mr Sean McEneaney Production Manager

Logistix Ireland Ltd
Swords Business Park
Swords Co. Dublin
Phone: 01-8084600 Fax: 01-8084642
Email: info@logistix.com
Web: http://www.logistix.com
SIC: 30020 Employees: 85
Turn Key Company
Mr Donal Walsh Managing Director
Ms Paula Walsh Personnel Officer
Mr Tim Hurley Sales Manager
Mr Richard Seavers IT Manager

Modus Media
Mclaughlin Road
National Technology Park
Limerick Co. Limerick
Phone: 061-485500 Fax: 061-485583
Email: reception_limerick@modusmedia.com
SIC: 30020 Employees: 200
Manufactures cd kits for computers
Mr John Heffernan Managing Director
Mr Ciaran Corrnan Finance Director

Offaly Computer Systems
OCS House Market Square
Tullamore Co. Offaly
Phone: 0506-23666 Fax: 0506-23606
Email: info@ocs.ie
Web: http://www.ocs.ie
SIC: 30020 Employees: 29
Computer Production & Training
Mr Michael Geoghegan Managing Director
Ms Mary Geoghegan Finance Director
Mr Mark Hughes Sales Director
Mr Pat Byrne Technical Director

Quantum Peripheral Products (Ireland)
Finnabair Industrial Estate
Dundalk Co. Louth
Phone: 042-9355200 Fax: 042-9355400
Email: postmaster@quantum.com
Web: http://www.quantum.com
SIC: 30020 Employees: 350
Hard Disc Drive Manufacture
Mr Kevin Devlin Chief Executive
Mr William O'Brien Financial Controller
Mr Ian McGowan-Smith Human Resources Mgr
Mr Leo Murphy Production Manager
Mr Murt O'Shea MIS Manager

Ribbontype Ltd
Bridge House
Bannow Road
Dublin 7
Phone: 01-8681125 Fax: 01-8681178
SIC: 30020 Employees: 23
Computer Form Handling Equipment
Mr John Morgan Managing Director
Ms Elaine Peppard Financial Controller
Mr Ronny Russell Sales & Marketing Manager

Viking Components Europe
3200 Lake Drive City West Business P
Dublin 24
Phone: 01-4660090 Fax: 01-4660120
Web: http://www.viking.ie
SIC: 30020 Employees: 102
Manufacture Distribution & Sales Of Computer Memory
Mr Don O'Callaghan Managing Director
Mr Chris Cowan Finance Manager
Ms Caroline Sweeney Human Resources Director
Mr Martin Morrissey Sales Director
Mr Martin Skerrit Computer Manager

Electrical Machinery Manufacture

31 Electrical Machinery Manufacture
31000 Electrical Products
31100 Electronic Sub-Assemblies
31101 Compact Discs (CD) Equipment Manufacture
31300 Insulated Wires/Cables
31400 Batteries & Accumulators
31500 Electric Lamps/Lighting Equipment
31600 Basic Electricity Equipment
31601 Electronic Equipment (Other)
31620 Electrical Installation Equipment
31621 Alarms/Signalling Equipment
31622 Electrical Equipment (Industrial)
31629 Electrical Equipment (Other)

Beaumark Service Co Ltd
Unit L3 Ballymount Drive
Walkinstown
Dublin 12
Phone: 01-4566384 Fax: 01-4508188
Email: admin@beaumark.ie
Web: http://www.beaumark.ie
SIC: 31000 Employees: 25
Manufacture Electrical Appliances
Mr Fran Wren Managing Director
Ms Margaret Genoccha Financial Controller
Mr Gordan Farrelly Production Manager
Ms Miriam O'Brien Office Manager

Bitech Engineering Ltd
Dunleer
Drogheda Co. Louth
Phone: 041-6851309 Fax: 041-6851456
Email: info@glendimplex.com
Web: http://www.glendimplex.com
SIC: 31000 Employees: 485
Electric/Gas Domestic Appliance Manufacturer
Mr Stephen Fullerton Chief Executive

Bose Corporation
Castleblayney Road
Carrickmacross Co. Monaghan
Phone: 042-9661988 Fax: 042-9661998
SIC: 31000 Employees: 140
Audio Speaker Manufacturer
Mr Pat McAdam Chief Executive
Mr Jim Curtis Finance Director
Mr Andrew Matthews Sales Director
Ms Martina O'Neil Computer Manager

Electrical Equipment

Braun Ireland Ltd
Dublin Road
Carlow Co. Carlow
Phone: 0503-76400 Fax: 0503-76404
Email: info@braun.de
Web: http://www.braun.de
SIC: 31000 Employees: 1000
Hair Care Products Electrical & Gas
Mr Christian Leonard Managing Director
Mr Brian Rice Director of Finance
Mr John Fitzgerald Personnel Director
Mr Des McEvoy Materials Manager

Control Equipment
4056 Kingswood Drive
City West Business Campus
Dublin 24
Phone: 01-4526733 Fax: 01-4660563
Email: info@cedl.ie
Web: http://www.cedl.ie
SIC: 31000 Employees: 60
Manufacture Electrical Switch Gear
Mr David Hayde Managing Director
Mr Vincent McDermot Financial Controller
Ms Elaine O'Reilly Sales & Marketing Manager
Mr Tom Lawlor Production Manager
Mr Declan Kilmartin Computer Manager

Domotec Ltd
Naas Road
Dublin 12
Phone: 01-4602855 Fax: 01-4503259
SIC: 31000 Employees: 23
Manufacturer/Distribution of White Goods
Mr Peter Donohoe Managing Director
Mr Owen Cummins Accountant
Mr Christie Deering Dispatch Manager

Eurotech Ireland Ltd
Unit E 61 Heather Road
Sandyford Industrial Estate
Dublin 18
Phone: 01-2957811 Fax: 01-2957885
Email: info@eurotek.ie
Web: http://www.eurotek.ie
SIC: 31000 Employees: 25
Audio Visual Equipment
Mr John Roche Managing Director
Mr Drago Radick Finance Manager
Ms Deirdre Elworthy Personnel Officer

Garo Electrical Agencies Ltd
126 Broombridge Close
Glasnevin
Dublin 11
Phone: 01-8303499 Fax: 01-8306307
Email: info@garo.ie
Web: http://www.garo.ie
SIC: 31000 Employees: 32
Manufacture & Retail Electrical Products
Mr Phelim Hamill Managing Director
Mr Joe Ree Finance Manager
Mr Paul Fox Sales & Marketing Manager

GB Manning Electrical Contractors (Cork) Ltd
East lodge
Carraigtwohill
Cork Co. Cork
Phone: 021-4882480 Fax: 021-4882486
SIC: 31000 Employees: 70
Electricial
Mr John Manning Managing Director

GMX Ireland Ltd
Stadavoher Industrial Estate
Thurles Co. Tipperary
Phone: 0504-23801 Fax: 0504-23181
SIC: 31000 Employees: 300
Electrical Components Manufacturers
Mr Emile Morvan General Manager
Mr Liam McCarthy Financial Controller
Ms Deirdre Deasy Human Resources Manager
Mr Sean Gilmore Production Manager
Ms Mairead Donegan Computer Manager

Irish Driver-Harris Co Ltd
Ballymount Trading Estate
Lower Ballymount Road
Dublin 12
Phone: 01-4506935 Fax: 01-4503330
Email: info@idh.ie
Web: http://www.idh.ie
SIC: 31000 Employees: 120
Electric Cable Manufacturer
Mr Tony Harford General Manager
Mr Jim Kinsella Finance Manager
Mr Tom Gibney Computer Manager

LVP Conveyors Ltd
Unit 13 Newtown Industrial Estate
Coolock
Dublin 17
Phone: 01-8477244 Fax: 01-8477079
Email: sales@conveyors.ie
Web: http://www.conveyors.ie
SIC: 31000 Employees: 50
Conveyor Manufacture
Mr Geoffrey White General Manager
Ms Marian Lamb Office Manager
Mr Steven Mulqueeney Sales & Marketing Manager
Mr Tommy Buggley Production Manager

Microtherm
Bruff
Kilmallock Co. Limerick
Phone: 061-382281 Fax: 061-382557
Email: microtherm@eircom.net
SIC: 31000 Employees: 65
Manufacture Electro Mechanical Bimetal Thermostats
Mr Brendan Corrigan Managing Director
Ms Annette Bulfin Finance Manager
Ms Lily Gleeson Production Manager

Neltronic Ltd
John F Kennedy Industrial Estate
Naas Road
Dublin 12
Phone: 01-4503560 Fax: 01-4552789
Email: neltronic@eircom.net
Web: http://www.neltronic.ie
SIC: 31000 Employees: 30
Calibration & Electrical Components
Mr John Nelson Managing Director
Ms Pauline O'Brien Financial Controller
Mr Owen Nelson Sales Director

Pembroke Electrical Ltd
UD2, Station Road Business Park
Clondalkin
Dublin 22
Phone: 01-4570202 Fax: 01-4570206
Email: info@pembroke.iol.ie
SIC: 31000 Employees: 50
Electrical Manufacture
Mr John Hughes Managing Director

PRP Ireland Ltd
Carrigaline
Cork Co. Cork
Phone: 021-4372839 Fax: 021-4374465
Email: prp@eircom.net
SIC: 31000 Employees: 25
Manufacture Extrusions & Thermoforming
Mr Eoin Lane General Manager

Renley
Unit 2 Section O, Ballymount Industrial Estate
Walkinstown
Dublin 12
Phone: 01-4198094 Fax: 01-4505574
Email: accounts@renley.ie
SIC: 31000 Employees: 60
Manufacturing of Electrical Equipment
Mr Declan McGrath Managing Director
Ms Louise Behan Finance Manager
Mr Eric Mather Sales Director
Mr Philip Sweeney Computer Manager

Spleodar Teo
Ballyconnell Industrial Estate
Falcarragh
Letterkenny Co. Donegal
Phone: 074-35361 Fax: 074-35884
Email: spleodar@eircom.net
SIC: 31000 Employees: 55
Electric Fencing
Mr Art Wilson Managing Director
Mr Robert Rowlette Finance Manager
Mr John Kelly Sales Manager

Total Retail Control
TRC House
Dundrum Road
Dublin 14
Phone: 01-2963155 Fax: 01-2963333
Email: info@trcepos.com
Web: http://www.trcepos.com
SIC: 31000 Employees: 25
Electronic Point of Sale/Cash Registers
Mr Patrick Hesnan General Manager
Mr David Douglas Finance Manager
Mr Rory O'Malley Sales & Marketing Manager
Mr Sean Martin Product Development Manager

Volex Interconnect Ireland
Breaffy Road
Castlebar Co. Mayo
Phone: 094-23444 Fax: 094-23741
Web: http://www.volex.com
SIC: 31000 Employees: 800
Electric Cable Mfr
Mr John Corcoran Managing Director
Ms Catherine Brennan Finance Director
Mr Joe Gilmore Sales Director
Mr Paul Harte IT Director

Weber Sensors Ireland Ltd
IDA Industrial Estate
Monraed Road
Naas Co. Kildare
Phone: 045-879774 Fax: 045-879035
Email: captor@indigo.ie
Web: http://www.captor.ie
SIC: 31000 Employees: 24
Sensors
Mr Brendan Blacklock General Manager

WPB
Carrigaline Industrial Estate
Carrigaline
Cork Co. Cork
Phone: 021-4372131 Fax: 021-4372423
Email: post@wpb.ie
Web: http://www.wpb.ie
SIC: 31000 Employees: 50
Electronic Buzzers & Alarms
Mr Colm Burke Managing Director

Acra Control Ltd
Landscape House
Landscape Road
Dublin 14
Phone: 01-2951264 Fax: 01-2951265
Email: mail@acracontrol.com
Web: http://www.acracontrol.com
SIC: 31100 Employees: 30
Electronic Components
Mr Fergal Bonner Managing Director
Ms Ann Murphy Accounts
Mr Aaron McNeilis Hardware Director

Autotote Worldwide Services
Athlone Road
Ballymahon
Longford Co. Longford
Phone: 0902-32666 Fax: 0902-32668
Email: postmaster@autotote-wws.ie
Web: http://www.autotote.ie
SIC: 31100 Employees: 50
Electronic Wagering Systems
Mr James Gilmore Managing Director
Mr Con O'Brien Financial Controller
Mr Noel King Production Manager
Mr Conor Gray IT Manager

Electrical Equipment

Bourns Electronics Ireland Ltd
Mahon Industrial Estate
Blackrock
Cork Co. Cork
Phone: 021-4357001 Fax: 021-4515292
Email: info@bourns.com
Web: http://www.bourns.com
SIC: 31100 Employees: 300
Manufacture Network Resistors & Electrical Component
Mr Douglas Kelleher Chief Executive
Mr Sean O'Sullivan Financial Controller
Mr Denis Cronin Personnel Manager
Mr Brian Gibson Sales & Marketing Manager
Mr Patrick Humphreys Production Manager
Mr Kieran Gardiner MIS Manager

CITI Ireland Ltd
Abbeyfeale Industrial Estate
Abbeyfeale
Limerick Co. Limerick
Phone: 068-31555 Fax: 068-31709
Email: info@cit-ireland.com
Web: http://www.cit-ireland.com
SIC: 31100 Employees: 120
Electronic Components Manufacturer
Mr Maurice Dore President
Mr John Joe O'Carroll Financial Controller
Ms Anne Kennedy Personnel Manager
Ms Joan O'Connell Sales & Marketing Manager
Mr Michael Sullivan Production Manager

Com 21
Unit 4400 Cork Airport Business Park
Kinsalev Road
Cork Co. Cork
Phone: 021-7305800 Fax: 021-4321972
Email: info@com21.com
Web: http://www.com21.com
SIC: 31100 Employees: 60
Cable Modem Design
Mr Charles Cheevers Managing Director

Convex Electrical Ltd
Unit 8 Shanowen House
Shanowen Road Santry
Dublin 9
Phone: 01-8622330 Fax: 01-8622350
Email: info@convex.ie
Web: http://www.convex.ie
SIC: 31100 Employees: 30
Electrical Assembly
Mr Emmett McAuley Manager

Dovatron (Ireland) BV
Kilbarry Industrial Estate
Dublin Hill
Cork Co. Cork
Phone: 021-4300530 Fax: 021-4307572
Email: info@dovatron.com
Web: http://www.dovatron.com
SIC: 31100 Employees: 1400
Electronics Assembly Company
Mr Michael Corkery Managing Director
Mr Richard Foskin Finance Manager
Ms Sharon Looney Personnel Manager
Mr John O'Sullivan IT Manager

Electronic Concepts Europe Ltd
IDA Estate, Galway Road
Oughterard
Galway Co. Galway
Phone: 091-552432 Fax: 091-552387
Email: ecicaps@iol.ie
Web: http://www.eci-capacitors.com
SIC: 31100 Employees: 73
Manufacture Electronic sub-assemblies
Mr Finian Carney Managing Director
Ms Jane Cooke Financial Controller
Mr Conor Gibney Sales & Marketing Manager
Ms Breda Molloy Production Manager
Mr Michael Feeney IT Manager

Faac Electronics (Ireland) Ltd
Burton Hall Road
Foxrock
Dublin 18
Phone: 01-2954220 Fax: 01-2954687
Email: info@faac.ie
SIC: 31100 Employees: 150
Electronic Control Equipment Manufacture
Mr Donal Moriarty General Manager
Mr Patrick Fitzgerald Financial Controller
Mr Tony McHugh Plant Manager
Mr Alan Coapes Production Manager
Mr David Bergin IT Manager

Feasa Enterprises Ltd
Holland Road
The National Technological Park
Limerick Co. Limerick
Phone: 061-330333 Fax: 061-330452
Email: sales@feasa.ie
Web: http://www.feasa.ie
SIC: 31100 Employees: 30
Electronic Support
Mr Eamon O'Toole General Manager
Ms Eleanor Noonan Financial Controller
Mr Tim Davern Sales & Marketing Manager
Mr Mike Crowley Operation Manager

Info Lab Ltd
Unit 16
Annacotty Industrial Estate
Limerick Co. Limerick
Phone: 061-330666 Fax: 061-330668
SIC: 31100 Employees: 70
Cable Fillers/Toner Manufacture
Mr Jack Brennan Managing Director
Mr Michael Holmes Financial Controller

Kel Electronics Ltd
Unit 1 Ballymaley Business Park
Gort Road
Ennis Co. Clare
Phone: 065-6867500 Fax: 065-6828106
SIC: 31100 Employees: 75
Printed Circuit Boards
Mr David Howley General Manager
Mr Sean Norris Accounts Manager
Mr Albert O'Halloran Production Manager
Mr Noel Hynes Quality/IT Manager

Lisk Ireland
Ennis Road
Gort
Galway Co. Galway
Phone: 091-631510 Fax: 091-633011
Email: lisk@boinet.ie
SIC: 31100 Employees: 100
Solenoid Switch Manufacturer
Mr Frank Quinn Managing Director
Mr Gabriel Moran Financial Controller
Mr John Tully Manufacturing Manager

M & L Manufacturing Ltd
IOC Chapelizod Road
Chapelizod
Dublin 20
Phone: 01-6263477 Fax: 01-6262957
Email: mlmanuf@indigo.ie
SIC: 31100 Employees: 24
Electrical Components
Mr Jimmy Mulroy Managing Director
Ms Susan Brady Accounts Manager
Mr Michael McCormack Marketing Manager

M/a Com Eurotec
Loughmahon Industrial Estate
Skehard Road
Cork Co. Cork
Phone: 021-4808338 Fax: 021-4359935
Email: info@macom.com
Web: http://www.macom.com
SIC: 31100 Employees: 250
Electronic Component Manufacture
Mr Brian McCoy Managing Director
Mr Harry Quinlan Sales & Marketing Manager
Mr Gerald O'Connor IT Manager

Manufacturers Services Athlone Ltd
Business & Technology Park
Garrycastle Industrial Estate
Athlone Co. Westmeath
Phone: 0902-20800 Fax: 0902-72621
Email: info@manserve.com
Web: http://www.msl.com
SIC: 31100 Employees: 550
Manufacturing Services
Mr Tony Boyle Managing Director
Mr John Sweetman Finance Manager
Ms Mary Naughton Personnel Director
Mr Michael Steenson Production Manager
Mr Peter Diggins Computer Manager

MDR Shannon
Bunbeg Industrial Estate
Bunbeg
Letterkenny Co. Donegal
Phone: 075-31133 Fax: 075-31597
Email: sales@mdrfastboard.com
Web: http://www.mdrfastboard.com
SIC: 31100 Employees: 76
Manufacture Printed Circuit Boards
Mr Donal Bolger Managing Director
Ms Susan Feirtear Financial Controller
Mr Mick Crossan Sales Manager
Mr Terry Quinn Production Manager
Mr Anthony McCafferty Computer Manager

Microsemi Ireland
Industrial Estate
Gort Road
Ennis Co. Clare
Phone: 065-6840044 Fax: 065-6822298
Email: postmaster@microsemi.com
Web: http://www.microsemi.ie
SIC: 31100 Employees: 170
Electronic Components Manufacture
Mr Richard Finn General Manager
Mr Eamon Keane Financial Controller
Ms Patricia Moloney Personnel Manager
Mr Fergal Downey Computer Department

Millstreet Contract Electronic Ltd
West End
Millstreet
Cork Co. Cork
Phone: 029-70607 Fax: 029-70821
SIC: 31100 Employees: 60
Electronic Assembly
Ms Marie Fitzgerald Manager

Molex Ireland Ltd
Shannon Industrial Estate
Shannon Co. Clare
Phone: 061-471566 Fax: 061-702700
Web: http://www.molex.com
SIC: 31100 Employees: 700
Electronic Sub-Assemblies
Mr Pat Kirby Managing Director
Mr Malachy Darcy Finance Manager
Mr John O'Brien Personnel Manager
Mr Liam Buckley Production Manager
Mr Tom Ryan Computer Manager

Pulse Engineering Ireland
Dunmore Road
Tuam Co. Galway
Phone: 093-70300 Fax: 093-70301
SIC: 31100 Employees: 108
Manufacture & Design of Electronic Components
Mr Michael Gilmartin Managing Director
Ms Patricia Nolan Personnel Manager

Ship Company Ltd
Killarney Road
Macroom Co. Cork
Phone: 026-41314 Fax: 026-42083
Email: sales@ship.ie
Web: http://www.ship.ie
SIC: 31100 Employees: 35
Printed Circuit Boards
Mr Sten Bjorsell Managing Director
Ms Noreen Lynes Finance Manager
Mr Niall Kelleher Sales Manager
Ms Mary O'Leary Production Manager

SMTC
Derrybeg Industrial Estate
Donegal Co. Donegal
Phone: 075-31266 Fax: 075-31723
Email: postmaster@do.smtc.com
Web: http://www.smtc.com
SIC: 31100 Employees: 220
Manufacture Cable Harnesses For Telecommunications Industry
Mr Pat Moore Operations Director

Teradyne Ireland Ltd
Blanchardstown Industrial Estate
Blanchardstown
Dublin 15
Phone: 01-8202299 Fax: 01-8203586
Web: http://www.teradyne.com
SIC: 31100 Employees: 330
Back Panel Interconnect Systems Manufacturing
Mr Colm Fitzpatrick General Manager
Mr Liam Foster Finance Manager
Mr Ian Walsh Personnel Manager
Mr Tony Painter Sales & Marketing Manager
Mr Gerry Shaw Production Manager
Ms Yi Zhang Computer Manager

Tolga Services Ltd
Mungret Enterprise Centre
Mungret Street
Limerick Co. Limerick
Phone: 061-418343 Fax: 061-418348
Email: tolga@tinet.ie
SIC: 31100 Employees: 90
Electrical Sub Assemblies & Light Engineering
Mr John O'Connell Managing Director
Mr Jim O'Connell Financial Controller

Transnova Teo
Costello Industrial Estate
Costello
Galway Co. Galway
Phone: 091-572245 Fax: 091-572175
Email: info@transnova.ie
Web: http://www.transnova.ie
SIC: 31100 Employees: 40
Electronic Sub Assemblies
Ms Nora Nee Managing Director
Mr Patrick McHugh Sales Manager
Mr Seamus Gillespie Technical Director

Maxell Europe Ltd
Poppintree Industrial Estate
Finglas
Dublin 11
Phone: 01-8343707 Fax: 01-8343767
Email: info@maxell.com
Web: http://www.cu.maxell.com
SIC: 31101 Employees: 95
CD Replication
Mr Masahiro Suzuki Chief Engineer
Mr Denis Dwyer General Manager
Mr John Dooley Production Manager

Raidtec Corporation
Castle Road
Little Island
Cork Co. Cork
Phone: 021-4353440 Fax: 021-4353799
Email: raidtec@raidtec.ie
Web: http://www.raidtec.com
SIC: 31101 Employees: 100
Disc Arrays & Sub Systems
Mr Noel May Managing Director
Mr Michael O'Brien Finance Manager
Mr Pat Kerr Personnel Manager
Ms Orla Donohoe Sales Manager
Mr Philip Scott Production Manager
Mr Don Moriarty Computer Manager

Act Manufacturing Europe
Unit 2008 City West Business Park
Naas Road
Dublin 24
Phone: 01-4035200 Fax: 01-4035299
Email: info@actirl.com
Web: http://www.actirl.com
SIC: 31300 Employees: 120
Cable Assemblies PCB
Mr Lee Boggi Managing Director
Mr Paul Goheen Customer Services Manager
Ms Catherine Tully Production Manager

Capital Fencing
Stanaway Drive
Kimmage
Dublin 12
Phone: 01-4901401 Fax: 01-4561371
Web: http://www.capitalfencing.com
SIC: 31300 Employees: 35
Chainlink Mesh, Palisade Fence, Welded Mesh,Gates & Railings
Mr Joseph Thompson Managing Director
Mr Don Lynch Financial Controller
Mr Tom Carey Sales & Marketing Manager

Harrington Insulation
Maharees
Castlegregory
Tralee Co. Kerry
Phone: 066-7139163 Fax: 066-7139163
SIC: 31300 Employees: 50
Insulated Wires/Cables
Mr Thomas Harrington Managing Director

Keytech Products Ltd
Garryglass Industrial Estate
Ballysimon Rd
Limerick Co. Limerick
Phone: 061-318888 Fax: 061-318889
Email: info@keytech.global.cie
Web: http://www.keytech.ie
SIC: 31300 Employees: 120
Cable Product Assembly
Mr Ian Berry Managing Director
Mr Dermot Coffey Finance Manager
Mr Govind Basnet DP Manager

Kromberg & Schubert Ireland
Industrial Estate
Cork Road
Waterford Co. Waterford
Phone: 051-375955 Fax: 051-373714
Email: kroschu@indigo.ie
SIC: 31300 Employees: 300
Cable Harness Manufacturer
Mr Michael Lynch General Manager
Mr Frank Moriarty Financial Controller
Ms Julie O'Hanlon Personnel Manager
Mr Jim Lacey Sales/Marketing Manager
Mr Michael Lynch Manufacturing Manager
Mr Keith Erskine IT Manager

Electrical Equipment

Methode Electronics
Unit 11 Annacotty Industrial Estate
Annacotty
Limerick Co. Limerick
Phone: 061-330013 Fax: 061-330803
Email: info@methode.ie
Web: http://www.methode.com
SIC: 31300 Employees: 166
Manufacture Cables for Computers
Mr Joe Sheehan Managing Director
Mr Dan Donovan Financial Controller

Nexans Ireland Ltd
Cornamaddy Industrial Estate
Athlone Co. Westmeath
Phone: 0902-75001 Fax: 0902-74968
Web: http://www.nexansirelandltd.com
SIC: 31300 Employees: 110
Electric Cable Manufacturer
Mr John Shea Managing Director
Mr Tommy Greene Financial Controller
Mr Paddy Hynes Manufacturing Director
Mr Patrick Hunt Computer Manager

Qualtech Ltd
Parkmore Business Park West
Ballybrit
Galway Co. Galway
Phone: 091-756677 Fax: 091-752418
Email: qualtech@mmqualtech.ie
Web: http://www.mmqualtech.ie
SIC: 31300 Employees: 100
Cable Manufacturer
Mr Michael Connelly Managing Director
Ms Jane Delwood Financial Controller
Mr John Power Sales & Marketing Manager
Ms Kendra Glynn IT Manager

Wampfler Ltd
Lathaleere Industrial Estate
Baltinglass
Wicklow Co. Wicklow
Phone: 0508-81168 Fax: 0508-81006
Email: info@wampfler.com
Web: http://www.wampfler.com
SIC: 31300 Employees: 40
Maufacturers of Flexible Cables Systems
Mr Brian Bible Managing Director
Mr David Lord Finance Manager
Ms Elizabeth Gibbons Personnel Manager

Wessels Cable Ltd
Aghafad
Longford Co. Longford
Phone: 043-41011 Fax: 043-41376
Email: info@wessel.ie
Web: http://www.wessel.ie
SIC: 31300 Employees: 180
Electrical Cables
Mr Tom Flynn General Manager
Mr Tim Bowler Plant Manager

Wexford Electronix
Trinity Street
Wexford Co. Wexford
Phone: 053-42599 Fax: 053-44429
SIC: 31300 Employees: 525
Cable Harness Manufacturer
Mr Brian Gill Managing Director
Mr Richard Rice Finance Manager
Mr Dermot Hynes Personnel Manager
Mr Michael Furlong Engineering Manager
Mr Fergus Sinnott DP Manager

Willich Insulations Ltd
Clondalkin Industrial Estate
Dublin 22
Phone: 01-4571129 Fax: 01-4571173
Email: willich@indigo.ie
SIC: 31300 Employees: 50
Insulation Wiring
Mr Pat Kelly Managing Director
Ms Eileen Warde Financial Controller

Convertec Ltd
Whitemill Industrial Estate
Wexford Co. Wexford
Phone: 053-70100 Fax: 053-70101
Email: convertec@convertec.ie
Web: http://www.convertec.de
SIC: 31400 Employees: 74
Manufacture Power Supplies
Mr Werner Wolfe Managing Director
Mr Colm O'Callaghan Finance Manager
Mr Michael Carey Production Manager

Schaefer Ireland
Unit 7 Bantry Enterprise Centre
Bantry Co. Cork
Phone: 027-51580 Fax: 027-51581
Email: schaefer@tinet.ie
SIC: 31400 Employees: 50
Manufacture Power Supplies
Mr Pierce Enderson General Manager
Ms Margaret Cooney Personnel Officer

TDI
Carrigtwohill Industrial Estate
Carrigtwohill
Cork Co. Cork
Phone: 021-4882130 Fax: 021-4882131
Web: http://www.tdipower.com
SIC: 31400 Employees: 100
Manufacture Power Supplies
Mr Paul Deasy General Manager
Ms Mary Menamin Financial Controller

Falks Lighting
84 Terenure Road East
Dublin 6
Phone: 01-4904813 Fax: 01-4907811
SIC: 31500 Employees: 50
Lighting-Equipment
Mr Kevin Rooney Manager
Mr Joe Kenny Finance Manager
Ms Vivian Cavanagh Personnel Officer
Ms Anette Olthert Computer Manager

James Hackett Ltd
Whitestown Drive
Tallaght Business Park
Dublin 24
Phone: 01-4527606 Fax: 01-4527743
Email: orders@jameshackett.ie
Web: http://www.jameshackett.ie
SIC: 31500 Employees: 32
Manufacture Lampshades & Lighting
Mr James Hackett Managing Director
Mr Michael Murphy Production Manager

Lampost Construction Co Ltd
Greenore Industrial Estate
Greenore
Dundalk Co. Louth
Phone: 042-9373554 Fax: 042-9373378
Email: lampost@iol.ie
SIC: 31500 Employees: 25
Manufacturer Of Lamp Posts
Mr Oliver Murphy Director

National Emergency Lighting
Newmarket Industrial Estate
Dublin 8
Phone: 01-4531388 Fax: 01-4531604
SIC: 31500 Employees: 26
Emergency Lighting
Mr John Fitzsimons Managing Director

William Cox Ireland Ltd
Robinhood Industrial Estate
Clondalkin
Dublin 22
Phone: 01-4500300 Fax: 01-4500481
Email: admin@williamcox.ie
SIC: 31500 Employees: 85
Rooflight Manufacturer
Mr William Burbridge Managing Director
Mr Gerry Hegarty Financial Director
Ms Donna Nugent Personnel Manager
Mr Peter Cowley Sales/Marketing Director
Mr Jack McHugh Operations Director

Nuvotem Teo
Crolly
Letterkenny Co. Donegal
Phone: 075-48666 Fax: 075-48139
Email: info@nuvotem.com
Web: http://www.nuvotem.com
SIC: 31600 Employees: 70
Manufacture Transformers
Mr Patrick Grady Managing Director
Mr Paul Gallagher Financial Controller
Mr Tim Boyle Production Manager
Mr Declan Grady Computer Manager

Abrel Products Ltd
Raheen Industrial Estate
Raheen
Limerick Co. Limerick
Phone: 061-304566 Fax: 061-304567
Email: info@abrel.com
Web: http://www.abrel.com
SIC: 31601 Employees: 25
Electronic Equipment - Manufacturing & Design
Mr Paul Comfort Managing Director

ADC Bar Code Systems
Unit 54 Bracken Road
Sandyford Industrial Estate
Dublin 18
Phone: 01-2957377 Fax: 01-2076766
Email: info@adcbarcodes.com
Web: http://www.adcbarcodes.com
SIC: 31601 Employees: 35
Bar Code Systems
Mr Alan O'Malley Managing Director
Mr Paddy Gough Finance Manager
Mr Declan Torsney Sales Manager
Mr Bill Arbuckle Production Manager
Ms Dearbhla Carmody Services Manager

Analog Devices BV
Raheen Industrial Estate
Limerick Co. Limerick
Phone: 061-229011 Fax: 061-308448
Email: info@analog.com
Web: http://www.analog.com
SIC: 31601 Employees: 1450
Integrated Circuits Manufacture
Mr Robert McAdam Vice President
Mr Eamon McAvinue Finance Manager
Mr Alistair Purdy Personnel Manager
Mr Mike Britchfield Sales & Marketing Manager

Anecto Ltd
Mervue Industrial Estate
Galway Co. Galway
Phone: 091-757404 Fax: 091-757387
Email: sales@anecto.com
Web: http://www.anecto.com
SIC: 31601 Employees: 40
Testing On Electronic Goods
Mr Frank Cashman Manager
Ms Anne Reddington Accounts

Ashtech House
Ballybin Road
Ashbourne
Navan Co. Meath
Phone: 01-8351744 Fax: 01-8352359
Email: info@bmcmanufacturing.ie
Web: http://www.bmcmanufacturing.ie
SIC: 31601 Employees: 75
Switchgear Manufacturing
Mr Brendan Meehan Managing Director
Mr Justin Murphy IT Manager

Automated Vending
Unit 34 Parkwest Enterprise Centre
Nangor Road
Dublin 12
Phone: 01-4533666 Fax: 01-4597781
Email: automatedvending@hotmail.com
SIC: 31601 Employees: 60
Vending Machines
Mr Ray Elson Manager
Ms Ann McClay Personnel Manager
Mr Brendan Mallon Sales Manager
Mr Kevin Burns Computer Manager

Ballyneety Manufacturing Services
Ballysimon Road
Limerick Co. Limerick
Phone: 061-301511 Fax: 061-311534
Email: admin@bmsirl.ie
Web: http://www.bmsirl.com
SIC: 31601 Employees: 30
Electronic Test Equipment
Mr Liam Ryan Managing Director
Mr Tom Costello Finance Manager
Mr Jackie Nelligan General Manager

Bart Whelan Electric
Chapel Street
Charleville
Cork Co. Cork
Phone: 063-89345 Fax: 063-89499
SIC: 31601 Employees: 25
Electronics
Mr Bart Whelan Manager

Betatherm Ireland Ltd
Ballybrit Business Park
Galway Co. Galway
Phone: 091-753238 Fax: 091-753615
Email: postmaster@betatherm.com
Web: http://www.betatherm.com
SIC: 31601 Employees: 120
Manufacture Electrical Components
Mr Terence Monaghan Chief Executive Officer
Mr Steven Meagher Finance Manager
Mr Paul O'Shaughnessy Sales & Marketing Manager
Ms Mary Kenny Operation Manager
Mr Gerry Savage IT Manager

CBE Concannon Group
CBE House
IDA Estate
Claremorris Co. Mayo
Phone: 094-71755 Fax: 094-62036
Email: sales@cbe.ie
Web: http://www.cbe.ie
SIC: 31601 Employees: 64
Cash Registers & Suppliers
Mr Gerard Concannon Chief Executive Officer
Mr Seamus Murray Financial Controller
Mr John Henry Managing Director
Mr Michael Cattigan Production Manager

Celestica Ireland
Balheary Industrial Park
Swords Co. Dublin
Phone: 01-8077000 Fax: 01-8077011
Email: info@celestica.com
Web: http://www.celestica.com
SIC: 31601 Employees: 800
Electronic Manufacturers and Service Providers
Mr Donal Casey Chief Executive
Mr Tony Campion Human Resources Director
Mr Tim O'Shea Operation Manager
Mr Frank Duffy IT Manager

Electrical Equipment

Connaught Electronics
Dunmore Road
Tuam Co. Galway
Phone: 093-25128 Fax: 093-25133
Email: info@cel.ie
Web: http://www.cel-europe.com
SIC: 31601 Employees: 200
Electronics Manufacturers
Mr Joe McBreen Chief Executive
Mr Paul Lufer Financial Controller
Ms Caroline Reddington Personnel Manager
Mr Alan Moran Sales & Marketing Manager
Mr Brendan Fahey Production Manager
Mr Mike Burke IT Manager

Connemara Electronics Ltd
Carrigaline Industrial Estate
Carrigaline
Cork Co. Cork
Phone: 021-4371559 Fax: 021-4371415
Email: connemara.electronics@connelec.ie
Web: http://www.beha.com
SIC: 31601 Employees: 55
Electronic Test Devices
Mr George Kennedy Managing Director
Mr Terry O'Reilly Finance Manager
Ms Dolores Kennedy Sales & Marketing Manager
Mr Brian McCarthy Production Manager

Credit Card Systems Ireland Ltd
Coolmine Industrial Estate
Clonsilla
Dublin 15
Phone: 01-8216611 Fax: 01-8216164
Email: ccs@fimak_group.ie
Web: http://www.fimakgroup.ie
SIC: 31601 Employees: 35
Embossing & Incoding on Credit Cards
Mr Andrew Mackey Managing Director
Mr Sandy Wilson Company Accountant
Mr David McManus Sales Director
Mr Matt Harris Operations Manager

Curtronics Ltd
Unit M6 Smithstown Industrial Estate
Shannon Co. Clare
Phone: 061-360770 Fax: 061-364909
Email: info@curtronics.ie
Web: http://www.curtronics.ie
SIC: 31601 Employees: 80
Mobile Phone Components
Mr Eddie Curran General Manager
Ms Kitty Curran Personnel Director

Data Display Co Ltd
Deerpark Industrial Estate
Ennistymon
Ennis Co. Clare
Phone: 065-7071242 Fax: 065-7071311
Email: ddisplay@iol.ie
Web: http://www.data-display.com
SIC: 31601 Employees: 120
Manufacture Electronic Displays
Mr Kevin Neville Manager
Mr Noel Stapleton Financial Controller
Mr Eugene Phillips Personnel Manager
Mr Paul Neville Sales Manager
Mr Gerry Sadler Computer Manager

Datac Control International Ltd
Unit 19 Enterprise Centre
Pearse Street
Dublin 2
Phone: 01-6717377 Fax: 01-6717470
Email: info@datac-control.com
Web: http://www.datac-control.com
SIC: 31601 Employees: 200
Scada & Telemetry Company
Mr Cyril Kerr Managing Director
Mr Sean Dunne Financial Controller
Mr Raymond O'Flaherty Sales Manager
Mr Eamon Lawler Production Manager

Eltex Manufacturing Ltd
Railway Road
Templemore
Thurles Co. Tipperary
Phone: 0504-31433 Fax: 0504-31002
Email: info@eltex.ie
Web: http://www.eltex.ie
SIC: 31601 Employees: 50
Electronic Stop Devices
Mr Frank Morris Managing Director
Mr Pat Gormley IT Manager
Mr Seamus O'Dwyer Production Manager

Embassy Components
68 Kenyon Street
Nenagh Co. Tipperary
Phone: 067-29144 Fax: 067-41684
Email: embassy@iol.ie
SIC: 31601 Employees: 93
Electronic Equipment - Manufacturing & Design
Mr Tony Hompton Manager

Ericsson Systems Expertise Ltd
Ericsson Software Campus
Athlone Co. Westmeath
Phone: 0902-74601 Fax: 0902-31304
Web: http://www.ericsson.net
SIC: 31601 Employees: 500
Electronics
Mr Michael Gallagher Managing Director
Mr Martin Ryan Finance Manager
Mr Michael McGan Human Resources Manager

Factron Ltd
Unit 12 Ashbourne Industrial Park
Ashbourne
Navan Co. Meath
Phone: 01-8352718 Fax: 01-8353159
Email: gfactron@eircom.net
SIC: 31601 Employees: 25
Manufacture Electronic Circuit Boards
Mr Gerald Francis Managing Director

Furey Vending
Claregalway
Galway Co. Galway
Phone: 091-791161 Fax: 091-793201
SIC: 31601 Employees: 35
Vending
Mr Kevin Furey Proprietor

GDS
Display House, Broomhill Bus Complex
Broomhill Road, Tallaght
Dublin 24
Phone: 01-4521122 Fax: 01-4521277
SIC: 31601 Employees: 28
Graphics & Display Systems
Mr Nick Brittan Managing Director
Ms Jackie Curtis Financial Controller
Mr Alan Leckie Director of Personnel

General Semiconductor Ireland
IDA Industrial Estate
Harnetts Cross
Macroom Co. Cork
Phone: 026-41401 Fax: 026-42176
Email: info@gensemi.com
Web: http://www.gensemi.com
SIC: 31601 Employees: 830
Manufacture Electronics
Mr Steven Cowman Managing Director
Mr Peter O'Sullivan Financial Controller
Mr Michael Larkin Human Resources Manager
Mr Ken Murphy Sales & Marketing Manager
Ms Anne Sloane Information Technology Manager

Gentech Electronics Ltd
Unit 7 Garry Glass Industrial Estate
Ballysimon Road
Limerick Co. Limerick
Phone: 061-316077 Fax: 061-310995
Email: gentech@iol.ie
Web: http://www.gentechireland.com
SIC: 31601 Employees: 25
Subcontract Manufacture of Electronics
Mr Matthew Kavanagh Managing Director
Mr Maurice McNernen Finance Manager

Great Island Vending
Tay Road
Cobh Co. Cork
Phone: 021-4811528 Fax: 021-4811528
SIC: 31601 Employees: 85
Vending Machines
Mr Kevin O'Flynn Director

Klockner Moeller Ireland
Unit 94B Lagan Road
Dublin Industrial Estate
Dublin 11
Phone: 01-8300400 Fax: 01-8300537
Email: klockner@iol.ie
SIC: 31601 Employees: 40
Manufacture Electrical Switch Gear
Mr Derek Farrell Commercial Director
Mr Harry Farrell Marketing Director
Mr Shane Madden Production Director

Litho Circuits Ltd
Carbery Cottage
Caherass, Croom
Limerick Co. Limerick
Phone: 061-419251 Fax: 061-397444
Email: info@litho-circuits.com
Web: http://www.litho-circuits.com
SIC: 31601 Employees: 25
Electronic Equipment - Manufacturing & Design
Mr Frank Keohane Managing Director
Mr Noel Parkes Sales & Marketing Manager

Littelfuse Ireland
Ecco Road
Dundalk Co. Louth
Phone: 042-9335401 Fax: 042-9332532
Email: smtp@littelfuse.com
Web: http://www.littelfuse.com
SIC: 31601 Employees: 250
Electronic Components
Mr Pat McCarry Managing Director
Mr Jim Kennedy Financial Controller
Mr Pat McCarry Human Resources Manager
Mr Walter Kitchen Supply Chain Manager
Mr Richard Dalton Global Manufacturing Manager
Mr Alan O'Connor IT Co-Ordinator

Massana Ltd
5 Westland Square
Dublin 2
Phone: 01-6023999 Fax: 01-6023977
Email: info@massana.com
Web: http://www.massana.com
SIC: 31601 Employees: 32
Electronic Equipment Engineering
Mr Paul Costigan Branch Manager

Micam Ltd
Sean Moyland Park
Mallow Co. Cork
Phone: 022-21345 Fax: 022-21891
Email: sales@micam.com
Web: http://www.mican.com
SIC: 31601 Employees: 85
Industrial Laminate & Printed Circuit Boards
Mr Neil Hogan Proprietor
Mr Pat Dunlea Finance Manager
Mr Pat Kelleher Personnel Manager
Mr Martin Faulkner Sales & Marketing Manager
Mr Kevin O'Connor

Electrical Equipment

Microfilm Data Ltd
Unit 7B Sunshine Industrial Estate
Crumlin
Dublin 12
Phone: 01-4731901 Fax: 01-4731904
Email: micdat@iol.ie
Web: http://www.iol.ie/~micdat
SIC: 31601 Employees: 23
Document Imaging & Scanning
Mr Richard Bates Managing Director

Nec Semiconductors Ltd
Ballivor
Navan Co. Meath
Phone: 0405-67100 Fax: 0405-67101
Email: info@nec.ie
Web: http://www.nec.ie
SIC: 31601 Employees: 350
Electronic Manufacturers
Mr Larry Murtagh Managing Director

O'Shea Electrical
Euro Business Park
Little Island
Cork Co. Cork
Phone: 021-4510700 Fax: 021-4510739
SIC: 31601 Employees: 80
Electronic Equipment (Other)
Mr John Hackett Managing Director
Ms Noreen McCarthy Finance Manager
Mr John Hartnett Personnel Manager
Mr Brian Nolan Sales & Marketing Manager
Mr Declan Lordan Marketing Manager

Optronics Ireland
Enterprise Ireland
Glasnevin
Dublin 9
Phone: 01-8082426 Fax: 01-8082283
Email: optronics@enterprise-ireland.com
Web: http://www.tcd.ie/optronics
SIC: 31601 Employees: 30
Lasers Optrelectronics Development
Mr Austin Duke Programme Director
Ms Susan Hanna Administrator
Ms Kim McDonald Administrator

PEI Technologies
Enterprise Ireland
Glasnevin
Dublin 11
Phone: 01-8372326 Fax: 01-8372411
Email: info@pei-tech.ie
Web: http://www.pei-tech.ie
SIC: 31601 Employees: 58
Research, Design, Development for Electronics
Mr Joe Madden Director
Ms David Flood Finance Manager
Ms Margaret Halligan Sales & Marketing Manager

PMC Sierra
IDA Business Park
Dangan
Galway Co. Galway
Phone: 091-519900 Fax: 091-519901
Email: info@pmc-sierra.com
Web: http://www.pmc.com
SIC: 31601 Employees: 40
Electronic Design
Mr Pat Sheehan Managing Director
Mr Charles Gillanders IT Manager

Power One
Raheen Business Park
Raheen
Limerick Co. Limerick
Phone: 061-332888 Fax: 061-335284
Email: info@power-one.com
Web: http://www.power-one.com
SIC: 31601 Employees: 32
Powers Supplies - Manufacturing & Design
Mr Antoin Russell Manager
Mr Frank Cassidy Finance Manger
Mr Dara Crowe Sales Manager
Mr David Keating Production Manager

Premier Vending
15 Douglas Street
Cork Co. Cork
Phone: 021-4315606 Fax: 021-4322418
Email: russbara@iol.ie
SIC: 31601 Employees: 30
Cigarette Vending Machines
Mr Brian Russell Proprietor

Realtime Technology
Clonshaugh Industrial Estate
Dublin 17
Phone: 01-8486112 Fax: 01-8487861
Email: realtime@realtime.ie
Web: http://www.realtime.ie
SIC: 31601 Employees: 80
Manufacture To Electronic Industry
Mr Patrick White Managing Director
Mr Paul Hennigan Financial Controller

REM
Raheen Industrial Estate
Raheen
Limerick Co. Limerick
Phone: 061-303306 Fax: 061-303307
Email: rem@gandonenenterprises.ie
Web: http://www.gandonenenterprises.ie
SIC: 31601 Employees: 75
Electronics
Mr Paudie Murphy General Manager
Mr Michael Cronin Financial Controller
Mr Sohrab Nezamabad Operation Manager

SELC Ireland Ltd
Industrial Estate
Belmullet
Ballina Co. Mayo
Phone: 097-81200 Fax: 097-81400
Email: selc@iol.ie
Web: http://www.selc.ie
SIC: 31601 Employees: 55
Electronic Manufacture
Mr Jerome McDonnell Manager

Siemens Ltd
Fitzwillam Place
Lesson Close
Dublin 2
Phone: 01-6684727 Fax: 01-2162399
Email: info@siemens.com.ie
Web: http://www.siemens.com.ie
SIC: 31601 Employees: 600
Electronic Products/Services
Mr Richard Crowe Managing Director
Mr John O'Keefe Financial Controller
Mr Gary O'Callaghan Sales Manager
Mr Ciaran Creaner Operations Manager

Solectron Ireland
Clonshaugh Industrial Estate
Dublin 17
Phone: 01-8484222 Fax: 01-8484900
Web: http://www.selectron.com
SIC: 31601 Employees: 500
Electronics Manufacture
Mr Brian Brown General Manager

Static Vision Specialists
Ballybrit Upper Industrial Estate
Monivea Road
Galway Co. Galway
Phone: 091-770577 Fax: 091-756135
Email: sales@svs.ie
Web: http://www.svs.ie
SIC: 31601 Employees: 93
Electronic Equipment & Supplies
Mr Philip Debane Partner
Ms Louise Kenny Finance Manager
Mr Martin Craven Partner

Stella Doradus Industrial Ltd
Coolfin
Portlaw
Waterford Co. Waterford
Phone: 051-387145 Fax: 051-387244
Web: http://www.stelladoradus.com
SIC: 31601 Employees: 93
Electronics
Mr Frank Browne Managing Director

Western Automation Research & Development
Poolboy
Ballinasloe Co. Galway
Phone: 0905-43359 Fax: 0905-43094
Email: info@westernautomation.com
Web: http://www.westernautomation.com
SIC: 31601 Employees: 26
Manufacture Residual Count Devices
Mr Patrick Ward Managing Director
Mr Philip O'Farrell Financial Controller
Mr Myles McCarthy Operation Manager

Western Retail Systems
Merrion House
Liosbaun Industrial Estate
Galway Co. Galway
Phone: 091-753377 Fax: 091-756678
SIC: 31601 Employees: 93
Cash Registers & Supplies
Mr Peter Greaney Managing Director

Electrofast
Excelwork, Bluebell Avenue
Dublin 12
Phone: 01-4504581 Fax: 01-4602178
Email: sales@excelelectric.ie
SIC: 31620 Employees: 80
Mfr/Dist Electrical Installation Materials
Mr Eamon Cullen Managing Director
Mr Tony Brady Finance Manager
Mr Cathal McConville Sales Manager

General Monitors
Ballybrit Business Park
Galway Co. Galway
Phone: 091-751175 Fax: 091-751317
Email: info@gmil.ie
Web: http://www.gmil.ie
SIC: 31621 Employees: 45
Manufacture Fire Detection Equipment
Mr Denis Connolly Managing Director
Mr Cecil Lennihan Financial Controller
Mr William Higgins Sales Manager
Mr Des Hennessy Production Manager

ASC Ltd
River View Park
Ballytrasma, Lissardagh
Cork Co. Cork
Phone: 021-7336577 Fax: 021-7336572
Email: offices@eircom.net
SIC: 31622 Employees: 30
Manufacture of Electrical Equipment
Mr Noel Meehan Manager

Byrnes Electrical Wholesalers
Unit 2C O'Briens Road
Carlow Co. Carlow
Phone: 0503-42044 Fax: 0503-42068
SIC: 31622 Employees: 30
Electrical Equipment & Supplies
Mr Eamon McPhillips Managing Director

C & D Technologies Ltd
Bay 132 Shannon Industrial Estate
Shannon Co. Clare
Phone: 061-474126 Fax: 061-474141
Email: info@cdtechno2.com
Web: http://www.cdpowerelectronics.com
SIC: 31622 Employees: 52
Manufacture Converters
Mr Sean Murphy Managing Director

Production Equipment Ltd
Riverside Commercial Estate
Tuam Road
Galway Co. Galway
Phone: 091-755557 Fax: 091-751299
Email: sales@productionequipment.ie
Web: http://www.productionequipment.ie
SIC: 31622 Employees: 40
Electrical Fencing & Other Agri Products
Mr Tom Keady Managing Director
Mr John Mitchell Finance Manager

South East Electrical Wholesale
Tullow Road
Carlow Co. Carlow
Phone: 0503-33494 Fax: 0503-33496
Email: seew@eircom.net
SIC: 31622 Employees: 30
Manufacture of Electrical Equipment
Mr Brian Doyle Managing Director

Transistor Devices Europe Ltd
Carrigtwohill Industrial Estate
Carrigtwohill
Cork Co. Cork
Phone: 021-4853020 Fax: 021-4882131
Web: http://www.tdipower.com
SIC: 31622 Employees: 100
Manufacture Power Supplies
Mr Paul Deasy General Manager
Ms Mary Monaghan Financial Controller
Mr Des Daly IT Manager

Vendepac Ireland
36 Western Parkway Business Centre
Lower Ballymount Road
Dublin 12
Phone: 01-4564670 Fax: 01-4564680
Email: info@vendepac.co.uk
Web: http://www.vendepac.co.uk
SIC: 31622 Employees: 70
Vending Machines
Mr Andrew Hanley Technical Manager
Ms Angela Leeman New Business Development

Anord Electric Controls Ltd
Coes Road Industrial Estate
Dundalk Co. Louth
Phone: 042-9332268 Fax: 042-9338907
Email: anord@eircom.net
Web: http://www.anord.ie
SIC: 31629 Employees: 110
Manufacture Electrical Switch Boards
Mr Anthony Nordon Managing Director
Mr Fergus McArdle Financial Director
Ms Eileen Nordon Personnel Manager
Mr Peter McConville Sales Manager
Mr John Doherty Production Manager
Mr Stephen Murphy IT Manager

Chilton Electric
Ardee Road
Dunleer
Drogheda Co. Louth
Phone: 041-6851404 Fax: 041-6851941
Email: chiltonelectric@compuserve.com
SIC: 31629 Employees: 280
Manufacturers of Domestic Electrical Appliances
Mr Muris Flynn Managing Director
Mr Olan Walsh Financial Controller
Mr Michael Murphy Production Manager
Mr David Ross Computer Manager

Excelsys Technologies Ltd
Unit 4 Swords Business Park
Swords Co. Dublin
Phone: 01-8900933 Fax: 01-8901358
Web: http://www.excelsys.com
SIC: 31629 Employees: 35
Manufacture Power Supplies
Mr Frank Devitt Managing Director
Mr David Redmond Accountant
Mr Darren Greenan Systems Manager

Hitech Electronics Ltd
Mountbellew
Ballinasloe Co. Galway
Phone: 0905-79301 Fax: 0905-79415
Email: hitechel@iol.ie
SIC: 31629 Employees: 80
Manufacture of Electrical Appliances
Mr Peter Callan Managing Director
Ms Theresa Noon Finance Manager
Ms Geraldine Geraghty Sales Manager
Mr Charles O'Donoghue Production Manager
Mr Patrick Callan Materials Manager

Kieran Electrical Ltd
Unit H3 Ballycureen
Frankfield
Cork Co. Cork
Phone: 021-4310910 Fax: 021-4315811
SIC: 31629 Employees: 30
Manufacture Electrical Equipment & Supplies
Mr Peter Kiernan Manager

Kostal Ireland
Mountmahon
Abbeyfeale
Limerick Co. Limerick
Phone: 068-31444 Fax: 068-31674
Email: info@kostal.com
Web: http://www.kostal.com
SIC: 31629 Employees: 1000
Automotive Components Manufacturers
Mr Michael Genster Manager
Mr Paul Morris Financial Controller
Mr John Mangan Personnel Manager
Mr Holger Muller Sales Manager
Mr Brendan Walsh Production Manager
Mr Eric Haneton IT Manager

Kraus & Naimer (Irl) Ltd
Bay 145 Shannon Free Zone
Shannon Co. Clare
Phone: 061-471922 Fax: 061-471084
Email: postmaster@krausnaimer.ie
SIC: 31629 Employees: 150
Manufacture & Distribute Electrical Switch Gear
Mr PJ MacGoey General Manager
Ms Pauline Lowe Financial Controller
Ms Carmel Ryan Personnel Officer
Mr Oisin Burke Technical Sales Engineer
Mr Eoin Fitzgerald Production Director
Ms Una O'Brien Computer Manager

MGM Electronics Ltd
Gortlandroe Industrial Estate
Nenagh Co. Tipperary
Phone: 067-33722 Fax: 067-33724
Email: info@mgmelec.iol.ie
Web: http://www.mgmelec.iol.ie
SIC: 31629 Employees: 45
Manufacture Electrical Components
Mr John Geehan Managing Director
Mr Jack Kennedy Production Manager

Moran Electrical
Knockkranny
Westport Co. Mayo
Phone: 098-28877 Fax: 098-28997
Email: moranelectrical@eircom.net
SIC: 31629 Employees: 30
Manufacture Electrical Equipment & Supplies
Mr Michael Moran Proprietor

Novum Overseas Ltd
Kilmore Road
Artane
Dublin 5
Phone: 01-8473266 Fax: 01-8473246
Web: http://www.novum.ie
SIC: 31629 Employees: 140
Commercial Refrigeration Manufacture
Mr Richard Sheridan Managing Director
Mr Anthony Giles Finance Manager

Power Engineering
Ring
Dungarvan Co. Waterford
Phone: 058-46271 Fax: 058-46452
Email: info@powerflo.ie
Web: http://www.powerflo.ie
SIC: 31629 Employees: 35
Manufacture Of Electrical Equipment
Mr John Power Manager
Mr James Byrne Accountant
Mr Frank Lynch Production Director

Theo Benning GMBH
Whitemill Industrial Estate
Wexford Co. Wexford
Phone: 053-43155 Fax: 053-41841
Email: info@benning.ie
SIC: 31629 Employees: 160
Manufacture Electrical Test Equipment
Mr Charles Baron General Manager
Ms Eilish O'Connor Finance Manager
Mr Pat Nugent Personnel Manager

Walden Electrical Contracting
3 Anglesea Street
Clonmel Co. Tipperary
Phone: 052-23677 Fax: 052-22286
Email: tgw@iol.ie
Web: http://www.waldenelectrical.com
SIC: 31629 Employees: 50
Electrical Installations
Mr Thomas Walsh Partner
Ms Pamela Corcoran Finance Manager
Ms Audrey O'Donoghue Personnel Manager
Mr Walter Holden Partner

Radio, TV & Communication Manufacture

32 Radio, TV & Communication Manufacture
32100 Control Systems
32201 Telephone Equipment
32202 Radio & Electronic Capital Goods
32300 Non Active Components

ABB Process Automation
Finnabair Industrial Park
Dundalk Co. Louth
Phone: 042-9385100 Fax: 042-9385124
Email: hr.dept@ie.abb.com
Web: http://www.abb.com/ie
SIC: 32100 Employees: 95
Automatic Control Systems Manufacture
Mr Tom O'Reilly Managing Director
Ms Margaret Nolan Financial Controller
Ms Elizabeth Lennon Personnel Manager
Mr Frank Carolan Marketing Manager
Mr John McKeever IT Manager

BS & B Safety Systems Ltd
Raheen Industrial Estate
Raheen
Limerick Co. Limerick
Phone: 061-227022 Fax: 061-227987
Email: info@bsb.ie
Web: http://www.bsb.ie
SIC: 32100 Employees: 83
Safety Systems
Dr Joe Isso General Manager
Mr Seamus Hickey Accountant
Ms Geraldine Raddie Personnel Director
Mr Walter Kennedy Sales Manager
Mr Noel Narnett MIS Manager

Kinetics Fluid Systems Ltd
89B Lagan Road
Dublin Industrial Estate
Dublin 11
Phone: 01-8305088 Fax: 01-8305291
Email: kinetics@iol.ie
SIC: 32100 Employees: 30
Manufacture Mass Flow Controls
Mr Peter English General Manager
Mr Billy Mulcahy Financial Controller
Mr Chris Delaney Personnel Manager
Mr PJ Ryan Computer Manager

Logstrup (Ireland) Ltd
Dunmore Road
Tuam Co. Galway
Phone: 093-24833 Fax: 093-70901
Email: info@logstrup.ie
Web: http://www.logstrup.com
SIC: 32100 Employees: 65
Manufacture Control Panels
Mr Sean Mulryan Managing Director
Mr John Clarke Financial Controller
Mr Rory O'Connell IT Manager

Eircom Business Systems
Estuary House
Henry Street
Limerick Co. Limerick
Phone: 061-312345 Fax: 061-400922
Email: info@eircom.ie
Web: http://www.eircom.ie
SIC: 32201 Employees: 45
Telephone Equipment
Mr Tim Brosnan Manager
Mr Pat Toland Sales Manager

Electromaster Ltd
73 Mespil Road
Dublin 4
Phone: 01-6601611 Fax: 01-6601575
Email: electromaster@eircom.net
Web: http://www.electromaster.ie
SIC: 32201 Employees: 28
Telephone Equipment & Maintenance & Service
Mr James Dunne Managing Director
Mr Jim Condon Finance Manager
Mr Paul Doyle Sales Manager
Mr Brendan Ryan IT Manager

Motorola B V
Newtown Park
Holybanks
Swords Co. Dublin
Phone: 01-8408866 Fax: 01-8408290
Web: http://www.motorola.com
SIC: 32201 Employees: 1700
Manufacture Mobile Phones
Mr Noel Fogarty Site General Manager
Mr John O'Connor Financial Controller
Mr John Lenihan MIS Manager

Soft-Ex
South County Business Park
Leopardstown
Dublin 18
Phone: 01-2416600 Fax: 01-2956290
Email: info@soft-ex.net
Web: http://www.soft-ex.net
SIC: 32201 Employees: 100
Communications Management Solutions
Mr Henry Woods Chief Executive Officer
Mr Ian Sparling Chief Financial Officer
Mr Ken Francis Sales & Marketing Manager
Mr John O'Regan Computer Manager

Tecnomen Ltd
Shannon Industrial Estate
Shannon Co. Clare
Phone: 061-702200 Fax: 061-702201
Email: sales@tecnomen.ie
Web: http://www.tecnomen.ie
SIC: 32201 Employees: 125
Telephone Telegraph Apparatus
Mr Paul Fitzgerald Managing Director
Ms Anne Hannan Financial Controller
Ms Jackie Crampton Personnel Manager
Mr Philip Hayes Sales Manager
Mr Alan Copley Operation Manager

Amatech ECM
Baile Na hAbhann
Galway Co. Galway
Phone: 091-506900 Fax: 091-506901
Email: info@amatech.ie
Web: http://www.amatech.com
SIC: 32202 Employees: 30
Radio Frequency ID Tags & Smart Cards
Mr Seamus O'Keeffe Manager

Medical, Precision & Optical Manufacture

33 Medical, Precision & Optical Manufacture
33000 Precision Instruments
33100 Medical/Surgical Equipment
33200 Measuring/Checking Apparatus
33201 Medical Diagnostic Equipment
33401 Spectacles/Unmounted Lenses
33402 Optical Precision Instruments
33403 Photographic & Cinematography Equipment

Clanmorris Enginering Services
6-7 Thomas Street
Limerick Co. Limerick
Phone: 061-416400 Fax: 061-413036
Email: ces@iol.ie
SIC: 33000 Employees: 100
Precision Engineering
Mr Michael Noonan Managing Director
Ms Jackie McInerney Financial Controller
Mr Eugene O'Laughan Personnel Manager

Cork Precision Tool Co Ltd
Lehanaghmore Road
Togher
Cork Co. Cork
Phone: 021-4963611 Fax: 021-4317279
Email: info@corkprecision.ie
Web: http://www.corkprecision.ie
SIC: 33000 Employees: 35
Precision Tools
Mr James Barrett Managing Director
Ms Patricia O'Regan Accountant
Ms Angela Barrett Office Manager
Mr Finbar Twomey Production Manager

Roscommon Precision Castings
Racecourse Road
Roscommon Co. Roscommon
Phone: 0903-26457 Fax: 0903-25068
Email: rpcl@iol.ie
SIC: 33000 Employees: 41
Precision Castings
Mr Patrick Naughton General Manager
Mr Syl Murray Financial Controller
Mr Steve Doherty Sales Manager
Mr Michael Bergin Production Manager
Ms Amanda Mee Sales Co-ordinator

SPS International Ltd
Shannon Industrial Estate
Shannon Co. Clare
Phone: 061-471155 Fax: 061-716584
Email: postmaster@spstech.com
Web: http://www.spstech.com
SIC: 33000 Employees: 250
Precision Tools Manufacturer
Mr Tim Ryan Chief Executive
Ms Orla Begley Financial Controller
Mr Gerry Phelan Personnel Manager
Mr Pat Monaghan Marketing Manager
Mr Sean Burke Operation Manager
Mr Carl Goldsworthy Computer Manager

Techniform Ltd
Unit 219 Industrial Estate
Waterford Co. Waterford
Phone: 051-373489 Fax: 051-379920
Email: techsm@iol.ie
SIC: 33000 Employees: 50
Precision Metal Work
Mr Dennis Foley Managing Director
Mr Gordon Wilkins Financial Controller

Abbott Ireland
Ballytivnan
Sligo Co. Sligo
Phone: 071-55600 Fax: 071-55601
Email: info@abbott.com
Web: http://www.abbott.ie
SIC: 33100 Employees: 1500
Disposable Hospital Products
Mr Mike Warmth Managing Director
Mr James Egan Finance Manager
Mr Sean Treacey Human Resource Manager
Mr Brendan Duggan Product Development Manager
Mr Tom Horkin IT Manager

Alcon Irelnd
Cork Business & Technological Park
Model Farm Road
Cork Co. Cork
Phone: 021-4344355 Fax: 021-4865165
Email: recruit@alconlreland.com
Web: http://www.sum-tech.com
SIC: 33100 Employees: 100
Manufacture Medical/Laser Products
Mr Sean Magee Managing Director
Ms Janet Hand Financial Controller
Ms Linda O'Flynn Personnel Manager
Ms Jackie Murphy Production Manager
Mr Tim Walsh MIS Manager

Ardagh Dental Supply Company
Unit 4 Docklands Innovation Park
128-130 East Wall Road
Dublin 3
Phone: 01-8551600 Fax: 01-8363991
SIC: 33100 Employees: 34
Dental Equipment & Supplies
Mr John McEvoy Managing Director
Ms Colette McEvoy Accounts Manager
Mr Glenn McEvoy Sales Manager

Baxter Healthcare Ltd
Moneen Road
Castlebar Co. Mayo
Phone: 094-22244 Fax: 094-22956
Web: http://www.baxter.com
SIC: 33100 Employees: 850
Health Care Equipment Manufacturer
Mr Chris Williams General Manager
Mr Tom Canavan Financial Controller
Ms Maureen O'Malley Human Resources Manager
Mr Harry Keenan Sales & Marketing Manager
Mr Tom Canavan IT Manager

Medical Equipment

BD Consumer Healthcare
Pottery Road
Kill O' The Grange
Dun Laoghaire Co. Dublin
Phone: 01-2854800 Fax: 01-2854332
Email: info@europe.bd.com
Web: http://www.europe.bd.com
SIC: 33100 Employees: 600
Manufacture Medical Devices
Mr Liam Downey Managing Director
Mr Niall Caffrey Finance Manager
Mr Noel Caffrey Human Resources Manager
Mr Michael O'Neill Sales & Marketing Manager
Mr Peter Cullen Production Manager
Mr Jim McQuinn MIS Manager

BD Medical Systems
Donore Road
Drogheda Co. Louth
Phone: 041-9837721 Fax: 041-9839066
Email: info@bd.com
Web: http://www.bd.com
SIC: 33100 Employees: 250
Medical Instruments
Mr Liam Downey Managing Director
Mr Niall Caffery Finance Manager
Mr Seamus MacKenna Personnel Manager
Mr Jim Woods Engineering Manager

Becton Dickinson & Co Ltd
Pottery Road
Kill O The Grange
Dun Laoghaire Co. Dublin
Phone: 01-2025222 Fax: 01-2854332
SIC: 33100 Employees: 400
Manufacture of Medical Devises
Mr Liam Downey General Manager

Boston Scientific (Irl) Ltd
Ballybrit Business Park
Galway Co. Galway
Phone: 091-756300 Fax: 091-757398
Email: info@bsci.com
Web: http://www.bsci.com
SIC: 33100 Employees: 2500
Manufacture of Medical Devices Healthcare
Mr David Toohey Managing Director
Mr Paul Curtis Financial Controller
Mr Peter Rowley Personnel Administrator
Mr Bernard Collins Vice President
Mr Liam Molloy Production Manager
Mr Tom Fitzgibbon Computer Manager

Cook Ireland Ltd
O'Halloran Road
National Technological Park
Limerick Co. Limerick
Phone: 061-334440 Fax: 061-334441
Email: info@cook.ie
Web: http://www.cookgroup.com
SIC: 33100 Employees: 90
Medical Equipment Manufacturing
Mr Bill Doherty Managing Director
Ms Angela Maloney Finance Manager
Ms Alice O'Dwyer Personnel Manager
Mr Barry Slowey Sales & Marketing Manager
Mr Gerard Sinnin Production Manager
Mr Geroid Murphy Computer Manager

Creganna Ltd
Ballybane Industrial Estate
Galway Co. Galway
Phone: 091-757801 Fax: 091-757850
Email: info@creganna.ie
Web: http://www.creganna.ie
SIC: 33100 Employees: 130
Manufacture Electronic Componets & Medical Parts
Mr Ian Quinn Managing Director
Mr Padraic Clarke Finance Manager
Mr Neill Quinn Personnel Manager
Mr Michael Moore Sales Manager
Ms Deirdre Hartman Computer Manager

Donovan Medical Equipment
Brookpark Industrial Estate
Dunmanway Co. Cork
Phone: 023-45522 Fax: 023-45827
SIC: 33100 Employees: 40
Surgical Implants Manufactures
Ms Eileen Coughlan Director
Mr Joe Portley Technical & Operations Manager

Fannin Healthcare Ltd
72 Lagan Road
Dublin Industrial Estate
Dublin 11
Phone: 01-8309211 Fax: 01-2954777
Email: info@fannins.com
SIC: 33100 Employees: 200
Medical Equipment Manufacture
Mr Peter Woods Managing Director
Mr Jude Carey Financial Controller
Ms Jacinta O'Leary Personnel Manager
Mr John Brew Sales & Marketing Director
Ms Ann O'Neill Manufacturing Supervisor

HLFBM Murphy Ltd
John Street
New Ross Co. Wexford
Phone: 051-421623 Fax: 051-421179
Email: hlfbmfr@iol.ie
SIC: 33100 Employees: 30
Curtains Screens & Bedding for Hospitals
Ms Hilary Murphy Managing Director
Mr George Murphy Financial Controller
Mr Finbar Murphy Sales & Marketing Manager

Hollister Ltd
Rehins
Ballina Co. Mayo
Phone: 096-22066 Fax: 096-21237
Email: hollist@hollister.iol.ie
Web: http://www.hollister.com
SIC: 33100 Employees: 300
Medical Products Manufacturer
Mr Pat O'Malley Plant Manager
Mr Hugh Hanly Financial Controller
Mr John O'Reilly Personnel Manager
Mr Brendan McClaren Distribution/Marketing Manager

Homecare Medical Supplies
Knock Road
Claremorris Co. Mayo
Phone: 094-81361 Fax: 094-81370
SIC: 33100 Employees: 60
Medical/Surgical Equipment
Mr Peter McGuinness Manager

Humancare Ltd
Jamestown Business Park
Jamestown Road, Finglas
Dublin 11
Phone: 01-8640990 Fax: 01-8640890
Web: http://www.humancare.ie
SIC: 33100 Employees: 30
Incontinence Protection
Mr Martin Fallon Managing Director
Ms Carol O'Shea Financial Controller
Mr David Ronaldson Sales Manager

Insilco Technologies
Carraroe Industrial Estate
Galway Co. Galway
Phone: 091-595108 Fax: 091-595069
Email: info@insilco.technology.com
SIC: 33100 Employees: 160
Manufacture Medical Electronic Components
Ms Rita Lalor Managing Director
Mr Joe McHugh Finance Manager
Mr Enda Bonner Computer Manager

Integrity Data Associates Ltd
Mervue Industrial Estate
Galway Co. Galway
Phone: 091-758366 Fax: 091-755635
Email: bridges@eircom.net
Web: http://www.bridges.ie
SIC: 33100 Employees: 50
Dental Equipment & Supplies
Mr Frank Fox Managing Director
Mr Brendan Burke Sales Director

Interventional Technologies Europe Ltd
Lisnenan Industrial Estate
Letterkenny Co. Donegal
Phone: 074-26377 Fax: 074-27456
Web: http://www.interventionaltch.com
SIC: 33100 Employees: 40
Medical Device Manufacturer
Mr Ed Pannek Managing Director
Mr Justin Welsh Accounts Manager
Ms Bernadette Doherty Customer Services Manager
Mr Brian McLaughlin Production Manager

Intraveno Healthcare
86 Broomhill Road
Tallaght
Dublin 24
Phone: 01-4520388 Fax: 01-4520864
Web: http://www.intraveno.com
SIC: 33100 Employees: 35
Medical Supplier
Mr Dara Murphy Financial Controller

Irish Ostomy Products
20-21Talbot Street
Dublin 1
Phone: 01-8554216 Fax: 01-8555880
SIC: 33100 Employees: 25
Medical Equipment Suppliers
Mr David Murray Managing Director

Isotron Ireland Ltd
Sragh Industrial Estate
Sragh Road
Tullamore Co. Offaly
Phone: 0506-46058 Fax: 0506-52616
Email: isotron@iol.ie
Web: http://www.isotron.co.uk
SIC: 33100 Employees: 30
Contract Sterilisation Medical Devices
Mr Michael O'Neill Managing Director
Ms Geraldine Cummins Financial Administrator
Mr Patrick Lewis IT Director

Johnson & Johnson Ireland
Belgard Road
Tallaght
Dublin 24
Phone: 01-4510544 Fax: 01-4510204
Email: info@jnj.com
Web: http://www.jnj.com
SIC: 33100 Employees: 102
Healthcare Products Manufacturer
Mr Eunan Friel Managing Director
Mr Michael Brown Finance Director
Ms Mary Mulkern Human Resources Director
Mr Sean Lovett Sales Director
Mr Paul O'Rourke Computer Manager

Maspac
Mervue Business Park
Galway Co. Galway
Phone: 091-751089 Fax: 091-751099
Email: maspac@iol.ie
Web: http://www.maspac.com
SIC: 33100 Employees: 42
Contract Medical Devices Manufacturer
Mr Ravinder Gill Managing Director
Ms Gill Manminder Human Resources Director
Mr Tony Killarney Operation Director

McCormack Dental Ltd
33 James's Street
Dublin 8
Phone: 01-4548733 Fax: 01-4547733
Email: info@mccormacdental.ie
Web: http://www.mccormacdental.ie
SIC: 33100 Employees: 25
Dental Equipment & Supplies
Mr Aidan McCormac Managing Director
Mr Richard Kenny Sales Director

McGhan Ltd
Kilbride Industrial Estate
Arklow Co. Wicklow
Phone: 0402-39502 Fax: 0402-39821
Email: inark@indigo.ie
Web: http://www.mcghan.com
SIC: 33100 Employees: 170
Silicone Implant Medical Devices
Mr John McQuaid Managing Director
Mr Declan Daly Financial Controller
Mr Edward Ryan MIS Manager

Medtronic AVE
Parkmore Business Park West
Ballybrit
Galway Co. Galway
Phone: 091-757261 Fax: 091-752472
Email: postmaster@medtronic.com
Web: http://www.medtronic.com
SIC: 33100 Employees: 1400
Manufacturers of Cardiology Products
Mr Peter Walsh Managing Director
Mr Pat Cunningham Finance Manager
Ms Dorothy Kelly Personnel Manager
Mr Sean O'Connor Production Manager
Mr Frank Anderson Computer Manager

Merit Medical Supplies
Parkmore Business Park West
Ballybrit
Galway Co. Galway
Phone: 091-703700 Fax: 091-771888
Email: info@merit.ie
Web: http://www.merit.com
SIC: 33100 Employees: 150
Manufacture Medical Devices
Mr Mark Butler Manager
Mr Bernard Birkett Finance Manager
Ms Deirdre O'Brien Personnel Manager
Mr Gearoid Quinn European Financial Controller
Ms Anne Pearce Production Manager
Mr Dave McNeill Computer Manager

Millipore Ireland BV
Tullagreen
Carrigtwohill
Cork Co. Cork
Phone: 021-4883666 Fax: 021-4883048
Email: info@millipore.com
SIC: 33100 Employees: 300
Medical Filtration Equipment
Mr Michael O'Dea Plant Manager
Ms Barbara Hooley Financial Controller
Ms Doreen Freeman Personnel Manager
Mr David Skelton Facilities Manager

Olympus Diag
Lismeehgan Callisham Mills
Ennis Co. Clare
Phone: 065-6831123 Fax: 065-6831122
SIC: 33100 Employees: 250
Medical Diagnostics
Mr Michael Crowe Manager

Pall Ireland
Rosanna Road
Tipperary Co. Tipperary
Phone: 062-82600 Fax: 062-82680
Email: info@pall.com
Web: http://www.pall.com
SIC: 33100 Employees: 250
Medical Filters & Hydraulics Manufactures
Mr Padraig Barry General Manager
Mr Paul Condon Financial Controller
Ms Catherine Manning Personnel Manager
Ms Susan McMullan Production Supervisor
Mr John Leamy Production Engineer

Piercan Ireland Ltd
Kenmare
Killarney Co. Kerry
Phone: 064-41317 Fax: 064-41367
SIC: 33100 Employees: 24
Manufacture Latex Laboratory Gloves
Mr John Holland Plant Manager
Ms Tina O'Sullivan Accounts Manager

Resound Ireland Ltd
Cork Business & Technology Park
Model Farm Road
Cork Co. Cork
Phone: 021-4345270 Fax: 021-4345266
Email: info@resound.com
Web: http://www.resound.com
SIC: 33100 Employees: 180
Hearing Aids Manufacturers
Mr Mark Walsh General Manager
Mr Sean Gayer Financial Controller
Ms Patricia Tracey Personnel Manager
Ms Frances Burke Production Manager
Ms Niamh Mason IT Manager

Stafford - Millar (Irl) Ltd
IDA Industrial Estate
Dungarvan Co. Waterford
Phone: 058-20200 Fax: 058-20299
Email: info@gsk.com
Web: http://www.gsk.com
SIC: 33100 Employees: 400
Dental Equipment & Supplies
Mr Vincent Cortin Managing Director
Mr John Dempsey Financial Controller
Mr Martin Hulihan Computer Manager

Stryker Howmedica Osteonics
IDA Industrial Estate
Carrigtwohill
Cork Co. Cork
Phone: 021-4532800 Fax: 021-4532850
Email: info@howost.com
Web: http://www.howost.com
SIC: 33100 Employees: 283
Medical Manufacturing Company
Mr Pat Forristal Managing Director
Mr Paul Holland Financial Controller
Ms Jan Harte Personnel Manager

TFX Medical
Unit 7-8 Annacotty Industrial Estate
Annacotty
Limerick Co. Limerick
Phone: 061-331906 Fax: 061-330725
Email: info@tfx.ie
Web: http://www.tfx.ie
SIC: 33100 Employees: 80
Manufacturing Medical Tubing & Devices
Mr Gerry Kiely General Manager
Ms Liz Stack Finance Manager
Ms Margaret Sweeney Personnel Manager
Ms Catherine Lee Production Manager
Mr Geoff Redmond Technical Manager

Trulife Ltd
Unit 3 Cookstown Industrial Estate
Tallaght
Dublin 24
Phone: 01-4511755 Fax: 01-4525790
Email: prodtn@trulife.ie
Web: http://www.trulife.ie
SIC: 33100 Employees: 100
Medical Products Manufacture
Mr Noel Murphy Chief Executive
Mr David Devine Financial Controller
Ms Helen Grehan Personnel Manager
Ms Jean Twohig Sales & Marketing Manager
Ms Kerry McMahon Production Manager
Mr Terry Carolan IT Manager

Tyco Health Care
Sragh Industrial Estate
Tullamore Co. Offaly
Phone: 0506-41311 Fax: 0506-27200
Email: info@tyco.com
Web: http://www.tyco.com
SIC: 33100 Employees: 1500
Medical Devices Manufacturer
Mr Tom Shields Managing Director
Mr Paddy White Financial Controller
Mr Gerry Thorp Personnel Manager
Mr John Carroll IT Manager

Avery Berkel Ireland
Unit 2 Western Industrial Estate
Naas Road
Dublin 12
Phone: 01-4600088 Fax: 01-4600096
Email: info@averyberkel.com
Web: http://www.averyberkel.com
SIC: 33200 Employees: 100
Weighing Machine Manufacturers
Mr Kieran Killoran Manager
Mr John Bodley Finance Manager

Cylon Controls Ltd
Unit 14 IDA Enterprise Centre
East Wall Road
Dublin 3
Phone: 01-8366626 Fax: 01-8365108
Email: askus@cylon.ie
Web: http://www.cylon-controls.com
SIC: 33200 Employees: 60
Energy & Analysis Systems
Mr Sean Giblin Managing Director
Ms Collette Caulfield Accounts Manager
Mr John O'Driscoll Sales Manager
Mr Gerald Mulvey Operations Director
Mr Eamon Kelly Resource & Development Officer

Hanson Industries (Ireland)
Cleveragh Industrial Estate
Sligo Co. Sligo
Phone: 071-42057 Fax: 071-45158
SIC: 33200 Employees: 110
Scales Manufacturer
Mr Chris Duggan General Manager
Ms Marion Prendergast Accounts Manager
Mr Jim Henry Production Manager
Ms Ann Lee DP Manager

Interparts (Drumalee) Ltd
Dublin Road
Cavan Co. Cavan
Phone: 049-4331777 Fax: 049-4361277
SIC: 33200 Employees: 40
Tachographs
Mr Phelim Costello General Manager
Mr Donal McAdam Finance Manager

MC Building Chemicals Ltd
Killycard
Castleblayney Co. Monaghan
Phone: 042-9740607 Fax: 042-9746222
Email: mcbuilding@eci.iol.ie
Web: http://www.eci.iol.ie
SIC: 33200 Employees: 45
Quality Control Test Equipment
Mr Hans Wiehn Managing Director
Ms Rosemary Marry Financial Controller
Ms Alice Duffy Personnel Manager
Mr Peter Goergen Sales Manager
Mr Andy Wheelan Production Manager

Panametrics Ltd
Bay 148 Shannon Industrial Estate
Shannon Co. Clare
Phone: 061-471377 Fax: 061-471359
Email: info@panametrics.ie
Web: http://www.panametrics.ie
SIC: 33200 Employees: 70
Manufacture Measuring Equipment
Mr Jim Gibson General Manager
Mr Jim Kearns Finance Manager
Mr Pat Hegarty Production Manager
Mr Jim Horgan Computer Manager

Precia Molen
Ashbourne Business Park
Ashbourne
Navan Co. Meath
Phone: 01-8353084 Fax: 01-8351213
Email: gtech@iol.ie
SIC: 33200 Employees: 25
Scales & Weighing Equipment
Ms Pamela Furlong Managing Director
Mr Chris Mulligan Sales Manager

Renishaw (IRL) Ltd
Swords Business Park
Swords Co. Dublin
Phone: 01-8131111 Fax: 01-8131122
Web: http://www.renishaw.com
SIC: 33200 Employees: 100
Measuring Equipment Manufacturer
Mr Mark Moloney Managing Director
Mr Martin Cooney Financial Controller
Ms Ann Byrne Personnel Officer
Ms Lorraine Toohey Sales
Mr Glen Doyle Computer Manager

Shop Equipment Ltd
Unit 4052 Kingswood Drive
City West Business Campus
Dublin 24
Phone: 01-6775648 Fax: 01-8721598
SIC: 33200 Employees: 50
Scales & Weighing Equipment
Mr Paul Evans Managing Director
Mr John Carey Financial Controller
Mr Jim Keever Sales Manager
Mr Kevin Barry IT Manager

Ansamed
Abbeytown
Boyle Co. Roscommon
Phone: 079-63038 Fax: 079-63039
Email: sales@ansa.com
Web: http://www.ansamed.com
SIC: 33201 Employees: 62
Medical Supplies
Mr Rory O'Connor Managing Director
Ms Barbara Meehan Finance Director
Ms Antoinette McTigue Production Director
Mr Paul O'Donnell Research & Development Directo

Bayer Diagnostics Manufacturing Ltd
Chapel Lane
Swords Co. Dublin
Phone: 01-8132222 Fax: 01-8132111
Email: diagnostics@byer.ie
Web: http://www.byerdiag.com
SIC: 33201 Employees: 350
Diagnostic Equipment
Mr Dan Meyaard Managing Director
Mr Andy Kettle Finance Manager
Ms Lynne DeSherbinin Personnel Manager
Mr Bill Penderville Director
Mr Alastair MacNaughton Production Manager
Mr Brendan Farrell IT Manager

BD Medical Equipment Ltd
Donore Road
Drogheda Co. Louth
Phone: 041-9837724 Fax: 041-9839066
SIC: 33201 Employees: 200
Manufacture Medical Equipment
Mr Liam Downey General Manager
Mr Jim McQuinn IT Manager

Beckman Coulter Ireland
Mervue Business Park
Mervue
Galway Co. Galway
Phone: 091-753125 Fax: 091-751404
Web: http://www.beckman.com
SIC: 33201 Employees: 114
Diagnostic Equipment /Medical Rotor s
Dr Clare O'Donovan General Manager
Mr Derek Bryan Human Resource Manager
Mr John O'Grady Production Manager
Mr Michael McDonagh MIS Co-ordinator

Biocompatibles Cardiovascular Ireland
Mervue Business Park
Galway Co. Galway
Phone: 091-752930 Fax: 091-752943
Web: http://www.biocompatible.co.uk
SIC: 33201 Employees: 100
Medical Devices Manufacturing
Mr Andrew Ferguson Chief Executive
Mr Brendan McLaughlin Financial Controller
Mr Mike Byron IT Manager

Deroyal Europe Ltd
Virginia Road
Kells Co. Meath
Phone: 046-80100 Fax: 046-80110
Email: info@deroyal.com
Web: http://www.deroyal.com
SIC: 33201 Employees: 90
Medical Goods
Mr Tony O'Shea Managing Director
Ms Margaret Flaherty Finance Manager
Mr John Sourke Customer Services Manager
Ms Carol Crowley Computer Manager

Guidant Corporation
Cashel Road
Clonmel Co. Tipperary
Phone: 052-81000 Fax: 052-81002
Email: guidance@iol.ie
Web: http://www.guidance.com
SIC: 33201 Employees: 800
Manufacture Pacemakers
Ms Deb Russell Managing Director
Mr Kieran Rossiter Finance Manager
Mr Chris Harrold Personnel Director

Keaney Medical Ltd
Clinton House
Unit 6 Greenhills Business Park
Dublin 24
Phone: 01-4596585 Fax: 01-4596634
Email: info@keaneymedical.iol.ie
SIC: 33201 Employees: 30
Hospital Equipment & Supplies
Mr Gerry Keaney Managing Director
Mr Chris Keaney Finance Manager
Ms Denise Lawson Sales Manager

Lake Region Manufacturing Company
Butlersland
New Ross Co. Wexford
Phone: 051-425511 Fax: 051-425522
SIC: 33201 Employees: 250
Medical Goods
Mr John Harris General Manager
Mr Tony Carroll Financial Controller
Ms Ruth Warren Marketing Manager

Medi-Kleen Ltd
Corcanree Business Park
Dock Road
Limerick Co. Limerick
Phone: 061-303477 Fax: 061-303479
Email: medikleen@iol.ie
Web: http://www.medikleen.com
SIC: 33201 Employees: 32
First Aid Supplies and Services
Ms Sandra Fleming Managing Director
Ms Audrey Birmingham Finance Manager

Mednova Ltd
Unit 3 IDA Enterprise Park
Tuam Road
Galway Co. Galway
Phone: 091-758288 Fax: 091-758272
Email: info@mednova.ie
SIC: 33201 Employees: 70
Medical Devices
Mr John O'Shaughnessy Managing Director
Mr Paul Gilson General Manager
Ms Rosemary Reilly Personnel Officer
Mr Charles Taylor Sales & Marketing Manager

Orthorest Sales
Milltown
Monaghan Co. Monaghan
Phone: 047-82422 Fax: 047-84697
Email: neesonbl@eircom.net
Web: http://www.orthorest.ie
SIC: 33201 Employees: 28
Medical Goods
Mr Conor Mulhall Partner
Ms Ann-Marie Neeson Partner
Mr Niall Neeson Production Manager

Reagecon Diagnostics Ltd
Bay K13 Shannon Industrial Estate
Shannon Co. Clare
Phone: 061-472622 Fax: 061-472642
Email: sales@reagecon.ie
Web: http://www.reagecon.com
SIC: 33201 Employees: 60
Chemical Water Testing Equip
Mr John Barron Managing Director
Mr Enda Jordan Financial Controller
Mr Brian Kelly Sales & Marketing Director

Trinity Biotech Plc
IDA Business Park
Southern Cross Road
Bray Co. Wicklow
Phone: 01-2769800 Fax: 01-2769888
Email: info@trinitybiotech.ie
Web: http://www.trinitybiotech.com
SIC: 33201 Employees: 170
Medical Goods
Mr Ronan O'Caoimh Chairman & CEO
Mr Jonathan O'Connell Chief Financial Officer
Mr Michael Foley IT Manager

Bausch & Lomb Ireland
Unit 424 Industrial Estate
Cork Road
Waterford Co. Waterford
Phone: 051-355001 Fax: 051-377042
Email: info@bausch.com
Web: http://www.bausch.com
SIC: 33401 Employees: 1300
Contact Lens Manufacturers
Mr James Kennedy Vice President
Mr Paul Lyng Financial Controller
Mr Dave Mullis Personnel Manager
Ms Ashling Manning Sales Representative
Mr Colin Grant Operations Manager
Mr John Geary IT Manager

Essilor Ireland
Raheen Industrial Estate
Limerick Co. Limerick
Phone: 061-227533 Fax: 061-229313
SIC: 33401 Employees: 100
Glass Lens
Mr James Crampton General Manager
Ms Madeline O'Connor Financial Manager
Ms Angela Keogh Sales & Marketing Manager
Mr Ken Browne Administration Manager

Sola ADC Lenses Ltd
Whitemill Industrial Estate
Wexford Co. Wexford
Phone: 053-63700 Fax: 053-41671
Web: http://www.sola.com
SIC: 33401 Employees: 450
Opthalmic Lens Manufacturer
Mr Derek Mernagh Chief Executive
Mr Peter Lyons MIS Manager

Organic Lens Manufacturing Ltd
Industrial Estate
Gort Road
Ennis Co. Clare
Phone: 065-6840300 Fax: 065-6840304
SIC: 33402 Employees: 150
Optical Lenses
Mr Jim Crampton General Manager
Ms Madeline O'Connor Finance Manager
Mr Colm Ryan Personnel Manager
Mr Pat Morris Production Manager
Mr Ken Brown IT Manager

Sumicem Optoelectronics Irl Ltd
National Technological Park
Plassey
Limerick Co. Limerick
Phone: 061-331100 Fax: 061-331331
Email: info@sumicem.ie
Web: http://www.sumicem.com
SIC: 33402 Employees: 77
Fibre Optic Coupners Manufacturing
Mr Masao Shimo President
Mr Patrick Thornton Finance Manager
Ms Laura Collins Sales Director

Visionplus
Eyre Square
Galway Co. Galway
Phone: 091-568717 Fax: 091-568809
SIC: 33402 Employees: 25
Optical Goods- Ophthalmic
Mr Noel Meehan Managing Director
Mr Kevin Matthews Personnel Manager
Ms Rachael Murphy Sales Manager
Ms Jennifer Staunton IT Director

Donegal Camera Centre
Quay Street
Donegal Co. Donegal
Phone: 073-23477 Fax: -
Email: donegalcameracent@eircom.net
Web: http://www.donegalcameracentre.ie
SIC: 33403 Employees: 23
Photographic Equipment & Supplies
Mr Mark Wickham Proprietor

Pemberton Marketing Ltd
United Drug House
Belgard Road
Dublin 24
Phone: 01-4041888 Fax: 01-4596916
Email: info@pemberton.ie
Web: http://www.pemberton.ie
SIC: 33403 Employees: 200
Photographic Equipment & Supplies
Mr Jody Walshe Manager
Mr Declan Gilroy Finance Manager
Mr Vincent Long Personnel Manager
Ms Marie Bonar Sales Manager
Ms Michael Campbell Production Manager
Mr Johnny Philips Computer Manager

Motor Vehicles, Trailers Manufacture

34 Motor Vehicles, Trailers Manufacture
34100 Motor Vehicles/ Engines
34101 Internal Combustion Engines
34200 Motor Vehicle Bodies
34202 Trailers/ Semi-Trailers
34203 Caravans Manufacture & Sales
34300 Motor Vehicle Parts
34301 Hydraulic Equipment

Duffy Coachbodies Ltd
Industrial Estate
Coes Road
Dundalk Co. Louth
Phone: 042-9334312 Fax: 042-9332270
Email: duffylimousine@tinet.ie
SIC: 34200 Employees: 25
Coach Builders
Mr Gerard Duffy Proprietor

Elm Motors Ltd
Ennis Road
Limerick Co. Limerick
Phone: 061-451577 Fax: 061-451020
Email: elmmotors@eircom.net
SIC: 34200 Employees: 25
Motor Vehicle Bodies
Mr Pat Kennedy Manager
Ms Aideen Fitzpatrick Finance Manager
Ms Ellen Kennedy Sales & Marketing Manager

ESTA Manufacturing & Sales Ltd
Kildare Road
Athy Co. Kildare
Phone: 0507-32088 Fax: 0507-32066
Email: general@estams.com
Web: http://www.estams.com
SIC: 34200 Employees: 25
Motor Panels Design & Manufacture
Mr Jim McGuinness Managing Director
Mr Seamus Rowan Accountant
Mr John Mullaniff Personnel Manager
Mr Liam Tallon Sales & Marketing Manager

Euro Coach Builders
Derrybeg Industrial Estate
Letterkenny Co. Donegal
Phone: 075-31528 Fax: 075-31930
SIC: 34200 Employees: 44
Coach Builders
Mr Joe Ferry Managing Director
Mr Columba Duggan Works Manager

James Mangan & Son
Dublin Road
Edenderry
Tullamore Co. Offaly
Phone: 0405-31311 Fax: 0405-31363
Email: manganjames@eircom.net
SIC: 34200 Employees: 25
Coach Builders
Mr James Mangan General Manager
Mr Michael Duffy Finance Manager
Mr Patrick Haughton Sales Manager
Mr Patrick Mangan Production Manager

James Murphy & Son (MFG)
Dublin Road
Dundalk Co. Louth
Phone: 042-9334284 Fax: 042-9333993
SIC: 34200 Employees: 25
Commercial Vehicle Body Builders
Mr Francis Murphy Proprietor
Mr Peter Nordon Financial Controller
Mr Tom Downey Production Manager

Thompson Engineering
Hanover
Carlow Co. Carlow
Phone: 0503-31624 Fax: 0503-42897
Email: thomeng@eircom.net
SIC: 34202 Employees: 100
Trailers/ Semi-Trailers - Manufactures
Mr Paddy Thomas Managing Director
Mr William Flattery Finance Manager
Mr Gerry Hayden Sales Manager

Toughline
Naas Industrial Estate
Naas Co. Kildare
Phone: 045-897553 Fax: 045-876291
Email: info@toughline.iol.ie
SIC: 34202 Employees: 50
Trailers/ Body Builders
Mr Brendan Ronan Managing Director
Mr Hugh McGlinn Finance Manager
Mr Brian Walsh Sales Manager
Mr Michael Behan Production Manager
Mr Pat Carson Computer Manager

Alps Electric Ireland
Clara Road
Millstreet Town
Cork Co. Cork
Phone: 029-70677 Fax: 029-70603
Email: info@alps.ie
Web: http://www.alps.ie
SIC: 34300 Employees: 450
Manufacture Automotive Parts
Mr Alex Ashida Managing Director
Mr William Kiely Finance Manager
Ms Breda Flagherty Personnel Manager
Mr John Foley Operations Manager
Mr Gerry Murphy IT Manager

Beru Electronics Gmbh Branch Ireland
Monavalley Industrial Estate
Tralee Co. Kerry
Phone: 066-7125111 Fax: 066-7125883
Email: personnel@beru.com
Web: http://www.beru.com
SIC: 34300 Employees: 320
Sparkplug/Glowplug Manufacture
Mr Paul Stepanek General Manager Technical
Mr Shay Cleary General Manager Commercial
Ms Gemma Carty Personnel Officer

C & C Lenwood Ltd
Longmile Road
Walkinstown
Dublin 12
Phone: 01-4501044 Fax: 01-4568502
Email: info@lenwoodcc.ie
Web: http://www.lenwoodcc.ie
SIC: 34300 Employees: 40
Car Parts & Accessories
Mr John Kavanagh Proprietor
Mr David Geoghan Financial Controller
Mr Authur Collier Marketing Director

Flair Filtration & Dollinger
Ballycasheen
Killarney Co. Kerry
Phone: 064-33322 Fax: 064-33371
Email: sales@flairirl.iol.ie
Web: http://www.dollinger/ireland
SIC: 34300 Employees: 60
Filters
Mr James Doherty Managing Director
Mr Denis Reidy Accounts Manager
Mr Tom Punch Production Manager
Mr Patrick Dennehy General Manager

HP Chemie Pelzer Ltd
IDA Industrial Estate
Waterford Co. Waterford
Phone: 051-376516 Fax: 051-375457
SIC: 34300 Employees: 130
Sound Proof Insulation for Auto Industry
Mr Tony Kavanagh Managing Director
Mr Paul Jacob Financial Controller
Mr Damien McGuire Production Director
Mr Colm Doris Research & Development Officer

Johnson Manufacturing Co Ltd
Moneen Road
Castlebar Co. Mayo
Phone: 094-23755 Fax: 094-23752
Email: johnsonltd@eircom.net
Web: http://www.johnsonmanufacturing.com
SIC: 34300 Employees: 40
Automotive Parts-Fuel Tanks & Air Pressure Tanks
Brakes systems
Mr Alexander Bannon Managing Director
Ms Anne Marie Wilmot Accounts Manager
Ms Deirdre Stakelem Sales Manager
Mr Florent Borotto Operation Manager

Kirchhoff Ireland Ltd
Lisnennan Industrial Estate
Letterkenny Co. Donegal
Phone: 074-22422 Fax: 074-24932
Email: kirchhoff@eircom.net
Web: http://www.homepage.eircom.net/~kirchhoff
SIC: 34300 Employees: 62
Car Parts Manufactures
Mr Ulrich Schroeder Managing Director
Ms Francoise Arnaud-Kieran Finance Manager
Mr Pat McNally Sales Manager
Mr Sean McDermot Computer Manager

Motogen Group
Tower House, Crossbeg Industrial Estate
Upper Ballymount Road
Dublin 24
Phone: 01-4508366 Fax: 01-4506762
Email: info@motogen.ie
Web: http://www.motogen.ie
SIC: 34300 Employees: 60
Motors & Generator Sales
Mr Maurice Lynch Managing Director
Ms Jacinta Buckley Personnel Manager

PR Reilly Ltd
221-239 Howth Road
Killester
Dublin 5
Phone: 01-8336924 Fax: 01-8531297
Email: sales@prreilly.com
Web: http://www.prreilly.com
SIC: 34300 Employees: 45
Motor Vehicle Parts & Accessories
Mr Brian Torley Manager
Mr Barry Deane Accounts Manager

Schmitter Ireland Ltd
Langford Street
Killorglin
Killarney Co. Kerry
Phone: 066-9761700 Fax: 066-9761724
Email: info@schmitterireland.com
SIC: 34300 Employees: 28
Precision Pipes Components (Cars)
Mr Rolf Bacham General Manager
Mr Patrick Sheehan Production Manager

Turnex Ltd
Waterford Industrial Park
Cork Road
Waterford Co. Waterford
Phone: 051-372098 Fax: 051-370588
Email: info@turnex.ie
Web: http://www.turnex.ie
SIC: 34300 Employees: 50
Equipment Components-Vehicle Manufacturers
Mr Ray Breen Managing Director
Mr Jim Burns Accounts Manager
Mr Darren Waugh Operations Manager
Mr Pat Dunfay Production Director

Advanced Technical Concepts Ltd
Sixmilebridge, Frederick Square
Ennis Co. Clare
Phone: 061-369334 Fax: 061-369347
Email: info@atc-ireland.com
Web: http://www.atc-ireland.com
SIC: 34301 Employees: 25
Seals, Gaskets & Hydraulic Equipment
Mr Noel Clifford Proprietor

Hi Power (Ireland) Ltd
Ballincolly
Dublin Hill
Cork Co. Cork
Phone: 021-4301742 Fax: 021-4303296
Email: hipower@hipower.ie
Web: http://www.hipower.ie
SIC: 34301 Employees: 50
Hyrdraulic Equipment Suppliers
Mr Dermot Tracey Managing Director
Mr Declan Casey Finance Manager
Ms Mary Kelleher Personnel Manager
Mr Michael Wren Sales & Marketing Manager

Lex Hydraulic Service Ltd
Ballymount Road
Naas Road
Dublin 22
Phone: 01-4594700 Fax: 01-4591776
Email: postmaster@lex.ie
SIC: 34301 Employees: 28
Material Handling
Ms Deirdre Tully Office Manager

Moog Ltd
Ringaskiddy
Cork Co. Cork
Phone: 021-4519000 Fax: 021-4519001
Email: info@moog.ie
Web: http://www.moog.com
SIC: 34301 Employees: 155
Manufacturing Electronic Controlled Equipment
Mr John Scannell General Manager
Mr Kevin McDaid Financial Controller
Ms Helga Haussmann Personnel Manager
Mr Mark Stockil Computer Manager

Nelson Hydraulics Ltd
U54 Cookstown Industrial Estate
Tallaght
Dublin 24
Phone: 01-4510622 Fax: 01-4510893
Email: neldub@eircom.net
SIC: 34301 Employees: 40
Hydraulic Sales & Service
Mr Alan Gray Manager
Mr Tony Keegan Sales Manager

Pressure Hydraulics Ltd
Centaur Street
Carlow Co. Carlow
Phone: 0503-43601 Fax: 0503-43731
Email: phcarlow@iol.ie
Web: http://www.pressure-hydraulics.com
SIC: 34301 Employees: 40
Pressure Hydraulics
Mr Robin Connolly Managing Director
Ms Hilda Ruddock Accounts Manager
Mr Noel Fallon Sales Director

Priority Drilling
162 Clontarf Road
Dublin 3
Phone: 01-8331826 Fax: 01-8334060
SIC: 34301 Employees: 50
Drilling Contractors & Testers
Mr Austin Kenny Director

Redwood Hydraulics Ltd
2 Midleton
Cork Co. Cork
Phone: 021-4613922 Fax: 021-4632601
SIC: 34301 Employees: 38
Hydraulics Manufacturing
Mr Tim Crotty Manager

Status Hydraulics Ltd
Unit1B Cookstown Industrial Estate
Tallaght
Dublin 24
Phone: 01-4514333 Fax: 01-4624495
Email: status@indigo.ie
Web: http://www.status.ire.sm
SIC: 34301 Employees: 40
Hydraulic Equipment
Mr Hugh Hannigan Managing Director
Ms Catriona McCann Personnel Manager
Mr Niall Houlihan Sales Manager

Transport Equipment Manufacture

35	**Transport Equipment Manuf**
35100	Shipbuilding/ Repairing
35200	Railway/Tramway Vehicles
35300	Aerospace Repairs/Manufactures
35400	Motorcycles & Parts
35420	Pedal Cycles and Parts
35500	Vehicles (Other)

Cork Dockyards Ltd
Rushbrook
Cork Co. Cork
Phone: 021-4811831 Fax: 021-4811595
Email: cdltd@eircom.net
Web: http://www.corkdockyard.com
SIC: 35100 Employees: 50
Ship Repair
Mr Walter Hamilton Managing Director
Ms Susan Gardiner Accountant
Mr Joe Forde Property Manager

Mooney Boats
St Catherines Road
Killybegs
Donegal Co. Donegal
Phone: 073-31152 Fax: 073-31632
Email: mboats@iol.ie
SIC: 35100 Employees: 30
Boat Building & Repairs Services
Mr Michael Mooney General Manager

Rappel Enterprises Ltd
North Quay
Arklow Co. Wicklow
Phone: 0402-32126 Fax: 0402-39839
SIC: 35100 Employees: 30
Shipbuilders
Mr Billy Tyrell Manager

Aerospace Industries Ltd
Unit 5 Balbriggan Business Park
Balbriggan North
Lusk Co. Dublin
Phone: 01-8439310 Fax: 01-8439310
Email: sales@aerospaceindustry.com
Web: http://www.aerospaceindustry.com
SIC: 35300 Employees: 50
Aircraft Spare Parts Exporters
Mr Barry McGovern Managing Director
Mr Brian Tonnie Finance Manager
Mr Brendan McGrath Personnel Manager
Ms Ann Hennigan Sales Manager

Befab Safeland Ltd
Bay C15/16
Shannon Industrial
Shannon Co. Clare
Phone: 061-471844 Fax: 061-471463
SIC: 35300 Employees: 23
Aircraft Arresting Systems & Safety Equipment
Mr Alex O'Sullivan Managing Director
Mr Edward Hynes Accounts Manager
Mr John Ryan Marketing Manager
Mr John Cleary Production Manager

Devtec Ltd
20 Viscount Avenue
Airways Industrial Estate
Dublin 17
Phone: 01-8426688 Fax: 01-8426020
Email: devtec@iol.ie
SIC: 35300 Employees: 34
Manufacture Aircraft Parts
Mr Kieran Mulhall Managing Director
Mr Patrick Smith Financial Controller
Ms Mary Fox Personnel Manager
Mr Brian Reid Sales & Marketing Manager
Mr Rory Broderick Operations Manager
Mr Gerard Fenner Quality Manager

Garrett Engine Boosting Systems
Unit 411 IDA Industrial Park
Cork Road
Waterford Co. Waterford
Phone: 051-376411 Fax: 051-355352
Email: info@honeywell.com
Web: http://www.honeywell.com
SIC: 35300 Employees: 1500
Automotive Foundry and Forge
Mr John Hickey Managing Director
Mr Richard Hogan Financial Controller
Mr David Mullis Personnel Officer
Mr Jim Grace Operations Director
Ms Lisa O'Callaghan Computer Analyst

JET Technology Centre (Wood Group JTC)
Ridgewell House
Hollywood
Ballyboughal Co. Dublin
Phone: 01-8433466 Fax: 01-8433849
Email: support@jtc.ie
Web: http://www.jtc.ie
SIC: 35300 Employees: 58
Overhaul Aircraft Components
Mr Pat McEvoy Managing Director
Mr Les Cronin Sales & Marketing Manager
Mr Ciaran Costello Engineering Manager
Mr Stuart Burn IT Manager

PWA International Ltd
Naas Road
Rathcoole
Dublin 24
Phone: 01-4588100 Fax: 01-4588978
Web: http://www.pwai.ie
SIC: 35300 Employees: 160
Aircraft Repairs & Maintenance
Mr Owen McClave General Manager
Mr Michael Gleeson Financial Controller
Mr Paul O'Reilly Systems Controller

Ruibear Motair Teoranta
Bunbeg Industrial Estate
Bunbeg
Letterkenny Co. Donegal
Phone: 075-31880 Fax: 075-31884
Email: enquiries@rmt.ie
Web: http://www.rmt.ie
SIC: 35300 Employees: 150
Automotive Components Manufacturing
Mr Paul Gribben Managing Director
Mr Neil Gaynor Financial Consultant
Ms Cordelia Nicshearraigh Administration Assistant
Mr Ralph O'Leary Sales Manager
Mr Seamus Grant Operations Manager

Shamrock Aviation Services
Airport Waterford
Waterford Co. Waterford
Phone: 051-872809 Fax: 051-872809
SIC: 35300 Employees: 30
Aircraft Repairs & Maintenance
Mr Keith Furnell Manager

Shannon Aerospace
Shannon Airport
Shannon Co. Clare
Phone: 061-370000 Fax: 061-361100
Email: info@sal.ie
Web: http://www.shannonaerospace.com
SIC: 35300 Employees: 850
Aircraft Maintenance
Mr Martin Kaiser Managing Director
Mr Pat Shine Head of Finance
Ms Niamh O'Connor Head of Human Resources
Mr Seven Domke Head of Sales & Marketing
Mr Tom Caffrey Head of Production
Mr Ray Wallis Head of IT

Smyth Aerospace Manufacturing Ltd
U13 Distribution Centre
Shannon Co. Clare
Phone: 061-474766 Fax: 061-474768
SIC: 35300 Employees: 70
Aircraft Dealers & Supplies
Mr Joe Smith Managing Director

SRAM Ireland
IDA Industrial Estate
Ballylynch
Carrick On Suir Co. Tipperary
Phone: 051-641414 Fax: 051-641688
Web: http://www.sram.com
SIC: 35400 Employees: 200
Gears For Bikes
Mr Joseph Greene Manager
Ms Jenifer Mullally Accounts Manager
Mr Diarmuid Leahy Personnel Manager
Mr Padraic Halpin Operation Manager
Mr Robert Smith IT Manager

Auto Conversions Ltd
Frederick Street
Clara
Tullamore Co. Offaly
Phone: 0506-31386 Fax: 0506-31319
Email: wilkerltd@eircom.net
SIC: 35500 Employees: 60
Manufacture & Lease Mini Buses
Mr Noel Kerrigan Managing Director
Mr Brendan Dowling Financial Controller

Auto Diesel Services
Dock Road
Limerick Co. Limerick
Phone: 061-229430 Fax: 061-301921
SIC: 35500 Employees: 23
Other Vehicles
Mr John Naughton Managing Director

Sifco Turbine Components
Mahon Industrial Estate
Blackrock Co. Cork
Phone: 021-4357901 Fax: 021-4521200
Web: http://www.sifco.ie
SIC: 35500 Employees: 400
Overhall of Lazer Jet Engines
Mr Tim Creen Managing Director
Mr Michael Shorten Financial Controller
Mr Liam Linehan Personnel Manager
Mr Sean Kelly Sales Manager
Ms Margaret Stack Computer Manager

Tony Gray & Sons Ltd
Hill Of Down
Enfield
Navan Co. Meath
Phone: 0405-46210 Fax: 0405-46325
Email: info@tonygray.ie
Web: http://www.tonygray.ie
SIC: 35500 Employees: 30
Truck & Trailer Bodies
Mr Philip Gray Managing Director
Mr PJ Keogan Sales Manager
Mr Patrick Gray Production Manager

Furniture & Other Manufacture

36	Furniture Manufacture
36130	Kitchen Manufacture
36140	Furniture Manufacture
36200	Jewellery etc Manufacture
36300	Musical Instruments
36400	Sports Goods
36500	Toys & Games Manufacture
36600	Miscellaneous Manufacture
36620	Brushes/Brooms
36630	Manufactured Products (Other)

Acorn Parks Co Ltd
Main Street
Rathcoole
Dublin 24
Phone: 01-4588202 Fax: 01-4588437
Email: acorn@acornpark.net
Web: http://www.acornpark.net
SIC: 36130 Employees: 60
Kitchen & Bedroom Manufacture
Mr Eugene Moore Managing Director
Ms Jillian O'Toole Office Manager

Brogan Jordan Homestyle Ltd
48-52 Cork Street
Dublin 8
Phone: 01-4533669 Fax: 01-4536471
Email: info@broganjordan.com
SIC: 36130 Employees: 25
Kitchen Cabinets & Units
Mr Finbarr Brogan Managing Director
Mr Joe Henehan Sales Manager
Mr Noel Jordan Production Director

Collier Kitchen Supplies
31A Jones Road
Dublin 3
Phone: 01-8551000 Fax: 01-8551104
Email: sales@collierkitchen.ie
Web: http://www.collierkitchen.ie
SIC: 36130 Employees: 30
Kitchen Manufacture
Mr John Law Manager
Ms Mairead Grieve Personnel Manager
Mr Michael O'Donnell Sales & Marketing Manager

Furniture Manufacture

Country Kitchens
The Old School House
Ballymore Eustace
Naas Co. Kildare
Phone: 045-864169 Fax: 045-864473
Email: gorcountrykitchens@eircom.net
Web: http://www.countrykitchens.com
SIC: 36130 Employees: 25
Kitchen Manufacturers
Mr Gerard O'Rourke Managing Director

Gowan Group
1 Herbert Avenue
Merrion Road
Dublin 4
Phone: 01-2601677 Fax: 01-2601672
Email: info@gowangroup.ie
Web: http://www.gowanmerrion.com
SIC: 36130 Employees: 240
Motor Dist/Kitchen Appliances
Mr Michael Dwan Chief Executive

Mica Post Form Ltd
Unit 1C St Margarets Industrial Est
Ballymun
Dublin 11
Phone: 01-8423622 Fax: 01-8423329
Email: mica@iol.ie
SIC: 36130 Employees: 30
Kitchen Manufacture
Mr Noel Pitcher Managing Director
Mr David Pitcher Finance Manager

Springhill Woodcrafts Ltd
Kernanstown Industrial Estate
Carlow Co. Carlow
Phone: 0503-42288 Fax: 0503-43230
Email: sales@springhill.ie
Web: http://www.springhill.ie
SIC: 36130 Employees: 38
Fitted Kitchens & Bedrooms
Mr Eamon Tynan Managing Director
Mr Brendan Doyle Finance Manager
Ms Pauline Murphy Sales Director

Abbeylands Furniture Ltd
Newgate
Kells Road
Navan Co. Meath
Phone: 046-21691 Fax: 046-29530
Email: sales@abbeylandsfurniture.ie
SIC: 36140 Employees: 42
Furniture Manufacturers
Ms Caroline Horgan Managing Director
Ms Ann Glynn Office Manager
Mr Barry Fitzpatrick Sales Director

Ashleaf Furniture Ltd
Beechmount Industrial Estate
Navan Co. Meath
Phone: 046-29089 Fax: 046-28061
Email: sales@ashleaf.com
SIC: 36140 Employees: 27
Manufacture Soft Furniture
Mr Eamonn Kane Manager
Mr Morgan Padayachee Financial Controller

Bargaintown Ltd
Queen Street
Dublin 7
Phone: 01-6774015 Fax: 01-6713626
SIC: 36140 Employees: 45
Furniture
Mr Alan Prendergast Managing Director

Bedroom Elegance Ltd
Unit 3 Grand Canal Harbour
Dublin 8
Phone: 01-4543124 Fax: 01-4534760
Email: bedroom@indigo.ie
SIC: 36140 Employees: 34
Furniture Manufacturer
Mr Thomas Farrell Manager
Mr Graham O'Reilly Financial Controller
Mr Brian O'Connor Sales Manager

Bedrooms Direct
Unit 4 Belgard Industrial Estate
Tallaght
Dublin 24
Phone: 01-4517666 Fax: 01-4526967
SIC: 36140 Employees: 28
Furniture
Mr Liam Delaney Manager
Mr Glen Delaney Sales Manager

Byrne & O'Loughlin Ltd
Grangeway Unit 100
Baldoyle Industrial Estate
Dublin 13
Phone: 01-8320875 Fax: 01-8325771
Email: sales@bol.ie
Web: http://www.bol.ie
SIC: 36140 Employees: 25
Manufacture Display Units
Mr Barry O'Loughlin Proprietor

C L F Ltd
Unit 20 Finglas Business Centre
Jamestown Road Finglas
Dublin 11
Phone: 01-8646820 Fax: 01-8646822
SIC: 36140 Employees: 55
Furniture Manufacturers
Ms Niamh Cameron Proprietor

Cawleys Furniture Ltd
Unit 54/56 Cherry Orchard Ind Estate
Dublin 10
Phone: 01-6268182 Fax: 01-6265997
Email: cawleys@indigo.ie
SIC: 36140 Employees: 50
Furniture Manufacturer
Mr Edward Cawley Proprietor

City Furniture Ltd
Beechmount Industrial Estate
Navan Co. Meath
Phone: 046-27084 Fax: 046-28389
SIC: 36140 Employees: 40
Furniture Manufacturer
Mr Kevin Fitzpatrick Manager
Ms Pamela Fitzpatrick Office Manager
Mr Christy Fitzsimmons Production Manager

Connolly Furniture Ltd
Emyvale
Monaghan Co. Monaghan
Phone: 047-87236 Fax: 047-87568
SIC: 36140 Employees: 34
Furniture Manufacturers
Mr Francis Connolly Manager
Mr Paul Connolly Sales Manager
Mr Michael Duffy Production Manager

Crannac Co-Op Society Ltd
Mullaghboy Industrial Estate
Navan Co. Meath
Phone: 046-21217 Fax: 046-21809
Email: crannaccoop@yahoo.co.uk
SIC: 36140 Employees: 40
Furniture Manufacture
Mr Paddy Brennan Managing Director
Ms Margaret Davis Sales Manager
Mr Paul Mongey Production Manager

Farrell Bros
Dundalk Road
Ardee Co. Louth
Phone: 041-6853418 Fax: 041-6853620
Email: info@farrells.com
Web: http://www.farrells.com
SIC: 36140 Employees: 90
Wooden Office Furniture Manufacture
Mr Oliver Farrell Managing Director
Mr Joe McCreesh Finance Manager
Ms Louise Farrell Sales (Ireland)
Mr Brendan Farrell Production Manager
Mr Adrian Crawley IT Director

Finline Furniture Ltd
New Inn
Emo
Portlaoise Co. Laois
Phone: 0502-26219 Fax: 0502-26237
Email: info@finlinefuniture.ie
Web: http://www.finlinefuniture.ie
SIC: 36140 Employees: 40
Furniture Manufacturer
Mr Kieran Finane Manager

Fitzgerald Kitchens
Bective Street
Kells Co. Meath
Phone: 046-40066 Fax: 046-40564
Email: fitzkit@iol.ie
SIC: 36140 Employees: 24
Furniture Manufacturing
Ms Mary Fitzgerald Director

Flanagans
Deerpark Road, Mount Merrion
Blackrock Co. Dublin
Phone: 01-2880218 Fax: 01-2881336
Email: flan@iol.ie
Web: http://www.theflanagan.com
SIC: 36140 Employees: 50
Furniture Manufacturer
Mr Peter Flanagan Proprietor
Ms Patricia Cassidy Finance Manager
Mr Gerard Cooper Computer Manager

Galtee Wood Products Ltd
Cork Road
Ballylanders
Kilmallock Co. Limerick
Phone: 062-46855 Fax: 062-46863
Email: galteewood@eircom.net
SIC: 36140 Employees: 101
Furniture Manufacture
Mr Sean Ryan Managing Director
Mr Noel Molan Financial Controller
Mr Gerry Fox Production Manager
Mr Jimmy O'Shaughnessy Computer Manager

Glenwood Furniture
Dunraymond
Monaghan Co. Monaghan
Phone: 047-71515 Fax: 047-83027
Email: info@glenwoodfurniture.ie
Web: http://www.glenwoodfurniture.ie
SIC: 36140 Employees: 28
Furniture-Manufacturing
Mr Gerry Murphy Managing Director
Mr Adrian McKirnan General Manager
Ms Deirdre Finan Director

Hallmark Furniture Co Ltd
Glaslough
Monaghan Co. Monaghan
Phone: 047-88163 Fax: 047-88237
Email: hallmarkfurn@eircom.net
SIC: 36140 Employees: 30
Furniture Manufacturer
Mr David Flack Managing Director
Mr William Flack Sales Director

Home Lee Bedding (1975) Ltd
Weir Road
Tuam Co. Galway
Phone: 093-24345 Fax: 093-25102
Email: info@homeleebedding.ie
SIC: 36140 Employees: 60
Manufacture Beds
Mr Martin Buckley Joint Managing Director
Mr Pat Sheehy Financial Controller
Mr Barry Buckley Joint Managing Director
Mr Tom Gibbons Production Manager

House Of Denmark
Unit 11 Rosemount Business Park
Blanchardstown
Dublin 11
Phone: 01-8224777 Fax: 01-8224788
Email: Info@houseofdenmark.ie
Web: http://www.houseofdenmark.ie
SIC: 36140 Employees: 30
Furniture and Kitchens
Mr Carsten Stensho Proprietor

JE Coyle Ltd
Plantation
Monaghan Co. Monaghan
Phone: 047-82155 Fax: 047-84164
Email: jecoyle@john.coyle.ie
SIC: 36140 Employees: 130
Furniture Manufacture
Mr Anthony Coyle Managing Director
Ms Irene Clarke Finance Manager
Mr Stanley Carlton Personnel Manager
Ms Karen Coyle Sales & Marketing Manager
Mr John Nally Computer Manager

JJ McCreery Ltd
Grand Canal Place
James Street
Dublin 8
Phone: 01-4533952 Fax: 01-4532192
Email: info@jjmccreery.ie
Web: http://www.jjmccreery.ie
SIC: 36140 Employees: 30
Office Furniture Manufacturer
Mr Noel McCreery Managing Director
Ms Deirdre Brown Accountant
Mr Gerard Martin Sales Director

Kilrush Trading Company Ltd
Cooraclare Road
Kilrush Co. Clare
Phone: 065-9051777 Fax: 065-9051408
SIC: 36140 Employees: 47
Furniture Manufacturer
Mr Michael Broderick General Manager
Ms Caroline Broderick Accounts Manager

Laverty Design Workshops
Dunkineely
Donegal Co. Donegal
Phone: 073-37178 Fax: 073-37286
Email: info@laverty.ie
Web: http://www.laverty.ie
SIC: 36140 Employees: 23
Manufacture Furniture
Mr Gerry Laverty Managing Director
Ms Jean Blain Sales & Marketing Manager

M & A Moran Ltd
Beechmount Industrial Estate
Navan Co. Meath
Phone: 046-23851 Fax: 046-22997
Email: mamoran@tinet.ie
SIC: 36140 Employees: 100
Furniture Manufacturer
Mr Aidan Moran Joint Managing Director
Mr Joe Ledgewidge Sales Manager
Mr Paddy Duffy Production Manager

McKenna & Cairns
Bree
Castleblayney Co. Monaghan
Phone: 042-9746270 Fax: 042-9740942
Email: mckennacairns@eircom.net
SIC: 36140 Employees: 30
Fixtures and Fittings Manufacturer
Mr Tony McKenna Partner
Mr Peter Cairns Partner

McNally & Finlay Ltd
Latlurcan
Monaghan Co. Monaghan
Phone: 047-81366 Fax: 047-84056
Email: info@rossmorefurniture.ie
SIC: 36140 Employees: 90
Furniture Manufacture
Ms Laura McNally Director
Ms Rose Hughes Company Secretary
Mr Bertie Hamilton Personnel Officer

Michael McGoona Furniture Ltd
Beechmount Industrial Estate
Navan Co. Meath
Phone: 046-22281 Fax: 046-22284
Email: mcgoona@eircom.net
SIC: 36140 Employees: 28
Furniture Manufacture
Mr Michael McGoona Managing Director
Ms Caroline Murphy Finance Manager

Modular Cold Store Manufacture Ltd
50 Coneyhall
Mornington
Drogheda Co. Louth
Phone: 041-9828866 Fax: 041-9828866
Email: modular@indigo.ie
SIC: 36140 Employees: 85
Cold Storage & Manuf of Panel Doors
Mr Pat Byrne Proprietor
Mr Charlie Ward Personnel Manager
Mr Dick Doyle Sales & Marketing Manager

Navan Sofa Centre
Last Unit Beechmount
Industrial Estate
Navan Co. Meath
Phone: 046-72950 Fax: 046-27063
SIC: 36140 Employees: 30
Furniture
Mr Thomas McGoona Manager

Neeson Brothers Ltd
Milltown
Belturbet Co. Cavan
Phone: 047-82210 Fax: 047-84697
Email: sales@neeson.com
Web: http://www.neeson.com
SIC: 36140 Employees: 25
Furniture Manufacture
Mr Conor Mulhall Proprietor
Ms Anne-Marier Neeson Manager

Nolan Kitchens Ltd
Hawthorn House Oak Road
Western Industrial Estate
Dublin 12
Phone: 01-4567621 Fax: 01-4502599
SIC: 36140 Employees: 45
Furniture Manufacturer
Mr John Nolan Managing Director
Mr Paul Nolan General Manager

O'Donnell Design Ltd
Baltimore Road
Skibbereen Co. Cork
Phone: 028-22274 Fax: 028-22267
Email: info@odonnelllfurniture.com
SIC: 36140 Employees: 34
Furniture Manufacturer
Mr Jim O'Donnell Director
Mr Sean Spillane Sales Manager

Protea Pine Ltd
2 St Peter's Industrial Estate
Walkinstown
Dublin 12
Phone: 01-4508983 Fax: 01-4553065
SIC: 36140 Employees: 50
Furniture Manufacturer
Ms Maura Prendergast Managing Director
Mr Sean Collins Finance Manager
Ms Bernie Mc Keown Human Resources Manager
Mr Mickey McComb Sales Manager

Raheen Engineering Ltd
Beechwood Close
Boghall Road
Bray Co. Wicklow
Phone: 01-2829019 Fax: 01-2829957
Email: info@ihs.ie
Web: http://www.ihs.ie
SIC: 36140 Employees: 25
Hospital Furniture Manufacture
Mr Vincent Farrell Managing Director
Mr Chris Moore Sales Manager
Mr Paddy Murphy Production Manager

Reilly Bros
Richmond Street
Longford Co. Longford
Phone: 043-46332 Fax: 043-45118
Email: sales@reillybrothers.ie
Web: http://www.reillybrothers.ie
SIC: 36140 Employees: 25
Furniture Manufacture
Mr Michael Reilly Proprietor

Scotstown Furniture Ltd
Bough
Scotstown
Monaghan Co. Monaghan
Phone: 047-89324 Fax: 047-89637
Email: info@mcolumb.iol.ie
SIC: 36140 Employees: 25
Furniture Manufacturer
Mr Padraig Columb Sales & Marketing Manager
Ms Siobhan Columb Company Secretary

Sherry Bros
Scotstown
Monaghan Co. Monaghan
Phone: 047-89309 Fax: 047-89592
Email: sherrybr@tinet.ie
SIC: 36140 Employees: 109
Furniture Manufacturer
Ms Brenda Sherry Managing Director
Mr Matt McCrudden Sales Manager
Mr Sean Morgan Production Manager
Ms Maura McKay DP Manager

SS Quinn Ltd
Ballybay Road
Monaghan Co. Monaghan
Phone: 047-81653 Fax: 047-82128
Email: sfquinn@eircom.net
SIC: 36140 Employees: 25
Furniture Manufacture
Ms Phyllis Moffett Managing Director

T O'Higgins Manufacturing Ltd
Rahoon Road
Shantalla
Galway Co. Galway
Phone: 091-522411 Fax: 091-522403
SIC: 36140 Employees: 100
Furniture Manufacturer & Hardware Store
Mr Michael O'Higgins Managing Director
Mr William Coneely Finance Manager
Ms Geraldine Egan Computer Manager

Topform Ltd
Tubber Road
Gort
Galway Co. Galway
Phone: 091-631616 Fax: 091-631619
Email: info@topform.ie
Web: http://www.topform.ie
SIC: 36140 Employees: 50
Industrial Worktops Manufacturer
Mr Paul Glynn Managing Director
Mr John Le Gar Accountant
Ms Maria Lyons Sales Manager

Woodland Products Ltd
The Mills
Emyvale
Monaghan Co. Monaghan
Phone: 047-87211 Fax: 047-87754
SIC: 36140 Employees: 60
Furniture Manufacture
Mr Patrick Treanor Joint Managing Director
Mr Harry Gillanders Joint Managing Director

J & Z Blackman
34 Anne's Lane
Dublin 2
Phone: 01-6772587 Fax: 01-6791640
Email: sales@blackman.iol.ie
SIC: 36200 Employees: 38
Manufacture Jewellery
Mr David Blackman Proprietor
Mr John Higgins Financial Controller
Mr Tommy Reichental Production Manager

MMI Group Ltd
Insignia House, JFK Park
Bluebell
Dublin 12
Phone: 01-4509577 Fax: 01-4504819
Email: sales@mmi-group.com
Web: http://www.mmi-group.com
SIC: 36200 Employees: 30
Corporate Gifts & Celtic Jewellery Manufacturer
Mr Enda Wood Director

TJH
Pleasant House Pleasant Lane
Pleasant Street
Dublin 8
Phone: 01-4762112 Fax: 01-4762113
Email: info@tjh.ie
SIC: 36200 Employees: 60
Jewellery Manufacturing
Ms Kela Ledwidge General Manager

Azzurri Ireland Ltd
Kilcohan Industrial Estate
Kilcohan
Waterford Co. Waterford
Phone: 051-850066 Fax: 051-850442
Email: postmaster@azzurri.ie
Web: http://www.teamkit.ie
SIC: 36400 Employees: 40
Sport & Leisure Wear Manufacturer & Fire Industrial Wear
Mr John Molloy Managing Director
Ms Miriam Molloy Director
Mr Joe O'Brien Production Manager

Bucas Ltd
Togher Industrial Estate
Cork Co. Cork
Phone: 021-4963353 Fax: 021-4312941
Email: admin@bucas.com
Web: http://www.bucas.com
SIC: 36400 Employees: 45
Equestrian Products Manufacturers
Mr Alf Casselbrant Proprietor
Ms Helen Frost Finance Manager
Ms Liz Kelly Personnel Manager
Mr Douglas Venn Sales & Marketing Manager
Ms Louise Manning Production Manager

Cascade Designs Ltd
Dwyer Road
Midleton Co. Cork
Phone: 021-4621400 Fax: 021-4632583
Email: cascadedesigns@indigo.ie
Web: http://www.cascadedesigns.com
SIC: 36400 Employees: 100
Sports Goods & Camping Equipment
Mr Joe McSwiney General Manager
Mr Bryan Ahern Finance Manager
Ms Laura O'Donavan Human Resource Co ordinator
Mr Bruno Drews Sales Manager
Mr Ken Cotter Operations Manager
Mr Pearse McClennan MIS Manager

Penn Raquet Sports Co Ireland
Lynn Road
Mullingar Co. Westmeath
Phone: 044-41511 Fax: 044-41064
Email: info@pennraquet.ie
Web: http://www.pennraquet.ie
SIC: 36400 Employees: 160
Tennis Ball Manufacturers
Ms Rosemary Traynor VP Of Operations
Ms Carol Shearan Manufacturing Clerk
Ms Margaret Tynan Customer Services Manager
Mr Pat McKerr Plant Manager
Ms Lisa Guing Systems Manager

Tretorn Sport Ltd
New Industrial Estate
Portlaoise Co. Laois
Phone: 0502-21333 Fax: 0502-22118
Email: tretorn@tretorn.ie
Web: http://www.tretorn.com
SIC: 36400 Employees: 100
Tennis Ball Manufacturers
Mr Michael MacCaughey Managing Director
Mr Pat Coffee Financial Controller
Mr Roy Bulfin Production Manager

Hasbro Ireland
Cork Road
Waterford
Phone: 051-331100 Fax: 051-331133
Email: info@hasbro.com
Web: http://www.hasbro.com
SIC: 36500 Employees: 400
Toy & Game Manufacturer
Mr Pat Gilhooly Chief Executive
Mr John Harrison Finance Director
Mr John Lennon HR Manager
Mr Tony Ruane Operations Manager
Mr John Lombard IT Manager

Kimble Manufacturing Ltd
Bachelors Walk
Dundalk Co. Louth
Phone: 042-9336574 Fax: 042-9333251
Email: kimble@iol.ie
Web: http://www.kimble.ie
SIC: 36500 Employees: 30
Amusements Suppliers
Mr James McCann Manager
Ms Linda Doyle Finance Manager
Ms Linda Rodgers Personnel Manager

Krakajack
Athenry Road
Loughrea
Galway Co. Galway
Phone: 091-841144 Fax: 091-847116
Email: krak@iol.ie
SIC: 36500 Employees: 45
Manufacture of Christmas Crackers
Ms Jean Molloy Operations Manager
Ms Peg Devine Financial Accountant
Ms Jeanette McDonnell Sales & Marketing Manager
Mr John Fahy Production Manager

Advanced Materials Ltd
Tougher Industrial Estate
Kildare Co. Kildare
Phone: 045-438477 Fax: 045-438498
Email: info@advmacl.ie
SIC: 36600 Employees: 45
Process Foam
Mr Tom Lane Proprietor
Mr Robert Doyle Sales Manager

Daelgate Ltd
Salcombe House
Robinhood Industrial Estate
Dublin 22
Phone: 01-4569288 Fax: 01-4569296
SIC: 36600 Employees: 35
Manufacture Gillette & Oral B Products
Mr Anthony Delacey Managing Director
Mr Hugh Daly Finance Manager
Mr Brian Noble Sales Manager

Display Contracts International Ltd
4 Greencastle Parade, Malahide Road Indust Est
Coolock
Dublin 17
Phone: 01-8770030 Fax: 01-8770031
Email: info@displaycontracts.com
Web: http://www.displaycontracts.com
SIC: 36600 Employees: 35
Exhibition & Display Equipment Manufacturer
Mr Jim O'Brien Managing Director
Ms Barbara Donald Financial Controller
Ms Adrienne O'Brien Sales & Marketing Manager

Keelings Casing Ltd
Roslin
Saint Margarets
Swords Co. Dublin
Phone: 01-8407969 Fax: 01-8407970
SIC: 36600 Employees: 25
Manufactures Casing
Mr Fred Keelan

Litepac Ltd
Granard
Longford Co. Longford
Phone: 043-86155 Fax: 043-86489
SIC: 36600 Employees: 47
Manufacture & Distribute Insulation
Mr Thomas Feehan Manager
Mr Liam McCaffrey Finance Manager
Mr Paddy Mohan Group Sales Manager
Mr Declan Power Computer Manager

Merenda Ltd
Park Road
Manorhamilton Co. Leitrim
Phone: 072-55105 Fax: 072-55296
Email: sales@merenda.com
Web: http://www.merenda.com
SIC: 36600 Employees: 35
Edge Banding Manufacture
Mr Oliver Haslette Managing Director
Ms Joan Haslette Finance Manager
Ms Margaret Dolan Personnel Manager
Ms Siobhan Haslette Sales & Marketing Manager
Mr Sean Gilligan Production Manager

Nomadic Display (Irl) Ltd
Louisburgh
Westport Co. Mayo
Phone: 098-66011 Fax: 098-66025
Web: http://www.nomadicdisplay.com
SIC: 36600 Employees: 60
Portable Exhibition Equipment Manufacturers
Mr Tom Wilson Managing Director
Mr Jerome Gannon Accounts Manager

Qualceram Shires
South Quay
Arklow Co. Wicklow
Phone: 0402-31288 Fax: 0402-31292
Email: info@qualceram-shires.com
Web: http://www.qualceram.ie
SIC: 36600 Employees: 250
Bathroom Suite Manufacture & Distribution
Mr John O'Loughlin Managing Director
Mr Aidan Clince Company Secretary
Mr John Byrne Sales & Marketing Director
Mr Tom Byrne Production Manager
Mr Trevor Broughall Computer Manager

Sealcon
Newbridge Business Park
Newbridge Co. Kildare
Phone: 045-431007 Fax: 045-437902
Web: http://www.barlopackaging.com
SIC: 36600 Employees: 80
Manufacture Food Containers
Mr Christy Howard Manager
Mr Ian Menszies Finance Manager
Mr John Larkin Sales Manager
Mr Fergal Barry Computer Manager

Seamar Ltd
Kilbarry Industrial Estate
Dublin Hill
Cork Co. Cork
Phone: 021-4394800 Fax: 021-4395794
Email: seamar@eircom.net
SIC: 36600 Employees: 70
Manufacture Industrial Products & Hotel Amenities
Mr John Cornally Managing Director
Ms Marianne Collins Financial Controller
Ms Claire Meehan Sales & Marketing Manager
Mr Shane Cornally IT and Purchasing Manager

Solatrex International Ltd
Bay F20 Shannon Free Zone
Shannon Co. Clare
Phone: 061-472722 Fax: 061-472816
Email: solatrex@iol.ie
Web: http://www.solatrex.com
SIC: 36600 Employees: 25
Quartz Watches & Clocks Distributors & Manufacturers
Mr Tom Flynn Managing Director
Ms Brid Guinnane Finance Manager
Ms Mary Colbert Sales & Marketing Manager

Textile Tape Company Ltd
Donore Road Industrial Estate
Drogheda Co. Louth
Phone: 041-9871094 Fax: 041-9835662
Email: ttco@iol.ie
SIC: 36600 Employees: 35
Manufacture Tape for Shoe Industry
Mr Declan Keehan Managing Director
Mr Jim Hanlon Office Manager

Vigitek Ltd
Holland Road
National Technological Park
Limerick Co. Limerick
Phone: 061-336900 Fax: 061-335411
Email: mail@vigitek.com
Web: http://www.vigitek.com
SIC: 36600 Employees: 50
Manufacture Visual Inspection Systems
Mr John Mallon Managing Director
Mr Eoin Kierse Financial Controller
Ms Nichola McGowan Personnel Manager
Mr Conor O'Neill International Business Directo
Ms Grainne Bermingham IT Manager

D O'Sullivan & Co Ltd
South Douglas Road
Cork Co. Cork
Phone: 021-4892813 Fax: 021-4893180
Email: dosco@iol.ie
SIC: 36620 Employees: 70
Brush Manufacturer
Mr James McGrath Managing Director
Mr Michael O'Sullivan Finance Manager
Mr Finbar O'Sullivan Production Manager

Varian Co Ltd
652 South Circular Road
Kilmainham
Dublin 8
Phone: 01-4534226 Fax: 01-4536263
SIC: 36620 Employees: 35
Brush Manufacturers
Mr Patrick Varian Managing Director
Mr Tom Byrne Finance Manager

Castle Brand Co
Tyone
Nenagh Co. Tipperary
Phone: 067-31711 Fax: 067-31659
Email: castlebrand@eircom.net
Web: http://www.castlebrand.com
SIC: 36630 Employees: 60
Cookware Manufacturers
Mr George Henderson Managing Director
Mr Gerry O'Dowd Sales Manager
Mr Jim Magher Operations Manager

Exitex Ltd
Mount Pleasant
Dundalk Co. Louth
Phone: 042-9371244 Fax: 042-9371221
SIC: 36630 Employees: 48
Draught Excluders Manufacturer
Mr Brian Allport Managing Director
Mr Des Grey Sales Director
Mr Adrian Grey Computer Manager

Fitzsimons Pallets
Blackhall Place
Mullingar Co. Westmeath
Phone: 044-48424 Fax: 044-41323
SIC: 36630 Employees: 30
Manufacturing Pallets & Crates
Mr Declan Fitzsimons Proprietor

Flexachem Manufacturing
Donnybrook Commercial Centre
Donnybrook, Douglas
Cork Co. Cork
Phone: 0214-363742 Fax: 021-4891297
Email: flexachem@iol.ie
SIC: 36630 Employees: 40
Manufacture Pumps Pipes & Valves
Mr Michael O'Connell Managing Director
Mr Jim Sheeran Finance Manager
Ms Agnes Mullins Sales Manager

Fragrance Boutique Ltd
Fragrance House
The Marina
Malahide Co. Dublin
Phone: 01-8455200 Fax: 01-8455490
Email: sales@fragrance-boutique.com
Web: http://www.fragrance.ie
SIC: 36630 Employees: 30
Gift Manufacturer
Mr Roy Donaldson Managing Director
Mr Nigel Kerley Finance Manager
Ms Paula Hackett Personnel Officer

Irishshop LLC
Unit 2a Santry Hall Industrial Park
Santry
Dublin 9
Phone: 01-8161118 Fax: 01-8161119
SIC: 36630 Employees: 50
Irish Souvenirs Manufacturers
Mr Daniel Nelhy Managing Director

John Hinde Ltd
71-73 Heather Road
Sandyford Industrial Estate
Dublin 18
Phone: 01-2941111 Fax: 01-2941071
Email: info@johnhinde.com
Web: http://www.johnhinde.com
SIC: 36630 Employees: 30
Manufacturer & Distribution of Souvenir Products
Mr Niall Howard Managing Director
Mr Dermot Caffrey Finance Manager
Mr Martin Walsh Production Manager

Oral B Laboratories
Green Road
Newbridge Co. Kildare
Phone: 045-437200 Fax: 045-433830
Email: info@oralb.com
Web: http://www.oralb.com
SIC: 36630 Employees: 450
Oral Care Products Manufacture
Mr Gerry Kierans General Manager
Mr Brian Rice Finance Manager
Ms Anne Scally Personnel Manager
Mr Ger Cummins Production Manager
Ms Hilary May IT Co-ordinator

Saehan Media Irl Ltd
Hazelwood House
Hazelwood
Sligo Co. Sligo
Phone: 071-44524 Fax: 071-44527
SIC: 36630 Employees: 400
Manufacture Video Tapes
Mr K Kim Managing Director
Mr HW Park Finance Manager
Mr Gary Byrne Human Resources Director

Schutz Ireland Ltd
Townmore
Killala
Ballina Co. Mayo
Phone: 096-33044 Fax: 096-33044
SIC: 36630 Employees: 24
Manufacture Packaging for Coca Cola
Mr Ciaran Bailey Manager

Unilever Ireland
Whitehall Road
Rathfarnham
Dublin 14
Phone: 01-2984344 Fax: 01-2984397
SIC: 36630 Employees: 500
Manufacture & Distribution of Consumer Goods
Mr Jules Norten Chief Executive
Mr D Staveley Director of Finance

Recycling

37	Recycling
37100	Scrap Dealers
37200	Recycling of Non-Metal Waste & Scrap

Galway Metal Company Ltd
Oranmore
Galway Co. Galway
Phone: 091-794358 Fax: 091-790218
Email: galwaymetal@eircom.ie
SIC: 37100 Employees: 40
Scrap Metal Processing
Mr Patrick Walsh Managing Director
Mr Tom Grealy Finance Manager

Connect Industries
Unit 8 IDA Small Business Centre
Tuam Road
Galway Co. Galway
Phone: 091-770207 Fax: 091-770208
Email: annmarie@connect.iol.ie
Web: http://www.connectind.ie
SIC: 37200 Employees: 70
Recycling
Mr Michael Connolly Managing Director
Mr Peter Dunican Finance Manager
Mr Hugh McNally Sales & Marketing Manager
Mr Damian Brereton Computer Manager

Hammond Metal Recycling
Pigeon House Road
Dublin 4
Phone: 01-6675335 Fax: 01-6675345
SIC: 37200 Employees: 35
Recycling of Non-Metal Waste & Scrape
Mr Joe Corcaran Manager

Pac Sort Ltd
Coes Road
Dundalk Co. Louth
Phone: 042-9336426 Fax: 042-9336428
Email: pacsort@psl.com
SIC: 37200 Employees: 25
Recycling
Mr Malachy Lynch Managing Director

Rehab Recycling Partnership
The Rehab Building
Kylemore Road, Ballfermot
Dublin 10
Phone: 01-8422944 Fax: 01-6260549
Email: info@gandonenterprises.ie
Web: http://www.rehabrecycling.ie
SIC: 37200 Employees: 96
Recycling
Mr Bob Rowate General Manager
Mr Ashley Balbirnie Chief Executive

Thornton's Recycling Centre
Killeen Road
Dublin 10
Phone: 01-6235133 Fax: 01-6235131
Email: info@thorntons-recycling.ie
Web: http://www.thorntons-recycling.ie
SIC: 37200 Employees: 50
Recycling Waste
Mr Padraig Thornton Managing Director
Mr Eamon Flanagan Finance Manager
Ms Carmel Thornton Personnel Manager
Mr Aidan Kenny Sales Manager
Mr Tom Craig Production Manager

Electricity & Gas Supply

40	Electricity & Gas Supply
40101	Electricity Production
40102	Energy Distribution
40103	Electricity Distribution
40200	Public Gas Supply
40210	Energy Production

ESB Power Station
Great Island
Campile
New Ross Co. Wexford
Phone: 051-388161 Fax: 051-388114
Email: info@esb.ie
Web: http://www.esb.ie
SIC: 40101 Employees: 100
Power Station
Mr Ciaran Sweeney Station Manager
Ms Margaret O'Connor Administrator
Mr Gerry Ryder Production Manager

ESB
27 Lower Fitzwilliam Street
Dublin 2
Phone: 01-6765831 Fax: 01-6615376
Email: postmaster@esb.ie
Web: http://www.esb.ie
SIC: 40103 Employees: 8500
Electricity Supply Board
Mr Ken O'Hara Chief Executive
Mr Tony Donnelly Group Finance Director
Mr Sean O'Driscoll Personnel Director
Mr Richard Hayden MD Business Services
Mr Michael Power Power System Control Manager
Mr Michael Leahy IT Manager

Construction

45	Construction
45100	Site Preparation
45110	Demolition Companies
45210	Construction/Building Companies
45211	Building Maintenance & Repair
45213	Civil Engineering
45215	Chimney Builders
45216	Prefabricated Buildings
45217	Timber Frame Buildings
45218	Loft Conversions
45220	Roofing Contractors
45230	Roads, Airfields & Sports Facilities
45240	Construction of Water Projects
45310	Electrical Contractors
45311	Electrical Engineers
45330	Plumbers
45331	Heating Engineers
45400	Building Completion Work
45410	Plasterers
45420	Joiners & Carpenters
45421	Joinery Companies
45431	Flooring Contractors
45441	Painters/Decorators
45442	Glazing
45451	Fencing
45452	Shopfitting/Officefitting
45453	Installation Fixtures/Fittings

Irish Geotechnical Services Ltd
U26 Newbridge Industrial Estate
Newbridge Co. Kildare
Phone: 045-431088 Fax: 045-433145
Email: igsl@iol.ie
SIC: 45100 Employees: 55
Site Investigations
Mr John Clancy Contracts Manager
Mr Pat O'Gorman Finance Manager
Mr Steven McSweeney IT Director

Liffey Development Dublin Ltd
Boulter House
Naas Road, Clondalkin
Dublin 22
Phone: 01-4594333 Fax: 01-4592543
Email: liffey@indigo.ie
SIC: 45100 Employees: 100
Site Development
Ms Teresa Dunne Managing Director

Scafform Ltd
Newcourt Business Park
St Margaret's
Dublin 10
Phone: 01-6266601 Fax: 01-8567086
SIC: 45100 Employees: 40
Scaffolding Contractors
Mr Eugene O'Doherty Managing Director
Mr Paul Delaney Financial Controller
Mr John Butler Director
Mr Sean McAnulty Sales Manager
Mr Donal Molloy Operations Manager

Albert Enterprises Ltd
Unit 2 Redcow Interchange Estate
Turnpike Road Ballymount
Dublin 22
Phone: 01-4640333 Fax: 01-4640338
Email: albertenterprises@eircom.net
Web: http://www.albertenterprises.com
SIC: 45210 Employees: 60
Building Contractors
Mr William Smyth Managing Director
Mr Mark Allen Accounts
Ms Caroline Bell Group Administrator

B & C Contractors
Church Street
Carrickmacross Co. Monaghan
Phone: 042-9661124 Fax: 042-9661481
SIC: 45210 Employees: 30
Building Contractors
Mr Michael McBride Managing Director
Mr Colm McBride Finance Manager
Mr Jim McBride Sales Director

Brendan Byrne & Son Ltd
Carrowclaggan
Louisburgh
Westport Co. Mayo
Phone: 098-66146 Fax: 098-66036
SIC: 45210 Employees: 28
Construction
Mr Brendan Byrne Proprietor

Brendan Duffy Construction Ltd
Ardee Road
Dundalk Co. Louth
Phone: 042-9331659 Fax: 042-9335757
Email: info@bduffyconstruction.com
Web: http://www.bduffyconstruction.com
SIC: 45210 Employees: 40
Builders - General Contractors
Mr Brendan Duffy Managing Director
Ms Barbara McCourt Finance Manager
Mr Gerard Martin IT Manager

Bresc Estates Ltd
Monread Court
Sallins Road
Naas Co. Kildare
Phone: 045-866033 Fax: 045-897237
Email: bresc@iol.ie
SIC: 45210 Employees: 25
Building Contractors
Mr Frank Cleary Managing Director

Bride View Development Ltd
Sallybrook Industrial Estate
Glanmire
Cork Co. Cork
Phone: 021-4821644 Fax: 021-4821320
SIC: 45210 Employees: 50
Building Company
Mr Declan O'Mahony Managing Director
Mr Tom O'Keefe Sales Manager

Broomfield Construction Co Ltd
Bree
Castleblayney Co. Monaghan
Phone: 042-9740559 Fax: 042-9740832
SIC: 45210 Employees: 35
Building Contractors
Mr Patrick Murphy Foreman / Manager

Byrne & Byrne Ltd
Ryland Road
Bunclody
Enniscorthy Co. Wexford
Phone: 054-77377 Fax: 054-77422
SIC: 45210 Employees: 30
Builders
Mr Bart Byrne Partner
Mr Nicholas Byrne Partner

C & M Construction Co Ltd
Noel Barbannon House, Castle Street
Ashbourne
Navan Co. Meath
Phone: 01-8352506 Fax: 01-8352509
SIC: 45210 Employees: 45
Building Company
Ms Christine Doyne Director
Mr Bill Thompson Finance Manager
Mr Gerry McGeehan Sales Manager

C F Structures Ltd
Fox & Geese
Naas Road
Dublin 12
Phone: 01-4504283 Fax: 01-4566457
SIC: 45210 Employees: 60
Building Contractors
Mr Tim McAnulty Manager

Construction

Carty Construction Ltd
Ballisodare
Sligo Co. Sligo
Phone: 071-67788 Fax: 071-30949
Email: info@cartygroup.com
Web: http://www.cartygroup.com
SIC: 45210 Employees: 30
Plant Hire and Contractors
Mr Pat Carty Partner
Mr Aidan Carty Partner

Cedar Building Co Ltd
Abbeylands
Arklow Co. Wicklow
Phone: 0402-37315 Fax: 0402-37492
Email: cedarbuildingcompany@eircom.net
SIC: 45210 Employees: 70
Building & Civil Engineering
Mr Eddie Holly Managing Director
Mr Matt McDonagh Financial Controller
Mr Stephen O'Halloran Sales Manager
Mr Pat O'Halloran Production Director

Coffey Construction Ltd
Castlewood
Athenry Co. Galway
Phone: 091-844356 Fax: 091-844519
Email: info@coffeyconstruction.com
Web: http://www.coffeyconstruction.com
SIC: 45210 Employees: 400
Builders & Civil Engineering Contractors
Mr Patrick Coffey Managing Director
Mr Gerry Fahy Finance Manager
Mr Tom Coffey Sales Director
Mr John Callaghan Contracts Manager
Mr Tiernan O'Rourke IT Manager

Cusack Construction
Ballyfore
Edenderry
Tullamore Co. Offaly
Phone: 0405-31075 Fax: 0405-31257
Email: info@cusackconstruction.oceanfree.com
Web:
http://www.cusackconstruction.oceanfree.com
SIC: 45210 Employees: 80
Construction/Building Company
Mr Alan Cusack Proprietor

Cusack Homes
Dublin Road
Trim
Navan Co. Meath
Phone: 046-31517 Fax: 046-31517
Email: cusackhomes@eircom.net
SIC: 45210 Employees: 40
Construction/Building Company
Mr John Cusack Proprietor

Custom House Docks Development Co
14 Wellington Road
Ballsbridge
Dublin 4
Phone: 01-6683791 Fax: 01-6680265
Email: centralmail@hardwick.ie
SIC: 45210 Employees: 25
Property Development
Mr Mark Kavanagh Chairman
Mr David Maguire Accounts Manager
Mr Brian Owens Personnel Director
Mr David McGuire Sales Director
Mr Maurice Tunney Computer Manager

Dartmouth Building Works Ltd
Dartmouth House, 11 Ballymount Road
Clondalkin
Dublin 22
Phone: 01-4594011 Fax: 01-4594810
SIC: 45210 Employees: 30
Builders - General Contractors
Mr Gerard Doherty Managing Director
Ms Lorraine Merriman Financial Administrator
Mr Paul Merriman Sales Manager

Descon Construction Ltd
Ballyrichard
Carrigtwohill
Cork Co. Cork
Phone: 021-4321800 Fax: 021-4613166
Email: desconk@indigo.ie
Web: http://www.descon.ie
SIC: 45210 Employees: 25
Pile - Driving Contractors
Mr Kevin McDonnell Manager

Drumlohan Enterprise's Ltd
Ballynorth
Askeaton
Limerick Co. Limerick
Phone: 061-392301 Fax: 061-392531
SIC: 45210 Employees: 50
Building Company
Mr Seamus Braddish Manager

Eamonn Duignan
Hayes House
Hayestown
Navan Co. Meath
Phone: 046-24616 Fax: 046-24619
SIC: 45210 Employees: 25
Property Developers
Mr Eamonn Duignan Managing Director
Ms Rita Burtenshaw Accounts Manager

Ellen Construction Ltd
Whitestown Lower
Baltinglass
Wicklow Co. Wicklow
Phone: 045-404030 Fax: 045-404044
Email: ellen@indigo.ie
SIC: 45210 Employees: 25
Builders - General Contractors
Mr Michael Doran Manager
Mr John Whelan Chief Estimator

Finlay Bros (Builders) Ltd
Church Road
Tullamore Co. Offaly
Phone: 0506-21089 Fax: 0506-21097
SIC: 45210 Employees: 35
Construction/Building Companies
Mr Tommy Finlay Proprietor

G & T Crampton Ltd
Sandymount Buildings
Simmons Court Road, Ballsbridge
Dublin 4
Phone: 01-6680691 Fax: 01-6683408
Email: gtc@indigo.ie
SIC: 45210 Employees: 241
Building Company
Mr Philip Crampton Joint Managing Director
Mr Hal Hosford Financial Director
Mr Tommy Moloney Training/Personnel Manager
Mr Clive Chattie IT Manager

Glenbeigh Construction Ltd
Tyrrelstown Way
Damastown Business Park
Dublin 15
Phone: 01-8227008 Fax: 01-8227009
SIC: 45210 Employees: 25
Builders - General Contractors
Ms Pauline Anand Secretary

Glenbrier Ltd
Dunmoe Lodge
Hayes
Navan Co. Meath
Phone: 046-24495 Fax: 046-24979
SIC: 45210 Employees: 50
Builders - General Contractors
Mr Pat Burke Director
Mr Kieran Fay Finance Manager

Glynns Tuam Ltd
Ballygaddy Road
Tuam Co. Galway
Phone: 093-24482 Fax: 093-28745
Email: glynns@tinet.ie
SIC: 45210 Employees: 28
Building providers
Mr Pauric Glynn Managing Director
Mr Brian Flesk Director of Finance

Green Glens Development
Main Street
Millstreet
Cork Co. Cork
Phone: 029-70039 Fax: 029-70305
Email: ncdel@eircom..net
SIC: 45210 Employees: 50
Property Development Company
Mr Barry Duggan Managing Director
Mr Laurence Luddy Financial Controller
Ms Margaret Creedon IT Manager

Gypsum Industries plc
Kingscourt
Cavan Co. Cavan
Phone: 042-9667104 Fax: 042-9667221
Email: tom.farrell@btb.com
Web: http://www.gypsum.com
SIC: 45210 Employees: 50
Building Company
Mr John Byrne Manager

JFL Group Ltd
43 Lower Salthill
Galway Co. Galway
Phone: 091-522485 Fax: 091-524943
Email: jfl@stewart.ie
SIC: 45210 Employees: 60
Building-Engineering Contracts
Mr Sean Stewart Managing Director
Mr Gerry Conway Financial Controller

JJ Rhatigan & Co Ltd
Heritage Hall
Kirwan's Lane
Galway Co. Galway
Phone: 091-565676 Fax: 091-566861
Email: buildings@jjrhatigan.iol.ie
SIC: 45210 Employees: 100
Building Company
Mr Padraic Rhatigan Managing Director
Mr Thomas Kelly Financial Controller
Mr Sean Rhatigan Purchasing Manager
Ms Anne Marie Keogh Computer Manager

Joe Wallace Construction Ltd
Main Street, The Square
Glin
Limerick Co. Limerick
Phone: 068-34353 Fax: 068-34069
SIC: 45210 Employees: 39
Construction Company
Mr Joe Wallace Managing Director

John Paul & Co
Dundrum Business Park
Dundrum Road
Dublin 14
Phone: 01-2156100 Fax: 01-2981710
Email: info@johnpaulconstruction.com
Web: http://www.johnpaulconstruction.com
SIC: 45210 Employees: 305
Construction Company
Mr Donal O'Brien Managing Director
Mr Des Bruton Group Finance Director
Mr Connor O'Donnell Office Manager
Mr Ray Mescal Sales & Marketing Director
Mr James Mitchell Senior Computer Manager

Construction

John Paul Construction Ltd
Unit 1 Euro Business Park
Little Island
Cork Co. Cork
Phone: 021-4524444 Fax: 021-4524990
Email: info@johnpaulconstruction.com
Web: http://www.johnpaulconstruction.com
SIC: 45210 Employees: 30
Builders - General Contractors
Mr Liam Casey Regional Manager

John Sisk & Son Ltd
Naas Road, Wilton Works,
Clondalkin
Dublin 22
Phone: 01-4504589 Fax: 01-4091550
Email: info@sisk.ie
Web: http://www.sisk.ie
SIC: 45210 Employees: 1748
Construction
Mr Thomas Costello Managing Director
Mr Connor Dunne Financial Director
Mr Barry Patterson Company Secretary
Mr Maurice Healy Marketing Manager
Mr Joe Gaffney IT Manager

Joseph Lane & Sons Ltd
Monaghan Road
Cork Co. Cork
Phone: 021-4965233 Fax: 021-4965067
Email: info@jlaneandsone.ie
Web: http://www.cedarlan.ie
SIC: 45210 Employees: 80
Building Contractors
Mr Joseph Lane Managing Director
Mr Kevin Lane Finance Manager
Mr John Coughlan Computer Manager

Keane Building Services
3 St Senan's Road
Enniscorthy Co. Wexford
Phone: 054-37055 Fax: 054-37965
Email: info@celtichomes.com
Web: http://www.celtichomes.ie
SIC: 45210 Employees: 150
Builders - General Contractors
Mr Joe Keane Managing Director

Kearney Contracts
36D Merchants Dock
Merchants Road
Galway Co. Galway
Phone: 091-569299 Fax: 091-569287
SIC: 45210 Employees: 60
Building Contractor
Mr John Kearney Proprietor

Kelland Homes
Ballymount House
Ballymount Road, Kingswood
Dublin 24
Phone: 01-4593146 Fax: 01-4591650
SIC: 45210 Employees: 160
Construction Company
Mr Patrick Kelly Chief Executive
Mr Michael O'Connor Financial Controller
Mr Tony Cunniffe Purchasing Manager

Kenny Builders & Co Ltd
Bridgewater Court
Harvey's Quay
Limerick Co. Limerick
Phone: 061-411934 Fax: 061-414795
SIC: 45210 Employees: 25
Builders
Mr Paul Byrne Contracts Manager
Ms Moira Ryan Finance Manager
Ms Triona Bresnihna Sales & Marketing Manager

Kenny Developments
Kenny Group House
Ros Ard Cappagh Road
Galway Co. Galway
Phone: 091-590590 Fax: 091-591195
Email: kennygroup@tinet.ie
SIC: 45210 Employees: 70
Building Contractors
Mr John Kenny Chief Executive
Mr Mike Pender Financial Controller
Ms Barbara Kenny Personnel Manager

Keohane & Company Ltd
Dublin Executive Office Centre
Red Cow, Naas Road
Dublin 22
Phone: 01-4642140 Fax: 01-4592891
Email: keohanedub@tinet.ie
SIC: 45210 Employees: 40
Builders -Main Contractors
Mr James O'Hara Contracts Director
Mr Paul O'Reilly Accountant

Kilcawley Building & Civil Engineering
Stradhill Road
Sligo Co. Sligo
Phone: 071-62206 Fax: 071-69463
Email: kilcawleysltd@eircom.net
Web: http://www.kbce.com
SIC: 45210 Employees: 30
Building Contractors
Mr Tom Kenny Director
Mr Brendan Henry Contract Director

Kildare Building Co Ltd
Bride Street
Kildare Co. Kildare
Phone: 045-521644 Fax: 045-522502
SIC: 45210 Employees: 30
Building Contractors
Mr John Kindregan Managing Director
Mr Joe Brown Financial Controller

Kilmoney Construction Ltd
Carrigaline
Old Waterpark
Cork Co. Cork
Phone: 021-4372198 Fax: 021-4372198
SIC: 45210 Employees: 40
Construction
Ms Carmel Connell Manager

Kingston Construction Ltd
Apollo Buildings
Dundrum Road
Dublin 14
Phone: 01-2986047 Fax: 01-2960738
Email: kingston@indigo.ie
SIC: 45210 Employees: 45
Builders - General Contractors
Mr Myles Carrie Managing Director
Ms Colette Griffin Financial Controller

KMMS Construction Ltd
Airglooney Business Park
Tuam Co. Galway
Phone: 093-24200 Fax: 093-26499
SIC: 45210 Employees: 50
Construction Company
Mr Mike O'Shaughnessey Managing Director

Lissadell Construction
111 Ludford Road
Dundrum
Dublin 16
Phone: 01-2983610 Fax: 01-2984847
SIC: 45210 Employees: 25
Master Builders
Mr Mel Columb Managing Director

M Fitzgibbon (Builders) Ltd
Darragh
Ennis Co. Clare
Phone: 065-6838770 Fax: 065-6838178
Email: mfitzgibbonbuilders@eircom.net
SIC: 45210 Employees: 90
Building and Civil Engineering Company
Mr Martin Fitzgibbon Proprietor

McInerney Construction Ltd
Rathfarnham Gate
Rathfarnham
Dublin 14
Phone: 01-4909900 Fax: 01-4909951
Email: reception@dublin.mcinerney.ie
Web: http://www.dublin.mcinerney.ie
SIC: 45210 Employees: 400
Construction & Property Development
Mr Tommy Drumm Director
Mr Dan O'Driscoll General Manager

McInerney Holdings Plc
29 Kenilworth Square
Rathgar
Dublin 6
Phone: 01-2985700 Fax: 01-4962055
Email: reception@mcinerney.ie
Web: http://www.mcinerney.ie
SIC: 45210 Employees: 400
Construction/Property Development
Mr Barry O'Connor Managing Director
Mr Frank Ferguson Finance Manager
Ms Catherine McNaughton Personnel Manager
Mr Mark Shakespeare Treasurer
Mr Joe McNamara Construction Manager
Mr Greg McCambridge Computer Manager

Mealey Construction Co Ltd
O'Brien Road
Carlow Co. Carlow
Phone: 0503-41537 Fax: 0503-41566
Email: mealeycon@tinet.ie
SIC: 45210 Employees: 25
Builders Firms
Mr Pat Mealey Managing Director

Michael McNamara & Co
Grattan Bridge House
3 Upper Ormond Quay
Dublin 7
Phone: 01-8725311 Fax: 01-8733084
Email: info@michaelmlmcnamara.ie
Web: http://www.michaelmlmcnamara.ie
SIC: 45210 Employees: 334
Building Contractors
Mr Bernard McNamara Managing Director
Mr Chris Hurst Financial Director

Michael Reynolds & Sons Ltd
Breffni Crescent
Carrick On Shannon Co. Leitrim
Phone: 078-20231 Fax: 078-20640
Email: reynoldsltd@esatclear.ie
SIC: 45210 Employees: 35
Builders/Civil Engineering Contractors
Mr Patrick Reynolds Managing Director

MJ Clarke & Sons Ltd
Whitechurch Road
Rathfarnham
Dublin 14
Phone: 01-4933386 Fax: 01-4935886
SIC: 45210 Employees: 40
Building Contractors
Mr Michael Clarke Managing Director
Ms Mary Agnew Finance Manager

Mulhern Builders Ltd
Ballina Road
Crossmolina
Ballina Co. Mayo
Phone: 096-31239 Fax: 096-31386
Email: mulhern@iol.ie
SIC: 45210 Employees: 25
Builders Firms
Mr Kieran Mulhern Managing Director

Construction

Ned O'Shea & Sons Construction Ltd
Rock Business Centre
Tralee Co. Kerry
Phone: 066-7121240 Fax: 066-7126319
Email: jamesos@iol.ie
SIC: 45210 Employees: 70
Building Company
Mr Ned O'Shea Managing Director
Mr James O'Shea Sales & Marketing Director

Noel Frisby Construction Ltd
1-2 Canada Street
Waterford Co. Waterford
Phone: 051-875409 Fax: 051-841515
Email: info@frisbyhomes.com
Web: http://www.frisbyhomes.com
SIC: 45210 Employees: 60
Construction Company
Mr Noel Frisby Proprietor
Mr Tom Greene Accountant

Noonan Construction Co Ltd
13 Melifont Avenue
Dun Laoghaire Co. Dublin
Phone: 01-2801197 Fax: 01-2801206
SIC: 45210 Employees: 64
Building Contractors
Mr Kieran Noonan Managing Director
Mr Eamon Cahill Finance Director
Mrs Rory Noonan Human Resources Manager
Mr Neil Noonan Sales & Marketing Director
Mr Kevin Gilmore Production Manager
Mr Stephen Moriarty Computer Manager

O'Flynn Construction Co Ltd
Melbourne House
Model Farm Road
Cork Co. Cork
Phone: 021-4343111 Fax: 021-4343053
Email: ofc@oflynnconstruction.ie
Web: http://www.oflynnconstruction.ie
SIC: 45210 Employees: 80
Building Company
Mr Michael O'Flynn Managing Director
Mr Brian O'Neill Finance Manager

O'Malley Construction Co Ltd
Augustine House
St Augustine Street
Galway Co. Galway
Phone: 091-509970 Fax: 091-564503
Email: info@omalley-construction.ie
SIC: 45210 Employees: 130
Construction Company
Mr Frank O'Malley Managing Director
Ms Helen Casserly Finance Manager
Mr David Casserly IT Manager

O'Sheas
White Street
Cork Co. Cork
Phone: 021-4270474 Fax: 021-4963842
Email: info@osheasbuilders.com
SIC: 45210 Employees: 90
Building Contractors
Mr Aidan O'Shea Manager
Mr Joe Fitzgerald Finance Manager

Paddy Burke Builders Ltd
Atlantic Road
Lisdoonvarna
Ennis Co. Clare
Phone: 065-7074234 Fax: 065-7074277
Email: pbbuild@eircom.net
SIC: 45210 Employees: 120
Building Contractor
Mr Paddy Burke Managing Director

Padraig Moneley Ltd
Kilsaran
Dundalk Co. Louth
Phone: 042-9372173 Fax: 042-9372530
Email: pmltd@iol.ie
SIC: 45210 Employees: 40
Building & Engineering
Mr Patrick Moneley Managing Director

Patrick Brock & Sons
Pottery Road
Dun Laoghaire Co. Dublin
Phone: 01-2852033 Fax: 01-2852339
SIC: 45210 Employees: 82
Building Contractors
Mr Patrick Brock Proprietor
Ms Penny Horsham Office Manager

Patrick Fallon Construction
Donore Road
Drogheda Co. Louth
Phone: 041-9832550 Fax: 041-9833461
SIC: 45210 Employees: 60
Construction Company
Mr Patrick Fallon Proprietor

Peter Mountaine & Sons Ltd
Dorset Lane
Dublin 1
Phone: 01-8742306 Fax: 01-8742332
SIC: 45210 Employees: 50
Builders - General Contractors
Mr Camillus Mountaine Managing Director

Pierse Contracting Ltd
Birmayne House
Mulhuddart
Dublin 15
Phone: 01-8205811 Fax: 01-8217361
Email: info@pierse.ie
Web: http://www.pierse.ie
SIC: 45210 Employees: 700
Irish Home Builders Association
Mr G Pierse Chairman
Mr F O'Nolan Company Secretary
Mr M Flick Managing Civil Engineer

PJ Walls Ltd
City Junction Business Park
North Cross, Malahide Road
Dublin 17
Phone: 01-8064600 Fax: 01-8064666
Email: build@pjwalls.ie
Web: http://www.pjwalls.ie
SIC: 45210 Employees: 360
Construction Company
Mr Pat Veale Managing Director
Mr Maurice O'Carroll Finance Manager
Mr Pat McDevitt Sales Manager
Mr Eugene O'Shea Contracts Director

PJ & EJ Doherty Ltd
37 Quay Street
Dundalk Co. Louth
Phone: 042-9336455 Fax: 042-9338971
Email: dohertydevelopements@btinternet.com
Web: http://www.dohertybuild.com
SIC: 45210 Employees: 30
Building Contractors
Mr P J Doherty Proprietor
Mr Kieran McParland Sales & Marketing Manager

R & B Construction Ltd
11a Berkeley Road
Dublin 7
Phone: 01-8309244 Fax: 01-8302181
SIC: 45210 Employees: 30
Construction Company
Mr Terence Roche Director
Ms Nuala Coussey Accounts Manager

R & B O'Connor Construction Ltd
Kilbride
The Ballagh
Enniscorthy Co. Wexford
Phone: 053-36261 Fax: 053-36466
SIC: 45210 Employees: 30
Builders
Mr Brendan O'Connor Manager
Ms Marie Murphy Office Manager

R McDonald & Sons Ltd
The Cove
Tramore
Waterford Co. Waterford
Phone: 051-386655 Fax: 051-386677
SIC: 45210 Employees: 60
Construction Company
Mr Pat McDonald Director

South Eastern Construction
Dublin Road
Kilmacow
Waterford Co. Waterford
Phone: 051-885221 Fax: 051-885595
Email: seconstruction@eircom.net
SIC: 45210 Employees: 50
Builders
Mr Tom Kent Managing Director
Ms Mavis Kelly Accountant
Ms Anne Counts Sales Manager

South Midland Construction Ltd
St. Margarets Road, Dubber Cross
Finglas
Dublin 11
Phone: 01-8580200 Fax: 01-8361050
Email: dubber@eircom.net
Web: http://www.smcgroup.ie
SIC: 45210 Employees: 230
Construction Company
Mr Phelim Moylan Managing Director
Mr Cormac O'Reilly Financial Controller
Mr Simon Black Personnel Manager

T McGurk & Co Ltd
Ballyjamesduff Co. Cavan
Phone: 049-8544143 Fax: 049-8544758
SIC: 45210 Employees: 35
Builders
Mr Joseph McGurk Managing Director

Tarmax Co Ltd
Drennanstown
Rathangan
Kildare Co. Kildare
Phone: 045-524520 Fax: 045-524618
SIC: 45210 Employees: 25
Builders Firms
Mr Seamus Mannion Managing Director

Terence Harvey Contracts Services
1 Lissin Glen, Ballybogan Road
Glasnevin
Dublin 11
Phone: 01-8306777 Fax: 01-8305893
SIC: 45210 Employees: 200
Builders - General Contractors
Mr Terence Harvey Proprietor
Mr Gary McKeown Financial Controller
Mr Kevin McDonnell Personnel Manager
Mr Tony Gorman Sales & Marketing Manager

Thomas McDonogh & Sons
Merchants Road
Galway Co. Galway
Phone: 091-566111 Fax: 091-567774
Email: info@mcdonogh.ie
Web: http://www.mcdonogh.ie
SIC: 45210 Employees: 50
Construction Company
Mr Thomas McDonagh Chairman
Mr Michael Ryan Chief Financial Officer
Mr James Kennedy Chief Executive Officer

Construction

Tom Hayes Ltd
The Green
Killaloe
Ennis Co. Clare
Phone: 061-376240 Fax: 061-376252
Email: hayesbuild@eircom.net
SIC: 45210 Employees: 80
Building & Civil Engineering Contractors
Mr Tom Hayes Managing Director
Mr Laurence Flanagan Finance Manager
Mr Tom Haskett Personnel Manager
Mr Ronnie Slevin Sales & Marketing Manager
Mr Tom Burke Computer Manager

Tom O'Leary Construction
57 High Street
Killarney Co. Kerry
Phone: 064-35015 Fax: 064-35684
Email: tolcons2@eircom.net
SIC: 45210 Employees: 25
Builders - General Contractors
Mr Tom O'Leary Proprietor
Mr Gerry Sheehan Financial Controller

Townlink Construction Ltd
10 Greenhill Business Park
Dublin 24
Phone: 01-4627131 Fax: 01-4627137
Email: build@townlink.ie
Web: http://www.townlink.ie
SIC: 45210 Employees: 40
Building & Construction
Mr T Walsh Director
Ms Maria Whelan Finance Manager

Treform Ltd
14 Ardilaun Road
Newcastle
Galway Co. Galway
Phone: 091-523125 Fax: 091-585096
Email: treform@eircom.net
SIC: 45210 Employees: 130
Building Contractors
Mr Augustine Tracey Managing Director

Tricastle Ltd
Merchants Court
Merchants Quay
Dublin 8
Phone: 01-6776691 Fax: 01-6777081
Email: tricastle@eircom.net
SIC: 45210 Employees: 100
Construction Company
Mr Richard McGarry Managing Director

Tyron Ltd
61 Shantalla Road
Beaumont
Dublin 9
Phone: 01-8375656 Fax: 01-8375188
Email: tyronltd@tyron.ie
SIC: 45210 Employees: 25
Building & Civil Engineering Contractors
Mr Brendan Monaghan Managing Director
Ms Mary Monaghan Financial Administrator

Vincent Ruane Builders Ltd
Church Road
Ballina Co. Mayo
Phone: 096-22382 Fax: 096-21113
SIC: 45210 Employees: 60
Building Contractors
Mr Vincent Ruane Manager
Ms Breda Reid Finance Manager
Mr Padraig Farrell Computer Manager

William F Rowley Ltd
4a Villa Park Road
Blackhorse Avenue
Dublin 7
Phone: 01-8383336 Fax: 01-8381503
SIC: 45210 Employees: 50
Building Contractors
Mr Padraic Rowley Managing Director
Mr Jim Burgan Finance Manager

Woodgreen Builders Ltd
23 Temple Lane South
Templebar
Dublin 2
Phone: 01-6719093 Fax: 01-6773804
SIC: 45210 Employees: 40
Builders - General Contractors
Mr Joe Kenny Manager

Active Services
Unit 9 Craftmasters
Greenhills Industrial Estate
Dublin 12
Phone: 01-4601980 Fax: 01-4601982
Email: activeg1@iol.ie
SIC: 45211 Employees: 100
Building -Maintenance & Contract Cleaning
Ms Bernadette Horn Manager

Keating Insulation
Old Mill
Castlebridge
Wexford Co. Wexford
Phone: 053-59866 Fax: 053-59134
Email: keatinginsulation@eircom.net
SIC: 45211 Employees: 26
Insulation of Houses
Mr Liam Keating Managing Director
Ms Marie Donnelly Finance Manager
Mr Larry Lambert Sales Manager

Limerick Civic Trust
Bishops Palace, Church Street
Kings Island
Limerick Co. Limerick
Phone: 061-313399 Fax: 061-315513
SIC: 45211 Employees: 90
Listed Buildings Restoration
Mr Denis Leonard Director
Ms Irene Hyland Computer Manager

Masonry Fixing Services Ltd
Unit 83 Cherry Orchard Industrial Estate
Ballyfermot
Dublin 10
Phone: 01-6268391 Fax: 01-6263493
SIC: 45211 Employees: 40
Masonry Fixing Service
Mr Gerard Carroll Managing Director
Ms Maria Priestley Financial Director
Mr Frank Cullen Personnel Manager

Acutool Ltd
Jamestown Business Park
Finglas
Dublin 11
Phone: 01-8640466 Fax: 01-8640474
Email: sales@acutool.ie
Web: http://www.acutool.com
SIC: 45213 Employees: 35
Precision Engineering
Mr Frank McAuliffe Managing Director
Ms Anne Redmond Financial Controller
Mr Noel Madigan Sales Manager

Ascon Ltd
Kill
Naas Co. Kildare
Phone: 045-886400 Fax: 045-877264
Email: ascon@ascon.ie
Web: http://www.asconrohcom.ie
SIC: 45213 Employees: 1600
Civil Engineers & Building Contractors
Mr Brendan Barrett Managing Director
Mr Brian Fitzpatrick Company Secretary
Mr Tom Bambrick IT Manager

AWP Engineering Ltd
Unit 1, Block 13, Ballybane Ind Est
Galway Co. Galway
Phone: 091-751800 Fax: 091-756799
Email: awpeng@tinet.ie
SIC: 45213 Employees: 30
Precision & Production Engineering
Mr Des Rooney Managing Director

Brian McCarthy Ltd
Unit 6, Quinn Road Business Park
Ennis Co. Clare
Phone: 065-6828772 Fax: 065-6828432
Email: mccarthybrian@eircom.net
SIC: 45213 Employees: 140
Civil Engineering Contractors
Mr Brian McCarthy Proprietor
Mr Alan McCarthy Finance Manager

C M G Construction
Castlemahon
Limerick Co. Limerick
Phone: 069-72795 Fax: 069-72796
Email: cmgltd@iol.ie
SIC: 45213 Employees: 31
Civil Engineering Contractors
Mr Tom Collins Managing Director

Damien McKay
Drumany
Letterkenny Co. Donegal
Phone: 074-29243 Fax: 074-29242
SIC: 45213 Employees: 31
Civil Engineering Consultants
Mr Damien McKay Managing Director

Duggan Brothers (Contractors)
Richmond
Templemore
Thurles Co. Tipperary
Phone: 0504-31311 Fax: 0504-31258
Email: info@duggan-brothers.ie
SIC: 45213 Employees: 180
Civil Engineering & Building
Mr Kevin Duggan Managing Director
Mr Joe Gleeson Financial Controller
Mr Chris Oakes Marketing Manager
Mr Pat Heffernan Plant Manager

Energy Service Engineers
The Mall
Waterford Co. Waterford
Phone: 051-873301 Fax: 051-854843
Email: info@esb.ie
Web: http://www.esb.ie
SIC: 45213 Employees: 381
Engineers
Mr John Hadden General Manager

Glenrue Ltd
Kilcruttin Industrial Estate
Tullamore Co. Offaly
Phone: 0506-24555 Fax: 0506-24556
SIC: 45213 Employees: 31
Civil Engineering Contractors
Mr Seamus Egan General Manager

Hanley Development Ltd
Bushfield
Charlestown
Claremorris Co. Mayo
Phone: 094-54265 Fax: 094-54484
SIC: 45213 Employees: 31
Civil Engineering Contractors
Mr Michael Hanley Director

Hegarty Demolition Ltd
17 Main Street
Rathfarnham
Dublin 14
Phone: 01-4905058 Fax: 01-4905678
SIC: 45213 Employees: 100
Civil Engineers
Mr Sean Hegarty Managing Director
Mr Joe Flannery Finance Manager

Construction

Irishenco Construction Ltd
Hartwell Upper
Kill
Naas Co. Kildare
Phone: 045-877322 Fax: 045-877304
Email: info@irishenco.ie
Web: http://www.irishenco.ie
SIC: 45213 Employees: 60
Civil Engineering
Mr Bill O'Regan Managing Director
Mr Pat Farrell Accountant

John J Fleming Construction Co Ltd
New Cork Road
Bandon Co. Cork
Phone: 023-20600 Fax: 023-20610
Email: info@flemingconstruction.ie
Web: http://www.flemingconstruction.ie
SIC: 45213 Employees: 80
Civil Engineers & General Builders
Mr John Fleming Managing Director
Mr Vincent O'Donavan Administration Manager

Jons Civil Engineering Co Ltd
Duleek
Drogheda Co. Louth
Phone: 041-9823682 Fax: 041-9823264
Email: jonsheadoffice@esatclear.ie
SIC: 45213 Employees: 125
Civil Engineering Contractors
Mr John Pentony Director
Ms Susan Gleeson Computer Manager

JSL Group Ltd
43 Lower Salthill
Galway Co. Galway
Phone: 091-522815 Fax: 091-524943
Email: jsl@stewart.ie
SIC: 45213 Employees: 50
Building/Civil Engineers
Mr Sean Stewart Manager

Langan Associates
Rathronan House
Ardagh
Limerick Co. Limerick
Phone: 069-76144 Fax: 069-76130
SIC: 45213 Employees: 31
Civil Engineering Consultants
Mr John Scaman Managing Director

Loftus Civil Engineering
Kilbarry House
Dublin Hill
Cork Co. Cork
Phone: 021-4393655 Fax: 021-4395006
Email: info@loftus.eng.ie
Web: http://www.loftus.eng.ie
SIC: 45213 Employees: 70
Civil Engineering
Mr John Loftus Director
Ms Marie Loftus Finance Manager
Mr Sean Loftus Sales Manager
Ms Hilary Loftus Production Manager
Ms Evelyn Horgan Computer Manager

MacContractors Ltd
12 Grove Lawn
Malahide Co. Dublin
Phone: 01-8452125 Fax: 01-8451405
Email: engineering@maccontractors.iol.ie
SIC: 45213 Employees: 200
Building & Civil Engineering
Mr Brendan McGrath General Manager
Ms Elaine Keoghan Accounts Manager

McCartney Contractors Ltd
Moynalty
Kells Co. Meath
Phone: 046-44444 Fax: 046-44183
Email: drydoc@iol.ie
SIC: 45213 Employees: 32
Landscaping & Sportsfield Draining
Mr Alan McCartney Managing Director
Ms Lucy Carolan Accounts Manager

McGinty & O' Shea Ltd
Sarsfield Court Industrial Estate
Glanmire
Cork Co. Cork
Phone: 021-4821719 Fax: 021-4866436
Email: info@mos.iol.ie
SIC: 45213 Employees: 100
Civil Engineering
Mr Jim O'Shea Managing Director
Ms Margaret Fitzpatrick Financial Controller
Mr Dan Murphy Sales Manager

Murphy International Ltd
Great Connell
Newbridge Co. Kildare
Phone: 045-431384 Fax: 045-431635
Email: mil@iol.ie
SIC: 45213 Employees: 165
Civil Engineering
Mr Bernard Murphy Managing Director
Mr William Byrne Director/Company Secretary
Mr Pat Fox Sales Manager

P & S Plant Hire
Drumuck
Stradone
Cavan Co. Cavan
Phone: 049-4330115 Fax: 049-4330462
SIC: 45213 Employees: 60
Civil Engineering Contractors, Plant Hire & Quarries
Mr Sean Smith Proprietor

P Elliott & Co Ltd
49 Church Street
Cavan Co. Cavan
Phone: 049-4331066 Fax: 049-4331537
Email: pelliott01@eircom.net
SIC: 45213 Employees: 150
Civil Engineering Contractor
Mr Mark Elliott Chief Executive
Ms Mary Keegan Group Accountant
Mr Noel Elliott Jnr Contracts Director

Patrick Mulcair Engineering
Ballyclough
Ballysheedy
Limerick Co. Limerick
Phone: 061-414874 Fax: 061-414767
Email: mulcair@indigo.ie
SIC: 45213 Employees: 550
Civil Engineering
Mr Pat Mulcair Managing Director
Mr Connor Gilligen Financial Controller
Mr Eamonn O'Dowd Contracts Director

Peter O'Loughlin Ltd
13 Thomas Street
Waterford Co. Waterford
Phone: 051-876362 Fax: 051-871907
SIC: 45213 Employees: 50
Civil Engineering Contractor
Mr Peter O'Loughlin Managing Director
Mr Patrick Slevin Sales & Marketing Manager

PJ Edwards & Co Ltd
Kennelsfort Road
Palmerstown
Dublin 20
Phone: 01-6268329 Fax: 01-6260340
Email: pje@iol.ie
SIC: 45213 Employees: 50
Civil Engineering
Mr Greg Edwards Managing Director

PJ Walls Ltd
Rosemount Office Park
Glandore Road
Dublin 9
Phone: 01-8374143 Fax: 01-8369800
Email: info@pjwalls-civil.ie
SIC: 45213 Employees: 50
Civil Engineering
Mr Eamon Corcoran Managing Director
Mr Ronan Nelvin Finance Manager
Mr Paddy Smith Computer Manager

Redmond Civil Engineering
Kildavin, Bunclody
Enniscorthy Co. Wexford
Phone: 054-76262 Fax: 054-76519
Email: rce@eircom.net
SIC: 45213 Employees: 31
Civil Engineering Contractors
Mr Kieran Redmond Managing Director
Mr Michael Redmond Sales Director

RSK Ltd
U15 Crough Cresent, Crag Ind Estate
Clondalkin
Dublin 22
Phone: 01-4578188 Fax: 01-4578188
Email: taraleebrennan@eircom.net
SIC: 45213 Employees: 240
Civil Engineering
Mr Martin Dwyer Managing Director

SIAC Construction Ltd
Monastery Road
Clondalkin
Dublin 22
Phone: 01-4591188 Fax: 01-4591207
Email: siac@siac.ie
Web: http://www.siac.ie
SIC: 45213 Employees: 500
Construction Civil Engineering
Mr Finn Lyden Managing Director
Mr Bernard McGlade Finance Manager
Ms Lynne McSherry Personnel Director
Mr Michael Feighery Company Secretary
Mr Clinton Quinless IT Manager

Sorensen Construction & Plant Co Ltd
Forge Hill Cross
Kinsale Road
Cork Co. Cork
Phone: 021-4968917 Fax: 021-4965544
Email: sales@sorensen.ie
SIC: 45213 Employees: 80
Civil Engineering Contractors
Mr Olaf Sorensen Managing Director
Mr Kieran Horgan Financial Controller
Mr Eamon McCarthy Sales Manager

Wills Brothers Plant Hire Ltd
Ballylahan Bridge
Foxford
Westport Co. Mayo
Phone: 094-56221 Fax: 094-56221
SIC: 45213 Employees: 25
Civil Engineering Contractors
Mr James Wills Proprietor
Mr Charles Wills Computer Manager

Dublin Container & Transport Services
Tolka Quay
Dublin 3
Phone: 01-8557334 Fax: 01-8365403
Email: dcats@eircom.net
SIC: 45216 Employees: 30
Building Prefabrications
Mr Seamus O'Gara Managing Director
Mr David Balch Sales Director

Extraspace
Craig Avenue Business Park
Clondalkin
Dublin 22
Phone: 01-4570366 Fax: 01-4570326
Email: info@extraspace.ie
Web: http://www.extraspace.ie
SIC: 45216 Employees: 50
Manufacture Portacabins & Containers
Mr Connor Hanratty Managing Director

Roankabin Group
Oldmill Town
Kill,
Naas Co. Kildare
Phone: 045-886100 Fax: 045-886101
Email: info@roankabin.ie
Web: http://www.roankabin.ie
SIC: 45216 Employees: 30
Portable Accomodation
Mr Paddy McEvoy Managing Director
Mr Gary Davitt Finance Manager
Mr Gerry Diggins Joint Managing Director

Century Homes Ltd
Clones Road
Monaghan Co. Monaghan
Phone: 047-81270 Fax: 047-84397
Email: salesdesk@century.ie
Web: http://www.centuryhomes.ie
SIC: 45217 Employees: 200
Manufacture Timber Frame Houses
Mr Gerald McCaughey Managing Director
Ms Bernie McAdams Financial Controller
Ms Kerry McNally Personnel Manager
Mr Paul McDonald Sales & Marketing Director
Mr Jonathan Smyth IT Manager

Ramstown Development
Ramstown
Gorey Co. Wexford
Phone: 055-22099 Fax: 055-22130
Email: info@ramstown.com
SIC: 45217 Employees: 25
Manufacturer of Timber Framed Houses
Mr Thomas Miler Manager

Asphalt Roofing Ltd
Ballyraggett
Kilkenny Co. Kilkenny
Phone: 056-33249 Fax: 056-67001
SIC: 45220 Employees: 40
Roofing Contractors
Mr John O'Brien Managing Director

CCR Ltd
Unit 5 Block B
Ballymount Cross Business Park
Dublin 24
Phone: 01-4569633 Fax: 01-4569637
SIC: 45220 Employees: 130
Roofing Contractors
Mr Niall Cormican Managing Director

Celtic Roofing Ltd
Unit 16 Westpoint Business Park
Dublin 15
Phone: 01-8206600 Fax: 01-8206649
Email: celticroofing@iol.ie
SIC: 45220 Employees: 35
Roofing Contractors
Mr Carl Gygax Managing Director

Fitzharris Construction Ltd
Maudlins
New Ross Co. Wexford
Phone: 051-420420 Fax: 051-420450
Email: info@indigo.ie
SIC: 45220 Employees: 30
Roofing Contractors
Mr William Fitzharris Proprietor
Ms Catrina Whelan Computer Manager

Gerard F May Roofing Ltd
Waterway House, Crag Crescent
Clondalkin Industrial Estate
Dublin 22
Phone: 01-4570666 Fax: 01-4571039
Email: info@gfmay.com
Web: http://www.gfmay.com
SIC: 45220 Employees: 35
Roofing Contractor
Mr Gerard May Managing Director
Mr Paul Brian Finance Manager
Ms Gillian Smith Office Manager

H & E Costello Roofing Ltd
9 Robinhood Road
Clondalkin
Dublin 22
Phone: 01-4508863 Fax: 01-4569660
Email: roofing@handecostello.iol.ie
Web: http://www.costelloroofing.ie
SIC: 45220 Employees: 35
Roofing Contractors
Mr Eamon Costello Proprietor

Lynch Roofing Systems
Market Street
Ballaghadereen
Castlerea Co. Roscommon
Phone: 0907-60041 Fax: 0907-60685
Email: lynchroof@indigo.ie
Web: http://www.lynchroof.com
SIC: 45220 Employees: 40
Roofing Contractors
Mr Colman Lynch Managing Director

Multiroofing Systems Ltd
Unit 62 Cookstown Industrial Estate
Tallaght
Dublin 24
Phone: 01-4596660 Fax: 01-4514753
SIC: 45220 Employees: 50
Roofing Contractors
Mr Barry Sharkey Managing Director

PJ Quinn Ltd
Po Box 23
New Ross Co. Wexford
Phone: 051-428316 Fax: 051-428458
SIC: 45220 Employees: 65
Roofing & Cladding Contractors
Mr PJ Quinn Managing Director
Mr Edward Kent General Manager
Ms Patricia Quinn Sales & Marketing Manager

MacLochlainn Ltd
21 Prospect Road
Dublin 9
Phone: 01-8309107 Fax: 01-8309526
SIC: 45230 Employees: 40
Roadmarkings
Mr Andrew Berry General Manager

MacLochlainn Roadmarkings
Parnell Street
Thurles Co. Tipperary
Phone: 0504-23355 Fax: 0504-23587
Email: maclochl@iol.ie
SIC: 45230 Employees: 25
Road Marking Contractors
Mr Cathal General Manager

Morrissey Dan (Ireland) Ltd
Balleese Wood Quarry
Rathdrum
Wicklow Co. Wicklow
Phone: 0404-46399 Fax: 0404-46399
SIC: 45230 Employees: 25
Tarmacadam Contractors
Mr Dan Morissey Managing Director

The Paving Division
Adrienne Monastery Road
Clondalkin
Dublin 22
Phone: 01-4593194 Fax: 01-4592679
Email: paving@siac.ie
SIC: 45230 Employees: 40
Roads & Paving Services
Ms Vivienne Moore Managing Director

Thornton G Ireland Ltd
Portuma
Galway Co. Galway
Phone: 0509-41955 Fax: 0509-41956
Email: gtisports@eircom.net
SIC: 45230 Employees: 40
Sports Field Construction
Mr Paul Copage General Manager

Tracey Enterprises Ltd
St Michael's, Dundrum Road
Dundrum
Dublin 14
Phone: 01-2984300 Fax: 01-2980122
SIC: 45230 Employees: 120
Tarmac Manufacturing
Mr Gerry Fitzpatrick General Manager
Mr Patsy Monaghan Production Director

Focus Communications Ireland Ltd
64 Moyle Road, Dublin Industrial Estate
Glasnevin
Dublin 11
Phone: 01-8306864 Fax: 01-8302512
SIC: 45240 Employees: 100
Trenching Contractors
Mr Tony O'Brien Managing Director
Mr Gary Smyth Financial Controller

AGB Electrical Contractors Ltd
Knockrea Ballinlough Road
Ballinlough
Cork Co. Cork
Phone: 021-4962433 Fax: 021-4962285
Email: abgelect@indigo.ie
SIC: 45310 Employees: 30
Electrical Contractors
Mr Julian O'Sullivan Managing Director

Ascal Electrical
100 Kimmage Road West
Dublin 12
Phone: 01-4555479 Fax: 01-4559713
Email: ascal@indigo.ie
SIC: 45310 Employees: 25
Electrical Contractors - General
Mr Brendan Mullin Manager

Breen Electrical Co Ltd
12 Upper Ormond Quay
Dublin 7
Phone: 01-6711854 Fax: 01-8731087
Email: breenel@iol.ie
SIC: 45310 Employees: 25
Electrical Contractors
Mr Ivan Hammond Managing Director

Brian Kelly Manufacturing
Main Street
Ballaghadereen
Castlerea Co. Roscommon
Phone: 0907-60033 Fax: 0907-60326
SIC: 45310 Employees: 25
Electrical Contractors
Mr Brian Kelly Manager

CEI (Cork) Ltd
Oldchurch St Mary's
Montenotte
Cork Co. Cork
Phone: 021-4551717 Fax: 021-4551719
Email: cei@eircom.net
SIC: 45310 Employees: 70
Electrical Contractors - Industrial
Mr Tom Buckley Proprietor
Mr Eugene Hall Contract Manager

CG Services Ltd
Ballycurreen
Airport Road
Cork Co. Cork
Phone: 021-4317571 Fax: 021-4313794
Email: info@cgservices.ie
Web: http://www.cgservices.ie
SIC: 45310 Employees: 170
Electrical Contractors
Mr Chris Granby Managing Director
Mr Lou Knapmann Finance Manager

Construction

CJ Ryder Lawlor Ltd
85-86 Amiens Street
Dublin 1
Phone: 01-8742558 Fax: 01-8747525
Email: info@cjrl.ie
Web: http://www.cjrl.ie
SIC: 45310 Employees: 95
Electrical Contractors
Mr Des Kelly Managing Director
Mr John Ryder Finance Manager

CMK Electrical Services Ltd
Manor-Kilbride
Blessington
Naas Co. Kildare
Phone: 01-4582494 Fax: 01-4582750
SIC: 45310 Employees: 25
Electrical Contractors
Mr Patrick O'Toole Manager

Crowe Engineering Ltd
Feltrim Industrial Park
Drynam Road
Swords Co. Dublin
Phone: 01-8407769 Fax: 01-8407772
SIC: 45310 Employees: 150
Electrical Contractors
Mr Tom Barron Chairman
Mr James Kavanagh Finance Director
Mr Pat Brown Contracts Director

Dan Sugrue & Co Ltd
Russell Street
Tralee Co. Kerry
Phone: 066-7122183 Fax: 066-7123086
Email: sugrue@indigo.ie
SIC: 45310 Employees: 40
Electrical Contractor
Mr Dan Sugrue Managing Director
Ms Sheila Tangney Finance Manager

Designer Electric Ltd
27 Annamoe Terrace
North Circular Road
Dublin 7
Phone: 01-8681817 Fax: 01-8381983
Email: deselec@indigo.ie
Web: http://www.designerelectric.ie
SIC: 45310 Employees: 80
Electrical Contractors - General
Mr Michael Stone Managing Director

Electrical Rewind Service (Limerick)
38/39 Thomas Street
Limerick Co. Limerick
Phone: 061-417070 Fax: 061-419122
Email: sales@electricalrewind.ie
SIC: 45310 Employees: 80
Electrical Contractors
Mr Daniel Lehane Managing Director
Ms Grainne Lehane Finance Manager
Mr Tom Ryan Personnel Manager
Mr Michael Ryan Sales & Marketing Manager
Mr Tom McGann Computer Manager

Elenco Engineering Ltd
9 Belvedere Place
Dublin 1
Phone: 01-8554077 Fax: 01-8554026
Email: management@elenco.ie
Web: http://www.elenco.ie
SIC: 45310 Employees: 120
Electrical & Technical Contractors
Mr Alan Simpson Managing Director
Ms Sinead Byrne Finance Manager
Mr Maurice McHugh Personnel Director
Mr Dave Regan Computer Manager

FB Aragoran Services
Unit 1 Clonroad Business Park
Ennis Co. Clare
Phone: 065-6820530 Fax: 065-6820019
Email: m.tambling@aragoran.ie
SIC: 45310 Employees: 40
Electrical Sub-Contractors
Mr Fergus Blake General Manager
Mr Cyril McMahon Marketing Manager

Fitzgibbon Electrical Services Ltd
2 Doctor Croke Place
Clonmel Co. Tipperary
Phone: 052-21586 Fax: 052-21777
Email: fesl@eircom.net
SIC: 45310 Employees: 30
Electrical Contractors
Mr Mark Fitzgibbon Managing Director
Mr Anthony Fitzgibbon Finance Manager

Geoghegan Electrical
7/8 Butterly Business Park
Artane
Dublin 5
Phone: 01-8488353 Fax: 01-8488363
Email: geoghegan@iol.ie
SIC: 45310 Employees: 70
Electrical Contractors
Mr Gerry Geoghegan Managing Director
Mr John Rush Finance Manager

H Shiels Ltd
18b Goldenbridge Industrial Estate
Inchicore
Dublin 8
Phone: 01-4540441 Fax: 01-4530312
Email: hshiels@eircom.net
SIC: 45310 Employees: 60
Electrical Contractors
Mr Harry Shiels Managing Director
Mr Noel Madden Contract Manager

HTE Ltd
Drumconrath
Navan Co. Meath
Phone: 041-6854228 Fax: 041-6854367
Email: hte@dna.ie
SIC: 45310 Employees: 120
Electrical Contractors
Mr Louis Tighe Managing Director
Ms Rita Thompson Finance Manager

IIF Process Mechanical & Electrical
PO Box No 683, Sarsfield Road Wilton
Cork Co. Cork
Phone: 021-4346880 Fax: 021-4346881
Email: info@iifpmec.ie
Web: http://www.iifpmec.ie
SIC: 45310 Employees: 250
Electrical & Mechanical Contractors
Mr Andrew O'Gorman Managing Director
Mr John Burke Financial Controller
Mr Edwin Kenny Sales & Marketing Manager

Irish Energy Management Ltd
8 Ballycurreen Industrial Estate
Kinsale Road
Cork Co. Cork
Phone: 021-4320480 Fax: 021-4320479
Email: info@iem.ie
Web: http://www.iem.ie
SIC: 45310 Employees: 30
Electrical Contractors/Energy Consultants
Mr John Maloney Partner
Mr Steven Flint Partner
Mr Tom Lynch Partner
Mr Peter Shortland Computer Manager

John Fletcher Ltd
The Whitehouse
Main Street, Portarlington
Portlaoise Co. Laois
Phone: 0502-23276 Fax: 0502-23916
Email: jfl@eircom.net
SIC: 45310 Employees: 35
Electrical Contractors
Mr John Fletcher Managing Director

JP Byrne Electrical Ltd
36 Parkwest Enterprise Centre
Dublin 12
Phone: 01-6269556 Fax: 01-6269782
Email: jpbyrneelec@eircom.net
SIC: 45310 Employees: 30
Electrical Contractors
Mr Paul Byrne Managing Director
Mr Derek Byrne Sales Director

Kirby Group
1 Wolsley Street
Dublin 8
Phone: 01-4540411 Fax: 01-4547589
Email: dublin@kirbyelec.ie
Web: http://www.kirbyelec.ie
SIC: 45310 Employees: 600
Electrical Contractors
Mr Fergus Froll Managing Director

L Redmond Electrical Ltd
Hawthorn Avenue, Eastwall
Dublin 3
Phone: 01-8364040 Fax: 01-8364026
Email: redelec@eircom.net
SIC: 45310 Employees: 35
Electrical Contractors
Mr Liam Redmond Managing Director

McGrattan Kenny McCaffrey Ltd
Unit 4 Block 9 Riverview
Business
Dublin 12
Phone: 01-4605360 Fax: 01-6683086
SIC: 45310 Employees: 60
Electrical & Mechanical Contractors
Mr Frank McCaffrey Managing Director
Mr John Walsh Finance Manager

O'Kane Engineering Ltd
Herberton Road
Glenview Industrial Estate
Dublin 12
Phone: 01-4542759 Fax: 01-4543963
Email: info@okane-eng.com
Web: http://www.okane-eng.com
SIC: 45310 Employees: 150
Electrical Contractors
Mr Leo O'Kane Managing Director
Ms Maureen Mallon Administration Manager
Mr Derek Hammond Operation Manager

O'Leary Electrical
213 Botanic Avenue
Dublin 9
Phone: 01-8377128 Fax: 01-8377128
Email: polelect@indigo.ie
SIC: 45310 Employees: 30
Electrical Contractors
Mr O'Leary Partner
Ms Mary O'Leary Personnel Director
Mr Padraig O'Leary Partner

Phoenix Electrical Ltd
Coes Road
Dundalk Co. Louth
Phone: 042-9330011 Fax: 042-9330013
Email: phoenixelectrical@eircom.net
SIC: 45310 Employees: 45
Electrical Contractors
Mr PJ Loughran Manager

R-Tec Teoranta
Baile An Tagairt, An Spideal
Galway Co. Galway
Phone: 091-553111 Fax: 091-553417
SIC: 45310 Employees: 70
Electrical Contractors
Mr Ray O'Donnchadha Managing Director
Ms Barbara O'Donnell Personnel Manager
Mr Fergal Kyme Production Manager

Ray Staunton Electrical Ltd
Kildysart Road
Clarecastle
Ennis Co. Clare
Phone: 065-6838158 Fax: 065-6838100
Email: rsel@eircom.net
Web: http://www.rsel.ie
SIC: 45310 Employees: 60
Electrical Contractors
Mr Ray Staunton Proprietor

Reihill Electrical Ltd
Turners Cross
Cork Co. Cork
Phone: 021-4319929 Fax: 021-4319929
SIC: 45310 Employees: 30
Electrical Contractors - General
Mr Anthony Crowley Proprietor

Rotary M & E Services Ltd
Esmond Avenue
Fairview
Dublin 3
Phone: 01-8369175 Fax: 01-8367034
Email: rotary@indigo.ie
SIC: 45310 Employees: 100
Electrical & Mechanical Contractors
Mr Gerry Collins Managing Director
Mr Robert McClean Finance Manager
Mr Maurice Leen Marketing Manager

Schneider Electric Manufacturing
Maynooth Road
Celbridge
Naas Co. Kildare
Phone: 01-6012250 Fax: 01-6012251
Email: info@scheiderelectric.ie
Web: http://www.scheiderelectric.ie
SIC: 45310 Employees: 366
Electrical Contactor/Industrial Contractors
Mr Alan Leroy General Manager
Mr Austin McDermott Financial Controller
Ms Maura McEvoy Personnel Manager
Mr Jim Rice Sales Director
Mr John Sexton Production Manager

SCI Ireland
Rathhealy Road
Fermoy Co. Cork
Phone: 025-31777 Fax: 025-31104
Email: info@sci.com
Web: http://www.sci.com
SIC: 45310 Employees: 750
Electrical Contractors
Mr Christopher White Managing Director
Mr Owen O'Regan Financial Controller
Ms Cassie Fitzpatrick Personnel Manager
Mr Brian Martin Sales & Marketing Manager
Mr Patrick Holmes IT Manager

Sean Ahern Ltd
5 Corn Market Street
Cork Co. Cork
Phone: 021-4273227 Fax: 021-4272718
Email: ahernelec@eircom.net
SIC: 45310 Employees: 100
Electrical Contractors
Mr Sean Ahern Proprietor
Mr John Nolan Accountant

Tim Kelly Electrical Contractors Ltd
Claremorris Road
Ballinrobe
Claremorris Co. Mayo
Phone: 092-41283 Fax: 092-41670
Email: timkelly@iol.ie
SIC: 45310 Employees: 73
Electrical Contracting
Mr Tim Kelly Managing Director

Update Technology
90 Upper Churchtown Road
Churchtown
Dublin 14
Phone: 01-6710266 Fax: 01-6710086
Email: info@updatetech.ie
Web: http://www.updatetechnology.ie
SIC: 45310 Employees: 60
Electrical Contractors
Mr Eamonn O'Riordin Managing Director
Ms Rachel Slattery Finance Manager
Mr Tim O'Riordan Sales Manager

Vincent Doherty Ltd
11a Tivoli Avenue
Harolds Cross Road
Dublin 6w
Phone: 01-4963156 Fax: 01-4963449
Email: info@vdoherty.com
Web: http://www.vdoherty.com
SIC: 45310 Employees: 30
Electrical Contractors
Mr Vincent Doherty Manager

W Malone & Sons
117 Cork Street
Dublin 8
Phone: 01-4543755 Fax: 01-4544173
Email: enquiries@malone-electrical.ie
Web: http://www.malone-electrical.ie
SIC: 45310 Employees: 45
Electrical Contractors
Mr Bill Malone Proprietor

William Farrell Ltd
Grange House Unit 94 Foxrock Avenue
Dublin 18
Phone: 01-2836455 Fax: 01-2836493
SIC: 45310 Employees: 25
Electrical Contractors
Mr William Farrell Managing Director
Ms Marty Farrell Company Secretary

Winthorp Engineers Ltd
2 Adelphi Quay
Waterford Co. Waterford
Phone: 051-843311 Fax: 051-843321
Email: info@waterford.winthrop.ie
Web: http://www.waterford.winthrop.ie
SIC: 45310 Employees: 70
Electrical Contractors
Mr Gerard O'Leary Manager
Mr Margaret Burchall Financial Controller

WW Electrical Ltd
160 St Peters Road
Walkinstown
Dublin 12
Phone: 01-4567183 Fax: 01-4567877
SIC: 45310 Employees: 40
Electrical Contractors
Mr Terry Wall Partner
Ms Brenda Kane Office Manager

Brooklyn Engineering Service
Unit 8, 78 Furze Road
Sandyford Industrial Estate
Dublin 18
Phone: 01-2691648 Fax: 01-2942433
Email: info@brooklyn.ie
Web: http://www.brooklyn.ie
SIC: 45311 Employees: 150
Electrical Engineering
Mr William Johnston Managing Director
Mr Dermot MacNamara Sales & Marketing Manager
Mr John Traynor Computer Manager

PEM Ltd Precision Engineering
Mullingar Business Park
Mullingar Co. Westmeath
Phone: 044-40729 Fax: 044-43518
Email: info@pem.ie
Web: http://www.pem.ie
SIC: 45311 Employees: 34
Electrical Engineers
Mr Richard Edert Managing Director
Ms Kim Brown Finance Manager
Mr Heinz O'Connor Personnel Manager
Mr Liam McCauley Sales Manager
Mr Ambrose Doyle Computer Manager

Suir Engineering Ltd
32 Upper Mountail Street
Dublin 2
Phone: 01-6787466 Fax: 01-6787473
Email: info@suireng.ie
Web: http://www.suireng.com
SIC: 45311 Employees: 450
Electrical Engineering
Mr Edward Walsh Manager
Ms Grainne Rice Marketing Manager
Mr Paul Hayes IT Manager

Ashbrook Engineering
Unit 4-5 Southern Cross Business Park
Boghall Road
Bray Co. Wicklow
Phone: 01-2861322 Fax: 01-2861473
SIC: 45331 Employees: 75
Heating Insulation
Mr Eamon Walsh Managing Director
Ms Lorraine Byrne Personnel Manager
Mr Frank Aherne Computer Manager

BJ Duffy & Sons Ltd
25 Camden Street Lower
Dublin 2
Phone: 01-4753081 Fax: 01-4753753
SIC: 45331 Employees: 25
Heating Contractors
Mr Brendan Duffy General Manager

D Harris Heating & Plumbing Ltd
149 North Strand Road
Dublin 3
Phone: 01-8741151 Fax: 01-8740299
SIC: 45331 Employees: 40
Heating Contractors - Industrial
Mr David Harris Managing Director
Mr Paul Kiberd Finance Manager
Ms Ann Cooper Head of Computers

L Lynch & Co Ltd
Unit 16 Fonthill Industrial Park
Fonthill Road North
Dublin 22
Phone: 01-6261144 Fax: 01-6262588
Email: info@llynch.com
Web: http://www.llynch.com
SIC: 45331 Employees: 200
Heating Contractors - Industrial
Mr Sean Smith Manager
Mr Conor Lynch Finance Manager
Ms Eileen Ryan Office Manager

BMD & Co Ltd
Lee Road
Cork Co. Cork
Phone: 021-4541499 Fax: 021-4546794
SIC: 45400 Employees: 145
Building Contractor
Mr John Bowen Manager

Cafferty Developments Ltd
18 Castletown Estate
Leixlip
Naas Co. Kildare
Phone: 01-6244203 Fax: 01-6246883
SIC: 45400 Employees: 40
Groundwork & Excavation Contractors
Mr Tony Cafferty Managing Director

Construction

CLG Builders
Dock Road
Limerick Co. Limerick
Phone: 061-303274 Fax: 061-303439
SIC: 45400 Employees: 245
Pipe Laying Contractor
Mr Eugene Feaheny Manager
Mr Anthony Fahy Finance Manager

Plaster & Drywall Ltd
13 Brompton Lawn
Castleknock
Dublin 15
Phone: 01-8216576 Fax: 01-8216576
SIC: 45410 Employees: 60
Plastering
Mr Pat Grey Manager

Sean Cunnane Plasters
Adrigoole
Kiltimagh
Claremorris Co. Mayo
Phone: 094-88290 Fax: 094-88494
SIC: 45410 Employees: 30
Plastering
Mr Sean Cunnane Proprietor

Burke Joinery Ltd
Unit 1 Kylemore Park South
Ballyfermot
Dublin 10
Phone: 01-6268129 Fax: 01-6268175
Email: info@burkejoinery.ie
Web: http://www.burkejoinery.ie
SIC: 45420 Employees: 30
Joinery Products
Mr John Burke Proprietor
Mr Michael Burke Finance Manager
Mr Michael Meehan Personnel Manager

Dunnes Workshop Ltd
Rahugh
Kilbeggan
Mullingar Co. Westmeath
Phone: 044-23188 Fax: 044-23130
SIC: 45420 Employees: 60
Joiners & Carpenters
Mr Brian Scally Manager

Geraghty & Co Ltd
Carraghy
Claregalway
Galway Co. Galway
Phone: 091-797193 Fax: 091-797336
SIC: 45420 Employees: 45
Joiners & Carpenters
Mr Eugene Geraghty Managing Director
Ms Mary Geraghty Administration Manager

Irish Joinery
Unit 6 Mayfield Business Park
Cork Co. Cork
Phone: 021-4551788 Fax: 021-4551799
Email: theirishjoinery@oceanfree.net
SIC: 45420 Employees: 30
Joinery Works
Mr PJ Dennehy Proprietor

Joseph O'Halloran & Son Ltd
Tuam Road
Galway Co. Galway
Phone: 091-755601 Fax: 091-755351
SIC: 45420 Employees: 40
Joiners & Carpenters
Mr Richard O'Halloran Managing Director

Murnane & O'Shea Ltd
Glengarriff Road
Bantry Co. Cork
Phone: 027-50198 Fax: 027-51430
Email: most@eircom.net
SIC: 45420 Employees: 200
Joiners & Carpenters
Mr Daniel Murnane Managing Director
Mr Jerry Enright Company Secretary
Mr Andrew Moore Sales & Marketing Manager

Bonmahon Joinery & Upvc
Coolraclaire
Waterford Co. Waterford
Phone: 051-292123 Fax: 051-292294
SIC: 45421 Employees: 23
Joinery & Upvc
Mr John Roche Manager
Ms Mary Roche Office Manager
Ms Rosemary Walsh Sales Manager

Daingean Joinery Ltd
Daingean
Tullamore Co. Offaly
Phone: 0506-53097 Fax: 0506-53274
SIC: 45421 Employees: 33
Joinery
Mr Noel Waters Manager
Mr Michael Clarke Finance Manager

Dalgan Wood Industry
Dalgan Road
Shrule
Galway Co. Galway
Phone: 093-31270 Fax: 093-31377
Email: dwi@eircom.net
SIC: 45421 Employees: 50
Joinery/PVC Windows
Mr Peter McCarthy General Manager
Mr Billy Ryan Personnel Manager

Doherty Joinery
Killbegs
Donegal Co. Donegal
Phone: 073-31551 Fax: 073-32955
SIC: 45421 Employees: 35
Joinery Company
Mr Eugene Doherty Manager

Dolan Bros Joinery
Moyle Road
Dublin Industrial Estate
Dublin 11
Phone: 01-8303844 Fax: 01-8303184
Email: info@dolansbrothers.com
Web: http://www.dolansbrothers.com
SIC: 45421 Employees: 50
Joinery
Mr Seamus Dolan Managing Director
Mr Michael Dolan Financial Controller
Mr Michael Tanaman Marketing Manager
Mr Derek Ryan Production Manager
Ms Monica Dolan Accounts Manager

J McNally Joinery Ltd
Walshestown
Lusk Co. Dublin
Phone: 01-8433022 Fax: 01-8433367
SIC: 45421 Employees: 40
Joinery Company
Mr Joe McNally Managing Director

Kelly Bros Ltd
Rossmore Industrial Estate
Monaghan Co. Monaghan
Phone: 047-81157 Fax: 047-84162
Email: kbltd@eircom.net
SIC: 45421 Employees: 30
PVC & Joinery Work
Mr John Kelly Managing Director
Mr Paul Loane Accounts Manager
Mr Maurice McCarey Production Manager

Munster Joinery Ltd
Lacka Cross
Ballydesmond
Mallow Co. Cork
Phone: 064-51151 Fax: 064-51311
Email: munsterj@iol.ie
SIC: 45421 Employees: 400
Wood Products (Semi-finished)
Mr Donal Ring Chief Executive
Mr Paddy Tobin Financial Controller
Ms Christine Bradley Personnel Manager
Mr Tom Nugent Sales & Marketing Manager
Mr Jerry Coffee IT Manager

P J McLoughlin & Sons Ltd
Dublin Road
Longford Co. Longford
Phone: 043-46317 Fax: 043-46636
SIC: 45421 Employees: 35
Joiners Building Contractors
Mr Martin McLoughlin Manager

Tom Durkin & Co
Jamestown Road
Inchicore
Dublin 8
Phone: 01-4536155 Fax: 01-4532668
SIC: 45421 Employees: 30
Joinery Works
Mr Tom Durkin Proprietor
Mr Derek Arkins Production Manager
Ms Evelyn Brierley Office Manager

Truwood Ltd
Drumcondra
Emyvale
Monaghan Co. Monaghan
Phone: 047-87581 Fax: 047-87832
Email: truwoodltd@eircom.net
SIC: 45421 Employees: 30
Specialist Joinery
Mr Philip McKenna Managing Director
Ms Olive McKenna Finance Manager
Ms Carmel Meehan Personnel Manager
Mr Al McKenna Sales & Marketing Manager

Bosal Ireland Ltd
Naas Road
Dublin 12
Phone: 01-4565644 Fax: 01-4566447
SIC: 45431 Employees: 23
Floors - Mezzanine
Mr Henry Harding Managing Director

Cableplan Ltd
Park House Kylemore Park North
Ballyfermot
Dublin 10
Phone: 01-6268888 Fax: 01-6268889
SIC: 45431 Employees: 30
Flooring
Mr David O'Brien Proprietor

Crown Flooring
Ballyquirke
Moycullen
Galway Co. Galway
Phone: 091-555202 Fax: 091-555639
SIC: 45431 Employees: 30
Floor Manufacturing
Mr Alan O'Toole Managing Director

Lackagh Concrete Ltd
Menlo
Galway Co. Galway
Phone: 091-768608 Fax: 091-768608
SIC: 45431 Employees: 30
Floor Manufacturing
Mr John Dempsey Managing Director

PG Power Distribution Ltd
Ballymount Road Lower
Walkinstown
Dublin 12
Phone: 01-4505553 Fax: 01-4501173
Email: pgpower@iol.ie
SIC: 45431 Employees: 31
Floor & Rail Coverings
Mr Mike Moffett Managing Director
Mr Alan Lawless Finance Manager
Ms Siobhan Cleary Personnel Manager

Wallguard Ireland
50 Cherry Orchard Industrial Estate
Dublin 10
Phone: 01-6265547 Fax: 01-6264403
Email: mvoh@iol.ie
SIC: 45431 Employees: 30
Flooring Contractors
Mr Ian O'Halloran Manager

Construction

Euro-Clad
Unit 4 Newhall Industrial Estate
Naas Co. Kildare
Phone: 045-435470 Fax: 045-435472
Email: info@euroclad.ie
Web: http://www.euroclad.ie
SIC: 45432 Employees: 25
Roof Cladding
Mr John Barrett Manager

Mak Fastener Specialists Ltd
Unit 57 Cookstown Industrial Estate
Tallaght
Dublin 24
Phone: 01-4519900 Fax: 01-4624019
Email: admin@mak.iol.ie
SIC: 45432 Employees: 30
Fasteners for Cladding Roofing & Construction
Mr Michael McDonald Managing Director
Ms Catherine Lawlor Accounts Manager
Mr Brian Rossiter Sales & Marketing Manager

Abdec
4 Brown Street South
Dublin 8
Phone: 01-4540576 Fax: 01-4544789
Email: doylebc@iol.ie
SIC: 45441 Employees: 30
Painting & Decorating Contractors
Mr Joe Whelan Managing Director
Mr Kieran Doyle Finance Manager

JS McCarthy Painting Contractors
Mount Tallant Avenue
Terenure
Dublin 6w
Phone: 01-4906327 Fax: 01-4904130
Email: info@capco.ie
Web: http://www.capco.ie
SIC: 45441 Employees: 60
Painting Contractors
Mr Tom Mintern Managing Director
Mr John Keavney Financial Controller
Ms Geraldine Farrelly Personnel Manager
Mr Francis Coogan Computer Manager

Keenan Decorators Ltd
4a Upper Abbey Street
Dublin 1
Phone: 01-8720382 Fax: 01-8720369
SIC: 45441 Employees: 70
Painting & Decorating Contractors
Mr Mark Keenan Managing Director

Knights Industrial Services Ltd
Davitt Road
Dublin 12
Phone: 01-4559511 Fax: 01-4559616
Email: knights@eircom.net
Web: http://www.knights.ie
SIC: 45441 Employees: 30
Industrial Painting Contractors
Mr Tony O'Brien Managing Director
Mr Con Mulcahy Financial Controller
Mr Clive Saab Sales Director

Leixlip Decorating Contractors Ltd
Westgate House, Station Road
Leixlip
Naas Co. Kildare
Phone: 01-6244819 Fax: 01-6244819
Email: idc@eircom.net
SIC: 45441 Employees: 30
Painting & Decorating Contractors
Mr William Fox Managing Director

Top Tech Ireland
U1 Poppintree Industrial Estate
Finglas
Dublin 11
Phone: 01-8362322 Fax: 01-8081410
Email: sales@toptech.ie
Web: http://www.rennicks.com
SIC: 45441 Employees: 70
Painting, Spraying & Moulding
Mr Jim Forde Chief Executive
Ms Jo Carton Financial Controller
Mr Gerry McGowan Sales & Marketing Manager
Mr Paul Clarke General Manager

Athlone Glass & Windows
Clonowen Road
Athlone Co. Westmeath
Phone: 0902-92979 Fax: 0902-92013
SIC: 45442 Employees: 35
Glazing
Mr Liam Watkins Partner
Mr Noel Watkins Partner

Classic Windows Ltd
Classic Commercial Park, Killumney
Ovens
Cork Co. Cork
Phone: 021-4875833 Fax: 021-4875844
Email: classicw@iol.ie
Web: http://www.classicwindow.ie
SIC: 45442 Employees: 32
Aluminium/PVC Windows & Conservatories
Mr Harry Matson Managing Director
Mr David Callaghan Sales Manager

Costello Doors
Unit 3, Kylemore Road
Ballyfermot
Dublin 10
Phone: 01-6269895 Fax: 01-6262518
SIC: 45442 Employees: 45
Glazing
Mr Patrick Power Managing Director

Eden Aluminium Ltd
Monasteroris Industrial Estate
Tullamore Co. Offaly
Phone: 0405-31093 Fax: 0405-31433
Email: info@edenaluminium.iol.ie
SIC: 45442 Employees: 55
Windows Doors & Conservatories
Mr Patsy O'Gara Managing Director

Hele PVC Windows Ltd
Mahon Industrial Estate
Blackrock
Cork Co. Cork
Phone: 021-4357116 Fax: 021-4357591
Email: helepvc@indigo.ie
SIC: 45442 Employees: 28
Windows & Doors
Mr Heinrich Lentzy Managing Director
Mr Brendan Lynch Finance Manager
Mr Chris Lentzy Personnel Manager
Mr Gerard Kavanagh Production Manager

Myra Glass Co Ltd
5-7 New Street
Dublin 8
Phone: 01-4532622 Fax: 01-4531377
Email: myraglass@eircom.net
SIC: 45442 Employees: 25
Glazier
Mr Sean Sloane Managing Director
Ms Ann Fitzroy Credit Controller
Mr Sean Ward Sales Director

Ryan Windows
Unit 7 Parkwest Enterprise Centre
Nangor Road
Dublin 12
Phone: 01-6267869 Fax: 01-6260769
SIC: 45442 Employees: 36
Glazier
Mr Martin Ryan Managing Director
Mr Sean Ryan Director

Thomas Dunne & Sons Ltd
Malahide Road Industrial Park
Newtown Park
Dublin 17
Phone: 01-8471511 Fax: 01-8471257
Email: dunnesgl@iol.ie
SIC: 45442 Employees: 55
Glazing Contractors
Mr William Dunne Managing Director
Ms Joanne Tormey Financial Controller
Mr Connor Waddell Sales Manager
Ms Olive Shaw Administrator

Tipperary Glass Ltd
Railway Road
Templemore
Thurles Co. Tipperary
Phone: 0504-32192 Fax: 0504-32195
Email: info@tipperaryglass.ie
Web: http://www.tipperaryglass.ie
SIC: 45442 Employees: 50
Glazing
Mr Nicholas Cody Managing Director
Ms Therese Maher Finance Manager

Waters Glass & Glazing Ltd
40 Maylor Street
Cork Co. Cork
Phone: 021-4273291 Fax: 021-4273325
Email: info@waterglass.ie
Web: http://www.waterglass.ie
SIC: 45442 Employees: 25
Glass & Glazing
Mr Stephen Barber Partner
Mr David Barber Partner

Ashley Martin Ltd
Carndonagh Industrial Estate
Carndonagh
Lifford Co. Donegal
Phone: 077-29000 Fax: 077-29500
Email: ashleymartin@eircom.net
Web: http://www.ashleymartin.com
SIC: 45452 Employees: 33
Shopfitters
Mr John Duffy General Manager
Ms Marie Duffy Finance Manager
Mr Anthony McGonigle Production Manager

Charles Johnston & Sons Ltd
38 Capel Street
Dublin 1
Phone: 01-8725277 Fax: 01-8725228
SIC: 45452 Employees: 23
Shopfitting Displays
Mr Andrew Johnston Managing Director
Mr Paddy Ferrons Sales Manager

John O'Connell Furniture
Dunshaughlin Industrial Estate
Dunshaughlin
Navan Co. Meath
Phone: 01-8258101 Fax: 01-8258103
Email: info@johnoconnellfurniture.iol.ie
SIC: 45452 Employees: 25
Bar Fixtures & Fittings
Mr John O'Connell Managing Director
Mr David O'Connell Director

Kleerex International
Unit 151 Grange Drive
Baldoyle Ind Estate Baldoyle
Dublin 13
Phone: 01-8394650 Fax: 01-8394651
SIC: 45452 Employees: 150
Merchandising & Pop Fixtures
Mr Michael Ryan Managing Director
Mr Alan Victory Financial Controller
Mr Paul Carroll Ireland Manager
Mr Bill Duggan Production Manager

Manning Group
9 Cookstown Industrial Estate
Belgard Road, Tallaght
Dublin 24
Phone: 01-4511122 Fax: 01-4597011
Email: jmf@indigo.ie
SIC: 45452 Employees: 42
Shopfitting, Office Fitting & Builders
Mr James Manning Senior Managing Director
Mr Eric Doyle-Higgins Financial Controller
Mr John Hynes DP Systems Manager

Storage Systems Ltd
Coolock Industrial Estate
Coolock
Dublin 17
Phone: 01-8470956 Fax: 01-8479892
Email: sales@storagesystems.ie
Web: http://www.storagesystems.ie
SIC: 45452 Employees: 35
Shop & Office Fittings
Mr Jimmy Rock Managing Director
Mr Hubert Darcy Financial Controller
Mr Niall Rock Sales Director

Westmann
Weir Road
Tuam Co. Galway
Phone: 093-25280 Fax: 093-25478
SIC: 45452 Employees: 39
Shop Fitters
Mr Frank Reynolds Proprietor

DD O'Brien & Company Ltd
126 Harolds Cross
Dublin 6w
Phone: 01-4979423 Fax: 01-4979330
Email: info@ddobrien.com
Web: http://www.ddobrien.com
SIC: 45453 Employees: 54
Wall & Floor Finishes
Mr Daniel O'Brien Managing Director
Mr Paul Glackin Financial Controller

Fayco Pressings Ltd
Ballyboggan Industrial Estate
Finglas
Dublin 11
Phone: 01-8308041 Fax: 01-8308787
Email: sales@fayco.ie
Web: http://www.fayco.ie
SIC: 45453 Employees: 25
Shelving & Storage Equipment
Mr Jack Fay Managing Director
Mr Tom Reynolds Sales Manager
Mr William Stewart Production Manager
Mr Niall Kinsley Computer Manager

Kingspan Insulation Ltd
Bree Industrial Estate
Castleblayney Co. Monaghan
Phone: 042-9795000 Fax: 042-9746129
Email: general.enquirys@kil.kingspan.ie
Web: http://www.kil.kingspan.ie
SIC: 45453 Employees: 46
Insulated Panels manufacturing
Mr Aaron O'Kane Managing Director
Mr Sean O'Hagan Financial Controller
Ms Margaret McArdle Office Manager
Mr Ralph Mannion Sales Manager

Cars/Cycles Sales, Maintenance /Repair

50 Cars/Cycles Sales, Maintenance/Repair
50100 Car Sales/Dealers
50103 Commerical Vehicle Sales
50200 Motor Vehicle Repair/Service
50300 Car Parts/Accessories
50301 Tyre Exhaust Centres
50302 Car Radio Dealers
50400 Motorbike Shops
50500 Petrol Filling Stations

Alfa Romeo Ireland
Turnpike Road
Naas Road
Dublin 22
Phone: 01-4034499 Fax: 01-4034455
SIC: 50101 Employees: 30
Motor Dealers
Mr Paddy Corcoran Managing Director
Mr Dominic Holmes Financial Controller

Annesley Motor Group
20 Ballybough Road
Dublin 3
Phone: 01-8555991 Fax: 01-8366956
Email: info@annesleymotors.ie
SIC: 50101 Employees: 50
Motor Dealers
Mr Jeremy Byrne Managing Director
Mr Eoin McCoy Financial Controller
Ms Anna Preston Company Secretary
Mr Patrick Byrne Sales Director

Annesley Williams Ltd
The Old Airport Road
Cloghran
Swords Co. Dublin
Phone: 01-8428855 Fax: 01-8428918
Email: info@annesleywilliams.ie
Web: http://www.annesleywilliams.ie
SIC: 50101 Employees: 30
Motor Vehicle Sales Repair Service
Mr Jim Williams Proprietor
Mr Derek Brady General Manager

Ashley Motors
305/309 North Circular Road
Dublin 7
Phone: 01-8380614 Fax: 01-8386398
Email: ashleym@iol.ie
SIC: 50101 Employees: 60
Ford Dealer & Car Repairs
Mr Matt Smyth Managing Director
Mr Chris O'Malley Accounts Manager
Mr Eamonn Grant Sales Manager

Auto Boland Ltd
Dublin Road
Newrath
Waterford Co. Waterford
Phone: 051-876558 Fax: 051-879379
Email: autoboland@eircom.net
SIC: 50101 Employees: 25
Volvo/Honda Dealers
Mr Anthony Boland Managing Director

Avis Johnson & Perrott
Emmet Place
Cork Co. Cork
Phone: 021-4281100 Fax: 021-4281122
SIC: 50101 Employees: 240
Motor Vehicle Sales & Hire
Mr David Whitaker Managing Director
Mr Eric Roe Financial Controller
Mr John O'Neill Computer Manager

Ballsbridge Motors
162 Shelbourne Road
Ballsbridge
Dublin 4
Phone: 01-6689651 Fax: 01-6602535
Email: bmotors@indigo.ie
SIC: 50101 Employees: 35
Car Sales
Mr Seamus Ryan General Manager
Ms Marion Jones Finance Manager
Ms Deirdre McMahon Assistant General Manager
Mr Finbar Quinn Brand Manager

BK Motors
Tolka Bridge
Drumcondra
Dublin 9
Phone: 01-8373762 Fax: 01-8369352
Email: info@bkmotors.net
Web: http://www.bkmotors.net
SIC: 50101 Employees: 23
Citroen Dealers
Mr Alan Farrington Managing Director
Mr Philip Gorman Finance Manager

Blackwater Motors
Dublin Road
Fermoy Co. Cork
Phone: 025-49500 Fax: 025-49555
Email: info@blackwatersmotors.ie
Web: http://www.blackwatersmotors.ie
SIC: 50101 Employees: 30
Car Dealers - New & Used
Mr David Quike Manager
Mr Kieran Crowley Finance Manager

Blanchardstown Renault
Coolmine Business Park
Blanchardstown
Dublin 15
Phone: 01-8200155 Fax: 01-8200156
SIC: 50101 Employees: 30
Renault Dealers
Mr Fergus O'Rourke Manager
Mr Damien Callaly Finance Manager
Mr John Quilter Sales Manager

BMW Maxwell Motors Ltd
Temple Road
Blackrock Co. Dublin
Phone: 01-2885085 Fax: 01-2885177
Email: sales@maxwellmotors.ie
Web: http://www.maxwellmotors.ie
SIC: 50101 Employees: 35
Motor Vehicles Sales
Mr Charles Day Managing Director
Ms Christine Gorman Financial Controller
Mr James Hennessy Sales Director

Boland's Car Dealers
Cork Road
Waterford Co. Waterford
Phone: 051-872122 Fax: 051-850664
Email: info@bolands.com
SIC: 50101 Employees: 30
Mitsubishi & BMW Dealer
Mr Jim Boland Managing Director
Mr Greg Byrne Sales Manager

Brady's Garage
Navan Road
Castleknock
Dublin 15
Phone: 01-8213053 Fax: 01-8210620
Email: info@bradysdublin.ie
Web: http://www.bradysdublin.ie
SIC: 50101 Employees: 30
VW Audi & Mercedes Benz Dealer
Mr Gerry Brady Managing Director
Mr Tom Roddy Accounts Manager

Car Sales

CAB Motor Co Ltd
Monaghan Road
Cork Co. Cork
Phone: 021-4963222 Fax: 021-4963561
Email: sales@cab.motors.ie
Web: http://www.cab-motors.ie
SIC: 50101 Employees: 50
Ford Dealer
Mr Conor Cavanagh Managing Director
Mr Donal McCarthy Financial Controller
Mr Michael Mullins Sales Director

Cahir 4x4 Centre
Clonmel Road
Cahir Co. Tipperary
Phone: 052-41883 Fax: 052-43001
SIC: 50101 Employees: 53
Car Dealers
Mr Pat Lawrence Managing Director

Cavanagh's of Fermoy
Fermoy Co. Cork
Phone: 025-32252 Fax: 025-32345
Email: sales@cavanagh.fdi.ie
Web: http://www.cavanaghoffermoy.com
SIC: 50101 Employees: 35
Car Sales, Servicing & Parts
Mr Thomas Cavanagh Proprietor
Mr Connor O'Keefe Sales Manager
Mr Mat Hegarty Computer Manager

Central Garage
Emmet Street
Mountmellick
Portlaoise Co. Laois
Phone: 0502-24105 Fax: 0502-24814
Email: info@centralgarage.ie
Web: http://www.centralgarage.ie
SIC: 50101 Employees: 70
Nissan Dealers
Mr Richard Forrestal Proprietor
Ms Iris Forrestal Personnel Manager
Mr Frank Fitzpatrick Sales Manager
Mr Jim Keating Computer Manager

Chapmans
Killbury Ltd
Dublin Road
Kildare Co. Kildare
Phone: 045-521203 Fax: 045-521785
Email: chapmans@iol.co.uk
Web: http://www.chapmans.ie
SIC: 50101 Employees: 25
Volvo/Rover/Land Rover
Mr Pat Dunlea Managing Director
Mr Paddy Hartnett Sales Manager

Cogan's Garage Ltd
Cork Road
Carrigaline
Cork Co. Cork
Phone: 021-4852500 Fax: 021-4852525
Email: cogans@cogans.ie
Web: http://www.cogans.ie
SIC: 50101 Employees: 50
Motor Dealership
Mr James Cogan Managing Director
Ms Margaret Murphy Financial Controller
Mr Conor Leary Sales Manager

Crawford's Opel Centre
Beach Road
Sandymount
Dublin 4
Phone: 01-6686011 Fax: 01-6685384
Email: info@crawfords.ie
Web: http://www.crawfords.ie
SIC: 50101 Employees: 80
Opel Car Dealer
Mr David Crawford Chief Executive
Mr Stephen Finn Accounts Director
Mr Pat Ryan Sales Director

Denis Mahony Ltd
Kilbarrack Road
Dublin 5
Phone: 01-8322701 Fax: 01-8393174
Email: fleet.services@avis.ie
Web: http://www.avis.ie
SIC: 50101 Employees: 64
Car Dealers
Mr John Mahony Managing Director
Mr John O'Callaghan Financial Controller
Mr John Collins Company Secretary
Mr Oliver Hughes Sales Manager

Dunleas Of Kilcullen
Naas Road, Kilcullen
Kildare Co. Kildare
Phone: 045-481397 Fax: 045-481716
Email: info@chapmans.ie
SIC: 50101 Employees: 25
Car Dealers - New & Used
Mr Pat Dunlea Proprietor
Ms Patricia Talt Financial Controller
Mr Paul Carley Dealer Principal

Esmonde Motors Ltd
Stillorgan Hill
Stillorgan
Blackrock Co. Dublin
Phone: 01-2886821 Fax: 01-2110099
Email: info@esmonde.ie
Web: http://www.esmondemotors.ie
SIC: 50101 Employees: 40
Car Dealers - New & Used
Mr Harold Murray Managing Director
Mr Rory Saunders Finance Manager
Mr Mark Purcell Sales Manager

Europa Mazda Centre
Motor Services Ltd
Newtown Avenue
Blackrock Co. Dublin
Phone: 01-2881624 Fax: 01-2831435
Email: emcsales@indigo.ie
SIC: 50101 Employees: 60
Mazda Dealers
Mr Brendan Grace General Manager
Mr Richard Patton Sales Manager

Fermoy Nissan Ltd
Dublin Road
Fermoy Co. Cork
Phone: 025-31555 Fax: 025-32201
Email: info@nissan.ie
Web: http://www.nissan.ie
SIC: 50101 Employees: 25
Car Sales & Repairs
Mr Pat McCarthy Managing Director
Mr Tom Howard Accounts Manager
Mr Bertie O'Regan Service Manager

Finn Reddy Motor
South Circular Road
Kilmainham
Dublin 8
Phone: 01-4732288 Fax: 01-4732770
Email: info@finnreddy.com
Web: http://www.finnreddy.com
SIC: 50101 Employees: 33
Car Dealers - New & Used
Mr Dave Sim Managing Director
Mr Owen Reddy Sales Manager

Frank Hogan Ltd
Dublin Road
Limerick Co. Limerick
Phone: 061-416000 Fax: 061-416043
Email: sales@frankhogan.ie
SIC: 50101 Employees: 50
Mercedes VW & Audi Dealers
Mr Frank Hogan Proprietor
Mr Paul Hogan Sales Director

Gowan Distributors
Gowan House
Naas Road
Dublin 12
Phone: 01-4092400 Fax: 01-4509620
Email: gallicsales@gdl.ie
Web: http://www.peugeot.ie
SIC: 50101 Employees: 63
Car Sales
Mr James Mulligan Manager
Mr Tony Maher Finance Manager
Mr David McConnell Sales Manager

Greenhall Motors Ltd
Charleville Road
Buttevant
Mallow Co. Cork
Phone: 022-23338 Fax: 022-23416
Email: greenhall.buttevant.sales@net.opel.com
SIC: 50101 Employees: 25
Opel Dealers
Ms Kim O'Shea Managing Director

H B Dennis Motors Ltd
48-52 New Street
Dublin 8
Phone: 01-4110100 Fax: 01-4110160
Email: sales@hbdennis.com
Web: http://www.hbdennis.com
SIC: 50101 Employees: 30
Car Sales, Car Servicing & Car Parts
Mr John Dennis Managing Director
Ms Catherine Keirns Finance Manager
Mr Tiernan Heartagan Sales Director

HB Dennis Motors (Fairview) Ltd
48-52 New Street
Dublin 8
Phone: 01-4536433 Fax: 01-4110160
Web: http://www.hbdennis.com
SIC: 50101 Employees: 100
Car Sales
Mr John Dennis Managing Director
Mr Paul Webb Financial Controller
Mr Tiernan Hartigan Sales Manager

Hi Way Services Ltd
Dublin Road
Tuam Co. Galway
Phone: 093-24215 Fax: 093-25107
Email: sales@hi-way.fdi.ie
Web: http://www.hi-way.fdi.ie
SIC: 50101 Employees: 40
Ford Dealers
Mr Vincent Cunniffe Managing Director

Hugh Boggan Motors Ltd
Carriglawn
Newtown Road
Wexford Co. Wexford
Phone: 053-43788 Fax: 053-42165
SIC: 50101 Employees: 55
Toyota Dealers
Mr Hugh Boggan Managing Director

J & M Cars
Dublin Road
Cavan Co. Cavan
Phone: 049-4361271 Fax: 049-4361277
SIC: 50101 Employees: 50
New & Used Car Dealers
Mr Joe Gormley Proprietor
Mr Donal McAdam Financial Controller
Mr Paddy Donnery Sales Manager

JJ Fleming
Tuam Road
Galway Co. Galway
Phone: 091-755451 Fax: 091-751658
SIC: 50101 Employees: 25
Car Sales/Dealers
Mr Pat Fleming Managing Director

Car Sales

Joe Duffy (Motors) Ltd
Griffith Avenue Extension
Dublin 11
Phone: 01-8342577 Fax: 01-8346597
Email: info@joeduffymotors.ie
Web: http://www.joeduffymotors.ie
SIC: 50101 Employees: 35
Motor Sales
Mr Owen Crinigan Managing Director
Mr Angus Donohoe Accountant
Mr Tony Hempenstall Sales & Marketing Manager

Kenilworth Motors
348 Harolds Cross Road
Dublin 6w
Phone: 01-4923757 Fax: 01-4922241
SIC: 50101 Employees: 25
Opel
Mr Brian Priestman Director
Ms Anne Fitzsimons Accounts Manager

Kerry Motor Works
Mileheight
Killarney Road
Tralee Co. Kerry
Phone: 066-7121555 Fax: 066-7123054
SIC: 50101 Employees: 25
Ford Dealer/Car Repairs
Mr Leslie Benner Manager
Mr Tim Teahan Finance Manager
Mr Kieran Griffin Sales Manager

Lee Garage Ltd
11-13 South Terrace
Cork Co. Cork
Phone: 021-4313344 Fax: 021-4314359
Email: leegar@indigo.ie
SIC: 50101 Employees: 44
Car Dealers
Mr Frampton Jeffrey Director
Mr Tim Crowley Finance Manager
Mr Liam Leahy Marketing Manager
Mr Michael Hennessy Service Manager
Ms Christina O'Riordan Computer Manager

Lissalan Motors
12-13 Lapps Quay
Cork Co. Cork
Phone: 021-4272877 Fax: 021-4272899
SIC: 50101 Employees: 24
Mitsubishi
Mr Denis Murphy Managing Director
Mr Sean Farley Financial Controller
Mr Tom O'Manie Sales Manager
Mr Tom Ivers Operation Manager

McCarricks Garage
Sligo Road
Tubbercurry
Sligo Co. Sligo
Phone: 071-86222 Fax: 071-20033
Email: mccarricks@iol.ie
Web: http://www.mccarricks.com
SIC: 50101 Employees: 40
Peugeot & Saab Dealers
Mr Noel McCarrick Proprietor
Mr Vincent Hunt Personnel Manager
Mr Michael Kerrigan Sales Manager

McCoy Motors
Lucan Bypass
Lucan Co. Dublin
Phone: 01-6241223 Fax: 01-6280199
SIC: 50101 Employees: 24
Toyota Garage
Mr Conor McCormack Manager

Mexgrave T/A Enniscorthy Motor Co
Old Dublin Road
Enniscorthy Co. Wexford
Phone: 054-33337 Fax: 054-34793
Email: enniscorthymotorcompany@eircom.net
SIC: 50101 Employees: 30
Car & Farm Machinery Dealers
Mr Diarmuid Boland Managing Director
Mr Michael O'Keefe Company Accountant
Mr Colman Doyle Sales Manager

Mongey Plunkett Motors
109 Upper Dorset Street
Dublin 1
Phone: 01-8301400 Fax: 01-8302710
Email: mongeyplunkett@eircom.net
Web: http://www.mongeyplunkettmotors.com
SIC: 50101 Employees: 28
Peugeot Dealers Car Repairs & Contract Hire
Mr Peter Mongey Joint Managing Director
Mr David Moore Finance Manager
Mr Tom O'Connor Sales Manager
Mr Theo Plunkett Joint Managing Director

Motor World Ltd
Carrigrohane Road
Cork Co. Cork
Phone: 021-4542344 Fax: 021-4344842
Email: ffitzpatrick@motorworld.ie
SIC: 50101 Employees: 25
Car Dealer
Mr John Hamill Managing Director
Mr John Keating Finance Manager
Mr Finbar Fitzpatrick Sales Manager

Murphy & Gunn Ltd
Rathgar Avenue
Rathgar
Dublin 6
Phone: 01-4068600 Fax: 01-4068666
Email: info@mgunn.ie
Web: http://www.murphygunn.ie
SIC: 50101 Employees: 80
Toyota & Lexus Dealers
Mr Tom Murphy Proprietor
Mr Eddie Fogarty Sales Manager

Noel Deasy Cars
New Mallow Road
Cork Co. Cork
Phone: 021-4395024 Fax: 021-4397658
SIC: 50101 Employees: 40
Car Dealers
Mr Noel Deasy Managing Director
Ms Evelyn O'Connor General Manager

O'Mara's Motors (Limerick) Ltd
Ennis Road
Limerick Co. Limerick
Phone: 061-451611 Fax: 061-326602
SIC: 50101 Employees: 26
Car Sales/Dealers
Mr Noel Daly Managing Director
Ms Anne Quinn Financial Controller

O'Sullivan & Hansbury Motors Ltd
Kilrush Road
Ennis Co. Clare
Phone: 065-6820312 Fax: 065-6840120
Email: sulhan@iol.ie
SIC: 50101 Employees: 50
Citroen & Peugeot Dealers
Mr John O'Sullivan Executive Director
Ms Claire O'Reilly Financial Controller
Mr John Ryan General Manager
Mr Darren Hayes Sales Manager
Mr Noel Gavin Computer Manager

Oliver Walsh Motors (Hyundai Dealership)
Lahinch Road
Ennis Co. Clare
Phone: 065-6842122 Fax: 065-6843133
SIC: 50101 Employees: 53
Hyundai Dealership
Mr Rory McAllister General Manager

Park Motors
218 North Circular Road
Dublin 7
Phone: 01-8387211 Fax: 01-8383566
Email: park@indigo.ie
Web: http://www.parkmotors.com
SIC: 50101 Employees: 30
VW Audi & Mercedes Benz Dealer
Mr Brendan Smyth General Manager
Mr Donal Duggan Sales Manager

Pat Dunlea & Sons
Naas Road
Kilcullen
Kildare Co. Kildare
Phone: 045-481299 Fax: 045-481716
SIC: 50101 Employees: 25
Nissan Dealers
Mr Pat Dunlea Managing Director
Ms Patricia Talt Finance Manager
Mr Hugh Pitt Sales & Marketing Manager

Pat Keogh Ltd
Tipperary Road
Limerick Co. Limerick
Phone: 061-313355 Fax: 061-312311
SIC: 50101 Employees: 25
BMW & Nissan Dealers
Mr Patrick Keogh Managing Director
Mr Paul McDonagh Business Manager

Rathdown Motors
Terenure
Dublin 6
Phone: 01-4903084 Fax: 01-4920908
Web: http://www.rathdownmotors.ie
SIC: 50101 Employees: 30
Motor Sales/Car Servicing & Parts
Mr Mark Turley Managing Director
Mr Keith Browne Office Manager
Mr Martin Speirin Sales Manager

Ray O'Brien Ltd
Moorfield
Newbridge Co. Kildare
Phone: 045-431130 Fax: 045-434916
Email: info@rayobriensgroup.com
Web: http://www.rayobriensgroup.com
SIC: 50101 Employees: 50
Car Dealers
Mr Ray O'Brien Managing Director
Ms Nora Skeehan Financial Controller
Mr Anthony Murray Personnel Manager

Rialto Motors Ltd
Springfield House
Herberton Road
Dublin 12
Phone: 01-4542755 Fax: 01-4536882
Email: sales@rialto.ie
Web: http://www.rialto.ie
SIC: 50101 Employees: 30
Ford Dealers
Mr Frank O'Neill Proprietor
Mr Brendan O'Neill Finance Manager

Rice & Roddy Ltd
Newry Road
Dundalk Co. Louth
Phone: 042-9334603 Fax: 042-9333948
Email: sales@riccroddy.ie
Web: http://www.riccroddy.ie
SIC: 50101 Employees: 30
Car Dealers & Motor Factors
Mr Maurice Roddy Partner
Mr Eamonn McCartan Finance Manager
Mr Derek Malone Sales Manager
Mr Patsy Rice Partner

Car Sales

Saab Scanveco Ltd
Long Mile Road
Dublin 12
Phone: 01-4504243 Fax: 01-4506291
Email: ajn@ohm.ie
SIC: 50101 Employees: 25
Car Importers
Mr Robert Barden Managing Director

Singland Motors
Dublin Road
Limerick Co. Limerick
Phone: 061-331933 Fax: 061-335864
Email: sales@singlandmotors.com
Web: http://www.singlandmotors.com
SIC: 50101 Employees: 55
Rover & Land Rover Dealers
Mr Noel Kearney Proprietor
Mr Ivor Myles Sales Manager

Skoda - Eurauto Ltd
Naas Road
Dublin 12
Phone: 01-4094444 Fax: 01-4094419
SIC: 50101 Employees: 150
Car Dealers - New & Used
Mr Nigel Flaherty Director
Mr M Fagen Finance Director
Mr Jim Foller Personnel Manager
Mr J Coffee Sales Director
Mr E Farrell Director

South Dublin Ford Centre
Whitechurch Road
Rathfarnham
Dublin 14
Phone: 01-4934605 Fax: 01-4944675
Email: sales@sdfc.ie
Web: http://www.fdi.ie/southd/
SIC: 50101 Employees: 30
Ford Dealers
Mr Cormac Hughes Managing Director
Mr Jim Tobin Accounts Manager
Mr Denny Donaldson Personnel Director
Mr Aidan Kane Sales Manager

T Sheils & Co Ltd
Ennis Co. Clare
Phone: 065-6821509 Fax: 065-6821993
Email: accounts@shiels.fdi.ie
Web: http://www.shiels.ie
SIC: 50101 Employees: 65
Ford Dealers
Mr Thomas Sheils Proprietor

Thomas Sheils & Co
Gort Road
Ennis Co. Clare
Phone: 065-6821035 Fax: 065-6821993
Email: sales@sheils.iol.ie
SIC: 50101 Employees: 50
Ford Dealer
Mr Thomas Sheils Managing Director
Mr John Hill Sales Manager

Tom Murphy
Morgan Street
Waterford Co. Waterford
Phone: 051-876614 Fax: 051-878200
Email: tmcs@indigo.ie
SIC: 50101 Employees: 45
Mercedes/ Audi/ VWDealers
Mr Tom Murphy Managing Director
Mr Dave Keown Sales Director

Top Car Newmarket
Charleville Road
Newmarket
Mallow Co. Cork
Phone: 029-60007 Fax: 029-60866
Email: info@topcarnewmarket.com
Web: http://www.topcarnewmarket.com
SIC: 50101 Employees: 23
Car Sales
Mr Finbar O'Sullivan Managing Director
Mr Tim O'Sullivan Finance Manager
Mr Brian Hanafin Sales Manager

Tractamotors (Blanchardstown) Ltd
Main Street
Blanchardstown
Dublin 15
Phone: 01-8216622 Fax: 01-8216020
SIC: 50101 Employees: 24
Car Dealers & Car Repairs
Mr Brendan Crawford Managing Director
Mr Jim McDermot Finance Manager
Mr Greg Crawford Sales Manager
Mr Don Coyle Production Manager

Turner's Cross Motors
Kinsale Road
Cork Co. Cork
Phone: 021-4962500 Fax: 021-4961505
Email: tcross@indigo.ie
SIC: 50101 Employees: 45
Car Sales
Mr Richard Cleary General Manager
Mr Declan Brougham Financial Controller

Walden Motor Company
172-175 Parnell Street
Dublin 1
Phone: 01-8730400 Fax: 01-8727234
Email: cars@walden.ie
Web: http://www.walden.ie
SIC: 50101 Employees: 48
Motor Trade
Mr Vincent Wallace Managing Director
Mr Paul Ellis Financial Controller
Mr Billy Wallace Sales Director

White & Delahunty Opel Centre
Pearse Road
Sallynoggin
Dun Laoghaire Co. Dublin
Phone: 01-2851266 Fax: 01-2853648
Email:
whiteanddelahunty.dublin.sales@net.opel.com
SIC: 50101 Employees: 40
Car Dealers
Mr Noel White Partner
Mr Niall Burke Accountant
Mr Jimmy Delahunty Partner

Wilton Motors
Bishopstown Road
Wilton
Cork Co. Cork
Phone: 021-4544655 Fax: 021-4544417
SIC: 50101 Employees: 45
Renault Dealers
Mr Moss Kennedy Manager
Mr Douglas Johnston Manager

Windsor Belgard Ltd
Belgard Road
Tallaght
Dublin 24
Phone: 01-4516877 Fax: 01-4513269
Email: sales@windsor-belgard.ie
SIC: 50101 Employees: 41
Main Nissan Dealer/Car Repairs & Service
Mr Tom Magee Managing Partner
Mr Robert Lawson Business Manager
Mr Clare Carol Personnel Officer
Mr Ken Carey Sales Director
Mr Michael Herbert Managing Partner

Windsor Deansgrange
Deansgrange Road
Blackrock Co. Dublin
Phone: 01-2896622 Fax: 01-2896622
Email: info@windsor-deansgrange.ie
Web: http://www.windsor.ie
SIC: 50101 Employees: 27
Car Dealers - New & Used
Mr Stephen Briggs Director
Mr Douglas Ryan Sales Person
Ms Mary Cumiskey Sales Person

Windsor Motors
355 South Circular Road
Rialto
Dublin 8
Phone: 01-4540800 Fax: 01-4541712
Email: postmaster@windsor.ie
Web: http://www.windsor.ie
SIC: 50101 Employees: 60
Car Sales
Mr Gabriel Keane Chief Executive
Mr Robert Nolan Financial Controller
Ms Margaret Fagan Company Secretary
Mr Robert O'Neill MIS Manager

Winfield Motors
Maxwell Road
Rathmines
Dublin 6
Phone: 01-4973338 Fax: 01-4973754
Email: info@winfieldmotors.ie
Web: http://www.winfieldmotors.ie
SIC: 50101 Employees: 30
Ford Dealers & Car Repairs
Mr Seamus Byrne Partner
Mr Martin Mannion Partner
Mr Noel Barton Computer Manager

Clareview Motors Ltd
Ennis Road
Limerick Co. Limerick
Phone: 061-206077 Fax: 061-326766
SIC: 50102 Employees: 30
Used Car Sales
Mr John Leahy Proprietor
Ms Rosemarie Fogarty Finance Manager
Ms Caroline Healy Human Resources Manager
Mr John Culleton Director
Mr Alex McConky IT Manager

Crosson Opel Centre
Malahide Road
Dublin 17
Phone: 01-8474311 Fax: 01-8479801
Email: sales@crossoncars.ie
Web: http://www.crossoncars.ie
SIC: 50102 Employees: 75
Car Dealership/Service/Parts
Mr John O'Reilly Managing Director
Ms Katherine Maher Accountant
Mr Eddie Coughlan Sales Manager

Fitzpatrick Car Sales
Dublin Road
Kildare Co. Kildare
Phone: 045-522533 Fax: 045-522245
Email: sales@fitzpatrickgarages.ie
SIC: 50102 Employees: 90
Car Sales & Repairs
Mr Sean Lyons Managing Director
Mr Andy Fitzpatrick Finance Manager
Mr Charlie Heffernan Sales Manager

Gowan Motors
23-24 Parkgate Street
Dublin 8
Phone: 01-6710333 Fax: 01-6710832
Email: info@gowanmerrion.com
Web: http://www.gowanparkgate.com
SIC: 50102 Employees: 34
Car Sales Dealership
Mr Brian Smith Managing Director
Mr Griffith O'Reilly Accountant

Car Sales

Kilkenny Truck Centre
Callan Road
Kilkenny Co. Kilkenny
Phone: 056-22830 Fax: 056-22657
Email: ktc@indigo.ie
SIC: 50102 Employees: 50
Car & Truck Sales
Mr John O'Neill Manager
Mr George Prizeman Accounts Manager
Mr Cathal O'Neill Sales Manager

Merlin Car Auctions
Ashbourne
Co Meath
Phone: 01-4599300 Fax: 01-4599330
Email: info@wca.ie
Web: http://www.wca.ie
SIC: 50102 Employees: 60
Car Auctions
Mr Sean Boland Managing Director
Mr James Butler Financial Controller
Ms Joanne Cranley Personnel Manager
Mr Eugene Mulligan Operation Manager
Mr Kevin Morbin Computer Manager

Moran's Garage
Mail Road
Dingle
Tralee Co. Kerry
Phone: 066-9151129 Fax: 066-9151553
Email: morans@dingletours.com
SIC: 50102 Employees: 40
Garage
Mr Sean Moran Proprietor

AOC Commercials Ltd
Springhill
Carrigtwohill
Cork Co. Cork
Phone: 021-4883322 Fax: 021-4883889
Email: aocadmin@eircom.net
SIC: 50103 Employees: 30
Isuzu/Scania Commercials
Mr Aidan O'Connor Proprietor
Mr Pat Curtin Financial Controller
Mr Michael O'Regan Personnel Manager
Mr George Peare Sales & Marketing Manager

Irish Commercials (Sales) Ltd
Naas Industrial Estate
Naas Co. Kildare
Phone: 045-879881 Fax: 045-875462
SIC: 50103 Employees: 55
Vehicle Sales
Mr Brendan Horan Managing Director
Mr Peter Horan Finance Manager
Mr Brian Murphy Director

Kearys of Cork Ltd
Grange
Douglas
Cork Co. Cork
Phone: 021-4361800 Fax: 021-4363322
Email: info@kearys.ie
Web: http://www.kearys.ie
SIC: 50103 Employees: 120
Commercial Vehicle Sales
Mr Bill Keary Chief Executive
Mr Noel O'Donovan Financial Controller

McCarthy Commercials Ltd
Watergrasshill
Cork Co. Cork
Phone: 021-4889147 Fax: 021-4889415
SIC: 50103 Employees: 78
Sales Parts & Service of Volvo Trucks
Mr Dermot Murphy General Manager
Mr Michael McCarthy Sales & Marketing Manager
Mr Colman McCarthy Services Manager
Ms Veronica Toomey Computer Manager

McDonnell Commercials Ltd
Duraymond
Monaghan Co. Monaghan
Phone: 047-83588 Fax: 047-84121
Email: info@mcdonnellcommercial.ie
Web: http://www.mcdonnellcommercial.ie
SIC: 50103 Employees: 32
Commercial Vehicle Sales
Mr Brian McDonnell Proprietor

McElvaney Motors Ltd
Dublin Road
Monaghan Co. Monaghan
Phone: 047-81596 Fax: 047-82715
Email: info@mcelvaney.com
SIC: 50103 Employees: 50
Commercial Vehicle Sales
Mr Oliver McElvaney Manager
Mr Reggie Patel Administrator

Opel Ireland Ltd
Heather Road
Sandyford Industrial Estate
Dublin 18
Phone: 01-2959800 Fax: 01-2959831
Email: opelreception@ie.opel.com
Web: http://www.opel.com
SIC: 50103 Employees: 60
Commercial Vehicle Sales
Mr Lede Alukema Managing Director
Mr John Doody Financial Controller

Padraig Cawley Commercials Ltd
Drinaghan
Sligo Co. Sligo
Phone: 071-60783 Fax: 071-69500
Email: sales@cawleycommercials.iol.ie
SIC: 50103 Employees: 40
Mitsubishi/Scania Trucks
Mr Padraig Cawley Proprietor
Mr Roy Kilfeather Human Resources Manager
Mr Michael Harte Sales Manager

Sheridan Truck & Plant Sales
Arden Road
Tullamore Co. Offaly
Phone: 0506-51366 Fax: 0506-41605
Web: http://www.sheridanplant.com
SIC: 50103 Employees: 30
Commercial Vehicles - Sales Service
Mr David Mullen Managing Director
Mr Brian Coffey Sales Manager

Suirhall Commercials
Ballylynch
Carrick On Suir Co. Tipperary
Phone: 051-640194 Fax: 051-640429
SIC: 50103 Employees: 35
Mechanical Engineering
Mr Dan O'Connor Managing Director
Mr Brian Elmes Sales Manager

T & F Gilmore Ltd
Shercock Road
Kingscourt
Cavan Co. Cavan
Phone: 042-9667126 Fax: 042-9667329
Email: info@gilmores.ie
Web: http://www.gilmores.ie
SIC: 50103 Employees: 60
Commericial Vehicle Sales
Mr Ken Gilmore Managing Director
Mr John Fitzmorris Finance Manager

Westward Group
Strokestown
Roscommon Co. Roscommon
Phone: 078-33029 Fax: 078-33454
SIC: 50103 Employees: 42
Commercial Vehicle Sales
Mr Pat Kenny Managing Director
Mr Joseph Compton Financial Controller

Westward Scania
Strokestown
Roscommon Co. Roscommon
Phone: 078-33068 Fax: 078-33707
Email: importer@westwardscania.com
Web: http://www.westwardscania.com
SIC: 50103 Employees: 45
Importers of Scania
Mr Pat Kenny Proprietor
Mr Joe Crann Sales & Marketing Manager

AA Mobile Windscreens
Naas Industrial Estate
Naas Co. Kildare
Phone: 051-857599 Fax: 045-876047
SIC: 50200 Employees: 40
Windscreen Replacement
Mr Eugene Hall Managing Director
Ms Caroline McGlinchy Financial Controller
Mr Declan Powers Operations Manager

Autoglass
Unit 19 Golden Bridge Industrial Estate
Inchicore
Dublin 8
Phone: 01-4542651 Fax: 01-4543227
Email: admin@autoglassireland.com
SIC: 50200 Employees: 60
Windscreen Replacement
Mr Philip Egan Managing Director
Ms Karen Ward Sales Manager

Autoglaze Ltd
39/41 Crumlin Road
Dolphin's Barn
Dublin 12
Phone: 01-4538555 Fax: 01-4540974
Email: info@autoglaze.ie
Web: http://www.autoglaze.ie
SIC: 50200 Employees: 36
Replacement Glass/Sunroofs/Windscreens
Mr John Ryan Managing Director
Ms Kathleen Mahon Financial Controller

Carroll & Kinsella Killeen Ltd
1a-2a Bluebell Industrial Estate
Naas Road
Dublin 12
Phone: 01-4503526 Fax: 01-4602081
Email: info@carollkinsella.ie
Web: http://www.carollkinsella.ie
SIC: 50200 Employees: 50
Crash Repairs
Mr Stephen Browne General Manager
Mr Brian Ahern Finance Manager

Clontarf Motors Ltd
46 Clontarf Road
Clontarf
Dublin 3
Phone: 01-8332258 Fax: 01-8335632
Email: renault@iol.ie
Web: http://www.clontarfmotors.com
SIC: 50200 Employees: 24
Motor Vehicle Repair/Service
Mr Paddy Stephen Manager
Mr Noel Howley Sales Manager

Dennehy's Cross Garage
Dennehy's Cross
Cork Co. Cork
Phone: 021-4542846 Fax: 021-4544020
SIC: 50200 Employees: 55
Motor Vehicle Repair/Service
Mr Sean Kenny General Manager
Mr Eamon Dennehy Sales Director

Car Sales

DG Opel
Navan Road
Dublin 15
Phone: 01-8385222 Fax: 01-8387890
Email: info@dgopel.ie
Web: http://www.dgopel.ie
SIC: 50200 Employees: 40
Motor Vehicle Repair/Service
Mr Michael Fitzsimons Managing Director
Mr Dominic Brooks Financial Director

Drumcondra Auto Repairs Ltd
3 Castleforbes Road
North Wall Quay
Dublin 1
Phone: 01-8374966 Fax: 01-8374740
SIC: 50200 Employees: 35
Vehicle Body Repair Specification/DOE Test Centre
Mr John Foran Director
Ms Eileen Dore Accounts Manager

EP Mooney & Co Ltd
Long Mile Road
Walkinstown
Dublin 12
Phone: 01-4195800 Fax: 01-4603296
Email: info@epmooney.com
Web: http://www.epmooney.com
SIC: 50200 Employees: 70
Garage Operators
Mr Pauric Mooney Managing Director
Ms Aileen Morrissey Finance Manager
Ms Bernie Clare Human Resources Manager
Mr Sean O'Leary Sales Manager
Ms Suzanne Kearns IT Support Manager

J Murphy & Sons (Motors) Ltd
Ballymount
Clondalkin
Dublin 22
Phone: 01-4592069 Fax: 01-4594263
SIC: 50200 Employees: 25
Mitsubishi Trucks & Repairs
Mr Michael Murphy Managing Director
Ms Deirdre Tait Accounts Manager
Mr Seamus O'Grady Sales Manager

Jackson's Garage Ltd
Farnham Street
Cavan Co. Cavan
Phone: 049-4331700 Fax: 049-4361437
Email: info@jacksons-ford.com
Web: http://www.jacksons-ford.com
SIC: 50200 Employees: 30
Ford/Vehicle Body Repair Specification
Mr David Jackson Managing Director

Koping Motors
Naas Road
Dublin 12
Phone: 01-4080400 Fax: 01-4568899
Email: koping@iol.ie
Web: http://www.kopingmotors.com
SIC: 50200 Employees: 50
Mechanical Garage
Mr Paul Mooney Managing Director
Mr Brendan Kelly Manager

Louth Transport Ltd
Readypenny
Dundalk Co. Louth
Phone: 042-9379168 Fax: 042-9379289
Email: loutrans@eircom.net
SIC: 50200 Employees: 80
Bus/Coach Refurbishment
Mr Frank Mullen Managing Director
Mr John Mullen Director

Micheal McKeon Motors Ltd
Bective Street
Kells Co. Meath
Phone: 046-40681 Fax: 046-40749
Email: mckeonmotors@eircom.net
SIC: 50200 Employees: 30
Motor Vehicle Repair/Service
Mr Micheal McKeon Managing Director

Par Fit Ltd
Old School House Works
Cloughran
Swords Co. Dublin
Phone: 01-8407880 Fax: 01-8407847
Email: parfit@indigo.ie
SIC: 50200 Employees: 25
Coach Building
Mr Charlie Fitzsimons Managing Director

PJ O'Hea & Co Ltd
26 St Patricks Quay
Cork Co. Cork
Phone: 021-4276657 Fax: 021-4273675
Email: pjohea@eircom.net
SIC: 50200 Employees: 31
Garage Operators
Mr Jim Oliver Managing Director
Mr David O'Halloran Financial Controller

SCR Garages Ltd
Davitt Road
Inchicore
Dublin 12
Phone: 01-4505149 Fax: 01-4555786
SIC: 50200 Employees: 27
Motor Vehicle Repair/Service
Mr Philip Jones Manager

Soraghan Auto Care
Unit 3 Phoenix Industrial Estate
Navan Road, Castleknock
Dublin 15
Phone: 01-8380333 Fax: 01-8380322
Email: info@centralmotor.ie
SIC: 50200 Employees: 40
Collision Repair Specialists
Mr Robert Soraghan Managing Director
Mr Bruce Soraghan Finance Manager
Mr Dennis Soraghan Sales & Marketing Director

Summerhill Commercials
125 Summerhill
Dublin 1
Phone: 01-8556116 Fax: 01-8365335
SIC: 50200 Employees: 30
Commercial Garage
Mr Tom Hendran Managing Director

Sweeney & Forte (Motors) Ltd
56 Howth Road
Clontarf
Dublin 3
Phone: 01-8332301 Fax: 01-8334229
Email: sales@sweeneyfortemotors.ie
Web: http://www.sweeneyfortemotors.ie
SIC: 50200 Employees: 30
Motor Vehicle Repairs/Services & Car Sales
Mr Gaetano Forte Managing Director

DAF Distributors
Naas Road
Clondalkin
Dublin 22
Phone: 01-4034100 Fax: 01-4591864
Email: daf@ohm.ie
SIC: 50300 Employees: 100
Commercial Vehicles - Accessories & Parts
Mr Tommy Smith Director
Mr Donald Forbes Finance Manager

DAF Truck Services Cork Ltd
Tramore Road
Cork Co. Cork
Phone: 021-4962400 Fax: 021-4962566
Email: info@truckservices.ie
Web: http://www.truckservices.ie
SIC: 50300 Employees: 50
Commercial Vehicles - Accessories & Parts
Mr Patrick Ferriter Manager
Mr Barry Bradfield Finance Manager
Mr John O'Mahony Sales Manager

Federal Mogul Champion Products
IDA Industrial Estate
Monread Road
Naas Co. Kildare
Phone: 045-876031 Fax: 045-897095
SIC: 50300 Employees: 90
Spark Plug Components
Mr William Brophy General Manager
Mr Liam O'Rourke Accounts Controller
Mr Andy Kirk Marketing Manager
Mr Vincent Maloney Computer Manager

Higgins Motorpark Ltd
The Terryland Roundabout
Headford Road
Galway Co. Galway
Phone: 091-741111 Fax: 091-741108
Web: http://www.motorpark.iol.ie
SIC: 50300 Employees: 60
Car Sales Parts & Services
Mr Gerry Halloran General Manager
Mr PJ O'Mahony Financial Controller
Mr Tony Barber Sales Manager

Intertool Ireland Ltd
8 Old County Road
Dublin 12
Phone: 01-4542733 Fax: 01-4544824
SIC: 50300 Employees: 24
Car Parts/Tools
Mr Jim McDermot Manager
Mr Fintan Lawlor Financial Controller

Iralco
Collinstown
Mullingar Co. Westmeath
Phone: 044-66600 Fax: 044-66690
SIC: 50300 Employees: 600
Car Decorative Trim
Mr Jurgen Marl Managing Director
Mr Derek Anderson Financial Controller
Mr Martin Wilson Personnel Manager
Mr Iain Balfour Chief Executive Officer
Mr Martin Heduvan Engineering Manager
Mr Pat O'Reilly Computer Manager

J H McLoughlins Ltd
Ballymany
Newbridge Co. Kildare
Phone: 045-431281 Fax: 045-431244
Email: sales@jhmcloughlin.com
SIC: 50300 Employees: 55
Car Parts/Accessories
Mr John McLoughlin Managing Director
Mr Ken McLoughlin Director

O'Leary's Garage
Lissarda
Cork Co. Cork
Phone: 021-7336146 Fax: 021-7336386
SIC: 50300 Employees: 25
Garage Parts & Service
Mr Pat O'Leary Proprietor
Mr Donal O'Donovan Sales Manager

Stewart's Garages Ltd
Greenhills Road
Dublin 24
Phone: 01-4624072 Fax: 01-4624075
Email: stewarts@iol.ie
Web: http://www.stewartsgarages.com
SIC: 50300 Employees: 30
Car Alarms & Security Devices
Mr David Stewart Proprietor

Truck Dealers International
Naas Road
Dublin 12
Phone: 01-4564747 Fax: 01-4503156
Email: ivecotdi@eircom.net
SIC: 50300 Employees: 50
Commercial Vehicles - Accessories & Parts
Mr Robert Harris Managing Director
Mr Patsy Kealey Sales Director

Advance Pitstop
Naas Road
JFK Drive
Dublin 12
Phone: 01-4504622 Fax: 01-4600490
Email: e-mailadvanced@iol.ie
SIC: 50301 Employees: 185
Tyres/Exhausts/Brakes/Shocks
Mr Richard O'Keefe Manager
Mr Con Culhane Financial Controller
Mr Terry Lennon Sales & Marketing Manager

Glanworth Tyres
Unit B1 Kylemore Park West
Balistorm
Dublin 10
Phone: 01-8900909 Fax: 01-6266770
Web: http://www.glanworthtyres.com
SIC: 50301 Employees: 30
Tyres Retreading & Remoulding
Mr Tom Whelahan Sales Manager

Kwik Fit
Malahide Road
Dublin 17
Phone: 01-6778506 Fax: 01-8672808
Web: http://www.kwik-fit.com
SIC: 50301 Employees: 110
Exhausts - Manufacturing & Repairs
Mr Pat Curran Managing Director
Mr Eamonn Connelly Finance Controller

Tractamotors Ltd
Dublin Road
Cavan Co. Cavan
Phone: 049-4331188 Fax: 049-4331642
Email: info@tractamotors.ie
SIC: 50301 Employees: 40
Tyre Sales/Hardware/Agriculture
Mr Niall Murray Managing Director
Mr Sean Reihill Financial Controller
Mr Kieran Murray Sales Manager

Frank Keane Holdings
John F Kennedy Drive
Naas Road
Dublin 12
Phone: 01-2405666 Fax: 01-4508509
Email:
SIC: 50302 Employees: 138
Vehicle/Hi-Fi Distribution
Mr Frank A Keane Director

Arena Service Station Ltd
Church Street
Askeaton
Limerick Co. Limerick
Phone: 061-392122 Fax: 061-392631
SIC: 50500 Employees: 40
Supermarket & Petrol
Mr Patrick Sheahan Proprietor
Mr William Sheahan Financial Controller
Mr Michael Sheahan Sales Manager

Belmont Service Station
126 Sandford Road
Dublin 6
Phone: 01-4978209 Fax: 01-4978299
Email: belmontsstn@eircom.net
SIC: 50500 Employees: 25
Service Stations - Petrol
Mr Barry O'Flynn Manager

Castle Service Station Ltd
Butterly Business Park
Dublin 5
Phone: 01-8475666 Fax: 01-8475875
SIC: 50500 Employees: 30
Petrol Filling Station
Ms Andrea Butterly Managing Director

Cherryorchard Service Station
Ballyfermot Road
Dublin 10
Phone: 01-6266066 Fax: 01-6232891
Email: cherryorch@eircom.net
SIC: 50500 Employees: 25
Service Station
Mr Thomas Ormond General Manager
Mr Joe Barrett Finance Manager

Claremount Filling Station
The Ward
Dublin 11
Phone: 01-8351437 Fax: 01-8353674
SIC: 50500 Employees: 40
Petrol Filling Station
Mr Johnny Brady Proprietor

Duffy Motors Newbridge Ltd
Naas Road
Newbridge Co. Kildare
Phone: 045-431340 Fax: 045-432744
SIC: 50500 Employees: 25
Shell Filling Station & Convenience Store/Cars Sales
Mr Pat Duffy Partner

John Bolger & Co (Forecourts) Ltd
Millands
Gorey Co. Wexford
Phone: 055-22494 Fax: 055-22495
SIC: 50500 Employees: 25
Service Station
Mr David Bolger Manager

Mulroys Supermarket & Off Licence
Moneen
Castlebar Co. Mayo
Phone: 094-21359 Fax: 094-21359
SIC: 50500 Employees: 30
Filling Station Off Licence & Supermarket
Mr Sean Mulroy Proprietor

Shell Select Glasnevin
Finglas Road
Dublin 11
Phone: 01-8348600 Fax: 01-8307021
Email: shellglasnevin@eircom.net
SIC: 50500 Employees: 25
Shell Petrol Station
Mr John Byrne Managing Director

Statoil Filling Station
Dublin Road
Bray Co. Wicklow
Phone: 01-2861288 Fax: 01-2861288
SIC: 50500 Employees: 24
Service Station
Mr Garry Healy Store Manager

Car Sales

Wholesale Commission & Trade

51 Wholesale & Commission Trade
51200 Agricultural Supplies Distribution
51230 Live Animals Distribution
51300 Food/ Drink Distribution
51310 Fruit & Vegetable Wholesale
51380 Fish Wholesale
51390 Cash & Carry
51420 Clothing & Textiles Distribution
51430 Electrical Products Distribution
51460 Pharmaceutical Distribution
51510 Coal/Gas Retail/ Distribution
51511 Oil & Petroleum Products Distribution
51520 Metals/Ores Distribution
51530 Building Supplies/Distribution
51540 Hardware/Household Goods Distribution
51541 Bathroom Equipment Suppliers
51542 Plumbers Supplies/Merchants
51610 Machinery & Equipment Distribution
51611 Motor Vehicles/Part Distribution
51651 Catering Equipment
51652 Catering Suppliers
51700 Distribution/General Wholesalers

Alltech Biotechnology
Sarney
Summerhill Road
Dunboyne Co. Meath
Phone: 01-8252244 Fax: 01-8252245
Email: info@alltech-bio.com
Web: http://www.alltech-bio.com
SIC: 51200 Employees: 50
Animal Feed Suppliers
Mr Jack O'Shea General Manager
Mr Liam Rooney Finance Manager
Ms Niamh Crosbie Sales & Marketing Manager
Mr Craig Ferry Production Manager

Brett Brothers Ltd
Industrial Estate
Callan
Kilkenny Co. Kilkenny
Phone: 056-25140 Fax: 056-25353
Email: admin@brettbrothers.ie
Web: http://www.brettbrothers.ie
SIC: 51200 Employees: 75
Agricultural Suppliers
Mr James Brett Managing Director
Mr Michael Walsh Finance Manager
Mr Sean Brett Sales Manager
Mr Colm Ryan Production Manager

Goldcrop Ltd
Centre Park Road
Cork Co. Cork
Phone: 021-4312211 Fax: 021-4313619
Email: goldcrop@general.ie
SIC: 51200 Employees: 70
Agricultural & Horticultural Seed/Chemical Wholesale
Mr Finbar Murphy Manager Director
Mr John Holland Finance Manager
Mr Gerry Buckley Warehouse Manager
Mr Brendan O'Kelly Computer Manager

Grassland Fertilisers Ltd
75 Merrion Square
Dublin 2
Phone: 01-6613211 Fax: 01-6625093
SIC: 51200 Employees: 200
Agricultural Merchants & Supplies
Mr Paul Clerkin General Manager

Interchem Ltd
29 Cherry Orchard Industrial Estate
Dublin 10
Phone: 01-6267211 Fax: 01-6265818
SIC: 51200 Employees: 40
Distribution of Animal Health Products & Chemicals
Mr Michael Barrett Managing Director
Mr Nicholas Forristal Finance Manager
Mr John Duffy Sales & Marketing Manager
Mr Gary Beirne Production Manager
Mr Larry Doherty Office Manager

John Bolger & Company Ltd
Station Road
Milltown Ferns
Enniscorthy Co. Wexford
Phone: 054-66232 Fax: 054-66278
SIC: 51200 Employees: 200
Agricultural Supplies Distribution & Hardware
Mr David Bolger Managing Director
Mr Andy Mahar Financial Controller
Mr John Bolger Sales & Marketing Manager
Mr Gary Norman IT Manager

Joseph Stewart Ltd
Commills
Boyle Co. Roscommon
Phone: 079-62009 Fax: 079-62739
SIC: 51200 Employees: 50
Animal Feed Suppliers
Mr Trevor Stewart Managing Director
Mr Tom Cantillon Finance Manager
Mr Neil Stewart Sales Manager

Kennedy Agri Services T/A Londis
Main Street
Killeshandra Co. Cavan
Phone: 049-4334412 Fax: 049-4334412
SIC: 51200 Employees: 25
Agri Supplies
Mr Vincent Kennedy Proprietor
Mr Brian Kennedy Sales & Marketing Manager

Liffey Mills
Bunnow
Roscrea Co. Tipperary
Phone: 0505-21794 Fax: 0505-23444
SIC: 51200 Employees: 50
Agricultural Merchants & Suppliers
Mr Barry Lissy Proprietor
Mr Matthew Kennedy Manager

Power Seeds
Portglorian
Kilcock
Naas Co. Kildare
Phone: 01-6287541 Fax: 01-6287545
Email: info@powerseeds.ie
Web: http://www.powerseeds.ie
SIC: 51200 Employees: 43
Wholesale Agricultural Distribution
Mr Gerry Griffiths Managing Director
Mr Martin Lynch Financial Controller
Mr Liam Farrell Personnel Manager
Mr Michael Flavin Plant Manager

R & H Hall Ltd Operations Division
Centre Park Road
Cork Co. Cork
Phone: 021-4911777 Fax: 021-4962529
Email: longm@laws.ie
SIC: 51200 Employees: 30
Grain Merchants
Mr Hilliard Bryan Operations Director

T & J Farrington Ltd
Rathcoffey
Donadea
Naas Co. Kildare
Phone: 045-868194 Fax: 045-861046
SIC: 51200 Employees: 40
Agricultural Supplies
Mr Larry MacHale Joint Managing Director
Mr Edward Gilmartin Production Director
Mr Peadar Montgomery DP Manager

Birr Co-op Livestock Mart
Fair Green
Birr Co. Offaly
Phone: 0509-20136 Fax: 0509-21368
SIC: 51230 Employees: 24
Livestock Auctioneer
Mr William Rigney Managing Director

Tattersalls (Ireland)
Fairyhouse Road
Ratoath
Navan Co. Meath
Phone: 01-8864300 Fax: 01-8864303
Web: http://www.tattersalls.ie
SIC: 51230 Employees: 25
Bloodstock Sales
Mr Edmond Mahoney Chief Executive
Mr Liam Dunne Finance Director
Mr Simon Kerins Advertising Executive

Allied Distributive Merchants Ltd
Sunshine Industrial Estate
160A Crumlin Road
Dublin 12
Phone: 01-4114000 Fax: 01-4114083
Email: info@londis.iol.ie
Web: http://www.londis.ie
SIC: 51300 Employees: 1400
Wholesale Distribution - exclusive rights to Londis
Mr Michael Irwin Chief Executive
Mr Aidan Corcoran Company Secretary
Mr Eddie O'Callaghan Personnel Manager
Mr Paddy McGarry Sales Manager
Mr Joe O'Brian Operation Manager

Allied Foods Ltd
Unit 24 Cookstown Estate
Tallaght
Dublin 24
Phone: 01-4513800 Fax: 01-4513564
Email: info@alliedfoods.ie
Web: http://www.alliedfoods.ie
SIC: 51300 Employees: 245
Food/Drink Distribution
Mr Mitchell Barry Chief Executive
Mr Peter Mallon Finance Manager
Mr Michael Deagan Sales & Marketing Manager

Anthony Donnelly & Sons Fruit
54 North King Street
Dublin 7
Phone: 01-8724542 Fax: 01-8722989
Email: info@donnelly.ie
Web: http://www.donnelly.ie
SIC: 51300 Employees: 55
Fruit & Vegetables Distributors
Mr Brian Donnelly Managing Director
Mr Oscar Lambe Financial Controller
Mr Harry McNamee Sales & Marketing Manager

Ballon Meats
Raheen Ballon
Carlow Co. Carlow
Phone: 0503-59132 Fax: 0503-59102
Email: ballon@iol.ie
SIC: 51300 Employees: 40
Meats Wholesale
Mr Fred Salter Managing Director
Mr John Salter Sales Director

Barry & Fitzwilliam Ltd
Ballycurreen Industrial Estate
Airport Road
Cork Co. Cork
Phone: 021-4320900 Fax: 021-4320910
Email: admin@barryfitz.iol.ie
SIC: 51300 Employees: 65
Wine & Spirit Importers & Wholesalers
Mr Michael Barry Managing Director
Mr David Murphy Finance Manager

Barry Galvin Wines & Spirits
37 Bandon Road
Cork Co. Cork
Phone: 021-4316098 Fax: 021-4314209
Email: galvinwines@eircom.net
SIC: 51300 Employees: 60
Wines Spirits Ales Wholesaler
Mr Barry Galvin Proprietor
Mr Steven Dwyer Accountant
Ms Carol Cregan IT Manager

Barry's Kinsale Ltd
Pearse Street
Kinsale Co. Cork
Phone: 021-4772162 Fax: 021-4774204
SIC: 51300 Employees: 40
Meats-Wholesale
Mr John Barry Managing Director
Ms Katrina Murphy Sales Director

Boyne Valley Foods
Platin
Drogheda Co. Louth
Phone: 041-9870300 Fax: 041-9870339
Email: info@boynevalley.com
Web: http://www.boynevalley.com
SIC: 51300 Employees: 220
Food Distribution
Mr Malachy McCluskey Chief Executive
Mr Denis Moynihan Financial Director
Mr Michael Finlay Sales Director
Mr John McCluskey Production Manager
Mr Michael Dalton IT Manager

BR Marketing
204 Northwest Business Park
Blanchardstown
Dublin 15
Phone: 01-8227688 Fax: 01-8227695
Email: webmngr@brmark.ie
Web: http://www.brmark.ie
SIC: 51300 Employees: 35
food Distrbutors
Mr William Rochford Managing Director
Mr Michael Rochford Finance Manager
Ms Miriam Walker Sales& Marketing Manager
Mr Eamon Bolton IT Manager

Browne's Beer Wine & Spirit Brokers
Naas Industrial Estate
Naas Co. Kildare
Phone: 045-879099 Fax: 045-876696
Email: info@irelandonwine.com
SIC: 51300 Employees: 55
Alcohol Brokers
Mr Niall Browne Managing Director
Ms Eileen O'Flaherty Office Manager

Carton Brothers
Unit 8 Besser Drive
Clondalkin Industrial Estate
Dublin 22
Phone: 01-4570777 Fax: 01-4570525
SIC: 51300 Employees: 504
Poultry Distribution
Mr Vincent Carton Chief Executive
Mr Willy Sinott Financial Controller
Ms Carol Gordon Personnel Manager
Mr Peter Fitzpatrick Sales Director
Mr Sean Hartnett IT Manager

CKS
276a Glasnevin Avenue
Dublin 11
Phone: 01-8340342 Fax: 01-8362245
Email: cks@cks.ie
Web: http://www.cks.ie
SIC: 51300 Employees: 30
Food Distribution
Mr Brendan Kavanagh Managing Director
Mr Liam Farrell Finance Manager

 Wholesale & Distribution

Clayton Love Distribution Ltd
Jamestown Road
Inchicore
Dublin 8
Phone: 01-4536035 Fax: 01-4533733
Email: cldist@iol.ie
SIC: 51300 Employees: 50
Frozen Food Distribution
Mr John Mulhern Managing Director
Mr John Keogh Finance Manager
Mr Gerry Early Sales & Marketing Manager
Mr James O'Reilly Computer Manager

Clonlara Wholesale Distributors Ltd
Clonlara
Ennis Co. Clare
Phone: 061-354780 Fax: 061-354055
SIC: 51300 Employees: 45
Wholesale Food Distributor
Mr John Tuffy Chief Executive
Mr Seamus Tuffy Marketing Manager
Mr Richard Lombard Credit Controller

Coca Cola Killarney
Fair Hill
Killarney Co. Kerry
Phone: 064-31042 Fax: 064-34069
SIC: 51300 Employees: 23
Soft Drinks Distribution
Mr Jim Fleming General Manager
Mr Tom Lyne Accounts Manager

Corrib Food Products
Kiltullagh
Athenry
Galway Co. Galway
Phone: 091-848004 Fax: 091-848071
Email: info@corribfood.com
Web: http://www.corribfood.com
SIC: 51300 Employees: 150
Poultry & Frozen Foods Distribution
Mr Stan Lawless Chief Executive
Mr John Lydon Accountant
Mr Stan Lawless Personnel Officer
Mr David Mannion Computer Manager

Costello & McDermott Ltd
Rathredmond
Ballinrobe
Claremorris Co. Mayo
Phone: 092-41039 Fax: 092-41761
Email: costelloandmcdermott@eircom.net
SIC: 51300 Employees: 30
Frozen & Chilled Food Distributors
Mr Peter Costello Director
Mr Jarlath Ward Financial Controller
Mr Eamon McDermott Director

Dawn Fresh Foods Ltd
Killenaule Road
Fethard
Clonmel Co. Tipperary
Phone: 052-31115 Fax: 052-31463
Email: sales@dawnfreshfoods.iol.ie
SIC: 51300 Employees: 100
Distribution Of Catering Foods
Mr Gerry Rafferty General Manager
Ms Fionnuala Scully Sales Manager
Mr John Staunton Operation Manager
Mr John Quelly Quality Manager

Donegal Meat Processors
Drumnashear
Carrigans
Lifford Co. Donegal
Phone: 074-40228 Fax: 074-40109
SIC: 51300 Employees: 260
Food & Drink Distribution
Mr Brian Gribben Manager
Mr Liam Connolly Finance Manager
Mr Norbert Quinn Sales & Marketing Manager

Drover Foods Ltd
Whitemill Industrial Estate
Wexford Co. Wexford
Phone: 053-41434 Fax: 053-46002
Email: drover@iol.ie
SIC: 51300 Employees: 40
Frozen Food Distribution
Mr Gerry Bernard Managing Director
Mr Noel McCormack Finance Manager
Mr Denis Doyle Sales Manager
Mr Steven Bryan Production Manager
Ms Siobhan Whelan Computer Manager

Edward Dillon & Company
25 Mountjoy Square East
Dublin 1
Phone: 01-8193300 Fax: 01-8555852
SIC: 51300 Employees: 75
Wines & Spirits - Distribution
Mr John Pearson Managing Director
Mr Liam Murray Finance Manager
Mr Tom Duffy Commercial Director
Mr Paul Condell IT Manager

Edward Joyce
Summerhill House
Meelick
Limerick Co. Limerick
Phone: 061-451663 Fax: 061-451663
SIC: 51300 Employees: 40
Meats-Wholesale
Mr Edward Joyce Managing Director

Fine Wines Limerick
Vintage House, 42 Roches Street
Limerick Co. Limerick
Phone: 061-416501 Fax: 061-417276
Email: info@finewines.ie
SIC: 51300 Employees: 100
Wine Importers
Mr Ralph Parks Managing Director
Mr Robert Keane Finance Manager
Mr John Blake Sales & Purchasing Manager

First Ireland Spirits Company Ltd
Mountrath Road
Abbeyleix
Portlaoise Co. Laois
Phone: 0502-31944 Fax: 0502-31975
SIC: 51300 Employees: 40
Wine & Spirits Wholesalers
Mr Joe Lynch Managing Director

GH Lett & Company Ltd
Mill Park Brewery
Enniscorthy Co. Wexford
Phone: 054-33544 Fax: 054-35222
Email: ghlettco@gofree.indigo.ie
SIC: 51300 Employees: 30
Wholesale Distribution of Wines & Spirits/ Beers/ Ales/ Minerals
Mr Douglas Lett Managing Director

Glynn Meat Exports
Prospect Hall
Patrickswell
Limerick Co. Limerick
Phone: 061-355233 Fax: 061-355021
SIC: 51300 Employees: 40
Meats - Wholesale
Mr John Glynn Manager

HJ Heinz Company Ireland
Stradbrook House
Stradbrook Road
Blackrock Co. Dublin
Phone: 01-2805757 Fax: 01-2801957
Email: hjheinz@clubi.ie
Web: http://www.heinz.com
SIC: 51300 Employees: 461
Food Distributor
Mr John O'Reilly Managing Director
Mr Joe Mohan Financial Controller
Ms Linda Dillon Marketing Manager

Irish Draft Systems
Unit 8 Quinn Road, Business Park
Ennis Co. Clare
Phone: 065-6820742 Fax: 065-6843160
SIC: 51300 Employees: 30
Drink Dispensing Service
Mr Fintan Meaney Managing Director

JD Enterprises
Ruaens, Balyclough
Mallow Co. Cork
Phone: 022-22782 Fax: 022-27034
Email: blackwater@indigo.ie
SIC: 51300 Employees: 41
Coffee Importers & Merchants
Mr Tony O'Driscoll Managing Director
Mr Martin Long Finance Director
Mr Ger McGrath Sales Director

John J Galvin & Son Ltd
Clieveragh
Listowel Co. Kerry
Phone: 068-21088 Fax: 068-21020
SIC: 51300 Employees: 27
Wholesale Beverages
Mr John Galvin Proprietor

Johnson Brothers Ltd
PO Box 821, Ballymount Avenue
Walkinstown
Dublin 12
Phone: 01-4523000 Fax: 01-4516696
SIC: 51300 Employees: 300
Sales & Distribution of International Branded Foods
Mr David Skerritt Managing Director
Mr Hugh Daly Finance Director

Kielys Distribution Ltd
Unit 22 Cookstown Industrial Estate
Tallaght
Dublin 24
Phone: 01-4610677 Fax: 01-4610577
Email: dublinwarehouse@kielys.iol.ie
SIC: 51300 Employees: 40
Warehouse & Distribution
Mr Michael Kiely Managing Director
Mr Michael Toomey Operation Manager

Kraft Foods Ireland Ltd
47 Pembroke Road
Ballsbridge
Dublin 4
Phone: 01-6052600 Fax: 01-6052626
SIC: 51300 Employees: 50
Food/Beverage & Confectionery Distributors
Mr Charles Walshe Managing Director
Mr Karl Young Finance Manager
Mr Gerry McGrath Sales Director
Mr Ken Ryan Computer Manager

Macrus
Ballymount Industrial Estate
Ballymount Road
Dublin 24
Phone: 01-4500666 Fax: 01-4510975
SIC: 51300 Employees: 40
Distributors of frozen food
Mr Dermot McGreal Proprietor
Mr Tom Reddy Sales Manager

Marcus Distribution Ltd
Ballymount Cross Industrial Estate
Tallaght
Dublin 24
Phone: 01-4501614 Fax: 01-4501975
SIC: 51300 Employees: 30
Frozen Foods Distribution
Mr Dermot McGreal Managing Director

Matt O'Brien
Kilcock
Naas Co. Kildare
Phone: 01-6287819 Fax: 01-6287189
SIC: 51300 Employees: 41
Coffee Importers & Merchants
Mr Matt O'Brien Proprietor

Wholesale & Distribution

Monaghan Bottlers
Tirkeenan
Monaghan Co. Monaghan
Phone: 047-82244 Fax: 047-84689
Email: mbl@eircom.net
SIC: 51300 Employees: 27
Beer/Wine/Spirit/Wholesale & Importer
Mr Pat Ronayne General Manager
Mr Seamus McManus Financial Controller

Munster Wholefoods Ltd
Farranfore
Killarney Co. Kerry
Phone: 066-9764691 Fax: 066-9764692
Email: info@mwf.ie
Web: http://www.mwf.ie
SIC: 51300 Employees: 23
Wholesale of Health Food
Mr Martin Benham Managing Director

Nash Beverages Ltd
Unit 8 Dockland Business Estate
Dock Road
Limerick Co. Limerick
Phone: 061-401555 Fax: 061-401550
SIC: 51300 Employees: 85
Wholesale Distribution to the Licence Trade
Mr Greg Canty General Manager
Mr Martin Deignan Financial Controller
Mr Paul Aherne Personnel Manager
Mr Owen O'Hea Sales Manager
Mr Kieran McMahon Systems Manager

Nest Box Egg Company
Lurganmore
Castleblayney Co. Monaghan
Phone: 042-9740000 Fax: 042-9740057
Email: info@nestbox.iol.ie
SIC: 51300 Employees: 30
Eggs - Wholesale
Ms Adrienne McGuiness Managing Director
Mr Brain Eivers Manager

O'Kane Castlemahon Food Services
Naas Industrial Estate
Naas Co. Kildare
Phone: 045-876648 Fax: 045-875653
Email: okanefoodsirl@eircom.net
SIC: 51300 Employees: 100
Poultry & Frozen Foods Distribution
Mr Graham Steward Managing Director
Mr Vincent O'Donoghue Group Finance Director
Mr Bill Lattimore Group Marketing Director
Mr Ronan Murphy IT Manager

P Henshaw Ltd
Finglas Bridge
Dublin 11
Phone: 01-8347711 Fax: 01-8347608
SIC: 51300 Employees: 40
Meat Wholesalers
Mr Peter Henshaw Managing Director
Mr Noel McSherry Financial Controller
Mr Eddie Henshaw Sales Director
Mr Troy Henshaw Production Manager

Packaging Resources Ltd
Unit 260 Holly Road
Western Industrial Estate
Dublin 12
Phone: 01-4569572 Fax: 01-4508351
Email: info@udv.com
SIC: 51300 Employees: 70
Store & Ship Liqueur
Mr Roddy Lyons Managing Director
Mr Jack O'Riordan Finance Manager
Mr Gavin Doyle Personnel Manager
Mr Brian O'Hara Operation Director
Mr Terry O'Toolis Computer Manager

RHM Foods (Ireland) Ltd
Unit 108-109 Bann Road
Glasnevin
Dublin 11
Phone: 01-8300411 Fax: 01-8308591
SIC: 51300 Employees: 180
Food Distributors
Mr Canice Kelly Managing Director
Mr Pat Robinson Financial Director
Mr Mark Dorman Sales & Marketing Director

Richmond Marketing
Unit 292 Beech Road
Western Industrial Estate
Dublin 12
Phone: 01-4601671 Fax: 01-4601570
Email: info@richmondmarketing.com
Web: http://www.richmondmarketing.com
SIC: 51300 Employees: 35
Soft Drinks & Suppliers
Mr Barry Connolly Managing Director
Ms Geraldine Russell Financial Controller
Mr Colm Storey Sales Director

Southern Fruit Distributing Co Ltd
Lehenaghmore, Togher
Cork Co. Cork
Phone: 021-4964322 Fax: 021-4964449
SIC: 51300 Employees: 25
Fruit & Veg Wholesalers
Mr Peter Collins Managing Director
Mr John O'Donavan Sales & Marketing Manager
Mrs Deirdre Collins Computer Manager

Stafford Lynch
Willsborough Industrial Estate
Clonshaugh
Dublin 17
Phone: 01-8670555 Fax: 01-8670795
SIC: 51300 Employees: 70
Food Distribution
Mr David O'Neill Managing Director
Mr Ciaran Moore Financial Controller
Mr Gerry Penrose Credit & Adminstration Manager
Ms Shannon Mullen Sales & Marketing Manager
Mr Hugh Hennessy Operation Manager

T Hanrahan & Sons Ltd
Raheen Business Park
Raheen
Limerick Co. Limerick
Phone: 061-302277 Fax: 061-301526
Web: http://www.completecuisine.com
SIC: 51300 Employees: 50
Frozen Food Distribution
Mr Thomas Hanrahan Managing Director
Mr Eddie Hanrahan Financial Controller

Teatime Express
Arkle Road, Sandyford Ind Estate
Foxrock
Dublin 18
Phone: 01-2952021 Fax: 01-2958708
SIC: 51300 Employees: 30
Flour Confectionery
Mr John Sherry Managing Director
Mr Donal Hogan Financial Controller
Ms Marie Mullaney Sales & Marketing Manager

Tennant & Ruttle Distribution
Unit 2 Allied Industrial Estate
Kylemore Road
Dublin 10
Phone: 01-6231610 Fax: 01-6231771
Email: tandr@indigo.ie
SIC: 51300 Employees: 45
Confectionery Distribution
Mr Geoffrey Beggs Managing Director
Mr Ray Woodroofe Financial Controller

Tullys Wholesale
Carlow Co. Carlow
Phone: 0503-47744 Fax: 0503-47738
Email: tullyltd@iol.ie
SIC: 51300 Employees: 40
Wine & Spirits Wholesalers
Mr Paddy Tully Managing Director

Union Food Distributors Ltd
Ballisodare
Sligo Co. Sligo
Phone: 071-62298 Fax: 071-60396
SIC: 51300 Employees: 55
Frozen Food Distribution
Mr Derek Pugh Managing Director
Mr John Feeney Financial Controller
Mr Norman Pugh Sales & Marketing Manager

United Beverages Sales
Finches Industrial Park
Long Mile Road
Dublin 12
Phone: 01-4502000 Fax: 01-4509004
Email: info@unibev.iol.ie
Web: http://www.unibevol.ie
SIC: 51300 Employees: 266
Soft Drinks Manufacture & Distribution
Mr Brian Farrell Chief Executive
Mr John McKernan Sales Director

Van Den Bergh Foods Ltd
Whitehall Road
Rathfarnham
Dublin 14
Phone: 01-2169400 Fax: 01-2961349
SIC: 51300 Employees: 250
Food Distributors
Mr Jules Noten Managing Director
Mr Derek Spaveley Financial Controller
Mr Donal O' Connell Human Resources Director
Mr Christian Kleine Sales Director

Wexford Quality Foods Ltd
Carrigduff
Bunclody
Enniscorthy Co. Wexford
Phone: 054-77917 Fax: 054-77919
SIC: 51300 Employees: 26
Food Processors
Mr PJ Darcy Chief Executive

Wholefoods Wholesale Ltd
Unit 3D Kylemore Industrial Estate
Killeen Road
Dublin 10
Phone: 01-6262315 Fax: 01-6261233
SIC: 51300 Employees: 30
Food/Drink Distribution
Ms Rosemary Byrne Manager
Ms Maria Rooney Accounts Manager
Mr Declan McDermott Production Manager

WJ Duffy Ltd
Belleek
Ballina Co. Mayo
Phone: 096-22576 Fax: 096-71102
SIC: 51300 Employees: 60
Wholesale Bakers
Mr John Duffy Managing Director
Mr Tony Duffy Finance Manager
Mr Derek Duffy Sales & Marketing Manager

Banana Importers of Ireland Ltd
Unit 7 Lehanaghmore
Togher
Cork Co. Cork
Phone: 021-4965243 Fax: 021-4965619
SIC: 51310 Employees: 25
Fruit & Vegetables
Mr Dickie Kieran Manager

Wholesale & Distribution

Bertie Glancy & Sons
Bishop Street
Elphin
Castlerea Co. Roscommon
Phone: 078-35039 Fax: 078-35194
SIC: 51310 Employees: 30
Fruit Importers
Mr John Glancy Proprietor
Mr Greg Glancy Finance Manager

Country Crest Ltd
Rathmooney
Lusk Co. Dublin
Phone: 01-8437061 Fax: 01-8439492
Email: info@countrycrest.ie
SIC: 51310 Employees: 50
Potatoes - Wholesale
Mr Michael Hoey Managing Director
Mr John Clarke Finance Manager

Dublin Meath Growers Society
Broughan
The Ward
Dublin 11
Phone: 01-8361629 Fax: 01-8361830
Email: dngco@gofree.indigo.ie
SIC: 51310 Employees: 40
Vegetables Wholesale
Mr Pat O'Conner Manager

Fyffes Group Ireland
1 Beresford Street
Dublin 7
Phone: 01-8095555 Fax: 01-8730546
Email: postmaster@fyffes.com
Web: http://www.fyffes.com
SIC: 51310 Employees: 500
Fruit & Vegetable Distribution
Mr David McCann Chief Executive
Mr Stephen McAdam Finance Manager
Mr Michael Clerkin Personnel Manager
Mr Tony McLoughlin Sales Manager
Mr Joe Fallon Director of IT

John Gilmartin & Co Ltd
Attifinlay
Carrick On Shannon Co. Leitrim
Phone: 078-20037 Fax: 078-20265
SIC: 51310 Employees: 30
Wholesale Grocers
Mr Sean Gilmartin Managing Director
Mr Harry Liard Personnel Manager

O'Shea Brothers
Ardclone
Piltown
Carrick On Suir Co. Tipperary
Phone: 051-643152 Fax: 051-643419
Email: osheabro@indigo.ie
SIC: 51310 Employees: 100
Wholesale Fruit & Vegetable
Mr John O'Shea Managing Director
Mr Michael Hennebry Finance Manager
Ms Marie Fitzpatrick Sales Manager

Breizon Ltd
Dalrida Minna
Inverin
Galway Co. Galway
Phone: 091-572157 Fax: 091-572246
SIC: 51380 Employees: 30
Fish Wholesaler
Mr Loic Trahan Managing Director
Mr Guenael Trahan Personnel Manager

C Fish
Main Street
Dunkineely
Donegal Co. Donegal
Phone: 073-37254 Fax: 073-37270
Email: cfish@indigo.ie
SIC: 51380 Employees: 44
Fish Wholesale
Mr Charles Vial Manager

Carrokeel Seafoods Ltd
The Pier
Killala
Ballina Co. Mayo
Phone: 096-32755 Fax: 096-32777
Email: killala@carokeel.iol.ie
SIC: 51380 Employees: 100
Fish Distributors
Mr Brendan Chambers Managing Director
Mr Ray Moran Financial Controller
Ms Noreen Vessey Sales & Marketing Manager
Mr Kevin Rice Production Manager
Ms Emma Chambers General Manager

Dunn's Sea Fare Ltd
Jamestown Business Park
Finglas
Dublin 11
Phone: 01-8643100 Fax: 01-8643109
Email: sales@dunns.ie
Web: http://www.dunns.ie
SIC: 51380 Employees: 55
Fish Processors & Salmon Smokers
Mr Peter Dunn Managing Director
Mr Derek Davey Accountant
Mr Billy Whelan Sales Manager
Mr Tommy Hanlon Production Manager
Mr Paul Dunn Computer Manager

Fingal Seafoods Ltd
North Road
Finglas
Dublin 11
Phone: 01-8342111 Fax: 01-8346888
Email: fingal@indigo.ie
SIC: 51380 Employees: 30
Fish Wholesale & Export
Mr Neil McCarthy Managing Director
Mr William McGrane Finance Manager
Mr Brian Sunderland Production Director

Iasc Mara Teo
Rossaveal Pier
Ballinahown
Galway Co. Galway
Phone: 091-572136 Fax: 091-572271
Email: iascmara@iol.ie
Web: http://www.irishrail.ie
SIC: 51380 Employees: 45
Fish Wholesale
Mr Cathal Groonell Managing Director
Mr Daniel Hoctor Financial Controller

Kerry Fish Ltd
Renard Point
Cahirciveen
Killarney Co. Kerry
Phone: 066-9473131 Fax: 066-9472553
SIC: 51380 Employees: 35
Fish Sales
Mr Liam Quinlan Managing Director
Ms Mary O'Shea Finance Manager
Mr Ronan Quinlan Sales Manager

O'Cathain Iasc Teo
The Woods
Dingle
Tralee Co. Kerry
Phone: 066-9151322 Fax: 066-9151746
Email: cathain@eircom.net
SIC: 51380 Employees: 70
Fish Wholesale
Mr Owen Keane Managing Director
Mr Richard Keane Production Manager
Mr Martin O'Neill Personnel Manager
Mr Joe O'Brien Sales & Marketing Manager

Oceanpath Ltd
11a West Pier
Howth
Dublin 13
Phone: 01-8321605 Fax: 01-8321607
Email: info@oceanpath.ie
SIC: 51380 Employees: 27
Seafood Specialists
Mr Alan Ecock Managing Director

South East Fish Distributors
Kerlogue Industrial Estate
Rosslare Road
Wexford Co. Wexford
Phone: 053-46651 Fax: 053-46654
Email: info@southeastfishdist.ie
SIC: 51380 Employees: 70
Fish Wholesale and Processing
Mr Alex Scallan Managing Director
Mr Brendan Hogan Financial Controller
Ms Kay Lambert Sales Director

Ted Brown Ltd
Baile na Buaile
Dingle
Tralee Co. Kerry
Phone: 066-9151933 Fax: 066-9151977
SIC: 51380 Employees: 30
Fish Wholesale And Processing
Mr Ted Brown Managing Director

Ban Ard Sweet Cash & Carry Ltd
Ballycureen Industrial Estate
Cork Co. Cork
Phone: 021-4312717 Fax: 021-4963015
Email: banard@indigo.ie
SIC: 51390 Employees: 40
Cash & Carry
Mr Declan O'Sullivan Managing Director
Mr Frank McCarthy Finance Manager
Ms Shirley O'Sullivan Sales Director

BWG Foods Ltd
Greenhills Road
Walkinstown
Dublin 12
Phone: 01-4602153 Fax: 01-4503660
Email: reception@bwg.ie
SIC: 51390 Employees: 750
Cash & Carry
Mr Leo Crawford Chief Executive
Mr Frank Mooney Financial Controller
Ms Margaret Sheridan Personnel Manager
Mr Alex Bannaghan Sales Director
Mr Stephen Daly IT Director

C Clifford & Sons Ltd
Basin View
Tralee Co. Kerry
Phone: 066-7121833 Fax: 066-7123355
SIC: 51390 Employees: 25
Cash & Carry
Mr Peter Clifford Managing Director

GW Biggs & Company Ltd
The Square
Bantry Co. Cork
Phone: 027-50196 Fax: 027-50352
Email: btagency@eircom.net
SIC: 51390 Employees: 150
Multi Trading Group
Mr Maurice O'Keeffe Managing Director
Mr Michael Hennebry Finance Director
Mr Micheal Henry Sales Director

H Murphy & Co Ltd
Millpark Road
Enniscorthy Co. Wexford
Phone: 054-33152 Fax: 054-33974
SIC: 51390 Employees: 23
Wholesale Cash & Carry
Mr David Murphy Joint Managing Director
Ms Bernadette Kennedy Finance Manager
Mr Philip Murphy Director

James A Barry & Company
Upper Quartertown
Mallow Co. Cork
Phone: 022-30100 Fax: 022-30179
SIC: 51390 Employees: 130
Cash & Carry - Wholesalers
Mr James Barry Proprietor
Mr Paul Barry Financial Controller
Mr David O'Sullivan Sales Manager

Wholesale & Distribution

Leydens Cash & Carry
158A Richmond Road
Fairview
Dublin 3
Phone: 01-8376074 Fax: 01-8376174
Email: sales@leydens.ie
Web: http://www.leydens.ie
SIC: 51390 Employees: 50
Cash & Carry
Ms Mary Duffy Chief Executive
Ms Anne Duffy Financial Controller
Mr Eugene Collins Personnel Manager
Mr James Duffy Sales Director

M & P O'Sullivan Ltd
Doughcloyne Ind Estate, Sarsfield Road
Wilton
Cork Co. Cork
Phone: 021-4546322 Fax: 021-4342020
Email: mpos@eircom.net
SIC: 51390 Employees: 54
Cash & Carry
Mr Patrick O'Sullivan Managing Director
Mr Frank Berry Financial Controller

Managan Bros Ltd
Dublin Road
Collooney
Sligo Co. Sligo
Phone: 071-67944 Fax: 071-67933
Email: mangancy@eircom.net
SIC: 51390 Employees: 70
Cash & Carry
Mr Gerry Munnelly Managing Director

Mangan Bros Ltd
Ashline
Kilrush Road
Ennis Co. Clare
Phone: 065-6824011 Fax: 065-6828708
Email: info@mangan.ie
Web: http://www.manganbros.ie
SIC: 51390 Employees: 190
Cash & Carry & Wholesalers
Mr Gabriel Mangan Managing Director
Mr John Lillis Finance Director
Ms Monica Ringrose Personnel Director
Mr Thomas Keane Sales Director
Mr John Mangan Systems Manager

Masterlink Transport Group
New Twotot House, Limerick Road
Mallow Co. Cork
Phone: 022-30800 Fax: 022-30888
Email: info@masterlinkgroup.com
Web: http://www.masterlinkgroup.com
SIC: 51390 Employees: 70
Distributors Warehouse
Mr Michael O'Regan Managing Director
Mr John Field Sales Manager

Musgrave Group Plc
Airport Road
Ballycurreen
Cork Co. Cork
Phone: 021-4522222 Fax: 021-4522244
Email: c&c@musgrave.ie
Web: http://www.musgrave.ie
SIC: 51390 Employees: 2595
Grocery Wholesale, Cash & Carry
Mr Seamus Scally Manager
Mr Michael Walsh Financial Director
Mr Cliff Hillard Human Resources Director
Mr Michael Nason Production Manager
Mr Brian Mahony IT Director

Padraic Tuffy Ltd
Bohernasup
Ballina Co. Mayo
Phone: 096-21300 Fax: 096-70500
Email: info@tuffys.net
Web: http://www.tuffys.net
SIC: 51390 Employees: 25
Cash & Carry
Mr Padraic Tuffy Proprietor
Mr John Tuffy Finance Manager

Tolan Foods Service
Merlin Park Industrial Estate
Galway Co. Galway
Phone: 091-741848 Fax: 091-741888
Email: info@tolan.com
Web: http://www.tolan.com
SIC: 51390 Employees: 55
Cash & Carry for Caterers
Mr Martin Tolan Managing Director
Mr Luke Birmingham Sales Manager
Mr Tom Moran Operation Manager

Triumph Distribution/ M50 Cash and Carry
Unit 39 JFK Road
JFK Industrial Estate
Dublin 12
Phone: 01-4500655 Fax: 01-4500638
Email: triumph@iol.ie
Web: http://www.iol.ie/triumphdistribution
SIC: 51390 Employees: 30
Cash and Carry
Mr Richard Smyth Managing Director
Mr Stewart Smyth Sales Manager

Value Centre Cash & Carry
Greenhills Road
Walkinstown
Dublin 12
Phone: 01-4090300 Fax: 01-4503660
SIC: 51390 Employees: 2000
Cash & Carry - Wholesalers
Mr Connor Whelan Managing Director
Mr Aidan Keenan Finance Manager

George J Crampton & Co Ltd
36-39 James Street
Dublin 8
Phone: 01-4538637 Fax: 01-4547744
SIC: 51420 Employees: 35
Upholstery Importers
Mr Ronald Crampton Managing Director
Mr Norman Kinnarr Finance Manager
Mr Derek Crampton Sales & Marketing Manager
Ms Sarah Dolan Computer Manager

Hickey & Co Ltd
Parkgate House
Parkgate Street
Dublin 8
Phone: 01-6778361 Fax: 01-6718023
Email: hickey@iol.ie
SIC: 51420 Employees: 100
Fabric & Trimmings Wholesalers
Mr Ian Donnelly Managing Director
Mr Thomas Jackson Finance Manager
Ms Una Nolan Personnel Manager
Mr Myles Donnelly Marketing Director
Mr Noel McShane Computer Manager

Joy Clothing Ltd
41 A-B Drury Street
Dublin 2
Phone: 01-6713659 Fax: 01-6795982
Email: joy@indigo.ie
SIC: 51420 Employees: 60
Clothing - Wholesale
Mr John Suttle Proprietor
Mr Patrick Rafter Financial Controller

M Drummy Ltd
Churchfield Commercial Park
Churchfield Avenue
Cork Co. Cork
Phone: 021-4304408 Fax: 021-4393887
Email: info@eccoirl.com
Web: http://www.ecco.com
SIC: 51420 Employees: 80
Footwear Wholesalers
Mr James Lyons Managing Director
Mr Tom Meade Finance Director
Ms Eileen Houlihan Personnel Administrator
Mr Richard Higgins General Manager

Michael Heather
58-64 Upper Dominick Street
Dublin 7
Phone: 01-8725044 Fax: 01-8726845
Email: sales@michaelh.ie
Web: http://www.ei.irishfashion.com/michael-h
SIC: 51420 Employees: 200
Clothing Wholesaler Retailer
Mr Michael Heather Manager
Mr Con Gallagher Finance Manager
Mr Simon Dowling Sales & Marketing Manager
Ms Lynda Heather Design
Ms Bernie Connell Designer

O'Sullivan Safety Ltd
Long Mile Road
Dublin 12
Phone: 01-4098500 Fax: 01-4568501
Email: sales@osullivan-safety.ie
SIC: 51420 Employees: 60
Clothing & Textiles Distribution
Mr Donal O'Sullivan Managing Director
Mr Shane Harkin Finance Manager

Rag Trade Distribution Ltd
Unit D14 Ballymount Cross Ind Estate
Dublin 24
Phone: 01-4508211 Fax: 01-4503236
Email: info@ragtradedistribution.ie
Web: http://www.ragtradedistribution
SIC: 51420 Employees: 30
Clothing Distribution
Mr Donal Mackey Managing Director

Spring Grove Services
Millfield
Mallow Road
Cork Co. Cork
Phone: 021-4301225 Fax: 021-4502988
SIC: 51420 Employees: 70
Linen Supply & Protective Clothing
Mr Sean Murphy Plant Manager
Ms Muireann Lawlor Finance Manager
Ms Patricia Hanover Sales Manager

Toplion Sportswear Ltd
A6 Parkway Business Centre
Ballymount Cross
Dublin 24
Phone: 01-4509194 Fax: 01-4509294
Email: admin@toplion.com
Web: http://www.toplion.com
SIC: 51420 Employees: 30
Sportswear Distributor
Mr Paul Dean Managing Director
Mr John Burke Financial Controller

Whelan Footwear Distributor
Lisnasaran
Cootehill Co. Cavan
Phone: 049-5552118 Fax: 049-5552637
Email: whelans@eircom.net
SIC: 51420 Employees: 56
Footwear Wholesalers
Mr Martin Whelan Managing Director
Ms Margaret McPhilips Financial Controller
Mr Austin Dempsey Marketing Manager
Ms Connie Whelan Personnel/DP Manager

Wrangler Ireland Ltd
Unit 5 Broomhill Business Park
Tallaght
Dublin 24
Phone: 01-4598471 Fax: 01-4510948
SIC: 51420 Employees: 25
Clothing Distribution
Mr Niall MacNeaney Area Director
Mr Paddy Emmerson Personnel Manager

All Ireland Group
Unit 2 Baldonnell Business Park
Naas Road
Dublin 22
Phone: 01-4123000 Fax: 01-4123099
Email: sales@connect-agency.ie
Web: http://www.connect-agency.ie
SIC: 51430 Employees: 80
Electrical Distribution
Mr Simon Maddock Managing Director
Mr Dan Laffan Group Controller
Ms Mary Hannon Customer Services

AP Haslam Ltd
14 Sunshine Industrial Estate
Crumlin Road
Dublin 12
Phone: 01-4532522 Fax: 01-4532949
Email: sales@aphaslam.ie
Web: http://www.aphaslam.ie
SIC: 51430 Employees: 30
Industrial Electrical Equipment Distribution
Mr Paul Haslam Managing Director
Mr Vincent Foran General Manager

BB Distribution
291 Whiteheather Industrial Estate
South Circular Road
Dublin 8
Phone: 01-4730885 Fax: 01-4730966
Email: info@bbdist.com
SIC: 51430 Employees: 35
Electrical Suppliers & Providers
Mr Denis Vallely General Manager
Mr Brian Callinan Finance Manager
Ms Maria Campbell Personal Assistant

Beaver Distribution
Greenhill's Road
Tallaght
Dublin 24
Phone: 01-4515211 Fax: 01-4517127
Email: info@beaverdistribution.ie
Web: http://www.beaverdistribution.ie
SIC: 51430 Employees: 70
Electrical Products Distribution
Mr Paul Welden Manager
Mr Philip Galligan Financial Controller

Broderick Electrical & Pumps Services
165 North Main Street
Youghal Co. Cork
Phone: 024-93032 Fax: 024-93819
Email: dbroderickandsons@eircom.net
SIC: 51430 Employees: 25
Electrical Pumps - Distribution & Servicing
Mr Denis Broderick Proprietor

Brother International Ltd
Airways Industrial Estate, Boeing Road
Santry
Dublin 17
Phone: 01-8424777 Fax: 01-8424517
Email: info@brother.ie
Web: http://www.brother.com
SIC: 51430 Employees: 25
Distribution of Electrical Appliances
Mr Sean Sheehan Manager
Ms Niamh Kenny Financial Controller
Ms Angela Levins Company Secretary
Mr Ray Darcy Technical Support Manager

Caulfield Industrial Ltd
Tuam Road
Galway Co. Galway
Phone: 091-795007 Fax: 091-795055
Email: sales@caulfieldindustrial.ie
SIC: 51430 Employees: 150
Electrical Suppliers/Wholesalers
Mr Edward Caulfield Managing Director
Mr Gerry Kelly Accountant

Charles Nolan Ltd
Techna House
Dublin 6w
Phone: 01-4901239 Fax: 01-4901274
Email: sales@cnolan.ie
Web: http://www.cnolan.ie
SIC: 51430 Employees: 50
Electrical Distribution
Mr Richard Nolan Managing Director
Mr Joe Kenny Finance Manager
Mr Pat McCann Sales Manager
Ms Anette Olphhert Computer Manager

Charlie Shiels Wholesale Ltd
U3/4 Goldenbridge Industrial Estate
Inchicore
Dublin 8
Phone: 01-4545844 Fax: 01-4545845
SIC: 51430 Employees: 35
Electrical Suppliers/Wholesale
Mr Charlie Shiels Proprietor
Mr Tom Pentony Financial Controller
Mr Brian Nels Sales & Marketing Manager

Clarity
Clarity House
Belgard Road
Dublin 24
Phone: 01-4500222 Fax: 01-4601500
Email: info@clarity.ie
Web: http://www.clarity.ie
SIC: 51430 Employees: 100
Computer Distribution
Mr Adrian Foley Managing Director
Mr Laurence Slavin Finance Manager
Ms Veronica Philips Sales Director
Mr Richard Cullen Production Manager

Dimpco Ltd
Airport Road
Cloghran
Swords Co. Dublin
Phone: 01-8424833 Fax: 01-8424943
Email: dimpco@dimpco.ie
Web: http://www.dimpco.ie
SIC: 51430 Employees: 120
Electrical Distributor
Mr Brendan McDonald Managing Director
Mr Tony Brennan Financial Controller
Mr Pat McCarthy Personnel Manager
Mr Martin Byrne Sales & Marketing Manager

Eastern Electrical
Coes Road
Dundalk Co. Louth
Phone: 042-9337101 Fax: 042-9337193
SIC: 51430 Employees: 300
Electrical Wholesale
Mr Hugh McGee Managing Director
Mr Sean McKenny Company Accountant
Ms Marian Grey Computer Manager

Edmundsons Electrical
15/19 Hendrick Street
Dublin 7
Phone: 01-6775413 Fax: 01-6775601
SIC: 51430 Employees: 360
Electrical Distributors
Mr Ronnie Stevenson Managing Director
Mr Kieran Whelan Financial Controller
Mr George Nusson Sales & Marketing Manager
Ms Bernie Cassidy Computer Manager

Egan Electrical Equipment Ireland Ltd
K1 Ballymount Drive
Dublin 12
Phone: 01-4564635 Fax: 01-4564639
Email: eganelect@eircom.net
SIC: 51430 Employees: 30
Electrical Equipment & Supplies - Wholesale
Mr Alan Moore Managing Director

Electro-Diesel (Ireland)
Kylemore Park West
Ballyfermot
Dublin 10
Phone: 01-6264366 Fax: 01-6266471
SIC: 51430 Employees: 40
Electrical Distributors
Mr Brian O'Brien Managing Director
Mr Tony Barton General Manager
Mr Harry Griffith Marketing Director
Mr Stephen Connolly IT Manager

Emcee Distribution Ltd
3B Avonbeg Industrial Estate
Longmile Road
Dublin 12
Phone: 01-4567911 Fax: 01-4506088
Email: sales@emcee.ie
SIC: 51430 Employees: 25
Computer Distribution
Mr Maurice Cohan Managing Director
Ms Bertha Cohan Financial Controller

Excelelectric
Excel Works
Bluebell Avenue
Dublin 12
Phone: 01-4500600 Fax: 01-4602178
Email: sales@excelelectric.ie
Web: http://www.excelelectric.ie
SIC: 51430 Employees: 60
Electrical Goods
Mr Eamon Cullen Managing Director
Mr Tony Brady Financial Controller

Hicken Lighting
17 Lower Bridge Street
Dublin 8
Phone: 01-6777882 Fax: 01-6774145
Email: info@hickenlighting.com
Web: http://www.hickenlighting.com
SIC: 51430 Employees: 35
Lighting Distributors
Ms Deirdre Baker Managing Director

Honeywell Control Systems Ltd
Unit 1 Robinhood Business Park
Robinhood Road
Dublin 22
Phone: 01-4565944 Fax: 01-4565947
Email: info@honeywell.com
Web: http://www.honeywell.com
SIC: 51430 Employees: 30
Sales & Service of Process Control Systems
Mr Greg Connelly Area Manager
Mr Declan Coughlin Sales Manager

Irish Security
Rockchapel
Mallow Co. Cork
Phone: 029-69173 Fax: 029-69056
Email: isd@eircom.net
SIC: 51430 Employees: 25
Distribute Security Products
Mr Patrick O'Connor Managing Director

Led Group Ltd
Moeran Road
Walkinstown
Dublin 12
Phone: 01-4550770 Fax: 01-4550779
Email: info@led.ie
Web: http://www.led.ie
SIC: 51430 Employees: 150
Lighting & Electrical Distributors
Mr Michael Slein Managing Director
Mr Brendan Bergin Finance Manager
Mr Derek Slein Export Director
Mr Fergal Warren Computer Manager

Wholesale & Distribution

M Kelliher & Sons (1935) Ltd
Ballymullen
Tralee Co. Kerry
Phone: 066-7121144 Fax: 066-7121775
Email: info@kelliher.com
Web: http://www.kelliher.com
SIC: 51430 Employees: 25
Electrical Wholesaler
Mr Paddy Sugrue Managing Director
Mr Dennis Kelliher Financial Controller

Mitsubishi Electric Ireland
Westgate Business Park
Ballymount
Dublin 24
Phone: 01-4198800 Fax: 01-4198890
Email: sales.info@mei.mee.com
Web: http://www.mitsubishi.ie
SIC: 51430 Employees: 40
Electrical Goods
Mr Fergus Madigan President
Mr Martin Maher Head of Finance
Mr Dennis Boyd Sales & Marketing Manager

National Electrical Wholesalers
New Wapping Street
Dublin 1
Phone: 01-8555201 Fax: 01-8555144
Email: new@new.ie
SIC: 51430 Employees: 32
Electrical Equipment & Supplies - Wholesale
Mr Alan Collin Managing Director
Mr Philip Brady Company Secretary

OBF Distributors Ltd
Unit 182 Western Industrial Estate
Naas Road
Dublin 12
Phone: 01-4504644 Fax: 01-4504757
Email: sales@obf.com
SIC: 51430 Employees: 40
Electric Cable Distribution
Mr Tommy Lyons Managing Director
Mr Noel Gough Finance Manager
Ms Carol Rutherford Personnel Manager
Mr Derek Gill Sales Contact
Mr Oisin O'Brien Production Manager

Philips Electronics Ireland
Newstead
Clonskeagh
Dublin 14
Phone: 01-7640000 Fax: 01-7640152
Web: http://www.philips.com
SIC: 51430 Employees: 300
Electronic Products Distribution
Mr Cel O'Reilly Managing Director
Mr Larry Keaveny Company Secretary
Ms Adrienne Ryan Human Resources Manager
Mr Albert Brookes Sales Manager
Mr Pat Ahearn IT Manager

Radionics Ltd
Glenview Industrial Estate
Herberton Road
Dublin 12
Phone: 01-4536099 Fax: 01-4153111
Web: http://www.radionics.ie
SIC: 51430 Employees: 63
Electrical Suppliers/Wholesale
Mr John Fitzgerald General Manager
Mr Gerard Monaghan Financial Controller
Mr Aidan Kenny Personnel Manager
Mr Paul Doyle Sales Manager
Ms Cathy Lee Computer Manager

T O'Reilly Electrical Supplies
5 Golden Bridge Industrial Estate
Dublin 8
Phone: 01-6712011 Fax: 01-6791543
Email: electric@indigo.ie
SIC: 51430 Employees: 360
Electrical Wholesalers
Mr Declan O'Reilly Managing Director
Mr Terence Tierney Financial Controller
Mr Damien Gore Sales Manager

Abbott Laboratories Ireland Ltd
Unit 1 Broomhill Business Park
Tallaght
Dublin 24
Phone: 01-4517388 Fax: 01-4517765
SIC: 51460 Employees: 3000
Pharmaceutical Distribution and Marketing
Ms Bonnie Shawl Managing Director
Mr Basil Blakeney Finance Manager
Ms Majella McAneney Personnel Manager
Ms Francis Finnerty IT Manager

Boehringer Ingelheim Ltd
31 Sandyford Office Park
Blackthorn Avenue
Dublin 18
Phone: 01-2959620 Fax: 01-2959624
Email: info@boehringer-ingelheim.com
Web: http://www.boehringer-ingelheim.com
SIC: 51460 Employees: 30
Pharmaceuticals
Mr Albert Roche General Manager
Mr Colin Edwards Finance Manager
Mr Albert Roche Personnel Manager
Mr Martin O'Brien Sales Manager

Boilbau & Boyd Ltd
Unit 11a Parkmore Industrial Estate
Walkinstown
Dublin 12
Phone: 01-4507077 Fax: 01-4507946
Email: bboyd@iol.ie
SIC: 51460 Employees: 50
Pharmaceutical
Mr Gerry Hayden Managing Director
Mr David Ivory Financial Controller
Mr Michael Griffin Sales & Marketing Manager
Mr Colin Cronin Computer Manager

Cahill May Roberts Group Plc
Pharmapark
Chapelizod
Dublin 20
Phone: 01-6305555 Fax: 01-6305599
Email: cmr@cmrg.ie
SIC: 51460 Employees: 210
Pharmaceutical Wholesalers
Mr Pat Tracey Managing Director
Mr Colm O'Connor Finance Manager
Mr Gerry McSweeney Personnel Manager
Mr David Sweeney Sales Director
Mr Conor O'Brien Operation Manager

Co-operative Animal Health Ltd
Tullow Industrial Estate
Tullow
Carlow Co. Carlow
Phone: 0503-51251 Fax: 0503-51856
Web: http://www.cahl.ie
SIC: 51460 Employees: 90
Distribution of Veterinary Products
Mr Pat McCarthy Managing Director
Mr Paddy McEvoy Financial Controller
Mr Pat Tallon Sales Manager
Ms Geraldine O'Sullivan IT Manager

Excel Medical Products Ltd
Chatsworth House Chatsworth Street
Castlecomer
Kilkenny Co. Kilkenny
Phone: 056-41283 Fax: 056-41745
Email: irishdoctors@tinet.ie
SIC: 51460 Employees: 50
Pharmaceutical Distribution
Ms Joanne Reilly Managing Director
Ms Ann Mahon Finance Manager
Ms Mary Brophy Sales Manager

Glaxo Smith Kline
Grange Road
Rathfarnham
Dublin 16
Phone: 01-4938811 Fax: 01-4069217
Email: ireland@gsk.com
SIC: 51460 Employees: 95
Pharmaceutical & Chemists - Wholesale
Mr Joe Lecouilliard Managing Director
Mr David Lechleiger Head of Finance/Co Secretary
Mr Gerry Farrelly Data Processing Manager

Janssen Pharmaceuticals
Little Island
Cork Co. Cork
Phone: 021-4978500 Fax: 021-4978550
Web: http://www.jnj.com
SIC: 51460 Employees: 200
Pharmaceutical Distribution
Mr Bryan Mohally General Manager

Klinge Pharmacia & Co
52 James Place East
Dublin 2
Phone: 01-6761681 Fax: 01-6761920
Email: info@dublin.klinge.ie
Web: http://www.dublin.klinge.ie
SIC: 51460 Employees: 355
Pharmaceutical Distribution
Mr Barry O'Sullivan Managing Director

Organon Ireland Ltd
Drynam Road
Swords Co. Dublin
Phone: 01-8074100 Fax: 01-8074101
Web: http://www.organnon.com
SIC: 51460 Employees: 600
Pharmaceutical Company
Mr John Mangan General Manager
Ms Margaret Larkin Financial Controller
Mr Lesley Richards Human Resources Manager
Ms Sarah MacDonald IT Manager

Pegler & Louden Ireland Ltd
Campbell House
Forge Hill, Kinsale Road
Cork Co. Cork
Phone: 021-4314544 Fax: 021-4314606
Email: sales@pol.ie
Web: http://www.pol.ie
SIC: 51460 Employees: 30
Distribution Pharmaceutical Goods
Mr Anthony Wornock Managing Director
Mr David Keating Finance Manager
Mr Tony Corbet Sales Director

Roche Product Ireland Ltd
3 Richview
Clonskeagh
Dublin 14
Phone: 01-2837977 Fax: 01-2837840
SIC: 51460 Employees: 40
Pharmaceutical & Chemists - Wholesale
Mr Mark Rodgers Managing Director
Mr Adrian McCann Administration Manager

Rottapharm Ltd
Damanstown Industrial Park
Mulhuddart
Dublin 15
Phone: 01-8852700 Fax: 01-8552792
SIC: 51460 Employees: 80
Pharmaceutical Products
Mr Pat Garrahy Managing Director
Mr Dominic Carroll Finance Manager

TP Whelehan Son & Co
North Road
Finglas
Dublin 11
Phone: 01-8342233 Fax: 01-8362271
Email: info@tpwhelan.ie
SIC: 51460 Employees: 50
Sales & Distribution of Human Healthcare Products
Mr Pat Keenan Chief Executive

Uni Phar
Belgard Road
Dublin 24
Phone: 01-2953501 Fax: 01-4041799
Email: dublin@uniphar.ie
Web: http://www.uniphar.ie
SIC: 51460 Employees: 210
Pharmaceutical Wholesale/Distribution
Mr Gerry Griffin Chief Executive
Mr David Mongey Finance Manager
Ms Rosemary Finnegan Sales & Marketing Manager
Mr Eugene Connell Systems Manager

United Drug Plc
United Drug House, Belgard Road
Tallaght
Dublin 24
Phone: 01-4598877 Fax: 01-4596918
Email: info@united-drug.ie
Web: http://www.united-drug.ie
SIC: 51460 Employees: 1400
Pharmaceutical Wholesale Distribution Services
Mr Liam Fitzgearald Chief Executive
Mr Barry McGrane Finance Director
Mr Vincent Long Human Resources Manager
Dr Philip Briers Group Marketing & Corporate Co
Mr Johnne Phillips IT Manager

Whelehan & Son
North Road
Finglas
Dublin 11
Phone: 01-8068600 Fax: 01-8362271
Email: info@tpwhelehan.ie
SIC: 51460 Employees: 140
Distribution of Cosmetic, Surgical, Veterinary & Pharmaceutical Products
Dr Pat Keenan Managing Director
Mr Gerard O'Neill Financial Director
Mr Donagh Barry Commercial Director
Ms Carol Roe Computer Manager

Bord Gais
Gasworks Road
Cork
Phone: 021-4534000 Fax: 021-4534001
Email: info@bordgais.com
Web: http://www.bge.ie
SIC: 51510 Employees: 750
Natural Gas Supply and Distribution
Mr Gerry Walsh Chief Executive
Mr Eamonn Nicholson Finance Manager
Mr Michael Kelly Human Resources Manager
Mr Paul O'Shaughnessy Marketing Manager
Mr Tom Doherty Chief Information Officer

Calor Gas Ireland (HQ)
Long Mile Road
Dublin 12
Phone: 01-4505000 Fax: 01-4506070
Email: info@calorgas.ie
Web: http://www.calorgas.ie
SIC: 51510 Employees: 1200
Distribution of Liquefied Petroleum Gas
Mr Ken Wilson Chief Executive Officer

Calor Kosangas Ltd
Whitegate
Midleton Co. Cork
Phone: 021-4661269 Fax: 021-4661491
Email: info@calorgas.ie
Web: http://www.calorgas.ie
SIC: 51510 Employees: 35
Bottled Gas Distributors
Mr Michael Kenefick Operations Manager

Campus Oil Ltd
25 Fitzwilliam Square
Dublin 2
Phone: 01-6763524 Fax: 01-6614704
Email: clashfern@eircom.net
SIC: 51511 Employees: 30
Oil Distribution
Mr Gerry McNamara Chief Executive
Mr Colm Moloney Financial Controller
Ms Caroline Keenan Office Manager
Mr Edmond O'Neill Sales Manager
Mr Philip O'Kennedy Operation Manager
Mr James Fiztgerald General Manager

Castrol (Ireland) Ltd
U1, Site 9 Northwest Business Park
Blanchardstown
Dublin 15
Phone: 01-8557771 Fax: 01-8242071
SIC: 51511 Employees: 25
Oil Retail/Distribution
Mr DM Bruen Chairman
Ms Maria Cleary Company Secretary

Donegal Oil Company Ltd
Port Road
Letterkenny Co. Donegal
Phone: 074-21633 Fax: 074-21902
Email: fuels@donegaloilco.ie
Web: http://www.donegaloilco.ie
SIC: 51511 Employees: 28
Oils- Fuel
Mr Arthur McMahon Managing Director
Ms Kathleen McFadden Office Manager

Emo Oil Ltd
Clonminam Industrial Estate
Portlaoise Co. Laois
Phone: 0502-22577 Fax: 0502-74750
Email: emo@iol.ie
Web: http://www.emo.ie
SIC: 51511 Employees: 150
Heating Oil Distribution
Mr Danny Murray Managing Director
Mr Gerry Wilson Financial Manager
Ms Maureen Boland Personnel Manager
Mr John O'Brien Marketing Manager
Mr Paul Leahy Operations Manager

Estuary Fuel
23 O'Curry Street
Limerick Co. Limerick
Phone: 061-319677 Fax: 061-311024
Email: info@estuaryfuel.ie
Web: http://www.estuaryfuel.ie
SIC: 51511 Employees: 50
Oil Distributor
Mr Tim O'Donoghue Managing Director
Mr Gerald O'Mahony Commercial Director
Mr Al Finucane Retail Sales

Morris Oil Co Ltd
Fiddown
Piltown
Kilkenny Co. Kilkenny
Phone: 051-643317 Fax: 051-643756
SIC: 51511 Employees: 28
Oil Importers/Distribution
Mr Max Morris Managing Director
Ms Ruth McHale Financial Controller
Mr Dan O'Shea Sales/Marketing

Primo Oil Co Ltd
Belgard Square South
Tallaght
Dublin 24
Phone: 01-4599699 Fax: 01-4598063
Email: primooil@indigo.ie
SIC: 51511 Employees: 90
Heating Oil Distribution & Petrol Filling Stations
Mr James Cummins Managing Director
Mr Gerard Mee Financial Controller
Mr Michael Hayden Sales Director

Rustic Oil Products
16 Business Park
Mullingar Co. Westmeath
Phone: 044-40502 Fax: 044-40029
Email: rustic@indigo.ie
SIC: 51511 Employees: 34
Oil Distribution
Mr Michael Donoghue Proprietor
Ms Lesley Doyle Secretary

Stafford Oils
Mosstown
Dunleer
Drogheda Co. Louth
Phone: 041-6861900 Fax: 041-6861945
SIC: 51511 Employees: 60
Supply Home Heating Oil
Mr Victor Stafford Managing Director
Mr Gerry Sheehan Financial Controller
Mr John Kennedy Sales & Marketing Manager

Suttons Oil Ltd
Centre Park Road
Cork Co. Cork
Phone: 021-4911700 Fax: 021-4911701
SIC: 51511 Employees: 50
Home Heating Oil & Petrol Distributors
Mr Joe O'Mahony Managing Director
Mr William Barry Sales Manager
Mr Pat Hourihan IT Manager

Sweeney Oil Ltd
Galway Road
Clifden
Galway Co. Galway
Phone: 095-21777 Fax: 095-21280
SIC: 51511 Employees: 25
Oil Retail & Distribution
Mr John Sweeney Managing Director
Ms Martina Carey Financial Controller

Tedcastles Oil Products Ltd
Promenade Road
Dublin 3
Phone: 01-8786911 Fax: 01-8786517
Email: info@top.ie
Web: http://www.top.ie
SIC: 51511 Employees: 100
Oil Retail/Distribution
Mr Donal Gordon Managing Director
Ms Sinead O'Connell Marketing Manager
Ms Paula O'Reilly Personnel Manager
Mr Liam Mortimer Sales Director
Mr Sean Hickey Computer Manager

Tex Oil Ltd
Alexander Road
Dublin 1
Phone: 01-8393036 Fax: 01-8558848
SIC: 51511 Employees: 80
Home Heating Oil Distribution
Mr Tom Kirrane Managing Director
Mr Dominic Morgan Financial Controller
Mr Tom Connelly Human Resources Manager
Mr Frank Webb Sales Manager
Ms Margaret Byrne Depot Manager

Texoil
Alexandra Road
Dublin 1
Phone: 01-8401303 Fax: 01-8558848
Email: info@texoil.ie
SIC: 51511 Employees: 53
Oil Distributors
Mr Tom Kirrane Managing Director
Ms Margaret Byrne Office Manager
Mr Paul Higgins Sales Representative

Three Rivers Oil Ltd
Provincial House
Patrick Street
Kilkenny Co. Kilkenny
Phone: 056-61277 Fax: 056-61473
Web: http://www.threeriversoil.com
SIC: 51511 Employees: 400
Oil Distributors
Mr Gerard Boylan Managing Director
Mr Richard O'Dwyer Financial Controller
Ms Margaret Fogarty Sales Manager
Mr Liam Conway Quality Co-ordinator

Tougher's Oil Distributors
PO Box 201, Tougher's Business Park
Newhall
Naas Co. Kildare
Phone: 045-432448 Fax: 045-436809
SIC: 51511 Employees: 130
Heating Oil Distributors & Petrol Service Stations
Mr Thomas Tougher Managing Director
Ms Pauline Craddock Finance Manager
Ms Paula Doyle Personnel Manager
Mr Robert Brennan Sales Director

Esso Ireland Ltd
Esso House
Stillorgan Road
Blackrock Co. Dublin
Phone: 01-2881661 Fax: 01-2887303
SIC: 51512 Employees: 94
Petrol Distributor
Mr Donal O'Sullivan Chairman
Mr David MacFarlane Financial Director
Mr Liam Doyle Human Resources Manager
Mr Declan Collier Sales Manager
Mr Arthur Choice IT Manager

Fingal Aviation Services Ltd
BP Depot
Dublin Airport
Swords Co. Dublin
Phone: 01-8445137 Fax: 01-8446131
Email: fingalaviation@eircom.net
SIC: 51512 Employees: 30
Aviation Fuel
Mr Bob Mulvanny Manager

Gem Oils Ltd
Regaskin
Cavan Co. Cavan
Phone: 049-4331077 Fax: 049-4361157
Email: sales@gemoils.ie
Web: http://www.gemoils.ie
SIC: 51512 Employees: 50
Oil & Lubricant Distributor
Mr Alec Milligan Managing Director
Mr Kevin McCabe Financial Controller
Mr Tom Fulton Sales & Marketing Manager
Mr Michael Brady Production/Logistics

Irish Shell
Shell House
Beech Hill, Clonskeagh
Dublin 4
Phone: 01-2838844 Fax: 01-2838320
Email: info@shellireland.com
Web: http://www.shellireland.com
SIC: 51512 Employees: 120
Oil Company
Mr Michael Forde Managing Director
Mr Michael Colgan Financial Controller
Mr William Barry Human Resources Manager
Mr Jim Gildea IT Operations Manager

Maxol Ltd
3 Custom House Plaza
IFSC
Dublin 1
Phone: 01-6076800 Fax: 01-6076850
Email: post@maxol.ie
Web: http://www.maxol.ie
SIC: 51512 Employees: 240
Marketing/Distribution of Oil Products
Mr Thomas J Noonan Chief Executive
Mr Laurance Donegan Accountant
Mr Frank Dormer Personnel/Admin Manager
Mr John Holmes Sales Manager-Retail Division
Mr Dennis Field Operations Manager
Mr Gary Boggan Computer Manager

Tankfreight (Ireland) Ltd
Alexandra Road
Dublin Port
Dublin 1
Phone: 01-8558850 Fax: 01-8551457
Email: postmaster@tankfreight.com
Web: http://www.tankfreight.com
SIC: 51512 Employees: 120
Bulk Haulage Petroleum Distribution
Mr David Brown Managing Director
Mr Andy Nicholson Finance Manager
Mr Andy Laurence Computer Manager

Engineering & Power Tools (Ireland) Ltd
Pollerton Industrial Estate
Carlow Co. Carlow
Phone: 0503-42424 Fax: 0503-41302
Email: sales@ept-irl.com
Web: http://www.ept-irl.com
SIC: 51520 Employees: 28
Distribution of Welding Engineering & Safety Equipment
Mr Seamus Doorley Managing Director

Frentech Engineering Ltd
Unit 102, Waterford Industrial Estate
Cork Road
Waterford Co. Waterford
Phone: 051-354633 Fax: 051-354816
Email: info@frentech.ie
Web: http://www.frentech.ie
SIC: 51520 Employees: 60
General Engineering Firm
Mr Bill Curtin Managing Director
Mr Martin Lynch Finance Manager
Mr Billy Power General Manager

Sherling & Sons Ltd
Jamestown Road
Inchicore
Dublin 8
Phone: 01-4533008 Fax: 01-4544322
Email: info@sherling.com
Web: http://www.sherling.com
SIC: 51520 Employees: 75
Steel Stockist
Mr Charlie Sherling Managing Director
Mr Frank Moore Finance Manager
Mr Rory Campion General Manager

Aircell Ltd
Loch Gowna
Cavan Co. Cavan
Phone: 043-83550 Fax: 043-83551
Email: aircell@aerobord.ie
Web: http://www.aerobord.ie
SIC: 51530 Employees: 25
Aeroboard Insulation Systems For Building Industry
Mr Henry Sheehan General Manager
Mr Richard Wolfe Financial Controller

Amalgamated Hardware Ltd
Naas Industrial Estate
Naas Co. Kildare
Phone: 045-876406 Fax: 045-866860
SIC: 51530 Employees: 25
Building Supplies
Mr Michael Byrne Managing Director
Ms Michael Kelly Financial Controller
Ms Michael Woods IT Officer

B D Flood
Hilltown
Oldcasle
Kells Co. Meath
Phone: 049-8541477 Fax: 049-8541311
Email: flood@iol.ie
Web: http://www.floodflooring.com
SIC: 51530 Employees: 200
Concrete Products
Mr John Flood Proprietor
Mr Tom Gallagher Finance Manager
Mr Tom McManus Sales Manager
Mr Gerry Doyle Production Manager

Briggs Roofing & Cladding
Marble Hill
Ballintemple
Cork Co. Cork
Phone: 021-4294522 Fax: 021-4294886
Email: info@briggs.ie
SIC: 51530 Employees: 55
Roofing & Cladding Products
Mr John Mohally Manager

Brooks Group Ltd
Bluebell, Naas Road
Dublin 12
Phone: 01-4783422 Fax: 01-4190040
Email: jwbrooks@iol.ie
SIC: 51530 Employees: 260
Builders Providers/Timber Merchants
Mr John Walsh Chief Executive
Mr Gerard Swarbrigg Group Financial Director
Mr Michael Garvey Personnel Manager
Mr Eugene Gilmore Sales & Marketing Director
Mr Neville Bryan Operations Manager
Ms Suzy Walsh Group IT Manager

Brooks Haughton Ltd
South Terrace
PO Box 100
Cork Co. Cork
Phone: 021-4275191 Fax: 021-4965522
SIC: 51530 Employees: 50
Building Supplies & Distribution
Mr Gerry McCarthy General Manager
Mr Peter Murray Finance Manager
Mr Tony Phelan Marketing Manager
Mr Brian McCarthy Production Manager

Buckleys Builders Providers
Ballysimon
Tipperary Road
Limerick Co. Limerick
Phone: 061-416844 Fax: 061-416418
Email: info@heitons.ie
SIC: 51530 Employees: 40
Wood Products and Builders Providers
Mr Gerard Maguire General Manager
Ms Josephine Colman Credit Controller

Capro Ltd
Mount Tallant Avenue
Terenure
Dublin 6
Phone: 01-4902755 Fax: 01-4920203
Email: info@capro.net
Web: http://www.capro.net
SIC: 51530 Employees: 400
Distributor of Specialised Building Products
Mr Brian Craig Managing Director
Mr John Keaveney Financial Controller
Ms Patricia Nolan Personnel Manager
Mr Terry Hayden Sales Director

Wholesale & Distribution

Charles Kelly Ltd
Ballymacool
Letterkenny Co. Donegal
Phone: 074-21477 Fax: 074-21324
Email: kellys@indigo.ie
SIC: 51530 Employees: 50
Builders Providers & Timber Merchants
Mr William Kelly Primary Manager
Mr Kieran O'Malley Finance Manager
Mr William Carr Sales Manager
Mr George Kelly Production Manager
Mr Gerard Kelly Computer Manager

Cleary & Doyle Contracting Ltd
Larkin's Cross
Wexford Co. Wexford
Phone: 053-65900 Fax: 053-65999
Email: info@clearydoyle.com
Web: http://www.clearydoyle.com
SIC: 51530 Employees: 300
Construction Products and Contractors
Mr John Doyle Joint Managing Director
Mr Alan Flynn Company Accountant
Mr Jim Lennon Office Manager
Mr Damian Donlon Sales Manager
Mr Ned Sullivan National Contracts Director
Mr Nell Connolly IT Executive

Clondalkin Builders Providers Ltd
Ninth Lock Road
Clondalkin
Dublin 22
Phone: 01-4592133 Fax: 01-4573753
Web: http://www.clondalkinbuildersproviders.com
SIC: 51530 Employees: 30
Building Supplies
Mr John Noonan Managing Director

Coen Holdings Ltd
Deerpark Industrial Estate
Oranmore
Galway Co. Galway
Phone: 091-790300 Fax: 091-790277
Email: coen@iol.ie
SIC: 51530 Employees: 150
Builders Providers
Mr Ainsley Tolland Chief Executive
Mr Michael Garvey Financial Controller
Mr Pat Forde Sales Manager

Cork Builders Providers Ltd
Westlink
Togher Industrial Estate
Cork Co. Cork
Phone: 021-4961700 Fax: 021-4961428
Email: sales@cork-build-prov.ie
Web: http://www.cork-build-prov.ie
SIC: 51530 Employees: 60
Building & Plumbing Supplies
Mr John Carter Managing Director
Mr Brian Murphy Sales Director
Mr Bernard McCarthy IT Manager

CRH Plc
Belgard Castle, Belgard Road
Clondalkin
Dublin 22
Phone: 01-4041000 Fax: 01-4041007
Email: mail@crh.ie
Web: http://www.crh.ie
SIC: 51530 Employees: 1000
Building Materials
Mr Liam O'Mahony Chief Executive
Mr Harry Sheridan Financial Director
Mr Jack Golden Director of Human Resources
Ms Lorraine Whelan Investor Relations Manager
Ms Fiona O'Sullivan Computer Manager

Designer Wholesale
Gort Road Industrial Estate
Ennis Co. Clare
Phone: 065-6844444 Fax: 065-6844412
SIC: 51530 Employees: 50
Wholesale Tiles
Mr David O'Connor Managing Director
Mr Eamon Gilmartin Sales Manager

Dublin Plywood & Veneer Company Ltd
22/27 North Brunswick Street
Dublin 7
Phone: 01-8732544 Fax: 01-8732943
Email: sales@dpv.ie
Web: http://www.dpv.ie
SIC: 51530 Employees: 50
Timber Importers
Mr John Rooney Managing Director
Ms Martha O'Byrne Finance Manager
Mr James McKeown Sales Director
Mr Thomas Kelly DP Manager

Dublin Providers Ltd
68 Old Kilmainham
Dublin 8
Phone: 01-4531046 Fax: 01-4541622
Email: info@kilmainham.ie
Web: http://www.kilmainham.ie
SIC: 51530 Employees: 910
Builders Providers
Mr Jeremiah Maher Managing Director
Mr Donal Murphy Finance Manager
Mr John Pearse DP Manager

EU Profiles Ltd
Dublin Road, Tullamaine
Kilkenny Co. Kilkenny
Phone: 056-25050 Fax: 056-63411
Email: info@dugganstee legroup.com
Web: http://www.dugganstee legroup.com
SIC: 51530 Employees: 150
Building Supplies/Distribution
Mr Frank Duggan Chairman
Ms Yvonne Duggan Finance Manager
Mr Michael Egan Sales Director

Frank Brogan Ltd
Bangor
Erris
Claremorris Co. Mayo
Phone: 097-83498 Fax: 097-83498
SIC: 51530 Employees: 40
Building Supplies
Mr Frank Brogan Managing Director

Freefoam Plastics Ltd
Central Commercial Park
Centre Park Road
Cork Co. Cork
Phone: 021-4966311 Fax: 021-4965273
Email: sales@freefoam.com
Web: http://www.freefoam.com
SIC: 51530 Employees: 80
Building Supplies/Distribution
Mr Tony Walsh Manager
Mr Aidan Harte Financial Controller
Ms Karen Feelan Sales & Marketing Manager

Ganly's of Athlone
Roscommon Road
Athlone Co. Westmeath
Phone: 0902-92036 Fax: 0902-92630
Email: sales@ganlyhardware.ie
Web: http://www.ganlyhardware.ie
SIC: 51530 Employees: 38
Building Supplies/Distribributors
Mr Michael Ganly Managing Director
Mr Padraic Farrell Finance Manager
Mr PJ Monaghan Sales Manager

Heiton Holdings Plc
Ashfield, Naas Road
Clondalkin
Dublin 22
Phone: 01-4034000 Fax: 01-4593696
Email: plc@heitons.ie
Web: http://www.heitons.ie
SIC: 51530 Employees: 1580
Steel/Timber / Builders Providers / Homecare / DIY
Mr Leo Martin Group Chief Executive
Mr Peter Byers Finance Director
Mr Finbar Moloney Personnel Manager
Mr Edward Kelly Commercial Director
Mr Paul Sherwood IT Manager

Heitons McFerran Ltd
Port Road
Letterkenny Co. Donegal
Phone: 074-21055 Fax: 074-24748
Email: postmaster@heitons.ie
Web: http://www.heitons.ie
SIC: 51530 Employees: 24
Builders Suppliers
Mr Daniel Borland Manager
Ms Grace Kelly Credit Controller

J E Telford Ltd
Mountrath
Portlaoise Co. Laois
Phone: 0502-32312 Fax: 0502-32735
Email: mountrath@telfords.net
SIC: 51530 Employees: 25
Builders Merchants DIY
Mr Des Telford Managing Director
Mr William Telford Partner

Kelly Timber
Kilshane Cross North Road
Finglas
Dublin 11
Phone: 01-8342207 Fax: 01-8342511
SIC: 51530 Employees: 180
Builders Providers
Mr Patrick Kelly Proprietor
Mr Damien Taheny Company Secretary
Mr Shane Moran Sales Manager
Mr Liam O'Brien Production Manager

Liam Rice Ltd
72 Seatown Place
Dundalk Co. Louth
Phone: 042-9334514 Fax: 042-9336130
Email: riceltd@iol.ie
SIC: 51530 Employees: 55
Building Supplies
Mr Liam Rice Managing Director
Ms Elizabeth McGuinness Financial Controller
Ms Irene McArdle Personnel Manager
Mr Eddie McGill Sales & Marketing Manager
Ms Barbara Markey IT Manager

MD O'Shea & Sons Ltd
7-8 Main Street
Killarney Co. Kerry
Phone: 064-31029 Fax: 064-37441
Email: mdoshea@iol.ie
SIC: 51530 Employees: 70
Building Supplies & DIY Superstore
Mr Paul O'Shea Managing Director
Ms Adele O'Reilly Finance Manager

Michael Cooney & Sons Ltd
Tibohine
Castlerea Co. Roscommon
Phone: 0907-70007 Fax: 0907-70104
SIC: 51530 Employees: 30
Builders Providers
Mr Brendan Cooney Proprietor

Morris's (Builders Providers) Ltd
The Manor
Waterford Co. Waterford
Phone: 051-874986 Fax: 051-877435
Email: morrisbp@eircom.net
SIC: 51530 Employees: 60
Building Suppliers
Mr Edward McBride General Manager

Newmans Sheeting Centre
Waterfall Avenue, Richmond Road
Drumcondra
Dublin 3
Phone: 01-8371099 Fax: 01-8370625
Email: sale@newmans-sheeting.ie
Web: http://www.newmans-sheeting.ie
SIC: 51530 Employees: 60
Timber & Laminated Board Suppliers
Mr Mark Newman Managing Director
Ms Patricia Caulfield Administration Manager
Mr Tom McEvoy Sales Director

Ryan Brothers (Ennis) Ltd
Toonagh Quarry
Ennis Co. Clare
Phone: 065-6837644 Fax: 065-6837047
SIC: 51530 Employees: 30
Building Supplies
Mr Martin Tierney Manager

Shannonside Building Supplies Ltd
Cappa Road
Kilrush
Ennis Co. Clare
Phone: 065-9051008 Fax: 065-9051301
SIC: 51530 Employees: 50
Building Supplies
Mr Daragh O'Flaherty Manager

Tegral Holdings Ltd
6 South Leinster Street
Dublin 2
Phone: 01-6763974 Fax: 01-6762820
SIC: 51530 Employees: 400
Roofing and Cladding Products
Mr David Graham Chief Executive
Mr Vincent O'Brien Financial Director
Mr John Peters Personnel Director
Mr Tom Richmond Sales Manager
Mr John Page DP Manager

Thomas Brooks
Upper Mayor Street
North Wall
Dublin 1
Phone: 01-8555333 Fax: 01-8550824
Email: brooks.thomas@upm-kymmene.com
Web: http://www.brooksgroup.ie
SIC: 51530 Employees: 30
Timber Merchants & Builders Providers
Mr Christie Conway Manager

TJ O'Mahony & Sons Ltd
Ballymount Cross
Ballymount Road, Tallaght
Dublin 24
Phone: 01-4508488 Fax: 01-4500415
Email: info@tjom.ie
SIC: 51530 Employees: 70
Building Supplies
Mr Tommy O'Mahony Managing Director
Mr Ken Phillip Accountant
Mr Colm O'Connor Sales & Marketing Manager
Mr John Barry Computer Manager

Ashbourne Distributors
Dublin Road
Ashbourne
Navan Co. Meath
Phone: 01-8352264 Fax: 01-8351512
Email: info@medtiles.com
Web: http://www.medtiles.com
SIC: 51540 Employees: 23
Tiles - Sales/Wholesale
Mr Michael McGinn Proprietor
Ms Denise Shannon Personnel Manager
Mr Jim Gartlan Sales Manager

B & G Ltd
Units E & F Greenhill Industial Estate
Greenhills Road
Dublin 12
Phone: 01-4569300 Fax: 01-4569335
Email: info@bgqhp.com
Web: http://www.bgqhp.com
SIC: 51540 Employees: 30
DIY Products Wholesaler
Mr Thomas Glency Managing Director
Ms Patricia Guard Credit Controller
Mr Timothy Maguire Personnel Manager
Mr Tony McNally Sales Director
Mr Adrian Carolan Operation Director
Mr Declan Connell Computer Manager

BL Hanly Ltd
JFK Avenue
Naas Road
Dublin 12
Phone: 01-4500444 Fax: 01-4500309
Email: info@blhanly.ie
Web: http://www.blhanly.ie
SIC: 51540 Employees: 25
Hardware Wholesalers
Mr Bruno Hanly Managing Director
Mr John Ward Financial Controller

Burke Bros Son & Company Ltd
Mill Lane, Navan Road
Ashtown
Dublin 15
Phone: 01-8387387 Fax: 01-8380045
Email: sales@burke-bros.ie
Web: http://www.burke-bros.ie
SIC: 51540 Employees: 40
Wholesale Hardware & Electrical Products
Mr Thomas Burke Managing Director
Mr Eugene Agnoli Finance Manager
Mr Tom Burke Jnr Personnel Manager
Mr Declan Ryan Sales Manager

CHM Ltd
Dough Cloyne Park Estate
Wilton
Cork Co. Cork
Phone: 021-4542177 Fax: 021-4343146
SIC: 51540 Employees: 25
Import & Distribute Hardware
Mr Simon O'Leary Managing Director
Mr Jim Ahern Sales & Marketing Manager

Cooper Hardware
Sunbury Industrial Estate
Ballymount Road
Dublin 12
Phone: 01-4506242 Fax: 01-4501005
Email: coopers@iol.ie
SIC: 51540 Employees: 50
Hardware & Household Goods Distribution
Mr David Cooper Managing Director
Mr Dermot Lally Finance Manager
Mr Peter McClure Sales Manager

Herron & Son Ltd
Finisklin Road
Sligo Co. Sligo
Phone: 071-61211 Fax: 071-69600
Email: purchasesatherron@eircom.net
SIC: 51540 Employees: 25
Hardware - Wholesale
Ms Margaret Forde Proprietor

Irish International Trading Corporation
Rocksavage
Cork Co. Cork
Phone: 021-4275161 Fax: 021-4313662
Email: iitc@iitc.ie
SIC: 51540 Employees: 90
Hardware Wholesale
Ms Hilary Browne Managing Director
Mr Noel Cleary Financial Controller
Mr Tadhg Healy Deputy Managing Director

Joseph Murphy (Ballina) Ltd
Lord Edward Street
Ballina Co. Mayo
Phone: 096-21344 Fax: 096-70549
SIC: 51540 Employees: 30
Hardware & Wholesale Distribution
Mr Peter Laing Managing Director
Mr Michael Collins Accountant
Ms Marian Flynn DP Manager

Wholesale & Distribution

KCC Ltd
Unit S4 Ballymount Industrial Estate
Ballymount Drive
Dublin 12
Phone: 01-4552421 Fax: 01-4567409
Email: sales@kcchardware.com
SIC: 51540 Employees: 40
Door Furniture Distribution
Mr Christopher Kilpatrick Managing Director
Mr John Keogh Finance Manager
Ms Margaret Drennan Human Resources Director
Mr Fergus Corcoran Sales Director
Mr Donald McLeod IT Systems Manager

Kitchenware Products (Ireland) Ltd
70-75 North Wall Quay
Dublin 1
Phone: 01-8559099 Fax: 01-8559131
Email: info@kitchenware-products.com
SIC: 51540 Employees: 35
Kitchenware Importers
Mr Jim Murphy Managing Director
Ms Deirdre Markey Financial Director
Mr Maurice Moore Sales Manager
Mr Liam Quinn Operations Director

Multy Products
Greenhills Road
Walkinstown
Dublin 12
Phone: 01-4602911 Fax: 01-4501317
Email: email@multy.ie
SIC: 51540 Employees: 40
Hardware Wholesalers
Mr Martin McManus Managing Director
Mr Pauric Tierney Personnel Manager
Mr Stephen Farrell Sales Manager

Profast Ltd
Unit 11 Western Industrial Estate
Naas Road
Dublin 12
Phone: 01-4566666 Fax: 01-4500198
Email: profast@indigo.ie
Web: http://www.profast.ie
SIC: 51540 Employees: 30
Engineering & Hardware Distribution
Mr Brendan Flynn Managing Director
Ms Nadine O'Gorman Accounts Manager
Mr Gary Flanagan Sales Director

Trinity Group Ltd
Maretim Court
Temple Road
Blackrock Co. Dublin
Phone: 01-2061500 Fax: 01-2790000
Email: postmaster@trinity-group.ie
Web: http://www.trinity-group.ie
SIC: 51540 Employees: 70
Hardware Supplier
Mr Robert Booth Managing Director
Mr Aidan Torney Finance Manager
Ms Diane Hodnett Sales Manager
Mr Tony Nason Operations Manager
Mr Dan Drummond IT Manager

American Standard Plumbing (Ireland) Ltd
M50 Business Park
Ballymount
Dublin 12
Phone: 01-4564525 Fax: 01-4564505
Email: americanstandarddublin@aseur.com
SIC: 51541 Employees: 30
Bathroom/Sanitaryware Distribution
Mr Brian Redmond Managing Director
Mr James Ward Finance Manager
Ms Sheila Kilbride Commercial Manager

Wholesale & Distribution

Davies Bathroom Centre
6/8 Richmond Avenue
Fairview
Dublin 3
Phone: 01-8376076 Fax: 01-8372863
SIC: 51541 Employees: 70
Bathroom Suites & Fittings
Mr Declan O'Donnell Managing Director
Mr Albert Carroll Financial Controller
Mr Liam Oonan General Manager

Flair International Ltd
Cavan Road
Bailieborough Co. Cavan
Phone: 042-9665382 Fax: 042-9665516
Email: info@flairinternational.com
SIC: 51541 Employees: 130
Shower Enclosures
Mr Gordon Provan Chief Executive Officer
Mr Peter Feeney Financial Controller
Mr David West Director
Mr Richard McManus IT Manager

Multi Products (Ireland)
Greenhills Road
Walkinstown
Dublin 12
Phone: 01-4501288 Fax: 01-4602765
Email: email@multi.ie
SIC: 51541 Employees: 50
Lighting & Bathroom Accessories
Mr Martin McMahon Chief Executive
Mr John Crofton Sales Director

Shiren Ireland
Broomhill Road
Tallaght
Dublin 24
Phone: 01-4515877 Fax: 01-4047640
Email: info@shires-bathrooms.co.uk
Web: http://www.shires-bathrooms.co.uk
SIC: 51541 Employees: 50
Bathroom Distributors
Mr Brendan Houller Managing Director
Mr David O'Dowd Personnel Officer

Tilesavers
70 North Wall Quay
Dublin 1
Phone: 01-8552606 Fax: 01-8364521
Email: info@tilesavers.ie
Web: http://www.tilesavers.ie
SIC: 51541 Employees: 400
Bathroom Suites & Fittings
Mr Ray Keegan General Manager
Ms Michelle O'Grady Operations Director
Mr Des Henry Sales Director

Walsh Bros Plumbing & Heating
Cappincur
Tullamore Co. Offaly
Phone: 0506-22553 Fax: 0506-24073
SIC: 51541 Employees: 40
Bathroom Suites & Fittings, Tiles & Plumbimg
Mr Gerry Walsh Director
Ms Mary Coughlan Finance Manager
Mr David Walsh Sales Director

Amari Cork Ltd
Unit 18 Monahan Road Ind Estate
Cork Co. Cork
Phone: 021-4316750 Fax: 021-4316753
Email: info@amari-cork.com
Web: http://www.amari-cork.com
SIC: 51542 Employees: 50
Pipes & Pipeline Fittings
Mr Robin Malcolm Managing Director

Arcon Heating & Plumbing Ltd
6-7 Glenview Industrial Estate
Herberton Road
Dublin 12
Phone: 01-4541384 Fax: 01-4544220
SIC: 51542 Employees: 36
Plumbing & Heating Equipment
Mr Anthony Callaghan Managing Director
Mr Ron O'Connor Financial Director

Ashworth Frazer Ltd
Hibernian Industrial Estate
Tallaght
Dublin 24
Phone: 01-4527522 Fax: 01-4514621
SIC: 51542 Employees: 45
Pipes & Pipeline Fittings
Mr Colin Wilson Managing Director
Mr Greg Donovan Financial Controller
Mr John Flannery Sales Director

Cavanagh Foundry Ltd
Roscrea Road
Birr Co. Offaly
Phone: 0509-20277 Fax: 0509-21726
Email: info@cavanagh.ie
Web: http://www.cavana.ie
SIC: 51542 Employees: 45
Produce Manhole Covers & Frames
Mr Para Freeman General Manager
Ms Chrissy Powers Finance Manager
Mr Declan Ryan Sales Manager

Cavmac Hose Manufacturers
Cootehill Co. Cavan
Phone: 049-5552340 Fax: 049-5552312
Email: cavmac@eircom.net
SIC: 51542 Employees: 24
Hoses & Hose Accessories
Mr Aidan O'Connor Managing Director

Coppercraft Ltd
Kylemore Park West
Ballyfermot
Dublin 10
Phone: 01-6265146 Fax: 01-6265146
Email: info@coppercraft.ie
Web: http://www.coppercraft.ie
SIC: 51542 Employees: 28
Plumbing Supplies
Mr Dave Madigan Managing Director

Heat Merchants
Moydrum Road
Athlone Co. Westmeath
Phone: 0902-24000 Fax: 0902-24050
Email: info@heatmerchants.ie
Web: http://www.tubstiles.ie
SIC: 51542 Employees: 200
Heating & Plumbing Suppliers - Wholesale & Sales
Mr Michael Lucitt Managing Director
Mr Jim Carey Financial Controller
Mr Phillip Grey Personnel Manager

Heatmerchants Ltd
5 Curragh Road
Turners Cross
Cork Co. Cork
Phone: 021-4968134 Fax: 021-4317760
SIC: 51542 Employees: 30
Plumbing Supplies
Mr Roy McCarthy General Manager
Mr Martin O'Conlon Sales Manager

Heritage Bathrooms Ire Ltd
Unit 7 North West Business Park
Ballycoolin
Dublin 15
Phone: 01-8128200 Fax: 01-8128233
SIC: 51542 Employees: 30
Bathroom Supplies
Mr Karl Muldoney Manager

M Beatty & Co Ltd
Church Street
Loughrea
Galway Co. Galway
Phone: 091-841403 Fax: 091-841677
Email: beattys@indigo.ie
SIC: 51542 Employees: 30
Plumbing Supplies
Mr Michael Shield Managing Director

PH Ross Ltd
12-32 Old Cabra Road
Dublin 7
Phone: 01-8385666 Fax: 01-8388319
SIC: 51542 Employees: 28
Heating Merchants
Mr Patrick O'Rourke Managing Director
Mr Tom Redmond Finance Manager
Ms Susanne Peppers Computer Manager

Weldon Plastics
Cashel House
Boreenmanna Road
Cork Co. Cork
Phone: 021-4291442 Fax: 021-4291711
Email: weldon@weldon.ie
SIC: 51542 Employees: 30
Pipes & Pipeline Fittings
Mr Denis O'Callaghan General Manager
Mr Cathal O'Mahony Finance Manager
Mr James O'Driscoll Sales Manager

AC Tape & Packaging
Parkway Business Centre
Balymount Cross
Dublin 24
Phone: 01-4600488 Fax: 01-4600499
Email: sales@njb.ie
SIC: 51610 Employees: 26
Packaging & Machinery Distribution
Mr John Brady Managing Director
Mr Edward Nevin Sales Manager

Acco Rexel Ltd
Clonshaugh Industrial Estate
Clonshaugh
Dublin 17
Phone: 01-8488011 Fax: 01-8488033
Email: info@acco-rexel.ie
Web: http://www.accoeurope.com
SIC: 51610 Employees: 55
Distribution of Office & Computer Equipment
Mr Brendan Cole Managing Director
Mr Henry McGannon Finance Manager
Ms Ruth Connaughton Human Resources Manager
Mr Brian Mooney Sales Manager
Ms Marian Healy Head of Computer Department

Ardmac
Coe's Road Industrial Estate
Dundalk Co. Louth
Phone: 042-9336711 Fax: 042-9331681
Email: info@ardmac.com
Web: http://www.ardmac.iol.com
SIC: 51610 Employees: 400
Cleanroom Construction
Mr Kevin McAnallen Chief Executive
Mr Frank Keenan Financial Controller
Ms Hanna McAnallen Personnel Manager
Mr Conor Murphy Sales & Marketing Manager
Mr Dermot McKenna Manufacturing Manager
Mr Damien Lacey Computer Manager

Astra Business Systems Ltd
Hollybrook House
55 Naas Road
Dublin 12
Phone: 01-4500111 Fax: 01-4508339
Email: sales@astracopy.com
Web: http://www.astracopy.com
SIC: 51610 Employees: 30
Office Equipment Sales
Mr John Cousins Managing Director
Mr John McGrath Sales Director

Wholesale & Distribution

Atkins McKenzies
Carrigrohane Road
Cork Co. Cork
Phone: 021-4542811 Fax: 021-4343140
Email: smsales@atkins.ie
Web: http://www.atkins.ie
SIC: 51610 Employees: 200
Supply Agricultural & Horticultural Machinery
Mr Peter Wolfe Managing Director
Mr Robert McCutcheon Financial Controller

BSS (Ireland) Ltd
White Heather Industrial Estate
301 South Circular Road
Dublin 8
Phone: 01-4165100 Fax: 01-4165165
Email: sales@bssgroup.com
Web: http://www.bssuk.co.uk
SIC: 51610 Employees: 42
Marketing & Distribution -
Heating/Plumbing/Pipeline/Mechanical Service
Equipment
Mr Liam Keating Managing Director
Mr Patrick Burton Financial Controller
Mr Brendan Coghlan Operations Manager
Mr John Brophy Product Director

Crane Care Lifting Services Ltd
Unit 10 Hibernian Industrial Estate
Greenhills Road Tallaght
Dublin 24
Phone: 01-4519866 Fax: 01-4525275
Email: crane@eircom.net
SIC: 51610 Employees: 30
Distribute Cranes
Mr Sean Dunne Managing Director
Ms Louise O'Brien Accounts Manager
Mr Sean McCaffery Sales Director

DSG Ireland
Unit 10B Calmount Park
Ballymount Avenue
Dublin 12
Phone: 01-4097160 Fax: 01-4521643
Email: sales@dsg.ie
Web: http://www.dsg.ie
SIC: 51610 Employees: 200
Office Machinery Distribution
Mr Peter Kelly Managing Director
Ms Cora Mooney Credit Controll Manager
Mr Derek Boyle Sales Director
Mr Jim O'Connor IT Sales Manager

Electrical & Pump Service Ltd
Quartertown Industrial Estate
Mallow Co. Cork
Phone: 022-21064 Fax: 022-31250
Email: sales@epsireland.com
Web: http://www.epsireland.com
SIC: 51610 Employees: 100
Distribution of Pumps
Mr Gerard Buckley Managing Director
Mr Liam Sheehan Finance Manager
Mr James Murphy Personnel Manager
Mr Tom Ruddy Production Manager
Mr Tom Palmer Computer Manager

Electro Automation
3 Ballymount Trading Estate
Walkinstown
Dublin 12
Phone: 01-4501770 Fax: 01-4567864
Email: electroautomation@iol.ie
Web: http://www.electroautomation.ie
SIC: 51610 Employees: 30
Computerised Car Parking Equipment Wholesalers
Mr Patrick Doherty Managing Director
Mr Declan Walsh Finance Manager
Mr Alfie Walsh Sales Manager
Mr Philip Clarke Production Manager

Equipment Company Of Ireland
JFK Drive, Naas Road
Dublin 12
Phone: 01-4500233 Fax: 01-4502041
Email: partsdub@ecijcb.ie
SIC: 51610 Employees: 80
Equipment Wholesalers
Mr Donal O'Sullivan Managing Director
Mr Tony Nicholson Finance Manager
Ms Mary O'Sullivan Sales Manager
Mr Pat Ryan Services Director

Fagan Office Supplies Ltd
16 Pearse Street
Mullingar Co. Westmeath
Phone: 044-40736 Fax: 044-43367
Email: faganofficesupplies@eircom.net
SIC: 51610 Employees: 50
Office Equipment Distribution
Mr John Fagan Managing Director
Ms Veronica Flanagan Accounts Manager
Mr Patrick Fagan Sales & Marketing Manager

Farmhand Ltd
Navan Road
Castleknock
Dublin 15
Phone: 01-8213455 Fax: 01-8213064
Email: info@farmhand.ie
Web: http://www.farmhand.ie
SIC: 51610 Employees: 30
Farm Machinery Distribution
Mr John Scrivener Managing Director
Ms Maureen Hamill Head of Accounts
Mr John Brady Director

FG Wilson Engineering Ltd
Unit 3c Sunbury Industrial Estate
Ballymount, Walkinstown
Dublin 12
Phone: 01-4508322 Fax: 01-4508836
Email: info@fgwilson.ie
Web: http://www.fgwilson.ie
SIC: 51610 Employees: 2000
Diesel Generators
Mr John Lloyd Manager

Genfitt Mayo Ltd
Kiltimagh
Claremorris Co. Mayo
Phone: 094-81377 Fax: 094-81615
Email: info@genfitt.ie
Web: http://www.genfitt.ie
SIC: 51610 Employees: 50
Hardware & Machinery Spares Wholesaler
Mr Larry McEllin Managing Director
Mr Pat Conlon Personnel Manager
Mr Noel Hyland Sales Manager
Mr Mark McEllin General Manager

Harold Engineering Ltd
214-220 Harolds Cross Road
Dublin 6w
Phone: 01-4971039 Fax: 01-4978091
Email: sales@haroldeng.ie
Web: http://www.haroldeng.ie
SIC: 51610 Employees: 60
Industrial & Garage Equipment
Mr Derek Whelan Chief Executive
Mr Aidan Kilgannon Sales Director

Henley Forklift Ireland Ltd
Henley Industrial Park
Killeen Road
Dublin 10
Phone: 01-6266438 Fax: 01-6265406
Email: dublin@henley.ie
Web: http://www.henley.ie
SIC: 51610 Employees: 598
Forklift Truck Distribution
Mr Patrick O'Connor Managing Director
Mr Paul Maxwell Financial Controller
Mr Des Sherry Sales & Marketing Manager
Mr Seamus Hurson Operation Director
Mr Mark Bagnall Computer Manager

Hevac Ltd
Murfield Drive, Naas Road
Dublin 12
Phone: 01-8301211 Fax: 01-8301990
Email: info@hevac.ie
Web: http://www.hevac.ie
SIC: 51610 Employees: 70
Domestic Heating Equipment Distributors
Mr John English Managing Director
Mr Paul Dunne Finance Manager
Mr Tom Scott Sales & Marketing Director
Ms Christina Harden Computer Manager

Hilti Fastening Systems Ltd
132 Dublin Industrial Estate
Glasnevin
Dublin 11
Phone: 01-8303422 Fax: 01-8303569
Web: http://www.hilti.com
SIC: 51610 Employees: 59
Construction Fixing & Fastenings Supplier
Mr Urs Hanselma General Manager
Mr Alfie McCrann Head of Credit Control
Mr Dominic McGrady Sales & Marketing Manager

Horizon Open Systems
Block U East Point Business Park
Dublin 3
Phone: 01-8055600 Fax: 01-8055601
Email: marketing@hos.horizon.ie
Web: http://www.hos.horizon.ie
SIC: 51610 Employees: 40
Distributors for Sun Micro Systems in Ireland
Mr Gary Coburn Manager
Mr Roland Noonan Sales Manager

Irish Farm & Garden Machinery Ltd
Hazelbrook
Malahide Co. Dublin
Phone: 01-8463922 Fax: 01-8461321
Email: info@farmandgardenltd.co.uk
Web: http://www.farmandgardenltd.co.uk
SIC: 51610 Employees: 26
Farm & Garden Machinery Distribution
Mr Paul Butterly Managing Director
Mr Jim Carton Accountant

JJ McQuillan Son & Company Ltd
34-36 Capel Street
Dublin 1
Phone: 01-8733944 Fax: 01-8733287
Email: sales@mcquillantools.ie
SIC: 51610 Employees: 45
Machinery/Tools Sales/Wholesalers
Mr Jay McQuillan Managing Director
Mr Niall Kenny Credit Controller

Kevin Broderick Ltd
1 Glenageary Avenue
Dun Laoghaire Co. Dublin
Phone: 01-2858011 Fax: 01-2855350
Email: info@broderick.ie
Web: http://www.broderick.ie
SIC: 51610 Employees: 25
Grass Cutting Machinery Distributors
Mr Noel Broderick Managing Director
Mr David Smyth Financial Controller
Mr Robert Foley Sales Director

Lister Machine Tools
PO Box 838
Bluebell Industrial Estate
Dublin 12
Phone: 01-4508866 Fax: 01-4509836
Email: sales@listermt.ie
SIC: 51610 Employees: 50
Machine Tool Distributors
Mr William Crawford Managing Director
Mr John Hynes Financial Controller
Mr Dominic Gall Personnel Manager
Mr Liam Sweeney Sales Director
Mr Andrew Hynes Systems Administrator

Wholesale & Distribution

Maxtor Ireland
Bray Business Park
Southern Cross Road
Bray Co. Wicklow
Phone: 01-2041100 Fax: 01-2864577
Web: http://www.maxtor.com
SIC: 51610 Employees: 100
Hard Drive Disc Distribution & Services
Ms Ita Brennan Managing Director
Ms Fiona Flynn Personnel Manager
Mr David Steadman Computer Manager

Modern Tool (Ireland) Ltd
John F Kennedy Avenue
Naas Road
Dublin 12
Phone: 01-4509488 Fax: 01-4509750
Email: modtool@iol.ie
SIC: 51610 Employees: 25
Machinery Distributors
Mr Liam Clifford Managing Director
Ms Yvonne O'Reilly Accounts Manager

Pitney Bowes (Ireland) Ltd
14a Parkmore Industrial Estate
Long Mile Road
Dublin 12
Phone: 01-4502252 Fax: 01-4505493
Email: foxja@pb.com
SIC: 51610 Employees: 65
Office Machinery Distribution
Mr Kevin Short Managing Director
Mr Derek Whelan Service Director
Ms Jane Kelly-Fox Marketing Manager

Quiptech Ltd
Riverside Commercial Estate, Tuam Road
Galway
Phone: 091-757800 Fax: 091-751299
Email: sales@equiptech.ie
Web: http://www.quiptech.ie
SIC: 51610 Employees: 25
Electronic Distribution
Mr Donal Murnane Managing Director
Mr John Mitchell Financial Controller
Mr Pat Gayer Sales Manager

RMI Ltd
Deansgrange Industrial Estate
Deansgrange
Blackrock Co. Dublin
Phone: 01-2892445 Fax: 01-2953354
Email: rmiltd@eircom.net
SIC: 51610 Employees: 30
Air Conditioning Suppliers
Mr Eamon Malloy Managing Director

Schindler Ltd
1 Ballymount Drive
Walkinstown
Dublin 12
Phone: 01-4500136 Fax: 01-4508526
SIC: 51610 Employees: 40
Lifting Equipment Distribution
Mr Colin Jeromson Managing Director
Mr Paddy O'Donohue Finance Manager
Mr Paul O'Toole Marketing Manager
Mr Owen Sexton Operations Manager
Mr Darren Doyle DP Manager

Scott & O'Shea
6 Western Parkway Business Centre,
Dublin 12
Phone: 01-4568901 Fax: 01-4568903
SIC: 51610 Employees: 30
Close Circuit Television Distribution
Mr Roger O'Shea Managing Director

Sureweld International Ltd
Fonthill
Lucan Co. Dublin
Phone: 01-6266242 Fax: 01-6262533
Email: info@sureweld.net
SIC: 51610 Employees: 60
Welding Machinery Suppliers
Mr Pat Hurney Managing Director
Mr Joe Lynch Credit Controller
Mr Ken Dunne Sales Manager

System Video Ltd
System House
Palmerstown Business Park
Dublin 20
Phone: 01-6232666 Fax: 01-6232030
Email: info@sysystemvideo.ie
Web: http://www.systemvideo.ie
SIC: 51610 Employees: 35
Audio Visual Suppliers & Installers
Mr Tom Carroll Managing Director
Mr David Carroll Sales Manager

Unidare Plc
Unit 6 Richview Office Park
Clonskeagh
Dublin 14
Phone: 01-2837111 Fax: 01-2603177
Email: email@unidare.ie
Web: http://www.unidare.ie
SIC: 51610 Employees: 680
Distribution of Engineered Products
Mr Paul Duggan Chief Executive Officer
Mr Kevin Gallen Finance Manager
Ms Margaret Cowley Personnel Manager
Ms Vicky Casey Management Accountant

Auto Diesel Electric Ltd
Dartmouth House
Kylemore Road
Dublin 10
Phone: 01-6232828 Fax: 01-6232588
Email: ade@indigo.ie
Web: http://www.ade.ie
SIC: 51611 Employees: 30
Wholesale Motor Parts
Mr Timothy Boyne Managing Director
Mr Alan Lyons Financial Controller
Mr Michael Cluskey Sales Manager
Mr Brendan O'Kane Computer Manager

Bridgestone/Firestone (Ireland) Ltd
Unit 4
Leopardstown Office Park
Dublin 18
Phone: 01-2952844 Fax: 01-2952858
Email: info@bfeurope.com
SIC: 51611 Employees: 42
Tyre Distribution
Mr Brian Condon Managing Director
Mr Michael Ryan Accounts Manager
Mr Frank White Sales Manager

D & S Roe Ltd
Unit D15 Ballymount Cross Ind Estate
Dublin 24
Phone: 01-4564410 Fax: 01-4564416
Email: dsroeltd@indigo.ie
SIC: 51611 Employees: 25
Wholesale Motor Factors
Mr Sean Roe Managing Director
Ms Anne Scott Accounts Manager
Mr Frank O'Brien Sales Manager

Dickson Bearings & Transmissions Ltd
Unit 7 Northern Cross Business Park
North Road, Finglas
Dublin 11
Phone: 01-8443000 Fax: 01-8443050
Email: sales@dicksonbearings.ie
Web: http://www.dicksonbearings.ie
SIC: 51611 Employees: 25
Industrial Engineering & Agricultural Bearing & Transmission Distributors
Mr Derek Dickson Managing Director
Mr John Dickson Director

Exide Batteries (Ireland) Ltd
Kore Development Park, JFK Drive
Blubell
Dublin 12
Phone: 01-4506533 Fax: 01-4602654
Email: exide@eircom.net
SIC: 51611 Employees: 25
Battery Wholesalers
Ms Vivienne Hughes Managing Director
Mr Philip Cullen Sales Manager

Fiat Auto Ireland Ltd
Fiat House, Turnpike Road
Naas Road
Dublin 22
Phone: 01-4034433 Fax: 01-4034455
Email: fiatauto@iol.ie
Web: http://www.fiat.ie
SIC: 51611 Employees: 40
Fiat Distribution
Dr Nicola Greco Chief Executive Officer
Mr Dominic Holmes Financial Controller
Mr Liam Sherlock After Sales Manager
Mr Stephen Walsh DP Manager

Glencullen Group
Kylemore Road
Ballyfermot
Dublin 10
Phone: 01-6260222 Fax: 01-6260241
Email: info@renault.ie
Web: http://www.renault.ie
SIC: 51611 Employees: 65
Vehicle Distribution
Mr Bill Cullen Chief Executive
Mr Mark Short IT Director

Gowan Group
1 Herbert Avenue, Merrion Road
Dublin 4
Phone: 01-2601677 Fax: 01-2601672
Email: info@gowangroup.ie
Web: http://www.gowanmerrion.com
SIC: 51611 Employees: 250
Motor Vehicle Distribution
Mr Michael Dwan Managing Director
Ms Tracey Davis Finance Manager
Mr Michael Aherne Sales Manager
Mr Paul Hamill Head of IT

Harris Assemblers Group
Naas Road
Dublin 12
Phone: 01-4602282 Fax: 01-4602284
Email: harrisgroup@eircom.net
SIC: 51611 Employees: 150
Truck Assemblers
Mr Robert Harris Chief Executive

Henry Ford & Son Limited
Elm Court
Boreenmanna Road
Cork Co. Cork
Phone: 021-4329277 Fax: 021-4329216
Email: postmaster@ford.ie
Web: http://www.ford.ie
SIC: 51611 Employees: 1300
Ford Distribution
Mr Eddie Murphy Managing Director
Mr George Kenny Finance Manager
Mr Terry O'Regan Human Resources Director
Mr David O'Driscoll Sales Manager
Mr Michael Corkery IT Manager

Irish Dunlop Company Ltd
Dunlop House Hibernian Indust Estate
Greenhills Road
Dublin 24
Phone: 01-4597070 Fax: 01-4597075
Email: sales@dunlop.ie
SIC: 51611 Employees: 55
Importation & Distribution of Parts/Garage Equipment
Mr Thomas Martin Managing Director
Mr Richard Warbrick Commercial Manager

Wholesale & Distribution

Motor Distributors Ltd
Naas Road
Dublin 12
Phone: 01-4503333 Fax: 01-4094419
SIC: 51611 Employees: 100
Car Distributors
Mr Bob O'Callaghan Chief Executive
Mr David O'Higgins Financial Director
Mr Jim Farrell Personnel Manager
Mr Tom O'Connor Sales/Marketing Director
Ms Marie Mackin Computer Manager

Motor Import Ltd
BMW House, John F Kennedy Drive
Naas Road
Dublin 12
Phone: 01-2405666 Fax: 01-4508509
Web: http://www.bmw.ie
SIC: 51611 Employees: 100
Import Vehicles
Mr Eugene O'Reilly Chief Executive
Mr Larry Heffernan Financial Director
Mr Dene McQuaid Marketing Manager
Mr Pat Allen Technical Director

National Vehicle Distribution
Churchtown Kilrane
Rosslare Harbour
Wexford Co. Wexford
Phone: 053-33313 Fax: 053-33408
Email: rosslare@nvd.ie
Web: http://www.nvd.ie
SIC: 51611 Employees: 100
Motors Vehicles Deliveries
Mr Andrew Boland Managing Director
Mr Michael Doyle Finance Manager
Mr Joe Batts General Manager

Nissan Ireland
Nissan House
Naas Road
Dublin 12
Phone: 01-4091100 Fax: 01-4091101
Email: sales@nissan.ie
Web: http://www.nissan.ie
SIC: 51611 Employees: 350
Motor Vehicle Distribution
Mr Gerard O'Toole Chairman
Mr Tony McLoughlin Financial Controller
Mr Padraig Boland Sales Director
Mr Pat Pearse IT Manager

O'Flaherty Holdings
33 Leeson Park
Dublin 6
Phone: 01-6605011 Fax: 01-6605231
SIC: 51611 Employees: 956
Motor Vehicle Distributors
Mr Tom O'Dowd Managing Director
Mr Jim Farrell Group Personnel Manager
Mr Bill Duffy Sales Manager
Ms Marie Macken IT Manager

OHM Group
Naas Road
Clondalkin
Dublin 22
Phone: 01-4591300 Fax: 01-4591864
Email: daf@ohm.ie
SIC: 51611 Employees: 110
Importation & Distribution of Motor Vehicles
Mr Declan McCourt Chief Executive
Mr Donal Forbes Financial Controller
Mr Thomas Smith Personnel Director
Mr Anthony Neville Marketing Manager
Mr Emmet Holland Computer Manager

PR Reilly Ltd
Karkraft House
Kilbarrack Industrial Estate
Dublin 5
Phone: 01-8320001 Fax: 01-8322993
Email: prreilly@iol.ie
SIC: 51611 Employees: 135
Sell & Distribute Motor Parts
Mr Norbert Reilly Chief Executive
Mr Barry Dean Financial Controller
Mr Frank Burn Sales Director
Ms Gina Sparks Data Processing Manager

Renault Distributors
Glencullen House
Kylemore Road
Dublin 10
Phone: 01-6055500 Fax: 01-6260241
Web: http://www.renault.ie
SIC: 51611 Employees: 70
Renault Vehicle Distributor
Mr Bill Cullen Chief Executive
Mr John O'Donnell Corporate Sales Director

Smith's Garage
North Road
Drogheda Co. Louth
Phone: 041-9831106 Fax: 041-9836332
SIC: 51611 Employees: 40
Car Sales & Repairs
Mr Micky Smith Managing Director

Swifco Ltd
Cork Road
Newcastlewest
Limerick Co. Limerick
Phone: 069-62106 Fax: 069-62522
SIC: 51611 Employees: 45
Motor Factors Wholesale
Mr Pat Harnett Director

Toyota Ireland
Toyota House
Killeen Road
Dublin 12
Phone: 01-4507088 Fax: 01-4507590
Email: marketing@toyota.ie
Web: http://www.toyota.ie
SIC: 51611 Employees: 200
Motor Vehicles Distributors
Mr David Shannon Managing Director
Mr Tom Armstrong Finance Manager
Mr Jim Cusack Personnel Manager
Mr Declan O'Halloran Sales & Marketing Director
Mr John Keane IT Manager

Transport Component Distributor Ltd
Unit 10 Parkmore Industrial Estate
Longmile Road
Dublin 12
Phone: 01-4504090 Fax: 01-4507176
Email: sales@transcomp.iol.ie
SIC: 51611 Employees: 50
Distribution of Truck Parts
Mr Harry Nash Managing Director
Mr David Breen Financial Controller
Mr Mark Keenan Sales & Marketing Manager

Broderick Brothers Ltd
JFK Industrial Estate
JFK Road
Dublin 12
Phone: 01-4509083 Fax: 01-4509570
Email: broderickbros@eircom.net
SIC: 51651 Employees: 45
Catering Equipment
Mr Michael Scanlon Managing Director
Mr Declan Godfrey Financial Director

OS Sheet Metal Ltd
Tramore Road
Cork Co. Cork
Phone: 021-4962077 Fax: 021-4963547
Email: osmetal@indigo.ie
SIC: 51651 Employees: 30
Catering Equipment
Mr Neil O'Shea Director
Mr Dairmuid Kellehar Accountant

Russell Will Ltd
Unit 5 Baldoyle Industrial Estate
Grange Road
Dublin 13
Phone: 01-8392064 Fax: 01-8322335
Email: russell.will@oreley.ie
SIC: 51651 Employees: 40
Disposable Catering Products
Mr David Will Managing Director
Ms Maria Conway Accounts Manager
Ms Mary Ryan Administration Manager
Ms Elizabeth Will Sales Manager
Ms Yvonne Murphy Computer Manager

Serviquip
U67 Cherry Orchard Industrial Estate
Cherry Orchard Industrial Estate
Dublin 10
Phone: 01-6231699 Fax: 01-6231702
Email: info@serviquip.ie
Web: http://www.serviquip.ie
SIC: 51651 Employees: 40
Catering Equipment Suppliers
Mr John Dunne Managing Director
Mr Jim Malone Finance Manager
Mr John Bow Sales & Marketing Manager

Thomas McLaughlin Ltd
138a Slaney Close, Dublin Ind Estate
Glasnevin
Dublin 11
Phone: 01-8306555 Fax: 01-8306556
Email: info@tmclaughlin.com
Web: http://www.tmclaughlin.com
SIC: 51651 Employees: 120
Catering Equipment
Mr Alastair McLaughlin Managing Director
Mr Gerry McDermott Personnel Director

Vending Products Ltd
Sandyford Industrial Estate
Foxrock
Dublin 18
Phone: 01-2952616 Fax: 01-2954367
SIC: 51651 Employees: 43
Disposable Catering Products
Mr Tom Coogan Managing Director
Ms Jacqueline Slater Accounts Manager
Ms Olivia Caslin Sales Manager

Deli Products
Greenogue Square
Greenogue Industrial Estate
Dublin 2
Phone: 01-4589432 Fax: 01-4586032
Email: info@deliproducts.ie
Web: http://www.deliproducts.ie
SIC: 51652 Employees: 30
Caterers Supplies
Mr Myles O'Brien Proprietor
Mr Stephen Heffernan Financial Controller
Mr Billy Reilly Sales Manager

Gate Gourmet Ireland
South Apron, Dublin Airport
Dublin 9
Phone: 01-8444093 Fax: 01-8446092
Email: tfg@indigo.ie
SIC: 51652 Employees: 200
In-Flight Catering
Mr Tony Finlayson-Green Managing Director
Mr Niall McInerney Finance Manager
Mr David Barry Personnel Director
Ms Niamh McCara Sales & Marketing Manager

Wholesale & Distribution

George Mogerley Ltd
Unit 10 K C R Industrial Estate
Kimmage
Dublin 12
Phone: 01-4909771 Fax: 01-4904087
Email: mogerley@eircom.net
SIC: 51652 Employees: 35
Catering Supplies
Mr David Mogerley Managing Director

Hugh Jordan & Company Ltd
Grand Canal Quay
Dublin 2
Phone: 01-6779498 Fax: 01-6715803
Email: info@hughjordan.com
Web: http://www.hughjordan.com
SIC: 51652 Employees: 50
Catering Equipment
Mr Fergus Jordan Managing Director
Ms Debbie Plunkett Human Resources Manager
Ms Caroline Bradley Computer Manager

Irish Merchants Group
Malahide Road Industrial Park
Newtown
Dublin 17
Phone: 01-8474333 Fax: 01-8474668
Email: irish-mer@indigo.ie
SIC: 51652 Employees: 100
Catering Equipment Suppliers
Mr Brendan Cooney Managing Director
Mr Brian Carolan Finance Manager
Mr Maurice Flanagan Operations Director
Mr Kevin Carey IT Officer

McCambridge Foods Ltd
Arkle Road
Sandyford Industrial Estate
Dublin 18
Phone: 01-2958867 Fax: 01-2958865
Email: info@mccambridgefoods.ie
SIC: 51652 Employees: 30
Catering Supplies
Mr Michael McCambridge Managing Director
Mr Brendan McCarthy Company Accountant
Mr Richard Terraton Marketing Executive
Mr John Daly Production Manager

ACD (Advanced Computer Distribution)
Unit 10-11 Deansgrange Ind Estate
Deansgrange
Blackrock Co. Dublin
Phone: 01-2898440 Fax: 01-2898448
Web: http://www.acd.ie
SIC: 51700 Employees: 25
Distribute Computers
Mr Michael Doyle Managing Director
Mr Declan Clancy Accounts Manager
Mr John Doherty General Manager
Ms Caroline Coyle Marketing Executive

Akzo Nobel
Malahide Road
Coolock
Dublin 17
Phone: 01-8474222 Fax: 01-8478831
Email: info@akzonobel.ie
SIC: 51700 Employees: 200
Distribution of Paint, Varnish & Lacquer
Mr PJ Gunne Managing Director
Mr Aidan Dunne Financial Controller
Ms Ita Mullen Personnel Manager
Mr Alan Duggan Retail Sales Manager
Mr Kevin Whelan Marketing Director
Mr Jeff Gallagher IT Officer

Alpha Marketing (Irl) Ltd
Unit D1 Ballymount Industrial Estate
Walkinstown
Dublin 12
Phone: 01-4568288 Fax: 01-4503152
Email: 3sixtydublin@eircom.net
Web: http://www.alphaofficefurniture.com
SIC: 51700 Employees: 135
Distribution of Office Furniture & Equipment
Mr Robin Black Managing Director
Mr Ian Bell Financial Controller
Mr John Kelly Sales Manager

Architectural & Metal Systems Ltd
Lehenaghmore, Togher
Cork Co. Cork
Phone: 021-4961111 Fax: 021-4961644
Web: http://www.ams.ie
SIC: 51700 Employees: 60
Wholesale PVC & Aluminium
Mr Chris Martin Managing Director
Ms Mary Loughran Financial Controller
Mr Pat O'Hara Sales & Marketing Director
Mr Pat Willis IT Manager

BJ Fitzpatrick Co Ltd
Grafton House, Ballymoss Road
Sandyford Industrial Estate
Dublin 18
Phone: 01-2958400 Fax: 01-2958498
SIC: 51700 Employees: 30
Wholesaler/ImporterJewellery Gift Trade
Mr John Fitzpatrick Managing Director
Ms Mary Kitson Finance Manager
Mr Martin Kinirons Sales Manager

C & C Wholesale Ltd
Kilcarbary Park Nangor Road
Clondalkin
Dublin 3
Phone: 01-8336962 Fax: 01-6305049
Email: info@cantrellandcochrane.com
Web: http://www.cantrellandcochrane.com
SIC: 51700 Employees: 130
Drinks Distributor
Mr Desmond Drumm Managing Director
Mr Pat Miley Financial Controller
Mr Paddy Doody Sales Director

Cabletron Systems Ltd
Shannon Industrial Estate
Shannon Co. Clare
Phone: 061-472022 Fax: 061-471259
Email: info@cabletron.com
Web: http://www.cabletron.com
SIC: 51700 Employees: 160
Distribution of Computer Products
Mr Roger Grant Vice President
Mr Terry McSweeney Finance Manager
Ms Breda Kissane Human Resources Manager
Mr Kevin Murphy Sales & Marketing Manager
Mr Tony Woods IT Manager

Calcul International Ltd
Bay F20 Shannon Industrial Estate
Shannon Co. Clare
Phone: 061-472722 Fax: 061-472816
Email: solatrex@iol.ie
Web: http://www.solatrex.com
SIC: 51700 Employees: 27
Distribution and Service Watches Clocks
Mr Tom Flynn Managing Director
Ms Brid Ginnuane Financial Controller
Ms Mary Colbert Sales Manager

Camida
Terrace House
New Quay
Clonmel Co. Tipperary
Phone: 052-25455 Fax: 052-25466
Email: info@camida.ie
Web: http://www.camida.ie
SIC: 51700 Employees: 35
Chemical Distributors
Mr David Anchell Managing Director
Ms Mary Britton Accounts Manager
Ms Orla Heenan Sales Manager
Ms Breda O'Dwyer Computer Manager

Careline Moving & Storage
Whitehall
Parteen
Limerick Co. Limerick
Phone: 061-326070 Fax: 061-326030
Email: inquiries@careline.ie
Web: http://www.careline.ie
SIC: 51700 Employees: 25
Furniture Removal, Storage & Distribution
Mr Mark Carey Managing Director
Ms Sharon Dore Financial Controller
Ms Maureen Gleeson Sales Manager
Mr Diarmuid Cullinan Computer Manager

Carlton Cards Ltd
Unit 4 Carriglea Industrial Estate
Naas Road
Dublin 12
Phone: 01-4566424 Fax: 01-4503773
Email: info@carltoncards.ie
SIC: 51700 Employees: 28
Greeting Card Distributor
Mr John Egan General Manager
Mr Tom Feeney Sales & Marketing Manager

Carroll Educational Supplies
U5 Western Industrial Estate
Dublin 12
Phone: 01-4567279 Fax: 01-4569998
Email: ces@indigo.ie
Web: http://www.carrolled.com
SIC: 51700 Employees: 24
Educational Supplies
Mr Gerry Carroll Managing Director
Ms Fionnuala Campion Sales Manager

Codico Distributors Ltd
Bracetown Business Park
Clonee
Navan Co. Meath
Phone: 01-8014011 Fax: 01-8014091
SIC: 51700 Employees: 100
Distribution
Mr Cliff Bond Managing Director

Coghlans Bakery Products Ltd
U4 Blackhorse House
Industrial Estate
Dublin 7
Phone: 01-8683066 Fax: 01-8683018
SIC: 51700 Employees: 25
Bakers & Confectioners - Wholesale
Mr Brendan Coghlan Manager

Corcoran Chemicals Ltd
Kingsbridge House
17/22 Parkgate Street
Dublin 8
Phone: 01-6778163 Fax: 01-6793521
Email: info@corcoranchemicals.com
Web: http://www.corcoranchemicals.com
SIC: 51700 Employees: 26
Chemical Distribution
Mr Ken Byrne Director
Mr John Reade Accounts Manager
Ms Nora Tisdall General Manager
Mr Andrew Byrne Director
Mr PV McGuire Director

Corporate Express Ireland
Woodford Business Park
Santry
Dublin 9
Phone: 01-6798899 Fax: 01-8623022
Web: http://www.cexp.ie
SIC: 51700 Employees: 95
Office Equipment
Mr John Fulham Managing Director
Mr Cal Keenan Financial Controller
Ms Jane Doolin Personnel Manager
Ms Maria McGinley Sales Manager
Ms Catherine Moran Computer Manager

Cuisine de France Ltd
Belgard Square
Tallaght
Dublin 24
Phone: 01-4057200 Fax: 01-4057290
Email: info@cuisinedefrance.ie
Web: http://www.cuisinedefrance.ie
SIC: 51700 Employees: 200
Food Products/Importers & Distribution
Mr Hugo Kane Managing Director
Mr Patrick McEniff Financial Controller
Mr PJ Gerard Personnel Manager
Mr Mark Gavin Sales Director
Mr Ronan McNamee Chairman

D O'Sullivan Print Supplies Ltd
Knockmitten Lane
Western Industrial Estate
Dublin 12
Phone: 01-4565788 Fax: 01-4507072
Email: kos@dos.iol.ie
Web: http://www.dos.iol.ie
SIC: 51700 Employees: 65
Print Supplies
Mr Gerard O'Sullivan Managing Director
Mr David Hughes Financial Controller
Mr Kieran O'Sullivan Head of Marketing
Mr John Donoghue Production Manager
Mr Matthew Kavanagh Computer Manager

Danfay Ltd
61D Sallynoggin Road
Dun Laoghaire Co. Dublin
Phone: 01-2859177 Fax: 01-2858810
Email: info@danfay.ie
SIC: 51700 Employees: 25
Importers Of Various Goods
Mr Terry Brooks Managing Director
Mr Tom Dunphy Financial Controller
Mr Colin Martin Sales Manager

Designer Homecentre Ltd
Mill Road, Car Park
Ennis Co. Clare
Phone: 065-6828400 Fax: 065-6840922
SIC: 51700 Employees: 40
Tiles Timber Fireplaces & Granite Worktops
Mr David O'Connor Managing Director
Mr Jack Kyan Financial Controller
Ms Bronagh Keane Human Resources Director
Mr Michael Enright Sales Manager

Dockrell Glass Distribution Ltd
Ballymount Cross
Tallaght
Dublin 24
Phone: 01-4500155 Fax: 01-4600100
Email: info@dockrellglass.ie
Web: http://www.dockrellglass.ie
SIC: 51700 Employees: 130
Glass Reprocessing/Distribution
Mr Martin Bates Managing Director
Ms Jennifer Halpin Financial Controller
Mr Liam Devlin Sales Manager
Mr Mike Kelly Production Director

Drammock Ltd
Unit 13 Airways Industrial Estate
Santry
Dublin 17
Phone: 01-8428444 Fax: 01-8428064
Email: drammock@eircom.net
Web: http://www.comfies.ie
SIC: 51700 Employees: 95
Disposable Baby Products
Mr Tommy Daly Managing Director
Mr Tim Murphy Finance Director
Mr John Dodd Personnel Manager
Mr Garrett Brady Sales Manager
Mr Michael MacCabe Engineering Manager
Ms Michelle Maxwell Computer Manager

EA Delany Ltd
Unit 139 Slaney Close
Glasnevin Industrial Estate
Dublin 11
Phone: 01-8303022 Fax: 01-8303314
SIC: 51700 Employees: 24
Wholesale Textiles Distributors
Mr Edmund Delaney Managing Director
Mr Brian Morton Financial Controller
Mr Padraig Flanery Sales Manager

Emerald Group
Temple House
Templeshannon
Enniscorthy Co. Wexford
Phone: 054-38333 Fax: 054-38222
Email: emergrp@indigo.ie
Web: http://www.emergrp.ie
SIC: 51700 Employees: 30
Distribution of Christmas Trees
Mr Noel Moran Managing Director
Ms Denise O'Sullivan Accountant
Mr David Barrett Personnel Director
Mr Gavin Fenelon Production Manager

Erin Foods Ltd
Slievenamon Road
Thurles Co. Tipperary
Phone: 0504-21588 Fax: 0504-21810
SIC: 51700 Employees: 150
Food Processing/Distribution
Mr Michael Curtin Chief Executive
Mr Brian Lyons Financial Controller
Mr Michael O'Sullivan Personnel Officer
Mr James Cass Marketing Manager
Mr Eileen Murphy Production Manager
Ms Nora Fitzpatrick Computer Services Manager

Exel
Furry Park Industrial Estate
Santry
Dublin 9
Phone: 01-8622200 Fax: 01-8622980
SIC: 51700 Employees: 700
Logistics/Freight Forwarding
Mr Michael O'Donoghue Managing Director
Mr Michael Sutton Finance Manager
Mr Terry Allen Sales Manager

FA Wyatt & Co Ltd
Unit 5 Airways Industrial Estate
Cloghran
Dublin 17
Phone: 01-8423522 Fax: 01-8423148
SIC: 51700 Employees: 30
Wholesale/Distribution
Mr Shane O'Callaghan Managing Director
Mr Tim Murphy Financial Director
Mr Gordon Mahon Commercial Director

Flannery's Nurseries Ltd
Staplestown
Donadea
Naas Co. Kildare
Phone: 045-869131 Fax: 045-869218
Email: flannurs@iol.ie
SIC: 51700 Employees: 25
Nursery Wholesale
Mr Sean Flannery Managing Director
Ms Martina Wyse Company Accountant
Mr Joe Judge Sales Manager
Ms Mary Farrell Production Manager

Fork Lift Centre
Ballymount Road
Dublin 12
Phone: 01-4508600 Fax: 01-4508919
Email: enquires@forklift.centre.ie
SIC: 51700 Employees: 30
Sales & Services of Fork Lifts
Ms Pat Crofield Managing Director
Mr Paul Perry Sales Manager

Fuji Photo Film (Ireland) Ltd
78 Lagan Road
Dublin Industrial Estate
Dublin 11
Phone: 01-8820200 Fax: 01-8309351
Email: sales@fugifilm.ie
Web: http://www.fugifilm.ie
SIC: 51700 Employees: 31
Photographic Equipment & Supplies- Wholesale
Mr Gerry O'Brien Managing Director
Mr John Cassidy Financial Controller
Mr Richard Brown Sales Manager
Mr Brian O'Kane Technical Services Manager

Furlong Carpets (Wholesale) Ltd
UA Ballymount Cross Industrial Est
Dublin 24
Phone: 01-4506011 Fax: 01-4505520
SIC: 51700 Employees: 50
Floor Covering Distributors
Mr Muir O'Loghlen Managing Director
Ms Edel O'Brien Financial Controller
Mr Eamon Murray Sales Manager
Ms Tina Elliott Computer Manager

Gen-Weld Safety Equipment Ltd
Ballysimon Road
Limerick Co. Limerick
Phone: 061-311520 Fax: 061-316500
Email: sales@gws.iol.ie
SIC: 51700 Employees: 30
Distribute Health & Safety Equipment
Mr Bert Gleeson Managing Director
Mr Jim Murphy Finance Manager
Mr Pat O'Brien Sales Manager

Gill & Macmillan Ltd
Hume Avenue
Park West
Dublin 12
Phone: 01-5009500 Fax: 01-5009599
Email: sales@gillmacmillan.ie
Web: http://www.gillmacmillan.ie
SIC: 51700 Employees: 65
Publishers & Distributors
Mr Michael Gill Managing Director
Mr Dermot O'Dwyer Finance Director
Ms Gemma Connolly Personnel Manager
Mr Peter Thew Sales & Marketing Director
Ms Mairead O'Keele Production Director
Mr Vincent Hunt IT Manager

Grogan Brothers Ltd
Unit 5 Phoenix Industrial Estate
Ashtown
Dublin 15
Phone: 01-8387233 Fax: 01-8387232
Email: giltedge@indigo.ie
Web: http://www.giltedge.ie
SIC: 51700 Employees: 35
Menswear Wholesale
Mr Brian Grogan Managing Director
Mr Liam Reynolds Finance Manager
Mr Michael Grogan Personnel Manager
Mr Eamon Grogan Sales Manager

Hafele Ireland Ltd
Kilcoole Industrial Estate
Kilcoole
Bray Co. Wicklow
Phone: 01-2873488 Fax: 01-2873563
Email: info@hafele.ie
SIC: 51700 Employees: 35
Furniture Importers & Distributors
Mr Brendan Smith Managing Director
Ms Marie Barry Finance Manager
Mr John Murray Archeologists Hardware Manager
Mr Paul Butler Warehouse Manager
Mr Mick Smith General Manager

J Langdons Ltd
Burton Hall Road
Sandyford Industrial Park
Dublin 18
Phone: 01-2955533 Fax: 01-2957715
Email: info@jlangdon.ie
Web: http://www.jlangdon.ie
SIC: 51700 Employees: 59
Distribution Sports Gear
Mr Alan McFarlane Group Chief Executive
Mr David McFarlane Finance Manager
Ms Nicola Donegan Personnel Manager
Mr Dominic Mann Sales Director
Mr Anton Phelan Production Manager

JA Boland & Sons Ltd
Ferrybank
Wexford Co. Wexford
Phone: 053-23711 Fax: 053-24449
Email: info@bolandcars.ie
Web: http://www.bolandcars.ie
SIC: 51700 Employees: 45
Commercial Machinery Distribution
Mr Gerard Boland Managing Director

JMC Van Trans
Unit D Merrywell Industrial Estate
Ballymount
Dublin 12
Phone: 01-4602555 Fax: 01-4564860
Email: info@jmcvantrans.ie
Web: http://www.jmcvantrans.ie
SIC: 51700 Employees: 80
Warehousing & Distribution
Mr Gareth Murphy Managing Director
Ms Janet McCluskey Finance Manager
Mr Martin Fahey Sales Manager
Mr John McCluskey Computer Manager

KCR Stores
140 Terenure Road
Dublin 6w
Phone: 01-4905645 Fax: 01-4929971
SIC: 51700 Employees: 25
Newsagents Wholesale
Mr Paul Lynch Manager

Kennedy Group
Paddingstown
Clonee
Navan Co. Meath
Phone: 01-8252825 Fax: 01-8255608
Email: sales@kennedy-group.ie
SIC: 51700 Employees: 70
Abrasive Distributor
Mr Pat Kennedy Managing Director
Mr John Kennedy Financial Controller
Ms Breda Cribben-Doran Sales Manager
Mr Gerard Boyle IT Manager

Lennox Laboratory Supplies
JFK Drive
Naas Road
Dublin 12
Phone: 01-4552201 Fax: 01-4507906
Email: sales@lennoxlabs.com
Web: http://www.lennoxlabs.com
SIC: 51700 Employees: 55
Laboratory Supplies
Mr Eric McMorris Managing Director
Mr Tony Carton Financial Controller
Mr Greg Kearns Sales & Marketing Director

Lever Faberge
5th Floor, Plaza House, The Square
Tallaght
Dublin 24
Phone: 01-4043300 Fax: 01-4527137
Web: http://www.leverfaberge.ie
SIC: 51700 Employees: 140
Distribute Household Cleaners
Mr Shane Malone Managing Director
Mr Dermot Quigley Finance Manager
Mr Tom O'Reilly Sales & Marketing Director
Mr Martin Smyth Computer Manager

Lumley's Bakery
U21 Goldenbridge Industrial Estate
Inchicore
Dublin 8
Phone: 01-4733553 Fax: 01-4733556
SIC: 51700 Employees: 30
Bakers & Confectioners - Wholesale
Mr Dennis Lumley Manager
Ms Julie Headen Sales Manager

Martin Jennings Ltd
Neale Road
Ballindine
Claremorris Co. Mayo
Phone: 092-41611 Fax: 092-41746
Email: jenningssales@eircom.net
SIC: 51700 Employees: 80
Wholesalers
Mr Martin Jennings Managing Director

McHugh & Kramp
89 Broomhill Road
Tallaght Industrial Estate
Dublin 24
Phone: 01-4519222 Fax: 01-4519467
Email: info@mchugh-kramp.ie
Web: http://www.kol.ie/mchkramp
SIC: 51700 Employees: 45
Wholesalers Distributor
Mr Seamus McHugh Managing Director
Mr Derek McHugh Financial Controller

Medical Supply Co Ltd
Gamastown
Mulhuddart
Dublin 15
Phone: 01-8426644 Fax: 01-8224100
Email: msc@internet-ireland.ie
Web: http://www.medical-supply.ie
SIC: 51700 Employees: 30
Laboratory Ware & Instruments Suppliers
Mr Brendan Scully Managing Director
Mr Des Donegan Accounts Manager
Mr Noel Campbell Computer Manager

Merrimack Transformers
Industrial Estate
Rathangan
Kildare Co. Kildare
Phone: 045-524548 Fax: 045-524202
Email: merrimack@eircom.net
SIC: 51700 Employees: 30
Power Transformers & Distribution of Gate Automation Equipment
Mr Martin Shiel Managing Director
Mr Padraig Glennon Finance Manager
Mr John O'Neill Productions Manager

MMC Commercials Ltd
Mitsubishi House, JFK Drive,
Naas Road
Dublin 12
Phone: 01-4192300 Fax: 01-4600988
Email: info@mmc.ie
SIC: 51700 Employees: 150
Car & Truck Distribution
Mr Eugene O'Reilly Chairman
Mr Dermot Delaney Accountant
Mr Patrick Murphy Sales & Marketing Manager
Mr Paul Ancker Computer Manager

Modern Plant
Otter House, Naas Road
Clondalkin
Dublin 22
Phone: 01-4591344 Fax: 01-4592329
Email: sales@modernplant.ie
Web: http://www.modernplant.ie
SIC: 51700 Employees: 60
Distribute Industrial Components
Mr Henry Bolger Managing Director
Mr John Woods Financial Controller
Mr Brendan Conlon IT Manager

Nath Brothers Ltd
52-55 Drury Street
Dublin 2
Phone: 01-6715993 Fax: 01-6791837
Email: nathbros@indigo.ie
SIC: 51700 Employees: 200
Ladies & Gents Clothing Wholesalers
Mr Jagdish Sabherwal Managing Director

Newspread Ltd
7 Goldenbridge Industrial Estate
Inchicore
Dublin 8
Phone: 01-4537262 Fax: 01-4531081
SIC: 51700 Employees: 60
Newspaper Distribution
Mr Laurence Roe General Manager
Mr Gareth O'Donovan Financial Accountant
Ms Kathleen Ryan Sales Manager
Mr Chris Flynn Computer Manager

Oxygen Care Teoranta
Corrig Road, Sandyford Ind Estate
Foxrock
Dublin 18
Phone: 01-2953421 Fax: 01-2953366
SIC: 51700 Employees: 28
Distributors
Mr David Moran Director

P E O'Brien & Sons
Cookstown Industrial Estate
Tallaght
Dublin 24
Phone: 01-4510922 Fax: 01-4519071
SIC: 51700 Employees: 40
Tool Distrubutors & Wholesale
Mr Gerry Quinn Managing Director

Parkside Ireland Ltd
71 Cherry Orchard Industrial Estate
Ballyfermot
Dublin 10
Phone: 01-6268342 Fax: 01-6266689
Email: parkside@parksideirl.com
SIC: 51700 Employees: 25
Hygiene Products (Make and Distribute)
Mr Ronnie Fair Managing Director

Pat Hickey Wall & Floor Specialists
Murroe
Limerick Co. Limerick
Phone: 061-386523 Fax: 061-386080
SIC: 51700 Employees: 50
Tile wholesale
Mr Pat Hickey Proprietor

Paul Stuart Ltd
Tallaght Business Park
Whitestown
Dublin 24
Phone: 01-4523432 Fax: 01-4523967
Email: info@paulstuart.com
Web: http://www.paulstuart.com
SIC: 51700 Employees: 23
Distribution
Mr Stuart Smith Managing Director
Ms Gillian Smith Financial Controller
Mr Kevin Clancy Sales Manager

PBS Sales Ltd
Hibernian Industrial Estate
Greenhills Road
Dublin 24
Phone: 01-4596526 Fax: 01-4596527
Email: info@pbssales.ie
Web: http://www.pbssales.ie
SIC: 51700 Employees: 25
Import & Distribute Pet Products
Mr Liam Barrett Managing Director
Mr Eoin Connolly Accountant
Mr Eugene Barrett Sales Manager

Pilton Company Ltd
U2 Loughlinstown Industrial Estate
Loughlinstown, Ballybrack
Dublin 18
Phone: 01-2826444 Fax: 01-2826532
Email: ncv@iol.ie
Web: http://www.ncv.com
SIC: 51700 Employees: 76
Video Film Computer Games & Accessories Distributors
Mr Nick Furlong Managing Director
Mr Noel Geoghegan Sales Director
Mr Maurice White Operation Director
Mr Brian Gilligan IT Manager

Pump Services Ltd
Old Naas Road
Dublin 12
Phone: 01-4569999 Fax: 01-4568808
Email: info@pumpservices.ie
SIC: 51700 Employees: 42
Distribution of Fluid Handling Equipment
Mr Noel O'Kelly Managing Director
Ms Geraldine Kavanagh Financial Director
Ms Shirley Caslin Sales Director

Reynolds Systems Ireland
Ballymount Road
Clondalkin
Dublin 22
Phone: 01-4508809 Fax: 01-4565259
SIC: 51700 Employees: 35
Stockists/Distributors
Mr Dennis Kane Managing Director
Mr Fergus McNamara Company Accountant
Mr Joe Lawlor Sales Director

Sean Fitzpatrick (Wholesale) Ltd
4 John F Kennedy Avenue
John F Kennedy Industrial Estate
Dublin 12
Phone: 01-4508300 Fax: 01-4568348
Email: eoinfitz@indigo.ie
SIC: 51700 Employees: 31
Giftwear, Toys & Fancy Goods
Mr Eoin Fitzpatrick Managing Director
Ms Bronagh Kavanagh Finance Manager

Selex Ireland
Selex House, Old Dublin Road
Stillorgan Co. Dublin
Phone: 01-2782222 Fax: 01-2782200
SIC: 51700 Employees: 25
Photocopier Distributor
Mr Pat Brennan Director
Ms Mary Russell Accounts Manager
Ms Fiona Harrison Sales Manager
Mr Jim McEvoy Operation Manager
Mr Peter Wade IT Manager

Sharptext Ltd
M50 Business Park
Ballymount Road Upper
Dublin 12
Phone: 01-4193100 Fax: 01-4193111
Email: sharptext@sharptext.com
Web: http://www.sharptext.com
SIC: 51700 Employees: 120
Distribution of IT Products
Mr Paul White Managing Director
Mr Brian Griffin Sales Director

Slextronics International Ireland Ltd
National Technological Park
Plassey
Limerick Co. Limerick
Phone: 061-339400 Fax: 061-339401
Email: info@slextronics.com
Web: http://www.slextronics.com
SIC: 51700 Employees: 600
Distribution & Call Centre
Mr Ivan Herd Manager
Ms Siobhan Roche Human Resources Manager

Smith & Nephew Ireland Ltd
Pottery Road
Kill O'The Grange
Dun Laoghaire Co. Dublin
Phone: 01-2852222 Fax: 01-2852516
Email: info@smith-nephew.iol.ie
Web: http://www.smith-nephew.com
SIC: 51700 Employees: 95
Distribute Medical & Consumer Products
Mr John McKeown Managing Director
Mr Phillip O'Connor Financial Controller
Ms Clodagh Smith Marketing Manager
Mr Greg Walsh Operations Manager
Mr Seamus McGovern Business Systems Manager

SuperLeague Ireland Ltd
15 B Goldenbridge Industrial Estate
Dublin 8
Phone: 01-4535322 Fax: 01-4547075
SIC: 51700 Employees: 45
Juke Boxes Games Machines Pool Tables
Mr Brendan Murphy Director

Swedish Match Ireland
Unit 14 North West Business Park
Ballycoolin, Blanchardstown
Dublin 15
Phone: 01-8228500 Fax: 01-8223164
Email: sales@swedishmatch.ie
Web: http://www.swedishmatch.ie
SIC: 51700 Employees: 40
Marketing/Distribution of Matches
Mr Fintan Corrigan Managing Director
Mr Martin Thornton Financial Director
Mr Michael Sullivan Sales Director

Texaco Ireland Ltd
Texaco House, 83 Pembroke Road
Ballsbridge
Dublin 4
Phone: 01-6686822 Fax: 01-6684890
Email: info@texaco.ie
Web: http://www.texaco.ie
SIC: 51700 Employees: 800
Oil Distributors
Mr John Lynn General Manager
Ms Janette O'Sullivan Accounts Manager
Mr Paul Martin IT Officer

Ward Anderson
Film House
35 Upper Abbey Street
Dublin 1
Phone: 01-8044500 Fax: 01-8723687
SIC: 51700 Employees: 500
Film Distribution
Mr Leo Ward Managing Director
Mr Martin O'Dowd Financial Controller
Mr Robert Jameson Office Manager

Westex Ltd
3 Crosslands Industrial Estate
Walkinstown
Dublin 12
Phone: 01-4567826 Fax: 01-4503223
Email: wessales@indigo.ie
Web: http://www.westex.ie
SIC: 51700 Employees: 29
Distribution of Safety Equipment
Mr Michael Tynan Managing Director
Mr Raymond Devereux Financial Controller
Ms Helen O'Leary Sales & Marketing Manager

Wilo Pumps Ltd
Raheen Business Park
Raheen
Limerick Co. Limerick
Phone: 061-227566 Fax: 061-229017
Email: info@wilopumps.ie
SIC: 51700 Employees: 300
Pump Parts/Distribution
Mr Brendan Lyons Managing Director
Ms Margaret Meagher Administration Manager
Mr Kieran Barry Materials Manager
Mr Simon Ryan Production Manager

Wincanton (Ireland) Ltd
Promenade Road
East Wall
Dublin 3
Phone: 01-8555049 Fax: 01-8550015
Email: info@wincanton.co.uk
Web: http://www.wincanton.co.uk
SIC: 51700 Employees: 100
Transport and Distribution
Mr Con Sweeney Contracts Manager
Ms Dervla O'Brien Finance Manager

Wurth Ireland Ltd
Monaclonoe Industrial Estate
Ballysimon Road
Limerick Co. Limerick
Phone: 061-412911 Fax: 061-412428
Email: info@wurth.ie
Web: http://www.wurth.ie
SIC: 51700 Employees: 140
Distribution Company
Mr Michael Coffey Managing Director
Mr Dermot Quinn Financial Controller
Ms Lorraine Riddle Personnel Officer
Mr Noel Houlihan Sales Manager
Mr Jim Morany IT Manager

Zocalo Imports Ltd
Rathnure
Enniscorthy Co. Wexford
Phone: 054-55811 Fax: 054-55492
Email: info@zocalo.ie
Web: http://www.zocalo.ie
SIC: 51700 Employees: 30
Furniture - Wholesale
Mr Derry Conran Managing Director
Ms Derek Kehoe Sales Director

Retail & Repair

52121	Shopping Centre
52122	Catalogue Store
52123	Department Store
52210	Fruit & Veg
52220	Butcher
52230	Fish Monger
52240	Bakers
52250	Off Licences
52260	Tobacconist
52271	Supermarket
52272	Grocers
52273	Frozen Food Shop
52274	Confectionary Shop
52275	Delicatessans
52276	Multiple Food Store
52277	Health Food Shop
52278	Florist
52310	Chemists
52330	Cosmetics & Perfume Retail
52411	Fabric Retailer
52412	Carpet Sales
52420	Clothes Retail (Mixed)
52422	Clothes Retail (Children)
52423	Clothes Retail (Women)
52424	Clothes Retail (Men)
52425	Baby Goods Retail
52426	Knitwear Retailers
52431	Shoe Shop
52432	Leather Goods Retailer
52441	Furniture Retail
52442	Lighting Goods Retailer
52443	Soft Furnishers Retail
52451	Electrical Retailer
52452	HI-FI Dealers
52461	Hardware Store
52462	DIY Store
52471	Bookshop
52472	Newsagents
52473	Stationary - Suppliers/Retail
52474	Greeting Card Shop
52482	Photographic Equipment
52483	Music Shop
52484	Jewellers, Clocks & Coins
52485	Sport Shop
52486	Camping / Hiking Shop
52487	Angling/Fishing Shop
52488	Cycle Shop
52489	Toy Shop
52490	Picture Shops/Framers/Restore
52491	Art & Craft Shop
52492	Record Shop
52494	Gift Shop
52495	Mobile Phone Retailers
52496	Pet Shop
52497	Model Shop
52498	Glass & China Retail
52499	Discount Store
52510	Trift & Charity Shops
52520	Antiques
52610	Mail Order Company
52710	Shoe & Leather Goods Repair
52720	Repair - Consumer Goods

Argos
Level 2 The Square South Circuit
Tallaght
Dublin 24
Phone: 01-4622689 Fax: 01-4622695
SIC: 52123 Employees: 45
Department Stores
Mr Steve Taylor Manager
Ms Donna O Keefe Assistant Manager

Arnotts Plc
12b Henry Street
Dublin 1
Phone: 01-8050400 Fax: 01-8730109
Email: info@arnotts.ie
Web: http://www.arnotts.ie
SIC: 52123 Employees: 1000
Department Store
Mr James Duignan Managing Director
Mr Paul Donnelly Financial Controller
Ms Irene Canavan Personnel Manager
Mr Bill Kelly Operations Manager
Ms Maria Tyrrell Computer Manager

Boyers & Co Ltd
19/23 North Earl Street
Dublin 1
Phone: 01-8748667 Fax: 01-8745380
SIC: 52123 Employees: 150
Department Store Operators
Mr David O'Cionna Managing Director
Mr Paul Donnelly Financial Controller
Ms Margaret Chivers Personnel Manager
Ms Roz O'Shaughnessy Sales & Advertising Manager

BT2
28/29 Grafton Street
Dublin 2
Phone: 01-6056707 Fax: 01-6056750
SIC: 52123 Employees: 60
Department Stores
Ms Lisa Brown Store Manager

Burgess Department Store
1-7 Church Street
Athlone Co. Westmeath
Phone: 0902-72004 Fax: 0902-72545
Email: info@burgessofathlone.ie
Web: http://www.burgessofathlone.ie
SIC: 52123 Employees: 30
Department Store
Mr Frank Kenny General Manager

Cleary & Co (1941) Plc
18-27 Lower O'Connell Street
Dublin 1
Phone: 01-8786000 Fax: 01-8740644
Email: custserv@clearys.ie
Web: http://www.clearys.com
SIC: 52123 Employees: 350
Department Store
Mr Denis Ryan Chief Executive
Mr Patrick Timmins Company Secretary
Ms Amelda Crothmen Human Resources Manager
Ms Liza Jones Marketing Director
Mr Shaun Rippington Store Manager

Dunnes Stores Ltd
67 Upper Stephen Street
Dublin 8
Phone: 01-4751111 Fax: 01-4754405
Email: info@dunnesstores.ie
Web: http://www.dunnesstores.com
SIC: 52123 Employees: 11500
Department Store
Ms Margaret Heffernan Managing Director
Mr Pat O'Donoghue Financial Controller
Mr Tim O'Mahoney Human Resources Manager
Mr Darina Walsh
Mr John McNiff Stores Operation Manager
Mr Andrew Street IT Director

Frawleys
34-36 Thomas Street
Dublin 8
Phone: 01-4542273 Fax: 01-4540159
Email: info@frawleys.ie
Web: http://www.frawleys.ie
SIC: 52123 Employees: 40
Department Store
Mr Sean McEvoy Managing Director
Mr John Clohessy Finance Manager

Goods of Kilkenny
88-90 High Street
Kilkenny Co. Kilkenny
Phone: 056-22143 Fax: 056-61009
SIC: 52123 Employees: 50
Retail Department Store
Ms Vivian Good Managing Director
Ms Kitty O'Hallrahan Financial Controller
Ms Margaret Murphy Personnel Manager

Heatons Ltd
Heaton House, IDA Business Park
Tallaght
Dublin 24
Phone: 01-4519811 Fax: 01-4519199
SIC: 52123 Employees: 600
Department Store
Mr John O'Neill Managing Director

Henry Lyons & Co Ltd
Lower O'Connell Street
Sligo Co. Sligo
Phone: 071-42616 Fax: 071-42616
SIC: 52123 Employees: 60
Department Store
Mr Richard Lyons Managing Director

Hore's Stores Ltd
31 South Main Street
Wexford Co. Wexford
Phone: 053-42200 Fax: 053-46471
SIC: 52123 Employees: 35
Department Stores
Mr Gerard Hore Managing Director

Hubert Tully Department Stores
87 & 110/111 West Street
Drogheda Co. Louth
Phone: 041-9831927 Fax: 041-9842656
SIC: 52123 Employees: 28
Department Store
Mr Hubert Tully Managing Director
Mr Greg Tully Sales Manager

J J Fennessy
31 William Street
Limerick Co. Limerick
Phone: 061-415879 Fax: 061-414644
SIC: 52123 Employees: 50
Department Stores
Mr John Fennessy Manager

John McElhinney Ltd
Main Street
Ballybofey
Lifford Co. Donegal
Phone: 074-31217 Fax: 074-31757
SIC: 52123 Employees: 115
Department Store
Mr John McElhinney Managing Director
Mr Seamus Bonner Financial Controller
Ms Eileen McDaid Personnel Officer

Marks & Spencer (Ireland) Ltd
24-29 Mary Street
Dublin 1
Phone: 01-8728833 Fax: 01-8728995
Email: info@marks-and-spencer.com
Web: http://www.marks-and-spencer.com
SIC: 52123 Employees: 1500
Retail Department Stores
Mr Steve Costello General Manager
Ms Phil Doyle Finance Manager
Mr Juan Pemberton Personnel Manager
Ms Carmel Bretheny Operations Manager
Ms Susan Hazzard IT Supervisor

Mary's Of Sligo
Castle Street
Sligo Co. Sligo
Phone: 071-41707 Fax: 071-41707
SIC: 52123 Employees: 50
Department Stores
Mr Patrick Joyce Managing Director

McGowans Customs Furniture
Kinlough
Sligo Co. Sligo
Phone: 072-42120 Fax: 072-41801
SIC: 52123 Employees: 134
Department Store
Mr Mark McKeown Manager

Paul's Ltd
12 High Street
Kilkenny Co. Kilkenny
Phone: 056-21289 Fax: 056-61561
Email: hughgo@indigo.ie
SIC: 52123 Employees: 50
Department Stores
Mr John Skuve Manager

Penneys
47 Mary Street
Dublin 1
Phone: 01-8727788 Fax: 01-8733532
Email: postmaster@primark.ie
Web: http://www.primark.ie
SIC: 52123 Employees: 3000
Department Stores
Mr Arthur Ryan Chairman
Mr Paddy Prior Finance Manager
Ms Breege O'Donoghue Director
Mr Seamus Halford Director of Store Operations
Mr Terry Greaves IT Manager

Roches Stores
54-62 Henry Street
Dublin 1
Phone: 01-8730044 Fax: 01-8730791
Email: info@roches-stores.ie
Web: http://www.roches-stores.ie
SIC: 52123 Employees: 3800
Department Store
Mr Stephen Barry Chief Executive
Mr Richard Pierce Financial Director
Mr Eugene Hanley Group Personnel Manager
Mr Robert Ward Marketing Manager
Mr Tony Lambert Group Systems Director

Salmons Department Store
Main Street
Ballinasloe Co. Galway
Phone: 0905-42120 Fax: 0905-42120
SIC: 52123 Employees: 40
Department Stores
Mr Thomas Salmon Managing Director
Mr Dermot Salmon Sales & Marketing Manager

Shaw & Sons Ltd
Centre Point
Portlaoise Co. Laois
Phone: 0502-21316 Fax: 0502-20719
Email: info@shaws.ie
Web: http://www.shaws.ie
SIC: 52123 Employees: 300
Department Store
Mr Mervyn Shaw Managing Director
Mr Sydney Finley Finance Manager
Mr David McMahon Personnel Manager
Mr Michael Brody DP Manager

Shaws of Carlow
8-11Tullow Street
Carlow Co. Carlow
Phone: 0503-31509 Fax: 0503-41522
SIC: 52123 Employees: 25
Department Store
Mr Clive Shaw Managing Director
Mr James Griffin Sales Director

TF Fleming Ltd
Church Square
Monaghan Co. Monaghan
Phone: 047-81344 Fax: 047-84370
SIC: 52123 Employees: 135
Department Store
Mr Gordon Fleming Managing Director
Mr Aidan McNeil Financial Controller
Ms Edna Fleming Company Secretary
Mr Richard Tiernan Shop Floor Manager
Ms Joan Maxwell DP Manager

Thomas Brown
88-95 Grafton Street
Dublin 2
Phone: 01-6795666 Fax: 01-6056750
Email: info@brownthomas.ie
Web: http://www.brownthomas.ie
SIC: 52123 Employees: 850
Retail Department Store
Mr Paul Kelly Managing Director
Mr Mark Byrne Financial Controller
Ms Mary Cryan Personnel Manager

W & G Hadden Ltd
15 Tullow Street
Carlow Co. Carlow
Phone: 0503-31650 Fax: 0503-41130
SIC: 52123 Employees: 50
Department Stores
Mr D Fennell Managing Director

Sam Dennigan & Co Ltd
Palmerstown
Dublin 20
Phone: 01-8350644 Fax: 01-8350944
SIC: 52210 Employees: 125
Fruit & Vegetables
Mr Sam Dennigan Joint Director
Ms Eva Croasdell Finance Manager
Ms Frances Leech Personnel Manager
Mr Liam Glennon Marketing Manager
Mr Ray Maher Production Manager
Mr Joe Dennigan Joint Director

Shellfish-de-la-Mer Ltd
Dinish Island
Castletownbere
Bantry Co. Cork
Phone: 027-70461 Fax: 027-70333
Email: fdlm@iol.ie
SIC: 52230 Employees: 50
Fish Retailers
Mr Peter O'Sullivan Managing Director

United Fish Industries
Donegal Road
Killybegs
Donegal Co. Donegal
Phone: 073-41800 Fax: 073-41847
Email: info@iaws.ie
SIC: 52230 Employees: 50
Fish Monger
Mr Michael Long Managing Director
Mr Tom O'Keeffe Sales Manager
Ms Berni Sheridan Technical Manager
Mr Denis Moran IT Manager

Buttercrust
Jamestown Road
Finglas
Dublin 11
Phone: 01-8362211 Fax: 01-8362923
Email: rbake@iol.ie
SIC: 52240 Employees: 100
Bakery
Mr Padraig Cribbin Managing Director
Mr Pat Fox Finance Manager
Mr Gus O'Reilly Sales Manager

Comerfords Bros Ltd
Industrial Estate
Newbridge
Naas Co. Kildare
Phone: 045-431770 Fax: 045-432618
SIC: 52240 Employees: 50
Bakery
Mr Peter Comerford Manager

Daniel Doherty Ltd
Gulladuff
Moville
Lifford Co. Donegal
Phone: 077-82014 Fax: 077-82213
SIC: 52240 Employees: 30
Bakery/Confectionery
Mr Daniel Doherty Managing Director
Ms Linda Farrell Accounts Manager
Mr Seamus Garrigle Marketing Manager
Mr Paddy Craig Production Manager

Edward Flahavan & Sons Ltd
Kilnagrange Mills
Kilmacthomas
Waterford Co. Waterford
Phone: 051-294107 Fax: 051-294308
Email: flahavan@tinet.ie
SIC: 52240 Employees: 40
Bakery Ingredients
Mr John Flahavan Managing Director
Mr John Meskill Financial Controller
Mr John Coffey Personnel Manager
Mr Pat Casey Sales Director
Mr John Noonan Marketing Director

Gallaghers Bakery Ltd Galard
Cashel
Ardara
Donegal Co. Donegal
Phone: 075-41167 Fax: 075-41777
SIC: 52240 Employees: 300
Bakery
Mr Declan Gallagher Manager
Ms Cathleen Gallagher Finance Manager

Irish Pride Bakery
Taghmon
Wexford Co. Wexford
Phone: 053-34136 Fax: 053-34251
Email: cahillk@irishpride.ie
Web: http://www.iaws.ie
SIC: 52240 Employees: 100
Bakery
Mr Ken Cahill Manager
Mr Cathal Ryan Sales Manager

J Spicer & Co Ltd
Athlumney Road
Navan Co. Meath
Phone: 046-21114 Fax: 046-21408
SIC: 52240 Employees: 110
Bakery
Mr Adrian McGrane General Manager
Ms Elizabeth Spicer Finance Manager
Mr Liam McAlerney Sales & Marketing Manager
Mr John Reilly Production Manager
Mr Vincent Byrne Computer Manager

Joseph Brennan Bakeries
Greenhills Industrial Estate
Walkinstown
Dublin 12
Phone: 01-4513933 Fax: 01-4514631
Email: info@brennan.iol.ie
SIC: 52240 Employees: 110
Bread
Mr Colm Brennan Managing Director
Ms Deborah Brennan Financial Controller
Mr Derek Beatty Sales Director
Mr Jim Hyland Manufacturing Director

Mack's Bakery
Thomas Street
Kiltimagh
Claremorris Co. Mayo
Phone: 094-81398 Fax: 094-81829
Email: macksbakery@tinet.ie
SIC: 52240 Employees: 50
Bakery
Mr Thomas McNicholas Managing Director
Mr Francis McNicholas Production Manager

Neville's Bakery
Kylemore Industrial Estate
Kill
Dublin 10
Phone: 01-6260288 Fax: 01-6231334
Email: nevilleb@indigo.ie
SIC: 52240 Employees: 50
Bakery
Mr Sean Maguire Manager
Ms Mary Lawlor Finance Manager

O'Hehirs Bakery
Unit 4A Cleveragh Industrial Estate
Sligo Co. Sligo
Phone: 071-44171 Fax: 071-44171
SIC: 52240 Employees: 50
Bakery
Mr Michael O'Hehir Proprietor
Ms Janet Gillan Accounts Manager

Old Mill Bakery
113 Phibsboro Road
Dublin 7
Phone: 01-8300175 Fax: 01-8302788
SIC: 52240 Employees: 70
Bakery Products
Mr Joe O'Brien Managing Director
Ms Dympna O'Brien Accounts Manager
Mr Chris Tiernan Sales Director
Mr Alan McGuire Production Manager
Mr Oliver Bright DP Manager

Pat The Baker Ltd
Moxham Street
Granard
Longford Co. Longford
Phone: 043-86523 Fax: 043-86331
Email: patthebaker@tinet.ie
SIC: 52240 Employees: 450
Bakers
Mr Paddy Higgins Managing Director
Mr James Higgins Financial Director
Ms Susan Pardoe Personnel Manager
Mr Michael Higgins Operations Director

Stafford Bakeries Ltd
IDA Industrial Estate
Clonattin
Gorey Co. Wexford
Phone: 055-22205 Fax: 055-21069
SIC: 52240 Employees: 90
Bakery a& Confectionery
Mr Sean Stafford Managing Director
Ms Una Stafford Accounts Manager
Mr Hugh Byrne Sales & Marketing Manager

Croughans Supervalu & Off Licence
5 Castlemaine Street
Athlone Co. Westmeath
Phone: 0902-73555 Fax: 0902-75611
SIC: 52250 Employees: 50
Off Licence
Mr John Croughan Proprietor
Mr Francis Keane Financial Controller
Mr Joseph Egan Off-Licence Manager

Findlater (Wine Merchant) Ltd
Magna Drive, Citywest Business Campus
Dublin 24
Phone: 01-4529112 Fax: 01-4529120
Email: sales@findlaters.com
Web: http://www.findlaters.com
SIC: 52250 Employees: 34
Wine & Spirits
Mr Keith McCarthy Managing Director
Mr Frode Dahl Finance Director
Mr Barry Geoghegan Sales Manager

Molloy Group
Block 2 Village Green
Tallaght
Dublin 24
Phone: 01-4515544 Fax: 01-4515658
Email: info@molloys.com
Web: http://www.molloys.com
SIC: 52250 Employees: 300
Retail Liquor Sales
Mr Kevin Molloy Managing Director
Mr Patrick Kelly Head of Finance
Ms Michelle Fogarty Head of Human Resources
Mr David Noble Sales & Marketing Manager
Mr Pat Hogan Operations Manager
Ms Helen Murray Head of IT

O'Donovan's Off Licence
Unit 27 St Patricks Woollen Mills
Cork Co. Cork
Phone: 021-4895746 Fax: 021-4893391
SIC: 52250 Employees: 120
Off Licence
Mr Joseph O'Donovan Managing Director
Mr Gary O'Donovan Sales Director

Stephens & Champ Ltd
Main Street
Killorglin
Killarney Co. Kerry
Phone: 066-9761117 Fax: 066-9761078
SIC: 52250 Employees: 40
Off Licences
Mr Padraig Condon Manager

Aidan Byrne Superstore
Bridge Street
Tullow
Carlow Co. Carlow
Phone: 0503-51132 Fax: 0503-51132
SIC: 52271 Employees: 25
Supermarket
Mr Charlie O'Toole Manager

Ardkeen Superstores Ltd
Dunmore Road
Waterford Co. Waterford
Phone: 051-874620 Fax: 051-871926
SIC: 52271 Employees: 170
Supermarket & Petrol Station
Mr Val Lambe Manager
Mr Gerald Jephson Accounts Manager

Ascot Stores Ltd
Bypass Road
Clonakilty Co. Cork
Phone: 023-33116 Fax: 023-34646
Email: sparclon@eircom.net
SIC: 52271 Employees: 55
Supermarket
Mr Ger Harte Managing Director
Ms Kathleen O'Mahony Finance Manager
Ms Eileen Hurley Office Manager
Ms Violet Twohig Floor Manager
Mr Roni Enright IT Manager

Brendan's Super Save
Unit 6B Rowlagh Shopping Centre
Dublin 22
Phone: 01-6262746 Fax: 01-6262746
SIC: 52271 Employees: 30
Supermarket
Mr Brendan Farley Proprietor

C & T Supermarket
8 Shenick Road
Skerries Co. Dublin
Phone: 01-8492727 Fax: 01-8492729
SIC: 52271 Employees: 35
Supermarkets
Mr Tom Stafford Manager

C Morton & Sons
15-17 Dunville Avenue
Rathmines
Dublin 6
Phone: 01-4971254 Fax: 01-4971978
Email: cmorton@iol.ie
SIC: 52271 Employees: 55
Supermarkets
Mr Eric Morton Proprietor
Mr Stan O'Reilly Finance Manager
Mr Larry Condon Store Manager

Carolans Londis Superstore
Beechmount Shopping Centre
Navan Co. Meath
Phone: 046-23800 Fax: 046-22893
SIC: 52271 Employees: 40
Supermarket
Mr Jim Carolans Manager
Ms Ann McGlew Finance Manager
Ms Paula Wall Office Manager
Mr Karl Flemming Sales & Marketing Manager

Caulfield Supermarket
Archer Street
Loughboy
Kilkenny Co. Kilkenny
Phone: 056-65404 Fax: 056-52912
Email: supervalue@eircom.net
SIC: 52271 Employees: 100
Supermarket
Mr Seamus Watters Manager
Ms Annette Manning Finance Manager
Ms Clare Doyle Supervisor

Centra Quickstop
Unit 7 Main Street
Finglas
Dublin 11
Phone: 01-8361104 Fax: 01-8643585
SIC: 52271 Employees: 30
Convenience Store
Mr Mark Fitzgerald Manager

Centra Stores
Main Street
Maynooth Co. Kildare
Phone: 01-6285247 Fax: 01-6285247
Email: info@centra.ie
Web: http://www.centra.ie
SIC: 52271 Employees: 25
Supermarkets
Mr Jerry Scally Manager

Cosmoline
Abbey Trinity
Tuam Co. Galway
Phone: 093-24146 Fax: 093-25111
Email: cosmo@esatclear.ie
SIC: 52271 Employees: 147
Supermarket
Mr Paul Merrins Director
Mr Joe Cummins Finance Manager
Mr Chris Donnelly Computer Manager

Crana Retailers
Cockhill Road
Buncrana
Lifford Co. Donegal
Phone: 077-61719 Fax: 077-63605
SIC: 52271 Employees: 50
Supermarkets
Mr Gerry Nelson Manager
Mr Patrick McBride Accounts Manager

D O'Connell & Co
Dunman Way
Cork Co. Cork
Phone: 023-45457 Fax: 023-45476
SIC: 52271 Employees: 24
Supermakets
Mr Derry O'Connell Managing Director
Ms Marguerite Galvin Accounts Manager
Mr John Galvin Sales Manager

Doyle's Centra
Main Street
Rathcoole
Dublin 24
Phone: 01-4589109 Fax: 01-4589109
SIC: 52271 Employees: 84
Supermarkets
Mr Karl O'Dwyer Manager

E & A Gilbride Ltd
Main Street
Emyvale
Monaghan Co. Monaghan
Phone: 047-87383 Fax: 047-87956
SIC: 52271 Employees: 32
Supermarket
Mr Kevin Gallagher Manager

Eurospar
Main Street
Rush Co. Dublin
Phone: 01-8437226 Fax: 01-8437742
SIC: 52271 Employees: 70
General Stores
Mr John Glennon Proprietor
Ms Julie Farrell Personnel Manager
Mr Ciaran Price Sales Manager

Garveys Group
117 Lower Rock Street
Tralee Co. Kerry
Phone: 066-7128166 Fax: 066-7128229
Email: garveys@esatclear.ie
SIC: 52271 Employees: 400
Supermarket Chain
Mr Thomas Garvey Managing Director
Mr Terry Dunne Financial Controller
Ms Marie Griffin Personnel Manager
Mr Kevin McCarthy Regional Manager

Garveys Supervalue
The Quay
Dungarvan Co. Waterford
Phone: 058-41628 Fax: 058-45084
Email: garveys@iolfree.ie
SIC: 52271 Employees: 130
Supermarket
Mr Sean Farrell General Manager

Gormley's Centra Supermarket
Circular Road
Letterkenny Co. Donegal
Phone: 074-23173 Fax: 074-26990
Email: centra@eircom.net
SIC: 52271 Employees: 55
Supermarket
Mr John Gormley Manager
Ms Katheen Gallagher Finance Director
Mr John Gormley Sales Director

Greaney Independent Supermarket
The Square
Swinford
Claremorris Co. Mayo
Phone: 094-51201 Fax: 094-51511
SIC: 52271 Employees: 24
Supermarket
Mr Lou Kelly Manager
Ms Myra Rouane Finance Manager

Higgins Foodstore
The Mall
Sligo Co. Sligo
Phone: 071-41701 Fax:
SIC: 52271 Employees: 23
Supermarkets
Mr Higgins

Hurley's Super Valu
Townpark
Mill Road
Midleton Co. Cork
Phone: 021-4631570 Fax: 021-4631410
SIC: 52271 Employees: 70
Supermarket
Mr John Hurley Proprietor

Iceland
35-38 Courtyard
Letterkenny Co. Donegal
Phone: 074-29112 Fax: 074-27629
Web: http://www.iceland.co.uk
SIC: 52271 Employees: 24
Supermarkets
Mr Brian McGarvey Managing Director

J Haslam & Son Ltd - Supervalu
25 Main Street
Birr Co. Offaly
Phone: 0509-20015 Fax: 0509-20377
SIC: 52271 Employees: 45
Supermarket
Mr Tim Dolan Manager

J O'Connor (Nenagh)
Nenagh Shopping Centre
Nenagh Co. Tipperary
Phone: 067-31022 Fax: 067-33449
SIC: 52271 Employees: 200
Supermarket
Mr Joseph O'Connor Managing Director
Ms Margaret Shanahan Financial Controller
Mr Rory O'Connor Sales Director

JC's Supermarket
Swords Shopping Centre
Rathbeale Road
Swords Co. Dublin
Phone: 01-8402884 Fax: 01-8403687
SIC: 52271 Employees: 150
Supermarket
Mr Joseph Savage Managing Director
Mr Phillip Harney Accountant
Mr Barry Savage Personnel Manager
Mr Bernard Walsh Store Manager

Laurel Mount Ltd
Unit 10 Laurel Lodge Shopping Centre
Castleknock
Dublin 15
Phone: 01-8224720 Fax: 01-8224876
SIC: 52271 Employees: 25
Centra Food Market
Mr Paul Donlon Managing Director

Londis
Main Street
Clane
Naas Co. Kildare
Phone: 045-868236 Fax: 045-861352
Email: doolans@ginep.ie
Web: http://www.ginep.ie
SIC: 52271 Employees: 55
Supermarket
Mr Nicholas Crowley Manager

Mace
Cartron Village
Sligo Co. Sligo
Phone: 071-41479 Fax: 071-42871
Email: info@mace.ie
Web: http://www.mace.ie
SIC: 52271 Employees: 25
Supermarkets
Mr Keith Dillon Proprietor

Martin Divilly's Quality Foodhall
Unit 9/10 Westside Shopping Centre
Galway Co. Galway
Phone: 091-523947 Fax: 091-523947
SIC: 52271 Employees: 23
Supermarket
Mr Martin Divilly Proprietor

McConnons Supervalu
Main Street
Castleblayney Co. Monaghan
Phone: 042-9746005 Fax: 042-9746630
Email: jimoconnor@eircom.net
SIC: 52271 Employees: 70
Supermarket
Mr Vincent Quinn Manager

McHugh Centra
Unit 17 Edenmore Shopping Centre
Raheny
Dublin 5
Phone: 01-8478122 Fax: 01-8670141
SIC: 52271 Employees: 40
Supermarkets
Mr Gerry McHugh Managing Director
Mr Paddy Hobbs Store Manager

Moriarty Group
Unit 15 Palmerstown Centre
Kennelsfort Road
Dublin 20
Phone: 01-6235805 Fax: 01-6235807
Email: superval@indigo.ie
SIC: 52271 Employees: 350
Supermarket
Mr Luke Moriarty Managing Director
Mr Chris Harmon Finance Manager
Mr Shea Smith Sales Director

Nolan Supermarkets Ltd
49 Vernon Avenue
Clontarf
Dublin 3
Phone: 01-8338361 Fax: 01-8332789
Email: eomalley@nolans.ie
Web: http://www.nolans.ie
SIC: 52271 Employees: 120
Supermarket
Mr Richard Nolan Managing Director
Mr Gerard Claffey Financial Controller
Ms Emer O'Malley Sales Manager
Mr Dermot Kelly Store Manager

O'Connor Group Ltd
Shop Street
Westport Co. Mayo
Phone: 098-26300 Fax: 098-26321
Email: info@oconnor.ie
SIC: 52271 Employees: 100
Supermarket
Mr Noel Kavanagh Director
Ms Ashley Wilson Finance Manager
Ms Caroline Heagney Sales & Marketing Manager

O'Connors Super-Valu
The Square
Claremorris Co. Mayo
Phone: 094-62242 Fax: 094-62243
SIC: 52271 Employees: 60
Supermarket
Mr Pat O'Brien Manager

O'Gorman Ltd
15 Main Street
Carrickmacross Co. Monaghan
Phone: 042-9661387 Fax: 042-9661704
SIC: 52271 Employees: 25
Supermarket
Mr Ralph Johnson Manager
Mr Gerry Daly Finance Manager
Ms Margaret Kearns Company Secretary

Retail

O'Kelly Londis
Cleveragh Road
Sligo Co. Sligo
Phone: 071-70190 Fax: 071-70204
SIC: 52271 Employees: 25
Supermarkets
Mr Sean O'Kelly Manager

O'Sheas Supervalue Ltd
Castle Street
Ballyragget
Kilkenny Co. Kilkenny
Phone: 056-33122 Fax: 056-33122
SIC: 52271 Employees: 25
Supermarket
Mr Kevin O'Shea Manager

P Twohig & Sons Ltd
Kanturk
Mallow Co. Cork
Phone: 029-50069 Fax: 029-50322
Email: twohigsb@eircom.net
SIC: 52271 Employees: 75
Supermarket
Mr Michael Twohig Proprietor
Ms Maria O'Mahony Finance Manager

Pats Centra Supermarket
The Square
Bettystown
Drogheda Co. Louth
Phone: 041-9827252 Fax: 041-9827548
SIC: 52271 Employees: 25
Supermarket
Mr Patrick Boshell Proprietor

Pettits Supermarket
St Aidans Shopping Centre
Wexford Co. Wexford
Phone: 053-24055 Fax: 053-23203
Email: pettitts@pettitts.ie
Web: http://www.pettitts.ie
SIC: 52271 Employees: 630
Supermarket
Mr Desmond Pettitt Managing Director
Ms Geraldine Roche Financial Controller
Ms Cathy O'Leary Personnel Manager
Ms Siobhan O'Keeffe Marketing Manager
Ms Julie Hanton DP Manager

Quealey's Supervalu
Frances Street
Kilrush
Ennis Co. Clare
Phone: 065-9051885 Fax: 065-9051737
SIC: 52271 Employees: 80
Supermarket
Mr Dennis Nolan Manager
Ms Eileen Dillon Accounts Manager

Riordans Ltd
Courthouse Road
Fermoy Co. Cork
Phone: 025-31275 Fax: 025-32972
Email: riordansfermoy@indigo.ie
SIC: 52271 Employees: 40
Supermarkets
Mr Michael Riordan Proprietor

Shinnicks
22 McDermot Place
Fermoy Co. Cork
Phone: 025-31360 Fax: 025-31333
SIC: 52271 Employees: 25
Supermarkets
Mr Brian Shinnick Proprietor

Superquinn
PO Box 99, Sutton Cross
Dublin 13
Phone: 01-8325700 Fax: 01-8326544
Email: talk@superquinn.ie
Web: http://www.superquinn.ie
SIC: 52271 Employees: 4800
Supermarket
Mr Fergal Quinn Chief Executive
Mr Vincent O'Doherty Chairman

Superquinn
PO Box 99
Sutton Cross
Dublin 13
Phone: 01-8167100 Fax: 01-8167150
Email: talk@superquinn.ie
Web: http://www.superquinn.ie
SIC: 52271 Employees: 3520
Supermarket
Mr Feargal Quinn Managing Director
Mr Frank Murphy Finance Manager
Mr Eammon Quinn Sales & Marketing Manager
Mr Eric Hayes IT Manager

Supervalu (McNamaras)
Westvillage
Ballincollig
Cork Co. Cork
Phone: 021-4870719 Fax: 021-4870547
SIC: 52271 Employees: 200
Supermarkets
Mr John Heffernan Manager

Tesco Ireland
PO Box 3 Gresham House
Marine Road
Dun Laoghaire Co. Dublin
Phone: 01-2808441 Fax: 01-2800136
Email: postmaster@tesco.ie
Web: http://www.tesco.ie
SIC: 52271 Employees: 18540
Supermarkets
Mr Maurice Pratt Managing Director
Ms Heather Butler Human Resources Manager
Mr Brendan Guidera Store Operations manager
Mr Donal Loftus IT Director

Whoriskeys Spar Supermarket
The Mall
Ramelton
Letterkenny Co. Donegal
Phone: 074-51022 Fax: 074-51006
SIC: 52271 Employees: 30
Supermarket
Mr Hugo Whoriskeys Proprietor
Ms Janette Brolley Accountant

Conway's Spar Shop
Fairyhouse Road
Ratoath
Navan Co. Meath
Phone: 01-8256160 Fax: 01-8256850
SIC: 52272 Employees: 35
Groceries Coal & Gas Retail
Mr Noel Conway Proprietor

Eight To Twelve
23 Fitzwilliam Square
Dublin 2
Phone: 01-6762205 Fax: 01-6619575
SIC: 52272 Employees: 1850
Convenience Stores
Mr John Clohisey Chief Executive
Mr Karl Brennan Finance Manager

Fresh Food Centre
54/55 Upper William Street
Limerick Co. Limerick
Phone: 061-413161 Fax: 061-400477
SIC: 52272 Employees: 35
Fresh Food
Mr Edward Drew Managing Director

Jl Johnston 1959 Ltd
Thurles Co. Tipperary
Phone: 0504-21586 Fax: 0504-21599
SIC: 52272 Employees: 40
Grocery
Mr Wayne Johnston Co-Manager
Mr James Kavagnagh Co-Manager

John Foy
54 Market Street
Cootehill Co. Cavan
Phone: 049-5552122 Fax: 049-5552360
SIC: 52272 Employees: 35
Food Store/Hardware
Mr John Foy Proprietor
Ms Charlene Gillespie Supervisor

Poldys Fresh Foods Ltd
Naas Industrial Estate
Naas Co. Kildare
Phone: 045-874495 Fax: 045-875623
Email: info@greenisle.ie
Web: http://www.greenisle.ie
SIC: 52273 Employees: 80
Frozen Foods
Mr Albert Gallagher Managing Director
Mr John Munnelly Financial Controller
Ms Rose Keely Human Resources Manager

Sara Lee Ireland Ltd
Park Road
Killarney Co. Kerry
Phone: 064-39400 Fax: 064-33720
Email: info@saralee.com
Web: http://www.eu.saralee.com
SIC: 52273 Employees: 60
Frozen Food Manaufacture
Mr Paul Magowan Manager
Mr Gerard Doyle MIS Manager

McCambridges Of Galway Ltd
38-39 Shop Street
Galway Co. Galway
Phone: 091-562259 Fax: 091-561802
Email: retail.com@iol.ie
SIC: 52275 Employees: 25
Delicatessens
Mr Owen McCambridge Managing Director

Boots Chemist
12 Grafton Street
Dublin 2
Phone: 01-6773173 Fax: 01-6773228
SIC: 52310 Employees: 1000
Chemist Shop
Ms Deirdre Burns Chief Executive
Mr John Kingston Financial Controller
Mr Nick Hudson Marketing Manager
Mr David Aylward IT Manager

CH Chemists Ltd
31 The Mall
Tralee Co. Kerry
Phone: 066-7128271 Fax: 066-7126585
Email: chchemist@eircom.net
Web: http://www.chtralee.com
SIC: 52310 Employees: 40
Chemists
Mr Peter Harty Pharmacist
Mr Kevin O'Riordan General Manager

Hickey Pharmacy Ltd
Hilltop Business Centre
Station Road, Raheny
Dublin 5
Phone: 01-8328433 Fax: 01-8328447
Email: hickeypharm@netscape.net
SIC: 52310 Employees: 70
Pharmacy
Mr Paddy Hickey Managing Director
Mr Stephen Butler Finance Manager
Ms Brenda Greene Sales & Marketing Manager

Hunter's Pharmacy
48 O'Connell Street
Sligo Co. Sligo
Phone: 071-42696 Fax: 071-44133
SIC: 52310 Employees: 25
Chemists
Mr Trevor Hunter Proprietor

Kencin Roxboro Pharmacy
Roxboro Shopping Centre
Roxboro
Limerick Co. Limerick
Phone: 061-418232 Fax: 061-418232
SIC: 52310 Employees: 80
Chemists
Ms Mary Mulrooney Pharmacist

Phelan's Pharmacy
Carrigaline
Cork Co. Cork
Phone: 021-4371600 Fax: 021-4372009
Email: phelanph@indigo.ie
Web: http://www.phelans.ie
SIC: 52310 Employees: 120
Chemists
Mr Connor Phelan Pharmacist

Rice Steele & Co Ltd
Unit 31 Cookstown Industrial Estate
Tallaght
Dublin 24
Phone: 01-4510144 Fax: 01-4521875
SIC: 52310 Employees: 50
Chemists
Mr John McCormack Managing Director
Ms Imelda Lowe Accounts Manager
Mr Eugene Ryder Sales & Marketing Manager

Sam McCauley's Ltd
3-7 Redmond Square
Wexford Co. Wexford
Phone: 053-22422 Fax: 053-21670
Email: paulm@smcc.ie
Web: http://www.smcc.ie
SIC: 52310 Employees: 70
Pharmacy
Mr Patrick McCormac Director

Body Shop
82 Grafton Street
Dublin 2
Phone: 01-6713725 Fax: 01-6713901
Email: info@the-body-shop.com
Web: http://www.the-body-shop.com
SIC: 52330 Employees: 250
Cosmetics & Haircare Products
Mr Peter McDonald Manager
Ms Ciara O'Reilly Accounts Manager

Orco Sales Ltd
18 Exchange Street Upper
Dublin 8
Phone: 01-6719424 Fax: 01-6718232
Email: enquiries@fashionhsc.com
Web: http://www.fashionhsc.com
SIC: 52330 Employees: 33
Fashion Accessories
Mr Stephen Finn Managing Director

Cork Square Deal Centre Ltd
16-21 Washington Street
Cork Co. Cork
Phone: 021-4274045 Fax: 021-4274048
SIC: 52412 Employees: 50
Floor Covering & Furniture
Mr Patrick Herlihy Managing Director
Ms Kate Geary Finance Manager
Ms Tara George Personnel Manager
Mr Adrian Hughes Sales & Purchasing Manager

Des Kelly Carpets Ltd
1A Prospect Road
Glasnevin
Dublin 9
Phone: 01-8302433 Fax: 01-8308687
SIC: 52412 Employees: 170
Carpet & Furniture Retailers
Mr Desmond Kelly Managing Director
Mr Alan Toomey Financial Controller
Mr Greg Kelly Sales Manager

Michael Murphy & Co Ltd
Edward Street
Newbridge Co. Kildare
Phone: 045-431868 Fax: 045-433580
SIC: 52412 Employees: 80
Carpet Sales
Mr Michael Murphy Managing Director

Munster Carpets
Grange
Douglas
Cork Co. Cork
Phone: 021-4892854 Fax: 021-4891027
Email: sales@munstercarpets.ie
Web: http://www.munstercarpets.ie
SIC: 52412 Employees: 55
Carpet Retailer
Mr Paul Callaghan Managing Director
Mr Pat Quinnlin Financial Controller
Mr Sean Kelly Sales & Marketing Manager

TC Matthews Carpets Ltd
The Wool Centre, Greenhills Road
Walkinstown
Dublin 12
Phone: 01-4503822 Fax: 01-4602013
Email: sgolden@ctmatthews.ie
Web: http://www.tcmatthews-carpets.ie
SIC: 52412 Employees: 30
Carpets Retailer
Mr Thomas Matthews Managing Director
Mr Fergus Flynn Finance Manager
Mr Peter Dixon Sales & Marketing Manager

Youghal Carpet Yarns
Killacloyne
Carrigtwohill
Cork Co. Cork
Phone: 021-4883333 Fax: 021-4883018
Email: info@youghalcarpetyarns.com
Web: http://www.youghalcarpetyarns.com
SIC: 52412 Employees: 200
Carpet
Mr Pat Curtin Director

Anthony Ryan Ltd
16-18 Sharp Street
Galway Co. Galway
Phone: 091-567061 Fax: 091-563160
SIC: 52420 Employees: 120
Drapery Store
Mr James Cawley Managing Director
Mr Anthony Ryan General Manager

Fashion Flo Ltd
79 Lagan Road
Dublin Industrial Estate
Dublin 11
Phone: 01-8372446 Fax: 01-8309617
Email: info@fashionflo.ie
Web: http://www.fashionflo.ie
SIC: 52420 Employees: 70
Clothes Retailers
Mr Frank Murphy Managing Director
Mr John Green Financial Controller

Kilkenny Shop
5-6 Nassau Street
Dublin 2
Phone: 01-6777066 Fax: 01-6773891
Email: info@kilkenny-shop.com
Web: http://www.kilkennygroup.com
SIC: 52420 Employees: 80
Clothing Shop
Ms Margaret Delworth Manager
Ms Sinead O'Toole Human Resources Manager
Mr Seamus Leahy Sales & Marketing Manager

Michael Guiney Ltd
11-12 North Earl Street
Dublin 1
Phone: 01-8724377 Fax: 01-8724124
SIC: 52420 Employees: 200
Clothing Retailer
Mr Michael Guiney Managing Director
Mr Philip Duffy Finance Manager

Murray & Son Ltd
Main Street
Charleville
Cork Co. Cork
Phone: 063-81225 Fax: 063-89478
Email: murson@iol.ie
Web: http://www.murson.ie
SIC: 52420 Employees: 40
General Retail Outfitters
Mr Michael Murray Managing Director
Mr John Murray Financial Controller
Mr Patrick Murray Director

A-Wear Ltd
26 Grafton Street
Dublin 2
Phone: 01-6717200 Fax: 01-6711251
Email: lbenford@a-wear.ie
Web: http://www.a-wear.ie
SIC: 52423 Employees: 250
Clothes Retail
Mr Paul Kelly Managing Director
Mr Mark Byrne Financial Controller
Ms Ann-Marie Flood Sales & Marketing Manager

Dorothy Perkins
Unit 201 Blanchardstown Town Centre
Dublin 15
Phone: 01-8221831 Fax: 01-8221869
SIC: 52423 Employees: 30
Ladies Fashions
Ms Janine Timmons Manager

Loretta Bloom Ltd
Tait Business Centre
Dominic Street
Limerick Co. Limerick
Phone: 061-311004 Fax: 061-311424
SIC: 52423 Employees: 60
Ladies Wear Co-ordinates
Mr Anthony Hartigan Managing Director
Ms Maureen Killion Personnel Manager
Ms Bernadette Tiernan Sales Director
Ms Antoinette Hartigan Credit Controller

Moderne Ltd
89-90 Patrick Street
Cork Co. Cork
Phone: 021-4270266 Fax: 021-4271894
Email: info@moderne.ie
Web: http://www.moderne.ie
SIC: 52423 Employees: 45
Ladies Fashions Retailers
Mr Ross O'Dowling Managing Director
Ms Linda Murphy Accountant

Pamela Scott
84 Grafton Street
Dublin 2
Phone: 01-6796655 Fax: 01-6792787
SIC: 52423 Employees: 50
Ladies Fashions
Mr Sean Barron Managing Director
Mr Robert Barron Finance Manager
Ms Maura Leahy Personnel Manager

Louis Copeland & Sons
39/41 Capel Street
Dublin 1
Phone: 01-8721600 Fax: 01-8733609
Email: louis@louiscopeland.com
Web: http://www.louiscopeland.com
SIC: 52424 Employees: 23
Menswear- Retail
Mr Louis Copeland Proprietor

Seale Clothing Ltd
Greencastle Parade
Coolock
Dublin 17
Phone: 01-8477011 Fax: 01-8477626
Email: info@bestsmenswear.com
Web: http://www.bestsmenswear.com
SIC: 52424 Employees: 70
Clothes Retail (Men)
Mr Diarmuid O'Brien Managing Director
Mr Niall Brogan Finance Manager
Mr John Smith Sales & Marketing Manager

Gaeltarra Knitwear Ltd
Tourmakeady
Claremorris Co. Mayo
Phone: 092-44015 Fax: 092-44025
Email: admin@gaeltarra.ie
Web: http://www.gaeltarra.ie
SIC: 52426 Employees: 35
Knitwear Retailers
Mr Bert Hanahoe Managing Director
Ms Marian Diskin Finance Manager
Ms Marian O'Malley Human Resources Manager
Mr Vincent Hennelly Sales Manager

Kilkenny Shoes Ltd
Padmore Barnes
Wolfe Tone Street
Kilkenny Co. Kilkenny
Phone: 056-21037 Fax: 056-61515
Email: padmore@iol.ie
Web: http://www.padmore.barnes.com
SIC: 52431 Employees: 80
Shoe Makers & Factory Shop
Mr Patrick Roberts Managing Director
Mr Robert Grogan Financial Director
Mr Frank Bryan Sales & Marketing Director
Mr Pat Stapleton Production Manager

Thomas Patrick Ltd
77 Grafton Street
Dublin 2
Phone: 01-6713866 Fax: 01-6772444
Email: info@thomaspatrick.com
SIC: 52431 Employees: 25
Footwear Retailers
Mr Thomas Fitzpatrick Managing Director
Ms Eilish Fitzpatrick Finance Manager
Ms Orla Fitzpatrick Sales & Marketing Director

At Home With Clerys
Blanchardstown Retail Park
Blanchardstown
Dublin 15
Phone: 01-8066077 Fax: 01-8211790
Email: info@clerys.ie
Web: http://www.clerys.ie
SIC: 52441 Employees: 24
Beds
Mr Stephen Maquire Managing Director

Greenwood Group
Cobh Cross Industrial Estate
Carrigtwohill
Cork Co. Cork
Phone: 021-4883400 Fax: 021-4883763
SIC: 52441 Employees: 25
Furniture Retail
Ms Dorothy Brady Manager

Meadows & Byrne Ltd
Blarney Wollen Mills
Blarney
Cork Co. Cork
Phone: 021-4344100 Fax: 021-4344220
Email: info@meadows-byrne.ie
Web: http://www.meadows-byrne.ie
SIC: 52441 Employees: 50
Giftware & Furniture
Ms Freda Hayse Chief Executive
Mr Robert Riordan Finance Manager

O'Carroll Furniture
3 Sandyford Office Park
Blackthorn Avenue
Dublin 18
Phone: 01-2604818 Fax: 01-2604816
SIC: 52441 Employees: 42
Furniture Retail
Mr Martin O'Carroll

Patrick Bruen
Dublin Road
Carrick On Shannon Co. Leitrim
Phone: 078-41300 Fax: 078-41205
SIC: 52441 Employees: 30
Furniture
Mr Patrick Bruen

Sherlock Bros Ltd
Beechmount Industrial Estate
Navan Co. Meath
Phone: 046-28386 Fax: 046-28504
SIC: 52441 Employees: 70
Retail Furniture Sales
Mr John Sherlock Managing Director

Western Postform Ltd
Galway Road
Ballinasloe Co. Galway
Phone: 0905-42566 Fax: 0905-43867
Email: info@westernpostform.ie
SIC: 52441 Employees: 45
Furniture Retail
Mr Seamus Shinners Manager
Ms Trina Hurley Financial Controller
Mr Austin O' Toole Office Manager
Mr Alan O' Grady Sales Manager

Wogan's Furniture & Carpets Ltd
Market Street
Ardee Co. Louth
Phone: 041-6853951 Fax: 041-6856205
Email: wogans@eircom.net
SIC: 52441 Employees: 30
Retail Furniture Sales
Mr Paul O'Brien General Manager
Mr Damien Rooney Financial Accountant

Parkersell Lighting Services (Irl)
U1/2 Cookstown Enterprise Park
Tallaght
Dublin 24
Phone: 01-4511277 Fax: 01-4511975
Email: geninfo@parkersell.ie
Web: http://www.parkersell.com
SIC: 52442 Employees: 30
Lighting Consultants
Mr Brendan Young Managing Director

DID Electrical
Belgard Road
Tallaght
Dublin 24
Phone: 01-4598600 Fax: 01-4598911
SIC: 52451 Employees: 60
Home Appliances Retailers
Mr John Doran General Manager
Mr Martin Fitzgerald Finance Manager
Mr Tony Pender Sales Manager
Ms Marian Woulfe Computer Manager

Dixons
Jervis Shopping Centre
Jervis Street
Dublin 1
Phone: 01-8781515 Fax: 01-8781524
SIC: 52451 Employees: 150
Electrical Goods
Mr John Dunleavy Manager
Mr Con Casey Personnel Officer

Dixons
17 Parkwest Industrial Estate
Nangor Road
Dublin 12
Phone: 01-6262430 Fax: 01-6262486
SIC: 52451 Employees: 38
Electrical Stores
Mr Paul Cahill Manager
Mr Chris Clynch Finance Manager
Ms Lisa Googan Sales Manager

Electricworld
Level 2 Unit 246 The Square
Tallaght
Dublin 24
Phone: 01-4597987 Fax: 01-4597237
SIC: 52451 Employees: 23
Retail of Electrical Goods & Computers
Ms Mary Griffin Manager

HMDS Ltd
22 Dawson Street
Dublin 2
Phone: 01-6623332 Fax: 01-6611088
Email: admin@hmgroup.iol.ie
SIC: 52451 Employees: 30
Electrical Retail
Mr Stephen Cloonan Managing Director

IBS
Unit 27 Cookstown Industrial Estate
Dublin 24
Phone: 01-4622646 Fax: 01-4622645
Email: sales@dublin.ibs.ie
Web: http://www.dublin.ibs.ie
SIC: 52451 Employees: 40
Retail Office Equipment & Servicing
Mr Jerry Carey Managing Director
Mr John Foley Financial Controller
Mr John Foley Financial Controller
Mr Neil Cumiskey Sales Manager
Mr Anne Griffen Computer Manager

JA Kilroy & Son Ltd
High Street
Tullamore Co. Offaly
Phone: 0506-21475 Fax: 0506-21988
Email: kilroy@eircom.net
SIC: 52451 Employees: 150
Electrical & Household Furniture Retail
Mr Michael Campbell General Manager
Mr Gerry O'Reilly Credit Controller
Mr Paddy Galvin Personnel Manager
Mr Pascal Keegan IT Manager

Kiely's
Woodlands
Killarney Co. Kerry
Phone: 064-31678 Fax: 064-35044
Email: kielytkl@iol.ie
SIC: 52451 Employees: 58
Electrical Retailer
Mr Seamus Kiely Managing Director
Mr Patrick Roe Financial Controller
Ms Karen Neher General Secretary
Mr Peter Fee Sales & Marketing Manager

Kitchen Accessories Ltd
Ninth Lock Road
Elmfield', Clondalkin
Dublin 22
Phone: 01-4570821 Fax: 01-4574614
Email: sales@kal.ie
SIC: 52451 Employees: 31
Kitchen Appliances Retailers
Mr Andy Humphreys General Manager
Mr Paul Thompson Financial Controller
Ms Regina Brennan Sales Director

Maddens
5 Parliament Street
Cork Co. Cork
Phone: 021-4277930 Fax: 021-4273962
Email: maddens@indigo.ie
SIC: 52451 Employees: 55
Electrical Retailer
Mr Michael Harold Manager
Mr David Madden Sales Manager

Power City Ltd
Greenhills Centre, Greenhills Road
Tallaght
Dublin 24
Phone: 01-4527597 Fax: 01-8223108
Email: info@powercity.ie
Web: http://www.powercity.ie
SIC: 52451 Employees: 200
Electrical Retailer
Mr John Butler Manager

Atkins
Carrigrohane Road
Cork Co. Cork
Phone: 021-4347370 Fax: 021-4542864
SIC: 52461 Employees: 65
Hardware Store
Mr Michael Concannon General Manager

Colman Doyle
66 South Main Street
Wexford Co. Wexford
Phone: 053-42084 Fax: 053-24467
SIC: 52461 Employees: 200
Hardware Store
Mr Colman Doyle Managing Director
Ms Colette Doyle Sales & Marketing Manager

Country Manor Brick
The Brick Yard, East Wall Road,
Dublin 1
Phone: 01-8550650 Fax: 01-8554743
Email: info@cmb.ie
Web: http://www.cmb.ie
SIC: 52461 Employees: 50
Brick Retailers
Mr Eugene Gregor Managing Director

Flynns Of Lackagh Ltd
Turloughmore
Galway Co. Galway
Phone: 091-797116 Fax: 091-797146
SIC: 52461 Employees: 40
Hardware Store
Mr Dermot Healey Managing Director
Mr Peter Murphy Sales Director

Garvey (Roscommon) Ltd T/A Garveys
Lanesboro Road
Roscommon Co. Roscommon
Phone: 0903-26293 Fax: 0903-27733
Email: info@garveys.ie
Web: http://www.garveys.ie
SIC: 52461 Employees: 25
DIY Store & Builders Merchants
Mr Sean Garvey Managing Director
Ms Marian Cunningham Financial Controller
Ms Christina Fallon Personnel Manager
Mr Seamus Corcoran Sales Manager

Griffin Hawe Ltd
22 Duke Street
Athy Co. Kildare
Phone: 0507-31221 Fax: 0507-38885
Email: griffinhawe@eircom.net
Web: http://www.griffinhawe.ie
SIC: 52461 Employees: 25
Hardware / Builders Providers
Mr Mervyn Griffin Manager
Mr Stuart Griffin Finance Manager

Horseware Products Ltd
Finnabair Industrial Estate
Dublin Road
Dundalk Co. Louth
Phone: 042-9389000 Fax: 042-9337671
Email: info@horseware.com
Web: http://www.horseware.com
SIC: 52461 Employees: 120
Horseware Products
Mr Tom MacGuinness Managing Director
Mr Jim Martin Financial Controller
Ms Anne Newell Personnel Manager
Mr Paul McAviney Sales Manager
Ms Anita Martin Computer Manager

J Coogan Farm Services Ltd
Lugduff
Tinahely
Arklow Co. Wicklow
Phone: 0402-38111 Fax: 0402-38286
SIC: 52461 Employees: 39
General Hardware & Farm Services
Mr Jim Coogan Managing Director
Ms Geraldine Coogan Accountant

Joyce & Sons Headford Ltd
Galway Road
Headford
Galway Co. Galway
Phone: 093-35643 Fax: 093-35625
SIC: 52461 Employees: 35
Hardware & Farming Building Supplies
Mr James Joyce Proprietor
Ms Mary Curran Finance Manager

JP Newson & Co Ltd
20-21 William Street
Limerick Co. Limerick
Phone: 061-414211 Fax: 061-311246
SIC: 52461 Employees: 40
Hardware Store
Mr James Luttrell Managing Director

Lenehan & Sons
124 Chapel Street
Dublin 1
Phone: 01-8730466 Fax: 01-8730471
Email: postmaster@lenehans.ie
Web: http://www.lenehans.ie
SIC: 52461 Employees: 35
Hardware Store
Mr Paddy Lenehan Managing Director
Mr Brendan Fanning Accounts Manager
Mr Mark Lenehan Administrator

M Donnelly & Co Ltd
Unit 18 Lee Road, Dublin Industrial Estate
Glasnevin
Dublin 11
Phone: 01-8304558 Fax: 01-8304809
Email: mdonn@iol.ie
SIC: 52461 Employees: 50
Hardware Store
Mr Martin Donnelly Managing Director
Mr Declan Brophy Accounts Manager

Michael Connolly & Sons Ltd
Pump Street
Bagenalstown Co. Carlow
Phone: 0503-21274 Fax: 0503-22072
SIC: 52461 Employees: 70
General Merchants
Mr Tom Connolly Proprietor

MRCB Ltd
12-13 Cornmarket
Dublin 8
Phone: 01-6040860 Fax: 01-6798858
Email: mrcbltd@eircom.net
SIC: 52461 Employees: 24
Retail Paint and Wallpaper
Mr Eugene Coghlan Office Manager

P Boland Ltd
22 Main Street
Arklow Co. Wicklow
Phone: 0402-32201 Fax: 0402-31382
SIC: 52461 Employees: 32
Hardware Store
Mr Anthony Fogarty Director
Ms Katrina Ivory Financial Controller

Patrick Sweeney & Co Ltd
Achill Sound
Westport Co. Mayo
Phone: 098-45211 Fax: 098-45313
SIC: 52461 Employees: 35
General Hardware & Grocery
Mr Rory Sweeney Managing Director

Quinns Superstore
Mill Street
Baltinglass
Wicklow Co. Wicklow
Phone: 0508-81266 Fax: 0508-81772
Email: quinnsb@indigo.ie
SIC: 52461 Employees: 25
Hardware Store
Mr Liam Quinn Managing Director
Mr Dan O'Leary Financial Controller

System Design Cork Ltd
SIAC House
Airport Road
Cork Co. Cork
Phone: 021-4968680 Fax: 021-4968552
SIC: 52461 Employees: 23
Hardware & Software computer design
Mr Ray Hynes Proprietor

Universal Providers
Kells Road
Kilkenny Co. Kilkenny
Phone: 056-62658 Fax: 056-62793
Email: upkilkenny@chadwicks.ie
SIC: 52461 Employees: 30
Hardware Store
Mr Vincent Maher Managing Director

Anvil Trading
22 Main Street
Bray Co. Wicklow
Phone: 01-2862814 Fax: 01-2760078
SIC: 52462 Employees: 25
DIY Supplies
Ms Maureen Flavin Manager

Retail

Hickeys Cork Ltd
9-12 Maylor Street
Cork Co. Cork
Phone: 021-4273281 Fax: 021-4275747
Email: info@hickeys.ie
Web: http://www.hickeys.ie
SIC: 52462 Employees: 1350
Paints & Electrical Hardware & Appliances
Mr Jim Luttrell Managing Director
Mr Gerry Walsh Sales & Marketing Manager

Homebase Ireland
Nutgrove Avenue
Churchtown
Dublin 14
Phone: 01-2983644 Fax: 01-2983644
Email: info@homebase.co.uk
Web: http://www.homebase.co.uk
SIC: 52462 Employees: 95
DIY Products
Mr Martin Quigg Manager
Mr Stewart Leighton Sales Manager

Lomac Tilemarket
74 Kylemore Road
Ballyfermot
Dublin 10
Phone: 01-6266955 Fax: 01-6266965
SIC: 52462 Employees: 250
Wall & Floor Tiles
Mr John Morrissey Showroom Manager

OSB Group
Hollymount Industrial Estate
Hollyhill
Cork Co. Cork
Phone: 021-4392166 Fax: 021-4946514
Email: info@osbgroup.com
Web: http://www.osbgroup.com
SIC: 52462 Employees: 70
DIY Store
Mr Pat Kennedy Managing Director
Mr Declan O'Flaherty Partner
Mr Anthony McGrath Sales & Marketing Manager
Mr Terry Buckley Production Manager
Mr Glen Hackett Computer Manager

Panelling Centre
144 Richmond Road
Dublin 3
Phone: 01-8841111 Fax: 01-8841177
Email: info@panelcentre.ie
Web: http://www.panelcentre.ie
SIC: 52462 Employees: 100
DIY Supplies
Mr Anthony Ridgeway Manager
Mr Mark Patterson Director

Patton DIY Ltd
Monaghan Shopping Centre
Dawson Street
Monaghan Co. Monaghan
Phone: 047-72900 Fax: 047-83442
SIC: 52462 Employees: 25
DIY Store
Mr David Patton Proprietor

Woodies DIY & Garden Centre
Belgard Road
Tallaght
Dublin 24
Phone: 01-4521353 Fax: 01-4521226
SIC: 52462 Employees: 260
DIY Store
Mr Ray Colman Managing Director
Mr Michael Ryan Financial Controller
Mr Brendan Morris Sales Manager

Eason & Son Ltd
80 Middle Abbey Street
Dublin 1
Phone: 01-8733811 Fax: 01-8733545
Email: eason@iol.ie
Web: http://www.eason.ie
SIC: 52471 Employees: 1300
Bookshops
Mr Martin Black Manager
Mr John Cudlipp Retail Director

Hodges Figgis & Co Ltd
56-58 Dawson Street
Dublin 2
Phone: 01-6774754 Fax: 01-6792810
Email: books@hodgesfiggis.ie
Web: http://www.hodgesfiggis.ie
SIC: 52471 Employees: 65
Bookshop
Mr Walter Pohli Managing Director
Mr Joe Collins Sales & Marketing Manager

Kennys Bookshop & Art Gallery
High Street
Galway Co. Galway
Phone: 091-562739 Fax: 091-568544
Email: queries@kennys.ie
Web: http://www.kennys.ie
SIC: 52471 Employees: 30
Art Gallery & Bookshop
Mr Conor Kenny Managing Director
Mr Tom Gilligan Accounts Manager
Ms Karen Golden Marketing Manager
Mr David Lohan Computer Manager

News Brothers Ltd
Sitecast Industrial Estate
Pouladuff Road
Cork Co. Cork
Phone: 021-4964355 Fax: 021-4964971
SIC: 52471 Employees: 50
Bookshops
Mr Gordon Bolton Manager

O'Mahony & Co Ltd
120 O'Connell Street
Limerick Co. Limerick
Phone: 061-418155 Fax: 061-414558
Email: omahonys@iol.ie
SIC: 52471 Employees: 60
Bookshop
Mr Frank O'Mahony Proprietor
Mr David O'Mahony Chairman

Waterstones
7 Dawson Street
Dublin 2
Phone: 01-6791415 Fax: 01-6791318
Email: info@waterstones.co.uk
Web: http://www.waterstones.co.uk
SIC: 52471 Employees: 30
Bookshop
Mr Alan Warnock Manager
Mr Sean McGowan Personnel Manager

Donovans Newsagents Ltd
Green Field Shopping Centre
Maynooth Co. Kildare
Phone: 01-6289408 Fax: 01-6291727
SIC: 52472 Employees: 30
Newsagents
Mr Sean Donovan Proprietor

Duffy Group Ltd
Gerry Duffy House, Old Bawn Shopping
Tallaght
Dublin 24
Phone: 01-4516621 Fax: 01-4516031
Email: info@duffygroup.ie
Web: http://www.duffygroup.ie
SIC: 52472 Employees: 105
Convenience Store
Mr Basil Duffy Managing Director
Mr Ciaran O'Cleirigh Financial Controller
Ms Margaret Kenny Personnel Manager
Mr Basil Duffy Sales Manager
Mr Pat Farrell Production/Operations Manager
Ms Cherie McGrane Computer Manager

Gem Northside
Unit 40 Northside Shopping Centre
Coolock
Dublin 5
Phone: 01-8471533 Fax: 01-8471533
SIC: 52472 Employees: 50
Newsagents
Mr Greg Rickard Managing Director
Ms Julie Dunne Manager

M & G Gallagher
97 Upper Rathmines Road
Dublin 6
Phone: 01-4964771 Fax: 01-4964724
Email: lateshop@eircom.net
SIC: 52472 Employees: 100
Bookshops and Newsagents
Mr Manus Gallagher Partner
Ms Alice Riordan Office Manager
Mr Brian Riordan IT Manager

Reads Of Nassau Street
24/25 Nassau Street
Dublin 2
Phone: 01-6796011 Fax: 01-6711684
SIC: 52472 Employees: 36
Newsagents - Stationery
Mr David O'Reilly Manager
Mr Michael O'Reilly Finance Manager
Mr Niall Mescall Sales Manager
Mr Gary O'Reilly Computer Manager

Reuters Ireland
Kestrel House
Clanwilliam Place
Dublin 2
Phone: 01-5001500 Fax: 01-5001501
Email: info@reuters.com
Web: http://www.reuters.com
SIC: 52472 Employees: 35
News Agency
Mr Patrick O'Reilly Managing Director
Mr Conor Murphy Financial Controller
Ms Tara O'Rourke Office Administrator
Ms Emer Goggins Sales & Marketing Manager
Mr Brian Reid Technical Manager

Bizquip Ltd
Arkle Road
Sandyford Business Park
Dublin 18
Phone: 01-2178000 Fax: 01-2178010
Email: generalinfo@bizquip.ie
Web: http://www.bizquip.ie
SIC: 52473 Employees: 56
Office Equipment & Stationery
Mr Jim Leyden Proprietor
Mr Darren Lowans Personnel Manager
Mr Nick Gaye Sales Director

Codex Office Products
89 Lagan Road
Dublin Industrial Estate
Dublin 11
Phone: 01-8822000 Fax: 01-8307180
Email: sales@codexltd.com
Web: http://www.codexltd.com
SIC: 52473 Employees: 55
Stationery
Mr Brendan Murphy Managing Director
Mr Turloch O'Sullivan Finance Manager
Ms Edel Spence Sales Director
Mr Alan Slattery Computer Manager

Data Print
Phoenix Industrial Estate
Navan Road
Dublin 15
Phone: 01-8367105 Fax: 01-8686166
SIC: 52473 Employees: 35
Listing Paper Retail & Printing
Mr James Skelton Managing Director
Mr Tom O'Hanlon Finance Manager

Ergoservices Ltd
251-255 Richmond Road
Fairview
Dublin 3
Phone: 01-8843200 Fax: 01-8843201
Email: sales@ergoservices.ie
Web: http://www.ergoservices.ie
SIC: 52473 Employees: 84
Printers Retail
Mr John Purdy Managing Director
Mr Mark Kenny Finance Manager
Mr Owen Ryan Personnel Director
Mr Roisin Gilroy Sales Manager

Field Boxmore Dublin Ltd
Fonthill Business Park
Fonthill Road
Dublin 22
Phone: 01-6236700 Fax: 01-6215120
Email: bpg@eircom.net
Web: http://www.avery.iol.ie
SIC: 52473 Employees: 100
Labels & Label Machines
Mr Bobby O'Connor General Manager
Ms Sandra Dillon Personnel Manager
Mr Gerry Malloy Sales & Marketing Director
Mr Sean Dowling Production Services Manager
Mr John Rowland IT Manager

Glen C Office Supplies Ltd
College Road
Lisbo Industrial Estate
Galway Co. Galway
Phone: 091-771199 Fax: 091-771171
SIC: 52473 Employees: 30
Office Supplies
Mr Tom Henly Managing Director

Spicers (Ireland)
4060 Kingswood Road
City West Business Campus
Dublin 24
Phone: 01-2457800 Fax: 01-2457799
Email: dublin@spicers.ltd.uk
Web: http://www.spicersnet.com
SIC: 52473 Employees: 60
Stationery
Mr Bill Maher Managing Director
Ms Geraldine Breen Financial Controller
Mr Graham Whelan Sales Manager

Viking Direct
Unit 35 Rosemount Business Park
Blanchardstown
Dublin 15
Phone: 01-8150600 Fax: 01-8150606
SIC: 52473 Employees: 150
Stationery
Ms Mary Nolan Manager

Camera Centre
56 Grafton Street
Dublin 2
Phone: 01-6775594 Fax: 01-6777977
Email: sales@cameracentre.iol.ie
SIC: 52482 Employees: 25
Photographic Retailer
Mr Seamus McCabe General Manager
Mr Damian Byrne Personnel Manager

Hahnel
Parnell Street
Bandon Co. Cork
Phone: 023-41606 Fax: 023-44963
Email: info@hahnel.ie
SIC: 52482 Employees: 35
Photographic Accessories
Mr Walter Hahnel Managing Director
Ms John McKeown Accounts Manager
Mr Chris Hahnel Sales & Marketing Manager
Mr Anthony O'Herlihy Production Manager
Mr Michael Hahnel Computer Manager

HMV
18 Henry Street
Dublin 1
Phone: 01-8732899 Fax: 01-8732936
SIC: 52483 Employees: 28
Music Store
Mr Des Lee Branch Manager

Sound City Galway Ltd
5 - 6 Shop Street
Galway Co. Galway
Phone: 091-564198 Fax: 091-509951
Email: info@musicireland.com
Web: http://www.musicireland.com
SIC: 52483 Employees: 60
Music Retail Outllet
Mr Des Hubbard General Manager
Mr Declan McEntee Personnel Manager

Dynasty
Block N2
Marina Commercial Park
Cork Co. Cork
Phone: 021-4318811 Fax: 021-4318727
Email: dynasty@iol.ie
SIC: 52484 Employees: 110
Retail Costume Jewellery
Mr Cyril Walsh Managing Director
Ms Angela Cahill Finance Manager
Ms Elizabeth O'Leary Human Resources Director

JWH Jewellers
Crescent Shopping Centre
Dooradoyle
Limerick Co. Limerick
Phone: 061-229566 Fax: 061-229025
Email: jwh@indigo.ie
SIC: 52484 Employees: 62
Jewellers
Mr Gerardine Harrison Proprietor

Solvar Exports
10 Harcourt Street
Dublin 2
Phone: 01-4780799 Fax: 01-4752370
Email: info@antnic.ie
Web: http://www.antnic.ie
SIC: 52484 Employees: 130
Jewellery Retail/Wholesale
Mr Anthony Overnik Managing Director
Mr Noel Coyle Finance Manager
Mr Colin Hadden Computer Manager

Weir & Son Ltd
96-99 Grafton Street
Dublin 2
Phone: 01-6779678 Fax: 01-6777739
Email: weirs@indigo.ie
SIC: 52484 Employees: 60
Jewellers
Mr David Andrews Joint Managing Director
Mr Tom Jenkinson Finance Manager
Mr David McCormick Personnel Manager

Champion Sports
Adare House Unit 6A Westgate Business Park
Ballymount
Dublin 24
Phone: 01-4190100 Fax: 01-4564036
Email: info@champion.ie
Web: http://www.champion.ie
SIC: 52485 Employees: 700
Sports Shop
Mr Paul McGlade Managing Director
Mr Liam Cunningham Finance Manager
Ms Fiona O'Malley Personnel Manager
Mr Michael Keith Sales & Marketing Manager
Mr Derek Buchannan Computer Manager

Connolly Sports
Loughgeorge
Claregalway
Galway Co. Galway
Phone: 091-798303 Fax: 091-798543
Email: conn1@indigo.ie
Web: http://www.connollysports.com
SIC: 52485 Employees: 60
Sports Retail
Mr Padraic Connolly Managing Director
Ms Cecilia Ruane Financial Controller
Ms Mary Fox Sales Director

Lifestyle Sports
Old Airport Road
Cloghran
Swords Co. Dublin
Phone: 01-8163100 Fax: 01-8163150
Email: info@lifestyle-sport.ie
Web: http://www.lss21.com
SIC: 52485 Employees: 600
Sports Goods & Equipment
Mr Andrew Sharkey Managing Director
Mr Tony McEntee Financial Controller
Ms Annemarie Keady IT Manager

McGuirk's Golf
Harbour Road
Howth
Dublin 13
Phone: 01-8393895 Fax: 01-8321653
Email: info@mcguirksgolf.ie
Web: http://www.mcguirksgolf.com.ie
SIC: 52485 Employees: 85
Golf Shop
Mr John McGuirk Managing Director
Ms Angela Maloney Finance Manager

Ben Eadair Fishing Company
1 West Pier
Howth
Dublin 13
Phone: 01-8393148 Fax: 01-8324090
Email: lettdorn@indigo.ie
SIC: 52487 Employees: 40
Fishing Company
Ms Muriel Doran Executive Director
Mr Tony Cuthbert Financial Controller
Ms Siobhan Doran Sales & Marketing Manager
Mr Sean Doran Operations Manager

Pride & Joy
13-20 Donaghmede Shopping Centre
Dublin 13
Phone: 01-8476107 Fax: 01-8476377
SIC: 52489 Employees: 25
Toy Shop
Mr Stephen Hinksman Managing Director

Smyths Toys Ltd
31a Mulvoy Commercial Centre
Sean Mulvoy Road
Galway Co. Galway
Phone: 091-743602 Fax: 091-743698
SIC: 52489 Employees: 400
Toy & Software Retailers
Mr Tony Smyth Managing Director
Mr Brian Donoghoe

Retail

Tommy's Wonderland
Unit 6b Northside Shopping Centre
Coolock
Dublin 17
Phone: 01-8477232 Fax: 01-8476311
SIC: 52489 Employees: 50
Toys and Fancy Goods Retailers
Ms Pauline McDonagh Manager

Avoca Handweavers Ltd
Millmount Mills
Kilmacanogue
Bray Co. Wicklow
Phone: 01-2867466 Fax: 01-2862367
Email: despatch@avoca.ie
Web: http://www.avoca.ie
SIC: 52491 Employees: 417
Hand Weavers
Mr Simon Pratt Manager
Mr A Coleman Personnel Manager
Ms Amanda Pratt Sales & Marketing Manager

D O'Sullivan (Graphic Supplies) Ltd
23-25 Grantham Street
Dublin 8
Phone: 01-4780422 Fax: 01-4782385
Email: telesales@dosgs.ie
Web: http://www.osullivangraphics.com
SIC: 52491 Employees: 48
Graphic Arts Suppliers
Mr Donal O'Sullivan Managing Director
Mr Terry Jackson Financial Controller
Mr Von Whittle Personnel Manager
Mr Julian O'Sullivan Computer Manager

Carroll's of Dublin Ltd
57 Upper O'Connell Street
Dublin 1
Phone: 01-8735587 Fax: 01-8735709
SIC: 52494 Employees: 120
Gift Shop
Mr Colm Carroll Managing Director
Mr John Browne Financial Controller
Mr Raymond O'Connell Sales Director
Mr Fran Kelly Computer Manager

Genesis Fine Arts
Mullingar Business Park
Mullingar Co. Westmeath
Phone: 044-43078 Fax: 044-43539
Email: genesisfinearts@eircom.net
Web: http://www.genesisfinearts.com
SIC: 52494 Employees: 60
Gift Shop Suppliers
Mr Tony Collins Managing Director
Mr Donald Bell Financial Controller
Mr Paul Dempsey Sales Manager
Mr Joe Duncan Production Manager
Ms Cathy O'Loughlin Computer Manager

House of Ireland Ltd
37-38 Nassau Street
Dublin 2
Phone: 01-6714543 Fax: 01-6791023
Email: info@houseofireland.com
Web: http://www.houseofireland.com
SIC: 52494 Employees: 30
Gift Retailers
Ms Eileen Galligan Managing Director
Ms Grace Galligan Sales Manager

Nicholas Mosse Pottery Ltd
Bennetsbridge
Kilkenny Co. Kilkenny
Phone: 056-27105 Fax: 056-27491
Email: sales@nicholasmosse.com
Web: http://www.nicholasmosse.com
SIC: 52494 Employees: 40
Giftware & Pottery
Mr Nicholas Mosse Managing Director

Aircall Wireless Solution
Clonskeagh Square
Dublin 14
Phone: 01-2698877 Fax: 01-2692596
Email: postmaster@aircall.ie
Web: http://www.aircall.ie
SIC: 52495 Employees: 30
Mobile Phone Repairs
Mr Owen Kavanagh Managing Director
Ms Maura Farrelly Financial Controller

Brightpoint (Ireland) Ltd
Oak Court Western Business Park
Dublin 12
Phone: 01-4603300 Fax: 01-4603330
Email: postmaster@brightpoint.ie
Web: http://www.brightpoint.ie
SIC: 52495 Employees: 70
Mobile Phone Retailers
Mr Jim Doak Chief Executive
Ms Gretta Hayes Sales Manager
Mr Eamon O'Leary ITManager

Cellular Connection
176 Pembroke Road
Dublin 4
Phone: 01-6600600 Fax: 01-6600666
Email: cellularconnection@eircom.net
SIC: 52495 Employees: 25
Mobile Phone Retailer
Mr Colin Hayes Managing Director
Ms Christina O'Reilly Manager

Cellular World
Unit T4 Birch Avenue
Stillorgan Industrial Park
Blackrock Co. Dublin
Phone: 01-2061000 Fax: 01-2061043
Email: info@cellularworld.ie
Web: http://www.cellularworld.ie
SIC: 52495 Employees: 800
Mobile Phone Retailer
Mr Ronan Murphy Director
Ms Aoife Short Finance Manager
Mr Derek McDonald Sales Manager

Eddie Totterdells Ltd
6 Upper George Street
Dun Laoghaire Co. Dublin
Phone: 01-2800203 Fax: 01-2844357
Email: totterdells@eircom.net
SIC: 52495 Employees: 50
Mobile Phone Retailer
Mr Derek Gallagher Manager
Ms Ann Burgess Personnel Manager

Person 2 Person
2 Slaney Drive Dublin Industrial Estate
Glasnevin
Dublin 11
Phone: 01-8601801 Fax: 01-8601842
Email: info@p2p.ie
Web: http://www.p2p.ie
SIC: 52495 Employees: 1150
Mobile Phone Retailer
Ms Josephine Conaghan Managing Director
Mr Derek Gleeson Finance Manager
Mr Alan Muldey Sales Manager

Talk To Me Ltd
5 Demesne Shopping Centre
Dundalk Co. Louth
Phone: 042-9338822 Fax: 042-9338811
Email: info@talktome.ie
Web: http://www.talktome.ie
SIC: 52495 Employees: 90
Mobile Phone Retailer
Mr Hugh McEvoy Proprietor
Ms Olivia Sunderland Finance Manager
Mr John Long Corporate Sales

Irish Dresden Ltd
Dromcolliher
Limerick Co. Limerick
Phone: 063-83030 Fax: 063-83192
Email: sales@irishdresden.iol.ie
SIC: 52498 Employees: 40
Glass & China Retail
Ms Johanna Saar General Manager
Ms Sabina Best Production Manager
Ms Sabina Saar IT Manager

Pound City
57 Moore Street
Dublin 1
Phone: 01-8731922 Fax: 01-8731604
SIC: 52499 Employees: 24
Discount Stores
Mr Andrew Shepherd General Manager

Pound World
Unit 270 Western Industrial Estate
Dublin 12
Phone: 01-4502272 Fax: 01-4502298
SIC: 52499 Employees: 200
Discount Stores
Mr Paul Hamill Manager
Mr Declan Malone Finance Manager
Ms Margaret O'Brien Personnel Manager

Flanagans of Buncrana Ltd
Shorefront, Buncrana
Lifford Co. Donegal
Phone: 077-62000 Fax: 077-62345
Email: flan@iol.ie
SIC: 52520 Employees: 30
Antique Furniture
Mr Brian Flanagan Managing Director
Mr Peter Flanagan Sales Manager
Mr Owen McGonigle Production Manager
Mr Jonathan Carey Computer Manager

Family Album
1/2 Upper O'Connell Street
Dublin 1
Phone: 01-8726600 Fax: 01-8745237
SIC: 52610 Employees: 57
Mail Order Retailing
Mr Ewan Byrne Managing Director
Mr Michael Murray Financial Controller
Ms Mary Rose Macken Personnel Manager
Ms Michelle O'Brien Marketing Manager
Ms Carmel Gartland Operations Manager

GUS Ireland Ltd
Unit 20 Chestnut Road
Western Industrial Estate
Dublin 12
Phone: 01-4502222 Fax: 01-4506888
Email: info@celtichampers.com
Web: http://www.celtichampers.com
SIC: 52610 Employees: 100
Mail Order Hampers
Mr Ewan Byrne Managing Director
Mr Michael Murray Finance Manager
Ms Yvonne Boyle Sales Manager
Ms Eileen Fitzgerald Computer Manager

Avonmore Electrical
Killarney Road
Rosekeen
Mallow Co. Cork
Phone: 022-47477 Fax: 022-47461
Email: avonmoreelectrical@eircom.net
SIC: 52720 Employees: 60
Electrical Repairs
Mr Jeremiah Sheehan Managing Director
Ms Bridget McGrath Financial Controller
Mr Pat O'Sullivan Sales & Marketing Manager

Hospitality

55 Hospitality
55110 Hotels
55121 Guesthouses
55122 Bed & Breakfast Accommodation (B&B)
55210 Self Catering & Hostels
55220 Caravan & Camping Sites
55231 Holiday Centres & Holiday Villages
55232 Farmhouse Accommodation
55301 Restaurants
55302 Cafes
55303 Take-Away Food Shops
55304 Pizza Parlours
55401 Private Licensed Social Clubs
55402 Public Houses
55403 Bars – Late & Food Licence
55404 Night Clubs
55510 Canteens & Messes
55520 Catering

Abberley Court Hotel
Belgard Road
Tallaght
Dublin 24
Phone: 01-4596000 Fax: 01-4621000
Email: abberley@iol.ie
SIC: 55110 Employees: 65
Hotel ***
Mr Brendan Flynn Managing Director
Mr Brian Flynn Finance Director
Ms Mary Byrne Human Resources Manager
Ms Louise McKeown Sales Manager
Ms Briege Flynn IT Manager

Abbey Court Hotel
Dublin Road
Nenagh Co. Tipperary
Phone: 067-41111 Fax: 067-41022
Email: info@nenagh-abbeycourt.ie
Web: http://www.nenagh-abbeycourt.ie
SIC: 55110 Employees: 70
Hotel ***
Mr Tom Walsh Managing Director
Mr Ger Heffernan Financial Controller
Ms Ann Masterson Sales Director

Abbey Glen Castle Hotel
Sky Road
Clifden
Galway Co. Galway
Phone: 095-21201 Fax: 095-21797
Email: info@abbeyglen.ie
Web: http://www.abbeyglen.ie
SIC: 55110 Employees: 45
Hotel ****
Mr Paul Hughes Proprietor
Mr Brian Hughes General Manager

Abbey Hotel
The Diamond
Donegal Co. Donegal
Phone: 073-21014 Fax: 073-23660
Email: whitegrp@iol.ie
Web: http://www.whites-hotels.com
SIC: 55110 Employees: 130
Hotel ***
Mr Jim White Manager
Ms Patricia Wilson Personnel Manager
Ms Sinead McGowan Sales & Marketing Manager
Mr Frank Brown IT Manager

Actons Hotel
Pier Road
Kinsale Co. Cork
Phone: 021-4772135 Fax: 0214-772231
Email: info@actonshotelkinsale.com
Web: http://www.actonshotelkinsale.com
SIC: 55110 Employees: 60
Hotel ***
Mr Jack Walsh General Manager
Ms Anne Murphy Financial Controller
Ms Laura Walsh Personnel Director
Ms Ann Marie Cross O'Connor Sales Manager

Adams Trinity Hotel
28 Dame Lane
Dublin 2
Phone: 01-6707100 Fax: 01-6707101
Email: reservations.adamstrinity@indigo.ie
SIC: 55110 Employees: 54
Hotel***
Mr Peter Hanahoe Proprietor
Ms Orla Crehan Personnel Manager
Ms Meave Carley Sales Director

Aghadoe Heights Hotel
Lakes of Killarney
Killarney Co. Kerry
Phone: 064-31766 Fax: 064-31345
Email: info@aghadoeheights.com
Web: http://www.aghadoeheights.com
SIC: 55110 Employees: 125
Hotel *****
Mr Pat Chawke General Manager
Ms Nora O'Mahoney Accountant
Mr Oliver Heffernan Operations Manager
Ms Emma Philips Sales & Marketing Manager

Aherlow House Hotel
Glen of Aherlow
Tipperary Co. Tipperary
Phone: 062-56153 Fax: 062-56212
Email: aherlow@iol.ie
Web: http://www.aherlowhouse.ie
SIC: 55110 Employees: 65
Hotel ***
Ms Frances Fogarty General Manager
Ms June Duggan Proprietor
Ms Una McMahon Sales & Marketing Manager

Allingham Arms Hotel
Main Street
Bundoran
Donegal Co. Donegal
Phone: 072-41075 Fax: 072-41171
SIC: 55110 Employees: 140
Hotel ***
Mr Peter McIntyre General Manager
Ms Elizabeth McIntyre Sales & Marketing Manager

Ardboyne Hotel
Dublin Road
Navan Co. Meath
Phone: 046-23119 Fax: 046-22355
Email: ardboyne@quinn-hotels.com
Web: http://www.quinn-hotels.com
SIC: 55110 Employees: 70
Hotel ***
Mr Michael McLaughlin General Manager
Ms Catherine Dunne Accountant
Ms Mary Fitzsimmons Personnel Manager
Ms Bernie McHugh Sales & Marketing Manager

Ardilaun House Hotel
Taylors Hill
Galway Co. Galway
Phone: 091-521433 Fax: 091-521546
Email: ardilaun@iol.ie
Web: http://www.ardilaunhousehotel.ie
SIC: 55110 Employees: 75
Hotel ****
Mr Tom MacCarthy General Manager
Ms Ann Silk Accounts Manager
Mr John Baughan Personnel Manager

Arlington Hotel
23/25 Bachelors Walk
O'Connell Bridge
Dublin 1
Phone: 01-8049100 Fax: 01-8049112
Email: arlington@tinet.ie
Web: http://www.arlington.ie
SIC: 55110 Employees: 100
Hotel ***
Mr Paul Keenan General Manager
Ms Joanna Simpson Financial Controller
Ms Clare Mills Office Manager
Ms Michelle Kelly Sales & Marketing Manager

Ashford Castle Hotel
Cong
Claremorris Co. Mayo
Phone: 092-46003 Fax: 092-46260
Email: ashford@ashford.ie
Web: http://www.ashford.ie
SIC: 55110 Employees: 200
Hotel *****
Mr Bill Buckley General Manager
Mr Colm Dalton Accounts Manager
Ms Paula Carroll Marketing Manager

Atlantic Coast Hotel
The Quay
Westport Co. Mayo
Phone: 098-29000 Fax: 098-29111
Email: achotal@iol.ie
Web: http://www.atlanticcoasthotel.com
SIC: 55110 Employees: 40
Hotels
Mr Jim Mulcahy General Manager
Ms Ann Downey Personnel Director
Ms Catherine O'Grady Sales Director

Ballyliffen Hotel
Ballyliffen
Clonmany
Lifford Co. Donegal
Phone: 077-76106 Fax: 077-76658
SIC: 55110 Employees: 50
Hotel**
Mr Michael McGonigle Manager
Ms Ann McGonigle Sales Manager

Ballynahinch Castle Hotel
Recess
Connemara
Galway Co. Galway
Phone: 095-31006 Fax: 095-31085
Email: bhinch@iol.ie
Web: http://www.ballynahinch-castle.com
SIC: 55110 Employees: 50
Hotel ****
Mr Patrick O'Flaherty General Manager

Ballyroe Heights Hotel
Ballyroe Heights
Ballyroe
Tralee Co. Kerry
Phone: 066-7126796 Fax: 066-7125066
Email: info@ballyroe.com
Web: http://www.ballyroe.com
SIC: 55110 Employees: 60
Hotel ***
Mr John Collins Proprietor
Mr Mark Sullivan Sales Manager

Baltimore Harbour Hotel
Baltimore
Cork Co. Cork
Phone: 028-20361 Fax: 028-20466
Email: info@bhrhotel.ie
Web: http://www.bhrhotel.ie
SIC: 55110 Employees: 40
Hotel ***
Mr Charles Cullinane Proprietor
Mr Gerry Murphy Accountant
Ms Fiona O'Sullivan Sales & Marketing Manager

Hospitality

Bartra House Hotel
Pearse Street
Ballina Co. Mayo
Phone: 096-22200 Fax: 096-22111
SIC: 55110 Employees: 45
Hotel **
Mr Paul Reagan Proprietor
Mr Noel Reagan Sales & Marketing Manager

Bell & Salmon Arms Hotel
95/97 Main Street
Carrick On Suir Co. Tipperary
Phone: 051-645555 Fax: 051-641293
Web: http://www.iol.ie/tip/bellsalm.htm
SIC: 55110 Employees: 100
Hotel
Mr Padraic Babbington Proprietor
Ms Catherine Babbington Sales & Marketing Manager

Berkeley Court Hotel
Lansdowne Road
Ballsbridge
Dublin 4
Phone: 01-6601711 Fax: 01-6617238
Web: http://www.berkeleycourthotel.com
SIC: 55110 Employees: 350
Hotel*****
Mr Joe Russell General Manager
Mr Noel Finnegan Financial Controller
Ms Kiera O'Dwyer Personnel Manager
Ms Anne Abberton Sales Manager
Mr David Murphy Accountant

Bewley's Hotel
Merrion Road
Ballsbridge
Dublin 4
Phone: 01-6681111 Fax: 01-6681999
Email: res@bewleyshotels.com
Web: http://www.bewleyshotels.com
SIC: 55110 Employees: 150
Hotel
Ms Clio O'Gara General Manager
Ms Elaine Cross Financial Controller

Blarney Park Hotel
Blarney
Cork Co. Cork
Phone: 021-4385281 Fax: 021-4381506
Email: info@blarneypark.com
Web: http://www.blarneypark.com
SIC: 55110 Employees: 100
Hotel ***
Mr Gerry O'Connor Managing Director
Ms Claire Cashin Personnel Manager
Mr Aidan Grimes General Manager

Bloomfield House Hotel
Tullamore Road
Mullingar Co. Westmeath
Phone: 044-40894 Fax: 044-43767
Email: bloomfieldhouse@eircom.net
SIC: 55110 Employees: 100
Hotel ***
Mr Seamus Laffan General Manager
Ms Kate Farrell Financial Controller
Mr John Short Sales & Marketing Manager

Blooms Hotel
Anglesea Street
Templebar
Dublin 2
Phone: 01-6715622 Fax: 01-6715997
Email: blooms@eircom.net
Web: http://www.blooms.ie
SIC: 55110 Employees: 60
Hotel ***
Mr Martin Keane Proprietor
Ms Jennifer Towell General Manager

Blue Haven Hotel
1-4 Pearse Street
Kinsale Co. Cork
Phone: 021-4772209 Fax: 021-4774268
Email: bluehaven@iol.ie
SIC: 55110 Employees: 50
Hotel ***
Mr Peter Cole General Manager
Mr Declan Delaney Assistant Manager

Boyne Valley Hotel
Dublin Road
Stameen
Drogheda Co. Louth
Phone: 041-9837737 Fax: 041-9839188
Email: reservations@boyne-valley-hotel.ie
Web: http://www.boyne-valley-hotel.ie
SIC: 55110 Employees: 70
Hotel***
Mr Michael McNamara Proprietor
Ms Denise Walsh Financial Controller
Mr Noel Comer Manager
Mr Clolin O'Rourke Production Manager

Bracken Court Hotel
The Square
Balbriggan Co. Dublin
Phone: 01-8413333 Fax: 01-8415118
Web: http://www.brackencourt.ie
SIC: 55110 Employees: 55
Hotel
Mr O'Sullivan Manager
Mr Chris Harmon Finance Manager
Ms Dervla O'Neill Sales Manager
Ms Serena O'Connor Computer Manager

Brandon Hotel
Princes Street
Tralee Co. Kerry
Phone: 066-7123333 Fax: 066-7125019
Email: louise@brandonhotel.ie
Web: http://www.brandonhotel.ie
SIC: 55110 Employees: 130
Hotel***
Ms Petra McDermott Managing Director
Mr Henry McCann Financial Controller
Ms Louise Langan Sales & Marketing Manager

Breaffy House Hotel
Breaffy
Castlebar Co. Mayo
Phone: 094-22033 Fax: 094-22276
Email: breaffyhotel@anu.ie
Web: http://www.breaffyhousehotel.com
SIC: 55110 Employees: 80
Hotel ***
Mr David Ryan General Manager
Ms Emma O' Toole Sales & Marketing Manager

Bridge Hotel
1 The Quay
Waterford Co. Waterford
Phone: 051-877222 Fax: 051-877229
Email: bridgehotel@treacyhotelsgroup.com
Web: http://www.treacyshotelgroup.com
SIC: 55110 Employees: 90
Hotel ***
Mr Jim Treacy Proprietor
Ms Rosemary Ahern Receptionist
Ms Catriona Byrne Sales & Marketing Manager

Bridge House Hotel & Leisure Club
Bridge Street
Tullamore Co. Offaly
Phone: 0506-22000 Fax: 0506-25690
Email: info@bridgehouse.com
Web: http://www.bridgehouse.com
SIC: 55110 Employees: 200
Hotel ****
Mr Colm McCabe General Manager
Mr John Hoare Financial Controller
Ms Paula McCabe Personnel Director

Bunratty Castle Hotel
Bunratty
Ennis Co. Clare
Phone: 061-364116 Fax: 061-364891
Email: info@bunrattycastlehotel.iol.ie
SIC: 55110 Employees: 140
Hotel***
Ms Deirdre Welsh General Manager
Mr Robert Riordan Finance Manager
Ms Freda Hayes Sales/Marketing Manager

Burkes Armada Hotel
The Spanish Point
Ennis Co. Clare
Phone: 065-7084110 Fax: 065-7084632
Email: armada@iol.ie
SIC: 55110 Employees: 50
Hotel & Self-Catering Cottages
Ms Claire Burke Partner
Mr John Burke Jnr General Manager
Ms June Burke Partner

Burlington Hotel
Upper Leeson Street
Dublin 4
Phone: 01-6605222 Fax: 01-6608496
Email: burlington@jurysdoyle.com
Web: http://www.jurysdoyle.com
SIC: 55110 Employees: 400
Hotel ****
Mr John Clifton General Manager
Ms Paula Someri-Kennedy Financial Controller
Ms Clara O'Dwyer Personnel Manager
Mr Niall Geoghegan Sales & Marketing Director

Buswells Hotel
25 Molesworth Street
Dublin 2
Phone: 01-6764013 Fax: 01-6762090
Email: buswells@quinn-hotels.com
Web: http://www.quinn-group.com
SIC: 55110 Employees: 50
Hotel ****
Mr Paul Gallagher General Manager
Ms Michelle McPhilips Office Manager
Ms Vari McGreevy Sales & Marketing Manager

Cabra Castle Hotel & Golf Club
Kingscourt
Cavan Co. Cavan
Phone: 042-9667030 Fax: 042-9667039
Email: cabrach@iol.ie
Web: http://www.cabracastle.com
SIC: 55110 Employees: 55
Hotel ****
Mr Howard Corscadden Manager
Ms Miriam Tierney Accounts Manager
Ms Colette Brady Sales & Marketing Manager

Cahir House Hotel
The Square
Cahir Co. Tipperary
Phone: 052-42727 Fax: 052-42727
Email: cahirhousehotel@eircom.ie
SIC: 55110 Employees: 50
Hotel ***
Mr Liam Duffy General Manager
Mr William Hanrahan Financial Controller

Camden Court Hotel
1 Camden Street
Dublin 2
Phone: 01-4759666 Fax: 01-4759677
Email: sales@camdencourthotel.com
Web: http://www.camdencourthotel.com
SIC: 55110 Employees: 70
Hotel***
Mr Derry Britton General Manager
Ms Susan McEvoy Finance Manager
Mr Gary Britton Personnel Manager
Ms Georgia Blake Sales & Marketing Manager
Ms Clara Clarke Computer Manager

Camden Hall Hotel
1 Upper Camden Street
Dublin 2
Phone: 01-4757906 Fax: 01-4757905
Email: camdenhallhotel@eircom.net
SIC: 55110 Employees: 50
Hotel***
Mr Eamon O'Reilly Proprietor
Mr Sean Harrington Finance Manager
Mr James O'Reilly General Manager

Carrickdale Hotel
Carricarnon
Ravensdale
Dundalk Co. Louth
Phone: 042-9371397 Fax: 042-9371740
Email: manager@carrickdale.com
Web: http://www.carrickdale.com
SIC: 55110 Employees: 30
Hotel ***
Ms Breige Savage General Manager

Carrigaline Court Hotel & Leisure Centre
Main Street
Carrigaline
Cork Co. Cork
Phone: 021-4371300 Fax: 021-4371103
Email: carrigcourt@eircom.net
SIC: 55110 Employees: 100
Hotel****
Mr John O'Flynn General Manager
Ms Bernadette Kirby Sales & Marketing Manager

Cashel Palace Hotel
Main Street
Cashel Co. Tipperary
Phone: 062-62707 Fax: 062-61521
Email: reception@cashel-palace.ie
Web: http://www.cashel-palace.ie
SIC: 55110 Employees: 50
Hotel ***
Mr Patrick Murphy Proprietor
Ms Eileen Walsh Accounts Manager
Ms Susan Murphy Operational Manager

Castle Hotel Group
2-4 Great Denmark Street
Dublin 1
Phone: 01-8746949 Fax: 01-8727674
Email: hotels@indigo.ie
Web: http://www.indigo.ie/~hotels
SIC: 55110 Employees: 50
Hotel **
Mr Fionn MacCumhaill Managing Director
Mr Kevin Fingleton Finance Manager
Ms Yvonne Evans Sales & Marketing Manager

Castle Ross Hotel
Killorglin Road
Killarney Co. Kerry
Phone: 064-31144 Fax: 064-31031
Email: castler@iol.ie
Web: http://www.towerhotelgroup.ie
SIC: 55110 Employees: 50
Hotel ***
Mr Danny Bowe General Manager
Mr Noel Ogle Financial Controller
Ms Michelle Thornton Sales & Marketing Manager

Castlecourt Hotel
Castlebar Street
Westport Co. Mayo
Phone: 098-25444 Fax: 098-28622
Email: info@castlecourthotel.ie
Web: http://www.castlecourthotel.ie
SIC: 55110 Employees: 200
Hotel ***
Mr Joe Corcoran Manager
Mr John O'Hora Finance Manager
Ms Cynthia Doyle Sales Manager

Castletroy Park Hotel
Dublin Road
Limerick Co. Limerick
Phone: 061-335566 Fax: 061-331117
Email: sales@castletroy-park.ie
Web: http://www.castletroy-park.ie
SIC: 55110 Employees: 105
Hotel ****
Mr Daragh O'Neill General Manager
Ms Geraldine Ryan Accountant
Ms Lynn Higgins Personnel Manager
Ms Ursula Cullen Sales & Marketing Manager

Celtic Ross Hotel Conference & Leisure Centre
Rosscarbery
Cork Co. Cork
Phone: 023-48722 Fax: 023-48723
Email: info@celticrosshotel.com
Web: http://www.celticrosshotel.com
SIC: 55110 Employees: 100
Hotel ***
Ms Nollaig Hurley General Manager
Mr Billy Clarke Accounts Manager
Ms Annemarie Hegarty Human Resources Director
Ms Kate Howry Sales & Marketing Manager
Mr Pat Reddan IT Manager

Central Hotel
The Diamond
Donegal Co. Donegal
Phone: 073-21027 Fax: 073-22295
Email: centralhotel@eircom.net
Web: http://www.whites-hotelsireland.com
SIC: 55110 Employees: 150
Hotel ***
Mr Michael Naughton Managing Director
Mr Paul Gallagher Accounts Manager
Ms Sinead McGowan Sales & Marketing Manager

Central Hotel
1-5 Exchequer Street
Dublin 2
Phone: 01-6797302 Fax: 01-6797303
Email: reservations@centralhotel.ie
Web: http://www.centralhotel.ie
SIC: 55110 Employees: 50
Hotel ***
Mr Guy Thompson General Manager
Ms Lisa Corr Receptionist

Christy's Hotel
Blarney
Cork Co. Cork
Phone: 021-4385011 Fax: 021-4385350
Email: christys@blarney.ie
Web: http://www.blarney.ie
SIC: 55110 Employees: 50
Hotel ***
Mr Derrick Matson General Manager

City West Hotel
Conference Leisure & Golf Resort
Saggart Co. Dublin
Phone: 01-4010500 Fax: 01-4588565
Email: info@citywesthotel.com
Web: http://www.citywesthotel.com
SIC: 55110 Employees: 350
Hotel****
Mr John Glynn Manager
Mr Richard Mahon Accounts Manager
Ms Wendy Grogan Sales & Marketing Manager

Clanbrassil Hotel
15 Clanbrassil Street
Dundalk Co. Louth
Phone: 042-9334141 Fax: 042-9328779
SIC: 55110 Employees: 45
Hotel**
Ms Anita McCann Manager
Ms Alison Murphy Sales & Marketing Manager

Clare Inn Hotel Ltd
Newmarket-on-Fergus
Dromoland
Ennis Co. Clare
Phone: 061-368161 Fax: 061-368622
Email: cro@lynchotels.ie
Web: http://www.lynchotels.ie
SIC: 55110 Employees: 130
Hotel ***
Mr Noel Mulhaire General Manager
Mr Joe Hughes Accounts Manager
Mr David Collins Sales & Marketing Manager

Clarence Hotel
6-8 Wellington Quay
Dublin 2
Phone: 01-4070800 Fax: 01-4070820
Email: reservations@theclarence.ie
Web: http://www.theclarence.ie
SIC: 55110 Employees: 120
Hotel ****
Mr Robert Van Eerde General Manager
Ms Jennifer Powell Chief Accountant
Ms Liz Wall Personnel Assistant
Ms Ailish Cantwell Sales & Marketing Manager

Clarion Brandon House Hotel
New Ross
Wexford Co. Wexford
Phone: 051-421703 Fax: 051-421567
Email: brandonhouse@eircom.net
SIC: 55110 Employees: 60
Hotel ***
Mr Patrick Quinn Proprietor
Ms Mary Walsh Financial Controller
Ms Mary Keating Sales Manager

Cliff House Hotel
Cliff Road
Ballybunion
Listowel Co. Kerry
Phone: 068-27777 Fax: 068-27783
Email: cliffhousehotel@eircom.net
Web: http://www.cliffhousehotel.net
SIC: 55110 Employees: 50
Hotel***
Mr Kevin O'Callaghan Manager

Clonea Strand Hotel & Leisure Centre
Clonea
Dungarvan Co. Waterford
Phone: 058-42416 Fax: 058-42880
Email: info@clonea.com
Web: http://www.amireland.com/clonea
SIC: 55110 Employees: 50
Hotel *** Leisure Centre & Swimming Pool
Mr Mark Knowles General Manager
Mr Mark Lenihan Group Financial Controller

Clontarf Castle Hotel
Castle Avenue
Clontarf
Dublin 3
Phone: 01-8332321 Fax: 01-8330418
Email: info@clontarfcastle.ie
Web: http://www.clontarfcastle.ie
SIC: 55110 Employees: 120
Hotel ****
Mr Enda O'Meara Managing Director
Mr John O'Connor Financial Controller
Ms Jane Flood Human Resources Manager
Ms Michelle Kelly Sales & Marketing Manager

Commons Inn
Commons Road
Cork Co. Cork
Phone: 021-4210300 Fax: 021-4210333
Email: info@commonsinn.com
Web: http://www.commonsinn.com
SIC: 55110 Employees: 80
Hotel
Mr Miles O'Neill Manager/Sales

Hospitality

Comrad International
Earlsfort Terrace
Dublin 2
Phone: 01-6765555 Fax: 01-6765424
Email: info@conrad-international.ie
Web: http://www.conrad-international.ie
SIC: 55110 Employees: 400
Hotel*****
Mr Michael Governey General Manager
Mr Kevin Gledhill Finance Manager
Ms Yvonne Brady Personnel Manager
Ms Sandra Cummins Sales & Marketing Manager

Connemara Coast Hotel
Furbo
Galway Co. Galway
Phone: 091-592108 Fax: 091-592065
Email: sinnotts@iol.ie
Web: http://www.sinnottshotel.com
SIC: 55110 Employees: 120
Hotel****
Mr Paul O'Meara Manager
Mr Peter Willams Finance Manager
Ms Gillian Chambers Personnel Manager
Ms Sarah Stewart Sales Manager

Conrad Dublin
Earlsfort Terrace
Dublin 2
Phone: 01-6028900 Fax: 01-6765424
Email: info@conraddublin.ie
Web: http://www.conraddublin.ie
SIC: 55110 Employees: 200
Hotel *****
Mr Michael Governey General Manager
Mr Kevin Gledhill Director of Finance
Ms Yvonne Brady Human Resources Manager

Corrib Great Southern Hotel
Renmore
Galway Co. Galway
Phone: 091-755281 Fax: 091-751390
Email: res@corribgsh.ie
Web: http://www.greatsouthernhotels.com
SIC: 55110 Employees: 100
Hotel****
Mr Michael Cunningham General Manager
Mr Michael O'Hare Financial Controller
Ms Karen Jones Sales & Marketing Manager

Court Hotel Killiney
Killiney Bay
Killiney
Dun Laoghaire Co. Dublin
Phone: 01-2851622 Fax: 01-2852085
Email: book@killineycourt.ie
Web: http://www.killineycourt.ie
SIC: 55110 Employees: 100
Hotel ***
Mr John O'Dowd Managing Director
Mr Joe Conlon General Manager
Mr Desmond Buckley Sales Manager

Crosbie Cedars Hotel
Rosslare
Wexford Co. Wexford
Phone: 053-32124 Fax: 053-32243
Email: info@crosbiecedar.iol.ie
SIC: 55110 Employees: 40
Hotel
Ms Liz Sinnott Managing Director

Davenport Hotel
Merrion Square
Dublin 2
Phone: 01-6073500 Fax: 01-6615663
Email: davenportres@ocallaghanhotels.ie
Web: http://www.davenporthotel.ie
SIC: 55110 Employees: 100
Hotel
Mr Weldon Mather General Manager
Mr Tom Rodgers Finance Manager
Ms Bridget McGreehan Personnel Manager
Ms Lucy Kelly Sales & Marketing Manager
Mr Gerry Colreavy Computer Manager

Dingle Skellig Hotel
Dingle
Tralee Co. Kerry
Phone: 066-9150200 Fax: 066-9151501
Email: dsk@iol.ie
Web: http://www.dingleskellig.com
SIC: 55110 Employees: 100
Hotel ****
Mr Philip Gavin Manager
Mr Thomas McCarthy Accountant
Mr Colin Ahern Senior Manager
Ms Caroline Boland Sales & Marketing Manager

Dinn Ri Hotel
Tullow Street
Carlow Co. Carlow
Phone: 0503-33111 Fax: 0503-30403
Email: dinnri@eircom.net
SIC: 55110 Employees: 105
Hotel**
Mr Sean McLaughlin Director
Ms Helen Stevenson Administrator
Ms Noleen Kealy Personnel Officer
Mr Brian Redmond Operations Manager

Dooley's Hotel
The Quay
Waterford Co. Waterford
Phone: 051-873531 Fax: 051-870262
Email: hotel@dooleys-hotel.ie
Web: http://www.dooleys-hotel.ie
SIC: 55110 Employees: 50
Hotel ***
Ms June Darrer Proprietor/Manager
Ms Gemma Murphy Accounts Manager
Ms Margaret Darrer Personnel Manager
Ms Helena Boyce Sales & Marketing Manager

Dooly's Hotel
Emmet Square
Birr Co. Offaly
Phone: 0509-20032 Fax: 0509-21332
Email: doolyshotel@esatclear.ie
Web: http://www.doolyshotel.com
SIC: 55110 Employees: 80
Hotel***
Ms Jo Duignan General Manager
Ms Alice Gleeson Finance Manager
Mr Paul Owens Personnel Officer
Mr David Conn Sales & Marketing Manager

Downhill House Hotel
Downhill Road
Ballina Co. Mayo
Phone: 096-21033 Fax: 096-21338
Email: thedownhillhotel@eircom.net
Web: http://www.downhillhotel.ie
SIC: 55110 Employees: 150
Hotel ***
Mr Michael McKeigue General Manager
Ms Josie Kirby Accountant
Ms Karen Moylett Personnel Manager
Ms Kay Devine Sales & Marketing Manager

Downshire House Hotel
Main Street, Blessington
Wicklow Co. Wicklow
Phone: 045-865199 Fax: 045-865335
Email: info@downshire.com
Web: http://www.downshire.com
SIC: 55110 Employees: 60
Hotel **
Ms Joan Flynn Manager

Dromhall Hotel Ltd
Muckross Road
Killarney Co. Kerry
Phone: 064-31431 Fax: 064-34242
Email: info@dromhall.com
Web: http://www.dromhall.com
SIC: 55110 Employees: 60
Hotel
Mr Derek Carroll

Dromoland Castle Hotel
Newmarket On Fergus
Ennis Co. Clare
Phone: 061-368144 Fax: 061-363355
Email: sales@dromoland.ie
Web: http://www.dromoland.ie
SIC: 55110 Employees: 200
Hotel *****
Mr Mark Nolan General Manager
Ms Marian Dalton McSherry Accounts Manager
Mr John Hehir Sales Director

Duhallow Park Hotel
Killarney Road
Clonmee
Navan Co. Meath
Phone: 029-56042 Fax: 029-56152
SIC: 55110 Employees: 45
Hotel ***
Mr Frank Kealy Proprietor
Ms Tracey Hoary Manager

Dunmore House Hotel & Golf Club
Muckross
Clonakilty Co. Cork
Phone: 023-33352 Fax: 023-34686
Email: dunmorehousehotel@eircom.net
Web: http://wwwdunmorehousehotel.com
SIC: 55110 Employees: 50
Hotel ***
Ms Carol Barrett General Manager
Ms Jenny O'Hea Finance Manager
Ms Ann-Marie Harte Manager
Ms Ann-Marie O'Carroll Sales & Marketing Manager

Dunraven Arms Hotel
Adare
Limerick Co. Limerick
Phone: 061-396633 Fax: 061-396541
Email: reservations@dunravenhotel.com
Web: http://www.dunravenhotel.com
SIC: 55110 Employees: 100
Hotel ****
Mr Brian Murphy General Manager
Mr Hugh Milne Finance Manager
Mr Louis Murphy Resident Manager

Earl of Desmond Hotel
Killarney Road
Tralee Co. Kerry
Phone: 066-7121299 Fax: 066-7121976
Email: earldes@eircom.net
SIC: 55110 Employees: 155
Hotel ***
Mr Michael Mannix General Manager

Europa Hotel
Dublin Road
Drogheda Co. Louth
Phone: 041-9837673 Fax: 041-9833116
SIC: 55110 Employees: 140
Hotel
Mr Hugh Curran Proprietor
Mr Richard Devine Manager

Fairways Hotel
Dublin Road
Dundalk Co. Louth
Phone: 042-9321500 Fax: 042-9321511
Email: info@fairways.ie
Web: http://www.fairways.ie
SIC: 55110 Employees: 150
Hotels
Mr Brian Quinn Proprietor
Mr Killian O'Grady Sales & Marketing Manager

Hospitality

Falls Hotel
Ennistymon
Ennis Co. Clare
Phone: 065-7071004 Fax: 065-7071367
Email: falls@iol.ie
Web: http://www.fallshotel.net
SIC: 55110 Employees: 60
Hotel ***
Mr Joe Leonard General Manager

Farnham Arms Hotel Ltd
Main Street
Cavan Co. Cavan
Phone: 049-4332577 Fax: 049-4362606
SIC: 55110 Employees: 60
Hotel ***
Mr Oliver Shiells General Manager
Ms Caroline Shiells Personnel Manager

Ferrycarraig Hotel
PO Box 11
Wexford Co. Wexford
Phone: 053-22999 Fax: 053-20982
Email:
Web: http://www.griffingroup.ie
SIC: 55110 Employees: 65
Hotel ****
Mr Mark Brown General Manager
Mr Michael O'Keefe Banqueting Manager
Ms Caroline Roche Sales & Marketing Manager

Ferrycarrig Hotel
PO Box 11
Wexford Co. Wexford
Phone: 053-20999 Fax: 053-20982
Web: http://www.griffingroup.ie
SIC: 55110 Employees: 120
Hotel & Gourmet Restaurant
Mr Mark Brown General Manager
Mr Michael O'Keefe Banqueting Manager
Ms Caroline Roche Sales & Marketing Manager

Finnstown Country House Hotel
Newcastle Road
Lucan Co. Dublin
Phone: 01-6280644 Fax: 01-6281088
Email: manager@finnstown-hotel.ie
Web: http://www.finnstown-hotel.ie
SIC: 55110 Employees: 50
Hotel ***
Mr Eoin Hickey Proprietor
Ms Marian Collins Accounts Manager
Ms Jenny Holmes Sales & Marketing Manager
Ms Paula Smith Operations Manager

Fir Grove Hotel
Cahir Hill
Mitchelstown Co. Cork
Phone: 025-24111 Fax: 025-84541
SIC: 55110 Employees: 50
Hotel **
Mr Pat Tangney Proprietor

Fitzpatrick Hotel Group
Corporate Office
Killiney
Dun Laoghaire Co. Dublin
Phone: 01-2845656 Fax: 01-2845655
Email: info@fitzpatricks.com
Web: http://www.fitzpatrickhotels.com
SIC: 55110 Employees: 520
Hotel Group
Mr Paddy Fitzpatrick Chairman
Ms Deirdre Clohessy Personnel Manager

Four Seasons Hotel
Simmonscourt Road
Ballsbridge
Dublin 4
Phone: 01-6654000 Fax: 01-6654099
Email: info@fourseasons.com
Web: http://www.fourseasons.com
SIC: 55110 Employees: 200
Hotel ****
Mr Michael Newcombe Hotel Manager

Galway Bay Conference & Leisure Centre
The Promenade
Salthill
Galway Co. Galway
Phone: 091-520520 Fax: 091-520530
Email: info@galwaybayhotel.net
Web: http://www.galwaybayhotel.net
SIC: 55110 Employees: 120
Hotel
Mr Dan Murphy General Manager
Ms Virginia Connolly Sales Manager

Glencairn Hotel & Leisure Centre
Monaghan Road
Castleblayney Co. Monaghan
Phone: 042-9746666 Fax: 042-9746521
SIC: 55110 Employees: 60
Hotel ***
Mr Patrick McFadden General Manager
Mr James Duffy Accounts Manager
Ms Kathleen Lavelle Sales & Marketing Manager

Glendalough Hotel
Glendalough
Bray Co. Wicklow
Phone: 0404-45135 Fax: 0404-45142
Email: info@glendaloughhotel.ie
SIC: 55110 Employees: 80
Hotel ***
Mr Patrick Casey General Manager
Ms Anna O'Meara Reception Manager
Mr Cormac O'Sullivan Sales & Marketing Manager

Gleneagle Hotel
Muckross Road
Killarney Co. Kerry
Phone: 064-36000 Fax: 064-32646
Web: http://www.gleneagle-hotel.com
SIC: 55110 Employees: 200
Hotel ***
Mr Patrick O'Donoghue Managing Director
Mr Derek Lee Financial Controller
Ms Susanne Kelly Personnel Manager
Ms Cara Fuller Corporate Sales Manager

Glenlo Abbey Hotel
Bushy Park
Galway Co. Galway
Phone: 091-526666 Fax: 091-527800
Email: glenlo@iol.ie
Web: http://www.glenlo.com
SIC: 55110 Employees: 70
Hotel *****
Mr Dermot Henry General Manager
Ms Pauline Kelly Accounts Manager
Ms Muriel Moffett Personnel Director
Mr Brian Burke Marketing Manager
Mr Dermot Henry Production Manager

Glenroyal Hotel & Leisure Club
Straffan Road
Maynooth Co. Kildare
Phone: 01-6290909 Fax: 01-6290919
Email: hotel@glenroyal.ie
Web: http://www.glenroyal.ie
SIC: 55110 Employees: 100
Hotel ***
Ms Helen Courtney General Manager
Mr Ray Grehan Sales Manager

Glentworth Hotel
Glentworth Street
Limerick Co. Limerick
Phone: 061-413822 Fax: 061-413073
Email: glentworthhotel@oceanfree.net
SIC: 55110 Employees: 50
Hotel
Mr Gerry Flynn General Manager
Ms Fiona Madden Accounts Manager

Glenview Hotel
Glen O The Downs
Delgany
Greystones Co. Wicklow
Phone: 01-2873399 Fax: 01-2877511
Email: glenview@iol.ie
Web: http://www.glenviewhotel.ie
SIC: 55110 Employees: 60
Hotel ***
Ms Anne Whelan General Manager
Mr Kenneth Fairley Personnel Manager
Ms Tracy Ashley Sales & Marketing Manager

Grand Hotel
Malahide Co. Dublin
Phone: 01-8450633 Fax: 01-8450987
Email: info@thegrand.ie
Web: http://www.thegrand.ie
SIC: 55110 Employees: 420
Hotel ****
Mr Mark Gannon General Manager
Ms Sinead Stone Sales & Marketing Manag
Mr Al Ryan Computer Manager

Grand Hotel
Denny Street
Tralee Co. Kerry
Phone: 066-7121499 Fax: 066-7122877
Email: info@grandhoteltralee.com
Web: http://www.grandhoteltralee.com
SIC: 55110 Employees: 60
Hotel ***
Mr Dick Boyle General Manager
Ms Ingrid Boyle Finance Manager
Ms Jennifer Crowley Stores Person

Grand Hotel
Abbey Street
Wicklow Co. Wicklow
Phone: 0404-67337 Fax: 0404-69607
Email: info@grandhotel.ie
Web: http://www.grandhotel.ie
SIC: 55110 Employees: 45
Hotel ***
Mr John Sullivan General Manager
Ms Edel O'Brien Financial Controller

Grand Parade Hotel
Grand Parade
Cork Co. Cork
Phone: 021-4274391 Fax: 021-4277187
SIC: 55110 Employees: 80
Hotel
Mr John Casey Manager

Great Northern Hotel
Bundoran
Donegal Co. Donegal
Phone: 072-41204 Fax: 072-41114
Email: reservations@greatnorthernhotel.com
Web: http://www.greatnorthernhotel.com
SIC: 55110 Employees: 75
Hotel ****
Mr Philip McGlynn General Manager
Ms Mary McGlynn Financial Controller

Great Southern Hotel
Rosslare Harbour
Wexford Co. Wexford
Phone: 053-33233 Fax: 053-33543
Email: res@rosslare.gsh.ie
Web: http://www.gsh.ie
SIC: 55110 Employees: 700
Hotel ***
Ms Roisin Buckley General Manager
Ms Mary O'Leary Accounts Manager
Mr Kieran Carroll Personnel Manager
Ms Catherine Cronin Sales & Marketing Manager

Hospitality

Great Southern Hotel
East Avenue
Killarney Co. Kerry
Phone: 064-31262 Fax: 064-31642
Email: res@killarney.gsh.ie
Web: http://www.gsh.ie
SIC: 55110 Employees: 100
Hotel ****
Mr Conor Hennigan General Manager
Mr Dan Neville Area Accountant
Ms Eilish Loughrey Personnel Manager
Ms Michelle King Sales & Marketing Manager
Mr Kevin Murphy Computer Manager

Great Southern Hotel
Eyre Square
Galway Co. Galway
Phone: 091-564041 Fax: 091-566704
Email: res@galway.gsh.ie
Web: http://www.greatsouthernhotels.com
SIC: 55110 Employees: 100
Hotel ****
Mr Fergal O'Connell Managing Director
Ms Karen Jones Sales & Marketing Manager
Mr Kevin Murphy DP Manager

Great Southern Hotel
Parknasilla
Sneem
Killarney Co. Kerry
Phone: 064-45122 Fax: 064-45323
Email: res@parknasilla.gsh.ie
Web: http://www.gsh.ie
SIC: 55110 Employees: 100
Hotel ****
Mr Jim Feeney General Manager
Ms Una McMahon Personnel Manager
Ms Catherine Cronin Sales & Marketing Manager

Great Southern Hotel
Dublin Airport
Swords Co. Dublin
Phone: 01-8446000 Fax: 01-8446001
Email: res@dubairport.gsh.ie
Web: http://www.gsh.ie
SIC: 55110 Employees: 80
Hotel
Mr Eamon Daly General Manager
Ms Mairead Carney Personnel Manager
Ms Avril Clarke Sales & Marketing Manager

Great Southern Hotel
6 Charlemont Terrace
Crofton Road
Dun Laoghaire Co. Dublin
Phone: 01-2808581 Fax: 01-2144805
Email: info@greatsouthernhotel.com
Web: http://www.greatsouthernhotels.com
SIC: 55110 Employees: 50
Hotel
Mr Eamonn McKeon Chief Executive
Ms Nuala Kilgallon Financial Controller
Ms Catherine Cronin Sales Manager
Ms Mary McKeon Operation Manager
Mr Kevin Murphy Computer Manager

Gregans Castle Hotel
Ballyvaughan
Ennis Co. Clare
Phone: 065-7077005 Fax: 065-7077111
Email: res@gregans.ie
Web: http://www.gregans.ie
SIC: 55110 Employees: 50
Hotel ****
Mr Peter Haden Proprietor
Mr Simon Haden Manager & Director

Gresham Hotel
23 Upper O'Connell Street
Dublin 1
Phone: 01-8746881 Fax: 01-8787175
Email: reservations@thegresham.com
Web: http://www.gresham-hotels.com
SIC: 55110 Employees: 300
Hotel ****
Mr Shay Livingstone General Manager
Mr Stephen Loftus Finance Manager
Ms Sharon Coleman Human Resources Manager
Mr John Cunningham Sales Manager

Greville Arms Hotel
Pearse Street
Mullingar Co. Westmeath
Phone: 044-48563 Fax: 044-48052
Email: grevillearmshotel@eircom.net
SIC: 55110 Employees: 166
Hotel ***
Mr John Cochrane Manager
Ms Sheila Weldon Finance Manager

Gullane's Hotel
Main Street
Ballinasloe Co. Galway
Phone: 0905-42220 Fax: 0905-44395
Email: gullaneshotel@eircom.net
SIC: 55110 Employees: 54
Hotel
Mr Thomas Gullane Proprietor

Harcourt Hotel
60 Harcourt Street
Dublin 2
Phone: 01-4783677 Fax: 01-4752013
Email: reservations@harcourthotel.ie
Web: http://www.harcourthotel.ie
SIC: 55110 Employees: 80
Hotel***
Ms Sally McGill Managing Director
Ms Ita Killelea Accountant
Mr Paul Glynn Sales & Marketing Manager
Mr Joseph Elmonem Financial Controller

Harveys Point Country Hotel
Harveys Point
Lough Eske
Donegal Co. Donegal
Phone: 073-22208 Fax: 073-22352
Email: harveyspoint@eircom.net
SIC: 55110 Employees: 60
Hotel***
Mr Marc Gysling Proprietor
Ms Siobhan McNulty Finance Manager
Ms Deirdre McGlone General Manager

Haydens Gateway Hotel
Dunloe Street
Ballinasloe Co. Galway
Phone: 0905-42347 Fax: 0905-42895
Email: cro@lynchhotels.com
Web: http://www.lynchhotels.com
SIC: 55110 Employees: 90
Hotel ***
Mr Joe Melody General Manager
Mr Joe Hughes Financial Controller
Ms Jacinta Knockton Personnel Manager
Mr David Collins Sales & Marketing Manager

Hayfield Manor
Perrott Avenue
College Road
Cork Co. Cork
Phone: 021-4315600 Fax: 021-4316839
Email: enquiries@hayfieldmanor.ie
Web: http://www.hayfieldmanor.ie
SIC: 55110 Employees: 60
Hotel *****
Ms Margaret Naughton Deputy General Manager
Ms Suzanne O'Mahony Sales & Marketing Manager

Hazel Hotel
Dublin Road
Monasterevin
Kildare Co. Kildare
Phone: 045-525373 Fax: 045-525810
Email: sales@hazelhotel.com
Web: http://www.hazelhotel.com
SIC: 55110 Employees: 50
Hotel***
Ms Margaret Kelly Proprietor
Mr John Kelly Sales & Marketing Manager

Herbert Park Hotel
Ballsbridge
Dublin 4
Phone: 01-6672200 Fax: 01-6672595
Email: reservations@herbertparkhotel.ie
Web: http://www.herbertparkhotel.ie
SIC: 55110 Employees: 90
Hotel****
Mr Ewan Plenderleith General Manager
Mr Killian Boland Finance Manager
Ms Rosemary Enright Personnel Manager
Ms Sorcha Moore Operations Manager

Hibernian Hotel
Main Street
Mallow Co. Cork
Phone: 022-21588 Fax: 022-22632
Email: info@hibhotel.com
Web: http://www.hibhotel.com
SIC: 55110 Employees: 60
Hotel ***
Ms Catherine Gyves General Manager
Mr Eamon Kearney Finance Manager

Hibernian Hotel
Eastmoreland Place
Ballsbridge
Dublin 4
Phone: 01-6687666 Fax: 01-6602655
Email: info@hibernianhotel.com
Web: http://www.hibernianhotel.com
SIC: 55110 Employees: 40
Hotel
Mr Neil Coffey General Manager
Ms Mary Daly Sales & Marketing Manager

Hillgrove Hotel
Old Armagh Road
Monaghan Co. Monaghan
Phone: 047-81288 Fax: 047-84951
Email: hillgrovehotel@quinn-hotels.com
Web: http://www.quinnhotels.com
SIC: 55110 Employees: 106
Hotel
Mr Ross Mealiff Manager
Mr Vari McGreavy Group Sales Manager

Hilton Hotel
Charlemont Place
Dublin 2
Phone: 01-4029988 Fax: 01-4029966
Email: reservations_dublin@hilton.com
Web: http://www.dublin.hilton.com
SIC: 55110 Employees: 150
Hotel
Mr Patrick Stapleton General Manager
Mr Jim Carlton Finance Manager
Ms Claire MacLeod Personnel Director
Ms Deirdre O'Brien Sales Manager

Hodson Bay Hotel
Roscommon Road
Athlone Co. Westmeath
Phone: 0902-92444 Fax: 0902-80520
Email: info@hodsonbayhotel.com
Web: http://www.hodsonbayhotel.com
SIC: 55110 Employees: 95
Hotel ***
Mr Michael Ducie General Manager
Mr Padraig Sugrue Accounts Manager
Ms Martina Comber Personnel Manager

Holiday Inn Dublin City Centre
99-107 Pearse Street
Dublin 2
Phone: 01-6703666 Fax: 01-6703636
Email: info@holidayinndublin.ie
Web: http://www.holidayinndublin.ie
SIC: 55110 Employees: 50
Hotel***
Mr John Moran Managing Director
Mr Alan Browne Financial Controller
Mr Kevin Finlay Sales & Marketing Manager

Holiday Inn Killarney
Muckross Road
Killarney Co. Kerry
Phone: 064-33000 Fax: 064-33001
Email: holidayinnkillarney@eircom.net
Web: http://www.holidayinnkillarney.com
SIC: 55110 Employees: 50
Hotel***
Mr David Hennessy General Manager
Ms Aisling O'Regan Financial Controller
Ms Brigeen Walsh Sales & Marketing Manager

Horse & Jockey Inn
Horse & Jockey
Thurles Co. Tipperary
Phone: 0504-44192 Fax: 0504-44747
Email: horseandjockeyinn@eircom.net
Web: http://www.horseandjockeyinn.com
SIC: 55110 Employees: 40
Hotel
Mr Tom Egan Proprietor
Mr Paul Meehan General Manager

Hotel Europe
Fossa
Killarney Co. Kerry
Phone: 064-31900 Fax: 064-32118
Email: sales@kih.liebherr.com
Web: http://www.iol.ie/khl
SIC: 55110 Employees: 200
Hotel *****
Mr Malcolm McKenzie Manager
Mr Hans Brunner Financial Controller
Mr Gerry Brown Sales & Marketing Director

Hotel Isaacs
48 Mac Curtain Street
Cork Co. Cork
Phone: 021-4500011 Fax: 021-4506355
Email: cork@isaacs.ie
Web: http://www.isaacs.ie
SIC: 55110 Employees: 40
Hotel ***
Ms Paula Lynch General Manager

Hotel Kilkenny
College Road
Kilkenny Co. Kilkenny
Phone: 056-62000 Fax: 056-65984
Email: kilkenny@griffingroup.ie
Web: http://www.griffingroup.ie
SIC: 55110 Employees: 120
Hotel ***
Mr Richard Butler General Manager
Ms Fiona Baynham Accounts Manager
Mr David Kelly Personnel Manager
Ms Fiona Fields Sales & Marketing Manager

Hotel Kilmore
Dublin Road
Cavan Co. Cavan
Phone: 049-4332288 Fax: 049-4332458
Email: kilmore@quinn-hotels.com
Web: http://www.quinnhotels.com
SIC: 55110 Employees: 200
Hotel ***
Mr Jim Burke General Manager
Ms Miranda Crowe Accounts Manager
Ms Sharon Crowe Sales & Marketing Manager

Hotel Minella
Colevile Road
Clonmel Co. Tipperary
Phone: 052-22388 Fax: 052-24381
Email: hotelminella@eircom.net
Web: http://www.hotelminella.ie
SIC: 55110 Employees: 70
Hotel ***
Ms Elizabeth Nallen Managing Director
Mr Bill Roche Financial Controller

Hotel Munster
Cathedral Street
Thurles Co. Tipperary
Phone: 0504-22305 Fax: 0504-26281
Email: info@munsterhotel.com
Web: http://www.munsterhotel.com
SIC: 55110 Employees: 60
Hotel***
Mr Gerry Clancy Proprietor
Mr Fergal Coghlan General Manager
Ms Martina Yearsley Sales & Marketing Manager

Hotel Westport
The Demesne
Newport Road
Westport Co. Mayo
Phone: 098-25122 Fax: 098-26739
Email: reservations@hotelwestport.ie
Web: http://www.hotelwestport.ie
SIC: 55110 Employees: 140
Hotel ***
Mr Gerry Walsh Manager
Mr Jarlath Hamilton Accountant
Mr Declan Heneghan Assistant Manager
Ms Ruth Farrell Sales & Marketing Manager

Ibis Hotel
Monastery Road
Clondalkin
Dublin 22
Phone: 01-4641480 Fax: 01-4641484
Email: info@ibishotel.com
Web: http://www.ibishotel.com
SIC: 55110 Employees: 90
Hotel **
Mr Alistair Smallwood General Manager
Ms Connie McDonnell Sales & Marketing Manager

Ibis Hotel
Headford Road
Galway Co. Galway
Phone: 091-771166 Fax: 091-771646
Web: http://www.ibishotel.com
SIC: 55110 Employees: 40
Hotel **
Ms Connie McDonnell General Manager

Inishowen Gateway Hotel
Railway Road
Buncrana
Lifford Co. Donegal
Phone: 077-61144 Fax: 077-62278
Email: inigatho@iol.ie
Web: http://www.globalgolf.com/irl/northwest/stay
SIC: 55110 Employees: 55
Hotel ***
Mr Patrick Doherty Director
Ms Marie Gill Financial Controller
Ms Rena Doherty Personnel Manager
Mr Sean O'Kane Sales Manager

International Best Western Hotel
Kenmare Place
Killarney Co. Kerry
Phone: 064-31816 Fax: 064-31837
Email: inter@iol.ie
Web: http://www.killarney-inter.com
SIC: 55110 Employees: 60
Hotel ***
Mr Terence Mulcahy General Manager

Jackson Court Hotel
29-30 Harcourt Street
Dublin 2
Phone: 01-4758777 Fax: 01-4758793
Email: info@jackson-court.ie
Web: http://www.jackson-court.ie
SIC: 55110 Employees: 60
Superior Hotel **
Ms Lesley-Ann Hayes General Manager
Mr Darren Power Accounts Manager

Jacksons Hotel
Ballybofey
Lifford Co. Donegal
Phone: 074-31021 Fax: 074-31096
Web: http://www.jacksons-hotel.ie
SIC: 55110 Employees: 130
Hotel ***
Mr Barry Jackson Proprietor
Mr Oliver O'Donnell Accounts Manager
Ms Kathleen McKendry Personnel Manager
Ms Laura Quigley Sales & Marketing Manager

Jurys Cork Inn
Anderson's Quay
Cork Co. Cork
Phone: 021-4276444 Fax: 021-4276144
Email: cork_inn@jurysdoyle.com
Web: http://www.jurysdoyle.com
SIC: 55110 Employees: 60
Hotel ***
Ms Julie-anne Brennan General Manager
Ms Imelda Murphy Accounts Manager
Ms Grace Gallagher Personnel Manager
Ms Linda Walsh Sales & Marketing Manager

Jurys Custom House Inn
Custom House Quay
Dublin 1
Phone: 01-6075000 Fax: 01-8290400
Email:
Web: http://www.jurysdoyle.com
SIC: 55110 Employees: 100
Hotel
Mr Edward Stephenson General Manager
Ms Helen Buckley Personnel Manager
Ms Linda Walsh Sales Manager

Jurys Doyle Hotel Group Plc
146 Pembroke Road
Ballsbridge
Dublin 4
Phone: 01-6070070 Fax: 01-6672370
Email: postmaster@jurysdoyle.com
Web: http://www.jurysdoyle.com
SIC: 55110 Employees: 1260
Group Head Office (Hotels)
Mr Pat McCann Managing Director
Mr Barry Sheehan Financial Director
Ms Jennifer Lee Personnel Manager
Mr Niall Geoghegan Sales & Marketing Manager

Jurys Hotel
Ferrybank
Waterford Co. Waterford
Phone: 051-832111 Fax: 051-832863
Email:
Web: http://www.jurysdoyle.com
SIC: 55110 Employees: 78
Hotel ***
Mr Stan Power General Manager
Mr Eddie Tobin Accountant
Ms Imelda McIntyre Personnel Manager
Ms Aine Aspel Sales Manager

Jurys Inn
Lower Mallow Street
Limerick Co. Limerick
Phone: 061-207000 Fax: 061-400966
Email: limerick_inn@jurysdoyle.ie
Web: http://www.jurysdoyle.com
SIC: 55110 Employees: 65
Hotel***
Mr Derek McDonnagh General Manager
Ms Laura Moore Sales Manager

Hospitality

Jurys Tara Hotel
Merrion Road
Blackrock
Dublin 4
Phone: 01-2694666 Fax: 01-2691027
Email: tara_hotel@jurysdoyle.com
Web: http://www.jurysdoyle.com
SIC: 55110 Employees: 70
Hotel ***
Ms Melissa Hynes General Manager
Ms Gail White Personnel Manager
Ms Michelle Bernie Sales Manager

Keadeen Hotel Ltd
Curragh Road
Newbridge Co. Kildare
Phone: 045-431666 Fax: 045-434402
Email: keadeen@iol.ie
Web: http://www.keadeenhotel.kildare.ie
SIC: 55110 Employees: 70
Hotel***
Ms Rose O'Loughlin Proprietor
Ms Bridie Clarke Accountant
Ms Heike Kober Personnel Manager
Ms Michelle Kelly Sales & Marketing Manager

Kees Hotel
Stranorlar
Ballybofey
Lifford Co. Donegal
Phone: 074-31018 Fax: 074-31917
Email: info@keeshotel.ie
Web: http://www.keeshotel.ie
SIC: 55110 Employees: 120
Hotel ***
Mr Richard Kee General Manager
Ms Valerie Hastings Accounts Manager
Ms Vicky Kee Sales & Marketing Manager

Kelly's Resort Hotel
Rosslare
Wexford Co. Wexford
Phone: 053-32114 Fax: 053-32222
Email: kellyhot@iol.ie
Web: http://www.kellys.ie
SIC: 55110 Employees: 170
Hotel**** & Leisure Centre
Mr William Kelly General Manager
Ms Joan Lambert Accounts Manager
Ms Sheila Malone Personnel & Training Manager
Mr John Lambert Computer Manager

Kilcoran Lodge Hotel
Kilcoran
Cahir Co. Tipperary
Phone: 052-41288 Fax: 052-41994
Email: kilcoran@eircom.net
Web: http://www.tipp.ie/kilcoran.htm
SIC: 55110 Employees: 54
Hotel ***
Ms Jacqueline Mullen Managing Director

Kildare Hotel & Country Club
Straffan
Kildare Co. Kildare
Phone: 01-6273333 Fax: 01-6017299
Email: hotel@kclub.ie
Web: http://www.kclub.ie
SIC: 55110 Employees: 150
Hotel*****
Mr Ray Carroll General Manager
Mr Patrick Cahill IT Director

Kilkee Castle
Castledermot
Kildare Co. Kildare
Phone: 0503-45156 Fax: 0503-45187
Email: kilkee@iol.ie
Web: http://www.kilkeecastle.ie
SIC: 55110 Employees: 50
Hotel ****
Mr Shane Cassidy Director
Ms Mary Kaye Finance Manager
Mr Paul Corrigan General Manager

Kilkenny River Court Hotel
The Bridge
John Street
Kilkenny Co. Kilkenny
Phone: 056-23388 Fax: 056-23389
Email: krch@iol.ie
Web: http://www.kilrivercourt.com
SIC: 55110 Employees: 80
Hotels
Mr Peter Wilson General Manager
Ms Patricia Cork Finance Manager
Mr Peter Wilson General Manager
Ms Breda Kehoe Sales & Marketing Manager

Killarney Court Hotel
Tralee Road
Killarney Co. Kerry
Phone: 064-37070 Fax: 064-37060
Email: stay@irishcourthotels.com
Web: http://www.irishcourthotels.com
SIC: 55110 Employees: 60
Hotel
Mr Robert Lyne Proprietor

Killarney Park Hotel
Kenmare Place
Killarney Co. Kerry
Phone: 064-35555 Fax: 064-35266
Email: info@killarneyparkhotel.ie
Web: http://www.killarneyparkhotel.ie
SIC: 55110 Employees: 80
Hotel *****
Mr Padraig Treacy Proprietor
Mr Donagh Davern General Manager
Ms Niamh O'Shea Sales & Marketing Manager

Killarney Ryan Hotel
Cork Road
Killarney Co. Kerry
Phone: 064-31555 Fax: 064-32438
Email: krh@gofree.indigo.ie
SIC: 55110 Employees: 120
Hotel ***
Mr Pat Galvin General Manager
Mr Gerry O'Sullivan Finance Manager
Mr Aidan Moynihan Personnel Manager
Ms Breeda Kelleher Reservations Manager

Killarney Towers Hotel
College Square
Killarney Co. Kerry
Phone: 064-31038 Fax: 064-31755
Email: towersky@iol.ie
SIC: 55110 Employees: 110
Hotel ***
Mr Frank McCarthy Managing Director
Ms Karen Horgan Personnel Director
Mr James Ormonde Sales & Marketing Manager

Killashee House Hotel
Killashee
Naas Co. Kildare
Phone: 045-879277 Fax: 045-879266
Email: sales@killasheehouse.com
Web: http://www.killasheehouse.com
SIC: 55110 Employees: 80
Hotel
Mr Odhran Lawlor Managing Director
Mr Liam Corr Personnel Manager
Ms Annemarie Hayes Sales Manager

Killeshin Hotel
Dublin Road
Portlaoise Co. Laois
Phone: 0502-21663 Fax: 0502-21976
Email: killeshinhotel@eircom.net
SIC: 55110 Employees: 50
Hotel ***
Mr PJ McCann Managing Director
Mr Frank Walsh Finance Manager
Mr Joe Carmody Operations Manager

Kilmurry Lodge Hotel
Dublin Road
Castletroy
Limerick Co. Limerick
Phone: 061-331133 Fax: 061-330011
Email: manager@kilmurry.com
Web: http://www.kilmurry.com
SIC: 55110 Employees: 100
Hotel **
Ms Siobhan Hoare Proprietor
Ms Lisa O'Brien Sales & Marketing Manager

Kingsley Hotel
Victoria Cross
Cork Co. Cork
Phone: 021-4800500 Fax: 021-4800527
Email: resv@kingsleyhotel.com
SIC: 55110 Employees: 90
Hotel ****
Mr Michael Roche General Manager
Mr Thomas McCarthy Finance Manager
Mr Seamus Heaney Sales & Marketing Manager

Leix County Hotel
Portlaoise Co. Laois
Phone: 0505-41213 Fax:
SIC: 55110 Employees: 50
Hotel *
Mr John Gaffney General Manager

Limerick Inn Hotel
Ennis Road
Limerick Co. Limerick
Phone: 061-326666 Fax: 061-326281
Email: limerick-inn@limerick-inn.ie
Web: http://www.limerick-inn.ie
SIC: 55110 Employees: 118
Hotels****
Mr John Fahey General Manager
Ms Nancy Keller Finance Manager
Mr Roger Beck Personnel Manager
Ms Patricia Ryan Sales & Marketing Manager

Limerick Ryan Hotel
Ardhu House
Ennis Road
Limerick Co. Limerick
Phone: 061-453922 Fax: 061-326333
Email: info@ryan-hotels.com
Web: http://www.ryan-hotels.com
SIC: 55110 Employees: 80
Hotel***
Mr Dermot Feeley General Manager
Mr Eddie Butler Head Accountant
Mr Vincent Hoban Personnel Manager

Lodge & Spa at Inchydoney Island
Clonakilty Co. Cork
Phone: 023-33143 Fax: 023-35229
Email: reservations@inchydoneyisland.com
Web: http://www.inchydoneyisland.com
SIC: 55110 Employees: 100
Hotel ****
Mr Michael Knox-Johnston Managing Director
Mr Des O'Dowd Financial Controller
Ms Hazel Knox-Johnston Sales Co-Ordinator

Longford Arms Hotel
24 Main Street
Longford Co. Longford
Phone: 043-46296 Fax: 043-46244
Email: longfordarms@eircom.net
Web: http://www.longfordarms.ie
SIC: 55110 Employees: 100
Hotel***
Ms Denise Batt General Manager

Majestic Hotel
Tramore
Waterford Co. Waterford
Phone: 051-381761 Fax: 051-381766
Email: info@majestichotel.ie
Web: http://www.majestichotel.ie
SIC: 55110 Employees: 50
Hotel ***
Ms Annette Devine Proprietor
Ms Sandra Faloon Front Office Manager

Hospitality

Maryborough House Hotel
Maryborough Hill
Douglas
Cork Co. Cork
Phone: 021-4365555 Fax: 021-4365662
Email: maryboro@indigo.ie
Web: http://www.maryborough.com
SIC: 55110 Employees: 60
Hotel ****
Mr Justin McCarthy General Manager
Mr Pat O'Doherty Finance Manager
Ms Mary Motherway Sales & Marketing Manager

McNamara's Hotel
Foyle Street
Moville
Lifford Co. Donegal
Phone: 077-82010 Fax: 077-82564
SIC: 55110 Employees: 50
Hotel **
Mr Billy Tyghe General Manager
Ms Kathleen McDonnell Personnel Manager

Menlo Park Hotel
Terryland
Galway Co. Galway
Phone: 091-761122 Fax: 091-761222
Email: menlopkh@iol.ie
Web: http://www.menloparkhotel.com
SIC: 55110 Employees: 50
Hotels
Mr David Keane Manager
Ms Edel Higgins Sales & Marketing Manager

Merrion Hotel
Upper Merrion Street
Dublin 2
Phone: 01-6030600 Fax: 01-6030700
Email: info@merrionhotel.com
Web: http://www.merrionhotel.ie
SIC: 55110 Employees: 240
Hotel *****
Mr Peter McCann General Manager
Mr Declan Burke Finance Manager
Ms Cathy Rigney Personnel Manager
Ms Christina Deeny Sales & Marketing Manager
Mr Owen McCarthy Computer Manager

Mespil Hotel
Mespil Road
Dublin 4
Phone: 01-6671222 Fax: 01-6671244
Email: mespil@leehotels.ie
Web: http://www.leehotels.ie
SIC: 55110 Employees: 200
Hotel ***
Mr Martin Holohan General Manager
Ms Mary Redding Finance Manager
Ms Monica Chawke Personnel Manager
Ms Emma Allen Sales & Marketing Manager
Ms Denise Campbell Front Office Manager

Midleton Park Hotel
Old Cork Road
Midleton Co. Cork
Phone: 021-4631767 Fax: 021-4631605
Email: info@midletonparkhotel.ie
SIC: 55110 Employees: 60
Hotel ***
Ms Clodagh Dunworth General Manager
Mr Thomas McCartney Jnr Financial Controller
Ms Daphne Beamish Sales & Marketing Manager

Mont Clare Hotel
Merrion Square
Dublin 2
Phone: 01-6073800 Fax: 01-6615663
Email: montclareres@ocallaghanhotels.ie
Web: http://www.montclarehotel.ie
SIC: 55110 Employees: 100
Hotel ****
Mr Brian Eaton General Manager
Mr Damien Alan Finance Manager
Ms Bridget McGreehan Human Resources Manager
Ms Lucia Kelly Sales & Marketing Manager
Mr Gerry Colreavy Computer Manager

Mont Clare Hotel
Merrion Square
Dublin 2
Phone: 01-6616799 Fax: 01-6615663
Web: http://www.ocallaghanhotels.ie
SIC: 55110 Employees: 50
Hotel ****
Mr Colm Heaton General Manager
Mr Tom Rodgers Finance Manager
Ms Bridget McGreehan Personnel Officer
Ms Lucia Kelly Sales & Marketing Director

Mount Errigal Hotel
Ballyraine
Letterkenny Co. Donegal
Phone: 074-22700 Fax: 074-25085
Email: info@mounterrigal.com
Web: http://www.mounterrigal.com
SIC: 55110 Employees: 130
Hotel ***
Mr Terry McEniff Managing Director
Mr Enda O'Donell Finance Manager
Ms Sharon McGlynn Personnel Director
Ms Loretta McEniff Marketing Executive

Mount Herbert Hotel
Herbert Road
Ballsbridge
Dublin 4
Phone: 01-6684321 Fax: 01-6607077
Email: info@mountherberthotel.ie
Web: http://www.mountherberthotel.ie
SIC: 55110 Employees: 100
Hotel
Mr John Loughran Managing Director
Mr Paul Loughran Director
Ms Michelle Feeney Personnel Manager

Mount Juliet Hotel
Thomastown
Kilkenny Co. Kilkenny
Phone: 056-73000 Fax: 056-73019
Email: info@mountjuliet.ie
Web: http://www.mountjuliet.ie
SIC: 55110 Employees: 150
Hotel****
Mr Richard Hudson General Manager
Mr Richard Lowry Financial Controller
Ms Margaret Fitzgerald Personnel Manager
Ms Jill O'Hare Sales & Marketing Director
Ms Dympna Kelly Computer Manager

Muckross Park Hotel
Muckross
Killarney Co. Kerry
Phone: 064-31938 Fax: 064-31965
Email: muckrossparkhotel@eircom.net
Web: http://www.muckrosspark.com
SIC: 55110 Employees: 50
Hotel ****
Ms Patricia Shanahan General Manager

Munster Arms Hotel
Oliver Plunkett Street
Bandon Co. Cork
Phone: 023-41562 Fax: 023-41562
Email: postmaster@munsterarmshotel.com
Web: http://www.munsterarmshotel.com
SIC: 55110 Employees: 50
Hotel ***
Mr Don O'Sullivan Director
Mr John McCarthy General Manager
Mr John Collins Director

Neptune Beach Hotel & Leisure Club
Bettystown
Navan Co. Meath
Phone: 041-9827107 Fax: 041-9827412
Email: info@neptunebeach.ie
Web: http://www.neptunebeach.ie
SIC: 55110 Employees: 150
Hotel ****
Mr Denis Redden Proprietor
Ms Sandra Ryan Assistant Manager
Ms Breffney Costello Manager

Newgrange Hotel
Bridge Street
Navan Co. Meath
Phone: 046-74100 Fax: 046-73977
Email: info@newgrangehotel.ie
Web: http://www.newgrangehotel.ie
SIC: 55110 Employees: 100
Hotel ****
Mr Noel J O'Mahony Manager
Mr Joseph Lynch Accountant
Ms Lorraine Cunningham Sales & Marketing Manager

Newpark Hotel
Castlecomer Road
Kilkenny Co. Kilkenny
Phone: 056-60500 Fax: 056-60555
Email: info@newparkhotel.com
Web: http://www.newparkhotel.com
SIC: 55110 Employees: 200
Hotel ***
Mr David O'Sullivan Manager
Ms Lena O'Neill Accounts Manager
Ms Orla Gray Sales & Marketing Manager

North Star Hotel
26-30 Amiens Street
Dublin 1
Phone: 01-8363136 Fax: 01-8363561
Email: norths@regencyhotels.com
Web: http://www.regencyhotels.com
SIC: 55110 Employees: 60
Hotel ***
Mr Dave Kylie General Manager
Mr Brian McGettigan Financial Controller
Ms Catherine McGettigan Personnel Manager
Mr James McGettigan Sales & Marketing Manager

Nuremore Hotel & Country Club
Ardee Road
Carrickmacross Co. Monaghan
Phone: 042-9661438 Fax: 042-9661853
Email: nuremore@eircom.net
Web: http://www.nuremore-hotel.ie
SIC: 55110 Employees: 100
Hotel ****
Ms Julie Gilhooly Proprietor
Mr PJ Dolan Finance Manager
Ms Helen Woods Sales & Marketing Manager
Mr Tony Walker General Manager

O'Sheas Hotel
19 Talbot Street
Dublin 1
Phone: 01-8365665 Fax: 01-8365214
Email: info@osheashotel.com
Web: http://www.osheashotel.com
SIC: 55110 Employees: 50
Hotel*
Mr John McCormack Manager
Mr John Moriarty Assistant Manager

Oak Wood Arms Hotel
Shannon Co. Clare
Phone: 061-361500 Fax: 061-361414
Email: reservations@oakwoodarms.com
Web: http://www.oakwoodarms.com
SIC: 55110 Employees: 60
Hotel ***
Mr Stephen Keogh General Manager
Mr Victor O'Sullivan Accounts Manager

Old Ground Hotel
O'Connell Street
Ennis Co. Clare
Phone: 065-6828127 Fax: 065-6828112
Email: oghotel@iol.ie
Web: http://www.flynnhotels.com
SIC: 55110 Employees: 85
Hotel ***
Mr Alan Flynn Proprietor
Ms Mary Gleeson General Manager

Ormond Hotel
7-11 Upper Ormond Quay
Dublin 7
Phone: 01-8721811 Fax:
Email: ormondqh@indigo.ie
SIC: 55110 Employees: 45
Hotel***
Ms Veronica Timlin Manager
Ms Helen McManus Sales & Marketing Manager

Ostan Gweedore
Bunbeg
Letterkenny Co. Donegal
Phone: 075-31177 Fax: 075-31726
Web: http://www.ostangweedore.com
SIC: 55110 Employees: 50
Hotel ***
Mr Charles Boyle Managing Director
Ms Trisha Doherty Sales & Marketing Manager

Ostan Radharc Na Mara
Sea View Hotel
Bunbeg
Letterkenny Co. Donegal
Phone: 075-31159 Fax: 075-32238
Email: ostanradharcnamara@eircom.net
SIC: 55110 Employees: 120
Hotel **
Mr James Boyle General Manager

Oyster Manor Hotel
Clarenbridge
Co. Galway
Phone: 091-796777 Fax: 091-796770
Email: reservations@oystermanorhotel.com
Web: http://www.oystermanorhotel.com
SIC: 55110 Employees: 40
Hotel ***
Ms Julianne Forde Proprietor
Ms Anne Forde General Manager

Park Hotel Kenmare
Kenmare
Killarney Co. Kerry
Phone: 064-41200 Fax: 064-41402
Email: info@parkkenmare.com
Web: http://www.parkkenmare.com
SIC: 55110 Employees: 50
Hotel *****
Mr Francis Brennan Proprietor
Mr John Brennan General Manager

Portobello Hotel & Bar
33 Richmond Street South
Dublin 2
Phone: 01-4752715 Fax: 01-4785010
Email: portobellohotel@indigo.ie
Web: http://www.portobellohotel.ie
SIC: 55110 Employees: 60
Hotel
Mr Finian McDonnell Proprietor
Ms Ursula Fox Personnel Manager

Prince of Wales Hotel
Church Street
Athlone Co. Westmeath
Phone: 0902-72626 Fax: 0902-75658
Email: sales@pwh-athlone.com
Web: http://www.pwhathlone.com
SIC: 55110 Employees: 50
Hotel***
Mr Paul Ryan Manager
Ms Mary Hanley Head of Accounts
Ms Gale Cooke-Allen Sales & Marketing Manager

Quality Benners Hotel
Castle Street
Tralee Co. Kerry
Phone: 066-7121877 Fax: 066-7122273
SIC: 55110 Employees: 45
Hotel ***
Mr Stephen Morrissey General Manager

Quality Hotel & Leisure Centre
Clogheen
Clonakilty Co. Cork
Phone: 023-35400 Fax: 023-35404
Email: qualityhotel@eircom.net
Web: http://www.qualityhotelclon.com
SIC: 55110 Employees: 40
Hotel
Mr David Henry General Manager
Ms Ann O'Sullivan Finance Manager
Mr David Henry Personnel Manager
Mr Raymond Kelleher Sales Manager

Quality Hotel & Leisure Centre Galway
Oranmore
Galway Co. Galway
Phone: 091-792244 Fax: 091-792246
Email: qualityhotelgalway@eircom.net
Web: http://www.qualityhotelgalway.com
SIC: 55110 Employees: 70
Hotel ***
Mr Dermot Comerford General Manager
Ms Edel Millar Finance Manager
Ms Majella Conroy Personnel Manager
Ms Rhona Carney Sales & Marketing Manager

Radisson SAS Saint Helen's Hotel
Stillorgan Road
Blackrock Co. Dublin
Phone: 01-2186000 Fax: 01-2186010
Email: info@dubzh.rdsas.com
Web: http://www.radisson.com/dublin.ie
SIC: 55110 Employees: 67
Hotel
Ms Suzanne Hazenberg General Manager
Ms Jackie Sandsord Sales & Marketing Manager

Randles Court Hotel
Muckross Road
Killarney Co. Kerry
Phone: 064-35333 Fax: 064-35206
Email: randles@iol.ie
Web: http://www.randlescourt.com
SIC: 55110 Employees: 50
Hotel ****
Ms Kay Randles Managing Director
Mr Tom Randle General Manager
Ms Susan Randles Sales & Marketing Manager

Rathkeale House Hotel
Main Street
Rathkeale
Limerick Co. Limerick
Phone: 069-63333 Fax: 069-63300
Email: rhh@iol.ie
SIC: 55110 Employees: 50
Hotel***
Mr Gerry O'Connor General Manager

Rathmines Plaza Hotel
Lower Rathmines Road
Dublin 6
Phone: 01-4966966 Fax: 01-4910603
Email: info@rathminescapital-hotel.com
Web: http://www.rathminescapital-hotel.com
SIC: 55110 Employees: 100
Hotels ***
Ms Frances Dempsey Manageress
Mr Hugh O'Doherty Finance Manager
Ms Ladonna Tallon Sales & Marketing Manager

Red Cow Morans Hotel
Red Cow Complex
Naas Road
Dublin 22
Phone: 01-4593650 Fax: 01-4591588
Email: reservations@morangroup.ie
Web: http://www.redcowhotel.com
SIC: 55110 Employees: 300
Hotel ****
Mr Kieran O'Donovan General Manager
Mr Pat Power Financial Controller
Ms Niamh Jordan Operations Manager

Regency Hotel Group
Swords Road
Whitehall
Dublin 9
Phone: 01-8373544 Fax: 01-8373174
Email: regency@regencyhotels.com
Web: http://www.regencyhotels.com
SIC: 55110 Employees: 300
Hotel***
Mr Brian McGettigan General Manager
Mr Tony Nolan Finance Director
Ms Lorraine McGettigan Sales Director
Mr Pat Heavey Operations Manager

Renvyle House Hotel
Renvyle
Connemara
Galway Co. Galway
Phone: 095-43511 Fax: 095-43515
Email: renvyle@iol.ie
Web: http://www.renvyle.com
SIC: 55110 Employees: 70
Hotel***
Mr Ronnie Connahan General Manager
Ms Maread McMacken Personnel Manager

Ripley Court Hotel
37 Talbot Street
Dublin 1
Phone: 01-8365892 Fax: 01-8561182
Email: sales@ripleycourt.com
Web: http://www.ripleycourt.com
SIC: 55110 Employees: 87
Hotel ***
Mr Austin Kelly Proprietor
Mr Frank Ruane Manager

River Island Hotel
25 Main Street Lower
Castleisland
Tralee Co. Kerry
Phone: 066-7142555 Fax: 066-7142544
SIC: 55110 Employees: 70
Hotel ***
Ms Margaret Hoey General Manager
Ms Karen Horgan Personnel Manager

Rochestown Park Hotel
Rochestown Road
Cork Co. Cork
Phone: 021-4892233 Fax: 021-4892178
Email: info@rochestownpark.com
Web: http://www.rochestownpark.com
SIC: 55110 Employees: 200
Hotel ****
Mr Liam Lally General Manager
Mr John Donovan Accounts Manager
Ms Dolores Barry Personnel Manager
Ms Claire Cullinane Sales & Marketing Manager

Royal Dublin Hotel
O'Connell Street
Dublin 1
Phone: 01-8733666 Fax: 01-8733120
Email: enq@royaldublin.com
Web: http://www.royaldublin.com
SIC: 55110 Employees: 40
Hotel ***
Mr David Brady General Manager
Mr Gerry Murphy Accountant
Ms Siobhan Tinnelly Sales & Marketing Manage

Royal George Hotel
110 O'Connell Street
Limerick Co. Limerick
Phone: 061-414566 Fax: 061-317171
Email: royalgeorgehotel@eircom.net
Web: http://www.royalgeorge.com
SIC: 55110 Employees: 140
Hotel ***
Mr Malcolm Stewart Proprietor
Mr Colm Battles Accounts Manager
Ms Vanessa Meare Sales & Marketing Manager

Hospitality

Royal Hoey Hotel
Mardyke Street
Athlone Co. Westmeath
Phone: 0902-75194 Fax: 0902-75194
Email: royalhoey@ebookireland.com
SIC: 55110 Employees: 45
Hotel **
Ms Mary Hoey Proprietor

Royal Hotel & Leisure Centre
Main Street
Bray Co. Wicklow
Phone: 01-2862935 Fax: 01-2867373
Email: royal@regencyhotels.com
Web: http://www.regencyhotels.com
SIC: 55110 Employees: 71
Hotel ***
Ms Maureen O'Connor General Manager
Mr Tom Molloy Operations Manager

Russell Court Hotel
21-25 Harcourt Street
Dublin 2
Phone: 01-4784066 Fax: 01-4781576
Email: reservations@russellcourthotel.ie
SIC: 55110 Employees: 100
Hotel ***
Mr Rangan Arunchelvan Managing Director
Ms Eileen Wright Sales & Marketing Manager

Ryan Hotels Plc
23 Upper O'Connell Street
Dublin 1
Phone: 01-8787966 Fax: 01-8786032
Email: ryan@indigo.ie
Web: http://www.ryan-hotel.com
SIC: 55110 Employees: 665
Hotel *****
Mr Patrick Coyle Chief Executive
Mr Robert Bastow Head of Finance
Mr Colm Molloy Personnel Manager
Mr John Cunningham General Manager

School House Hotel
2-8 Northumberland Road
Ballsbridge
Dublin 4
Phone: 01-6675014 Fax: 01-6675015
Email: school@schoolhousehotel.iol.ie
Web: http://www.schoolhousehotel.com
SIC: 55110 Employees: 50
Hotel****
Mr Bertie Kelly General Manager
Ms Carina Dunn Sales & Marketing Manager

Seven Oaks Hotel
Athy Road
Carlow Co. Carlow
Phone: 0503-31308 Fax: 0503-32155
SIC: 55110 Employees: 60
Hotel ***
Mr Michael Murphy Managing Director
Ms Kay Murphy Receptionist
Ms Kathleen Dooley Sales & Marketing Manager

Shandon Hotel
Port Na Blagh
Letterkenny Co. Donegal
Phone: 074-36137 Fax: 074-36430
Email: shandon@eircom.net
Web: http://www.shandonhotel.com
SIC: 55110 Employees: 73
Hotel ***
Mr Dermot McGlade Proprietor

Shannon Oaks Hotel & Country Club
Portumna
Galway Co. Galway
Phone: 0509-41777 Fax: 0509-41357
Email: sales@shannonoak.ie
Web: http://www.shannonoaks.ie
SIC: 55110 Employees: 50
Hotel ****
Mr Barry Maher General Manager
Ms Mary Mahony Accounts Manager
Mr Adrian Cummins Sales & Marketing Manager

Sheen Falls Lodge
Kenmare
Killarney Co. Kerry
Phone: 064-416002 Fax:
Email: info@sheenfallslodge.ie
Web: http://www.sheenfallslodge.ie
SIC: 55110 Employees: 100
Hotel *****
Mr Adrian Bartels Managing Director
Mr Maurice Guilfoyle Financial Controller
Ms Linda Lynch Personnel Manager
Ms Carmel Flynn Sales & Marketing Manager

Shelbourne Hotel
27 St Stephen's Green
Dublin 2
Phone: 01-6766471 Fax: 01-6616006
Email: shelbourneinfo@forte-hotels.com
Web: http://www.shelbourne.ie
SIC: 55110 Employees: 200
Hotel *****
Ms Jean Ricoux General Manager
Mr Ian Morrison Financial Controller
Ms Maeve Brench Personnel Manager
Ms Denise Gallagher Sales & Marketing Manager
Mr Owen O'Connell IT Manager

Sheldon Park Hotel
Kylemore Road
Dublin 12
Phone: 01-4601055 Fax: 01-4601880
Email: info@sheldonpark.ie
Web: http://www.sheldonpark.ie
SIC: 55110 Employees: 85
Hotel ***/ Leisure Centre
Mr Donnacha Roche General Manager
Ms Rosaleen Booth Finance Manager
Mr John Gannon Personnel Manager
Ms Elaine Molloy Sales & Marketing Manager

Skeffington Arms Hotel
Eyre Square
Galway Co. Galway
Phone: 091-563173 Fax: 091-561679
Email: info@skeffington.ie
Web: http://www.skeffington.ie
SIC: 55110 Employees: 80
Hotel ***
Mr John Callanan Managing Director
Ms Anne Carolan Accountant
Ms Juile Ann Keane Reservations Manager

Slieve Russell Hotel
Ballyconnell
Belturbet Co. Cavan
Phone: 049-9526444 Fax: 049-9526474
Email: slieve-russell@quinn-hotel.com
Web: http://www.quinn-hotel.com
SIC: 55110 Employees: 200
Hotel ****
Ms Sheila Grey General Manager
Ms Ciara Devlin Personnel Director
Ms Vari McGreevy Sales & Marketing Manager

Sligo Park Hotel
Pearse Road
Sligo Co. Sligo
Phone: 071-60291 Fax: 071-69556
Email: sligopk@leehotels.ie
Web: http://www.leehotels.ie
SIC: 55110 Employees: 70
Hotel ***
Ms Michelle Haugh General Manager
Ms Geraldine Keavney Accounts Manager
Mr Gerry Moore Personnel Manager
Ms Bernadette Coffey Sales & Marketing Manager

Sligo Southern Hotel & Leisure Centre
Strand Hill Road
Sligo Co. Sligo
Phone: 071-62101 Fax: 071-60328
Email: reservations@sligosouthernhotel.com
Web: http://www.sligosouthernhotel.com
SIC: 55110 Employees: 60
Hote & Leisure Centre
Mr Kevin McGlynn Manager
Ms Noreen Gaynor Finance Manager
Ms Elaine Duffy Assistant Manager
Ms Jackie McLoughlan Sales & Marketing Manager

Star Wood Hotels & Resorts
70 Penrose Wharf
Penrose Quay
Cork Co. Cork
Phone: 021-4279200 Fax: 021-4279211
Email: cork.rescrk@starwoodhotel.com
Web: http://www.starwoodhotelandresort.com
SIC: 55110 Employees: 280
Call Centre for Hotel Reservation
Ms Caroline Cooney Managing Director
Ms Catherine O'Shea Reservations Manager
Ms Eileen O'Grady Marketing & Finance Manager
Ms Cathy Mason IT Manager

Stephens Green Hotel
St Stephen's Green
Dublin 2
Phone: 01-6073600 Fax: 01-4781444
Email: info@ocallaghanhotels.ie
Web: http://www.ocallaghanhotels.ie
SIC: 55110 Employees: 280
Hotels
Ms Sally Hughes Manager
Ms Bridget McGreehan Personnel Manager
Ms Lucy Kelly Sales & Marketing Manager

Stillorgan Park Hotel
Stillorgan Road
Stillorgan
Blackrock Co. Dublin
Phone: 01-2881621 Fax: 01-2831610
Email: sales@stillorganpark.com
Web: http://www.stillorganpark.com
SIC: 55110 Employees: 100
Hotel ****
Mr Ronan Doran General Manager
Ms Berit Cannon Accounts Manager
Ms Carmel O'Riordan Personnel Manager
Ms Sharon Power Sales & Marketing Manager

Summerhill House Hotel
Enniskerry
Wicklow Co. Wicklow
Phone: 01-2867928 Fax: 01-2867929
Email: info@summerhillhousehotel.com
Web: http://www.summerhillhousehotel.com
SIC: 55110 Employees: 70
Hotel ***
Mr Michael Blake Manager
Ms Maura Demol Accountant
Ms Helen O'Reilly Front Office Manager

Talbot Hotel & Leisure Complex
Trinity Street
Wexford Co. Wexford
Phone: 053-22566 Fax: 053-23377
Email: talbotwx@eircom.net
Web: http://www.talbothotel.ie
SIC: 55110 Employees: 120
Hotel *** & Leisure Complex
Ms Ursula Sinnott General Manager
Ms Mary O'Leary Accounts Manager
Ms Maria O'Rourke Reservations Manager

Taylors Three Rock Hotel
Grange Road
Rathfarnham
Dublin 16
Phone: 01-4942999 Fax: 01-4946599
SIC: 55110 Employees: 100
Hotel
Mr Michael McDonald

Temple Gate Hotel
The Square
Ennis Co. Clare
Phone: 065-6823300 Fax: 065-6823322
Email: templegh@iol.ie
Web: http://www.templegatehotel.com
SIC: 55110 Employees: 60
Hotel ***
Mr John Madden General Manager
Ms Sinead Markham Sales & Marketing Manager

The Westin Dublin
At College Green
Dublin 2
Phone: 01-6451000 Fax: 01-6451234
Email: sales@westindublin.com
Web: http://www.westen.com
SIC: 55110 Employees: 180
Hotel
Mr Enda Mullen General Manager
Mr Patrick Divoll Finance Manager
Mr Shane Hodges Sales Manager

Tinakilly Country House & Restaurant
Rathnew
Wicklow Co. Wicklow
Phone: 0404-69274 Fax: 0404-67806
Email: wpower@tinakilly.ie
Web: http://www.tinakilly.ie
SIC: 55110 Employees: 70
Hotel****
Mr Raymond Power Proprietor
Mr Colm O'Flaherty Personnel Manager
Ms Josephine Power Sales & Marketing Manager

Torc Great Southern Hotel
Park Road
Killarney Co. Kerry
Phone: 064-31611 Fax: 064-31824
Email: res@sales.gsh.ie
Web: http://www.gsh.ie
SIC: 55110 Employees: 65
Hotel ***
Ms Freda Darcy General Manager
Mr Dan Neville Financial Controller
Ms Michelle King Sales & Marketing Manager

Tower Hotel
Quay Street
Sligo Co. Sligo
Phone: 071-44000 Fax: 071-46888
Email: towersl@iol.ie
Web: http://www.towerhotelgroup.ie
SIC: 55110 Employees: 300
Hotel ***
Mr Ian Highland Managing Director
Ms Michelle Thornton Finance Manager
Ms Margaret Davern Personnel Manager
Mr Eric Rothschild Sales & Marketing Manager

Tower Hotel & Leisure Centre
The Mall
Waterford Co. Waterford
Phone: 051-875801 Fax: 051-870129
Email: towerw@iol.ie
Web: http://www.towerhotelgroup.ie
SIC: 55110 Employees: 100
Hotel***
Mr Paul McDaid Manager
Mr Billy O'Sullivan Finance Manager
Ms Alison Redmond Personnel Director
Ms Michelle Thornton Sales & Marketing Manager
Ms Suzanne O'Reilly Computer Analyst

Towers Hotel
Lansdowne Road
Ballsbridge
Dublin 4
Phone: 01-6670033 Fax: 01-6605540
Email: info@jurysdoyle.com.
Web: http://www.jurysdoyle.com.
SIC: 55110 Employees: 200
Hotel*****
Mr Jim O'Brien General Manager
Ms Monica Morgan Personnel Manager

Towers Hotel
Glenbeigh
Killarney Co. Kerry
Phone: 066-9768212 Fax: 066-9768260
Email: towershotel@eircom.net
SIC: 55110 Employees: 40
Hotel ***
Ms Dolores Sweeney Proprietor
Mr Brendan Sweeney Proprietor

Trident Hotel
The Worlds End
Kinsale Co. Cork
Phone: 021-4772301 Fax: 021-4774173
Email: info@tridenthotel.com
Web: http://www.tridenthotel.com
SIC: 55110 Employees: 60
Hotel ***
Mr Hal McElroy Managing Director
Mr David Good Finance Manager
Mr Barry Gregg Operations Manager
Ms Una Wren Sales & Marketing Manager

Tulfarris Hotel & Golf Resort
Blessington Lakes
Wicklow Co. Wicklow
Phone: 045-867600 Fax: 045-867565
Email: info@tulfarris.com
Web: http://www.tulfarris.com
SIC: 55110 Employees: 110
Hotel****
Mr Jim Hayes Proprietor
Ms Catherine Hayes Sales & Marketing Manager

Tullamore Court Hotel
O'Moore Street
Tullamore Co. Offaly
Phone: 0506-46666 Fax: 0506-46677
Email: info@tullamorecourthotel.ie
Web: http://www.tullamorecourthotel.ie
SIC: 55110 Employees: 150
Hotel ****
Mr Joe O' Brien Managing Director
Ms Susan Bergin Accountant
Ms Ann McLoughlin Personnel Manager
Ms Ann Lynch Sales & Marketing Manager

Twelve Pins Hotel
Barna Village
Galway Co. Galway
Phone: 091-592368 Fax: 091-592485
Email: thetwelvepinshotel@eircom.net
Web: http://www.twelvepins.com
SIC: 55110 Employees: 35
Hotel ***
Mr Pat Lohan Proprietor
Ms Geraldine Lohan Personnel Manager

Two Mile Inn Hotel
Ennis Road
Limerick Co. Limerick
Phone: 061-326255 Fax: 061-453783
Email: info@twomileinnhotel.ie
Web: http://www.twomileinnhotel.ie
SIC: 55110 Employees: 50
Hotel ***
Mr John O'Connor General Manager
Mr Kieran O'Halloran Financial Controller
Ms Ann McGreal Sales & Marketing Manager

Welcome Inn Hotel Ltd
New Antrim Street
Castlebar Co. Mayo
Phone: 094-22288 Fax: 094-21766
Email: welcomeinn@eircom.net
SIC: 55110 Employees: 35
Hotel **
Ms Ann McHugh Director
Mr Philip Atkins Accounts Manager
Mr Joe O'Dea Personnel & General Manager

Hospitality

West County Conference & Leisure Hotel
Clare Road
Ennis Co. Clare
Phone: 065-6823000 Fax: 065-6823759
Email: reservations@lynchotels.com
Web: http://www.lynchotels.com
SIC: 55110 Employees: 200
Hotel ***
Mr Michael Lynch Group Managing Director
Mr Joe Hughes Group Financial Controller
Ms Catherine Shannon Group Personnel Officer
Ms Anne O'Toole Group Sales Director
Mr Matt Muller General Manager

West County Hotel
Chapelizod
Dublin 20
Phone: 01-6264011 Fax: 01-6231378
SIC: 55110 Employees: 50
Hotel **
Mr Gerry Cloghan Manager
Mr Larry Timmons Financial Controller
Mr Eamonn Fanely Sales & Marketing Manager

West Court Hotel
West Street
Drogheda Co. Louth
Phone: 041-9830965 Fax: 041-9830970
Email: westcourthotel@eircom.net
SIC: 55110 Employees: 65
Hotel ***
Ms Valerie Sherlock General Manager

Westport Inn Hotel
Mill Street
Westport Co. Mayo
Phone: 098-29129 Fax: 098-29250
Email: info@westportinn.ie
Web: http://www.westportinn.ie
SIC: 55110 Employees: 50
Hotels
Mr Brendan Kealy Manager
Ms Paula Coleman Sales Manager

White House Hotel
Ballinlough
Ballinasloe Co. Galway
Phone: 0907-40112 Fax: 0907-40993
SIC: 55110 Employees: 50
Hotel
Mr Martin Daly Manager

White Lady Hotel
Lower O'Connell Street
Kinsale Co. Cork
Phone: 021-4772737 Fax: 021-4774641
Email: wlady@indigo.ie
SIC: 55110 Employees: 50
Hotel***
Mr Anthony Collins Partner
Ms Anne Gavin Personnel Officer
Mr Ronan Minihane Partner

White's Hotel
George's Street
Wexford Co. Wexford
Phone: 053-22311 Fax: 053-45000
Email: info@whiteshotel.iol.ie
Web: http://www.whiteshotel.iol.ie
SIC: 55110 Employees: 150
Hotel ***
Mr Michael Connolly General Manager
Mr Liam Clancy Director

Woodlands Court Hotel
Southern Cross Road
Bray Co. Wicklow
Phone: 01-2760258 Fax: 01-2760298
Email: info@woodlandscourthotel.com
Web: http://www.woodlandscourthotel.com
SIC: 55110 Employees: 36
Hotel
Ms Eileen Murphy General Manager

Woodlands House Hotel
Adare
Limerick Co. Limerick
Phone: 061-605100 Fax: 061-396073
Email: reception@woodlands-hotel.ie
Web: http://www.woodlands-hotel.ie
SIC: 55110 Employees: 80
Hotel/Restaurant
Mr Richard Fitzgerald Proprietor
Ms Mary Mullane Financial Controller
Mr Michael Magner Personnel Officer
Ms Karen Brosnahan Sales & Marketing Manager

Wynn's Hotel
35-39 Lower Abbey Street
Dublin 1
Phone: 01-8745131 Fax: 01-8741556
Email: info@wynnshotel.ie
Web: http://www.wynnshotel.ie
SIC: 55110 Employees: 100
Hotel ***
Mr Neil Loftus General Manager

Yeats Country Hotel Golf & Country Club
Rosses Point
Sligo Co. Sligo
Phone: 071-77211 Fax: 071-77203
Email: yeatscountry@eircom.net
Web: http://www/sligoaccommodation.com/yeats
SIC: 55110 Employees: 60
Hotel ***
Ms Fiona McEniff Managing Director
Ms Brona Galvin Financial Controller
Ms Breda O'Dwyer General Manager

Castle Leslie
Glaslough
Monaghan Co. Monaghan
Phone: 047-88109 Fax: 047-88256
Email: ultan@castlelesley.ie
Web: http://www.castleleslie.ie
SIC: 55121 Employees: 35
Restaurant & Accommodation
Mr Sammy Lesley Managing Director
Mr Ultan Bannon Marketing Manager

Dunleer Grove Ltd
Main Street
Dunleer
Drogheda Co. Louth
Phone: 041-6851148 Fax: 041-6851594
Email: grovehousedunleer@eircom.net
SIC: 55121 Employees: 30
Guest House
Mr Michael McClelland Manager
Ms Catriona McClelland Sales Manager

An Oige
61 Mountjoy Street
Dublin 7
Phone: 01-8304555 Fax: 01-8305808
Email: anoige@iol.ie
Web: http://www.irelandyha.org
SIC: 55210 Employees: 50
Youth Hostel Organisation
Mr Ken Kilkenny President
Mr Pascal Keegan Honorary Treasurer
Ms Jacinta Moore Honorary National Secretary
Mr David Owens General Manager

Gold Coast Holidays Ltd
Ballinacourty
Dungarvan Co. Waterford
Phone: 058-42249 Fax: 058-43378
Email: clonea@indigo.ie
Web:
http://www.amireland.com/clonea/clonpage/cottage
s.html
SIC: 55210 Employees: 30
Golf Hotel and Holiday Cottages
Ms Ann McGrath Proprietor
Mr Mark Lenihan Finance Manager
Mr Martin Owens Group Sales Manager
Mr John Kiely General Manager

Hostels Management Ltd
9 Castle Avenue
Dublin 3
Phone: 01-8331721 Fax: 01-8330312
SIC: 55210 Employees: 40
Manage Hostels
Mr WJ Kiley Secretary

Trabolgan Holiday Centre
Whitegate
Middleton
Cork Co. Cork
Phone: 021-4661551 Fax: 021-4661698
Email: reservations@trabolgan.com
Web: http://www.trabolgan.com
SIC: 55231 Employees: 125
Holiday Centre
Mr Sean Woodgate General Manager
Ms Nuala Linnane Financial Controller
Ms Laura Manning Sales & Marketing Manager

Tyrconnell Group
Dinglei Coush
Bundoran
Donegal Co. Donegal
Phone: 072-42277 Fax: 072-42385
Email: cottages@donegalholidays.com
Web: http://www.donegalholidays.com
SIC: 55231 Employees: 300
Homes/Houses/Apartments to Let
Mr John McEniff Chief Executive Officer
Mr Padraig McGoldick Financial Controller
Mr Matt Britain Sales Director

Ashdale Catering Ltd
Bellview Lawn
Cork Co. Cork
Phone: 021-4277479 Fax: 021-4278175
SIC: 55301 Employees: 56
Fast Food Restaurant
Mr Martin McGinn Director

Ashtons Bar & Restaurant
11 Verge Mount
Clonskeagh
Dublin 6
Phone: 01-2600399 Fax: 01-2600399
SIC: 55301 Employees: 30
Restaurant
Mr Paul Kelly Manager

Bakery Restaurant Bistro & Wine Bar
Church Street
Wicklow Co. Wicklow
Phone: 0404-66770 Fax: 0404-66717
SIC: 55301 Employees: 23
Restaurants-Licensed
Ms Sally Stevens Manager

Banjo Sherlock's
Kennedy Road
Navan Co. Meath
Phone: 046-74688 Fax: 046-74689
SIC: 55301 Employees: 50
Restaurants
Mr Paul Tobin Manager

Burger King
21 Merrion Square
Dublin 2
Phone: 01-6796472 Fax: 01-6628231
Email: info@okr.ie
SIC: 55301 Employees: 850
Restaurants
Mr Patrick O'Leary Managing Director
Mr John O'Connor Finance Manager
Mr Ken Murphy Office Manager

Café Java
5 South Anne Street
Dublin 2
Phone: 01-6707239 Fax: -
SIC: 55301 Employees: 24
Restaurants
Mr Kieran Mulligan Proprietor
Ms Jennie Freyne Sales Manager

Clareview Taverns
The Balreask Arms
Trim Road
Navan Co. Meath
Phone: 046-78248 Fax: 046-78176
SIC: 55301 Employees: 25
Restaurant
Mr Seamus Daley Managing Director

Cookes Cafe
14 South William Street
Dublin 2
Phone: 01-6790536 Fax: 01-6790546
SIC: 55301 Employees: 25
Restaurant
Mr John Cooke Proprietor

Creamery Bar & Restaurant
Old Bunratty Road
Bunratty
Ennis Co. Clare
Phone: 061-364114 Fax: 061-364160
Email: info@creamerybar.com
Web: http://www.creamerybar.com
SIC: 55301 Employees: 25
Restaurant
Mr Paul Plunkett General Manager
Ms Michelle O'Brien Manager

Dominos Pizza
88 Lower Rathmines Road
Dublin 6
Phone: 01-4960577 Fax: 01-4965505
SIC: 55301 Employees: 37
Restaurants
Mr Kevin O'Driscoll Managing Director
Mr Mike Doyle Store Manager

Fitzers Restaurant
Temple Bar Square, Temple Bar
Dublin 2
Phone: 01-6790440 Fax: 01-6790445
Email: eat@fitzers.ie
Web: http://www.fitzers.ie
SIC: 55301 Employees: 30
Restaurant
Mr Ronnie Carr Manager

Four Star Pizza (Ireland) Ltd
51 Upper Georges Street
Dun Laoghaire Co. Dublin
Phone: 01-2843651 Fax: 01-2846403
Email: postmaster@fourstarpizza.ie
Web: http://www.fourstarpizza.ie
SIC: 55301 Employees: 80
Restaurant Operators
Ms Anne O'Leary Managing Director
Ms Anna Rowe Accountant

Gallaghers Boxty House Ltd
20/21 Temple Bar
Dublin 2
Phone: 01-6772762 Fax: 01-6779723
Email: postmaster@boxtyhouse.ie
Web: http://www.boxtyhouse.ie
SIC: 55301 Employees: 30
Restaurant
Mr Padraig Gallagher Managing Director
Ms Colette Smith Accounts Manager
Ms Maureen O'Flynn Manageress

GBC Restaurant & Coffee Shop
7 Williamsgate Street
Galway Co. Galway
Phone: 091-565988 Fax: 091-569263
SIC: 55301 Employees: 40
Restaurant
Mr Gerry McSweeney Proprietor
Ms Christina Murphy Accountant
Ms Margaret Nolan General Manageress
Ms Anne Hynes Sales & Marketing Manager

Hospitality

Gingerbread House
Paul Street
Cork Co. Cork
Phone: 021-4276411 Fax: 021-4275413
SIC: 55301 Employees: 30
Restaurant
Ms Zaniah Salem Proprietor
Ms Joanne Waring Finance Manager
Mr Ben Sutherland Sales Manager

Graham O'Sullivan
Lower Baggot Street
Dublin 2
Phone: 01-6764006 Fax: 01-6769014
Email: gos@indigo.ie
SIC: 55301 Employees: 170
Chain of Restaurants
Mr Patrick Meade Managing Director

Hudsons Bistro
30 Railway Street
Navan Co. Meath
Phone: 046-29231 Fax: 046-73382
SIC: 55301 Employees: 30
Restaurant
Mr Richard Hudson Proprietor

Huntsman Bar & Restaurant
College Road
Galway Co. Galway
Phone: 091-562849 Fax: 091-561985
Email: Huntsmaninn@indigo.ie
Web: http://www.huntsmaninn.ie
SIC: 55301 Employees: 30
Restaurant
Mr Steven Francis Proprietor
Mr Tony Newell Sales Manager

Kilkenny Design Centre
Killkenny Design Centre
Castle Yard
Kilkenny Co. Kilkenny
Phone: 056-22118 Fax: 056-65905
Email: info@kilkennydesigncentre.iol.ie
SIC: 55301 Employees: 25
Restaurant & Shop
Ms Kathleen Moran Proprietor
Ms Roseanne Hennessy Manager

Lemon Tree Café
27 Pearse Street
Mullingar Co. Westmeath
Phone: 044-42975 Fax: 044-42680
SIC: 55301 Employees: 30
Restaurant
Mr Brian Dominican Manager

Little Chef Cork
Blackash
Kinsale Road Roundabout
Cork Co. Cork
Phone: 021-4310730 Fax: 021-4310707
SIC: 55301 Employees: 30
Restaurant
Ms Caroline Walsh Manageress

LS Catering
First Floor 5 Upper O'Connell Street
Dublin 1
Phone: 01-8724313 Fax: 01-8724181
SIC: 55301 Employees: 30
Restaurant Proprietors
Ms Lorraine Sweeney Proprietor
Ms Norma Bollard Financial Controller

McDonald's Restaurants Ireland
7 Richview Office Park
Clonskeagh
Dublin 14
Phone: 01-2080020 Fax: 01-2080021
Email: info@Ireland.mcd.com
Web: http://www.Ireland.mcd.com
SIC: 55301 Employees: 2205
Restaurants
Mr Marcus Hewson Managing Director
Mr Paul O'Neill Financial Controller
Mr Tim Ackland Human Resources Manager
Mr Amir Afsar Field Services Manager

McSwiggans Bar & Restaurant
3 Eyre Street
Wood Quay
Galway Co. Galway
Phone: 091-568917 Fax: 091-568213
SIC: 55301 Employees: 80
Bar & Restaurant
Mr Tommy Smyth Managing Director
Ms Stephanie Healy Restaurant Manager

Mother Hubbards
Moyvalley
Athy Co. Kildare
Phone: 0405-51020 Fax: 0405-51358
SIC: 55301 Employees: 60
Restaurant
Mr Patrick Sweeney Proprietor
Ms Yvonne Sweeney Personnel Manager

Nancy Hands
30-32 Parkgate Street
Dublin 8
Phone: 01-6770149 Fax: 01-6770187
Email: nancyh@indigo.ie
SIC: 55301 Employees: 25
Pub/Restaurant
Mr Martin McCaffrey Managing Director
Mr Sean Foley Finance Manager
Ms Collette Cullen Office Manager

Old Dublin Restaurant
90/91 Francis Street
Dublin 8
Phone: 01-4542028 Fax: 01-4541406
SIC: 55301 Employees: 30
Restaurant
Mr Eamonn Walsh Proprietor

Old Schoolhouse
Coolbanagher
Church Road
Swords Co. Dublin
Phone: 01-8402846 Fax: 01-8405060
Email: sincater@indigo.ie
SIC: 55301 Employees: 30
Restaurant
Mr Brian Sinclair Proprietor
Ms Ann Sinclair Personnel Manager

Paddy Burkes
Clarenbridge
Galway Co. Galway
Phone: 091-796226 Fax: 091-796016
SIC: 55301 Employees: 40
Restaurant/Bar
Mr Matty Carr Proprietor

Patrick Guilbaud Restaurant
21 Upper Merrion Street
Dublin 2
Phone: 01-6764192 Fax: 01-6610052
SIC: 55301 Employees: 40
Restaurant
Mr Stephan Robin Manager

PI Restaurant
Washingtown Street
Cork Co. Cork
Phone: 021-4222860 Fax: 021-4273727
SIC: 55301 Employees: 35
Restaurant
Ms V Farrazin Manager

Probys Bistro
Probys Quay, Crosses Green
Cork Co. Cork
Phone: 021-4316531 Fax: 021-4975882
Email: info@probysbistro.com
Web: http://www.probysbistro.com
SIC: 55301 Employees: 40
Restaurant
Mr Michael Condon Manager

Reginald Lounge Bar
The Mall
Waterford Co. Waterford
Phone: 051-855087 Fax: 051-871026
SIC: 55301 Employees: 50
Restaurant/ Bar & Night club
Mr John Phelan Proprietor
Ms Josephine Phelan Finance Manager
Mr Pat Rocket Manager

Rocket Restaurants
7 South Anne Street
Dublin 2
Phone: 01-6797340 Fax: 01-6790040
SIC: 55301 Employees: 350
Restaurants
Mr Niall Fortune Managing Director
Mr Greg Malone Financial Controller
Mr Jonathon Parkhill Operations Manager

Select Service Partner
Level 5 Main Terminal Building
Dublin Airport
Swords Co. Dublin
Phone: 01-8444085 Fax: 01-8445360
SIC: 55301 Employees: 300
Restaurant
Ms Cathy Granby General Manager
Mr David Barry Finance Manager

Supermacs Ireland Ltd
1 O'Connell Street
Dublin 1
Phone: 01-8721828 Fax: 01-8734744
Web: http://www.supermacs.ie
SIC: 55301 Employees: 65
Restaurants
Mr Pat Mc Donagh Manager

Texas Steakout
116-117 O'Connell Street
Limerick Co. Limerick
Phone: 061-410350 Fax: 061-414440
Email: info@texassteakout.com
Web: http://www.texassteakout.com
SIC: 55301 Employees: 60
Restaurant
Mr Tony Enright Proprietor
Ms Margaret Bartley Manageress

The Loft Restaurant
16-20 Lord Edward Street
Sligo Co. Sligo
Phone: 071-46770 Fax: 071-46770
SIC: 55301 Employees: 30
Restaurants Licensed
Ms Fiona Burgess General Manager

Trastevere Italian Restaurant
Unit 1 Temple Bar Square
Dublin 2
Phone: 01-6708343 Fax: 01-6797182
SIC: 55301 Employees: 25
Restaurants
Mr Giovanni Cafolla Proprietor
Mr Carlo Alambi
Ms Karen Porter Manager

Hospitality

Waterfront Restaurant
Riversdale House Hotel
Kenmare
Killarney Co. Kerry
Phone: 064-41299 Fax: 064-41075
Email: riversdale@eircom.net
SIC: 55301 Employees: 45
Restaurant
Mr Peter O'Sullivan Proprietor
Ms Mary Wall General Manager

Yamamori Noodles
71 Great Georges Street South
Dublin 2
Phone: 01-4755001 Fax:
SIC: 55301 Employees: 45
Restaurants
Mr Duggan Maguire Manager

Bad Ass Cafe
9-11 Crown Alley
Temple Bar
Dublin 2
Phone: 01-6712596 Fax: 01-6712596
Email: bad-ass-cafe@hotmail.com
Web: http://www.badasscafe.com
SIC: 55302 Employees: 35
Café
Mr Brian Rowan Proprietor
Ms Carol Geraghty Finance Manager

Bendini & Shaw Sandwich Bar
4 Saint Stephen's Green
Dublin 2
Phone: 01-6718651 Fax: 01-6718643
SIC: 55302 Employees: 45
Sandwich Bars & Delivery Services
Mr Harry O'Kelly Managing Director

Bewley's Café
7 Hanover Street East
Dublin 2
Phone: 01-6775686 Fax: 01-8160770
Email: info@bewleys.com
Web: http://www.bewleys.com
SIC: 55302 Employees: 500
Coffee/Tea Supplier
Mr Patrick Bewley Managing Director
Mr John Thompson Finance Manager
Ms Sarah Power Sales Manager
Ms Deirdre Downes Computer Manager

Campbell Bewley Group
Northern Cross
Malahide Road
Dublin 9
Phone: 01-8160680 Fax: 01-8160681
SIC: 55302 Employees: 4850
Catering/Cafes
Mr Sam Cronan Chief Executive
Mr Michael O'Sullivan Group Finance Director
Ms Veronica Campbell Human Resources Director
Mr Barry Tweedy Sales & Marketing Director

O'Brien's Irish Sandwich Bar
23 South William Street
Dublin 2
Phone: 01-6715176 Fax: 01-4721401
Email: info@obriens.ie
Web: http://www.obrien.ie
SIC: 55302 Employees: 200
Sandwich Bars & Delivery Services
Mr Broddy Sweeney Manager
Mr Morris Knightly Personnel Manager
Ms Edel Nicholson Sales Manager

Bakers Corner
Kill O the Grange
Dun Laoghaire Co. Dublin
Phone: 01-2807782 Fax: 01-2302066
SIC: 55402 Employees: 40
Public House
Mr Conor O'Sullivan Manager

Ballyboden House
Rathfarnham
Dublin 16
Phone: 01-4932358 Fax: 01-4931707
SIC: 55402 Employees: 40
Public House
Mr Liam Bugler Proprietor
Mr Pascal Bugler Personnel Manager

Ballymun House Ltd
74 Willow Park Crescent
Finglas
Dublin 11
Phone: 01-8341893 Fax: 01-8361873
Email: willows@ballymunhouse.ie
SIC: 55402 Employees: 50
Public House
Mr Albert Martin Proprietor

Beaumont House
1 Shantalla Road
Beaumont
Dublin 9
Phone: 01-8371353 Fax: 01-8368405
SIC: 55402 Employees: 40
Pub Restaurant
Mr Dermott Carew Proprietor

Bloody Stream
Howth Railway Station
Howth
Dublin 13
Phone: 01-8395076 Fax: 01-8395321
Email: bloodys@iol.ie
SIC: 55402 Employees: 40
Public House
Mr Michael Wright Proprietor

Bosun Bar & Restaurant
Monkstown
Cork Co. Cork
Phone: 021-4842172 Fax: 021-4842008
SIC: 55402 Employees: 50
Public House & Restaurant
Mr Nicholas Moynihan Proprietor
Mr Michael Fitzgerald Financial Controller

Brady's
Main Street
Shankill
Dublin 18
Phone: 01-2820153 Fax: 01-2720504
SIC: 55402 Employees: 30
Public House
Mr John Brady Proprietor

Bridge Cafe Bar
10-12 Westmoreland Street
Dublin 2
Phone: 01-6708133 Fax: 01-6774021
Web: http://www.outonthetown.com/bridge
SIC: 55402 Employees: 35
Public House
Mr Colm Devine Manager

Capital Bars
40 Dawson Streer
Dublin 2
Phone: 01-6779021 Fax: 01-6774056
SIC: 55402 Employees: 900
Bar/Restaurant/Nightclub/Hotel Operator
Mr Roger Beaumont Proprietor

Carlsberg Sports Bar
103 O'Connell Street
Limerick Co. Limerick
Phone: 061-400417 Fax: 061-417922
Web: http://www.ravenhead.ie
SIC: 55402 Employees: 60
Public House, Restaurant & Niteclub
Mr Kieran Murray Proprietor
Ms Clodagh Murray General Manager

Castletown Inn
Upper Main Street
Cellbridge
Naas Co. Kildare
Phone: 01-6271158 Fax: 01-6271601
SIC: 55402 Employees: 30
Public House
Mr Noel Devine Proprietor

Clonsilla Inn
Weavers Row
Clonsilla
Dublin 15
Phone: 01-8213658 Fax: 01-8213658
SIC: 55402 Employees: 40
Public House
Mr Gary Murray Manager
Mr John McLaughlin Financial Controller

Coachmans
Airport Road
Cloghran
Swords Co. Dublin
Phone: 01-8401256 Fax: 01-8409808
SIC: 55402 Employees: 30
Pub/Restaurant
Mr Michael Flaherty General Manager

Dollymount House
366 Clontarf Road
Dublin 3
Phone: 01-8332701 Fax: 01-8331487
SIC: 55402 Employees: 65
Public House
Mr Leo Fitzgerald Proprietor
Ms Lisa Fitzgerald Personnel Manager

Eamon Doran
3a Crown Alley
Temple Bar
Dublin 2
Phone: 01-6799114 Fax: 01-6792692
SIC: 55402 Employees: 40
Public House
Ms Clare Doran Proprietor

Fiddlers Creek
Rockwood Parade
Sligo Co. Sligo
Phone: 071-41866 Fax: 071-41864
Web: http://www.sligoaccomodation.com/fiddlers
SIC: 55402 Employees: 40
Public House
Mr Enda Scanlon Partner
Mr Fergal Harrison Partner

Foxhunter
Ballydowd
Lucan Co. Dublin
Phone: 01-6262599 Fax: 01-6236131
SIC: 55402 Employees: 70
Public House
Mr Sean Slattery Manager
Ms Margaret White Finance Manager

Freestand Ltd
21 Eglington Street
Galway Co. Galway
Phone: 091-563073 Fax: 091-565376
Web: http://www.clubbing.com
SIC: 55402 Employees: 70
Public House/Nightclub
Mr Kevin Healy Proprietor

George
89 South Great Georges Street
Dublin 2
Phone: 01-4782983 Fax: 01-6704427
SIC: 55402 Employees: 45
Public House
Mr Peter McLaughlin General Manager

Hospitality

Gibneys Public House
New Street
Malahide Co. Dublin
Phone: 01-8450863 Fax: 01-8454289
SIC: 55402 Employees: 80
Public House & Off-Licence
Mr Tony Gibbons Proprietor

Goblet
Malahide Road
Dublin 5
Phone: 01-8327311 Fax: 01-8329824
Email: info@goblet.com
Web: http://www.goblet.com
SIC: 55402 Employees: 60
Public House
Mr James McGovern Proprietor
Mr Aidan McGovern Manager

Hanlons
Hanlons Corner
North Circular Road
Dublin 7
Phone: 01-8385261 Fax: 01-8385214
SIC: 55402 Employees: 50
Public House
Mr Tom McCormick Proprietor

Junction Bar & Rhythm Room Niteclub
97 Manor Street
Waterford Co. Waterford
Phone: 051-844822 Fax: 051-304167
Email: pikewood@eircom.net
SIC: 55402 Employees: 40
Public House
Mr Liam Crotty Partner
Mr Declan Walsh Partner

Kestrel House
Walkinstown Cross
Dublin 12
Phone: 01-4502097 Fax: 01-4500369
SIC: 55402 Employees: 25
Public House
Mr Larry Kelly Proprietor

Kings Head
15 High Street
Galway Co. Galway
Phone: 091-566630 Fax: 091-563592
Email: postmaster@kings-head.com
Web: http://www.kings-head.com
SIC: 55402 Employees: 40
Public House
Ms Marcella McGrath General Manager
Ms Maureen Quinn Accounts Manager
Ms Eithna Keilly Personnel Manager

Langton House Hotel
69 John Street
Kilkenny Co. Kilkenny
Phone: 056-65133 Fax: 056-63693
Email: langtons@aol.ie
SIC: 55402 Employees: 100
Hotel*** Public House Nightclub-Restaurant
Mr Eamon Langton Proprietor

Leinster Arms
Main Street
Maynooth Co. Kildare
Phone: 01-6286323 Fax: 01-6287218
SIC: 55402 Employees: 40
Public House
Mr Martin Brady Proprietor

Maltings Bar
2 Wood Street
Cork Co. Cork
Phone: 021-4278900 Fax: 021-4273502
Email: maltings@eircom.net
SIC: 55402 Employees: 40
Public House & Club
Mr Frank Sheehan Proprietor
Mr Mark Hefferan Manager

Michael O'Neill Ltd
2 Suffolk Street
Dublin 2
Phone: 01-6793656 Fax: 01-6790689
Email: mikeon@indigo.ie
Web: http://www.oneillsbar.com
SIC: 55402 Employees: 50
Public House
Mr Michael O'Neill Proprietor

Milestone Inn
Drogheda Street
Balbriggan Co. Dublin
Phone: 01-8412176 Fax: 01-8413099
SIC: 55402 Employees: 50
Public House & Restaurant
Mr James Reilly Proprietor

Monasterboice Inn
Monasterboice
Drogheda Co. Louth
Phone: 041-9837383 Fax: 041-9837485
SIC: 55402 Employees: 60
Public House
Ms Roseanne Donegan Proprietor

O'Riordan's Darby Arms
Main Street
Ballincollig
Cork Co. Cork
Phone: 021-4870854 Fax: 021-4875748
SIC: 55402 Employees: 80
Bar & Niteclub
Mr Michael O'Riordan Proprietor
Mr Kieran Calahan Manager

Old Oak
113-114 Oliver Plunkett Street
Cork Co. Cork
Phone: 021-4276165 Fax: 021-4276158
Email: oldoak@eircom.net
Web: http://www.oldoakbars.com
SIC: 55402 Employees: 65
Public House
Mr Peter Woods Proprietor
Mr Kevin Cotterell Financial Controller
Mr Gerard Kiely Manager

Old Orchard
Butterfield Avenue Orchard Complex
Rathfarnham
Dublin 16
Phone: 01-4943803 Fax: 01-4946705
Email: orchardi@iol.ie
Web: http://www.oldorchard.ie
SIC: 55402 Employees: 50
Public House & Off Sales
Ms Carol Dempsey Manager

P McCormack & Sons
67 Mounttown Lower
Dun Laoghaire Co. Dublin
Phone: 01-2805519 Fax: 01-2800145
Email: cormack@iol.ie
SIC: 55402 Employees: 40
Public House
Mr Patrick McCormack Proprietor
Ms Bronagh King Manager

Palmerstown House
Palmerstown
Dublin 20
Phone: 01-6262379 Fax: 01-6262382
SIC: 55402 Employees: 200
Public House
Mr Louis Fitzgerald Managing Director
Mr John Nash Sales & Marketing Manager

Piker Lodge
Loch Gowna
Cavan Co. Cavan
Phone: 043-83109 Fax: 043-83109
SIC: 55402 Employees: 24
Public House
Ms Tracey Clarke Proprietor

Polly Hops
Lucan Road
Newcastle
Clonmel Co. Tipperary
Phone: 01-6280295 Fax: 01-6213078
Email: pollyhop@iol.ie
SIC: 55402 Employees: 50
Public House
Mr James Spratt General Manager

Pulpit Bar
10 John Street
Waterford Co. Waterford
Phone: 051-844455 Fax: 051-844456
SIC: 55402 Employees: 50
Public House & Niteclub
Mr Declan Walsh Proprietor
Mr Liam Crotey General Manager

Quays Bar
Quay Street
Galway Co. Galway
Phone: 091-568347 Fax: 091-567405
SIC: 55402 Employees: 40
Public House
Mr Seamus McGettigan Manager

Queens
12 Castle Street
Dalkey
Dun Laoghaire Co. Dublin
Phone: 01-2854569 Fax: 01-2858345
Email: queens@club.ie
SIC: 55402 Employees: 50
Public House
Mr John Sheehan Proprietor

Reardens Bar
26 Washington Street
Cork Co. Cork
Phone: 021-4271969 Fax: 021-4278054
Email: info@reardens.com
Web: http://www.reardens.com
SIC: 55402 Employees: 100
Public House & Night club
Mr Paul Montgomery Proprietor
Mr Joe Belfra Financial Controller
Ms Karen Dukelow Marketing Manager

Shannon Knights Inn
Shannon Town Centre
Shannon Co. Clare
Phone: 061-361045 Fax: 061-361596
Email: shannonknights@eircom.net
SIC: 55402 Employees: 45
Public House/Restaurant/Nightclub/Off Licence
Mr Victor McSweeney Manager

Sinnotts Bar
South King Street
Dublin 2
Phone: 01-4784698 Fax: 01-4782598
Email: sinnotts@tinet.ie
SIC: 55402 Employees: 40
Public House
Mr Brian Burke General Manager

Station House
3-5 Station Road
Raheny
Dublin 5
Phone: 01-8313772 Fax: 01-8328291
SIC: 55402 Employees: 65
Public House
Mr Sean Quail Manager

Stillorgan Orchard
1 The Hill
Stillorgan
Blackrock Co. Dublin
Phone: 01-2888357 Fax: 01-2784138
Email: orchard@cafebar.net
Web: http://www.cafebar.net
SIC: 55402 Employees: 35
Public House
Mr Billy O'Dywer Manager

TGI Fridays
St Stephens Green Shopping Centre
Dublin 2
Phone: 01-4781233 Fax: 01-4781550
SIC: 55402 Employees: 60
Public House
Mr Alan Hare General Manager

The Kings Head
15 High Street
Galway Co. Galway
Phone: 091566-630 Fax: 091-563592
Email: kingshead@eircom.net
SIC: 55402 Employees: 35
Public House
Ms M McGrath General Manager

Yacht
73 Clontarf Road
Dublin 3
Phone: 01-8336364 Fax: 01-8336364
Email: info@theyachtclontarf.com
Web: http://www.theyachtclonarf.com
SIC: 55402 Employees: 50
Public House
Mr Richard Tobin Proprietor

Break For The Border
Lower Stephens Street
Dublin 2
Phone: 01-4780300 Fax: 01-4782910
Email: breakfortheborder@capitalbars.com
Web: http://www.bftb.com
SIC: 55403 Employees: 100
Restaurant/Bar/Niteclub
Mr George Burke General Manager
Mr Tony Leach Operation Manager

Burley Ltd
1 Crowe Street
Temple Bar
Dublin 2
Phone: 01-6707508 Fax: 01-6707559
Email:
SIC: 55403 Employees: 30
Bar & Restaurant
Mr Robbie Fox Proprietor

Davitts
The Quays
Dungarvan Co. Waterford
Phone: 058-44900 Fax: 058-41000
SIC: 55403 Employees: 50
Bar Restaurant & Nite Club
Mr Declan Hodman Manager

Harry's Bar
Bonemaine
Bridgend
Lifford Co. Donegal
Phone: 077-68444 Fax: 077-68664
SIC: 55403 Employees: 40
Bar & Restaurant
Mr Kevin Doherty Proprietor
Mr Garth O'Connor Manager

Keg
Main Street
Newbridge Co. Kildare
Phone: 045-431232 Fax: 045-432833
SIC: 55403 Employees: 45
Public House & Restaurant
Mr Pat McGinn Joint-Proprietor
Mr Owen Blake Manager
Mr Martin McGinn Joint Proprietor

MJ Finnegans
Dublin Road
Annacotty
Limerick Co. Limerick
Phone: 061-337338 Fax: 061-337171
Email: info@finnegansbar.com
Web: http://www.finnegansbar.com
SIC: 55403 Employees: 60
Bar & Resaurant
Mr Finbar Murphy Proprietor
Mr David Smiddy General Manager

New Wicklow Arms
Delgany
Greystones Co. Wicklow
Phone: 01-2874611 Fax: 01-2873878
Web: http://www.burn-group.com
SIC: 55403 Employees: 60
Public House/ Restaurant
Mr Robert Doyle Manager
Mr Billy Burn Personnel Manager
Mr Eddie Burn Sales & Marketing Manager

Central Park Galway Ltd
36 Upper Abbeygate Street
Galway Co. Galway
Phone: 091-565976 Fax: 091-567261
Email: cpbran@indigo.ie
Web: http://www.indigo.ie/~cpbran
SIC: 55404 Employees: 100
Night Club /Restaurant
Mr Ted Roberts General Manager

Conlons Restaurant Bar & Niteclub
5/9 Dublingate Street
Athlone Co. Westmeath
Phone: 0902-74376 Fax: 0902-72444
SIC: 55404 Employees: 80
Night Clubs
Mr Thomas Conlon Proprietor

Castleoak Catering Company Ltd
The Stables Courtyard
Univ of Limerick, Castletroy
Carrick On Shannon Co. Leitrim
Phone: 061-213527 Fax: 061-338120
SIC: 55520 Employees: 50
Catering
Ms Noreen O'Keeffe General Manager

Clarke's Home Bakery
54 New Cabra Road
Dublin 7
Phone: 01-8389724 Fax: 01-8684001
SIC: 55520 Employees: 30
Catering
Mr Noel Clarke Manager

Cuisine Express
Unit 16 Cookstown Business Centre
Tallaght
Dublin 24
Phone: 01-4622299 Fax: 01-4622686
SIC: 55520 Employees: 30
Catering Company
Ms Rachel Naylor Managing Director
Ms Angela Mahon General Manager

Egan Catering
Shelbourne Park, Greyhound Stadium
Ringsend
Dublin 4
Phone: 01-6608199 Fax: 01-6672422
SIC: 55520 Employees: 60
Catering Companies
Mr Thomas Egan Managing Director
Ms Suzanne Egan Finance Manager
Ms Ciara Egan Sales & Marketing Manager

Eurest Sutcliffe
Sutcliffe House
3 Eustace Street
Dublin 2
Phone: 01-6712700 Fax: 01-6796044
SIC: 55520 Employees: 1200
Catering
Mr Noel Mahony Chief Executive
Mr Paul Kenny Financial Director
Ms Mairead Nalty Personnel Manager
Mr Mike Molloy Sales Manager
Ms Brenda Mongey Office Manager

Fitzpatrick's
Glounthaune
Cork Co. Cork
Phone: 021-4353299 Fax: 021-4353093
SIC: 55520 Employees: 25
Catering
Ms Geraldine O'Neill Proprietor

Hooper Catering
45 Watson Road
Killiney
Dun Laoghaire Co. Dublin
Phone: 01-2352210 Fax: 01-2840702
Email: hooper@iol.ie
Web: http://www.hoopercatering.ie.nu
SIC: 55520 Employees: 25
Caterers
Mr Richard Hooper Managing Director

Management Catering Services Ltd
1 Terminus Mills
Clonskeagh Road
Dublin 6
Phone: 01-2837884 Fax: 01-2839797
Email: mcsplc@eircom.net
SIC: 55520 Employees: 300
Contract Caters
Mr Noel Forrester Managing Director
Ms Rena McDonald Finance Manager

Masterchefs
Muirfield Drive, Naas Road
Dublin 12
Phone: 01-6261466 Fax: 01-6261289
Email: sales@masterchefs.ie
Web: http://www.masterchefs.ie
SIC: 55520 Employees: 70
Catering
Mr Jamie Conlon Chief Executive
Mr Padraic O'Kane General Manager
Mr John Coghlan Production Director

SCG Holdings Ltd
Main Street
Castleblayney Co. Monaghan
Phone: 042-9740883 Fax: 042-9740977
Email: mas@iol.ie
SIC: 55520 Employees: 40
Catering Outlets
Mr Michael Smyth Director
Ms Elizabeth Smyth Secretary

Sodexho
23 Rock Hill
Main Street Blackrock
Dublin 4
Phone: 01-2833654 Fax: 01-2833991
Email: info@sodexho.com
Web: http://www.sodexho.ie
SIC: 55520 Employees: 1535
Industrial Caterers
Mr Desmond Doherty Managing Director
Mr Michael Purvis Financial Controller
Mr Malcolm Kelly Personnel Manager
Mr Eddie McGrath Sales & Marketing Manager
Ms Janine Patterson Quality Manager

Variety Foods Ltd
8 Rosemount Park
Ballycoolin
Dublin 11
Phone: 01-8226633 Fax: 01-8226262
Email: sales@variety.lls.com
Web: http://www.varietyfoods.net
SIC: 55520 Employees: 90
Suppliers To Catering Trade
Mr Henry Johnston Managing Director
Mr Gareth McAllister Financial Controller
Ms Wendy Wilson Personnel Director
Mr Barry Monaghan Regional Director
Mr Niall Johnston IT Manager

Wheelers Grill Room
Singland
Castletroy
Limerick Co. Limerick
Phone: 061-330955 Fax: -
SIC: 55520 Employees: 23
Catering
Mr Michael O'Leary Manager

With Taste Banqueting Services Ltd
Unit 60 Cherry Orchard Ind Estate
Dublin 10
Phone: 01-6268357 Fax: 01-6265241
Web: http://www.withtastebanqueting.ie
SIC: 55520 Employees: 200
Outside Caterers
Ms Fran Murrin Managing Director
Ms Sinead Spillane Financial Controller
Ms Geraldine Lyons Sales & Marketing Manager

Land Transport

60 Land Transport
60100 Urban Railways
60210 Bus Station/Depots
60220 Taxi Firms
60231 Coach Operators
60240 Road Haulage
60241 Furniture Removal
60249 Road Transport (Other)

Coras Iompair Eireann
Heuston Station
Dublin 8
Phone: 01-6771871 Fax: 01-7032276
Email: info@cie.ie
Web: http://www.cie.ie
SIC: 60100 Employees: 1000
Transport
Dr John Lynch Chairman
Mr Frank Crumlish Head of Group Finance
Mr John Sullivan Personnel Manager
Mr Noel Boyce Group IT Manager

Iarnrod Eireann
Connolly Station
Amien Street
Dublin 1
Phone: 01-8363333 Fax: 01-8364760
Email: info@irishrail.ie
Web: http://www.irishrail.ie
SIC: 60100 Employees: 5055
Railway Company
Mr Joe Meagher Managing Director
Mr Richard O'Farrell Manager Finance & Admin
Mr John Keenan Human Resources Manager
Mr Ray Kelly Manager Marketing Services
Mr Mick McMahon Manager Business Systems

Bus Eireann
Broadstone
Dublin 7
Phone: 01-8302222 Fax: 01-8309377
Email: info@buseireann.ie
Web: http://www.buseireann.ie
SIC: 60210 Employees: 2560
Provincial Bus Services
Mr Bill Lilley Chief Executive
Mr Martin Nolan Manager Finance & Accounting
Mr Des Tallon Manager Human Resources
Mr Barry Coyle Sales & Marketing Manager

Dublin Bus
59-60 Upper O'Connell Street
Dublin 1
Phone: 01-8720000 Fax: 01-8731195
Email: info@dublinbus.ie
Web: http://www.dublinbus.ie
SIC: 60210 Employees: 3200
Public Transport in the Greater Dublin Area
Dr Alan Westwell Managing Director
Ms Katrina Murphy Finance Manager
Mr Gerry Maguire Human Resources Manager
Mr Brendan Flynn Technical Manager

Athlone Cab Company
The Ark Dublin Gate Street
Athlone Co. Westmeath
Phone: 0902-75888 Fax: 0902-73188
SIC: 60220 Employees: 35
Cab Company
Ms Sharon Kearney Manager
Mr Pat Meade Financial Controller

Ballyowen Cabs
10 Village Centre
Lucan Co. Dublin
Phone: 01-6218888 Fax: 01-6282288
SIC: 60220 Employees: 40
Taxi & Taxicabs
Mr Barry McCann Proprietor

O'Brien Cab & Courier Services Ltd
34 Tradaree Court
Shannon Co. Clare
Phone: 061-362614 Fax: 061-362614
Email: obcabs@tinet.ie
SIC: 60220 Employees: 24
Taxis Firm
Mr Thomas O'Brien Proprietor

Phoenix Cab Co
91 Manor Street
Dublin 7
Phone: 01-6707333 Fax: 01-6793977
SIC: 60220 Employees: 50
Hackney Cars
Mr Tony Walsh Partner
Mr Tom Delaney Partner

Speeditaxis Ltd
Sweetbrier Rathuard
Ballysheedy
Limerick Co. Limerick
Phone: 061-318844 Fax: 061-411275
Email: speeditaxis@eircom.net
Web: http://www.limericktaxis.com
SIC: 60220 Employees: 35
Taxi Firm
Mr Philip O'Halloran Proprietor
Mr Philip O'Connor Accounts Manager

Taxi 2000
24 Thorn Castle Street
Ringsend
Dublin 4
Phone: 01-6617888 Fax: 01-2026807
SIC: 60220 Employees: 30
Taxi Service
Mr Joe Hannigan Financial Director

Terenure Taxi Cabs
120 Terenure Road North
Dublin 6
Phone: 01-4901111 Fax: 01-4920770
SIC: 60220 Employees: 140
Taxi & Taxicabs
Mr Derek McGovern Co-Proprietor
Mr Terry Kennedy Co-Proprietor

Alan Martin Coach Tours
Unit 13 Rosemount Business Park
Dublin 11
Phone: 01-8221122 Fax: 01-8209364
Email: amc@eircom.net
Web: http://www.amc.ie
SIC: 60231 Employees: 75
Coaches Charter Services
Mr Alan Martin Managing Director
Mr Paul Kiernan General Manager

Buckleys Tours
Woodlands Industrial Estate
Killarney Co. Kerry
Phone: 064-31945 Fax: 064-31903
Email: buckleys@iol.ie
SIC: 60231 Employees: 40
Coach Hire Company
Mr Mike Buckley General Manager
Mr Alan O 'Connor Transport Manager

City Cabs
New Market
Dublin 8
Phone: 01-4731333 Fax: 01-4733212
Email: citycabs@oceanfree.net
Web: http://www.citycabs.oceanfree.net
SIC: 60231 Employees: 25
Coaches/Charter Services/Taxis & Chauffeur
Ms Sarah Mullins Manager

Cronin's Coaches Ltd
Shannon Buildings
Mallow Road
Cork Co. Cork
Phone: 021-4309090 Fax: 021-4305508
Email: cork@croninscoaches.com
SIC: 60231 Employees: 70
Coach Hire
Ms Nora Cronin General Manager
Mr Pat Barratt Accountant

Dual Way Coaches
Keatings Park
Rathcoole
Dublin 24
Phone: 01-4580054 Fax: 01-4580808
Email: info@dualwaycoaches.com
Web: http://www.dualwaycoaches.co.uk
SIC: 60231 Employees: 30
Private Hire of Coaches
Mr Tony McCann Proprietor

Eirebus
25-27 City Quay
Dublin 2
Phone: 01-6715333 Fax: 01-6712973
Email: eirebus@iol.ie
SIC: 60231 Employees: 40
Coaches/Charter Services
Mr Jimmy Kelly Managing Director

Galvins Dunmanway Ltd
Dunmanway
Cork Co. Cork
Phone: 023-45125 Fax: 023-45407
Email: galvinscoaches@eircom.net
SIC: 60231 Employees: 25
Coach/Bus Hire
Ms Jenny Galvins Manager
Mr John Galvins Finance Manager

Transport

Achilles Express Road Services
Unit 9 Kinsealy Business Park
Kinsealy
Swords Co. Dublin
Phone: 01-8462400 Fax: 01-8462466
SIC: 60240 Employees: 40
Haulage Contractors
Mr Liam McGowan Manager
Mr Peter Barron Finance Manager

Andrew Weir Agencies (Ireland) Ltd
Conway House
East Wall Road
Dublin 3
Phone: 01-8552644 Fax: 01-8557234
Email: conwayshipping@tinet.ie
SIC: 60240 Employees: 25
Haulage
Mr Tony Ennis Manager

Autotrans Ltd
Cullinagh
Newcastle West
Limerick Co. Limerick
Phone: 069-62888 Fax: 069-62858
Email: info@autotrans.iol.ie
Web: http://www.autotrans.iol.ie
SIC: 60240 Employees: 56
Haulage Contractors
Mr Gerard Prendeville Manager
Ms Fiona Collins Accounts Clerk

Carna Transport Ltd
Main Street
Castleblayney Co. Monaghan
Phone: 042-9740537 Fax: 042-9746262
SIC: 60240 Employees: 78
Road Haulage
Mr Raymond Scullion Manager

Con Transport Ltd
Baldonnell Business Park
Baldonnell
Dublin 22
Phone: 01-2953635 Fax: 01-4660322
Email: contrans@indigo.ie
SIC: 60240 Employees: 60
Haulage Contactors
Mr Niall Hickey Managing Director
Ms Caroline Creighton Finance Manager

Cronin The Art of Moving
Tyrellstown Way
Damastown Industrial Park
Dublin 15
Phone: 01-8097000 Fax: 01-8097001
Email: relo@theartofmoving.com
Web: http://www.cronin-movers.ie
SIC: 60240 Employees: 50
Logistics
Ms Marian Foley Manager
Mr Dave Daley Finance Manager
Mr Damian Carroll Sales & Marketing Manager

DPF Consultants Ltd
T/A Alltrans
Upper Ballymount
Dublin 24
Phone: 01-4564511 Fax: 01-4564716
Email: info@altrans.ie
Web: http://www.altrans.ie
SIC: 60240 Employees: 35
Haulage & Warehousing
Mr Paul Touhey Managing Director
Ms Karen Philips Financial Controller

Fleming Transport
Block C Greenogue Industrial Estate
Rathcoole
Dublin 24 Co. Dublin
Phone: 01-4589933 Fax: 01-4589939
Email: info@fleming.transport.ie
Web: http://www.fleming.transport.ie
SIC: 60240 Employees: 60
Haulage Contractors
Mr John Joe Fleming Proprietor
Ms Jacqueline Moore Financial Controller
Mr Seamus Hennnesy Personnel Manager
Ms Ann Wilson Sales Director
Mr Paddy Farrell IT Manager

Hanlon Transport
Greenore
Dundalk Co. Louth
Phone: 042-9373136 Fax: 042-9373308
SIC: 60240 Employees: 25
Haulage Contractors
Mr John Hanlon Managing Director

Hughes Transport Ltd
Bond Road
Dublin 3
Phone: 01-8365995 Fax: 01-8366045
SIC: 60240 Employees: 30
Haulage Contractors
Mr Gerard Hughes Proprietor

J Toner & Sons Ltd
Unit 23 Cookstown Industrial Estate
Tallaght
Dublin 24
Phone: 01-4623080 Fax: 01-4623084
Email: enquiry@jtonerandsons.com
Web: http://www.jtoner&sons.com
SIC: 60240 Employees: 37
Haulage Contractors
Mr James Toner Proprietor

John McGarry Haulage Ltd
Abbeytown
Ballysadare
Sligo Co. Sligo
Phone: 071-30444 Fax: 071-30447
SIC: 60240 Employees: 33
Road Haulage
Mr Robert McNabb Managing Director
Ms Mary O'Malley Accounts Manager

Johnston Haulage Company Ltd
Blackchurch
Rathcoole
Dublin 24
Phone: 01-4588213 Fax: 01-4588261
Email: info@johnstonhaulage.ie
Web: http://www.johnstonhaulage.ie
SIC: 60240 Employees: 90
Haulage Contrators
Mr Albert Johnston Managing Director
Mr David Ensor Finance Manager
Ms Sandra Redden Personnel Manager
Mr Ivan Johnston DP Manager

JW Carnegie & Co Ltd
20A Sweetmanns Avenue
Blackrock Co. Dublin
Phone: 01-2831109 Fax: 01-2882458
SIC: 60240 Employees: 35
Haulage Contractors
Mr Dermot Carnegie Proprietor

Keenan International Transport Ltd
Benagh
Riverstown
Dundalk Co. Louth
Phone: 042-9376213 Fax: 042-9376422
Email: keenantransport@eircom.net
SIC: 60240 Employees: 50
Haulage Contractor
Mr Tommy Keenan Managing Director
Mr Joe Keenan Sales Director

Kehoe Transport
Pembroke
Carlow Co. Carlow
Phone: 0503-31359 Fax: 0503-41333
SIC: 60240 Employees: 25
Haulage Contactors
Mr Michael Grant Proprietor
Ms Annmarie McNamara Financial Controller

M Brannigan & Son Ltd
Talboths Inch
Freshford Road
Kilkenny Co. Kilkenny
Phone: 056-22141 Fax: 056-61469
Email: brann@indigo.ie
SIC: 60240 Employees: 30
Warehousing & Distribution
Mr Michael Brannigan Managing Director
Mr Eugene Paigeman Finance Manager
Mr Tony Pierce Personnel Manager
Ms Ashling Murphy Production Manager
Mr Gary Brennan Computer Manager

McArdle Transport Ltd
Callenberg
Inniskeen
Dundalk Co. Louth
Phone: 042-9378132 Fax: 042-9378402
Email: mcardletrans@iol.ie
SIC: 60240 Employees: 40
Haulage Contractors
Mr Michael McArdle Managing Director
Ms Grainne McKeown Financial Controller
Mr Frank Keenan Sales & Marketing Manager
Mr Martin McMahon IT Manager

McQuaid Transport
Bond Road
East Wall
Dublin 3
Phone: 01-8550075 Fax: 01-8550079
Email: mcquaid@tinet.ie
SIC: 60240 Employees: 65
Haulage Contactors
Mr Michael McQuaid Proprietor
Ms Geraldine O'Flanagan Financial Controller

Murphy Transport Ltd
Maryfield
Ballinlough Road
Cork Co. Cork
Phone: 021-4294400 Fax: 021-4293583
Email: mtl@tinet.ie
SIC: 60240 Employees: 40
Haulage Contractors
Mr Michael Murphy Managing Director
Mr John Lehane Finance Manager

Nolan Transport
Oaklands
New Ross Co. Wexford
Phone: 051-421965 Fax: 051-422808
Email: info@nolantransport.ie
Web: http://www.nolantransport.com
SIC: 60240 Employees: 200
Haulage Contractors
Ms Patricia Nolan Managing Director
Mr John Nolan IT Manager

O'Connell Transport & Warehousing Ltd
Brooklodge
Glanmire
Cork Co. Cork
Phone: 021-4821357 Fax: 021-4821112
Email: info@oconnellgroup.ie
Web: http://www.oconnellgroup.ie
SIC: 60240 Employees: 40
Container Haulage Specialists & Warehousing
Mr Edward O'Connell Manager
Mr Patsy Murphy Finance Manager
Mr Paddy O'Sullivan General Manager
Mr Bosco Creed Warehouse Manager

Transport

O'Donovan Transport (Cork) Ltd
Main Street
Carrigtwohill
Cork Co. Cork
Phone: 021-4883399 Fax: 021-4883705
Email: odt@odt.ie
SIC: 60240 Employees: 30
Haulage Contractors
Mr Patrick O'Donovan Proprietor
Mr Patrick Walsh Accountant
Ms Celine O'Donovan Sales & Marketing Manager
Mr Matt Mulcahy Computer Manager

O'Grady Freight Ltd
Clonbullogue
Edenderry
Tullamore Co. Offaly
Phone: 0405-30026 Fax: 0405-30124
Email: ogradytrans@tinet.ie
SIC: 60240 Employees: 25
Haulage Contactors
Mr Thomas O'Grady Managing Director

Prime Line Transport Ltd
Unit 1 Ashbourne Industrial Park
Ashbourne
Navan Co. Meath
Phone: 01-8353000 Fax: 01-8352300
SIC: 60240 Employees: 50
Haulage Contractors
Mr Danny Geoghan Managing Director

Reynolds Logistics Ltd
Alexandra Road
Dublin 1
Phone: 01-8170800 Fax: 01-8558829
Email: info@edminareynoldslogistics.com
Web: http://www.edminareynoldslogistics.com
SIC: 60240 Employees: 81
Haulage
Mr David Casey

Reynolds Tankers Ltd
Shell Dublin Terminal
Alexandra Road
Dublin 1
Phone: 01-4571124 Fax: 01-8558829
Email: info@reynolds-tankers.ie
Web: http://www.reynolds-tankers.ie
SIC: 60240 Employees: 50
Haulage Contractors
Mr Joe Reynolds Managing Director
Mr Barry Regan Finance Manager

Rice's Car Transport Ltd
Marshmeadow
New Ross Co. Wexford
Phone: 051-425444 Fax: 051-422551
Email: cartransport@iol.ie
Web: http://www.cartransport.ie
SIC: 60240 Employees: 55
Road Haulage
Mr Richard Rice Managing Director
Mr Gerard Henerick Financial Controller

Ryan Haulage Ltd
Ballywilliam
Enniscorthy Co. Wexford
Phone: 051-424949 Fax: 051 424949
SIC: 60240 Employees: 50
Haulage Contractors
Mr Gerry Ryan Managing Director
Mr John Ryan Sales Director

S Transport (Cork) Ltd
Central Park Road
Cork Co. Cork
Phone: 021-4311701 Fax: 021-4962913
SIC: 60240 Employees: 40
Haulage Contractors
Mr Terence Cronin Managing Director
Mr Jim O'Houlihan Company Accountant

Sean Delaney Haulage
Killalough Cross
Glanmire
Cork Co. Cork
Phone: 021-4821300 Fax: 021-4866509
SIC: 60240 Employees: 25
Haulage Contactors
Mr Sean Delaney Managing Director

Stephen Nolan Transport Ltd
Bond Drive Extension
East Wall
Dublin 3
Phone: 01-8366761 Fax: 01-8366763
Email: snt@indigo.ie
SIC: 60240 Employees: 25
Haulage Contractors
Mr James Nolan Proprietor

Trux Transport Ltd
Unit 45 Robinhood Industrial Estate
Clondalkin
Dublin 22
Phone: 01-4508058 Fax: 01-4507607
SIC: 60240 Employees: 35
Haulage Contractors
Mr John Keohane Managing Director
Mr John Ring Accounts Manager
Mr Peter Donoghue Sales Manager

Vanfleet Transport Ltd
Santry Industrial Estate
Santry
Dublin 9
Phone: 01-8620761 Fax: 01-8620794
Email: vanfleet@tinet.ie
SIC: 60240 Employees: 100
Haulage Company
Mr Tom Fitzsimmons Managing Director
Ms Mary Conlon Financial Controller
Ms Gretta Duffy Sales & Marketing Manager

Virginia Transport Ltd
Virginia
Cavan Co. Cavan
Phone: 049-8547403 Fax: 049-8547056
Email: enquiries@virginia-transport.ie
Web: http://www.virginia-transport.ie
SIC: 60240 Employees: 60
Road Haulage
Mr Sean Cole Managing Director
Mr Ray Cole Sales Manager

Williames Group
Blakes Cross
Belfast Road
Lusk Co. Dublin
Phone: 01-8437766 Fax: 01-8437213
SIC: 60240 Employees: 400
Haulage Contractors
Ms Mel Tomlin Managing Director
Mr Paul Boyd Finance Director
Ms Elena Luckyanenko Human Resources Director
Mr Lee Gannon Sales Director
Mr Joe Mercer Freight Director
Mr Stewart Bourke IT Manager

Allen Removals & Storage Ltd
Greenhills Estate
Tallaght
Dublin 24
Phone: 01-4513585 Fax: 01-4599039
Email: allenr@indigo.ie
Web: http://www.allenremovals.ie
SIC: 60241 Employees: 35
Removal & Storage
Mr Eamon Finn Managing Director

DJ Hanley Removal & Storage
Newtownmountkennedy
Bray Co. Wicklow
Phone: 01-2810416 Fax: 01-2810416
Email: removals@iol.ie
Web: http://www.hanley/removals.com
SIC: 60241 Employees: 25
Removals & Storage
Mr Declan Hanley Proprietor

Water Transport

61 Water Transport
61100 Sea Tansport

Arklow Shipping Ltd
North Quay
Arklow Co. Wicklow
Phone: 0402-39901 Fax: 0402-39902
Email: charting@asl.ie
Web: http://www.asl.ie
SIC: 61100 Employees: 275
Shipping
Mr James Tyrrell Managing Director
Mr Pat Corcoran Financial Director
Mr Michael Fitzpatrick IT Manager

Cleggan & Inishbofin Ferries Ltd
Cleggan
Galway Co. Galway
Phone: 095-44642 Fax: 095-44327
SIC: 61100 Employees: 26
Ferry Company
Mr Malachy King Managing Director

Dublin Maritime Ltd
Maritime House
North Wall
Dublin 1
Phone: 01-8741231 Fax: 01-6720510
Email: admin@dublin.hkcil.ie
Web: http://www.maritime.ie
SIC: 61100 Employees: 25
Shipping/Forwarding Agents
Mr Seamus Murphy Managing Director
Mr Michael Hogan Office Manager
Mr Franco Viale Sales Manager
Mr John Keogh DP Manager

Dublin Port
Port Centre
Alexandra Road
Dublin 1
Phone: 01-8876000 Fax: 01-8557400
Email: dubport@dublin-port.ie
SIC: 61100 Employees: 375
Port Authority
Mr Enda Connellan Chief Executive
Mr Michael Sheary Finance Manager
Mr Ken Whelan Human Resource Manager
Mr John Moore Store Manager
Mr Connor Farrell IT Manager

Irish Continental Group
Ferryport, Alexandra Road
Dublin 1
Phone: 01-8552222 Fax: 01-8552270
Email: info@irishferries.ie
Web: http://www.irishferries.com
SIC: 61100 Employees: 1165
Ferry Service
Mr Eamon Rothwell Chief Executive
Mr Gary O'Dea Group Finance Director
Mr Brendan McCarthy Group Human Resources Director
Mr John Reilly Operations Director

Transport

Irish Ferries
2/4 Merrion Row
Dublin 2
Phone: 01-6383333 Fax: 01-6610743
Email: info@irishferries.com
Web: http://www.irishferries.com
SIC: 61100 Employees: 30
Ferry Company
Mr Tommy Walsh Managing Director

Irish Mainport Holdings
Mainport
Monaghan Road
Cork Co. Cork
Phone: 021-4317900 Fax: 021-4317111
SIC: 61100 Employees: 250
Shipping
Mr Michael Ronayne Managing Director
Mr Donal Hurley Financial Director
Ms Cathy Giltina Personnel Director
Mr Donal McSweeney Operations

Marine Transport
Westland House
Rushbrooke
Cobh Co. Cork
Phone: 021-4811223 Fax: 021-4812645
SIC: 61100 Employees: 50
Ferry Company
Mr Mark Pearson Managing Director
Mr John O'Brien Financial Controller

Norse Merchant
Alexandra Road, Extension
Dublin Port
Dublin 1
Phone: 01-8551551 Fax: 01-8192941
Email: norse@aol.com
SIC: 61100 Employees: 400
Ferry Service
Mr Derek Cleary General Manager
Mr David Leathem Finance Manager
Ms Jemima Griffin-Cooke Personnel Manager
Ms Aaron McAleenan Sales & Marketing Manager
Mr Noel Byrne Operation Manager

P & O European Ferries Ltd
North Quay Extension
Dublin 1
Phone: 01-8557001 Fax: 01-8366472
Email: info@poirishsea.com
Web: http://www.poirishsea.com
SIC: 61100 Employees: 840
Shipping/Haulage
Mr Charles Green Chief Executive
Mr Declan Cleary Sales Manager

Port Of Cork Company
Custom House Street
Cork Co. Cork
Phone: 021-4273125 Fax: 021-4276484
Email: info@portofcork.ie
Web: http://www.portofcork.ie
SIC: 61100 Employees: 115
Port Authority
Mr Ted O'Neill Chief Executive
Mr Donal Crowley Finance Manager
Mr Pat Farnam Harbour Master

Stena Line
The Ferry Terminal
Dun Laoghaire Co. Dublin
Phone: 01-2047700 Fax: 01-2047620
Web: http://www.stenaline.com
SIC: 61100 Employees: 300
Sea Transport
Mr Vic Goodwin Route Director
Mr Francis Buckley Accountant
Mr Sean McBride Personnel & Training Manager
Mr Declan O'Sullivan Freight Sales Manager
Mr Eamonn Hewitt Communications Manager

Swansea Cork Ferries
52 South Mall
Cork Co. Cork
Phone: 021-4276000 Fax: 021-4275814
Email: scs@iol.ie
Web: http://www.swansea-cork.ie
SIC: 61100 Employees: 50
Ferry Company
Mr Thomas Hunter-Magowan Managing Director
Ms Gillian Harrington Finance Manager
Ms Millie Harrington Sales & Marketing Manager

Air Transport

62 Air Transport
62101 Air Transport – Passenger Airlines
62109 Air Transport – Other

Aer Arann
Connemara Airport
Galway Co. Galway
Phone: 091-593034 Fax: 091-593238
Email: aerarann@iol.ie
Web: http://www.iol.ie/resource/aerarann/
SIC: 62101 Employees: 70
Air Transport
Mr Padraig Keady General Manager
Mr Grainne Flaherty Finance Manager
Ms Marie Mulrooney Sales Manager

Aer Lingus (HQ)
Dublin Airport
Co. Dublin
Phone: 01-8862222 Fax: 01-8862157
Email: info@aerlingus.ie
Web: http://www.aerlingus.com
SIC: 62101 Employees: 6000
Airline Company
Mr Willie Walsh Group Chief Executive
Mr Brendan Byrne General Manager e-business
Mr Mark Martel Commercial Director
Mr Victor Garland Head Business Information Sys

Aer Lingus Ltd
Shannon Airport
Shannon Co. Clare
Phone: 061-471666 Fax: 061-715459
Email: info@aerlingus.ie
Web: http://www.aerlingus.ie
SIC: 62101 Employees: 800
Air Transport
Mr Chris Nash Station Manager
Ms Shelagh Grahame Personnel Manager
Mr Stephen Hunter Sales Manager
Mr Gerry McCormac Customer Services Manager

Aer Turas Teo
Corballis Park
Dublin Airport
Swords Co. Dublin
Phone: 01-8444131 Fax: 01-8446049
Email: aerturas@dublin.net
SIC: 62101 Employees: 55
Cargo & Passenger Operator - Airline
Mr Patrick Cousins Chief Executive
Mr Seamus O'Connell Financial Controller
Mr Frank Smyth Commercial Director
Mr Gerry Flannery Operations Superintendant

Air 2000 Ltd
Sun City Offices
Dublin Airport
Swords Co. Dublin
Phone: 01-7044857 Fax: 01-7044860
Email: info@air2000.com
Web: http://www.air2000.com
SIC: 62101 Employees: 900
Commercial Airline
Mr Kenneth Smith

Continental Airlines Inc
Suite 16, Level 2, Link Building
Dublin Airport
Swords Co. Dublin
Phone: 01-8145312 Fax: 01-8145313
Web: http://www.continental.com
SIC: 62101 Employees: 24
Airline
Mr Matthew McElroy Managing Director
Ms Oonagh Scully Finance Director
Mr Bryan Hughes Personnel Director
Ms Beatrice Cosgrove Sales Director
Ms Oonagh Scully Director - Information Systems

Donegal Airport
Carrickfinn
Kincasslagh
Letterkenny Co. Donegal
Phone: 075-48284 Fax: 075-48483
Email: donegalairport@eircom.net
Web: http://www.donegalairport.ie
SIC: 62101 Employees: 24
Airport
Ms Anne Bonner Director
Ms Anne Bonner Human Resources Manager
Ms Ellis Barrett Sales Manager
Mr Brendan O Baoill Production Manager

Kerry Airport
Farranfore
Tralee Co. Kerry
Phone: 066-9764644 Fax: 066-9764134
Email: info@kir.com
Web: http://www.kir.com
SIC: 62101 Employees: 25
Airport
Mr Peter Moore General Manager

Knock International Airport
Charlestown
Claremorris Co. Mayo
Phone: 094-67222 Fax: 094-67232
Email: info@west-irlholidays.ie
Web: http://www.knockinternationalairport.ie
SIC: 62101 Employees: 40
Air Transport
Mr Michael McGrath Airport Manager

Ryanair
Dublin Airport
Swords Co. Dublin
Phone: 01-8444400 Fax: 01-8121213
Email: info@ryanair.com
Web: http://www.ryanair.com
SIC: 62101 Employees: 1860
Airline
Mr Michael O'Leary Chief Executive
Mr Michael Cawley Group Financial Director
Ms Mary-Rose Mackin Personnel Director
Mr Tim Jones Marketing Manager
Mr Charlie Clifton Ground Operations Director
Ms Bronagh Kernan MIS Manager

Servisair Ltd
Shannon Airport
Shannon Co. Clare
Phone: 061-472340 Fax: 061-472386
Email: snnhandling@servisair.co.uk
Web: http://www.servisair.co.uk
SIC: 62101 Employees: 100
Airline Companies
Mr Tony Tulley Manager

Sligo Airport
Strandhill
Sligo Co. Sligo
Phone: 071-68280 Fax: 071-68396
Email: sxl@iol.ie
SIC: 62101 Employees: 25
Air Transport
Mr Joe Corcoran Manager
Ms Bernie Chambers Sales Manager

Cityjet
The Atrium Level 5 Terminal Building
Dublin Airport
Swords Co. Dublin
Phone: 01-8445588 Fax: 01-8446486
Email: info@cityjet.com
Web: http://www.cityjet.com
SIC: 62109 Employees: 350
Airline
Mr Geoffrey White Chief Executive
Mr Hugh Rodgers Finance Manager
Mr Jeremiah Lynch Personnel Manager
Mr Damian Manly Network Sales Manager
Mr Tony Regan Operation Manager
Mr Anthony Green Technical Director

Czech Airlines
Dublin Airport
Dublin 15
Phone: 01-8144626 Fax: 01-8444839
SIC: 62109 Employees: 75
Air Lines
Ms Sharon Greenhalgh Passenger Services Manager

Shamrock Logistics Ltd
Unit C4 Airport Business Park
Cloghran
Swords Co. Dublin
Phone: 01-8444571 Fax: 01-8444581
SIC: 62109 Employees: 44
Airline Transportation
Mr Micheal Dunne Manager

Wood Group JTC
Ridgewell House
Hollywood
Ballyboughal Co. Dublin
Phone: 01-8433642 Fax: 01-8433849
Email: support@jtc.ie
SIC: 62109 Employees: 70
Overhall Airplane Fuel Accessories
Mr Pat McEvoy Managing General
Mr Shaun Flood Finance Manager
Mr Les Cronan Sales & Marketing Manager
Mr Stewart Burn Computer Manager

Transport Supporting

63 Transport Supporting Services
63110 Cargo Storage, Handling & Warehousing
63210 Transport Services (Other)
63220 Support Services/Sea Transport
63221 Freight Forwarders
63230 Support Services/Air Transport
63301 Travel Agents & Tour Operators
63309 Tourist Offices/Services
63400 Transport Agencies – Other

Automation Transport Ltd
Tolka Quay Road
Dublin Port
Dublin 1
Phone: 01-8554388 Fax: 01-8554327
Email: info@crosbietankers.com
SIC: 63110 Employees: 50
Transport Storage & Warehousing
Mr Simon Crosbie Managing Director
Ms Alisa Murray Financial Controller

Beverly Records Management
13/17 Newmarket
Dublin 8
Phone: 01-4540235 Fax: 01-4542009
Email: brm@indigo.ie
Web: http://www.brm.ie
SIC: 63110 Employees: 28
Storage & Self Services Storage
Mr Ronan Byrne Managing Director

C & G Logistics Group
Westpoint Business Park, Navan Road
Mulhuddart
Dublin 15
Phone: 01-8208455 Fax: 01-8208457
Email: info@cglogistics.ie
Web: http://www.cglogistics.ie
SIC: 63110 Employees: 30
Warehouses (Bonded)
Mr David Dickson Managing Director
Mr Conrad Mason Finance Manager
Mr Pat Wogan Sales Manager

Dublin Port Company
Dublin Port House
32-34 Lower Grand Canal Street
Dublin 2
Phone: 01-6762259 Fax: 01-6762633
Email: dpt@eircom.net
SIC: 63110 Employees: 25
Shipping Agents
Mr Joseph Carrick Managing Director

Shreddit
Glenville Industrial Estate
26 Foster Avenue, Mount Merrion
Blackrock Co. Dublin
Phone: 01-2887982 Fax: 01-2883508
Email: storage@indigo.ie
SIC: 63110 Employees: 25
Document Storage
Mr Tom Hefferon Managing Director
Mr Francis Cummins Finance Manager
Mr Brian Hefferon Sales Manager
Mr Michael Kearns

Trans Stock Ltd
Christendom
Ferrybank
Waterford Co. Waterford
Phone: 051-832411 Fax: 051-843500
Email: info@trans-stock.com
SIC: 63110 Employees: 30
Bonded Warehouse
Mr Colm Brown Managing Director
Ms Gillian McAuley Financial Controller

DFDS Transport
Turnpike Road
Ballymount
Dublin 24
Phone: 01-4506399 Fax: 01-4051699
Email: info@dfdf.co.uk
Web: http://www.dfdf.co.uk
SIC: 63210 Employees: 175
Transport Services
Mr Jenn Neilsen Managing Director
Ms Loretta Neary Finance Director
Mr Brendan Murphy Sales Director
Mr Michael Doyle It Manager

Feehilys Executive Transport Ltd
2 Bridge Street
Sligo Co. Sligo
Phone: 071-43000 Fax: 071-70707
SIC: 63210 Employees: 25
Transport Company
Mr Daithi Shelly Manager

Hydro Hoist Ltd
Kernanstown Works
O'Brian Road
Carlow Co. Carlow
Phone: 0503-42529 Fax: 0503-41254
Email: hydrohoist@eircom.net
SIC: 63210 Employees: 35
Transport Industry Equipment
Mr Brian Fahy Managing Director

Independent Express Cargo
Northwest Business Park
Blanchardstown
Dublin 15
Phone: 01-8219999 Fax: 01-8212433
Email: logistics@indexp.com
Web: http://www.indexp.com
SIC: 63210 Employees: 30
Transport
Mr Owen Cook Managing Director

Irish Warehousing & Transport
Ocean House
Aran Court Aran Quay
Dublin 7
Phone: 01-8044800 Fax: 01-8730908
Email: iwt@iol.ie
Web: http://www.iwt-irl.com
SIC: 63210 Employees: 190
Service Company
Mr Frank Finan Joint Managing Director
Mr Pat Brophy Finance Director
Ms Celine Danaher Personnel Director
Mr Des McGarry Joint Managing Director

Leinster Farm Machinery
Rathmullen Road
Drogheda Co. Louth
Phone: 041-9836522 Fax: 041-9836586
Email: harvestmac@eircom.net
SIC: 63210 Employees: 25
Importing of Machinery
Mr Michael McGreene Managing Director

M50 Transport Services Ltd
13 Hazelwood Lane
Clondalkin
Dublin 22
Phone: 01-4593167 Fax: 01-4593167
SIC: 63210 Employees: 25
Transport Services
Mr Noel Fannin Managing Director

Murphy Sand & Gravel
6 Hampton Place
Balbriggan Co. Dublin
Phone: 01-8412827 Fax: 01-8412547
SIC: 63210 Employees: 30
Deliver Sand & Gravel
Mr Seamus Murphy Managing Director

National Toll Roads
Burton Court, Burton Hall Road
Sandyford
Dublin 18
Phone: 01-2063700 Fax: 01-2063701
SIC: 63210 Employees: 90
Toll Road/Bridge Development and Operators
Mr Thomas Roche Managing Director
Mr Kieran Farrell Financial Controller
Mr Anthony McCafferty Operations Manager
Mr John Fox Computer Manager

Seafield Holdings
19 Fitzwilliam Square
Dublin 2
Phone: 01-6611954 Fax: 01-6761090
SIC: 63210 Employees: 181
Property/Transport
Mr Jonathan Glanz Chief Executive

Shannon MRO
Shannon Airport
Shannon Co. Clare
Phone: 061-471533 Fax: 061-471241
Email: info@shannonmro.ie
Web: http://www.shannonmro.com
SIC: 63210 Employees: 150
Aircraft Maintenance
Mr Kevin Horton General Manager
Mr Kevin O'Sullivan Finance Director

Walsh Western International
Unit 1 Airport Business Park
Cloghran
Swords Co. Dublin
Phone: 01-8067150 Fax: 01-8067133
Email: customercare@ww-international.com
Web: http://www.ww-international.com
SIC: 63210 Employees: 300
International Transport
Mr John McDumphey General Manager
Mr Michael Broderick Accountant

West Link Tollbridge Ltd
Toll Plaza
Castleknock
Dublin 15
Phone: 01-8202000 Fax: 01-8211532
SIC: 63210 Employees: 100
Collect Tolls on Toll Bridges
Mr Tony McClafferty Managing Director
Mr Kieran Farrell Financial Controller
Mr Vincent Eves Human Resources Manager
Mr John Fox Computer Manager

Wilson Transport & Warehousing Ltd
Damastown Business Park, Macetown Road
Mullhuddart
Dublin 15
Phone: 01-8242044 Fax: 01-8242045
Email: info@wilsontransport.com
Web: http://www.wilsontransport.com
SIC: 63210 Employees: 30
Transport & Warehousing
Mr Dave Bergin Joint Managing Director
Mr Jonathan Carr Accounts Manager
Mr Alan Wilson Joint Managing Director
Mr Tom Fortune Sales & Marketing Manager

Dun Laoghaire Harbour Company
Harbour Lodge
Crofton Road
Dun Laoghaire Co. Dublin
Phone: 01-2801311 Fax: 01-2809607
Email: dlharbour@tinet.ie
SIC: 63220 Employees: 56
Harbour
Mr Michael Hanahoe Chief Executive

Geologistics (LEP) International
Unit 1& 2 Willsborough
Industrial Estate Clonshaugh
Dublin 17
Phone: 01-8166600 Fax: 01-8166601
SIC: 63220 Employees: 40
Shipping and Sea Transport
Mr Micheal Lynch Manager

Land Bridge Logistics
Malahide Road Industrial Park
Dublin 17
Phone: 01-8470316 Fax: 01-8474349
Web: http://www.ccs.ie/~landbridge
SIC: 63220 Employees: 75
Transport Services
Mr Jim Crawley Managing Director
Mr John Foram Financial Controller

ABX Logistics Ireland Ltd
U42 Park West Business & Industrial Park
Nangor Road
Dublin 12
Phone: 01-6161600 Fax: 01-6161610
Email: sales@kerstenhunik.ie
Web: http://www.abxlogistics.ie
SIC: 63221 Employees: 200
Shipping Company
Mr Gerard Ward Managing Director
Ms Collette Sheridan Financial Controller
Mr Paul Brennan Personnel Manager
Mr Conor Loughran Sales Manager
Mr Stephen White Head of IT

Ace Express Freight
100 Newtown Industrial Estate
Clonshaugh
Dublin 17
Phone: 01-8672777 Fax: 01-8672788
SIC: 63221 Employees: 40
Freight Agencies
Mr Philip Treacy Managing Director

Baxlabel Ltd
Unit R Northring Business Park
Cloghran
Dublin 9
Phone: 01-8621044 Fax: 01-8165473
Web: http://www.baxworld.com
SIC: 63221 Employees: 35
Freight Forwarding & Warehousing
Mr Gerry McCrudden Branch Manager
Ms Mary Murphy Financial Controller

Coastal Container Line Ltd
Coastal Terminal
Alexandra Road
Dublin 1
Phone: 01-8364833 Fax: 01-8364869
Email: info@coastalcontainer.ie
SIC: 63221 Employees: 60
Coastal Delivery Services
Mr Eamon Sullivan General Manager
Ms Anna Grainger Sales Manager
Mr Colm Walsh Operation Manager

Conway & Roadfreight Ltd
North Quay
Wicklow Co. Wicklow
Phone: 0404-67019 Fax: 0404-67120
Email: admin@conwayport.ie
Web: http://www.conwayport.ie
SIC: 63221 Employees: 45
Freight Forwarding
Mr Roy Conway Manager
Mr Harry Rice Finance Director

Country Wide
Falcon House
Ballough Cross
Lusk Co. Dublin
Phone: 01-8430000 Fax: 01-8430555
Web: http://www.countrywide-freight.ie
SIC: 63221 Employees: 50
Freight Company
Mr Donal McFerran Managing Director
Mr Trevor McMan Finance Manager
Mr Simon Dobin Depot Manager

Danzas Air Express International
Furry Park
Santry
Dublin 9
Phone: 01-8161000 Fax: 01-8161010
SIC: 63221 Employees: 150
Airfreight Forwarders
Mr Michael Lee Managing Director
Mr Aidan Farrelly Financial Controller
Ms Hilda Heggarty Personnel Manager
Mr Mark Feeney Sales Director

Duffy Express Freight Ltd
Cottage Farm
Newtowncunningham
Lifford Co. Donegal
Phone: 074-56333 Fax: 074-56281
Email: def@eircom.net
SIC: 63221 Employees: 60
Freight Transporters
Mr John Duffy Managing Director
Mr William Duffy Operations Manager

Eurosped
Unit 11 Cookstown Industrial Estate
Tallaght
Dublin 24
Phone: 01-4599500 Fax: 01-4599469
Email: euromode@indigo.ie
Web: http://www.eurosped.irl.com
SIC: 63221 Employees: 40
Freight Forwarding & Warehousing
Mr Joe Carton Manager
Mr Bill Childs Finance Manager
Mr Les Lawlor Operation Manager
Mr Declan Dunne IT Manager

Expeditors Ltd
9 Boeing Road
Airways Industrial Estate
Dublin 17
Phone: 01-8161805 Fax: 01-8161811
Email: info@expeditors.com
Web: http://www.expeditors.com
SIC: 63221 Employees: 300
Freight Company
Mr John Birmingham Managing Director
Mr Doug Sloane Finance Manager
Mr Kieran Delmar Sales & Marketing Manager
Mr Enda Duffy Computer Manager

Express Parcels Dublin Ltd
Unit G Bluebell Industrial Estate
Kylemore Road
Dublin 12
Phone: 01-4565909 Fax: 01-4602333
SIC: 63221 Employees: 83
Freight Forwarding & Warehousing
Mr Joe Heller Manager

Fashion Express Group
Breakwater Road
Ferry Port
Dublin 1
Phone: 01-8365655 Fax: 01-8365657
Email: sales@fashionexpress.ie
Web: http://www.fashionexpress.ie
SIC: 63221 Employees: 80
Freight Fowarding
Mr Fergus Treacy Managing Director
Ms Maureen Connolly IT Manager

FGL Freight Group Ltd
Unit 14 Rosemount Business Park
Ballycoolin
Dublin 11
Phone: 01-8208833 Fax: 01-8208900
Email: sales@fglfreight.com
Web: http://www.fglfreight.com
SIC: 63221 Employees: 30
Freight company
Mr Gerry Moran Managing Director

Fluskey Freight
Unit 31e Rosemount Business Park
Ballycoolin Road
Dublin 11
Phone: 01-8205650 Fax: 01-8205399
SIC: 63221 Employees: 50
Freight
Mr Arthur Fluskey Managing Director

FreightWatch International Ltd
Landscape House
Baldonnel
Dublin 22
Phone: 01-4661799 Fax: 01-4661756
Email: info@freightwatch.ie
Web: http://www.freightwatch.ie
SIC: 63221 Employees: 35
Freight company
Mr Terry Downes Managing Director

Intel WarehouseLtd
Thomastown Road
Knocktopher
Kilkenny Co. Kilkenny
Phone: 056-68800 Fax: 056-68849
Email: info@intelfreight.com
Web: http://www.intelfreight.com
SIC: 63221 Employees: 35
Freight Forwarding & Warehousing
Mr Ted Hoyne Joint Managing Director
Mr Alan Hoyne Joint Managing Director
Mr Sean Connors IT Officer

Interlink
Unit B1 B2 Corcanree Industrial Est
Dock Road
Limerick Co. Limerick
Phone: 061-480999 Fax: 061-300686
Email: express@limerick.interlink.ie
Web: http://www.limerick.interlink.ie
SIC: 63221 Employees: 50
Freight Company
Mr Morgan Leahy Managing Director
Mr Paul Kelly Accounts Manager

Irish Express Cargo Ltd
Rosemount Business Park
Ballycoolin Road
Dublin 11
Phone: 01-8111888 Fax: 01-8111800
Web: http://www.irishexpresscargo.com
SIC: 63221 Employees: 1500
Freight Forwarders
Mr Finn O'Sullivan Managing Director
Mr Tom Walsh Finance Manager
Ms Deirdre Giblin Personnel Manager
Mr Barbara Kearney Sales Manager
Mr Gerry Tirol Production Manager
Ms Josephine Eviston MIS Manager

James P Jones & Son Ltd
Unit 3 Kerlogue Industrial Estate
Rosslare Road
Wexford Co. Wexford
Phone: 053-44066 Fax: 053-44072
Email: info@jpjones.ie
Web: http://www.jonesintl.com
SIC: 63221 Employees: 30
Freight Forwarding & Warehousing
Mr Billy Redmond Manager

Jenkinson Agencies
36 Airways Industrial Estate
Santry
Dublin 17
Phone: 01-2411000 Fax: 01-2411098
Email: info@jenkinsonfreight.ie
Web: http://www.jenkinsonfreight.com
SIC: 63221 Employees: 30
Shipping Freight Company
Mr Ken Heade Managing Director
Ms Breda Nolan Finance Manager
Mr Mark Coyle Sales Manager

Lanigan International Freight Ltd
Unit 12 Blackwater Road
Dublin Industrial Estate
Dublin 11
Phone: 01-8308733 Fax: 01-8308748
Email: glanigan@laniganfreight.com
SIC: 63221 Employees: 30
Freight Forwarding & Warehousing
Mr George Lanigan Manager
Mr Tony Madden Financial Controller
Ms Lea Lanigan Sales & Marketing Manager

Mfasa Global Logistics
Furry Park Industrial Estate
Santry
Dublin 9
Phone: 01-8622200 Fax: 01-8622980
Web: http://www.excel.com
SIC: 63221 Employees: 130
Freight Forwarders
Mr Michael O'Donoghue Managing Director
Mr Michael Sutton Financial Controller
Ms Sally Goodwin Human Resources Manager
Mr Terry Allen Sales Manager

MSAS Global Logistics
Clyde House, The Quay
Waterford Co. Waterford
Phone: 051-854708 Fax: 051-853876
Email: info@msas.com
Web: http://www.msas.com
SIC: 63221 Employees: 100
Freight Forwarding & Warehousing
Mr Orn Kenny Managing Director

Online Logistics
Unit 6 North West Business Park
Ballycoolin
Dublin 15
Phone: 01-8222477 Fax: 01-8222609
Email: info@onlineclogistics.ie
SIC: 63221 Employees: 70
Freight Forwarders
Mr David Philpott Partner
Ms Jacinta Philipott Finance Manager
Mr Paul Leaph Partner

Patrick Monahan Drogheda Ltd
Merchants Quay
Drogheda Co. Louth
Phone: 041-9838887 Fax: 041-9835428
SIC: 63221 Employees: 60
Freight Forwarders/Ship Brokers
Mr William Lennon Managing Director

RMF Ireland Ltd
Damastown Industrial Park
Mulhuddart
Dublin 15
Phone: 01-8222300 Fax: 01-8222317
Email: dublin@rmf.ie
Web: http://www.rmf.ie
SIC: 63221 Employees: 40
Freight Forwarding
Mr Gosef Riedler Managing Director
Ms Olive Griffin Operations Manager

Shannon Transport & Warehousing Ltd
Monaclino Industrial Estate
Ballysimon Road
Limerick Co. Limerick
Phone: 061-416866 Fax: 061-416067
Email: info@shannontransport.ie
Web: http://www.shannontransport.ie
SIC: 63221 Employees: 120
Freight Forwarding
Mr Patrick Murrihy Managing Director
Ms Vera Kent Personnel Manager

Stafford Freight Ltd
Unit B Merrywell Business Park
Lower Ballymount Road
Dublin 12
Phone: 01-4509533 Fax: 01-4509144
Email: operations@anc.ie
SIC: 63221 Employees: 35
Freight Forwarding & Warehousing
Mr Gary Stafford Managing Director

Tibbett & Britten
Unit D1 Airport Business Park
Cloghran
Swords Co. Dublin
Phone: 01-8445545 Fax: 01-8445647
SIC: 63221 Employees: 70
Freight Forwarders
Mr Alan Johnston Managing Director
Ms Sandra McDonagh Finance Manager

TNT Express Worldwide
Cargo Terminal
Cork Airport
Cork Co. Cork
Phone: 021-4311293 Fax: 021-4313869
Email: info@tnt.com
Web: http://www.tnt.com
SIC: 63221 Employees: 220
Freight Company
Mr Conor McCarthy Operation Manager

Toga Freight Services Ltd
Kylemore Park North
Ballyfermot
Dublin 10
Phone: 01-6304244 Fax: 01-6304256
Email: info@togafreight.ie
Web: http://www.togafreight.com
SIC: 63221 Employees: 40
Shipping & Freight Forwarding
Mr Martin Gately Managing Director
Mr Fergal Maguire Finance Manager
Mr Peter Toner Sales & Personnel Manager
Mr Greg McDonald Production Manager
Mr Ed Farrell Computer Manager

Trans Global
Unit Q1 North Ring Business Park
Cloghran
Dublin 9
Phone: 01-8422777 Fax: 01-8425013
Email: postmaster@abtg.ie
Web: http://www.abtg.ie
SIC: 63221 Employees: 24
Freight Forwarding
Mr Gilly McCool Managing Director
Mr Paddy Pouch Sales & Marketing Manager

Two Way International Freight Ltd
Ballinstown
Ballyboughal Co. Dublin
Phone: 01-8433811 Fax: 01-8078090
SIC: 63221 Employees: 200
Freight Services
Mr Tom Kelly Managing Director
Mr John McSweeney Accounts Manager
Mr Matt Kelly Sales Executive
Mr Joe Kelly Operation Manager

Aer Rianta
Dublin Airport
Swords Co. Dublin
Phone: 01-8444900 Fax: 01-8144646
Email: info@aer-rianta.ie
Web: http://www.aer-rianta.ie
SIC: 63230 Employees: 2700
Airport Management
Mr John Burke Chief Executive
Mr Ray Gray Finance Director
Mr Oliver Cussan Director, Human Resources
Mr Robert Hilliard Director Dublin Airport
Mr Frank Cruise General Manager
Mr Brian Hampson Company Secretary

Abbey Travel
43-45 Middle Abbey Street
Dublin 1
Phone: 01-8047100 Fax: 01-8733163
Email: information@abbeytravel.ie
Web: http://www.abbeytravel.ie
SIC: 63301 Employees: 100
Travel Agents
Mr Jim Vaughan Managing Director
Mr Gary Donnelly Financial Manager
Mr Neil Horgan Personnel Manager
Mr Dermot Mulligan Sales & Marketing Manager

American Express BTC
61-63 South William Street
Dublin 2
Phone: 01-6175511 Fax: 01-6175544
SIC: 63301 Employees: 90
Travel Related services
Ms Annie Lawler Manager

Arrow Tours
40 West Street
Drogheda Co. Louth
Phone: 041-9831177 Fax: 041-9832288
Email: res@arrowtours.ie
Web: http://www.arrowtours.ie
SIC: 63301 Employees: 25
Travel Agent
Mr Edward Hurley Manager

Atlas Travel Service
9 College Green
Dublin 2
Phone: 01-6776620 Fax: 01-6711957
Email: info@atlas.ie
Web: http://www.atlas.ie
SIC: 63301 Employees: 40
Travel Agent
Mr Andrew McKenna Manager

BTI Ireland
Franklin House, 140-142 Pembroke Rd
Fallsbridge
Dublin 4
Phone: 01-6080011 Fax: 01-6601644
Email: info@btiirl.ie
Web: http://www.btiirl.ie
SIC: 63301 Employees: 50
Corporate Travel Agents
Mr Michael Enoch Manager
Mr Victor Gibson Financial Controller
Ms Sheila McCarthy Personnel Manager
Ms Tania Crinion Sales & Marketing Manager
Ms Linda Byrne IT Manager

Budget Travel Shop
134/135 Lower Baggot Street
Dublin 2
Phone: 01-6611403 Fax: 01-6618905
Email: postmaster@shopireland.com
Web: http://www.budgettravel.ie
SIC: 63301 Employees: 200
Tour Operator
Mr Eugene Corcoran Managing Director
Ms Barbara Hammond Group Financial Controller
Ms Jacinta McGlynn Personnel Manager
Mr Colm Conlon Sales Manager
Ms Geraldine Dunne IT Manager

Corporate Travel Partners
Lincoln House
Lincoln Place
Dublin 2
Phone: 01-6053900 Fax: 01-6053939
Email: corporatet@ctp.ie
Web: http://www.ctp.ie
SIC: 63301 Employees: 40
Travel Agent
Mr Joe Balfe Managing Director
Ms Conor McGarry Financial Controller
Ms Sheila Carey Office Manager
Ms Brenda O'Keefe Sales & Marketing Manager
Ms Valerie Metcalfe IT Manager

Dun Laoghaire Travel
12 Pembroke Road
Ballsbridge
Dublin 4
Phone: 01-6606321 Fax: 01-6606326
Email: asupport@indigo.ie
SIC: 63301 Employees: 30
Travel Agent
Mr Bob Evans Manager

Executive Travel Group Ltd
Jefferson House, Eglinton Road
Donnybrook
Dublin 4
Phone: 01-2697488 Fax: 01-2838404
Email: sclub@exectrav.ie
Web: http://www.executive.ie
SIC: 63301 Employees: 100
Travel Agents
Mr Arthur Harrow Managing Director
Mr Justin Caffery Financial Controller
Ms Niamh Byrne Personnel Manager
Mr Peter Lamb Marketing Manager

Falcon JWT
2nd Floor Block 5, Westland Square
Pearse Street
Dublin 2
Phone: 01-6056500 Fax: 01-6056598
Email: info@falconholidays.ie
Web: http://www.falconholidays.ie
SIC: 63301 Employees: 52
Tour Operators
Mr Bill Smith Managing Director
Mr Sean Ryan Finance Director
Mr Don Shearer Sales Director
Ms Carol Ann O'Neill Operations Director
Mr Bruce Crehan Computer Manager

Heffernans Travel
Douglas Village Shopping Centre
Douglas, Cork
Cork Co. Cork
Phone: 021-4271081 Fax: 021-4271863
Email: corporate@heff-travel.ie
Web: http://www.heff-travel.ie
SIC: 63301 Employees: 24
Travel Agents
Mr Ger Hanley Director
Ms Katherine Allen Accounts Manager
Mr Ger Hanley Executive Secretary
Mr Jim Hastings Operations Manager

Irish Travel Partners Ltd
3 Gardiner Place
Dublin 1
Phone: 01-8786288 Fax: 01-8786536
Email: inbound@travel-partners.ie
Web: http://www.travel-partners.ie
SIC: 63301 Employees: 23
Travel Agents
Ms Debbie Flynn Managing Director
Mr Ted O'Neill Finance Manager
Ms Fiona Robinson Personnel Manager
Mr Tim McStay Director-Special Products
Mr David Walsh Computer Manager

Irish Welcome Tours
4 Whitefriar
Aungier Street
Dublin 2
Phone: 01-4757007 Fax: 01-4785318
Email: info@irishwelcometours.com
Web: http://www.irishwelcometours.com
SIC: 63301 Employees: 25
Incoming Tour Operator
Mr John Waldron Managing Director
Mr Kevin O'Mara Finance Manager
Ms Bernadette O'Carroll Sales/Development Manager

Joe O'Reilly Travel Ltd
Blarney
Cork Co. Cork
Phone: 021-4385700 Fax: 021-4385257
Email: sales@jorgroup.com
Web: http://www.jorgroup.com
SIC: 63301 Employees: 25
Travel Agent
Mr Bernard O'Reilly Managing Director
Mr Michael Carey Finance Manager

Joe Walsh Tours Ltd
8 Baggot Street Lower
Dublin 2
Phone: 01-6763053 Fax: 01-6766572
Email: reservations@joewalshtours.ie
Web: http://www.joewalshtours.ie
SIC: 63301 Employees: 50
Travel Agents
Mr David Walsh Managing Director
Ms Maggie Carlin Finance Manager

John Cassidy Travel
24/25 Liffey Street Lower
Dublin 1
Phone: 01-8735000 Fax: 01-8735015
Email: holidays@cassidytravel.ie
Web: http://www.cassidytravel.com
SIC: 63301 Employees: 30
Travel Agents
Mr John Cassidy Proprietor

Neenan Travel Group
12 South Leinster Street
Dublin 2
Phone: 01-6079900 Fax: 01-6610695
Email: admin@neenantrav.ie
Web: http://www.neenantrav.ie
SIC: 63301 Employees: 40
Travel Agents
Mr Alan Neenan Director

O'Mara Travel Co Ltd
37 Main Street
Donnybrook
Dublin 4
Phone: 01-2696944 Fax: 01-2696705
Email: travel@omara-travel.com
Web: http://www.omara-travel.com
SIC: 63301 Employees: 26
Travel Agent
Ms Eileen O'Mara Walsh Managing Director
Ms Sinead Barry Finance Manager
Ms Fiona Herald Marketing Manager

Slatterys Travel
1 Russell Street
Tralee Co. Kerry
Phone: 066-7121722 Fax: 066-7125981
Email: travel@slattery.com
Web: http://www.slattery.com
SIC: 63301 Employees: 25
Travel Agent & Tour Operators
Mr David Slattery Proprietor
Mr Michael Slattery Finance Manager

Sunway Travel
114 Lower Georges Street
Dun Laoghaire Co. Dublin
Phone: 01-2886828 Fax: 01-2885187
Web: http://www.sunway.ie
SIC: 63301 Employees: 95
Tours Operator & Travel Agents
Ms Tanya Airey Proprietor
Mr Brian McGovern Finance Director
Ms Anita Kelly Sales Manager

Toolin Travel Ltd
86 Upper Drumcondra Road
Dublin 9
Phone: 01-8379282 Fax: 01-8375139
Email: sales@toolintravel.ie
Web: http://www.toolintravel.ie
SIC: 63301 Employees: 45
Travel Agents
Mr Frank Toolin Managing Director

Top Flight Holidays
1st Floor D'Olier Chambers
D'Olier Street
Dublin 2
Phone: 01-2401700 Fax: 01-6799498
SIC: 63301 Employees: 25
Tour Operators
Mr Tony Collins Chief Executive

Tour America
62 Middle Abbey Street
Dublin 1
Phone: 01-8780400 Fax: 01-8780269
Email: info@touramerica.com
Web: http://www.touramerica.com
SIC: 63301 Employees: 40
Travel Agents
Ms Mary McKenna Managing Director

Travel Care
Florence Road
Bray Co. Wicklow
Phone: 01-2864244 Fax: 01-2828622
Email: retail@travelcare.ie
SIC: 63301 Employees: 24
Travel Agents
Mr Brendan Quinn Managing Director
Ms Catherine May Finance Manager
Mr John Robinson Sales Manager

Travelcare Corporation
Florence Road
Bray Co. Wicklow
Phone: 01-2862722 Fax: 01-2865857
Email: corporate@travelcare.ie
Web: http://www.travelcare.ie
SIC: 63301 Employees: 27
Travel Agents
Mr John Robinson Director
Ms Catherine May Financial Controller
Ms Gabrielle Gilmartin Sales Manager

Tully's Travel
137 Tullow Street
Carlow Co. Carlow
Phone: 0503-31257 Fax: 0503-43555
Email: info@tullys.ie
SIC: 63301 Employees: 30
Travel Agent
Mr Joe Tully Managing Director
Ms Catherine Tully Accountant

Twohig Travel Agency Ltd
8 Burgh Quay
Dublin 2
Phone: 01-6772666 Fax: 01-6772691
SIC: 63301 Employees: 54
Travel Agents
Mr Edmund Burke Managing Director
Ms Ciara Kelly Accounts Manager

USIT World
19-21 Aston Quay
O'Connell Bridge
Dublin 2
Phone: 01-6778117 Fax: 01-6778843
Email: info@usitworld.com
SIC: 63301 Employees: 265
Student/Youth Travel
Ms Mairin Colleray Chief Executive

World Travel Centre
35 Pearse Street
Dublin 2
Phone: 01-6717058 Fax: 01-6777756
Email: info@worldtravel.ie
Web: http://www.worldtravel.ie
SIC: 63301 Employees: 25
Travel Agents
Ms Yvonne Kenny Manager
Mr Jimmy Lennox Sales Manager

Abbey Tours
City Gate
22 Lower Bridge Street
Dublin 8
Phone: 01-6799144 Fax: 01-6791486
Email: abbey@abbey.ie
Web: http://www.abbeytours.com
SIC: 63309 Employees: 60
Tour Company
Mr Brian McColgan Joint Managing Director
Ms Edel Roe Accounts Manager
Ms Jane Magnier Human Resources Manager
Ms Patricia McColgan Production Manager
Mr Per Henrik Ekstron IT Manager

Aillwee Cave Co Ltd
Ballyvaughan
Galway Co. Galway
Phone: 065-7077036 Fax: 065-7077107
Email: aillwee@eircom.net
Web: http://www.aillweecave.ie
SIC: 63309 Employees: 65
Show Cave - Guided Tours / Irelands Premier Showcave
Mr Roger Johnson Managing Director
Ms Maureen Gardiner Finance Manager
Ms Mary Droney General Manager
Ms Susan Johnson Sales & Marketing Manager
Mr Nicholas Johnson Computer Manager

Bord Failte Eireann
Baggot Street Bridge
Dublin 2
Phone: 01-6024000 Fax: 01-6024100
Web: http://www.ireland.travel.ie
SIC: 63309 Employees: 240
Tourist Board
Mr Niall Reddy Acting Chief Executive
Mr Chris Kane Secretary to the Board

Department of Tourism, Sport & Recreation
Kildare Street
Dublin 2
Phone: 01-6313800 Fax: 01-6611201
Email: web_master@tourism-sport.irlgov.ie
Web: http://www.irlgov.ie/tourism-sport
SIC: 63309 Employees: 80
Department of Tourism, Sport & Recreation
Ms Margaret Hayes Secretary General
Ms Caitriona Hennessy Assistant Principal Officer
Ms Susan McGrath Principal Officer

Dublin Tourism
Suffolk Street
Dublin 2
Phone: 01-6057700 Fax: 01-6057749
Email: info@visitdublin.com
Web: http://www.visitdublin.com
SIC: 63309 Employees: 64
Tourist Office
Mr Frank Magee Chief Executive
Ms Catherine Elliot Personal Assistant

Duchas Heritage Service
National Monuments DEPO
Muckross Road
Killarney Co. Kerry
Phone: 064-32402 Fax: 064-34352
SIC: 63309 Employees: 500
Heritage Service
Mr Terry Murphy Manager

Dun Na Sí Heritage Centre
Knockdomney
Moate
Athlone Co. Westmeath
Phone: 090-281183 Fax: 0902-81661
Email: dunnasimoate@eircom.net
SIC: 63309 Employees: 25
Cultural Institution
Ms Caroline Ganley Manager
Ms Bridie Hamm Treasurer
Ms Mary Conlon Secretary

Ireland Tourism Ltd
Victoria Place
Eyre Square
Galway Co. Galway
Phone: 091-563081 Fax: 091-537733
Email: info@irelandwest.ie
SIC: 63309 Employees: 40
Tourism Promotion/Development
Mr Brian Flynn Manager
Ms Anna Farrell Commercial Officer
Ms Sharon Brennan Services Executive
Mr Martin Bradley Tourism Officer

North West Regional Tourism Org. ltd
Lower John Street
Sligo Co. Sligo
Phone: 071-60336 Fax: 071-60360
Email: ireland-northwest@eircom.net
Web: http://www.ireland-northwest.travel.ie
SIC: 63309 Employees: 30
Tourist Information
Mr Michael Curley Manager
Ms Noreen Kiriehan Finance Manager
Ms Gemma Shannon Sales & Marketing Manager

Old Jameson Distillery
Bow Street
Smithfield Village
Dublin 7
Phone: 01-8072355 Fax: 01-8072369
Email: ojd@idl.ie
Web: http://www.whiskeytours.ie
SIC: 63309 Employees: 50
Visitor Centre
Mr Ray Dempsey Manager
Ms Kay Fitzsimons Account manager
Mr Jimmy O'Kane Deputy Manager

Powerscourt Gardens & House Exhibition
Enniskerry
Bray Co. Wicklow
Phone: 01-2046000 Fax: 01-2046900
Email: gardens@powerscourt.ie
Web: http://www.powerscourt.ie
SIC: 63309 Employees: 40
Tourism Attractions
Mr Tom Clarke Estate Manager
Ms Amanda Cloughley Financial Controller
Ms Sarah Slazenger Tourism & Personnel Manager

Shannon Heritage & Banquets
Bunratty Castle
Bunratty
Ennis Co. Clare
Phone: 061-361511 Fax: 061-361020
Email: liggyt@shannon-dev.ie
Web: http://www.shannonheritage.com
SIC: 63309 Employees: 200
Tourism
Mr Gerard Slattery Business Development Manager
Mr Kieran McNamara Finance Manager

SITA/Equant
Block 10B
Park West Business Park
Dublin 12
Phone: 01-6707272 Fax: 01-6301794
Web: http://www.panoramaholidays.ie
SIC: 63309 Employees: 50
Tour operators
Mr Niall McDonnell Chief Executive
Ms Mary Rankin Finance Manager
Ms Fiona Henwood IT Manager

South East Tourism (SERTA)
41 The Quay
Waterford Co. Waterford
Phone: 051-875823 Fax: 051-877388
Email: info@southeasttourism.ie
Web: http://www.southeasttourism.ie
SIC: 63309 Employees: 70
Regional Tourism
Mr Joe Palmer Regional Tourism Manager
Mr Luke Myers Sales Manager

St Marys Integrated
44 Nicholas Street
Limerick Co. Limerick
Phone: 061-318106 Fax: 061-318106
SIC: 63309 Employees: 41
Tours
Mr Paul Greamey Manager

TravelMad Ltd
Garland House Rathmines Park
Rathmines
Dublin 6
Phone: 01-4964228 Fax: 01-4964238
Email: info@travelmad.com
Web: http://www.travelmad.com
SIC: 63309 Employees: 80
Tourism on the Internet
Mr Alistair Kidd Managing Director
Mr Carl Butler Financial Controller
Mr Keith O'Reilly
Mr Jonathan Kidd Technolgy Director

Westport House Country Estate
Westport Co. Mayo
Phone: 098-25430 Fax: 098-25206
Email: info@westporthouse.ie
Web: http://www.westporthouse.ie
SIC: 63309 Employees: 100
Tourist Attraction
Mr Jeremy Altmont Proprietor

Engineering Works
Iarnrod Eireann, Inchicore Works
Inchicore
Dublin 8
Phone: 01-7033749 Fax: 01-7033775
SIC: 63400 Employees: 56
Transport
Mr John McCarthy Head Engineer

GP Fahey Division Engineer
Iarnrod Eireann
Limerick Junction
Tipperary Co. Tipperary
Phone: 062-51083 Fax: 062-52219
SIC: 63400 Employees: 25
Transport
Mr Gerry Fahey Manager

John Joe Flemming Transport
Carnmore West
Oranmore
Galway Co. Galway
Phone: 091-790000 Fax: 091-790200
Email: info@flemming.transport.ie
Web: http://www.flemming-transport.ie
SIC: 63400 Employees: 95
Transport Company
Mr John Joe Flemming Managing Director
Ms Anne Wilson Accounts Manager
Ms Jacqueline Moore Office Manager

O'Regan Transport
North Esk, Glanmire
Cork Co. Cork
Phone: 021-4354635 Fax: 021-4354710
SIC: 63400 Employees: 34
Transport Company
Mr Peter O'Regan Managing Director
Ms Janet Garry Office Manager

South Coast Transport Ltd
Corrin
Fermoy Co. Cork
Phone: 025-32435 Fax: 025-32739
Email: southcoast@indigo.ie
SIC: 63400 Employees: 40
Transporting Company
Mr John O'Flynn Managing Director
Mr Richard O'Flynn Finance Manager
Mr Pat O'Flynn Sales & Marketing Manager
Ms Cliona Hogan IT Officer

Post & Communications

64 Post & Telecommunications
64111 Post Offices
64112 Sorting Offices
64119 Postal Services
64120 Courier/Parcel Delivery Services
64201 Telecommunications
64202 Mobile Phone Service Providers

An Post
GPO
O'Connell Street
Dublin 1
Phone: 01-7057000 Fax: 01-7057663
Email: info@anpost.ie
Web: http://www.anpost.ie
SIC: 64111 Employees: 9450
Post Office
Mr John Hynes Group Chief Executive
Mr Ronan Byrne Chief Financial Officer
Mr John O'Hehir Human Resources Director
Mr Liam Sheehan Sales & Marketing Manager
Mr Willie Griffin Chief Operating Officer
Mr Gerry Bissett General IT Manager

Drogheda Head Office
West Street
Drogheda Co. Louth
Phone: 041-9838157 Fax: 041-9837718
SIC: 64111 Employees: 60
Post Office
Mr John Burns Manager

AM PM Super Couriers
Myles Balfe Centre, Naas Road
Dublin 12
Phone: 01-4642222 Fax: 01-4640382
SIC: 64120 Employees: 40
Couriers
Mr Val Dunlea Managing Director

City Air Express
93 Newtown Industrial Estate
Coolock
Dublin 17
Phone: 01-8484115 Fax: 01-8484117
Email: sales@cityairexpress.ie
Web: http://www.cityairexpress.ie
SIC: 64120 Employees: 25
Courier Service
Mr Adrian O'Connell Proprietor

Cyclone Courier
6 Upper Stephen's Street
Dublin 2
Phone: 01-4757000 Fax: 01-4757294
SIC: 64120 Employees: 100
Couriers
Mr Kevin Oliver Partner

DHL International
Collinstown Cross
Cloghran
Swords Co. Dublin
Phone: 01-8444744 Fax: 01-8701515
Email: info@ie.dhl.com
Web: http://www.dhl.ie
SIC: 64120 Employees: 500
International Couriers
Mr Peter Lomax General Manager
Mr Alan Smith Finance Manager
Mr Noel Byrne Sales & Marketing Manager
Mr Mike Farrell Operations Director
Mr Derek Monaghan Computer Manager

General Retail Express
JFK Park
Killeen Road
Dublin 12
Phone: 01-4500144 Fax: 01-4569896
SIC: 64120 Employees: 30
Courier service
Mr Anthony O'Regan Manager
Mr John Brosnan Finance Manager
Mr Patrick O'Regan Sales Manager

Interlink
Galway Road
Athlone Co. Westmeath
Phone: 0902-94823 Fax: 0902-94831
SIC: 64120 Employees: 700
Courier/Parcel Delivery
Mr Gavin Warwick Sales Manager
Mr James Lohan Chief Financial Officer
Mr Chris Burke Computer Manager

K & L Deliveries Ltd
Unit 1 Ballymount Cross Industrial Estate
Walkinstown
Dublin 12
Phone: 01-4501718 Fax: 01-4501709
Email: kld@indigo.ie
SIC: 64120 Employees: 50
Couriers
Mr Gordon O'Keeffe Proprietor
Mr John Sheehan Financial Controller

Nightline Express Delivery
Unit M1 Northring Business Park
Swords Road, Cloughran
Dublin 9
Phone: 01-8421177 Fax: 01-8423146
Email: info@nightline.ie
Web: http://www.nightline.ie
SIC: 64120 Employees: 70
Courier Service
Mr David Field Managing Director
Ms Caroline Daly Financial Administrator
Mr John Touhy Sales & Marketing Manager

SDS
Newlands
Naas Road
Dublin 12
Phone: 01-4591133 Fax: 01-4591149
Email: info@sds.ie
Web: http://www.sds.ie
SIC: 64120 Employees: 2000
Couriers - Central Parcel Office
Mr Peter Sweeney Director
Ms Pamela Porter Financial Controller
Mr John Westman Head of Sales & Marketing

Securicor Omega Express
Ballymount Road Lower
Walkinstown
Dublin 12
Phone: 01-2404402 Fax: 01-4569250
Web: http://www.securicor.com
SIC: 64120 Employees: 340
National Parcel Distribution
Mr Gareth Thornton General Manager
Mr Brendan Hand Finance Manager
Ms Gillian Park Personnel Manager
Mr Michael Brennan Sales Manager
Ms Maura Solan Computer Manager

Securispeed
Unit 12C
Santry Hall Industrial Estate
Dublin 9
Phone: 01-8425010 Fax: 01-8425103
SIC: 64120 Employees: 60
Couriers
Mr Kieran Kavanagh Manager

Post & Telecoms

Swift Couriers
Rockbrook House
Brookfield Terrace
Blackrock Co. Dublin
Phone: 01-2888410 Fax: 01-2883293
SIC: 64120 Employees: 30
Courier Service
Ms Siobhan Whelan Managing Director
Mr Tom O'Farrell Financial Controller
Ms Audrey Whelan Personnel Manager

Target Express Parcels Ltd
Unit 2 Rosemount Park Drive
Rosemount Business Park
Dublin 11
Phone: 01-8851866 Fax: 01-8851874
SIC: 64120 Employees: 200
Parcel Delivery
Mr Seamus McBride Managing Director

TNT Express Worldwide
Corballis Park Dublin Airport
Cloghran
Swords Co. Dublin
Phone: 01-8067888 Fax: 01-8067801
Web: http://www.tnt.com
SIC: 64120 Employees: 250
Couriers
Mr Ronnie Judge Manager
Mr Brian Gallagher Finance Manager
Ms Ann O'Donovan Human Resources Director

UPS (United Parcel Services)
Unit 134 Slaney Close
Dublin Industrial Estate
Dublin 11
Phone: 01-8304003 Fax: 01-8304160
Email: info@ups.com
Web: http://www.ups.com
SIC: 64120 Employees: 600
Parcel/Courier Service
Mr Stephen Kelly Managing Director
Mr Paul Switzer Accounts Manager
Ms Claire Bolger Employment Manager
Mr Fergus McCormack Business Dev Manager
Mr Tom McCreagh Operation Manager
Mr Paul Swaine IT Manager

West 1 International Rapid Despatch
Unit 9 The IDA Enterprise Centre
East Wall Road
Dublin 3
Phone: 01-8550700 Fax: 01-8550712
SIC: 64120 Employees: 50
Couriers
Mr Joe Fritsch Managing Director
Ms Marie Brannigan Plant Manager

Wheels Couriers
15 Belvedere Place
Dublin 1
Phone: 01-8551288 Fax: 01-8551292
SIC: 64120 Employees: 35
Couriers
Ms Bernie Kinsella Manager

Accuris Ltd
Eastpoint Business Park
Clontarf
Dublin 3
Phone: 01-2692322 Fax: 01-8875100
Web: http://www.accuris.ie
SIC: 64201 Employees: 120
Telecommunications Software
Mr Declan Kavanagh Chief Executive Officer
Mr Paul Smith Finance Manager
Ms Julie Conlon Personnel Manager
Mr Brian McDonagh Sales & Marketing Manager
Mr Simon Scott Computer Manager

Altion Ltd
AIB Investment House
Percy Place
Dublin 4
Phone: 01-6676888 Fax: 01-6600095
Email: rec@altion.com
Web: http://www.altion.com
SIC: 64201 Employees: 90
Telecommunications Software
Mr Magnus O'Driscoll Chief Operating Officer
Mr David Megan Finance Manager
Ms Laura Kineaby Human Resources Manager

Avaya Ireland
Cork Abbey
Bray Co. Wicklow
Phone: 01-2042000 Fax: 01-4182925
Web: http://www.avaya.ie
SIC: 64201 Employees: 380
Telecommunications
Ms Anne Marie Kenneally Director
Ms Fiona Nolan Marketing Director

Broadband Services International
Unit 3 Crag Avenue
Clondalkin Industrial Estate
Dublin 22
Phone: 01-4573336 Fax: 01-4575001
Email: mail@ashbourne-com.ie
Web: http://www.broadbandsvc.com
SIC: 64201 Employees: 70
Telecommunications
Mr Donagh Kelly Managing Director
Mr Brian Curran Finance Director
Ms Catherine Troy Human Resources Manager

C Sierra Communication
Knockmitten Lane North
New Nangor Road
Dublin 12
Phone: 01-4535911 Fax: 01-4537161
Email: info@sierracomm.ie
Web: http://www.sierra.ie
SIC: 64201 Employees: 200
Telecommunications/Civils
Mr Elliot Whyte Manager
Mr Steven Quinhan Finance Manager
Mr Elliott Whyte Personnell Manager

Cable & Wireless
1 Airton Road
Tallaght
Dublin 24
Phone: 01-4598333 Fax: 01-4040339
Email: info@cwplc.com
Web: http://www.cwplc.com
SIC: 64201 Employees: 280
Telecommunications
Mr Gordon Morrice Managing Director
Mr James Crowe Financial Controller
Mr Paul Byrne Sales Manager
Mr David Lister IT Manager

Carr Communications Ltd
Communications Centre
Booterstown Avenue
Blackrock Co. Dublin
Phone: 01-2785000 Fax: 01-2785001
Email: info@carrcommunications.ie
Web: http://www.carrcommunications.ie
SIC: 64201 Employees: 30
Telecommunications Company
Ms Dermot McCrum Managing Director
Ms Frances Fox Finance Manager
Mr Donal Cronin Director

Chorus - Business Services
3050 Lake Drive
Citywest Digital Park Co. Dublin
Phone: 01-4304000 Fax: 01-4112822
Email: business@chorus.ie
Web: http://www.chorus.ie
SIC: 64201 Employees: 25
Chorus Telecommunications - Business Services
Ms Sarah Lawless General Manager - Services

CMG Telecommunications
University Technological Park
Cork Co. Cork
Phone: 021-4933200 Fax: 021-4933201
Web: http://www.cmgtelecom.com
SIC: 64201 Employees: 95
Technical Support for Telecommunications
Mr Joe Walsh Manager
Ms Jacinta McCarthy Computer Manager

Digital Communications Management
Coral House, Airton Road
Tallaght
Dublin 24
Phone: 01-4597666 Fax: 01-4597022
Web: http://www.dcmgroup.com
SIC: 64201 Employees: 60
Telecommunications
Mr Alan Long Chief Executive
Mr Oran Maher Sales & Marketing Manager
Mr Tom Mullen IT Manager

Eircom Plc
St Stephens Green West
Dublin 2
Phone: 01-6714444 Fax: 01-6628316
Email: pressoffice@eircom.ie
Web: http://www.eircom.ie
SIC: 64201 Employees: 8500
Telecommunications
Mr Phil Nolan Chief Executive
Mr Peter Lynch Chief Financial Officer
Mr Tony O'Reilly Chairman
Mr Gerry O'Sullivan Group Corporate Relations

Equant Network Services International Ltd
25-26 Earlsfort Terrace
Dublin 2
Phone: 01-4025900 Fax: 01-4025920
Email: info@equant.com
Web: http://www.equant.com
SIC: 64201 Employees: 60
Telecommunications
Mr Sean Byrne Vice President
Mr Peter Cummings Finance Director
Ms Suzanne Farrelly Human Resources Manager
Mr Frank Mullan IT Manager

Esat Business
Grand Canal Plaza
1 Grand Canal Quay
Dublin 4
Phone: 01-4325000 Fax: 01-6704616
Email: info@esatbusiness.com
Web: http://www.esatbusiness.com
SIC: 64201 Employees: 1300
Business Telecommunications Provider
Ms Lucy Gaffney Managing Director
Mr Vincent Harrison Financial Controller
Ms Niall McPartland Personnel Manager
Mr Justin Kealy Sales & Marketing Director
Mr Martin Wickhan IT Director

Esat Fusion
Grand Canal Plaza
Upper Canal Street
Dublin 4
Phone: 01-2424000 Fax: 01-2424001
Email: info@esatfusion.ie
Web: http://www.esatfusion.ie
SIC: 64201 Employees: 300
Residential Telecommunication Company
Mr Derek Kickham Managing Director
Ms Kerry O'Keefe Personnel Director
Mr Mark Horgangaul Sales & Marketing Manager

GTS Ireland
GTS House
Barrow Street
Dublin 4
Phone: 01-6315000 Fax: 01-6315050
Web: http://www.gtseurope.com
SIC: 64201 Employees: 300
Telecommunications
Mr Michael O'Hara Managing Director
Mr Eoin Bolger Operations Director

Post & Telecoms

Interactive Enterprise
3098 Lake Drive
City West Business Campus
Dublin 24
Phone: 01-4660600 Fax: 01-4660284
SIC: 64201 Employees: 70
Communications
Mr Tom Higgins Managing Director
Mr Stephen Keveney Financial Controller
Mr William George Sales Manager

ITG Group
Unit 3 North Ring Business Park
Cloghran
Dublin 9
Phone: 01-8867422 Fax: 01-8427627
Email: info@itg.ie
Web: http://www.itg.ie
SIC: 64201 Employees: 340
Computer Maintenance & Computer Resale
Mr Michael Hickey Managing Director
Mr Tom Fee Financial Controller
Mr Tiernan Birmingham Sales Director

Lake Communications Systems Ltd
Beech House
Greenhills Road
Dublin 24
Phone: 01-4031000 Fax: 01-4520826
Email: postmaster@lake.ie
Web: http://www.lake.ie
SIC: 64201 Employees: 150
Telecommunications
Mr Anthony Birmingham Managing Director
Ms Caoimhin O'Laoi Finance Manager
Ms Clare McKenna Personnel Director
Mr Michael O'Dwyer Sales & Marketing Director
Mr Michael Tope Operations Manager
Mr Brian Kennedy Computer Manager

LM Ericsson
Beech Hill
Clonskeagh
Dublin 4
Phone: 01-2837222 Fax: 01-2072070
Email: info@eei.ericcson.se
Web: http://www.eei.ericcson.se
SIC: 64201 Employees: 1300
Telecommunications Products
Mr Ian Cahill Managing Director
Mr Joe Healy Financial Controller
Mr Noel Woods IT Director

Lucent Technologies
121 St Stephens Green
Dublin 2
Phone: 01-6768330 Fax: 01-4785645
Email: co2@lucent.com
Web: http://www.lucent.com
SIC: 64201 Employees: 240
Telecommunications
Mr Willy O'Connell Manager
Mr Chris Dickson Finance Manager
Ms Maura Begley IT Manager

MCI Worldcom
Lower Erne Street
Dublin 2
Phone: 01-6790404 Fax: 01-2468001
Email: sales@wcom.ie
Web: http://www.wcom.ie
SIC: 64201 Employees: 85
Telecommunications Provision
Mr David Hughes Managing Director
Mr John O'Connor Financial Controller
Ms Maria Kelly Personnel Manager
Mr Fergus Hynes Computer Manager

Midland Telecommunications Ltd
Unit 1 Daneswell Business Park
Tuam Road
Athlone Co. Westmeath
Phone: 0902-94776 Fax: 0902-94692
Email: midtel@iol.ie
SIC: 64201 Employees: 45
Telecommunications
Mr John Geehan Managing Director
Ms Bernie Doyle Accounts Manager

Nortel Network (Ireland) Ltd
Mervue Business Park
Galway Co. Galway
Phone: 091-757671 Fax: 091-755431
Email: info@nortelnetwork.com
Web: http://www.nortelnetwork.com
SIC: 64201 Employees: 3500
Telecommunications
Mr Brian Hagan Chief Executive
Mr Craig Steven Finance Manager
Mr Mark Cantwell Human Resources Manager
Mr Tom Murphy Sales Manager
Mr Fintan O'Flynn Informations Systems Manager

NTL
3rd Floor Embassy House
Ballsbridge
Dublin 4
Phone: 01-7998500 Fax: 01-7998515
Email: info@ntl.com
Web: http://www.ntl.com
SIC: 64201 Employees: 28
Telecoms & Internet Services
Mr Liam Duggan Managing Director
Ms Jane Courtney Sales Manager
Mr Eugene Kelly Computer Manager

Office of the Director of Telecom Regulation (ODTR)
Abbey Court Irish Life Centre
Lower Abbey Street
Dublin 1
Phone: 01-8049600 Fax: 01-8049680
Web: http://www.odtr.ie
SIC: 64201 Employees: 75
National Authority for Telecommunication Service
Ms Etain Doyle Director
Mr Michael Foy Finance Manager
Ms Ann-Marie O'Sullivan Personnel Manager

Performix Technologies
The Warehouse
35 Barrow Street
Dublin 4
Phone: 01-6778222 Fax: 01-2314701
SIC: 64201 Employees: 50
Call Centres Products Manufactures
Mr Cathal McGloin Chief Executive Officer

Spectel Ltd
21 Stillorgan Industrial Park
Stillorgan
Blackrock Co. Dublin
Phone: 01-2953116 Fax: 01-2953740
Email: post@spectel.ie
Web: http://www.spectel.ie
SIC: 64201 Employees: 60
Telecoms Design
Mr Gerard Moore Managing Director
Ms Ailish Macken Financial Controller
Mr Gerard Thornton Sales For Europe
Mr Gerry Roe Production Manager
Mr Paul Condon Computer Manager

Swiftcall Long Distance Ltd
294 Merrion Road
Dublin 4
Phone: 01-2057834 Fax: 01-2694184
Email: sales@swiftcall.com
Web: http://www.swiftcall.com
SIC: 64201 Employees: 170
Telecomms Company
Mr John Hynes Managing Director
Ms Deborah Glynn Accounts Administrator
Ms Deirdre O'Riordan Personnel Manager
Ms Tara Power Personnel Manager

The CoI 2002 Telecomms Group Ltd
15 Merchants Quay, Bessbroke
Iur Chinn Tra
Donegal, Co. Donegal
Phone: 1800-928992 Fax: 1800-928444
SIC: 64201 Employees: 41
Telecommunications Company
Mr Tom Murphy Managing Director
Ms Deborah Flynn Financial Controller
Mr Tom Lee Sales Director
Mr John Stewart IT Manager

Symphony Ireland
710 Robert Scott House
St Patricks Quay
Cork Co. Cork
Phone: 021-4557955 Fax: 021-4557950
SIC: 64201 Employees: 400
Telecommunications
Ms Teresa O'Connell Office Manager
Mr Gary Pryor Sales Director

Virtual Access
17/18 Trinity Enterprise Centre
Pearse Street
Dublin 2
Phone: 01-6041807 Fax: 01-6705380
Email: info@virtualaccess.com
Web: http://www.virtualaccess.com
SIC: 64201 Employees: 50
Telecommunications
Mr Henry Brankin Managing Director
Mr Barry Croucher Finance Manager

Worldcom
Ballybrit Business Park
Galway Co. Galway
Phone: 091-743000 Fax: 091-773864
Email: info@wcom.ie
Web: http://www.wcom.ie
SIC: 64201 Employees: 174
Telecommunication
Mr David Huges Managing Director

Meteor
4030 Kingswood Avenue
City West Business Park
Dublin 24
Phone: 01-4307000 Fax: 01-4307010
Email: info@meteor.ie
Web: http://www.meteor.ie
SIC: 64202 Employees: 300
Mobile Phone Communications Provider
Mr Pete Quinn Chief Executive Officer
Ms Cliodhna Whelan Financial Controller
Mr Conor Carmady Sales Manager
Mr Tony Stewart Lord IT Manager

RCI Service Solutions
Unit C 7 Station Road
Business Park Clondalkin
Dublin 22
Phone: 01-4579787 Fax: 01-4579790
Email: custsrvc-rci@clubi.ie
SIC: 64202 Employees: 25
Repair Mobile Phones
Mr Jeff Logie Service Centre Manager

Finance

Financial Intermediaries

65 Financial Intermediaries
65111 Bank Head Offices
65112 Building Society Head Offices
65121 Bank Branches
65122 Building Society Branches
65128 Bureau de Change
65129 Banking Services (Other)
65200 Financial Institutions - Other
65210 Financial Leasing
65220 Credit Unions
65222 Factoring
65239 Banking/Finance – Other

ABN Amro Bank (Irl) Ltd
ABN AMRO House
IFSC
Dublin 1
Phone: 01-6093800 Fax: 01-6093711
Email: info@ie.abnamro.com
Web: http://www.abnamro.com
SIC: 65111 Employees: 230
Merchant Bank
Mr Gerry Roseingrave Chief Executive Officer
Mr Steven Quinn Finance Manager
Mr Niall Glynn Personnel Manager
Mr Bernard Enright IT Manager

ACC Bank Plc
Charlemont Place
Abbey
Dublin 2
Phone: 01-4184184 Fax: 01-4184848
Email: info@accbank.ie
Web: http://www.accbank.ie
SIC: 65111 Employees: 640
Bank Head Office
Mr Colm Darling Chief Executive
Mr Eugene Murray Finance Manager
Ms Tara Glynn Personnel Director
Mr Mick Geoghegan Sales & Marketing Manager

AIB Bank Centre
Ballsbridge
Dublin 4
Phone: 01-6600311 Fax: 01-6603063
Email: info@aib.ie
Web: http://www.aib.ie
SIC: 65111 Employees: 9000
Bank (Head Office)
Mr Michael Buckley Group Chief Executive
Mr Con O'Sullivan Head of Group Finance
Mr Brian Gannon Head of IT Infrastructure

Anglo Irish Bank
Stephens Court
Stephens Green
Dublin 1
Phone: 01-6162000 Fax: 01-6702384
Email: postmaster@angloirishbank.com
Web: http://www.angloirishbank.ie
SIC: 65111 Employees: 300
Treasury Investment
Mr William McAteer Director
Mr John Hadden Senior Personnel Manager
Ms Mary Nolan Sales Manager
Mr Mike Campbell Computer Director

Bank Of America NA
Russell Court, IFSC
St Stephen's Green
Dublin 2
Phone: 01-4072100 Fax: 01-4072199
SIC: 65111 Employees: 45
Financial Services Management
Mr Diarmuid Connaughton Country Manager
Ms Catherine Meenaghan Country Ops Manager

Bank Of Ireland Group
Lower Baggot Street
Dublin 2
Phone: 01-6615933 Fax: 01-6615671
Email: info@boi.ie
Web: http://www.boi.ie
SIC: 65111 Employees: 15000
Bank Head Office
Mr Maurice Keane Chief Executive
Mr Paul D'Alton Finance Manager
Mr Kevin Flannaghan Human Resources Manager
Mr Patrick Waldron Sales & Marketing Manager

Bank Of Scotland
Canada House
65/68 St Stephens Green
Dublin 2
Phone: 01-4083500 Fax: 01-4757072
Email: info@bankofscotland.ie
Web: http://www.bankofscotland.ie
SIC: 65111 Employees: 210
Merchant Bank
Mr Mark Duffy Chief Executive
Mr Finian Daly Financial Controller
Mr Peter Brady IT Manager

Barclays Bank Plc
47/48 St Stephen's Green
Dublin 2
Phone: 01-6611777 Fax: 01-6623141
SIC: 65111 Employees: 65
Bank Branch
Mr Paul Shovlin Director
Ms Orla Scanlon Personnel Manager

Bear Stearns Bank Plc
Block 8 Harcourt Centre, IFSC
Charlotte Way
Dublin 2
Phone: 01-4026200 Fax: 01-4026237
Email: info@bear.com
Web: http://www.bearstearns.com
SIC: 65111 Employees: 65
Financial Services
Mr Pascal Lambert President & CEO
Mr David Rhind Head of IT

BNP Paribas
5 Georges Dock
IFSC
Dublin 1
Phone: 01-6712811 Fax: 01-6125100
Email: dublin.admin@bnpparibas.com
SIC: 65111 Employees: 175
Corporate Banking
Mr Michel Devibraye General Manager
Mr Norbert Kilty Financial Controller
Ms Patricia Walsh Human Resources Director
Mr Enda Cullen Sales & Marketing Manager
Mr Paul Byrne IT Manager

Central Bank of Ireland
PO Box 559
Dame Street
Dublin 2
Phone: 01-6716666 Fax: 01-6716561
Web: http://www.centralbank.ie
SIC: 65111 Employees: 660
Bank
Mr Maurice O'Connell Governor
Mr Pat Treanor Financial Controller
Mr Jim Cummins Human Resources and Planning
Mr Gerry McGrath Director General
Mr Hugh O'Donnell Corporate Services Manager
Mr Paddy O'Conaill IT Manager

City Bank
1 Northwall Quay
Dublin 1
Phone: 01-7023584 Fax: 01-6222222
SIC: 65111 Employees: 2000
Bank Branch
Mr Aidan Brady Chief Executive
Mr David Blackshaw Financial Controller
Mr Peter Brooks Personnel Manager
Ms Mary Ram Cash Management Sales
Mr Paul McEwen IT Manager

Commerzbank International (Ireland)
Commerzbank House, IFSC
Guild Street PO Box 7616
Dublin 1
Phone: 01-6491100 Fax: 01-6491299
Email: info@commerzbank.ie
Web: http://www.commerzbank.com
SIC: 65111 Employees: 31
Bank Branch
Mr John Bowden Managing Director
Mr Paul Windsor Accounts Manager
Mr Laurence Harris Assistant Manager

DePfa-Bank Europe Plc
International House
3 Harbourmaster Place, IFSC
Dublin 1
Phone: 01-6071600 Fax: 01-8290213
Email: info@depfa.ie
SIC: 65111 Employees: 70
Public Sector Lending
Mr Dermot Cahillane Managing Director
Mr Noel Reynolds Financial Controller
Ms Naimh Kenna Personnel Officer
Mr Joseph Dunne IT Manager

Deutsche Bank Group
Irish Life Centre
Dublin 1
Phone: 01-8051000 Fax: 01-8051111
Email: postmaster@db.com
Web: http://www.deutschebank.com
SIC: 65111 Employees: 170
Bank Branch
Ms Mary Campbell Managing Director
Ms Marian McKee Finance Manager
Ms Yvonne McGuiness Personnel Director
Mr Robert Gandy Computer Manager

Dresdner Bank (Ireland) Plc
La Touche House
IFSC
Dublin 1
Phone: 01-8181150 Fax: 01-8181159
Email: dbirl@dresdner-bank.ie
SIC: 65111 Employees: 50
Corporate Lending
Mr Werner Schwanberg Managing Director
Mr Thomas Kiefer Sales & Marketing Manager

First Active plc
Central Park
Lepoardstown
Dublin 18
Phone: 01-7092614 Fax: 01-2074900
Email: info@firstactive.com
Web: http://www.firstactive.com
SIC: 65111 Employees: 700
Bank Head Office
Mr Cormac McCarthy Managing Director
Mr Michael Torpey Finance Director
Mr Colm O'Riordan Sales & Marketing Manager
Mr Paul O'Reilly Computer Manager

Firste
Grand Canal Plaza
Grand Canal Street
Dublin 4
Phone: 01-6306000 Fax: 01-6306999
Email: info@firste.com
Web: http://www.firste.com
SIC: 65111 Employees: 50
Internet Bank
Mr Tom McFadden General Manager

GE Capital Woodchester
Park House Park Road
Waterford Co. Waterford
Phone: 051-875451 Fax: 051-841768
SIC: 65111 Employees: 25
Banking Services
Mr Jim Freeman Branch Manager

HBB Bank Ireland
International House, IFSC
3 Harbourmaster Place
Dublin 1
Phone: 01-6054100 Fax: 01-6054105
SIC: 65111 Employees: 35
Corporate Fund Management
Mr Gerry Heusel Director
Ms Heather Nesbitt Finance Manager
Ms Jacinta Breen Company Secretary
Mr David Garrett IT Manager

IIB Bank
91 Merrion Square
Dublin 2
Phone: 01-6619744 Fax: 01-6785034
Email: info@iib-bank.ie
Web: http://www.iib-bank.ie
SIC: 65111 Employees: 28
Merchant Bank
Mr Ted Meara Managing Director
Mr Ken Coffey Head of IT Services

Lombard & Ulster Banking Ltd
Ulster Bank Group Centre
Georges Quay
Dublin 2
Phone: 01-6085000 Fax: 01-6085001
Email: info@lombard.ie
Web: http://www.lombard.ie
SIC: 65111 Employees: 220
Banking
Mr Bernard Kingston Chief Executive
Ms Therese O'Brien Personnel Manager
Mr Anthony Cullen Computer Manager

National Irish Bank
3 Habourmaster Place
IFSC
Dublin 2
Phone: 01-6385000 Fax: 01-6385198
Email: info@nib.ie
Web: http://www.nib.ie
SIC: 65111 Employees: 2600
Bank
Mr Don Price Chief Executive

Pfizer International Bank Europe
La Touche House
IFSC
Dublin 1
Phone: 01-6700277 Fax: 01-6700466
Email: info@pfizer.com
Web: http://www.pfizer.com
SIC: 65111 Employees: 26
Financial Services
Mr Eddie Lee Chief Executive Officer

Post Office Savings Bank
General Post Office
O'Connell Street
Dublin 1
Phone: 01-7057000 Fax: 01-8723553
Email: info@anpost.ie
Web: http://www.anpost.ie
SIC: 65111 Employees: 1000
Financial Services
Mr John Hynes Chief Executive
Mr Ronan Byrne Director of Finance
Mr Justin Connolly Personnel Director
Mr John Daly Head of Finance
Mr Ciaran McGivern General IT Manager

PTSB Bank
Carysfort Avenue
Blackrock Co. Dublin
Phone: 01-2124000 Fax: 01-2124100
Email: info@tsbbank.ie
Web: http://www.tsbbank.ie
SIC: 65111 Employees: 1150
Bank
Mr Harry Loton Chief Executive

Ulster Bank
33 College Green
Dublin 2
Phone: 01-6777623 Fax: 01-6799468
Email: info@ulsterbank.com
Web: http://www.ulsterbank.com
SIC: 65111 Employees: 1400
Bank Head Office
Mr Daragh McMahon Manager
Mr Ivan Laird Financial Controller
Mr Noel Fitzpatrick IT Manager

Campion Insurances Ltd
Main Street
Urlingford Co. Co Kilkenny
Phone: 056-31202 Fax: 056-31448
Email: info@campionins.com
Web: http://www.campionins.com
SIC: 65112 Employees: 28
Building Society
Mr Jim Campion Manager
Ms Margaret Campion Finance Manager
Mr Jim Campion Personnel Manager
Mr Michael Sparron Sales & Marketing Manager
Mr Gavin Dixon Computer Manager

First Active Building Society
Head Office
Skehan House, Booterstown
Blackrock Co. Dublin
Phone: 01-7092070 Fax: 01-2885300
Email: info@firstactive.com
Web: http://www.firstactive.com
SIC: 65112 Employees: 100
Building Society
Mr Cormac McCarthy Chief Executive

Irish Life & Permanent Plc
56-59 St Stephen's Green
Dublin 2
Phone: 01-6615577 Fax: 01-6616515
Email: info@irishpermanent.ie
Web: http://www.irishpermanent.ie
SIC: 65112 Employees: 1750
Bank
Mr Billy Kane Group Chief Executive
Mr Peter Fitzpatrick Head of Finance
Mr Kevin Kenny Human Resources Manager
Mr Niall O'Grady Head of Marketing
Mr Fred Finlay Information Systems Manager

Irish Nationwide
Nationwide House
Grand Parade
Dublin 6
Phone: 01-4780022 Fax: 01-6096200
Email: info@irish-nationwide.com
Web: http://www.irish-nationwide.com
SIC: 65112 Employees: 200
Building Society
Mr Michael Fingleton Managing Director
Mr Dan Purcell Finance Manager
Mr D'arcy Donnelly Human Resources Manager
Ms Karen Meade Head of Marketing
Mr Derek Dunne IT Manager

Irish Permanent
12-13 Lower O'Connell Street
Dublin 1
Phone: 01-8788333 Fax: 01-8746391
Email: info@irishpermanent.ie
Web: http://www.irishpermanent.ie
SIC: 65112 Employees: 23
Building Society
Mr Charles Spillane Manager

AIB Tresurary
Iona House
Celburn Road
Dublin 4
Phone: 01-6417738 Fax: 01-6606757
Email: info@aib.ie
Web: http://www.aib.ie
SIC: 65121 Employees: 50
Bank Tresuary
Mr Jim O'Farrell Manager

Bank Of Ireland Card Services
33-35 Nassau Street
Dublin 2
Phone: 01-6770954 Fax: 01-6176037
Email: info@boi.ie
Web: http://www.boi.ie
SIC: 65121 Employees: 230
Bank of Ireland Card Services
Mr Aidan McEvoy Manager

Bank Of Ireland Group Finance
A3 Head Office
Lower Baggot Street
Dublin 2
Phone: 01-6043518 Fax: 01-6043553
Email: info@boi.ie
Web: http://www.boi.ie
SIC: 65121 Employees: 12000
Group of Finance For the Bank of Ireland
Mr Maurice Keane Managing Director
Mr Paul D'Alton Group Financial Controller
Mr Patrick Walton Sales & Marketing Manager
Mr Cyril Dunn IT Manager

Banklink Control
A.I.B.
Donnybrook House
Dublin 4
Phone: 01-2695200 Fax: 01-2830812
Email: ab@ab.ie
SIC: 65121 Employees: 400
Bank Branch
Mr Tom Burns Manager
Mr Gene Byrne Finance Manager
Ms Janice Mooney Personnel Manager
Mr Billy Finn Computer Manager

First Rate Bureau De Change Ltd
Hume House
Pembroke Road
Dublin 4
Phone: 01-6671566 Fax: 01-6671599
SIC: 65128 Employees: 23
Bureau De Change
Mr Joe Redmond Manager

Bank Of Ireland Credit Card Services
33/35 Nassau Street
Dublin 2
Phone: 01-6796015 Fax: 01-6718952
Email: info@boi.ie
Web: http://www.boi.ie
SIC: 65129 Employees: 180
Credit Card Services
Mr Tom Comerford Head of Credit Card Services
Ms Joan Talbot Acting Finance Manager
Mr Terry Carragher Marketing Manager

Helaba CommerzBank House
PO Box 3137
Guild Street, IFSC
Dublin 1
Phone: 01-6491500 Fax: 01-6491599
Email: infodublin@helaba.de
Web: http://www.helaba.de
SIC: 65129 Employees: 35
Banking Services
Mr Patrick Vangordon Managing Director
Mr Paul Murray Financial Controller
Ms Jenny McGurk Computer Manager

Rabo Bank
Georges Dock House
IFSC
Dublin 1
Phone: 01-6076174 Fax: 01-6701724
SIC: 65129 Employees: 45
Banking Services
Mr Fergus Murphy Managing Director
Ms Miriam Queally Finance Manager
Ms Claire Barrett Personnel Manager
Mr Colin Feehan Computer Manager

Allergan Services Ltd
The Sweepstake Centre
Ballsbridge
Dublin 4
Phone: 01-6142000 Fax: 01-6142099
Email: info@allergan.com
Web: http://www.allergan.com
SIC: 65200 Employees: 95
Financial Services for the Allergan Group
Mr David Flynn Operations Director
Mr Brian Golden Credit Controller
Ms Sonia Germaine Human Resources Manager
Mr Mike Slocun IT Manager

B I L Fund Services Ltd
Georges Quays
43 Townsend Street
Dublin 2
Phone: 01-6130444 Fax: 01-6130445
SIC: 65200 Employees: 100
Fund Services
Mr Robert Gough Managing Director

Bank Of Ireland Lifetime Management Services
Head Office,
Lower Baggot Street
Dublin 2
Phone: 01-7039500 Fax: 01-6620811
Email: info@lifetime.ie
Web: http://www.lifetime.ie
SIC: 65200 Employees: 330
Financial Services
Mr Roy Keenan Managing Director
Mr John Murphy Financial Controller
Ms Aveen Batt Personnel Manager
Mr Quentin Teggin Marketing Manager
Mr Dave Mitten Head of IT

Barclays Insurances Dublin
47 St Stephens Green
Dublin 2
Phone: 01-6618594 Fax: 01-6762430
Email: info@barclays.co.uk
Web: http://www.barclays.co.uk
SIC: 65200 Employees: 130
Financial Services
Mr Eamonn Slevin Chief Executive
Mr Steven Coombs Finance Manager
Mr Aidan Larkin Computer Manager

Bertelsmann Distribution Financial Services
Freeman House
Eastpoint Park Fairview
Dublin 3
Phone: 01-8554780 Fax: 01-8554792
Web: http://www.bolfs.ie
SIC: 65200 Employees: 240
Financial Services
Mr Mathias Miersich Managing Director
Ms Adrienne Bevins Financial Controller
Ms Ann Dinnigan Human Resources Manager
Mr Jorg Stimmer Sales & Marketing Manager
Mr Shay Carroll Operation Manager
Mr Noel Martin Systems Manager

BISYS Fund Managers Ltd
Brooklawn House, Crampton Avenue
Shelbourne Road
Dublin 4
Phone: 01-7903700 Fax: 01-6376400
SIC: 65200 Employees: 150
Fund Management Company
Mr Tony Mercure Managing Director

Caledonian Life
2-4 Merrion Row
Dublin 2
Phone: 01-6625150 Fax: 01-6620722
SIC: 65200 Employees: 100
Protection Savings & Pensions
Ms Aisling Nolan General Manager

Centurion Card Services
Temple House
Temple Road
Blackrock Co. Dublin
Phone: 01-2055111 Fax: 01-2883429
SIC: 65200 Employees: 40
American Express Cards
Mr Peter Egan Managing Director
Ms Joan Talbot Finance Manager
Ms Catrina Bradley Personnel Assistant
Ms Linda Omahonny Sales & Marketing Manager
Mr Ilan Bar-Kat IT Manager

Cogent Investment Operations Ireland Ltd
13 Exchange Place
IFSC
Dublin 1
Phone: 01-6702111 Fax: 01-6702149
Email: info@cogent.ie
Web: http://www.cogent.ie
SIC: 65200 Employees: 30
Offshore Fund Administration services
Mr Brian Goonan General Manager

Continental Finance & Adminitration
Unit 1, Sragh Industrial Estate
Tullamore Co. Offaly
Phone: 0506-25700 Fax: 0506-24919
SIC: 65200 Employees: 55
Financial Services
Mr Ian Breen Managing Director

Crana Financial Services
26 Upper Main Street
Buncrana
Lifford Co. Donegal
Phone: 077-61031 Fax: 077-61031
Email: cranafinancial@eircom.net
SIC: 65200 Employees: 60
Financial Services Insurance Aurtioneers
Mr Fergal McLoughlin Manager

Custom House Administration & Corporate Services
25 Eden Quay
Dublin 1
Phone: 01-8780807 Fax: 01-8780827
Email: info@customhousegroup.com
Web: http://www.customhousegroup.com
SIC: 65200 Employees: 85
Offshore Fund Set-Up & Administration
Mr David Blair Managing Director
Mr Glenn Wall Financial Controller
Mr Dermot Butler Chairman

D F Reidy & Company
10 The Crescent
Limerick Co. Limerick
Phone: 061-316454 Fax: 061-310636
SIC: 65200 Employees: 60
Mortgage Brokers & Services
Mr Keith Reidy Proprietor

Daiwa Securities Trust & Banking (Europe) Plc
Block 3 Harcourt Centre
Harcourt Road
Dublin 2
Phone: 01-4783700 Fax: 01-4783469
Email: kmceneff@deb.ie
Web: http://www.daiwasectab.com
SIC: 65200 Employees: 70
Financial Services - Fund Administration Bank
Mr Karl McEneff Executive Director
Ms Vanessa Trigg Human Resources Manager
Mr Donal O'Brien Trustee & Compliance Manager
Mr Brian Guyett Operation Director
Mr Darren Wayne Computer Manager

Donal O'Callaghan
76 Westbrook Ballymoneen Road
Galway Co. Galway
Phone: 091-590330 Fax: 091-590330
SIC: 65200 Employees: 60
Financial Brokers & Consultants
Mr Donal O'Callagahan Proprietor

Falcon Financial
Anne Street
Wexford Co. Wexford
Phone: 053-42912 Fax: 053-21009
SIC: 65200 Employees: 60
Mortgage Brokers & Services
Mr Syril Bardan Director

Fexco
Fexco House
12 Ely Place
Dublin 2
Phone: 01-6611800 Fax: 01-6610800
Email: info@fexco.ie
Web: http://www.fexco.ie
SIC: 65200 Employees: 97
Financial Services
Mr John Nagle Managing Director
Mr John McCarthy Finance Manager
Ms Julie Kennedy Personnel Manager
Mr Niall Brady Area Corporate Sales Manager

Financial Engineering Ltd
11 Pembroke Street
Cork Co. Cork
Phone: 021-4275000 Fax: 021-4275000
Email: fineng@iol.ie
Web: http://www.financial.ie
SIC: 65200 Employees: 60
Pension Scheme Consultants
Mr John Kelleher Managing Director

Fitzgerald Insurance Dungarvan Ltd
20 Grattan Square
Dungarvan Co. Waterford
Phone: 058-44011 Fax: 058-42875
SIC: 65200 Employees: 50
Insurance Brokers
Mr Liam Fitzgerald Partner
Mr Liam McCarthy Partner

Foreign Exchange Company of Ireland
Fexco Centre
Iveragh Road Killorglin
Killarney Co. Kerry
Phone: 066-9761258 Fax: 066-9761654
Email: kerry@fexco.ie
Web: http://www.fexco.com
SIC: 65200 Employees: 500
Financial Services
Mr John Nagle Managing Director
Mr Gerard Murphy Financial Director
Mr Michael Neilan Personnel Manager
Mr Dennis Crowley Marketing Director
Mr John Bowler Operations Manager
Mr Stephen O'Sullivan Technical Director

Friends First Life Assurance Company
Friends First House
29-31 Adelaide Road
Dublin 2
Phone: 01-6610600 Fax: 01-6616651
Email: info@life.friendsfirst.ie
Web: http://www.friendsfirst.ie
SIC: 65200 Employees: 550
Financial Services
Mr Adrian Heggarty Managing Director
Ms Una Sower Financial Controller
Ms Noreen Deegan Personnel Manager
Mr John Cunningham Sales & Marketing Manag
Mr Tom Browne Production Manager
Mr Sean Kennedy Computer Manager

Finance

GAM Fund Management
1 Saint Georges Dock
IFSC
Dublin 1
Phone: 01-6760630 Fax: 01-6702088
Web: http://www.gam.com
SIC: 65200 Employees: 111
Phones - Financial Management
Mr Craig Wallace Managing Director
Mr Michael Keane Head of Finance
Ms Annmarie O'Connor Personnel Director
Mr Darren Kirwan IT Manager

GE Capital Aviation Services Ltd (GECAS)
Aviation House
Shannon Free Zone
Shannon Co. Clare
Phone: 061-706500 Fax: 061-360888
Web: http://www.gcas.com
SIC: 65200 Employees: 120
Aircraft Financing and Leasing
Mr Brian Hayden Managing Director
Ms Connie Norris Personnel Manager
Mr Paul Barton Sales Manager
Mr Aidan O'Connell MIS Manager

Grafton Group Plc
Heron House Corrig Road
Sandyford Industrial Estate
Dublin 18
Phone: 01-2953377 Fax: 01-2954470
Email: info@graftonplc.com
Web: http://www.graftonplc.com
SIC: 65200 Employees: 1300
Financial Services
Mr Michael Chadwick Chairman
Mr Colm O'Nuallain Finance Manager
Mr Aidan O'Mara Human Resources Manager
Mr Michael Fox Computer Manager

H & C Finanacial Services Group Ltd
Oranmore Business Park
Galway Co. Galway
Phone: 091-788000 Fax: 091-788008
Email: tonyc@hcgroup.I
Web: http://www.hcgroup.ie
SIC: 65200 Employees: 250
Mortgage Advisors
Ms Hanna Kiley Managing Director
Mr Gerard Cuddy Director

Hamill Spence O'Connell
Adelaide House
90 Upper Georges Street
Dun Laoghaire Co. Dublin
Phone: 01-2808433 Fax: 01-2804472
SIC: 65200 Employees: 35
Financial Consultants/ Chartered Accountants
Mr Paul Spence Managing Director

HCM
8-11 Lower Baggot Street
Dublin 2
Phone: 01-6384200 Fax: 01-6620440
Email: info@hcmintl.com
Web: http://www.hcmintl.com
SIC: 65200 Employees: 100
Human Resources & Pension Funds
Mr Brendan O'Farrell Managing Director
Mr Donal Lawlor Financial Controller
Mr Connor Sheppard IT Manager

Hemisphere Management Ireland Ltd
Frederick House
South Frederick Street
Dublin 2
Phone: 01-6097200 Fax: 01-6725361
Email: info@hmil.ie
Web: http://www.hemisphereglobal.com
SIC: 65200 Employees: 90
Off-Shore Fund Administrators
Mr Ronan Daly Managing Director
Mr Paul Sinnott Chief Financial Officer
Ms Karen Tyrrell Production Manager

Hibernian Investment Managers
La Touche House
IFSC
Dublin 1
Phone: 01-6700950 Fax: 01-6700944
Email: him1@iol.ie
SIC: 65200 Employees: 48
Fund Management
Mr Pramit Goss Managing Director
Mr Paul Walton Accountant
Mr Dara Fitzgerald Sales & Marketing Manager
Mr Andrew Pomeroy Computer Manager

Hypovereinsbank Ireland
International House
3 Harbour Master Place
Dublin 1
Phone: 01-6054131 Fax: 01-6054105
Email: info@hypovereinsbank.de
Web: http://www.hypovereinsbank.de
SIC: 65200 Employees: 30
Corporate Lending
Mr Dieter Heusel Managing Director
Ms Heather Nesbitt Finance Manager

ICC Venture Capital Bank
72-74 Harcourt Street
IFSC
Dublin 2
Phone: 01-4155555 Fax: 01-6717797
Email: info@icc.ie
Web: http://www.icc.ie
SIC: 65200 Employees: 335
Asset Financing
Mr Michael Quinn Managing Director
Mr Martin Thornton Finance Manager

ICS Mortgage Store
12 Broad Street
Waterford Co. Waterford
Phone: 051-856770 Fax: 051-856578
Web: http://www.mortgagestore.ie
SIC: 65200 Employees: 35
Mortgage Brokers & Services
Ms Patricia Foskin Branch Manager

IFG Group
19 Fitzwilliam Square
Dublin 2
Phone: 01-6611954 Fax: 01-6761090
Web: http://www.ifggroup.ie
SIC: 65200 Employees: 270
Financial Services
Mr Richard Hayes Chief Executive

IFG Mortgages
Ground Floor 1 Rockford House
St Augustine Street
Galway Co. Galway
Phone: 091-563400 Fax: 091-567770
Web: http://www.ifgmortgages.ie
SIC: 65200 Employees: 80
Mortgage Brokers & Services
Mr Joseph Walsh Managing Director

International Banking Services
Ashford House
Tara Street
Dublin 2
Phone: 01-8740222 Fax: 01-8742304
Email: postmaster@aib.ie
Web: http://www.aib.ie
SIC: 65200 Employees: 2000
Financial Services
Mr Colm Doherty General Manager
Mr Norbert Bannan Finance Manager
Mr John Conway Human Resources Director

Investec Gandon Ltd
Andersen House
1 Harbourmaster Place IFSC
Dublin 1
Phone: 01-6701300 Fax: 01-6701330
Email: info@gandon-capital.ie
Web: http://www.gandon_capital.ie
SIC: 65200 Employees: 70
Corporate Risk Managment, Corporate Finance
Mr Michael Cullen Chief Executive
Mr Alan Byrne Financial Controller
Ms Brideen Downes Personnel Manager
Ms Annemarie Brennan Sales & Marketing Manager
Mr Kevin Ferguson Computer Manager

James Bruen & Sons Ltd
45 South Mall
Cork Co. Cork
Phone: 021-4270398 Fax: 021-4271508
SIC: 65200 Employees: 25
Pension Scheme Consultants
Mr Padraig O'Sullivan Managing Director

John Blackwell & Associates
112 The Quay
Waterford Co. Waterford
Phone: 051-852755 Fax: 051-852753
SIC: 65200 Employees: 60
Mortgage Brokers & Services
Mr John Blackwell Proprietor

KBC Acid Management
Georges Quay
Dublin 2
Phone: 01-6084339 Fax: 01-6084459
Email: info@kbcam.com
Web: http://www.kbcam.com
SIC: 65200 Employees: 73
Investment Management
Mr Gavin Caldwell Managing Director
Ms Anne O'Mhurchu Finance Manager
Ms Samantha McConnell Sales Director
Mr Ger Solan Computer Manager

Management International
1st Floor Europa House
Harcourt Street
Dublin 2
Phone: 01-4072228 Fax: 01-4752466
Email: info@bankofburmuda.com
Web: http://www.bankofburmuda.com
SIC: 65200 Employees: 108
Fund Administrators
Mr Gerard Brady Managing Director

Marsh Financial Services Ltd
Furbo
Galway Co. Galway
Phone: 091-592071 Fax: 091-592067
Email: marshfsg@marsh.com
Web: http://www.marsh.com
SIC: 65200 Employees: 100
Financial Services
Mr Ronan Bray Senior Financial Consultant

Mercer Ltd
St James House
25/28 Adelaide Road
Dublin 2
Phone: 01-4782866 Fax: 01-4782297
Web: http://www.mercer.com
SIC: 65200 Employees: 145
Pension Consultants/Actuaries
Mr James Kelly Chairman
Mr Noel Beecher Financial Director
Ms Martina Sheehan Personnel Manager
Mr Des Ryan Marketing Director
Mr Bernard Tymlin Systems Manager

Finance

Merrill Lynch Capital Markets Bank Ltd
Treasury Building, IFSC
Lower Grand Canal Street
Dublin 2
Phone: 01-6058500 Fax: 01-6058501
SIC: 65200 Employees: 235
Financial Services
Mr Michael D'Souza Chief Executive Officer
Mr Ben Hoey Finance Manager
Ms Margaret Lyng Personnel Manager
Mr John Woodworth Operations Manager
Mr Tony O'Hallaron Computer Manager

Molineux Investments Ltd
Bishop Street
Elphin
Castlerea Co. Roscommon
Phone: 078-35439 Fax: 078-35464
SIC: 65200 Employees: 23
Investment Trust Companies
Mr Dave Curry Proprietor

Mortgage Centre
Central Buildings O'Connell Street
Limerick Co. Limerick
Phone: 061-411410 Fax: 061-400140
Email: pssgs@indigo.ie
SIC: 65200 Employees: 60
Mortgage Brokers & Services
Mr Gerry Simms Manager

SEI Investments-Global Fund Services
Styne House
Upper Hatch Street
Dublin 2
Phone: 01-6382400 Fax: 01-6382499
Email: info@seic.com
Web: http://www.seic.com
SIC: 65200 Employees: 80
Financial Services
Mr James Cleary Managing Director
Mr Ian Flacke IT Manager

SFS Financial Services
Barrack Street
Charlestown
Claremorris Co. Mayo
Phone: 094-55128 Fax: 094-55131
Email: sfsfinance@eircom.net
Web: http://www.irelandwestproperty.com
SIC: 65200 Employees: 60
Financial Services
Ms Nuala McCarthy Managing Director

Tusa Financial Services
2-4 Upper Baggot Street
Dublin 4
Phone: 01-6684680 Fax: 01-6684668
SIC: 65200 Employees: 56
Financial Services
Mr Brian Mahony Chief Executive
Ms Ann Jones Finance Manager
Ms Julian Quinn Personnel Manager
Ms Aine McGriel Sales Manager
Ms Julian Quinn Technical Director

Whirlpool Ireland
Treasury Building
Lower Grand Canal Street
Dublin 2
Phone: 01-6046500 Fax: 01-6046799
Email: info@whirlpool.com
Web: http://www.whirlpool.com
SIC: 65200 Employees: 126
Shared Service Centre - Finance Department for Whirpool
Mr Steve Freeman Managing Director
Mr Frank Connolly Computer Manager

GE Capital Investments Plc
Woodchester House
Golden Lane
Dublin 8
Phone: 01-4784299 Fax: 01-4780000
Web: http://www.gecapital.com
SIC: 65210 Employees: 1600
Financial Institution
Mr John O'Connor Managing Director
Mr Declan Grogan Personnel Manager
Mr Adam Bacon Marketing Manager
Mr Denis Howard Production Manager
Mr Michael McGrath Computer Manager

GMAC Commercial Mortgage of Ireland
Clonmore
Mullingar Co. Westmeath
Phone: 044-32300 Fax: 044-32308
SIC: 65210 Employees: 67
Mortgage
Ms Claire Dooley Chief Executive

Irish Mortgage Corporation Ltd
3 Ely Place
Dublin 2
Phone: 01-6763654 Fax: 01-6619102
Email: info@irishmortgage.ie
Web: http://www.iol.ie/irishmortgage/
SIC: 65210 Employees: 55
Mortgage Advisors
Mr Derek Maguire Managing Director
Mr Kevin Day Accountant

MBNA Ireland
46 St Stephen's Green
Dublin 2
Phone: 01-6196010 Fax: 01-6196001
Email: info@mbna.com
Web: http://www.mbna.com
SIC: 65210 Employees: 240
Credit Card Banking
Ms Ciara Kennedy Manager

R & P Credit Ltd
126 South Circular Road
Dublin 8
Phone: 01-4532924 Fax: 01-4532924
Email: rpcredit@indigo.ie
SIC: 65210 Employees: 36
Loans
Mr Pat Quinn Managing Director
Mr Rod O'Leary Joint Manager

Health Services Staff Credit Union
5 High Street
Christchurch
Dublin 8
Phone: 01-6778648 Fax: 01-6778664
Email: info@hsscu.ie
Web: http://www.hsscu.ie
SIC: 65220 Employees: 23
Savings Banks
Mr Pat McDermott Manager

Oriel Credit Union Ltd
46 Quarter Road, Camlough
Dundalk Co. Louth
Phone: 1800-927222 Fax: 1800-928989
SIC: 65220 Employees: 25
Credit Unions
Mr Brian Mahoney Manager

Waterford Credit Union Ltd
1 Parnell Street
Waterford Co. Waterford
Phone: 051-873437 Fax: 051-872668
Email: info@waterfordcu.ie
Web: http://www.waterfordcu.ie
SIC: 65220 Employees: 25
Credit Unions
Mr Michael Doherty Manager

AIG Global Investment Group
AIG Centre, North Wall Quay
IFSC
Dublin 1
Phone: 01-2053924 Fax: 01-6720233
Email: dublin.reception.@aig.com
Web: http://www.aig.com
SIC: 65239 Employees: 300
Support to Fund Managers
Ms Orla Horn Managing Director
Ms Eilish Finan Finance Manager
Ms Bernadette Sexton Human Resources Director
Mr Colin O'Mahony Senior IT Manager

Allied Irish Finance Co Ltd
10 /11 West Street
Drogheda Co. Louth
Phone: 041-9836523 Fax: 041-9833265
Email: info@24houronline.ie
Web: http://www.24houronline.ie
SIC: 65239 Employees: 50
Financial Institution
Mr Declan Kelleher Manager
Mr Tom Keogh Finance & Leasing Manager
Mr Michael Murray Sales Director
Ms Deridre McManaman Computer Manager

Bermuda Trust (Dublin) Ltd
1st Floor Europa House
Harcourt Centre Harcourt Street
Dublin 2
Phone: 01-4072000 Fax: 01-4752466
Email: info@bankofbermuda.com
Web: http://www.bankofbermuda.com
SIC: 65239 Employees: 80
Custody & Trusteeship
Mr Gerald Brady Managing Director
Mr Henk Schra Computer Manager

Brinks Allied Ltd
Unit 25A Willsborough Clonshaugh
Industrial Estate Coolock
Dublin 17
Phone: 01-8486460 Fax: 01-8486467
Email: brinksal@indigo.ie
Web: http://www.indigo.ie
SIC: 65239 Employees: 120
Security Cash in Transit
Mr Bill Hoyne Managing Director
Ms Susan Reddin Financial Controller
Mr Alfy Brown Personnel Manager
Ms Siobhan Plunkett Sales Development Manager

Brown Brothers Harriman Fund Administration Ltd
80 Harcourt Street
Dublin 2
Phone: 01-4757840 Fax: 01-4757834
SIC: 65239 Employees: 48
Fund Management & Global Custody
Mr Jeffery Holland Director
Mr Pauric McBride Financial Controller
Ms Ciara O'Sullivan Administrative Officer
Mr Sean Peir Director

City Group
1 North Wall Quay
Dublin 1
Phone: 01-6225301 Fax: 01-6222222
Email: info@citycorp.com
Web: http://www.citycorp.com
SIC: 65239 Employees: 2000
Corporate Bank
Mr Aidan Brady Managing Director
Mr David Blackshaw Financial Controller
Mr Peter Brooks Human Resources Manager
Ms Tara O'Byrne Sales & Marketing Manager
Mr Paul McEwen Computer Manager

Cork Money Advice & Budgeting Services
Unit 33 Penrose Wharf
Penrose Quay
Cork Co. Cork
Phone: 021-4552080 Fax: 021-4552078
Email: info@cork.mabs.ie
Web: http://www.cork.mabs.ie
SIC: 65239 Employees: 250
Financial Services
Mr Dennis Corbet Managing Director

Dexia Fund Services (Dublin) Ltd
Georges Quay House
43 Townsend Street
Dublin 2
Phone: 01-6130400 Fax: 01-6130401
Email: info@bil-dexia.com
Web: http://www.dexia-bil.com
SIC: 65239 Employees: 50
Transfer Agency & Fund Accounting
Mr George Kohr Managing Director
Mr Marco Mondaini General Manager

Ergo Treasury Centre Ltd
4 Earlsfort Terrace
Dublin 2
Phone: 01-6623733 Fax: 01-6777044
Email: info@dbb.ie
Web: http://www.dbb.ie
SIC: 65239 Employees: 100
Treasury Centre
Mr Ronan Reid Manager
Mr Frank Conaty Finance Manager

IBT Trust & Custodial Services
Deloitte & Touche House
29 Earlsfort Terrace
Dublin 2
Phone: 01-4752211 Fax: 01-4751173
Email: info@ibtco.com
SIC: 65239 Employees: 80
Trustee & Custodial Services
Mr Raymond O'Neill Managing Director
Ms Kerys Gavigan Marketing Director
Ms Sarah Lee Computer Manager

International Fund Managers (Ire) Ltd
2nd Floor IFSC House
IFSC
Dublin 1
Phone: 01-6700660 Fax: 01-6701181
Web: http://www.ifm-ireland.com
SIC: 65239 Employees: 180
Financial Services
Mr Vic Holmes Managing Director
Mr Martin Anderson Finance Manager
Mr Peter Rowley Personnel Manager
Mr Martin Comiskey Computer Manager

International Fund Services (Ireland) Ltd
Block 1 Harcourt Centre
Harcourt Street
Dublin 2
Phone: 01-7075000 Fax: 01-7075100
Web: http://www.imsi.com
SIC: 65239 Employees: 200
Fund Management
Ms Mary Murphy Managing Director
Ms Dorothy Flattery Office Manager
Mr Derek Keating Computer Manager

Irish League of Credit Unions
33-41 Lower Mount Street
Dublin 2
Phone: 01-6146700 Fax: 01-6146701
Email: info@creditunion.ie
Web: http://www.creditunion.ie
SIC: 65239 Employees: 70
Support to Credit Unions
Mr Tony Smith General Secretary
Mr Tim Quinlan Head of Finance
Ms Catherine Devitt Head of Training
Mr Patrick Fay Operations Officer
Ms Lucy Browne Head of IT

Mellon Fund Administration (Dublin) Ltd
20-22 Hatch Street Lower
Dublin 2
Phone: 01-7905000 Fax: 01-7905010
Email: info@mellon.com
Web: http://www.mellon.com
SIC: 65239 Employees: 45
Fund Administrators
Mr Harley Murphy Managing Director

National Treasury Management Agency
Treasury Building
Lower Grand Canal Street
Dublin 2
Phone: 01-6762266 Fax: 01-6640890
Email: info@ntma.ie
Web: http://www.ntma.ie
SIC: 65239 Employees: 50
National Debt Management
Dr Michael Somers Chief Executive
Mr Brendan McDonagh Financial Controller
Mr Joe Hanrahan Personnel Manager
Mr Jim Farrell Director of Operations
Mr Ken Jordan IT Manager

Pembroke Capital Ltd
Pembroke House, IFSC
33-41 Lower Mount Street
Dublin 2
Phone: 01-6610900 Fax: 01-6612848
Email: pembroke.info@pcl.ie
Web: http://www.pcl.ie
SIC: 65239 Employees: 46
Aviation Finance
Mr Shane Cooke Chief Executive Officer
Mr Brian Goulding Finance Manager
Ms Simone Corcoran Personnel Manager
Mr Shane Lundgren Vice President of Marketing
Mr Barry Clegg IT Manager

PFPC International
Abbey Court Block C, IFSC
Lower Abbey Street
Dublin 1
Phone: 01-7903500 Fax: 01-7903510
Email: info@pfpc.com
Web: http://www.pfpcworldwide.com
SIC: 65239 Employees: 180
Funds Servicing / Marketing
Ms Joan Kehoe Managing Director
Ms Tara Murphy Finance Manager
Ms Lucy Tierney Human Resources Manager
Ms Ann Weaser Office Services Manager
Mr Paul Lord IT Manager

Pioneer Investments
3 Custom House Plaza
IFSC
Dublin 1
Phone: 01-6623600 Fax: 01-6364600
Email: info@piog.com
Web: http://www.pioneerfunds.com
SIC: 65239 Employees: 330
Fund Management
Mr Robert Richardson Managing Director
Ms Melissa O'Caoimh Finance Manager
Ms Una Kilduff Personnel Manager
Ms Rena Brennan Marketing Executive
Mr Tom McMahon Computer Manager

Rabobank Ireland plc
Georges Docks House
IFSC
Dublin 1
Phone: 01-6076100 Fax: 01-6701724
Email: info@dub.rabobank.com
Web: http://rabobank.info.nl//enels/default.htm
SIC: 65239 Employees: 45
Corporate Banking
Mr Hans van Griethuysen Managing Director
Mr Cian Dooley Finance Manager
Mr Adrian Whiteman Operations Manager
Mr Colm Feehan IT Manager

Tote
Leopardstown Racecourse
Foxrock
Dublin 18
Phone: 01-2895000 Fax: 01-2892019
Email: info@tote.ie
Web: http://www.tote.ie
SIC: 65239 Employees: 40
Credit Betting Section Of the Irish Racehorsing Authority
Mr Maurice Byrne Managing Director
Mr John White Manager

Insurance

66 Insurance
66001 Insurance Companies
66002 Insurance Broker
66003 Insurance Loss Adjuster

Accident & General International Ltd
34 Lower Abbey Street
IFSC
Dublin 1
Phone: 01-8748458 Fax: 01-8749201
Email: info@accidentgeneral.ie
Web: http://www.accidentgeneral.ie
SIC: 66001 Employees: 24
Insurance Broking
Mr Tom Duffy Managing Director
Mr Terry Gillan Finance Manager

Acorn Life
St Augustine Street
Galway Co. Galway
Phone: 091-562777 Fax: 091-535750
SIC: 66001 Employees: 200
Insurance Companies
Mr Gerry O'Connell Chief Executive
Mr Jonathan Gould Head of Finance
Mr Paddy Byrne Sales Manager

Aetna US Healthcare
Castleisland
Tralee Co. Kerry
Phone: 066-7142240 Fax: 066-7142228
Email: info@aetna.ie
Web: http://www.aetna.com
SIC: 66001 Employees: 90
Health insurance for US companies
Mr John Casey Managing Director
Ms Joan Griffin Finance Manager
Ms Katrina Keane Admin Supervisor
Mr Shane O'Neill Computer Manager

AIG Europe (Ireland) Ltd
Park House
Georges Avenue
Blackrock Co. Dublin
Phone: 01-2055901 Fax: 01-2783820
Email: postmaster@aig.ie
Web: http://www.aig.com
SIC: 66001 Employees: 100
Insurance & Financial Services - IT Section
Mr Conor Sexton Managing Director

Ark Life Assurance
8 Burlington Road
Dublin 4
Phone: 01-6681199 Fax: 01-6375737
Email: arklife@indigo.ie
Web: http://www.arklife.ie
SIC: 66001 Employees: 450
Life Assurance
Mr Billy Finn Managing Director
Mr Brian Woods Finance Manager
Mr Brian O'Connor Human Resources Manager
Mr Dermot O'Beirne Sales & International Director
Mr Declan McGovern DP Manager

BUPA (Ireland)
Mill Island
Fermoy Co. Cork
Phone: 025-32740 Fax: 025-42122
Email: choices@bupa.ie
Web: http://www.bupaireland.ie
SIC: 66001 Employees: 130
Health Insurance
Mr Martin O'Rourke Managing Director
Mr Niall Devereux Finance Manager
Ms Margaret Cleary Human Resources Manager
Mr Sean Murray Sales & Marketing Manager
Mr John O'Dwyer Operations Manager
Mr Donal Clancy IT Director

Canada Life Assurance HQ
Canada Life House
Temple Road
Blackrock Co. Dublin
Phone: 01-2102000 Fax: 01-2102020
Email: info@canadalife.ie
Web: http://www.canadalife.ie
SIC: 66001 Employees: 1000
Life Assurance
Mr Don Gallagher Managing Director
Mr Enda Murphy Financial Controller
Mr Richard Adams Personnel Officer
Mr Keiran Feelan Sales & Marketing Manager
Mr Kevin Lynch Computer Manager

Cork Brokers
Trinity House 3/4 South Mall
Cork Co. Cork
Phone: 021-4278922 Fax: 021-4278923
Email: info@newireland.ie
Web: http://www.newireland.ie
SIC: 66001 Employees: 86
Insurance Companies
Mr Denis Calahan Regional Sales Manager

Eagle Star Insurance Company Ltd
Eagle Star House
Ballsbridge Park
Dublin 4
Phone: 01-6670666 Fax: 01-6670644
Email: info@eaglestar.ie
Web: http://www.eaglestar.ie
SIC: 66001 Employees: 560
Insurance Company
Mr Ian Stewart Managing Director
Mr Shane Buggle Group Financial Controller
Mr Dermot Peakin Personnel Manager
Mr Kieran Murphy Sales Manager
Mr Eddie Lenehan IS Manager

Generali International Ltd
Navan Business Park
Athlumney
Navan Co. Meath
Phone: 046-74650 Fax: 046-74642
Email: irelandPB@genarali-guernsey.com
Web: http://www.generali-guernsey.com
SIC: 66001 Employees: 25
Life Assurance
Mr Paul Gillett Managing Director
Ms Margaret Lloyd Finance Manager
Ms Susanne Moran Administration
Ms Eimear Friel Computer Manager

Hansard Europe Ltd
PO Box 43 Enterprise House
Frascati Road
Blackrock Co. Dublin
Phone: 01-2112800 Fax: 01-2112850
Email: heladmin@hansard.com
Web: http://www.hansard.com
SIC: 66001 Employees: 25
Life Assurance
Ms Rachel Panagiodis Chief Executive Officer
Mr Vince Watkins Financial Controller
Mr Garvan Clarke Client Services Manager

Hibernian
Haddington Lodge
Haddington Road
Dublin 4
Phone: 01-6670288 Fax: 01-6686971
Email: info@hibernian.ie
Web: http://www.hibernian.ie
SIC: 66001 Employees: 1900
Insurance
Mr Pat McGorrian Chief Executive Officer
Mr Tony O'Riordain Group Finance Director
Mr Brian Dalton Personnel Director
Mr Kevin Garland IT Manager

Irish Life Assurance Co Ltd
Irish Life Centre
Lower Abbey Street
Dublin 1
Phone: 01-7042000 Fax: 01-7041900
Web: http://www.irishlifepermanent.ie
SIC: 66001 Employees: 3000
Insurance Company
Mr David Went Group Chief Executive
Mr Peter Fitzpatrick Financial Controller
Mr Niall Saul Personnel Manager
Ms Dervala Tomlin Sales & Marketing Manager
Mr John Gorry Production Manager
Mr Brad Finley IT Manager

Irish Pensions Trust Ltd
23-25 South Terrace
Cork Co. Cork
Phone: 021-4910900 Fax: 021-4910910
Email: postmaster@ipwmercer.com
Web: http://www.ipwmercer.com
SIC: 66001 Employees: 60
Pensions
Mr Noel Elliott Manager
Ms Jacinta Glancey Personnel Manager

L & P Financial Trustees Ltd
2-3 Terminus Mills
Clonskeagh Road
Dublin 6
Phone: 01-283 8788 Fax: 01-2838988
Email: info@lpgroup.ie
Web: http://www.lpgroup.ie
SIC: 66001 Employees: 35
Life, Pensions & Investment Consultants
Mr Gerry Langford Managing Director
Mr Shane Cowley Finance Director
Ms Mary Duffy Director
Ms Tracey Comerford IT Manager

New Ireland Assurance
9/12 Dawson Street
Dublin 2
Phone: 01-6172000 Fax: 01-6172800
Email: info@newireland.ie
Web: http://www.newireland.ie
SIC: 66001 Employees: 620
Insurance Company
Mr Roy Keenan Manager
Mr John Murphy Finance Manager
Mr Dermot Murray Sales Director
Mr David Mitten Computer Manager

Premier-Direct Insurance & Banking
Premier House
The Square Tallaght
Dublin 24
Phone: 01-4620222 Fax: 01-4620170
SIC: 66001 Employees: 300
Insurance & Banking Company
Mr Cathal Muckian General Manager
Mr Edward Byrne Financial Controller
Mr Brendan O'Driscoll Operations Manager

Prudential Europe Management Services Ltd
Montague House, Adelaide Road
Dublin 2
Phone: 01-6760747 Fax: 01-4765100
Web: http://www.prudentialeurope.com
SIC: 66001 Employees: 290
Life Assurance
Ms Edwina Fitzmaurice Managing Director
Mr Kieran McGettrick Finance Manager
Mr Mark Lawlor IT Director

QBE Insurance & Reinsurance (Europe) Ltd
St Stephen's Green House, IFSC
Earlsfort Terrace
Dublin 2
Phone: 01-6053800 Fax: 01-6614700
Email: info@qbe.europe.com
Web: http://www.qbe.europe.com
SIC: 66001 Employees: 400
International Insurance & Reinsurance
Mr Des Fogarty General Manager
Mr Gary Galvin Finance Manager
Ms Eileen Barry Human Resources Manager
Mr Steve Higginson Operation Manager
Mr Patrick Magee Computer Manager

Royal & Sun Alliance
13-17 Dawson Street
Dublin 2
Phone: 01-6798555 Fax: 01-6717625
Email: info@royalsunalliance.ie
Web: http://www.royalsunalliance.ie
SIC: 66001 Employees: 650
Insurance Company
Mr John Crebbin Manager

Royal Liver Assurance
4th Floor, Royal Liver House
1 Grand Parade
Dublin 6
Phone: 01-4962455 Fax: 01-4962337
Email: info@royal-liver.com
Web: http://www.royal-liver.com
SIC: 66001 Employees: 650
Insurance Company
Mr Derek Brennan Manager
Mr Ian Longley Treasury Manager
Ms Linda Martin Employee Relations
Ms Eileen Gorman General Administrator
Mr Ron Thompson IT Manager

Royal Liver Assurance
24 Denny Street
Tralee Co. Kerry
Phone: 066-7121473 Fax: 066-7121805
Email: info@royal-liver.com
Web: http://www.royal-liver.com
SIC: 66001 Employees: 100
Insurance Companies
Mr Brian Stynes Manager

Scottish Legal Life Assurance
7 Harcourt Street
Dublin 2
Phone: 01-4754222 Fax: 01-4757309
Email: marketing@scotlegal.com
Web: http://www.scotlegal.com
SIC: 66001 Employees: 100
Insurance Company
Mr Gerry Pounch Customer Service Manager
Mr Gregg Duffy Finance Manager
Mr Robert Donohoe Sales Manager (South)

Insurance

Scottish Provident
53 Fitzwilliam Square
Dublin 2
Phone: 01-6769400 Fax: 01-6382901
Email: scotprov@iol.ie
Web: http://www.scotprov.ie
SIC: 66001 Employees: 300
Insurance Company
Mr Peter Towers Chief Executive
Mr John Finnegan Financial Controller
Ms Tara Whelan Personnel Manager
Mr Eanna McCloskey Sales & Marketing Manager
Mr Paul Lageu Operations Manager

St Paul Ireland Insurance
Block 1 Harcourt Centre
Harcourt Street
Dublin 2
Phone: 01-6095600 Fax: 01-6095640
Web: http://www.stpaul.com/ireland
SIC: 66001 Employees: 78
Insurance Company
Mr Peter Hayden Managing Director
Mr Bernard Butler Sales & Marketing Manager

Standard Life Assurance Company
90 St Stephens Green
Dublin 2
Phone: 01-6397000 Fax: 01-6397262
Email: it@standardlife.ie
SIC: 66001 Employees: 400
Insurance
Mr Rory O'Riordan Director
Ms Fidelma Healy Personnel Manager
Mr Richard Lavelle Sales Manager

United Healthcare Ireland Ltd
International Business Centre
National Technological Park
Limerick Co. Limerick
Phone: 061-330177 Fax: 061-330188
Email: info@uhc.com
Web: http://www.uhc.com
SIC: 66001 Employees: 74
Insurance Company
Ms Niamh Frawley Manager
Ms Susan Fitzsimons Accounts Manager
Ms Nancy Fleming Personnel Manager
Mr Noel McCarthy IT Officer

Voluntary Health Insurance Board
VHI House
20 Lower Abbey Street
Dublin 1
Phone: 01-8724499 Fax: 01-7994091
Email: info@vhihealthcare.ie
Web: http://www.vhihealthcare.ie
SIC: 66001 Employees: 1000
Health Insurance Company
Mr Vincent Sheridan Chief Executive
Mr John Looney Financial Director
Ms Maureen Caulfield Personnel Manager
Mr Tony McSweeney Sales Manager
Mr John Creedon DP Manager

AA Insurance
22-23 Suffolk Street
Dublin 2
Phone: 01-6179950 Fax: 01-6775387
Email: aais@aaireland.ie
Web: http://www.aaireland.ie
SIC: 66002 Employees: 350
Insurance Brokers
Mr Pat Kiely Managing Director
Mr Colm Fallon Finance Manager
Mr Gary Freemantle Personnel Manager
Ms Mary Louise Bridgeman Sales & Marketing Manager

Aon & McDonagh Boland
10-12 Lansdowne Road
Dublin 4
Phone: 01-6059400 Fax: 01-6601187
Email: info@aon.com
Web: http://http://www.aon.com
SIC: 66002 Employees: 500
Insurance Brokers & Consultants
Mr Richard Endersen Chief Executive
Mr David Eagan Accounts Manager
Mr Owen Pepper Office Manager
Mr Billy Redmond Marketing Director

Aon Beech Hill
94 St Stephen's Green
Dublin 2
Phone: 01-6773100 Fax: 01-4784636
Email: info@aon.ie
Web: http://www.aon.ie
SIC: 66002 Employees: 50
Pensions & Insurance Brokers
Mr Kevin Goss Managing Director
Mr Patrick Egan Finance Manager
Mr Gerry Herbert Operations Manager

AXA
39/45 Wolfe Tone Street
Dublin 1
Phone: 01-8726444 Fax: 01-8729703
Email: info@axa.ie
Web: http://www.axa.ie
SIC: 66002 Employees: 1500
Insurance Company
Mr John O'Neill Chief Executive
Ms Emer Daly Director Financial Operations
Mr Colm McGattan Director of Human Resources
Mr Aidan Cassells Executive Director
Mr Padraic Millan Director - IT & MIS

Combined Insurance Company of Ireland
Merrion House, Merrion Road
Dublin 4
Phone: 01-2696522 Fax: 01-2838585
Web: http://www.aon.com
SIC: 66002 Employees: 25
Insurance Company
Mr John Hughes General Manager
Mr Ronan Neill Adminstration Manager
Ms Jenny Stokes Personnel Manager

Corn Market Insurance Brokers
Liberties House
Christchurch Square
Dublin 8
Phone: 01-4084000 Fax: 01-4084011
Email: postmaster@cornmarket.ie
SIC: 66002 Employees: 200
Investment & Insurance Brokers
Mr Mervyn Percival Chairman
Mr Michael Carroll Financial Controller
Mr Roddy Murphy Sales Manager
Mr Kieran Doherty Computer Manager

Coyle Hamilton International Ltd
7-9 South Leinster Street
IFSC
Dublin 2
Phone: 01-6616211 Fax: 01-6614369
Email: info@coyleham.ie
Web: http://www.coyleham.ie
SIC: 66002 Employees: 300
Insurance/Reinsurance/Investments/Pensions
Mr Bill Cooney Managing Director
Mr William Shannon Group Finance Director
Mr Barry Kinn Personnel Director
Mr Desmond O'Haloran Marketing Director
Mr Brian McLoughlin IT Manager

Culleton Insurances
Selskar Court
Wexford Co. Wexford
Phone: 053-23188 Fax: 053-24976
Email: info@culletons.com
Web: http://www.culletons.ie
SIC: 66002 Employees: 60
Insurance Broker
Mr Ciaran Culleton Managing Director
Mr Michael Corcoran Finance Manager
Mr Gary Johnston Office Manager
Ms Ann Jordan Sales Manager

Dolmen Insurance Brokers
Unit 44 Butterly Business Park
Artane
Dublin 5
Phone: 01-8672127 Fax: 01-8672123
Email: generalenquiry@dolmen-insurance.ie
SIC: 66002 Employees: 23
Insurance Brokers
Mr David Dillane Manager

FDC Financial Services Ltd
FDC House
Wellington Road
Cork Co. Cork
Phone: 021-4509022 Fax: 021-4509272
SIC: 66002 Employees: 300
Insurance Broker
Mr Jack Murphy Managing Director

Fitzgerald Insurances
23-24 The Quay
Waterford Co. Waterford
Phone: 051-873478 Fax: 051-877702
SIC: 66002 Employees: 45
Insurance Brokers & Life & Pensions
Mr Liam Dalton Managing Director
Ms Ann Quinn Finance Manager
Ms Orla Fitzgerald Sales & Marketing Manager

Frank Glennon Insurance
Charlemount House
Charlemount Place
Dublin 2
Phone: 01-7075800 Fax: 01-7075900
SIC: 66002 Employees: 90
Insurance Broker
Mr David Glennon Managing Director
Mr Tom Cummins Financial Controller

General Medical Services (Payments) Board
Raven House
Finglas
Dublin 11
Phone: 01-8343644 Fax: 01-8343589
Email: pburkegmspb@eircom.net
Web: http://www.gmspd.ie
SIC: 66002 Employees: 135
Medical Claims Processing
Mr Tom Flood Chief Officer
Ms Mary Hoolahan Accounts Manager
Ms Rita O'Brien Personnel Officer
Mr Gerald Byrne Pharmaceutical Officer
Mr Patrick Burke Computer Manager

Hodgins Percival & Associates Ltd
Iveagh Court
Harcourt Road
Dublin 2
Phone: 01-4783344 Fax: 01-4781066
Email: info@hodginspercival.ie
Web: http://www.hodginspercival.ie
SIC: 66002 Employees: 25
Insurance Brokers
Mr Guy Percival Managing Director
Mr Gregory Crowley Finance Director

Jardine Insurance Brokers Ltd
Warrington House
Mount Street Crescent
Dublin 2
Phone: 01-6609703 Fax: 01-6609750
Email: jltireland@eircom.net
SIC: 66002 Employees: 90
Insurance Brokers
Mr Patrick Howett Managing Director
Mr Paul Doherty Financial Controller
Mr Tom Glennane IT Manager

JF Dunne Insurances
37 North Main Street
Naas Co. Kildare
Phone: 045-876655 Fax: 045-876151
Email: insure@jfd.ie
Web: http://www.jfd.ie
SIC: 66002 Employees: 25
Insurance Brokers
Mr John Dunne Managing Director
Mr Paddy Solon Personnel Manager

Marsh Ireland
10-11 Leinster Street South
Dublin 2
Phone: 01-6182700 Fax: 01-6194661
Web: http://www.mmc.com
SIC: 66002 Employees: 1000
Insurance Brokers
Mr David Caird Manager
Mr Michael Holland Financial Controller
Mr Kieran McHugh Sales & Marketing Manager
Ms Carys Jones Computer Manager

MGM Financial Services Ltd
The Blackchurch
St Mary's Place
Dublin 7
Phone: 01-8308555 Fax: 01-8308581
SIC: 66002 Employees: 25
Insurance Brokers
Mr Fred Penco Managing Director
Mr Austin Garvey Finance Manager
Mr Eamon Porter Branch Manager
Mr Bernard Bennet Sales Manager

Mike Murphy Insurance Services Ltd
Ardfinnan House
17 Trinity Street
Dublin 2
Phone: 01-6714288 Fax: 01-6714582
Email: mmig@iol.ie
SIC: 66002 Employees: 45
Insurance Brokers
Mr Michael Murphy Managing Director
Mr Paul Doherty Financial Controller

O'Callaghan Insurance Ltd
46 Dublin Street
Dundalk Co. Louth
Phone: 042-9359000 Fax: 042-9333076
Email: insurance@oci.ie
Web: http://www.oci.ie
SIC: 66002 Employees: 50
Insurance Brokers
Mr Leo O'Callaghan Director

O'Driscoll & O'Neill Ltd
17/18 Herbert Place
Dublin 2
Phone: 01-6395800 Fax: 01-6395850
Email: info@odon.com
Web: http://www.odon.com
SIC: 66002 Employees: 35
Insurance Brokers
Mr Niall O'Driscoll Managing Director
Ms Adele Farrell Head of Accounts

O'Leary Insurances Ltd
6-7 South Mall
Cork Co. Cork
Phone: 021-4252100 Fax: 021-4271050
Email: info@olearyinsurances.ie
Web: http://www.olearyinsurances.ie
SIC: 66002 Employees: 120
Insurance Brokers & Consultants
Mr Anthony O'Leary Managing Director
Ms Toni Kelly Personnel Officer
Mr Anthony O'Sullivan Computer Manager

Penco NGM Insurances Ltd
The Black Church
St. Mary's Place
Dublin 7
Phone: 01-8308222 Fax: 01-8308581
SIC: 66002 Employees: 60
Insurance Agents & Brokers
Mr Fred Penco Managing Director
Ms Nicola Leonard Finance Manager
Mr Austin Garvet Sales Manager

Tyrrell Coakley Ltd
9 Eastgate Avenue, Eastgate Business Park
Little Island
Cork Co. Cork
Phone: 021-4270505 Fax: 021-4275540
Email: ijnsure@tyrrellcoakley.iol.ie
SIC: 66002 Employees: 32
Insurance Broker
Mr Donal Cronin Director
Mr Michael Bruen Sales & Marketing Manager
Mr John Hackett Computer Manager

Willis Management (Dublin) Ltd
80 Harcourt Street
Dublin 2
Phone: 01-4070500 Fax: 01-4070501
Email: info@willis.com
Web: http://www.willis.com
SIC: 66002 Employees: 40
Captive Insurance Management
Mr Ken Mahony Managing Director
Ms Siobhan Stanley Personnel Director

Wright Group Ltd
Cornmarket Custom House Quay
Wexford Co. Wexford
Phone: 053-41153 Fax: 053-41345
Email: broker@wrightgroup.ie
Web: http://www.wrightway.ie
SIC: 66002 Employees: 64
Insurance Brokers
Mr Tony Wright Manager
Mr Pat Wright Personnel Manager
Ms Breda Wright Computer Manager

Aston & Associates
Waverley Business Park
Old Naas Road
Dublin 12
Phone: 01-6604122 Fax: 01-4097319
Email: infotec@aston.ie
SIC: 66003 Employees: 24
Assessors & Adjusters
Mr Michael Cullen Managing Director
Mr Michael Twaley Finance Manager
Mr Mitch Wallis Computer Manager

Cleary Callanan & Associates
Ballybawn
Galway Co. Galway
Phone: 091-709700 Fax: 091-773277
Email: info@clearycallanan.com
Web: http://www.clearycallanan.com
SIC: 66003 Employees: 100
Public Loss Assessors
Mr Sean Cleary Managing Director
Ms Lorraine Larkin Finance Manager

McLarens Ireland
7/8 Harcourt Street
Dublin 2
Phone: 01-4782000 Fax: 01-4782908
SIC: 66003 Employees: 150
Loss Adjusters
Mr Robin Hamilton Director

Miller Farrell
Nutley Building Merrion Centre
Nutley Lane
Dublin 4
Phone: 01-6615344 Fax: 01-6615249
Email: info@farrells.ie
Web: http://www.farrells.ie
SIC: 66003 Employees: 140
Loss Adjusting & Management Consultants
Mr Malcolm Hughes Chairman
Mr John Magee Finance Manager
Ms Melissa Alexandra Personnel Director
Mr Danny Donoghue Marketing Director

Thornton & Partners
Ballymount Road Lower
Dublin 12
Phone: 01-6770848 Fax: 01-4607780
Email: info@thornpart.ie
SIC: 66003 Employees: 45
Assessors & Adjusters
Mr Peter Murphy Managing Director
Ms Caroline Higgins Computer Manager

Financial Services

67 Financial Services
67120 Stock Brokers
67200 Insurance – Other

BCP Stockbrokers
71-72 Upper Leeson Street
Dublin 4
Phone: 01-6684688 Fax: 01-6684246
Email: bcp@bcp.ie
Web: http://www.bcp.ie
SIC: 67120 Employees: 34
Stockbrokers
Mr Martin Kane Managing Director
Mr James Buckley Chairman
Ms Ursula Foley Company Secretary
Mr Trevor Cullen Director
Mr Trevor Gray DP Consultant

Bloxham Stockbrockers
IFSC
2-3 Exchange Place
Dublin 1
Phone: 01-8291888 Fax: 01-8291877
Email: bloxham@indigo.ie
SIC: 67120 Employees: 74
Stockbrokers
Mr Angus McDonnell Chief Executive
Mr Peter O'Carroll Financial Controller
Mr Martin Harte Human Resources Manager
Mr Tony Dorsaneo IT Manager

Davy International Ltd
49 Dawson Street, IFSC
Dublin 2
Phone: 01-6797788 Fax: 01-6712704
Email: davy@indigo.ie
Web: http://www.davy.ie
SIC: 67120 Employees: 350
International Stockbroker
Mr David Shubotham Chief Executive
Mr Peter Newman Chief Accountant
Mr Andrew Flynn Operation Manager
Mr Brendan Johnston Computer Manager

Dolmen Butler Briscoe
Dolmen Housw
4 Earlsfort Terrace
Dublin 2
Phone: 01-6777348 Fax: 01-6623737
Email: dolmen@iol.ie
Web: http://www.dbbi.com
SIC: 67120 Employees: 101
Stockbrokers
Mr Paul McGowan Joint Managing Director
Mr Andrew Byrne Financial Controller
Ms Paula Lonergan Senior Administrator
Mr Ronan Reid Joint Managing Director
Mr Paul Yates Head of IT

Goodbody Stockbrokers
Block B Ballsbridge Park
Dublin 4
Phone: 01-6670400 Fax: 01-6670422
Email: goodbody@goodbody.ie
Web: http://www.indigo.ie/goodbody/index.html
SIC: 67120 Employees: 372
Stockbrokers
Mr Roy Barrett Managing Director
Mr Vennon Rushe Finance Director
Ms Sarah Downing Personnel Manager
Mr Brian Delaney Head Of Private Clients
Mr Eamonn Glancy Chief Operating Officer
Mr Adrian Neville Head Of IT & Business Change

Irish Stock Exchange
28 Anglesea Street
Dublin 2
Phone: 01-6778808 Fax: 01-6719029
Email: info@ise.ie
Web: http://www.ise.ie
SIC: 67120 Employees: 30
Stock Exchange
Mr Tom Healey Chief Executive
Ms Geraldine Jones Finance Manager
Mr James Ferguson Operations Manager

Merrion Capital
3rd Floor Block C
Sweepstake Centre
Dublin 4
Phone: 01-2404100 Fax: 01-2404101
Email: info@merrion-capital.com
Web: http://www.merrion-capital.com
SIC: 67120 Employees: 50
Stockbroking
Mr John Conroy Chief Executive Officer
Mr Michael Hudson Finance Manager
Mr Shane Nolan Sales Manager
Mr Mark Lawlor Manager

Chubb Insurance Company of Europe SA
50 Dawson Street
IFSC
Dublin 2
Phone: 01-6707070 Fax: 01-6707271
Email: info@chubb.com
Web: http://www.chubb.com
SIC: 67200 Employees: 24
Commercial Provision of Risk Management Services
Mr Alan Sheil Managing Director
Mr Jackie Connolly Financial Controller
Ms Lillian Redmond Operations Manager

Cigna Healthcare
Dublin Road
Loughrea
Galway Co. Galway
Phone: 091-842222 Fax: 091-842429
Email: info@cigna.com
Web: http://www.cigna.com
SIC: 67200 Employees: 130
Healthcare Insurance
Mr Mike Stankard Managing Director
Mr John Lyons Production Manager

Risk Management International Ltd
Unit 2055 City West Business Campus
Naas Road
Dublin 24
Phone: 01-4038708 Fax: 01-4660426
Email: info@rmi.ie
Web: http://www.rmi.ie
SIC: 67200 Employees: 100
Company Security & Insurance
Mr Peadar Duffy Managing Director

Real Estate Activities

70	Real Estate Activities
70120	Owning/Dealing Real Estate
70201	Conference Centres/Organisers
70310	Estate Agents
70320	Auctioneers

Park Developments (Dublin Ltd)
Kirwan House
195 North Circular Road
Dublin 7
Phone: 01-8389989 Fax: 01-8379992
SIC: 70120 Employees: 135
Property Development
Ms Mary Collins Manager

Treasury Holdings
The Warehouse 35 Barrow Street
Grand Canal Quay
Dublin 4
Phone: 01-6188388 Fax: 01-6188389
Email: info@treasuryholdings.ie
Web: http://www.treasuryholdings.ie
SIC: 70120 Employees: 25
Property Development
Mr Maurice Harte Managing Director

Dublin Castle Conference Centre
Dublin Castle
Dublin 2
Phone: 01-6793713 Fax: 01-6797831
Email: dublincastle@eircom.net
Web: http://www.historic-centre.com
SIC: 70201 Employees: 100
Conference Centre
Mr Tommy O'Shaughnessy General Manager
Mr Dennis McCarthy Marketing Manager

Royal Dublin Society (RDS)
Merrion Road
Ballsbridge
Dublin 4
Phone: 01-6680866 Fax: 01-6604014
Web: http://www.rds.ie
SIC: 70201 Employees: 55
Exhibition Centre
Mr Shane Cleary Chief Executive
Mr Patrick Hanley Financial Controller
Ms Niamh Kelly Marketing Manager
Mr Brian Reed Chief Operations Manager
Mr Brian Reid IT Manager

Ballymore Properties
Hugenot House
35-38 St Stephens Green
Dublin 2
Phone: 01-6622300 Fax: 01-6622302
Email: info@ballymoreproperties.ie
Web: http://www.ballymoreproperties.ie
SIC: 70310 Employees: 32
Property Management
Mr Sean Mulryan Managing Director

Colliers Jackson Stops
51 Dawson Street
Dublin 2
Phone: 01-6333700 Fax: 01-6715156
Email: property@jacksonstops.ie
Web: http://www.jacksonstops.ie
SIC: 70310 Employees: 50
Estate Agent/Chartered Surveyors/Property Consultants
Mr Declan Stone Managing Director
Mr Marcus Magnier Sales Director
Mr Michael Donoghue IT Manager

Dunloe Ewart
9 Fitzwilliam Square
Dublin 2
Phone: 01-6764933 Fax: 01-6614322
SIC: 70310 Employees: 35
Property Investment
Mr Philip Byrne Managing Director
Mr Tim Kenny Financial Director
Ms Nicola Dult Computer Manager

Green Properties Plc
Styne House
Hatch Street Upper
Dublin 2
Phone: 01-2418400 Fax: 01-2418484
Email: office@greenpropertyplc.com
Web: http://www.greenpropertyplc.com
SIC: 70310 Employees: 100
Development
Mr Stephen Vernon Managing Director
Mr Danny Kitchen Finance Director

Gunne Property Consultants
164-166 Shelbourne Road
Ballsbridge
Dublin 4
Phone: 01-6682588 Fax: 01-6687890
Email: gen@gunne.ie
Web: http://www.gunneproperty.com
SIC: 70310 Employees: 200
Auctioneer/Valuer/Estate Agent
Mr Pat Gunne Managing Director - Commercial
Mr Eddie McNestry Financial Controller
Mr Eunan O'Carroll Residential MD
Mr Trevor Daly Company Secretary

Hamilton Osborne King
4 Main Street
Blackrock Co. Dublin
Phone: 01-2885011 Fax: 01-2880838
Email: info@hok.ie
Web: http://www.hok.ie
SIC: 70310 Employees: 150
Auctioneers/Valuers/Estate Agents
Mr Ronan O'Hara Manager
Mr Graham Slater Finance Manager
Ms Caroline Browne Human Resources Manager

HOK Residential
20 Dawson Street
Dublin 2
Phone: 01-6634300 Fax: 01-6634399
Email: info@hok.ie
Web: http://www.hok.ie
SIC: 70310 Employees: 120
Estate Agents/Auctioneers & Valuers
Mr Wade Wise Managing Director
Mr Nick Lagan Finance Manager
Ms Bernadette O'Higgins Marketing Manager

Irish Estates Management
Beresford Court
16 Beresford Place
Dublin 1
Phone: 01-7041400 Fax: 01-7041915
Email: solutions@irishestates.ie
Web: http://www.irishestates
SIC: 70310 Employees: 50
Estate & Property Managers
Mr Larry Kane Managing Director
Mr Peter Birthistle Company Secretary
Mr Darragh Harte Head of Property

Jones Lang LaSalle
10-11 Molesworth Street
Dublin 2
Phone: 01-6794622 Fax: 01-6795147
Email: info@joneslanglasalle.com
Web: http://www.joneslanglasalle.com
SIC: 70310 Employees: 55
Commercial Property Sales
Mr Pat McCaffrey Managing Director
Mr Fergal Walsh Finance Manager
Ms Margaret Mulholland Sales & Marketing Manager
Mr Phil Griffin Computer Manager

McCauley Properties
Malim Road
Moville
Lifford Co. Donegal
Phone: 077-82110 Fax: 077-82664
Web: http://www.mccauleypropertys.com
SIC: 70310 Employees: 27
Estate Agents
Mr Leo McCauley Proprietor

Palmer McCormack & Partners
65 St Stephen's Green
Dublin 2
Phone: 01-4784744 Fax: 01-4784553
Email: info@pmcc.ie
Web: http://www.pmcc.ie
SIC: 70310 Employees: 30
Estate Agents & Quantity Surveyors
Mr Patrick McCormack Managing Director
Mr Brendan Ward Financial Controller

Serco Services Ireland
Unit 30 Airways Industrial Estate
Clonshaugh
Dublin 17
Phone: 01-8621541 Fax: 01-8428166
Email: info@serco.ie
Web: http://www.serco.com
SIC: 70310 Employees: 270
Property Management
Mr Ray Foran Managing Director
Mr John King Company Secretary
Mr Mark Harper Business Development Director
Mr John McQuillian IT Manager

Douglas Newman Good
4/5 Trinity Street
Dublin 2
Phone: 01-6794088 Fax: 01-6799249
Email: info@dng.ie
Web: http://www.dng.ie
SIC: 70320 Employees: 250
Auctioneers
Mr Paul Newman Managing Director
Mr David Horgan Finance Manager
Mr Edmond Douglas Sales & Marketing Manager

Mason Estates
115a Rock Road
Booterstown
Bray Co. Wicklow
Phone: 01-2832355 Fax: 01-2831137
Email: info@masonestates.ie
Web: http://www.masonestates.ie
SIC: 70320 Employees: 40
Auctioneers
Mr Sean Mason Managing Director

Potterton Auctioneers
The Property Exchange
Emmet Street,Trim
Navan Co. Meath
Phone: 046-31391 Fax: 046-36538
SIC: 70320 Employees: 25
Auctioneers
Mr Thomas Potterton Manager
Mr Gerry Carney Finance Manager

Sherry Fitzgerald
Ormonde House, 12-13 Leeson Street
Dublin 2
Phone: 01-6399300 Fax: 01-6399389
Email: info@sherryfitz.ie
Web: http://www.sherryfitz.ie
SIC: 70320 Employees: 300
Auctioneers & Estate Agents
Mr Mark Fitzgerald Chief Executive
Mr James Barrett Financial Controller
Ms Jocelyn White Personnel Director

Spain Courtney Doyle
SCD House Waterloo Road
Dublin 4
Phone: 01-6140500 Fax: 01-6140555
Email: mail@spaincourtneydoyle.com
Web: http://www.spaincourtneydoyle.com
SIC: 70320 Employees: 25
Commercial Property Consultants
Mr David Courtney Partner
Mr Norman Green Accountant
Ms Deirdre Carpenter Personnel Manager

Wyse & Company
94 Lower Baggot Street
Dublin 2
Phone: 01-6616061 Fax: 01-6615616
Email: sales@wyse.ie
Web: http://www.wyse.ie
SIC: 70320 Employees: 34
Auctioneers
Mr Ben Gough Managing Director
Mr John Dennis Finance Manager
Mr John McKone Personnel Manager
Mr Peter Wyse Sales & Marketing Director
Mr George Murphy Computer Manager

Young Auctioneers
35 Ranelagh Village
Dublin 6
Phone: 01-4972600 Fax: 01-4975636
Email: info@youngsauctioneers.com
Web: http://www.youngsauctioneers.com
SIC: 70320 Employees: 24
Auctioneers
Mr Odran Young Managing Director
Mr Michael Kelly Personnel Manager

Hiring of Equipment

71 Hiring of Equipment
71000 Hiring & Leasing
71110 Car Hire
71210 Commercial Vehicle Hire
71230 Aircraft Leasing
71310 Hiring Agricultural Equipment
71320 Hiring Construction Equipment
71340 Hiring Machinery & Equipment (Other)
71401 Hire of Sporting & Recreational Equip
71403 TV/Video Rental
71405 Video Shops
71406 Catering Equipment Hire
71407 Dress Hire /Wedding Hire
71408 Hiring Consumer Goods

A-Plant
Ballysimon Road
Limerick Co. Limerick
Phone: 061-311388 Fax: 061-315840
SIC: 71000 Employees: 26
Plant Hire
Mr John Kennedy Managing Director
Mr John Owen Sales Manager

Celtic Linen Ltd
St Magdalens
Wexford Co. Wexford
Phone: 053-42244 Fax: 053-60806
Email: info@celticlinen.com
Web: http://www.celticlinen.com
SIC: 71000 Employees: 400
Hire of Linen goods
Mr Philip Scallan Managing Director
Mr Tommy Butler Group Finance Director
Mr John Ford Group Personnel Manager
Mr Martin Murphy General Manager
Mr Peter Scallan Director

Celtic Linen Services Ltd
Greenhills Road
Tallaght
Dublin 24
Phone: 01-4526122 Fax: 01-4599165
Email: info@celticlinen.com
Web: http://www.celticlinen.com
SIC: 71000 Employees: 24
Linen hire
Mr Paul Lyle General Manager
Mr Colm Cullen Sales Manager

Connacht Court Group Ltd
Henry Street
Galway Co. Galway
Phone: 091-582124 Fax: 091-581956
Email: ccggalway@eircom.net
SIC: 71000 Employees: 500
Laundry Rental Services
Mr Tom Joyce Managing Director
Ms Niamh Temple Finance Manager
Ms Anne-Marie Crain Personnel Manager
Ms Patricia Mullitan Sales & Marketing Director
Ms Susan O'Flynn Production Manager

Executive Towel Rental
Unit 8 Westlink Industrial Estate
Kylemore Road
Dublin 10
Phone: 01-6231100 Fax: 01-6235078
SIC: 71000 Employees: 30
Rental Of Towels
Mr Tommy Masterson Managing Director
Mr Patrick Brennan Finance Manager
Mr Eammon O'Carroll Sales & Marketing Manage
Mr Tony O'Brien Production Manager

H McLoughlin & Sons Ltd
Ballymagan
Donegal Co. Donegal
Phone: 077-63777 Fax: 077-63555
SIC: 71000 Employees: 25
Plant Hire
Mr Hubert Mc Loughlin Proprietor

J McG Plant Hire Ltd
Kildun
Ballycroy
Westport Co. Mayo
Phone: 098-49329 Fax: 098-36188
SIC: 71000 Employees: 30
Plant Hire
Mr James Corrigan Manager

Modular Automation Moleux Ltd
Smithstown Industrial Estate
Shannon Co. Clare
Phone: 061-363077 Fax: 061-361125
Email: info@modularauto.ie
Web: http://www.modularauto.ie
SIC: 71000 Employees: 60
Build Special Purpose Machinery
Mr Ron O' Brien Managing Director
Mr Mike Lane Operation Manager

Hiring Services

Roadmaster Caravans
Johnstown
Kilkenny Co. Kilkenny
Phone: 056-31201 Fax: 056-31550
SIC: 71000 Employees: 50
Caravans Mobile Homes & Office Accommodation
Mr Myles McCabe Managing Director
Mr Thomas Ryan Accountant
Ms Lorraine Nicholson Personal Assistant

Argus Rent A Car
Argus House
59 Terenure Road East
Dublin 6
Phone: 01-4904444 Fax: 01-4906328
Email: info@argus-rentacar.com
Web: http://www.argus-rentacar.com
SIC: 71110 Employees: 27
Car & Van Rentals
Ms Fiona Renton General Manager
Mr Niall Turley Finance Manager
Mr Greg Turley Personnel Manager

Avis Rent A Car
1 Hanover Street East
Dublin 2
Phone: 01-6057500 Fax: 01-6057520
Email: hanover@jandp.iol.ie
SIC: 71110 Employees: 23
Rent A Car Agency
Ms Deirdre O'Neill Director

Bandon Motors Ltd
Clonakilty Road
Bandon Co. Cork
Phone: 023-44422 Fax: 023-44350
SIC: 71110 Employees: 50
Car Rental & Sales
Mr Bob Clarke Managing Director
Mr Kevin Barry Sales Director

Cavanaghs of Charleville Ltd
Limerick Road
Charleville
Cork Co. Cork
Phone: 063-81561 Fax: 063-81833
Email: sales@cavanaghs.fdi.ie
Web: http://www.cavanaghs.com
SIC: 71110 Employees: 50
Car Hire & Ford Dealers
Mr Martin Condon Managing Director
Ms Carol Ryan Finance Manager
Mr Andrew Murphy General Manager/Director
Mr Liam Herlihy Sales Director
Mr Martin Ahearn Computer & Stationary Manager

Dan Dooley
Knocklong
Kilmallock Co. Limerick
Phone: 062-53103 Fax: 062-53392
Email: info@dan-dooley.ie
Web: http://www.dan-dooley.ie
SIC: 71110 Employees: 65
Car Hire
Mr Dan Dooley Managing Director
Mr Joseph McCarthy Financial Controller
Ms Mary Dooley Personnel Director
Mr James Dooley Company Secretary

Dooleys Motors
Court Place
Carlow Co. Carlow
Phone: 0503-31665 Fax: 0503-42118
Email: sales@dooleymotors.fdl.ie
SIC: 71110 Employees: 25
Motor Hire & Sales
Mr Anthony Dooley Proprietor
Mr Laurance Dillon Finance Manager
Mr Michael Denieffe Sales Manager
Ms Rowena Dooley Computer Manager

Foster Motor Co Ltd
Fosters Avenue
Mountmerrion
Blackrock Co. Dublin
Phone: 01-2884333 Fax: 01-2885365
Email: info@fostermotorco.ie
Web: http://www.fostermotorco.ie
SIC: 71110 Employees: 60
Car Leasing
Mr Ian MacNeill Director
Ms Patricia Farron Financial Controller
Mr Peter Quinn Sales & Marketing Manager

Hertz Europe Service Centre Ltd
IDA Business Park
Swords Co. Dublin
Phone: 01-8133550 Fax: 01-8406465
Web: http://www.hertz.ie
SIC: 71110 Employees: 1200
Car Hire
Mr Andrew Varley Director
Mr Brian Dixon Finance Manager
Ms Sarah Begley Personnel Manager
Mr Paul Birmingham IT Manager

Hertz Rent A Car
PO Box 23
Ferrybank
Wexford Co. Wexford
Phone: 053-23511 Fax: 053-22405
Email: talktohertz@tinet.ie
Web: http://www.hertz.com
SIC: 71110 Employees: 46
Car Hire
Mr Eamon Boland Managing Director
Mr Gerard Mullery Project Manager
Mr Sean Boland Sales & Marketing Director
Mr Robert Kenny IT Manager

Murray Group
Baggot Street, Bridge
Dublin 4
Phone: 01-6681777 Fax: 01-6142899
Email: murrays@europecar.iol.ie
Web: http://www.europecar.iol.ie
SIC: 71110 Employees: 146
Car/Van Rental
Mr Harold Murray Chief Executive
Mr Dan Kenny Financial Controller
Mr Billy Redden Personnel Manager
Mr Gareth O'Reilly Marketing Director
Mr Ronan Kehoe Operations Manager

National Car Rental
Centre Reservations
Centre Point, Centre Park Road
Cork Co. Cork
Phone: 021-4320755 Fax: 021-4320754
Web: http://www.nationalcar/europe.com
SIC: 71110 Employees: 90
Car Rental
Mr Jerry O'Riordan Managing Director
Mr Dave O'Regan Finance Manager
Mr Brian O'Riordan Computer Manager

Sheridan Waterford
Cork Road
Waterford Co. Waterford
Phone: 051-372891 Fax: 051-334810
SIC: 71110 Employees: 30
Ford Garage / Car Hire
Mr Tom Sheridan Managing Director
Mr Gerard Sheridan Sales Director

Sixth Car Rental
Dublin Airport
Swords Co. Dublin
Phone: 01-8444199 Fax: 01-8444199
Email: info@icrgroup.ie
Web: http://www.irishcarrentals.ie
SIC: 71110 Employees: 25
Car Rental
Mr Ray Murphy Manager
Mr Alan Doran Deputy Manager

Sligo Airport- Car Rentals
Sligo Airport
Strand Hill
Sligo Co. Sligo
Phone: 071-68386 Fax: 071-68396
Web: http://www.sligoairport.ie
SIC: 71110 Employees: 70
Car Hire
Mr Joe Corcoran Manager

Arevale PHH Vehicle Management
3rd Floor College Park House
20 Nassau Street
Dublin 2
Phone: 01-6040300 Fax: 01-6040791
SIC: 71210 Employees: 40
Allied vehicle management
Mr David Bennett Manager

Colm Burns Commercials
Dublin Road
Ballisodare
Sligo Co. Sligo
Phone: 071-60832 Fax: 071-61889
SIC: 71210 Employees: 35
Commerical Vehicle Hire
Mr John Burns Managing Director
Mr Turlough Burns Finance Manager
Mr Padraigh Hynes Sales Director

JJ Kavanagh & Sons
Main Street
Urlingford
Kilkenny Co. Kilkenny
Phone: 056-31106 Fax: 056-31172
Email: info@jjkavanagh.ie
Web: http://www.jjkavanagh.ie
SIC: 71210 Employees: 90
Coach Hire, Coach Tours and Local Services
Mr JJ Kavanagh Managing Director
Mr Tommy Wilson Finance Manager
Mr Paul Kavanagh Sales Manager
Ms Margaret Mullally IT Manager

National Truck Rental
30/40 Jones Road
Dublin 3
Phone: 01-8554233 Fax: 01-8554123
SIC: 71210 Employees: 50
Truck Rental
Mr Jim Byrne Managing Director
Mr Tony Morgan Personnel Manager
Mr John Murphy Sales Manager

Devis Air Finance
Airfinance House
Shannon Co. Clare
Phone: 061-360000 Fax: 061-360113
Email: info@devisairfinance.com
Web: http://www.devisairfinance.com
SIC: 71230 Employees: 40
Aircraft Leasing & Financing
Mr Patrick Blaney Chief Executive

Joe Reilly Plant Hire Ltd
Derryfadda
Bofeenaun
Ballina Co. Mayo
Phone: 096-51008 Fax: 096-51068
Email: joereilly@eircom.net
SIC: 71310 Employees: 35
Hiring Agriculture Equipment
Mr Joe Reilly Proprietor

Ashtead Plant Hire Co Ltd
Turnpike Industrial Estate
Ballymount
Dublin 22
Phone: 01-4568500 Fax: 01-4502196
Email: info@aplant.com
Web: http://www.aplant.com
SIC: 71320 Employees: 25
Small Plant Hire
Mr John Hansbury General Manager
Mr Hamish Oliphant Sales Manager

Breffini Plant Hire
42 Shanowen Road
Santry
Dublin 9
Phone: 01-8421955 Fax: 01-8421432
Email: sales@breffiniplant.iol.ie
SIC: 71320 Employees: 50
Plant Hire & Contractors
Mr Sean Flynn Proprietor
Mr Edward McAteer Finance Manager

Carey Tools
City Hall Quay
Cork Co. Cork
Phone: 021-4312222 Fax: 021-4317303
Email: info@careytools.com
Web: http://www.careytools.com
SIC: 71320 Employees: 60
Hiring Construction Equipment
Mr Kenneth Carey Managing Director
Mr William Clarke Financial Controller
Mr Brian Cummins Sales Manager

Connacht Scaffolding Ltd
Knock Road
Ballyhaunis Co. Mayo
Phone: 0907-30198 Fax: 0907-30336
SIC: 71320 Employees: 40
Hiring Construction Equipment
Mr Michael Murray Manager

Crane Hire Ltd (Accounts)
Scarsdale, Dalkey Avenue
Dalkey
Dun Laoghaire Co. Dublin
Phone: 01-2852022 Fax: 01-2852664
Email: info@cranehire.ie
Web: http://www.cranehire.ie
SIC: 71320 Employees: 30
Cranes - Hire
Ms Margaret Leary Managing Director
Mr Gerry Lally Sales Manager

Denis Moriarty Plant Hire
The Kerries View
Tralee Co. Kerry
Phone: 066-7121468 Fax: 066-7124759
Email: dmph@eircom.net
SIC: 71320 Employees: 40
Plant Hire
Mr Denis Moriarty Managing Director
Mr John Moriarty Personnel Officer

ECI (JCB)
J F Kennedy Drive
Naas Road
Dublin 12
Phone: 01-4502777 Fax: 01-4502041
Email: partsdub@ecijcb.ie
SIC: 71320 Employees: 45
Plant Hire
Mr Donal O'Sullivan Proprietor
Mr Tony Nicholson Finance Manager

Farrelly Plant Hire Ltd
Gravelmount
Castletown
Navan Co. Meath
Phone: 046-54160 Fax: 046-54539
SIC: 71320 Employees: 30
Plant Hire & Haulage Company
Mr Paddy Farrelly Managing Director

GK. Hire
12/20 East Road
East Wall
Dublin 3
Phone: 01-8742709 Fax: 01-8553218
Email: gkhire@eircom.net
Web: http://www.welcome.to/gkhire
SIC: 71320 Employees: 27
Equipment & Tool Hire
Mr Gerry Tuohy Managing Director
Ms Jennifer Keogh Financial Controller

GPT Plant & Tool Hire
Tuam Road
Galway Co. Galway
Phone: 091-755793 Fax: 091-752499
SIC: 71320 Employees: 100
Plant Hire & Contractors
Mr James Hughes Managing Director
Mr Brendan Maloney Financial Controller
Mr Pat Lane IT Manager

Havens Celbridge Hire Ltd
Main Street
Celbridge
Naas Co. Kildare
Phone: 01-6288171 Fax: 01-6288602
Email: haveneng@indigo.ie
SIC: 71320 Employees: 40
Hiring Construction Equipment & Sales
Mr Eamon Killgallon Managing Director
Mr William Molloy Sales Manager

Hinch Plant Hire Ltd
Mountmellick
Portlaoise Co. Laois
Phone: 0502-24201 Fax: 0502-24380
Email: hinch@gofree.indigo.ie
Web: http://www.hinchplant.com
SIC: 71320 Employees: 55
Plant Hire & Contracting
Mr Fintan Hinch Managing Director
Ms Teresa Hamill Finance Manager
Mr Tom Donoher Personnel Director
Mr Trevor Hinch Production Manager

J & D Daly Ltd
Unit 1 Mayfield Business Park
Old Youghal Road
Cork Co. Cork
Phone: 021-4551900 Fax: 021-4551911
Email: jnddaly@indigo.ie
SIC: 71320 Employees: 38
Plant Hire
Mr Richard Daly Managing Director
Ms Carol Daly Personnel Manager

JW Hire & Sales Ltd
Coolock Drive
Oscar Traynor Road
Dublin 17
Phone: 01-8342785 Fax: 01-8670187
Email: jwhire@indigo.ie
SIC: 71320 Employees: 35
Hiring Power Tools
Mr Joe White Managing Director
Mr John Calgey Sales Director

McHale Plant Sales Ltd
Birdhill
Tipperary Co. Tipperary
Phone: 061-379112 Fax: 061-379450
Email: info@mchaleplant.com
SIC: 71320 Employees: 30
Hiring and Sales Construction Equipment
Mr Michael McHale Managing Director
Mr Kevin Haltin Finance Manager
Mr John O'Brien Sales Manager
Mr Gerard Costelle Computer Manager

Monaghan Plant Hire
Old Cross Square
Monaghan Co. Monaghan
Phone: 047-82623 Fax: 047-83198
SIC: 71320 Employees: 40
Hiring Construction Equipment
Mr Padraig Watters Managing Director
Mr Eugene McMahon Sales Manager

Purcell Scaffolding Cork Ltd
Ballycurreen
Kinsale Co. Cork
Phone: 021-4961614 Fax: 021-4313526
Email: scaffolding@purcell.iol.ie
SIC: 71320 Employees: 24
Hiring Construction Equipment
Mr Peter Purcell Managing Director

Hiring Services

Rowland Civil Engineering & Plant Hire
Unit 3 Block B
Dunshaughlin Industrial Centre
Navan Co. Meath
Phone: 01-8258133 Fax: 01-8258144
SIC: 71320 Employees: 35
Plant Hire & Contractors
Ms Noreen Rowland Managing Director

Sutton Plant Hire Wexford Ltd
Broomhill
Fethard On Sea
New Ross Co. Wexford
Phone: 051-397143 Fax: 051-397241
Email: suttonplant@eircom.net
SIC: 71320 Employees: 27
Plant Hire
Mr James Sutton Proprietor

Swan Plant Hire (Dublin) Ltd
Ballymount Road
Walkinstown
Dublin 12
Phone: 01-4507219 Fax: 01-4600296
Email: sales@swanplant.ie
SIC: 71320 Employees: 60
Hiring Construction Equipment
Mr Brian Connolly Managing Director
Mr Jack O'Donoghue Personnel Manager

Thomas Brennan & Son
Ticknock
Sandyford
Dublin 18
Phone: 01-2956827 Fax: 01-2953838
SIC: 71320 Employees: 30
Plant Hire & Contractors
Mr Peter Brennan Proprietor
Mr Thomas Brennan Proprietor

Tony Kirwan Plant Hire Ltd
Ballybrack
Kilmacthomas
Waterford Co. Waterford
Phone: 051-294238 Fax: 051-294310
SIC: 71320 Employees: 40
Hiring Construction Equipment
Mr Tony Kirwan Proprietor

Waterford Hire Services Ltd
Unit 4 King's Meadow Retail Park
Ring Road
Waterford Co. Waterford
Phone: 051-833333 Fax: 051-833334
Email: info@waterfordhire.com
Web: http://www.waterfordhire.com
SIC: 71320 Employees: 40
Construction & Industrial DIY Equipment Hire
Mr Eamonn McKenna Managing Director

Willie Cosgrave Construction Ltd
Milebush
Castlebar Co. Mayo
Phone: 094-23028 Fax: 094-23028
SIC: 71320 Employees: 90
Hiring Construction Equipment
Mr Willie Cosgrave Proprietor
Mr Pat McDonagh Personnel Manager

Cloughvalley Agricultural Centre
Castleblayney Road
Carrickmacross Co. Monaghan
Phone: 042-9662532 Fax: 042 9664522
SIC: 71340 Employees: 50
Industrial Plant Hire & Agricultural products
Mr Michael Quinn Proprietor
Ms Bridget Quinn Office Manager

D Dennehy Ltd
Carrigtwohill
Cork Co. Cork
Phone: 021-4883300 Fax: 021-4883656
SIC: 71340 Employees: 43
Hiring Movables (Other)
Mr Finbar Dennehy Managing Director
Mr Sean Harte Finance Manager
Mr Jim Murray Production Manager

Hynes Plant & Tool Hire Ltd
Athenry Road
Tuam Co. Galway
Phone: 093-28418 Fax: 093-28546
SIC: 71340 Employees: 25
Plant Hire
Mr Bernard Hynes Manager
Ms Annette Hynes Accounts Manager

Martin Food Equipment Ltd
Gaskin Business Park
Coes Road
Dundalk Co. Louth
Phone: 042-9330366 Fax: 042-9330370
Email: info@martinfoodequip.com
Web: http://www.martinfoodequip.com
SIC: 71340 Employees: 56
Providers of Innovative Food Equipment Based Solutions
Mr Joe Bailey Managing Director
Mr Sean Murphy Operations Director
Mr Martin McGeough Sales Director
Mr Colin Maguire Financial Controller

P & O'Lynch (Plant Hire)
Roodstown
Ardee Co. Louth
Phone: 041-6856399 Fax: 041-6857626
SIC: 71340 Employees: 30
Plant Hire and Contractors
Mr Paul Lynch Director
Mr Oliver Lynch Director

Sam Hire Ltd
Red Cow Naas Road
Clondalkin
Dublin 22
Phone: 01-4594166 Fax: 01-4594155
Email: info@samhire.ie
Web: http://www.samhire.ie
SIC: 71340 Employees: 100
Plant Hire
Mr Eugene Heather Managing Director
Ms Margaret Tyndell Personnel Manager
Ms Pauline Heuston Sales Manager

Emerald Star Line
The Marina
Carrick On Shannon Co. Leitrim
Phone: 078-20234 Fax: 078-21433
Email: info@emerald-star.com
Web: http://www.emeraldstar.ie
SIC: 71401 Employees: 45
Boats-Charter & Hire
Mr Tim James Proprietor
Mr John Beirne Base Manager
Ms Lisa Stanford Reservations Manager

Movie Magic Ltd
Unit 1 Swords Business Park
Swords Co. Dublin
Phone: 01-8403746 Fax: 01-8900591
Email: info@moviemagic.ie
Web: http://www.moviemagic.ie
SIC: 71405 Employees: 60
Video and DVD Sales and Rental
Mr Leon Ellison Manager
Mr Ciaran Brennan Finance Manager
Ms Leon Ellison Office Manager

Xtra-Vision
Greenhills Road
Tallaght
Dublin 24
Phone: 01-4527722 Fax: 01-4511344
Email: info@xtravision.ie
Web: http://www.xtravision.ie
SIC: 71405 Employees: 1600
Video Shop
Mr Martin Higgins Chief Executive
Mr Tony Keatings Finance Manager
Mr Gerry McAuliffe Personnel Manager
Mr Dean O'Nolan Marketing Manager
Mr Seamus Quinn Computer Systems Manager

Hire All Party Hire
37-38 Spruce Avenue
Stillorgan Industrial Park
Blackrock Co. Dublin
Phone: 01-2953821 Fax: 01-2953011
Email: hireall@partyhire.ie
Web: http://www.partyhire.ie
SIC: 71406 Employees: 30
Catering Equipment Hire
Mr Pat Taylor General Manager
Mr Bill Begley Finance Manager

Fitzgerald Menswear Ltd
6 Barronstrand Street
Waterford Co. Waterford
Phone: 051-855055 Fax: 051-855162
SIC: 71407 Employees: 30
Dress Hire /Wedding Hire/Retail Menswear
Mr Tony Fitzgerald Managing Director

Pressco Jig & Tool Company Ltd
66 Mile Road
Glasnevin Industrial Estate
Dublin 11
Phone: 01-8301733 Fax: 01-8307675
Email: pressco@indigo.ie
Web: http://www.pressco.ie
SIC: 71408 Employees: 75
Hiring Consumer Goods
Mr John Byrne Managing Director
Mr Michael Hayes Financial Director

Western Pleasure Ltd
Galway Road
Tuam Co. Galway
Phone: 093-24472 Fax: 093-24079
Email: info@westernpleasure.ie
Web: http://www.westernpleasure.ie
SIC: 71408 Employees: 40
Hiring Consumer Goods
Mr John Fahy Managing Director

Computer & Related Activities

72 Computer & Related Activities
72100 Computer Consultancy
72200 Software/Information Products
72300 Data Processing
72400 Database Activities
72500 Repair of Office & Computing Equip
72601 Computer Services
72602 Network & Data Communications
72603 Computer Sales
72604 Computer Supplies
72605 Internet Providers/Services
72609 Computer Related Activities – Other

Allied Management Systems
Block B Irish Life Centre
Lower Abbey Street
Dublin 1
Phone: 01-4337300 Fax: 01-8781919
Email: hdq@amsys.ie
Web: http://www.amsys.ie
SIC: 72100 Employees: 55
IT Consultancy & Software Development
Mr Pat Ratcliffe Chief Executive Officer
Mr Michael McDonagh Financial Controller
Mr Philip O'Byrne Personnel Manager
Mr David Walsh Sales & Marketing Manager
Mr Tony O'Neill Technical Manager

Ashfield Computer Training
Main Street
Templeogue
Dublin 6w
Phone: 01-4926708 Fax: 01-4900020
Email: info@ashfieldcomputertraining.ie
Web: http://www.ashfieldcomputertraining.ie
SIC: 72100 Employees: 30
Computer Training
Ms Eileen McGinn Director
Ms Aisling Sweeney Accountant
Ms Tina Murray Office Manager

Brightsome Ltd
13-15 Fairview
Dublin 3
Phone: 01-8335005 Fax: 01-8335023
Email: sales@brightsome.com
Web: http://www.brightsome.com
SIC: 72100 Employees: 38
Computer Consultancy & Training
Mr Gerry Newman Managing Director
Ms Mary Eastwood Sales Manager

Cambridge Technology Partners
118-119 Lower Baggott Street
Dublin 2
Phone: 01-6079036 Fax: 01-6079001
Email: marketing@ctp.com
Web: http://www.ctp.com
SIC: 72100 Employees: 80
International Techology Consulting Firm
Mr Freddie Kavanagh Managing Director
Mr Richard Commins Finance Director
Ms Yvonne McCarthy Personnel Manager
Mr Michael Hoare Commercial Director

IDS Computer Services Ltd
3 Sandyford Business Park
Blackthorn Avenue
Dublin 18
Phone: 01-2604818 Fax: 01-2104816
Email: info@idsdataprocessing.co.uk
Web: http://www.idsmediagroup.com
SIC: 74141 Employees: 75
Data Analysis, Mining & Warehousing
Mr Martin Crilly Managing Director

Cap Gemini Ernst & Young
International House
20-22 Lower Hatch Street
Dublin 2
Phone: 01-6390100 Fax: 01-6390199
Email: info@capgemini.ie
Web: http://www.ie.cgey.com
SIC: 72100 Employees: 250
Software Consultants
Mr Eamon Doyle Managing Director
Ms Bridie Lynch Financial Controller
Ms Tereasa Hayden Personnel Manager
Ms Tina McVeigh Sales & Marketing Manager
Mr Tom Sheridan Computer Manager

Celtech Software International Ltd
East Point
Fairview
Dublin 3
Phone: 01-8558200 Fax: 01-8365509
Email: sales@cfil.ie
Web: http://www.cfil.ie
SIC: 72100 Employees: 30
Computer Consultancy
Mr Darragh Fanning Managing Director
Mr Stuart Cheehy Finance Manager
Ms Siobhan Murphy Personnel Manager
Mr Brian Davies Sales Manager

Clear Systems Solutions Ltd
Iveagh Court
6-8 Harcourt Road
Dublin 2
Phone: 01-4785291 Fax: 01-4785294
Email: info@clear.ie
Web: http://www.clearsys.ie
SIC: 72100 Employees: 27
Computer Consultancy
Mr Harry Dunne General Manager
Ms Fiona Lynch Sales Manager

Computer Department
School Nursing Building
Stevens Hospital
Dublin 8
Phone: 01-6352735 Fax: 01-6352740
SIC: 72100 Employees: 60
IT Consultancy
Mr Tony Carroll Manager

Connect Business Solutions
U13A, Corporate Park
Blanchardstown
Dublin 15
Phone: 01-8829000 Fax: 01-8829050
Web: http://www.cbsire.com
SIC: 72100 Employees: 73
Computer Consultancy
Mr Eugene McGinty Managing Director
Mr Gerry James Finance Manager
Mr Philip Fitzpatrick Sales & Marketing Manager
Mr Mike O'Brien Computer Manager

Core Computer Consultants
Core House
Pouladuff Road
Cork Co. Cork
Phone: 021-4947403 Fax: 021-4947432
Email: corecork@indigo.ie
SIC: 72100 Employees: 60
Computer Consultancy
Mr Sean Murphy Managing Director

Data Electronics Group Ltd
Unit 2 North West Business Park
Ballycoolin
Dublin 15
Phone: 01-4811600 Fax: 01-4811611
Email: info@dataelec.com
Web: http://www.dataelec.com
SIC: 72100 Employees: 50
Systems Consultants
Mr Maurice Mortell Managing Director
Mr Noel Kelly Finance Manager
Mr Brian Lineen Sales Marketing Manager
Mr Jason Kehoe Operations Manager
Mr Colm Bowles Technical Manager

EPC
100 North Kings Street
Dublin 7
Phone: 01-4740202 Fax: 01-4740208
Email: info@epc-int.com
Web: http://www.epc-int.com
SIC: 72100 Employees: 30
Computer Consultancy
Mr Colin Kennedy Managing Director
Mr Graham Collins Financial Controller
Ms Leanne Rooney Sales & Marketing Manager

Excaxe
20 Fitzwilliam Square
Dublin 2
Phone: 01-6629601 Fax: 01-6618650
Email: sales@harvard-group.com
Web: http://www.harvard-group.com
SIC: 72100 Employees: 25
Computer Consultancy
Mr Norman Carroll Managing Director
Mr Philip Naughton Finance Manager
Ms Eilish Mahon Personnel Manager
Mr Ross Brennan Sales & Marketing Manager

International Financial Systems Ltd
3 Dundrum Business Park
Dundrum Road
Dublin 14
Phone: 01-2964525 Fax: 01-2964627
Email: info@ifs.ie
Web: http://www.ifs.ie
SIC: 72100 Employees: 35
Computer Consultancy
Mr Ken Coldrick Managing Director
Mr Jim Duffy Head of Finance
Mr Paul Taggart Computer Manager

Iona Technologies Plc
Iona Building Shelbourne Road
Ballsbridge
Dublin 4
Phone: 01-6625255 Fax: 01-6372888
Email: info@iona.com
Web: http://www.iona.com
SIC: 72100 Employees: 290
Computer Consultancy
Mr Barry Morris Chief Executive
Mr Dan Demmer Chief Financial Officer
Ms Theresa Kelly Personnel Manager
Ms Fergal McDonnell Sales & Marketing Manager
Mr John Hughes IT Manager

IP Communications
251-255 Richmond Road
Dublin 3
Phone: 01-8843280 Fax: 01-8843282
Email: info@ip-comms.com
Web: http://www.ip-comms.com
SIC: 72100 Employees: 25
Computer Consultancy & Network
Mr John Purdy Managing Director
Mr Mark Kenny Finance Director
Mr Darren Costello Sales Director
Mr Mark Murphy IT Manager

Jefferson Computer Ltd
Jefferson House Eglinton Road
Donnybrook
Dublin 4
Phone: 01-2830244 Fax: 01-2830258
Email: sales@jefferson.ie
SIC: 72100 Employees: 25
Computer Consultancy
Mr Malachy Doherty Chief Executive
Mr Fintan Meagher Financial Controller
Mr Brendan Doyle Sales Manager

LAN Communications Ltd
Unit 3 Park Way House
Lower Ballymount Road
Dublin 12
Phone: 01-4093000 Fax: 01-4093001
Email: info@lancomms.ie
Web: http://www.lancomms.ie
SIC: 72100 Employees: 45
Computer Networking, Security & Management & Consultancy
Mr Sean McNamee Managing Director
Ms Anne Marie Cunningham Finance Manager
Mr Neil Wisdom Sales & Marketing Director
Mr Andrew O'Kelly IT Director

Moresoft Computers Ltd
Bracken House, Bracken Road
Sandyford Industrial Estate
Dublin 18
Phone: 01-6621711 Fax: 01-6621712
Email: training@moresoft.ie
Web: http://www.moresoft.ie
SIC: 72100 Employees: 38
Computer Consultancy
Mr Desmond Donnelly Managing Director
Mr Dermot Doyle Financial Controller

Orbism Ltd
Manor Street Business Park
Manor Street
Dublin 7
Phone: 01-6629440 Fax: 01-8689545
Email: info@orbism.com
Web: http://www.orbism.com
SIC: 72100 Employees: 50
Computer Consultancy
Mr John Fleming Chief Executive Officer
Mr Paul Tunney Chief Technical Officer

PA Consulting Group
Embassy House
Herbert Park Lane Ballsbridge
Dublin 4
Phone: 01-6684346 Fax: 01-6681771
Web: http://www.pa-consulting.com
SIC: 72100 Employees: 30
Computer Consultancy
Mr Michael Maguire Managing Director

SAP Service & Support Centre (Ireland)
East Point Business Park
Fairview
Dublin 3
Phone: 01-8054000 Fax: 01-8559285
Email: sap@iol.ie
Web: http://www.sap.com
SIC: 72100 Employees: 140
Support Services Centre for Computer Software
Mr Liam Ryan Managing Director
Ms Paula Finnegan Financial Controller
Mr Hans Ulmer IT Manager

Sureskills
14 Fitzwilliam Place
Dublin 2
Phone: 01-6763377 Fax: 01-2402233
Email: info@sureskills.com
Web: http://www.sureskills.ie
SIC: 72100 Employees: 25
Computer Training/Consultancy
Ms Alison Egan Managing Director
Mr Ross Bolton Sales Director

System Dynamics
14 Fitzwilliam Quay
Ringsend
Dublin 4
Phone: 01-6685522 Fax: 01-6685418
Web: http://www.systemdynamics.ie
SIC: 72100 Employees: 90
Software Consultancy
Mr Tony McGuire Managing Director
Ms Mary Purdue-Smyth Accounts Manager
Mr Dominic McMahon Human Resources Director
Ms Nora Ryder Sales & Marketing Manager
Mr Damien Pippet Technical Director

Vision Consulting Ltd
East Point Business Park
Fairview
Dublin 3
Phone: 01-2400200 Fax: 01-2400201
Email: postmaster@visions.com
Web: http://www.visions.com
SIC: 72100 Employees: 360
Computer Consultancy
Mr Billy Glennon Group Chief Executive
Mr Jim McLoughlin Finance Manager
Ms Grainne McCann Human Resources Director
Mr Ian Duffy Group Operations Director
Mr Gerald Adams Group Technical Director

A & G Technology Ltd
Unit B 7 Riverview Business Park
Nangor Road
Dublin 22
Phone: 01-4568600 Fax: 01-4568604
Email: agt@indigo.ie
SIC: 72200 Employees: 23
Computer Software & Hardware
Mr George McCormack Managing Director
Ms Moira McClean Personnel Manager
Mr Warren Daly Computer Manager

ADC
Galway Business Park
Dangan
Galway Co. Galway
Phone: 091-526611 Fax: 091-527351
Email: info@adc.com
Web: http://www.adc.com
SIC: 72200 Employees: 220
Computer Software Consultants
Mr Oliver Daniels Managing Director
Mr Patch McSweeney Finance Manager
Ms Geraldine Flanagan Personnel Manager
Mr Ivor Cunnigham Network Systems Manager

Airtel ATN Plc
Adelaide House
Adelaide Street
Dun Laoghaire Co. Dublin
Phone: 01-2842821 Fax: 01-2842816
Email: info@airtel-atn.com
Web: http://www.airtel-atn.com
SIC: 72200 Employees: 38
Software Development
Mr Kevin Jones Chief Executive Officer
Ms Mary Cooke Accountant
Mr Kieran Carrick Sales Manager
Mr Frank O'Connor Chief Technology Officer

Alcatel Ireland
Laragh
Bandon Co. Cork
Phone: 023-41060 Fax: 023-41542
Web: http://www.alcatel.com
SIC: 72200 Employees: 378
Manufacture Software
Mr John McGinley Managing Director
Mr Jim O'Donovan Financial Controller
Mr Joe Leonard Personnel Manager
Mr Michael Carney Sales & Marketing Manager
Mr Shane Monagh Software Manager

All Finanz
Allfinanz House Leopardstown Office Park
Foxrock
Dublin 18
Phone: 01-2952549 Fax: 01-2952554
Email: marketing@allfinanzinc.com
Web: http://www.allfinanzinc.com
SIC: 72200 Employees: 75
Software Development
Mr Jim Maher Chief Executive Officer
Mr David Wall Financial Controller
Mr Ross Maine Chief Technical Officer

AME Ltd
5 Dundrum Business Park
Dundrum
Dublin 14
Phone: 01-2079700 Fax: 01-2079701
Email: info@ame.ie
Web: http://www.ame.ie
SIC: 72200 Employees: 25
Program Management
Mr Jim O'Reilly Managing Director
Ms Georgina Cullen Finance Manager
Ms Lara Doyle Production Director
Ms Lara Doyle Computer Manager

AMT/Sybex Group
Oak House, Leopardstown Office Park
Foxrock
Dublin 18
Phone: 01-2958988 Fax: 01-2958990
Email: info@amt.sybex.com
Web: http://www.amt.sybex.com
SIC: 72200 Employees: 175
Software Development/Imaging Technology
Mr Pearse Mee Chief Executive
Mr Paul Reynolds Finance Director
Mr Paul Webster Sales Manager
Ms Katherine Moore Software Development

AOL Technologies Ireland Ltd
3030 Lake Drive
Citywest Business Campus, Rathcoole
Dublin 24
Phone: 01-4035000 Fax: 01-4035001
Email: info@aol.com
Web: http://www.aol.com
SIC: 72200 Employees: 200
Computer Software
Mr Manus Hanratty Managing Director
Mr Tom Carroll Financial Controller
Mr Alan Byrne IT Manager

Aspect Software
3 Westland Square
Pearce Street
Dublin 2
Phone: 01-6707699 Fax: 01-6707868
Email: info@aspect.ie
Web: http://www.aspect-software.com
SIC: 72200 Employees: 30
Software
Mr Gerry O'Connor Managing Director
Mr James Maughan Computer Manager

Attachmate Ireland
Bay D1, Shannon Industrial Estate
Shannon Co. Clare
Phone: 061-474666 Fax: 061-472733
Email: info@attachmate.com
Web: http://www.attachmate.com
SIC: 72200 Employees: 60
Software
Mr Liam O'Neill Managing Director
Mr Pat Wynne Financial Controller
Ms Carmel Pender Personnel Officer
Ms Marie McCrohan Customer Services Manager
Mr David Pender IT Manager

Avid Technology International BV
Carmenhall Road
Sandyford Industrial Estate
Dublin 18
Phone: 01-2950066 Fax: 01-2950079
Email: postmaster@avid.com
Web: http://www.avid.com
SIC: 72200 Employees: 60
Computer Software & Call Centre
Mr Patrick O'Beirne General Manager
Ms Adrienne Treanor Financial Controller
Ms Geraldine Stapleton Office Manager
Mr Carl Clarke Operations Manager
Mr Paul Reid IT Manager

Baltimore Technologies Ltd
39/41Park Gate Street
Dublin 8
Phone: 01-8816000 Fax: 01-8817000
Email: info@baltimore.com
Web: http://www.baltimore.com
SIC: 72200 Employees: 400
Computer Software
Mr Fran Rooney Chief Executive
Mr Paul McCauley Computer Manager

Banta Global Turnkey Group
Hollyhill Industrial Estate
Hollyhill
Cork Co. Cork
Phone: 021-4397515 Fax: 021-4397459
Email: info@bgt.com
Web: http://www.bgt.com
SIC: 72200 Employees: 300
Computer Software
Mr Tom King General Manager

BG Turnkey Services Ltd
Unit Q Raheen Industrial Estate
Raheen
Limerick Co. Limerick
Phone: 061-303888 Fax: 061-304043
Email: bentaglobal@limerick.ie
Web: http://www.limerick.ie
SIC: 72200 Employees: 150
Computer Software
Mr Joe Kavanagh General Manager
Mr Cathal Nagle Finance Manager

Big Picture Software
Unit 7 Inns Court
Winetavern Street
Dublin 8
Phone: 01-6776777 Fax: 01-6776614
Email: info@bigpicture.ie
Web: http://www.bigpicture.ie
SIC: 72200 Employees: 30
Software Development
Mr David Conroy Managing Director
Mr Stephen Connolly Financial Controller
Ms Rochelle Nelson Personnel Manager
Mr Simon English Sales Manager
Mr John Fenton IT Manager

Blackbird Data Systems Ltd
The National Technological Park
Plassey
Limerick Co. Limerick
Phone: 061-333188 Fax: 061-333133
Email: info@lk.blackbird.ie
Web: http://www.blackbirddatasystems.com
SIC: 72200 Employees: 40
Software Company
Mr Noel Clarke Managing Director
Mr Patrick Coleman Finance Manager
Ms Maureen McGreevy
Mr Aidan Curtis Computer Manager

BMC Software Europe
Ballymoss House, Carmanhall Road
Foxrock
Dublin 18
Phone: 01-2076800 Fax: 01-2076810
Email: info@bmc.com
Web: http://www.bmc.com
SIC: 72200 Employees: 35
Software Manufacturing
Mr Peter Dixon Finnegan General Manager
Mr Micheal Clohosey Finance Manager
Mr Kevin Priestly Computer Manager

Bowen Global Solutions (Ireland)
65-66 Lower Mount Street
Dublin 2
Phone: 01-6146300 Fax: 01-6146333
Email: ken.behan@bowenglobal.ie
Web: http://www.bowenglobal.ie
SIC: 72200 Employees: 100
Translate Software into Foreign Languages
Ms Wendy Hamilton General Manager
Mr Tom Gillanders Financial Controller
Mr Ken Behan Marketing Manager
Mr Dean Horrigan Testing Engineering Manager
Mr Gerry Fahey Computer Manager

Bromley Communications
Merchants House, Merchants Quay
Dublin 8
Phone: 01-4028100 Fax: 01-4028101
Email: sales@bromleygroup.ie
SIC: 72200 Employees: 40
Computer Software
Mr Matthew Maxwell Managing Director
Ms Kay Starling Personnel Manager
Mr Connor O'Kelly Sales & Marketing Manager

CADCO Evolution Ltd
Trafalgar House
Montenotte
Cork Co. Cork
Phone: 021-4551771 Fax: 021-4502148
Email: info@cadcoevolution.com
Web: http://www.cadcoevolution.com
SIC: 72200 Employees: 45
Software
Ms Anne O'Leary Managing Director
Ms Rosemary Browne Finance Manager
Mr Seamus Hurley Personnel Director
Ms Yvonne Sheahan Marketing Director

Cadence Design Systems
Eastpoint Business Park
Dublin 3
Phone: 01-8054300 Fax: 01-8054310
Email: postmaster@cadence.com
Web: http://www.cadence.com
SIC: 72200 Employees: 70
Computer Software
Mr Paul Talbot Managing Director
Mr John Wall Financial Controller
Ms Debbie Grimes Personnel Manager
Mr Brendan Pollard IT Support

CampusIT
Unit E Merrywell Business Park
Dublin 12
Phone: 01-6620144 Fax: 01-6620188
Email: info@campusit.net
Web: http://www.campusit.net
SIC: 72200 Employees: 60
Software Development
Mr Tony Sheridan Managing Director
Ms Nicola McCarthy Marketing Manager
Mr Gerry Doherty IT Manager

Cardbase Technologies
BIM House
Crofton Road
Dun Laoghaire Co. Dublin
Phone: 01-2843233 Fax: 01-2843220
Email: info@cardbase.com
Web: http://www.cardbase.com
SIC: 72200 Employees: 65
Software Company
Mr Aonghus Geraghty Managing Director
Mr Tom Cullen Financial Controller
Mr David O'Hagan Sales Manager
Mr Gerry Looby Technical Director

CCM Software Services Ltd
Argus House
Harolds Cross
Dublin 6w
Phone: 01-4538809 Fax: 01-4536533
Email: facility@facility.ie
Web: http://www.facility.ie
SIC: 72200 Employees: 27
Computer Software
Mr David Collery Manager
Ms Margaret Power Finance Manager
Ms Deirdre McSweeney Sales Manager

Clarus Corporation
The National Technological Park
Plassey
Limerick Co. Limerick
Phone: 061-338400 Fax: 061-335626
Email: reception@sai.ie
Web: http://www.cashbook.com
SIC: 72200 Employees: 50
Software Company
Mr Christopher Byrne General Manager
Ms Marian Shanahan Finance Manager
Ms Roisin Ghadi Personnel Officer
Mr Robert Moloney Sales Executive
Mr Ken Allen Computer Manager

Clockworks International
31 Upper Mount Street
Dublin 2
Phone: 01-6623438 Fax: 01-6623440
Email: sales@clockworks.ie
Web: http://www.clockworksintl.com
SIC: 72200 Employees: 70
Localisation / Multi Media Software
Mr PJ King Managing Director
Ms Jacinta Lambert Finance Manager
Ms Kate Collins Administrator
Mr Keith Donnelly IS Manager

Cognotec Ltd
2-4 Ely Place
Dublin 2
Phone: 01-6766455 Fax: 01-6766500
Web: http://www.cognotec.com
SIC: 72200 Employees: 195
Software Development
Mr Paul Fox Chief Technology Officer
Ms Sandra Bowen Financial Controller
Mr Colm Gorman H R Manager
Mr Stephen Butcher Sales Manager
Mr Michael Douglas IT Manager

Communicate Now
Unit 17 Carlow Shopping Centre
Carlow Co. Carlow
Phone: 0503-43700 Fax: 0503-40121
Email: commnow@iol.ie
Web: http://www.communications.ie
SIC: 72200 Employees: 27
Computer Games/Mobile Telephones/Internet Access
Ms Ella Hutton General Manager
Ms Marie McDermott Accountant

Compupac Ireland Ltd
Finisklin Industrial Estate
Sligo Co. Sligo
Phone: 071-62394 Fax: 071-69702
Email: sales@compupac.ie
Web: http://www.compupac.ie
SIC: 72200 Employees: 23
Software Company
Mr Michael Vickers Director
Ms Mary Ruddy Finance Manager
Ms Susanne McGarry Sales Manager
Mr Kevin Hunt IT Manager

Computer Applied Techniques
3 St James Terrace
Malahide Co. Dublin
Phone: 01-8450921 Fax: 01-8450136
Email: mail@captec.ie
Web: http://www.captec.ie
SIC: 72200 Employees: 28
Computer Consultants/Software Development
Mr Fred Kennedy Managing Director
Dr John Kennedy Research Director

Conduit
Conduit House, Block P1
East Point Business Park, Clontarf
Dublin 3
Phone: 01-8190000 Fax: 01-8190088
Email: info@conduit.ie
Web: http://www.conduit.ie
SIC: 72200 Employees: 1000
Computer Software / Telecommunications
Mr Liam Young Chief Executive Officer
Mr Rory Nealon Chief Executive Officer
Ms Lanna O'Reilly Call Centre Op Director
Mr Shane Buckley CEO Conduit Software
Mr Anthony Jordan IT Manager

CR2 Ltd
CR2 House Block,16 Joyce Way
Parkwest Business Park
Dublin 12
Phone: 01-4569677 Fax: 01-4569711
Email: info@cr2.com
Web: http://www.cr2.com
SIC: 72200 Employees: 100
International Banking Software
Mr Ron Downey Chief Executive Officer
Mr Conor Walsh Finance Manager
Ms Marian Skehill Human Resources Director
Mr Cian Kinsella Chief Executive Officer
Mr Gavin Killen IT Manager

Creative Labs (Ireland) Ltd
Ballycollin Business Park
Blanchardstown
Dublin 15
Phone: 01-8206444 Fax: 01-8205052
Email: info@creative.com
Web: http://www.creative.com
SIC: 72200 Employees: 350
Multimedia Software
Ms Merrion Brennan Managing Director
Ms Siobhan Phelan European Manager for Finance

Credo Group
Longport House Earlsfort Centre
Lower Leeson Street
Dublin 2
Phone: 01-6310200 Fax: 01-6310300
Email: marketing@credo.ie
Web: http://www.credo.ie
SIC: 72200 Employees: 70
Software Insurance
Mr Gerry Kelly Managing Director
Mr Ed O'Brien Financial Controller
Ms Anne Hayden Personnel Manager
Mr Gerry English Sales & Marketing Director
Mr John Morrisey Operation Manager
Mr Paul O'Dea Software Director

Critical Path
Knockmawn House
42-47 Lower Mount Street
Dublin 2
Phone: 01-2415000 Fax: 01-2415170
Email: info@cp.net
Web: http://www.cp.net
SIC: 72200 Employees: 105
Messaging Software
Mr Niall Cogan Managing Director
Mr Kevin McGrath Financial Controller
Mr Donal Brown Human Resources Manager
Mr Mark Owen Sales Manager
Ms Daragh Mullan Operations Manager
Mr Donal O'Callaghan IT Manager

CSK Software
Lisle House
33 Molesworth Street
Dublin 2
Phone: 01-6046300 Fax: 01-6622195
Email: enquiries@csksoftware.com
Web: http://www.csksoftware.com
SIC: 72200 Employees: 70
Software Development
Mr Gerry Giblin Manager
Ms Maureen Haskins Company Secretary
Ms Jennifer Dempsey Personnel Manager
Mr Ray Kehoe Sales & Marketing Manager
Mr Paul Sinnott Computer Manager

Dakota Group
Reillys Bridge
Roath Road
Dublin 11
Phone: 01-8308288 Fax: 01-8300280
Email: info@ormond.com
Web: http://www.ormond.com
SIC: 72200 Employees: 300
Printing/Packaging and Software
Mr Colum Kelleher Chairman/Chief Executive
Mr Kieran Condon Group Accountant
Mr Brendan Moles Group Operations Director

Dane-Elec Manufacturing
Spiddal Industrial Estate
Spiddal
Galway Co. Galway
Phone: 091-553000 Fax: 091-553050
Email: info@dane-elec.ie
Web: http://www.dane-elec.com
SIC: 72200 Employees: 80
Computer Software
Mr Dave Lalor Managing Director
Mr Tommy McDonagh Finance Manager
Ms Anne-Marie Nighriosa Human Resources Manager
Mr Ray Malloy Production Manager

Data Dimensions Ireland Ltd
Unit 2 Ballybrit Business Park
Galway Co. Galway
Phone: 091-771651 Fax: 091-771678
Web: http://www.datadimensions.com
SIC: 72200 Employees: 70
Computer Software
Mr John Costello Managing Director
Ms Angela Deacy Personnel Officer

Datacare Software Group
The Diamond Centre
Monaghan Co. Monaghan
Phone: 047-83084 Fax: 047-83099
Email: info@datacare.ie
Web: http://www.data-care.com
SIC: 72200 Employees: 23
Software Development
Mr John Kelly Managing Director
Mr Joe Daly Financial Controller
Ms Siobhan Leahy Sales Manager
Mr Kieran Kelly Senior Analyst/Programmer

Datalex Communications Ltd
Howth House
Harbour Road Howth
Dublin 13
Phone: 01-8391787 Fax: 01-8391781
Email: info@datalex.com
Web: http://www.datalex.com
SIC: 72200 Employees: 115
Software Sales
Mr Neil Wilson Managing Director
Mr Liam Boots Financial Controller
Ms Deirdre Reddin Logistics Administration
Mr Aidan Brogan Sales Manager
Mr Brian Dent Operation Manager
Mr John McQuillan Computer Manager

DDSI Ltd
Unit 1a University Technology Centre
Curraheen Road
Cork Co. Cork
Phone: 021-4925100 Fax: 021-4925101
Email: info@addsi.ie
Web: http://www.ddsi.ie
SIC: 72200 Employees: 65
Software Development
Mr John Murphy Director

Decision Support Systems Ltd
Hyde House
65 Adelaide Road
Dublin 2
Phone: 01-6619530 Fax: 01-6764655
Email: info@decision.ie
Web: http://www.decision.ie
SIC: 72200 Employees: 40
Computer Software Development
Mr Tony Stafford Managing Director
Ms Catherine Gilmore Finance Manager
Mr Brian McCrory Technical Manager

Delphi Technology Ltd
Linden Court The Plaza
Stillorgan
Blackrock Co. Dublin
Phone: 01-2782066 Fax: 01-2782563
Email: info@delphi.ie
Web: http://www.delphi.ie
SIC: 72200 Employees: 200
Software Consultancy
Mr James Walsh Managing Director
Ms Ann Webb Finance Manager
Ms Deirdre O'Sullivan Personnel Manager
Mr Noel Breen Sales & Marketing Manager
Mr Kevin Fennelly Network Manager

Diatec
93 Ranelagh Road
Dublin 6
Phone: 01-4960377 Fax: 01-4966544
Email: sales@diatec.ie
Web: http://www.diatec.ie
SIC: 72200 Employees: 45
Computer Software & General Stationery
Mr David Harpur Managing Director
Mr Joe Malone Accounts Manager
Mr Richard Harper Head Administrator
Mr Tony Duff Computer Manager

Dornan Manufacturing
Monaghan Road
Cork Co. Cork
Phone: 021-4962177 Fax: 021-4314196
Email: mail@dornan.net
Web: http://www.dornan.net
SIC: 72200 Employees: 30
Computer Software
Ms Jackie Dornan Managing Director
Mr Andrew Riordan Finance Manager
Mr Philip Coleman IT Officer

Dreytec Software
Block D, Charlemont Exchange, Charlemont Place
Dublin 2
Phone: 01-4189200 Fax: 01-4189210
Email: office@dreytec.com
Web: http://www.dreytec.com
SIC: 72200 Employees: 60
Software for private banking industry
Mr Torsten Beyer Managing Director
Mr John O'Callaghan Finance Manager
Ms Sarah Moore Personnel Manager
Mr Nigel Carter Sales Manager
Mr Brian Kiefel Computer Manager

DSCIE
Ballybrit Business Park
Ballybrit
Galway Co. Galway
Phone: 091-760541 Fax: 091-760542
Email: info@dscie.com
Web: http://www.dscie.com
SIC: 72200 Employees: 27
Computer Software
Mr John Walker Proprietor

Eland Technologies Ltd
24 South Frederick Street
Dublin 2
Phone: 01-6704300 Fax: 01-6704301
Web: http://www.elandtech.com
SIC: 72200 Employees: 90
Computer Software and Design
Mr Andres Cornelius General Manager
Ms Liz Convery Financial Controller
Ms Denise McNamara Personnel Director
Mr Conor Doherty Sales & Marketing Manager
Mr Ed Mannion IT Manager

Engage Technologies Ltd (Formely Belscan)
7-8 Mount Street, Crescent
Dublin 2
Phone: 01-6704101 Fax: 01-6704108
SIC: 72200 Employees: 23
Software Development
Mr Gerard O'Mahony Managing Director
Mr Paul Dunne Financial Controller
Mr Tom Lonergan Sales Manager
Mr Ger Keane IT Manager

Entropy Ltd
Unit 4a Sandyford Business Centre
Sandyford Industrial Estate
Dublin 18
Phone: 01-2940199 Fax: 01-2940121
Email: info@entropy.ie
Web: http://www.entropy.ie
SIC: 72200 Employees: 72
Computer Software
Mr Conal Lavery Managing Director
Mr Hugh Connolly Finance Manager
Ms Caroline McDaide Marketing Manager

Eon Technologies Ltd
Charlemont Exchange
Charlemont Street
Dublin 2
Phone: 01-4782932 Fax: 01-4752767
Email: info@eontec.com
Web: http://www.eon.com
SIC: 72200 Employees: 280
Computer Software
Mr James Callan Managing Director
Mr Colin Piper Technical Director

Epicor Software Ireland Ltd
Park House
North Circular Road
Dublin 7
Phone: 01-8681250 Fax: 01-8681255
Email: info@epicor.com
Web: http://www.pl.com
SIC: 72200 Employees: 60
Software Development & Call Centre
Mr Declan Finucane Managing Director
Ms Mairead Quilty Office Manager

Epionet
11 Marino Mart
Fairview
Dublin 3
Phone: 01-8339558 Fax: 01-8533241
Email: info@epionet.com
Web: http://www.itsysdev.com
SIC: 72200 Employees: 27
Computer Software Development
Mr Stephen Brogan Managing Director
Mr James Brennan Finance Manager
Mr Ambrose Curry Personnel Manager
Mr Liam McMahon Sales Manager

Eurologic Systems Ltd
Maple House, South County Business Park
Leopardstown
Dublin 16
Phone: 01-2958366 Fax: 01-2061299
Email: info@eurologic.com
Web: http://www.eurologic.com
SIC: 72200 Employees: 225
Software Development
Mr John Maybury Chief Executive Officer
Mr Ray O'Driscoll Financial Director
Mr Mike Stolz Sales Director
Mr David Verdon Production Manager
Mr Hans O'Sullivan Technical Director

Exact Software Ireland Ltd
Tentle House, Tentle Road
Blackrock Co. Dublin
Phone: 01-2698922 Fax: 01-2839429
Email: info@exactinternational.com
Web: http://www.exactinternational.com
SIC: 72200 Employees: 24
Software
Mr Douglas Notley Managing Director
Ms Sandra Sangro Finance Manager
Mr Jack General Computer Manager

Exaxe
20 Fitzwilliam Square
Dublin 2
Phone: 01-6618630 Fax: 01-6618650
Email: info@exaxe.com
Web: http://www.exaxe.com
SIC: 72200 Employees: 60
Software development
Mr Norman Carroll Chief Executive
Mr Philip Noughton Financial Controller
Ms Eilish Mahon Personnel Officer
Mr Ross Brennan Sales & Marketing Manager
Mr Tom Murray Computer Manager

Exceptis Technologies
Montague Court
Montague Street
Dublin 2
Phone: 01-4780077 Fax: 01-2416201
Email: info@exceptis.com
Web: http://www.exceptis.com
SIC: 72200 Employees: 65
Software Development
Mr Terry McWade Chief Executive Officer
Mr Eamon Keating Finance Manager
Ms Sarah Eustace Sales & Marketing Manager

EZ Management Ltd
Lurganboy
Carrick On Shannon Co. Leitrim
Phone: 072-56215 Fax: 072-56222
Email: info@ez-management.com
Web: http://www.ez-management.com
SIC: 72200 Employees: 27
Computer Software
Mr Eugene Bennett Manager

File Net Company Ltd
East Point Business Park
Fairview
Dublin 3
Phone: 01-8190100 Fax: 01-8190199
Email: info@filenet.com
Web: http://www.filenet.com
SIC: 72200 Employees: 75
Computer Software
Mr John McLaughlin Managing Director
Ms Mary Dunne Personnel Director
Mr Donal Forde Sales Manager
Mr Richard Carolan IT Manager

Fineos
Pembroke House
8-10 Lower Pembroke Street
Dublin 2
Phone: 01-6399700 Fax: 01-6399701
Email: info@fineos.com
Web: http://www.fineos.com
SIC: 72200 Employees: 250
Computer Software Company (Banking)
Mr Michael Kelly Managing Director
Mr Diarmuid Gahan Financial Director

Flextime Ltd
56 Blackthorn Road
Sandyford Industrial Estate
Dublin 18
Phone: 01-2954654 Fax: 01-2952083
Email: time@flextime.ie
Web: http://www.flextime.ie
SIC: 72200 Employees: 30
Time Recording Software & Hardware
Mr Ciaran Rowsom Managing Director
Ms Mary Rowsom Finance Manager
Ms Denise Prendergast Company Secretary
Mr Joachim Braune Software Development Director

Funcom Dublin Ltd
79-80 Furze Road
Sandyford Industrial Estate
Dublin 18
Phone: 01-2945160 Fax: 01-2945169
Email: info@funcom.ie
Web: http://www.funcom.com
SIC: 72200 Employees: 30
Design Computer Software
Ms Olivia White Managing Director
Ms Leona Kavanagh Secretary
Mr Joey Walsh IT Manager

Fusion Business Solutions
Block U
East Point Business Park
Dublin 3
Phone: 01-8055800 Fax: 01-8055801
Email: postmaster@fusion.ie
Web: http://www.fusion.ie
SIC: 72200 Employees: 56
SAP Solutions Computer Software
Mr Mark Little Managing Director
Mr Sean McRaymond Finance Manager
Mr Charles Acheson Sales & Marketing Manager
Ms Caroline Gill Computer Manager

G TECH Ireland Corporation
2nd Floor Irish Life Centre
Lower Abbey Street
Dublin 1
Phone: 01-8366377 Fax: 01-8366119
Email: info@gtech.com
Web: http://www.gtech.com
SIC: 72200 Employees: 70
Produce Software for National Lottery
Mr Declan Harkin Managing Director
Ms Miriam Cormack Finance Manager
Ms Mary Turkmen Human Resources Specialist
Mr Mark Fitzpatrick Operation Manager
Ms Jacinta Kielty Computer Manager

GEAC Enterprise Solutions Ireland
GEAC House
6 Sandyford Business Centre
Dublin 18
Phone: 01-2958555 Fax: 01-2958599
Email: info@geac.com
Web: http://www.geac.com
SIC: 72200 Employees: 50
Software Development
Mr Pat Chambers Managing Director
Ms Maeve Hogan Financial Controller
Mr Aidan Keogh Personnel Manager
Mr Neil Byrne Sales & Marketing Manager

Gradient Solutions Ltd
Ormond house
12 Lower leeson street
Dublin 2
Phone: 01-2400500 Fax: 01-2400501
Email: info@gradient.ie
Web: http://www.gradient.ie
SIC: 72200 Employees: 40
Computer Software
Mr Paschal Nee Managing Director
Mr Dave McCara Finance Director
Ms Denise Fay Sales Manager
Mr Gareth McDaid Computer Manager

Graham Technology Ireland Ltd
2A Ballybrit Business Park
Galway Co. Galway
Phone: 091-706000 Fax: 091-706066
Email: info@gtnet.com
Web: http://www.gtnet.com
SIC: 72200 Employees: 25
Software & Consultancv
Ms Fiona Graham Managing Director
Ms Caroline Collins Finance Manager

Herbst Computer Systems
Herbst House
Kilpoole Hill
Wicklow Co. Wicklow
Phone: 0404-67164 Fax: 0404-67363
Email: herbst@herbstgroup.com
Web: http://www.herbtsgroup.com
SIC: 72200 Employees: 30
Computer Software
Mr Michael Herbst Managing Director
Mr Mark Robinson Sales Manager

ICE Group
7 Father Griffin Road
Galway Co. Galway
Phone: 091-546700 Fax: 091-585070
Email: info@icegroup.ie
Web: http://www.icegroup.ie
SIC: 72200 Employees: 40
Sofware, Recruitment & Training
Ms Margaret Cox Managing Director
Mr Joe Tummon Financial Controller
Mr Felim McDonnell General Manager

Imagine Software
Unit 36 Southern Cross Business Park
Boghall Road
Bray Co. Wicklow
Phone: 01-2829888 Fax: 01-2861277
Email: info@imagine.ie
Web: http://www.imagine.ie
SIC: 72200 Employees: 27
Develop Computer Software
Mr Peter Doyle Managing Director

Infopoint Systems Ireland Ltd
Ballard House
Westside
Galway Co. Galway
Phone: 091-583030 Fax: 091-583031
Email: info@infopoint.ie
Web: http://www.infopoint.ie
SIC: 72200 Employees: 30
Design Computer Software
Mr Aidan Joyce Group Managing Director
Mr Jonathan Duggan Finance Manager
Mr Michael Rainey Personnel Manager
Ms Ann Walsh Sales Manager
Mr Kenneth Larkin Head of Software Engineering

Informix Software
4 Westgate Business Park
Ballymount
Dublin 24
Phone: 01-4564377 Fax: 01-4051140
Email: dublin@informix.com
Web: http://www.informix.com
SIC: 72200 Employees: 160
Database Software
Mr Terry Ralph General Manager
Mr Brendan Hunt Finance Manager
Ms Eileen Shanahan Personnel Manager
Ms Orla Ryan Sales Manager
Ms Suzanne Flood Production Manager
Mr Martin Wallace Computer Manager

Input Systems Ltd
383-384 Clontarf Road
Dublin 3
Phone: 01-8338100 Fax: 01-8338384
Email: info@input.ie
Web: http://www.input.ie
SIC: 72200 Employees: 25
Computer Software
Mr Geoff Keatings Managing Director

Integrity Software
South Dock Road
Camden Lock
Dublin 4
Phone: 01-6652000 Fax: 01-6670055
Email: sales@integritysoftwarer.ie
Web: http://www.integritysoftware.ie
SIC: 72200 Employees: 50
Software Solutions
Mr Mark Howell Managing Director
Ms Helena Mulcahy Finance Manager
Ms Noreen Kandean Sales Manager

Intellect Ltd
251-255 Richmond Road
Dublin 3
Phone: 01-8843255 Fax: 01-8843256
Email: sales@intellect.ie
Web: http://www.lntellect.ie
SIC: 72200 Employees: 23
Computer Software
Mr Ray Ryan General Manager

Interactive Services Ltd
Damastown Industrial Park
Mulhuddart
Dublin 15
Phone: 01-8111300 Fax: 01-8111301
Email: sales@interactiverser.com
Web: http://www.isl.ie
SIC: 72200 Employees: 180
Web Based Training Products
Mr Garrett Byrne Chief Executive Officer
Mr Ronan Murray Chief Finanacial Officer
Ms Diane Dignan Human Resources Manager
Ms Aideen Donohue Chief Operations Officer
Mr Mark Coffey Computer Manager

IPEC International Services
U23 Hills Industrial Estate
Lucan Co. Dublin
Phone: 01-6219459 Fax: 01-6219461
Email: sales@sfamipec.com
Web: http://www.sfamipec.com
SIC: 72200 Employees: 25
Service Office Semi-Conductors
Mr John Cooke Managing Director

Irish Medical Systems
Clara House Glenageary Park
Glenageary
Dun Laoghaire Co. Dublin
Phone: 01-2840555 Fax: 01-2840829
Email: info@imsmaxims.com
Web: http://www.imsmaxims.com
SIC: 72200 Employees: 100
Software for haelthcare market
Mr Brian Ennis Managing Director
Ms John Muir Director
Ms Geraldine O'Donnell Administrator
Mr Tom Holmes Sales & Marketing Manager
Ms Orla Jenkinson Production Director
Mr Terry Fossey Director

ISI Interact Services Ireland
The Firehouse
27-29 Bridgefoot Street
Dublin 8
Phone: 01-2809000 Fax: 01-6727671
Web: http://www.interactsi.ie
SIC: 72200 Employees: 45
Develop & Sell Computer Software
Mr Ian Spandau Managing Director
Ms Des Simmons Financial Controller
Mr Simon Fine Sales & Marketing Manager
Mr Fran McNally IT Officer

IT Design Ltd
Joyce Way Park West Business Park
Dublin 12
Phone: 01-4967766 Fax: 01-4323090
Email: info@itdesign.ie
Web: http://www.itdesign.com
SIC: 72200 Employees: 35
Software Development
Mr John Hearne Managing Director
Mr Ronan Rooney Personnel Officer
Mr Billy Dennigan Systems Administrator

Ivertec
Bridge Street
Cahirciveen
Killarney Co. Kerry
Phone: 066-9473333 Fax: 066-9473122
Email: info@ivertec.ie
Web: http://www.ivertec.com
SIC: 72200 Employees: 25
Computer Software
Mr Jimmy Sugrue Managing Director

JD Hackett & Co Ltd
17 Lower Baggot Street
Dublin 2
Phone: 01-6760301 Fax: 01-6614092
Email: info@jdh.ie
Web: http://www.jdh.ie
SIC: 72200 Employees: 40
Computer Software
Mr Frank Chambers Managing Director
Mr Joe Hackett Financial Controller
Mr Hugh Gallagher Computer Manager

Jefferson Payroll
Frankfort House, Vergemount Hall
Clonskeagh
Dublin 6
Phone: 01-2698311 Fax: 01-2698557
Email: edp@iol.ie
SIC: 72200 Employees: 50
Computer Software
Mr Malachy Doherty Managing Director
Mr David Corby General Admin & Accounts
Mr Des Mulvany Sales Manager

Keogh Software
Unit 1-2 Greenmount Office Park
Harold's Cross
Dublin 6w
Phone: 01-4548448 Fax: 01-4548555
Email: info@keogh-software.ie
Web: http://www.keogh-software.ie
SIC: 72200 Employees: 35
Computer Software
Mr Eamon Keogh Proprietor
Mr Andrew Lyall Financial Controller
Mr Mark Jones Software Manager

Kerridge Computer Systems
Anglesea House
Carysfort Avenue
Blackrock Co. Dublin
Phone: 01-2883355 Fax: 01-2883360
Email: irlsales@kerridge.com
Web: http://www.kerridge.com
SIC: 72200 Employees: 75
Computer Software Development
Mr Brendan Sullivan Managing Director
Mr Finbar O'Neill Financial Director
Ms Katy Pollard Personnel Manager
Mr Derek Dunne After Sales Manager
Mr Richard Treacy Technical Director

Kindle Banking Systems
East Point Business Park
Dublin 3
Phone: 01-8554555 Fax: 01-8554550
Email:
SIC: 72200 Employees: 455
Financial Software
Mr David Leech Chief Executive
Mr Conall Clancy Financial Controller

KPMG
Russell Court
St Stephens Green
Dublin 2
Phone: 01-4101000 Fax: 01-4121122
Email: info@kmpg.ie
Web: http://www.kmpg.ie
SIC: 72200 Employees: 100
Computer Software
Mr Jerome Kenney Managing Partner
Mr Gerard Flood Corporate Finance Manager

KPMG Consulting
Russell Court
St Stephens Green
Dublin 2
Phone: 01-4101444 Fax: 01-7081888
Email: ie-fm-kpmg@kpmgconsulting.ie
Web: http://www.kpmgconsulting.ie
SIC: 72200 Employees: 27
Computer Software Consultants
Mr John Condon Manager
Mr Mark Donaghy Sales & Marketing Manager

Lionbridge Technologies
Grattan House
Temple Road
Blackrock Co. Dublin
Phone: 01-2886200 Fax: 01-2886220
Email: info@lionbridge.com
Web: http://www.lionbridge.com
SIC: 72200 Employees: 100
Software Translation
Mr Noel Finnegan General Manager
Ms Deirdre Attridge Financial Controller
Ms Geraldine O'Donovan Human Resources Manager
Ms Helena Walshe Sales Manager
Mr Conor Smyth Group Head of IT

Lisheen Mine
Kiltoran
Moyne
Thurles Co. Tipperary
Phone: 0504-45600 Fax: 0504-45700
Email: info@lisheenmine.ie
Web: http://www.lisheenmine.ie
SIC: 72200 Employees: 280
Software Supply/Sales.Localisation
Mr Sean McCormack Chief Executive

Lotus Development
Unit 12 Airways Industrial Estate
Cloghran
Dublin 17
Phone: 01-8427222 Fax: 01-8427400
Email: info@lotus.com
Web: http://www.lotus.com
SIC: 72200 Employees: 664
Software Development/Manufacturer
Mr Michael Cusack Chief Executive
Mr Michael Shelton Financial Controller
Mr Sean O'Reilly Computer Manager

Marine Computation Services Ltd
Lismoyle House
Merchants Road
Galway Co. Galway
Phone: 091-566455 Fax: 091-566457
Email: info@mcs-international.com
Web: http://www.mcs-internet.com
SIC: 72200 Employees: 23
Engineering Software
Mr John Conroy Managing Director
Mr Des Higgins Accounts Manager

Matel Interactus
Adalaide House
7-8 Haddington Terrace
Dun Laoghaire Co. Dublin
Phone: 01-6638222 Fax: 01-2311119
SIC: 72200 Employees: 35
Computer Software
Mr Fergus Rigley General Manager
Mr Brian O'Neill Finance Manager

McKeown Software
2 Marshalsea Court
23 Merchants Quay
Dublin 8
Phone: 01-6715877 Fax: 01-4183101
Email: ireland@mckeown.com
Web: http://www.mckeown.com
SIC: 72200 Employees: 70
Computer Software
Mr Eamon Morris Director
Mr Brendan Coyne Financial Controller

Mentor Graphics (Ireland) Ltd
Bay 127 Shannon Free Zone
Shannon Co. Clare
Phone: 061-716200 Fax: 061-716202
Email: info@mentor.com
Web: http://www.mentorg.ie
SIC: 72200 Employees: 47
Software Duplication
Mr John O'Mara Managing Director

Microsoft European Operations Centre
Blackthorn Road
Sandyford Industrial Estate
Dublin 18
Phone: 01-2953826 Fax: 01-2953581
Web: http://www.microsoft.com
SIC: 72200 Employees: 1500
Software Manufacture & Distributors
Mr Kevin Dillon General Manager
Mr Pat Hale Finance Manager
Mr Phil Carney Personnel Manager
Ms Anne Riordan Marketing Manager
Mr Bernard Brogan Production Manager
Mr Neil Greaney IT Director

Microsol Ltd
Unit 28 Enterprise Centre
Pearse Street
Dublin 2
Phone: 01-6716255 Fax: 01-6716343
Email: microsol@iol.ie
Web: http://www.microsol.ie
SIC: 72200 Employees: 80
Development of Hardware & Software Products
Mr Denis O'Connor Chief Executive
Mr Martin Kelly Financial Controller
Mr Enda Mimnagh Sales Manager

Midia Distribution
Unit B Montone Business Park
Oak Road
Dublin 12
Phone: 01-4199700 Fax: 01-4199700
Email: info@midia.ie
Web: http://www.midia.ie
SIC: 72200 Employees: 40
Computer Software
Mr Tim Farrelly Managing Director
Mr Colin Quarry Finance Manager
Mr Andrew Healy Sales & Marketing Manager
Mr Eoin Mulligan Technical Director

Mobile Aware Ltd
3225 Lake Drive National Digital Pk
Citywest Business Campus
Dublin 24
Phone: 01-2410500 Fax: 01-2410501
SIC: 72200 Employees: 60
Software Technology
Mr Brian Collins Chief Executive Officer
Mr Chris Foxton Finance Officer
Ms Sinead Brennan Personnel Manager
Mr David McGeough Sales Manager
Mr Brian Kinane Computer Manager

Modus Media International
Clonshaugh Industrial Estate
Coolock
Dublin 17
Phone: 01-8036300 Fax: 01-8484014
Email: info@modusmedia.com
Web: http://www.modusmedia.com
SIC: 72200 Employees: 400
Computer Software
Mr Edward Nugent Managing Director
Ms Sandra Doyle Human Resources Manager

MPO (Ireland) Ltd
Blanchardstown Industrial Estate
Snugborough Road Blanchardstown
Dublin 15
Phone: 01-8221363 Fax: 01-8066064
Web: http://www.mpo.fr
SIC: 72200 Employees: 140
Manufacture Computer Games
Mr John Mullane Managing Director
Ms Sarah O'Callaghan Financial Controller
Ms Aine O'Sullivan Human Resources Manager
Mr Patrick Mongey Production Manager

National Instruments Ire
Willsborough Industrial Estate
Clonshaugh
Dublin 17
Phone: 01-8621540 Fax: 01-8673003
Web: http://www.ni.com
SIC: 72200 Employees: 45
Make Hardware Appliances For Computers
Mr Michael O'Conner Managing Director
Ms Ellen O'Dwyer Sales Manager

Network 365
Glencormack Business Park
Kilmacanogue
Bray Co. Wicklow
Phone: 01-2764500 Fax: 01-2764533
Email: info@network365.com
Web: http://www.network365.com
SIC: 72200 Employees: 64
Mobile Commerce Software
Mr Raomal Perera Chief Executive Officer
Mr Kevin McGrath Chief Finance Officer
Mr Pax Anderson VP of Sales
Ms Elaine Galbraith Director of Operations
Mr Denis Hennessy Chief Technical Officer

Novell
Treasury Building
Lower Grand Canal Street
Dublin 2
Phone: 01-6058000 Fax: 01-6058200
Web: http://www.novell.ie
SIC: 72200 Employees: 80
Software Networking
Ms Caroline Lonergan Chief Executive
Mr Gerry Reilly Personnel Manager
Mr Wayne Ross IT Manager

O & E Group Ltd
O & E House, Furze Road
Sandyford Industrial Estate, Foxrock
Dublin 18
Phone: 01-5001600 Fax: 01-5001699
Email: oegroup@indigo.ie
SIC: 72200 Employees: 60
Computer Software
Mr Michael Hassett Managing Director
Ms Jenny Hassett Finance Director
Mr Paschal Kennedy Sales Director
Ms Fiona Berkery IT Marketing Manager

Octagon
Beechill
Clonskeagh
Dublin 14
Phone: 01-2602497 Fax: 01-2602698
Email: info@octagon.ie
Web: http://www.octagon.ie
SIC: 72200 Employees: 30
Provide E Business Solutions
Mr Leo Kearns Managing Director
Mr Tom McCormaick Finance Manager
Ms Carol McHugh Sales & Marketing Executive

Office Integrated Solutions
114-115 Grafton Street
Dublin 2
Phone: 01-6764307 Fax: 01-6774034
Email: info@ois.ie
Web: http://www.e-purchasing.com
SIC: 72200 Employees: 25
Computer Software
Mr Tom Stringer Managing Director
Ms Mairead Casey Finance Manager
Mr Eoin Maguire Sales Manager

Oracle Europe
Oracle House
Herbert Street
Dublin 2
Phone: 01-8031000 Fax: 01-8031951
Email: info@oracle.com
Web: http://www.oracle.com
SIC: 72200 Employees: 1500
Software Manufacture & Sales
Mr Dermot O'Kelly Chief Executive

Peats World of Electronics
197/200 Parnell Street
Dublin 1
Phone: 01-8727799 Fax: 01-8727646
Email: shop@peats.com
Web: http://www.peats.com
SIC: 72200 Employees: 50
Computer Games
Mr Ken Peats Managing Director

Phoenix Technology Group
Phoenix House
32-34 Castle Street
Dublin 2
Phone: 01-6707722 Fax: 01-6707721
Email: solution@phoenix.ie
Web: http://www.phoenix.ie
SIC: 72200 Employees: 65
Computer Software
Mr John Feighan Managing Director
Ms Agnes Nugent Personnel Manager
Ms Brigid Walsh Business Development Manager

PKS
Avoca Centre
Temple Road
Blackrock Co. Dublin
Phone: 01-2833199 Fax: 01-6764909
Email: info@rajen.com
Web: http://www.rajen.com
SIC: 72200 Employees: 200
Computer Software Development
Mr John Colgan Managing Director
Ms Catriona Muldowney Secretary
Mr Willy Byrne Sales Manager

PMI Software Ltd
Hainault House, The Square
Tallaght
Dublin 24
Phone: 01-4040000 Fax: 01-4599794
Email: info@pmisoftware.com
Web: http://www.pmisoftware.com
SIC: 72200 Employees: 70
Software Promoters
Mr Larry Tobin Director
Mr Larry Westland Financial Controller
Ms Ann Doheny Office Manager
Ms Donna O'Shea Sales Manager
Mr Brian Priestly Production Manager

Point Information Systems Ltd
Embassy House
Ballsbridge
Dublin 4
Phone: 01-6767755 Fax: 01-6020101
Email: info@pointinfo.com
Web: http://www.pointinfo.com
SIC: 72200 Employees: 70
Software Developent
Mr Keith Holmes Vice President Research & Dev
Ms Anne Deacon Financial Controller
Mr Colm Feely IT Manager

POS Group
Glandore House Malahide Road
Balgriffin
Dublin 17
Phone: 01-8485599 Fax: 01-8485563
Email: possystems@tinet.ie
Web: http://www.possystems.ie
SIC: 72200 Employees: 50
Software Development
Mr Nicholas Connell Managing Director
Mr Terry Tew Financial Controller
Mr John Hatch Services Manager
Mr Ralph Llewellyn Software Development Manager

Precision Software Ltd
Castlewood House Castlewood Avenue
Rathmines
Dublin 6
Phone: 01-4060700 Fax: 01-4060799
Email: info@precisionsoftware.com
Web: http://www.precisionsoftware.com
SIC: 72200 Employees: 135
Software Development
Mr Joe Fitzpatrick Office Manager
Mr Billy Power Financial Controller
Ms Vivienne Gleeson Personnel Manager
Mr Robert Campbell Marketing Manager

Precision Software Ltd
31 The Mall
Waterford Co. Waterford
Phone: 051-870022 Fax: 051-858614
SIC: 72200 Employees: 80
Precision Software
Mr Brendan O'Donoghue Managing Director
Mr Billy Power Financial Controller

Premier Computer Group
Premier Group House
Camden Lock South Dock Road
Dublin 4
Phone: 01-6670011 Fax: 01-6670055
SIC: 72200 Employees: 70
Computer Software
Mr Mark Howell Managing Director
Ms Helena Mulcahy Finance Manager
Ms Bernadette Elliott Sales Manager
Mr Leo McCarthy IT Manager

Priority Data Systems Ltd
Priority House
63 Patrick Street
Dun Laoghaire Co. Dublin
Phone: 01-2845600 Fax: 01-2800311
Email: sales@prioritydata.ie
Web: http://www.prioritydata.ie
SIC: 72200 Employees: 44
Anti Virus Software & Technical Support
Mr Alec Florence Group Managing Director
Mr Eoin Kane Accounts Manager
Mr Kevin Hanley Personnel Manager
Mr Paul Hendrick Technical Director

Qualtrace Solutions
Cork Airport Business Park
Cork Co. Cork
Phone: 021-4807210 Fax: 021-4975229
Web: http://www.qualtrace.com
SIC: 72200 Employees: 40
Computer Software
Mr Donald Deaxy Chief Executive
Mr Francis Kenny Finance Manager
Mr Tim Bell Personnel Manager
Ms Maureen McDaid Sales & Marketing Manager

Quest Computing Ltd
31/33 Ushers court
Ushers Quay
Dublin 8
Phone: 01-6799933 Fax: 01-6799936
Email: info@quest.ie
Web: http://www.quest.ie
SIC: 72200 Employees: 35
Software Development & Consultancy
Mr Steve Wilson Managing Director
Mr Peter Howard Accounts Clerk
Mr Mervyn Coltan Personnel Manager

Qumas Ltd
Monahan Road
Cork Co. Cork
Phone: 021-4320050 Fax: 021-4320394
Email: cork@qumas.com
Web: http://www.qumas.com
SIC: 72200 Employees: 80
Computer Software
Mr David Grimes Joint Managing Director
Mr Michael Hennessey Finance Manager
Mr David Cronan Sales & Marketing Manager

RAM Technologies Ltd
Unit 5 The Court
Ashbourne Industrial Park, Ashbourne
Ashbourne Co. Meath
Phone: 01-8351504 Fax: 01-8351442
Email: sales@ramtechnologies.ie
Web: http://www.ramtechnologies.ie
SIC: 72200 Employees: 25
Computer Software/Duplication of CDR/Screen Print
Mr Cormac Lawless General Manager
Ms Darragh Duggan Sales Manager

Rand Worldwide
3016 Lake Drive City West Bus Campus
Naas Road
Dublin 24
Phone: 01-4660240 Fax: 01-4035899
Web: http://www.rand.com
SIC: 72200 Employees: 45
Computer Software
Mr Angelo Katfinos Manager
Ms Margaret Devereux Management Accountant

Resolution Technology Ltd
Ground Floor Hume House
Ballsbridge
Dublin 4
Phone: 01-6672634 Fax: 01-6672650
Email: quinlanl@restech.ie
SIC: 72200 Employees: 40
Software Services
Mr Cyril McGann Manager
Mr Gene Byrne Financial Controller

Riverdeep
3rd Floor Styne House
Upper Hatch Street
Dublin 2
Phone: 01-6707570 Fax: 01-6707626
Email: info@riverdeep.net
Web: http://www.riverdeep.net
SIC: 72200 Employees: 70
Computer Software
Mr Barry O'Callaghan Chief Executive Officer
Mr Dominic Griffin Technical Officer

Ross Systems Ltd
Clonard House
Sandyford Road
Dublin 16
Phone: 01-2954011 Fax: 01-2954012
Email: info@rossirl.ie
Web: http://www.rossinc.com
SIC: 72200 Employees: 30
Computer Software
Mr Lonan Byrne Managing Director

Sepro Telecom International Ltd
Unit 7 Dundrum Business Park
Windy Arbour
Dublin 14
Phone: 01-2964428 Fax: 01-4332199
Email: info@seprobilling.com
Web: http://www.seprobilling.com
SIC: 72200 Employees: 50
Computer Software
Mr Declan Ganter Executive Director
Mr Stephen Ryan Accountant
Mr Martin Morgan Head of Marketing

Siebel Systems Ireland Ltd
Galway Business Park
Dangan
Galway Co. Galway
Phone: 091-518400 Fax: 091-518432
Web: http://www.sibel.com/ireland
SIC: 72200 Employees: 50
Computer Software
Mr Seamus Kilbane Managing Director

Simultrans
River House
54-72 East Wall Road
Dublin 3
Phone: 01-4784567 Fax: 01-8556551
Email: Info@simultrans.ie
Web: http://www.simultrans.ie
SIC: 72200 Employees: 50
Localisation - Translating Software
Mr Glynn O'Leary Managing Director
Mr Darren Barlow Finance Manager

Software Resources Ltd
Heron House Corrig Road
Sandyford Business Park
Dublin 18
Phone: 01-2074700 Fax: 01-2074777
Email: info@srl.ie
Web: http://www.jdedwards.com
SIC: 72200 Employees: 40
Computer Software
Mr Joe Gorman Managing Director
Mr Derek McClean Financial Controller
Mr Ted Creed Technical Director

Software Spectrum Ltd
Merrion House
Merrion Road
Dublin 4
Phone: 01-2601788 Fax: 01-2601799
Web: http://www.softwarespectrum.com
SIC: 72200 Employees: 65
Software Products
Ms Rhonda Robati Director - European Operations
Mr David Flynn Financial Controller
Mr Donald Kehoe Sales & Marketing Manager
Mr Charles Watchorn Director Of European Operation
Mr Russell Gascoine Technical Manager

Softworks Computing Ltd
111 Main Street
Bray Co. Wicklow
Phone: 01-2866126 Fax: 01-2866135
Email: sales@softworks-computing.com
Web: http://www.softworks-computing.com
SIC: 72200 Employees: 25
Software Development
Mr Andrew Ferguson Managing Director
Ms Lisa Donohoe Financial Controller
Mr Paul O'Connell Customer Services Manager
Ms Leontia Brophy Senior Sales Executive
Mr Rene Kral Technical Director

SSE Ltd
Fitzwilliam Court
Leeson Close
Dublin 2
Phone: 01-2162900 Fax: 01-2162082
Email: info@sse.ie
Web: http://www.sse.ie
SIC: 72200 Employees: 60
Software Development
Mr Paul Dhesi Chief Executive Officer
Mr Gerry McMonagle Finance Director

Storm Technology Ltd
Galway Business Park
Upper Newcastle Road
Galway Co. Galway
Phone: 091-509770 Fax: 091-509771
Email: info@storm.ie
Web: http://www.storm.ie
SIC: 72200 Employees: 40
Computer Software
Mr Frank Boyle Managing Director
Mr Karl Flannery Sales Bus Development Manager

Sun Life Ireland
Unit 42
IDA Industrial Estate
Waterford Co. Waterford
Phone: 051-333303 Fax: 051-333310
Email: ireland_recruitment@sunlife.com
Web: http://www.sunlife.ie
SIC: 72200 Employees: 100
Software Services
Mr Brendan Maher Managing Director
Mr Patrick Bruen Financial Controller

System House Technology
South County Business Park
Leopardstown Road
Dublin 18
Phone: 01-2401000 Fax: 01-2401001
Email: info@systemhouse.ie
Web: http://www.systemhouse.com
SIC: 72200 Employees: 27
Computer Software
Mr Dermot Williams Managing Director
Ms Wendy Thornton Financial Controller
Mr Michael Phelan Sales Manager

Systems Solutions Ltd
Rosemount Court 89a Booterstown Ave
Blackrock Co. Dublin
Phone: 01-2781711 Fax: 01-2781733
Email: sales@syssol.ie
Web: http://www.syssol.ie
SIC: 72200 Employees: 25
Software Development
Mr Richard Mulcahy Managing Director
Mr Gerard O'Sullivan Financial Controller
Mr Austin Crowe Sales Manager
Mr David Rathorne Technical Services Director

Techmatic Ltd
Unit 1 Newgrange Business Park
Donore Road
Drogheda Co. Louth
Phone: 041-9841372 Fax: 041-9841370
Email: info@techmatic.iol.ie
Web: http://www.tech-matic.com
SIC: 72200 Employees: 25
Hardware Recycling & Software
Mr Tom Reilly Managing Director
Ms Deirdre Winters Finance Manager
Ms Michelle Bradley Personnel Manager
Mr Joe Hand Sales Manager
Mr Mark Meis Computer Manager

Telekinesys Research Ltd
7 Westland Court
Dublin 2
Phone: 01-6778705 Fax: 01-6767094
Email: info@havok.com
Web: http://www.havok.com
SIC: 72200 Employees: 30
Computer Software
Mr Hugh Reynolds Manager
Mr Mick Gallagher Financial Controller
Mr Alan Murphy Sales Manager
Mr Evin Levey Computer Manager

Torex Health Ireland
St John's Court
Swords Road
Dublin 9
Phone: 01-8420009 Fax: 01-8420927
Email: info@torex.com
Web: http://www.torex.com
SIC: 72200 Employees: 25
Software Development
Mr Dermot O'Neill Manager

Transware Ltd
2B Clonskeagh Square
Dublin 14
Phone: 01-2601997 Fax: 01-2601947
Email: info@transware.ie
Web: http://www.transware.ie
SIC: 72200 Employees: 120
Software Localisation
Mr Kieran McBrien Managing Director
Mr Bill Mullen Financial Controller
Mr Gerry Owens Sales & Marketing Manager
Mr Wayne O'Sullivan Director - Information Systems

Trilogie
Unit 91A Lagan Road
Glasnevin
Dublin 11
Phone: 01-8444066 Fax: 01-8444065
Email: info@trilog.ie
Web: http://www.trilog.ie
SIC: 72200 Employees: 25
Software Solutions / Digital Print CD & Enfillment
Mr Brian Deane Managing Director
Ms Miriam Wynne Finance Manager
Mr Tony Barry Sales Manager
Mr Paul McDonnell Operation Manager
Mr David Burke IT Manager

Trintech Technology
South County Business Park
Leopardstown
Dublin 18
Phone: 01-2074176 Fax: 01-2074190
Email: info@trintech.com
Web: http://www.trintech.com
SIC: 72200 Employees: 300
Software Company
Mr Cyril Maguire Managing Director
Mr Paul Byrne Financial Controller
Mr Conor Dowd Sales Manager
Mr Kim Searle Computer Manager

Vordel Ltd
Cranford House
Cranford Court
Dublin 4
Phone: 01-2153333 Fax: 01-2153334
Email: info@vordel.com
Web: http://www.vordel.com
SIC: 72200 Employees: 50
Software
Mr David Ryan Chief Executive Officer

Xiam Ltd
Alexandra House The Sweetsteaks
Block C Ballsbridge
Dublin 4
Phone: 01-6642400 Fax: 01-6319001
Email: info@xiam.com
Web: http://www.xiam.com
SIC: 72200 Employees: 30
Information Routers
Mr Robert Baker Managing Director

Zenith Technologies Ltd
Portgate Business Park
Ringaskiddy
Cork Co. Cork
Phone: 021-4370200 Fax: 021-4370299
Email: info@zentek.ie
Web: http://www.zentek.ie
SIC: 72200 Employees: 70
Software Development for Engineering Sector
Mr Brendan O'Regan Managing Director
Mr Mark MacIlwraith Financial Controller
Mr Brendan O'Connell Sales Manager

MTI Technology Ireland Ltd
Unit 5 Blanchardstown Corporate Park
Ballycoolin
Dublin 15
Phone: 01-8850500 Fax: 01-8850555
Email: info@ie.mti.com
Web: http://www.mti.co.uk
SIC: 72400 Employees: 30
Data Storage
Mr Nick Bolan Chief Executive
Mr Brian Dunne Financial Controller
Mr Adrian Peters MIS Co-Ordinator

Data Exchange
Clonshaugh Industrial Estate
Dublin 17
Phone: 01-8486555 Fax: 01-8486559
Email: info@dex2.com
Web: http://www.dex.com
SIC: 72500 Employees: 40
Maintenance & Repair Computer Equipment
Mr Maurice Regan Managing Director
Ms Aisling Clancy Accounts Manager
Mr Mike Holt European Sales Manager

Synstar International
Unit 50 Airways Industrial Estate
Santry
Dublin 9
Phone: 01-8429755 Fax: 01-8429937
Email: info@synstar.ie
SIC: 72500 Employees: 80
Computer Maintenance
Mr Ian Byrne Manager
Ms Siobhan Kenny Finance Manager
Mr Alan Whelan Sales Manager

AND Data Ireland Ltd
1a Ballybrit Business Park
Galway Co. Galway
Phone: 091-771333 Fax: 091-771344
Email: postmaster@and.com
Web: http://www.and.com
SIC: 72601 Employees: 75
Electronic Publishing & Software
Mr John Flannery Managing Director
Ms Cora Grimes Personnel Manager
Mr Dominic Gallagher Production Manager
Mr Tom Anglin Computer Manager

ARI Services Europe
Raheen Industrial Estate
Limerick Co. Limerick
Phone: 061-492000 Fax: 061-492266
Email: sales@arise-europe.com
Web: http://www.arise-europe.com
SIC: 72601 Employees: 50
Computer Service & Repair
Mr Joe Cahalane Managing Director
Mr Ger Moore Finance Manager
Ms Ann McMahon Personnel Manager
Mr Dan Wyngaard Computer Manager

ATI Technologies (Europe) Ltd
Swords Business Park
Swords Co. Dublin
Phone: 01-8077800 Fax: 01-8077820
Email: info@ati.com
Web: http://www.ati.com
SIC: 72601 Employees: 95
Graphics for Computers
Mr Patrick Redmond Managing Director

Berlitz Globalnet
3 West Pier Business Campus
Dun Laoghaire Co. Dublin
Phone: 01-2021200 Fax: 01-2021299
Email: info@berlitz.ie
Web: http://www.berlitz.ie
SIC: 72601 Employees: 450
Computer Translation Service
Mr Brian Kelly Chief Executive
Mr Ken Murphy Finance Manager
Mr David Silverlock Personnel Manager
Mr Michael Gavin Marketing Manager
Mr Wojtex Kosinski Computer Manager

CMS Peripherals Ltd
Kiltimagh
Claremorris Co. Mayo
Phone: 094-81871 Fax: 094-81874
Email: info@cmsperipherals.com
Web: http://www.cmsperipherals.com
SIC: 72601 Employees: 45
Computer Data Storage
Mr Frank Salmon Managing Director
Ms Elizabeth Froude Financial Controller
Mr Peadar Dolan Sales Manager
Mr James Wilkins Technical Manager

CSC Financial Services Group
5th Floor Marine House
Clanwilliam Place
Dublin 2
Phone: 01-6618288 Fax: 01-6618255
SIC: 72601 Employees: 150
Computer Programmers
Ms Noleen Lowry Managing Director
Ms Sarah Campbell Finance Manager
Ms Linda Rogers Personnel Manager
Ms Sandra Conroy Computer Manager

Data & Records Management Ltd
Benson House
6a Benson Street
Dublin 2
Phone: 01-6704367 Fax: 01-6704468
Email: datamc2@iol.ie
SIC: 72601 Employees: 35
Computer Recovery
Mr Eugene Gibney Managing Director
Mr Glen Reed Financial Controller

Dataconversion
25/26 Westland Square
Dublin 2
Phone: 01-6771466 Fax: 01-6771521
Email: info@dataconversion.ie
Web: http://www.dataconversion.ie
SIC: 72601 Employees: 80
Computing & Bureau Services
Mr Raymond O'Kelly Managing Director
Ms Carmel Gilroy Accounts Administrator
Ms Mary Killeen Personnel Manager
Mr Jimmy Fearon Sales & Marketing Director
Mr Dermot Killeen IT Director

DDC Ireland Ltd
Cork Business & Technology Park
Model Farm Road
Cork Co. Cork
Phone: 021-4341065 Fax: 021-4341568
Email: info@ddc-web.com
Web: http://www.ddc-web.com
SIC: 72601 Employees: 120
Data Conversion for aerospace industry
Mr Richard Buckley Managing Director
Ms Carmel Mulcahy Financial Controller
Mr Kieran Casey Production Manager
Mr Brian Cowman IT Manager

EDC Communications
355 North Circular Road
Dublin 7
Phone: 01-4535100 Fax: 01-4535101
Email: info@edccom.com
Web: http://www.edccom.com
SIC: 72601 Employees: 40
Network Design & Installation
Mr Damien Lynch Managing Director
Ms Flor Hill Finance Manager
Mr Roddy Devlin Network Support

Equator
25/26 Great Strand Street
Dublin 1
Phone: 01-8746923 Fax: 01-8746928
Web: http://www.eequator.com
SIC: 72601 Employees: 50
Computer Design
Mr Steven Killik Director

European Manufacturing Services Ltd
Unit 10D Airways Industrial Estate
Santry
Dublin 9
Phone: 01-8621600 Fax: 01-8621604
Email: info@ems.iol.ie
Web: http://www.euro-man.ie
SIC: 72601 Employees: 98
Solutions to the Computer Electronic Industry
Mr Frank Kilbride General Manager
Ms Olive O'Malley Financial Controller
Ms Deborah Reilly Personnel Manager
Mr Michael Malone Computer Manager

Galileo Ireland
Palmerston House
Fenian Street
Dublin 2
Phone: 01-6020444 Fax: 01-6020433
Email: info@galileo.ie
Web: http://www.galileo.ie
SIC: 72601 Employees: 62
Computer Reservation Services Systems
Mr Shay Mitchell Chief Executive
Mr Peter Cahill Financial Controller
Ms Alison Bell Marketing Manager
Mr Rob Cowan IT Manager

Horizon Technology Group Plc
Lower Glanmire Road
Cork Co. Cork
Phone: 021-4514700 Fax: 021-4514701
Web: http://www.horizon.ie
SIC: 72601 Employees: 300
Computers/Software Consultants/Training
Mr Charles Garvey Chief Executive
Ms Colette Murphy Finance Manager
Ms Danielle Kelly Human Resources Manager
Mr Donal O'Donoghue IT Administrator

I-flow Tech (Ireland) Plc
Watson & Johnson Innovation Centre
Mill Road
Greystones Co. Wicklow
Phone: 01-2873077 Fax: 01-2874524
Email: centralmailserver@iflow.ie
Web: http://www.iflow-tech.com
SIC: 72601 Employees: 51
Email/Internet/Fax Communication & Broadcasting
Mr Pete Williams Chief Executive Officer
Ms Sue Vialino Finance Director
Mr Abdlu Accko Personnel Officer
Mr Pabo McSillan Sales Director
Mr Llew Aambirga Operation Manager
Mr Dermot O'Solvon IT & MIS Manager

ICM Uni Comp
ICM House
Mountrath Road
Portlaoise Co. Laois
Phone: 0502-22651 Fax: 0502-20384
Email: sales@icmunicomp.ie
Web: http://www.icmunicomp.ie
SIC: 72601 Employees: 35
Process Control Systems for Feed Mill Business
Mr Ray Lawlor Managing Director
Mr Taco Camphuijsen Financial Controller
Ms Pauline Phelan Sales & Purchasing
Mr Pearse McNicholl Operations Manager

ICPC
Greencastle Parade
Coolock
Dublin 17
Phone: 01-8474711 Fax: 01-8474157
Web: http://www.icpc.ie
SIC: 72601 Employees: 42
Typesetting
Mr James McCague Managing Director
Mr Edward Bowe Computer Manager

Interface Business Information
Brighton House
121 Lower Rathmines Road
Dublin 6
Phone: 01-4060606 Fax: 01-4962212
Email: sales@interface.ie
Web: http://www.interface.ie
SIC: 72601 Employees: 25
Computer Company
Mr Paul French Managing Director
Ms Siobhan French Accounts Manager
Mr Jim Boland IT Manager

Irish Micro Film Systems
Unit A3 IDA Industrial Estate
Santry
Dublin 9
Phone: 01-8424144 Fax: 01-8424052
Email: imsi@indigo.ie
SIC: 72601 Employees: 120
Microfilming CD Rom Scanning
Mr Bob Doyle Managing Director
Mr Peter Murphy Financial Controller
Ms Lisa Brady Office Manager
Mr Peter Murphy Sales Manager
Mr Brian Campbell IT Manager

ISI Ireland Ltd
Block 2 International Business Ctr
Plassey National Technology Park
Limerick Co. Limerick
Phone: 061-330077 Fax: 061-330080
SIC: 72601 Employees: 80
Data Production
Ms Ann Donoghue General Manager
Mr Pascal Reagan Finance Manager
Ms Helen Alfred Operations Manager
Mr Clem Harrington IT Manager

IT Alliance
Floor 2, Park House
North Circular Road
Dublin 7
Phone: 01-8690200 Fax: 01-8690201
Email: info@italliancegroup.com
Web: http://www.italliancegroup.com
SIC: 72601 Employees: 280
IT Services
Mr Philip Magurie Chief Executive Officer
Mr Paul O'Brien Financial Controller
Mr Jackie Ellis Sales & Marketing Manager
Mr Paul Fannin Computer Manager

Jabil Global Service
Clonshaugh Industrial Estate
Dublin 17
Phone: 01-8427244 Fax: 01-8022990
Web: http://www.jabil.ie
SIC: 72601 Employees: 180
Computer Services
Mr Liam O'Halloran Managing Director
Mr Mark Doyle Financial Controller
Ms Aileen O'Toole Personnel Manager
Mr Frank Monaghan Sales Manager
Mr George McNamara Production Manager
Mr John O'Reilly IT Manager

JLS Technology Ltd
JLS House, Joyce Way Park West Business Park
Nangor Road
Dublin 12
Phone: 01-6209000 Fax: 01-6209019
Email: postmaster@jls.ie
Web: http://www.jls.ie
SIC: 72601 Employees: 40
Computer Services
Mr Robert Johnston Managing Director
Mr John Lynch Company Accountant
Mr John Sexton Sales & Marketing Director
Mr Paul Comerford Computer Manager

Local Government Computer Services Board
Phoenix House
27 Conyngham Road
Dublin 8
Phone: 01-6097000 Fax: 01-6097001
Email: info@lgcsb.ie
Web: http://www.lgcsb.ie
SIC: 72601 Employees: 100
Local Authority Computer Services
Ms Brid Carter Director
Ms Barbara Richardson Secretary

McGraw-Hill (Data Services) Ltd
Ballybrit Business Park
Ballybrit
Galway Co. Galway
Phone: 091-755577 Fax: 091-755199
Email: info@mcgrawhill.com
Web: http://www.mcgrawhill.com
SIC: 72601 Employees: 55
Computing & Bureau Services (Provide a Service Only)
Mr Damien Meaney Managing Director
Ms Karen Smith Financial Controller
Mr Colm Anglim IT Manager

Medrex Systems Ireland Ltd
Unit H LEDP
Roxboro Road
Limerick Co. Limerick
Phone: 061-400033 Fax: 061-400040
Email: medrex@iol.ie
Web: http://www.medrex-systems.com
SIC: 72601 Employees: 50
Micro Filming
Mr Anthony O'Carroll Managing Director
Mr Peter Allison Sales Manager
Mr Ray Ryan Production Manager
Mr Robert McInerney Head of IT

Orbis Information Systems
Avondale Business Park
Carysfort Avenue
Blackrock Co. Dublin
Phone: 01-2112320 Fax: 01-2090130
Email: info@orb-is.com
Web: http://www.orb-is.com
SIC: 72601 Employees: 26
Computer Systems Integrator
Mr Michael Gannon Managing Director
Ms Loretta Smyth Finance Manager
Mr John Tobin Sales & Marketing Director
Mr Vincent Mullally IT Manager

Orbiscom Ireland
3 Sandyford Park
Sandyford Industrial Estate
Dublin 18
Phone: 01-2945111 Fax: 01-2945119
Email: info@orbiscom.com
Web: http://www.orbiscom.com
SIC: 72601 Employees: 60
Computer Services
Mr David Brennan Manager
Ms Hazel Melbourne HR Director
Mr Gary Lyons Head of Development

Portable Software Solutions Ltd
31-33 Ranelagh Triangle
Dublin 6
Phone: 01-4974298 Fax: 01-4974892
Web: http://www.portablesolutions.com
SIC: 72601 Employees: 30
Computer Services
Mr Eric Browne Managing Director
Mr Brian Maguire Finance Manager
Mr Mark Peplow Personnel Manager
Mr Andrew Southgate Sales & Marketing Manager
Mr John Doyle Computer Manager

QC Data (Ireland) Ltd
Cork Business & Technology Park
Model Farm Road
Cork Co. Cork
Phone: 021-4341700 Fax: 021-4343645
Email: info@cork.qcdata.com
Web: http://www.qcdata.com
SIC: 72601 Employees: 100
Data Conversion/Management
Mr Michael Kelleher Managing Director
Ms Lindsay Sherwin Accounts Manager
Ms Michelle Dineen Personnel Officer
Mr Cathal O'Dwyer Financial Controller
Ms Caroline O'Leary Technical Services Manager

Tomorrows World Ltd
Block 1 Ushers Court
Ushers Quay
Dublin 8
Phone: 01-6798666 Fax: 01-6791810
Email: postermaster@tomorrows.ie
Web: http://www.iol.ie/~tworld/
SIC: 72601 Employees: 35
Computer Services
Mr Neville Kutner Managing Director
Ms Clodagh McGuire Finance Manager
Mr Colm Whelan Sales & Marketing Manager
Mr Terry Devine Operations Manager
Mr Keith Gibbons Computer Manager

TSM Control Systems
The Demense
Dundalk Co. Louth
Phone: 042-9335560 Fax: 042-9334422
Email: info@tsm-controls.com
Web: http://www.tsm-controls.com
SIC: 72601 Employees: 28
Process Control Factory
Mr Jim O'Callaghan Managing Director
Ms Suzanne Flynn Accounts Manager
Mr Paul Shields Factory Manager
Mr Martin Kirk Sales Manager
Mr Damien Halfpenny Operations Manager

Typeform Reproduction
Unit 7 Portside Business Centre
East Wall Road
Dublin 3
Phone: 01-8553855 Fax: 01-8553853
Email: info@typeform.ie
Web: http://www.typeform.ie
SIC: 72601 Employees: 30
Typesetting & Computer Imaging
Mr Robert Healy General Manager
Ms Julie Finglas Company Accountant
Mr Alan O'Reilly Computer Manager

Abacus Systems & Networks Ltd
Unit 2&3 Mulcahy Keane Indust Estate
Greenhills Road
Dublin 12
Phone: 01-4569587 Fax: 01-4600804
Email: sales@abacus.ie
Web: http://www.abacus.ie
SIC: 72602 Employees: 30
Network Systems
Mr Derek O'Callaghan Managing Director
Mr Ciaran Bauer Finance Manager
Mr Eoghan Johnson Sales Manager
Mr Joe Walsh Operation Director

APW
Mahon Industrial Estate
Blackrock
Cork Co. Cork
Phone: 021-4357201 Fax: 021-4357745
Email: info@apw-enclosures.com
Web: http://www.apw.com
SIC: 72602 Employees: 400
Electronic Data Interchange
Ms Carol Flack Managing Director
Mr Sean Dowling Finance Manager
Ms Ruth Dalton Personnel Manager
Mr Andrew O'Donovan Sales Manager

Bootstrap Ltd
Clonard House
Sandyford
Dublin 16
Phone: 01-2952629 Fax: 01-2952435
Email: sales@bootstrap.ie
Web: http://www.bootstrap.ie
SIC: 72602 Employees: 35
Network Integration
Ms Pauline White Managing Director
Ms Rosaleen Thomas Sales Director

Broadcom Eireann Research Ltd
Kestrel House
Clanwilliam Place
Dublin 2
Phone: 01-6761531 Fax: 01-6761532
Email: bd@broadcom.ie
Web: http://www.broadcom.ie
SIC: 72602 Employees: 62
Telecommunication Development
Mr Gerry Cahill Chief Executive
Ms Sharon Gaffney Financial Controller
Ms Carmel O'Brien Personnel Manager
Ms Michelle Lamont Marketing Manager
Mr Terry Turner Operations Manager
Mr John McCarthy IT Manager

Comnitel Technologies Ltd
Unit 2200, Airport Business Park
Kinsale Road
Cork Co. Cork
Phone: 021-7305600 Fax: 021-7305624
Email: info@comnitel.com
Web: http://www.comnitel.com
SIC: 72602 Employees: 40
Mobile Network Systems
Mr Declan Fox Partner
Mr Kieran Moynihan partner

Crescent Communications
UA3 Cookstown Business Centre
Tallaght
Dublin 24
Phone: 01-4610044 Fax: 01-4610892
Email: info@cresentcommunications.ie
Web: http://www.cresentcommunications.ie
SIC: 72602 Employees: 25
Data Communications
Mr Derek Gough Chairman
Mr Eric Rochford Managing Director
Mr Tommy Stenson Office Manager
Mr Alan Kennedy Sales Director
Mr Derek Bonner Technical Director

DCB Group
Unit 5 The Mill Building
The Malting
Bray Co. Wicklow
Phone: 01-2869432 Fax: 01-2769090
Email: info@dcbgroup.com
Web: http://www.inmac.co.uk
SIC: 72602 Employees: 25
Networking Cabling Suppliers
Mr Jimmy Tomkins Managing Director
Ms Teresa Maddock Finance Manager
Ms Fiona Ryan Sales & Marketing Manager

Esat Business - System Integration
The Winter Garden
Hanover Street East
Dublin 2
Phone: 01-6704433 Fax: 01-6704979
Email: info@esatbusiness.com
Web: http://www.esatbusiness.com
SIC: 72602 Employees: 35
Data Communications
Mr Paul Rache Manager
Mr Joe O'Mahony Finance Manager

International Data Processing Ltd
Behins
Listowel Co. Kerry
Phone: 068-40468 Fax: 068-40468
Email: breda@idp.iol.ie
Web: http://www.idp-ireland.com
SIC: 72602 Employees: 30
Data Communications
Ms Jennifer Boyle Managing Director

Kedington Group
Unit 70
Baldoyle Industrial Estate
Dublin 13
Phone: 01-8325665 Fax: 01-8325642
Email: info@kedington.ie
Web: http://www.kedington.ie
SIC: 72602 Employees: 150
Data Communications
Mr Chris Berkeley Managing Director
Mr Joseph Kirwan Financial Controller
Mr Christy Hynes Sales Manager
Mr Colm Goodson Computer Manager

Marconi Communications
Swords Business Park
Swords Co. Dublin
Phone: 01-8084444 Fax: 01-8084400
Email: postmaster@marconi.com
Web: http://www.marconi.com
SIC: 72602 Employees: 260
High Performance Networking Products
Mr Ken Doyle General Manager
Mr John Baird Financial Director
Ms Carol Cassidy Human Resources Manager
Mr Peter O'Reilly IT Manager

MDS
Bray Co. Wicklow
Phone: 01-2050044 Fax: 01-8366492
Email: info@mds.ie
Web: http://www.mds.ie
SIC: 72602 Employees: 100
Produce Telephone Systems
Mr Pat O'Toole Senior Software Engineer

Memorex Telex Ireland
88/89 Furze Road
Sandyford Industrial Estate
Dublin 18
Phone: 01-2075700 Fax: 01-2075701
Email: info@memorex.ie
Web: http://www.memorex.ie
SIC: 72602 Employees: 70
Computer Network Integrator
Mr Paschal Naylor Managing Director
Mr Kevin Cooney Finance Manager
Mr Roy Harte Sales Director
Mr John McHale Customer Engineering Manager

Qualcom Network Solutions
3-4 Lower Kevin Street
Dublin 8
Phone: 01-4750202 Fax: 01-4750203
Email: personnel@qualcom.ie
Web: http://www.qualcom.ie
SIC: 72602 Employees: 30
Network Solutions - Computer Re-Seller
Mr Ken Breen Managing Director
Mr Alan Smiley Personnel Manager

Apple Centre Typetec
Ballymount Road
Dublin 12
Phone: 01-5009000 Fax: 01-5009090
Email: sales@typetec.ie
Web: http://www.typetec.ie
SIC: 72603 Employees: 40
Computers Sales
Mr Tom Close Managing Director
Mr Tom O'Brien Finance Manager
Mr Peter Daly Personnel Manager
Ms Beryl Furlong Sales Manager
Mr Kevin O'Loughlin IT Manager

Billy Donnellan
Dunamon
Roscommon Co. Roscommon
Phone: 086-8119297 Fax:
SIC: 72603 Employees: 23
Computers
Mr Billy Donnellan Proprietor

CK Business Electronics Ltd
17-21 Temple Road
Blackrock Co. Dublin
Phone: 01-2055388 Fax: 01-2055377
Email: info@ck-business.ie
Web: http://www.ck-biz.ie
SIC: 72603 Employees: 220
Computer Sales/Engineering/Training
Mr Gerry Gray Managing Director
Mr Eamon Connaughton Financial Controller
Mr Barney Keegan Sales Manager

Coleman Computer Services
Cork Road
Fermoy Co. Cork
Phone: 025-32211 Fax: 025-31089
Email: info@coleman.ie
Web: http://www.coleman.ie
SIC: 72603 Employees: 30
Develop Computer Software
Mr Richard Mackessy Managing Director
Mr James Parker Finance Manager
Mr Dermot Harris Personnel Manager
Mr Declan McGinn Business Solutions Manager
Mr Dermot Harris Technical Services & Dev Mange

Compaq Ireland Ltd
5th Floor Park House
195 North Circular Road
Dublin 7
Phone: 01-8385433 Fax: 01-8385285
Email: info@compaq.ie
Web: http://www.compaq.ie
SIC: 72603 Employees: 2000
Computer Sales
Mr Tom Keating Managing Director
Mr Derek Doran Finance Manager
Ms Catherine Lamb Personnel Manager
Mr John McCormick Sales Director
Mr Denis Fricker Computer Manager

Compustore Ltd
2B Avonbeg Industrial Estate
Long Mile Road
Dublin 12
Phone: 01-4506255 Fax: 01-4502159
Email: info@compustore.ie
Web: http://www.compustore.ie
SIC: 72603 Employees: 200
PC Supplier
Mr Kevin Buckley Managing Director
Mr Gavin Murphy Sales Manager
Mr Robert McCarthy Head of Technology

Data Direct 2000 Ltd
6 Citygate
Bridge Court
Dublin 8
Phone: 01-6707000 Fax: 01-6707200
Email: ddirect@iol.ie
Web: http://www.ddirect.net
SIC: 72603 Employees: 30
Computer Sales
Mr Stephen Campbell Managing Director
Mr Ciaran Hennessey Sales Manager

Dell Computers
Boghall Road
Bray Co. Wicklow
Phone: 01-2860500 Fax: 01-2862020
Email: info@dell.com
Web: http://www.dell.com
SIC: 72603 Employees: 6000
Computer Telemarketing
Mr Maurice Cowey Managing Director
Mr Thomas Dittrich Financial Director
Ms Rosaleen Gillespie Human Resources Director
Mr Tim McCarthy Sales Manager

DFF
Unit 2 Parkway House
Western Parkway Business Park
Dublin 2
Phone: 01-4509465 Fax: 01-4509503
Email: postmaster@decision.ie
Web: http://www.decision.ie
SIC: 72603 Employees: 30
Computer Reselling
Mr Richard Nolan Managing Director
Mr Ciaran Murray Finance Manager
Mr John Kennedy Sales Director
Mr David Cathal Computer Manager

Direct Memory International Ltd
Unit 2 Kilnagleary Bus Park
Carrigaline
Cork Co. Cork
Phone: 021-4919053 Fax: 021-4919044
Email: sales@dmi.ie
Web: http://www.dmi.ie
SIC: 72603 Employees: 200
Computer Sales
Mr Stuart Matthews Managing Director
Mr Ted Daly Finance Director
Mr Fred Sorensen Sales Director
Mr Tom Lynch Director - Information Systems

Document Systems Group
Unit 10 Calmounc Business Park
Ballymount Road
Dublin 12
Phone: 01-4131300 Fax: 01-4521643
Email: sales@dsg.ie
Web: http://www.dsg.ie
SIC: 72603 Employees: 30
IT Equipment & Office Automation Products
Mr Peter Kelly Managing Director
Ms Cora Mooney Finance Manager
Mr Derek Boyle Sales & Marketing Director
Mr John Walsh MIS Manager

ICL Ireland Ltd
ICL House Harcourt Centre
Harcourt Street
Dublin 2
Phone: 01-4756761 Fax: 01-4753078
Web: http://www.icl.ie
SIC: 72603 Employees: 350
Computer Sales/Services
Mr Brian Baird Chief Operating Officer
Mr Martin Davies Financial Director
Ms Theresa Cunningham Personnel Manager
Mr Des Fitzgerald Sales Director
Mr Pierce Tolan Production Manager
Mr Roy Atkinson Computer Manager

Jones Business Systems
Asker Business Park
O'Brien Road
Carlow Co. Carlow
Phone: 0503-32595 Fax: 0503-43121
Web: http://www.jbsoffice.com
SIC: 72603 Employees: 30
Computer Sales
Mr Michael Condon Managing Director
Ms Catherine Jones Finance Manager
Mr Sean Jones Sales & Marketing Manager

Keating Computer Services
Calaveras
Hilltown
Cork Co. Cork
Phone: 021-4373395 Fax:
SIC: 72603 Employees: 23
Computers
Mr P. Keating Manager

Kingston Technologies Ltd
Blanchardstown Industrial Park
Snugborough Road Blanchardstown
Dublin 15
Phone: 01-8122888 Fax: 01-8128840
Email: info@kingston.ie
Web: http://www.kingston.ie
SIC: 72603 Employees: 115
Computers Memory
Mr C Lynn Managing Director
Mr David Cowan Financial Controller
Mr Brendan McSweeney Sales & Marketing Manager
Mr Glen Cheggwidden Computer Manager

Multis Ltd
Mervue Industrial Estate
Galway Co. Galway
Phone: 091-757343 Fax: 091 757548
Email: sales@multis.ie
Web: http://www.multis.ie
SIC: 72603 Employees: 60
Computers Sales & Manufacture
Mr Sean Keenan Manager
Mr Tom Hogan Sales Manager

O'Sullivan Graphics
23/25 Grantham Street
Dublin 8
Phone: 01-4780528 Fax: 01-4780172
Email: sales@dosgs.ie
Web: http://www.osullivangraphics.com
SIC: 72603 Employees: 50
Computer Sales & Graphic Supplies
Mr Donal O'Sullivan Managing Director
Mr Terry Jackson Finance Manager
Ms Yvonne Whittle Personnel Manager
Ms Debbie Laffan Sales Manager
Mr Julian O'Sullivan Computer Manager

PC World
Blanchardstown Centre
Dublin 15
Phone: 01-8025555 Fax: 01-8025500
Email: pcworld@indigo.ie
Web: http://www.pcworld.co.uk
SIC: 72603 Employees: 60
Computer Shop
Mr Terry Mabey Manager
Ms Lisa O'Kelly Deputy Manager

PFH Computers
East Gate Avenue
East Gate, Little Island
Cork Co. Cork
Phone: 021-2303000 Fax: 021-2303090
Email: sales@pfh.ie
Web: http://www.pfh.ie
SIC: 72603 Employees: 70
Computer Maintenance & Repairs
Mr Paul Hourican Managing Director

QCL Technologies
Westboro House
Mountenotte
Cork Co. Cork
Phone: 021-4551844 Fax: 021-4551855
Email: info@qclonline.ie
Web: http://www.qclonline.com
SIC: 72603 Employees: 25
Computer Sales & Services
Mr Sean Nevin Managing Director
Mr Jack Casey Financial Director
Mr John Levis IT Manager

Scienific Systems
Unit 3 Howth Junctions Business Park
Killbarrack
Dublin 5
Phone: 01-8395122 Fax: 01-8395133
Email: info@scisys.com
Web: http://www.scisys.com
SIC: 72603 Employees: 30
Computer Systems
Mr Mike Hopkins Press Director
Mr Colin McAndrew Financial Controller
Ms Liz Crehan Personnel Manager
Ms Roisin Cheshire Sales & Marketing Manager
Mr Frank Cass Production Manager
Mr Stephen O'Connor Computer Manager

Smyth Computer Systems Ireland
Dublin 24
Phone: 01-4510748 Fax: 01-4624745
Email: jsmyth@iol.ie
SIC: 72603 Employees: 23
Computers
Mr M Smyth

Xpert Technology
Unit 3 Furze Court, Furze Road
Sandyford Industrial Estate
Dublin 18
Phone: 01-2130100 Fax: 01-2957646
Email: info@xpert.ie
Web: http://www.xpert.ie
SIC: 72603 Employees: 40
Computer Hardware Sales & Service
Mr Aidan Farrell Managing Director
Mr Jim Redmond Company Secretary
Mr James Delaney Computer Manager

Avocent International
Avocent House, Shannon Free Zone
Shannon Co. Clare
Phone: 061-471877 Fax: 061-471871
Email: info@avocent.ie
Web: http://www.avocent.ie
SIC: 72604 Employees: 120
Computer Hardware
Mr Kieran McSweeney Manager
Mr Ian Barrett Finance Manager
Ms Anne Goggin Personnel Manager
Mr Aiden O'Driscoll Sales & Marketing Manager
Mr Jim Hodnett Production Manager
Ms Diane McInerney Computer Manager

Benchmark Electronics Ireland Ltd
Blanchardstown Industrial Park
Blanchardstown
Dublin 15
Phone: 01-8096200 Fax: 01-8096500
Email: postmaster@bench.com
Web: http://www.bench.com
SIC: 72604 Employees: 250
Contract Electronic Manufacturing - Computer Systems
Mr Dick Hogan Managing Director
Mr Liam Murphy Finance Manager
Mr Tommy Dwyer Human Resources Manager
Mr Bill O'Dwyer Commercial Manager
Mr Derek Ryan Operation Manager
Mr Kevin McQuillan IT Manager

Bryan S Ryan
Main Road
Tallaght
Dublin 24
Phone: 01-4524499 Fax: 01-4524845
Email: info@bryansryan.ie
Web: http://www.bryansryan.ie
SIC: 72604 Employees: 200
Computer Supplies & Accessories
Mr Gary Rafter Managing Director
Mr Andy Clarkin Finance Manager
Ms Adrianne Prendergast Sales & Marketing Manager
Mr Trevor Atkins Computer Manager

Cara Group
27 Willsborough Industrial Estate
Clonshaugh
Dublin 17
Phone: 01-6619066 Fax: 01-8473370
Email: info@cara.ie
Web: http://www.cara.ie
SIC: 72604 Employees: 300
Computer Equipment and Accessories
Mr David Little Managing Director
Ms Carina Ginty Marketing Director
Mr Joe McDonald Production Manager
Mr Tommy Swan IT Manager

Datapac Ltd
Hilton House, Ardee Road
Rathmines
Dublin 6
Phone: 01-4068080 Fax: 01-4961805
Email: wexford@datapac.ie
Web: http://www.datapac.ie
SIC: 72604 Employees: 120
Computer Services
Mr David Laird Managing Director
Ms Edel Creely Sales Manager
Mr John Hickey IT Manager

DC Kavanagh Ltd
43 Dolphins Barn Street
Dublin 8
Phone: 01-4544299 Fax: 01-4540532
Email: dck@indigo.ie
SIC: 72604 Employees: 40
Computer Forms
Mr Connor Kavanagh Managing Director
Mr Ronan Quinn Finance Manager
Ms Eileen Kavanagh Sales & Marketing Manager
Mr Stewart Sinclair Computer Manager

Dennison Ireland
Foxhole Industrial Estate
Youghal Co. Cork
Phone: 024-92301 Fax: 024-92864
Web: http://www.avery.co.uk
SIC: 72604 Employees: 50
Manufacturers of Office Documentation
Mr Michael Fitzgerald Operations Manager
Ms Beatrice Poletti Financial Controller

Earrai Plaisteacha Cumhachta EPC Teo
2 Aonad Baile Na Buaile
Dingle
Tralee Co. Kerry
Phone: 066-9152033 Fax: 066-9152036
Email: epcteo@iol.ie
SIC: 72604 Employees: 25
Computer Cables Supplies
Mr Bill Hadnett Managing Director

EMC Ireland
IDA Industrial Park
Ovens
Cork Co. Cork
Phone: 021-4873888 Fax: 021-4281523
Email: emcirelandhr@isus.emc.com
Web: http://www.emc.com
SIC: 72604 Employees: 1600
Computer Data Storage
Ms Veronica Perdisatt Managing Director
Mr Ger Cowhig Financial Controller
Mr Colm Condon Human Resources Director
Mr Rod Sutherland Sales & Marketing Manager
Mr Bob Savage Engineering Director
Mr JB McCarthy IT Support Officer

Fitzpatrick Business Systems Ltd
Mill House
Henry Street
Limerick Co. Limerick
Phone: 061-416646 Fax: 061-417219
Email: sales@fbs.ie
Web: http://www.fbs.ie
SIC: 72604 Employees: 50
Personal Computer Supplier
Mr Ciaran Fitzpatrick Managing Director
Mr Ger Jackson Finance Manager

Microwarehouse
Unit 13 Park West Business Park
Nangor Road
Dublin 22
Phone: 01-6160400 Fax: 01-6232800
Email: info@mwh.ie
Web: http://www.mwh.ie
SIC: 72604 Employees: 70
Computer Hardware/Software Distribution
Mr Pat Tynan Chief Executive
Ms Denise Collins Finance Director
Mr Rory Wilson Sales Director
Mr Mick O'Toole IT Manager

OKI Systems (Ireland) Ltd
The Square Industrial Complex
Tallaght
Dublin 24
Phone: 01-4049590 Fax: 01-4049591
Web: http://www.oki.ie
SIC: 72604 Employees: 62
Computer Equipment
Mr Vic Saunders Managing Director
Mr Jim Doyle Financial Director
Ms Susan Condon PA To Managing Director
Mr Martin Deignan Sales & Marketing Manager
Mr Chris Murphy IT Manager

Romak Computers Ltd
Coes Road
Dundalk Co. Louth
Phone: 042-9327270 Fax: 042-9327271
Email: sales@romak.ie
Web: http://www.romak.ie
SIC: 72604 Employees: 27
Computer Hardware
Mr Dermot McElroy Manager
Mr Tom McGeough Sales

Ronnie Moore Ltd
Unit 9A South Cork Industrial Estate
Bicars Road Pouladuff
Cork Co. Cork
Phone: 021-4277841 Fax: 021-4277014
Email: sales@ronniemoore.ie
Web: http://www.ronniemoore.ie
SIC: 72604 Employees: 32
Computer Supplies & Accessories
Mr Ronnie Moore Managing Director
Mr Eamon Quinlan Sales Manager

Smart Force
Block 7 & 8 Bellfield Office Park
Clonskeagh
Dublin 4
Phone: 01-2110700 Fax: 01-2830379
Email: info@smartforce.com
Web: http://www.smartforce.com
SIC: 72604 Employees: 500
Research and Development in e-learning
Mr Tom Marsh Director of Development
Mr Richard Butler Finance Manager
Ms Lucy O'Driscoll Sales Manager

Tec -Source Ltd
15 Rosemount Business Park
Ballycoolin
Dublin 11
Phone: 01-8323979 Fax: 01-8225121
Email: info@techsource.ie
Web: http://www.techsource.ie
SIC: 72604 Employees: 230
Computer Products
Mr Patrick Kinney Managing Director
Mr John McKeown Financial Controller
Mr Ken Finnegan Sales & Marketing Manager
Mr Paul Kinney IT Manager

Trinity Technology Group
Maretimo Court
Temple Road
Blackrock Co. Dublin
Phone: 01-2837799 Fax: 01-2790000
Email: info@trinity-group.ie
Web: http://www.trinitytechnology.com
SIC: 72604 Employees: 70
Computer Hardware
Mr Frank Ennis Managing Director
Ms Jane Walsh Finance Manager
Mr Robert Booth Sales Manager

UCD Computing Services
University College Dublin
Belfield
Dublin 4
Phone: 01-7062370 Fax: 01-2837077
Web: http://www.ucd.ie/computing
SIC: 72604 Employees: 100
Provide Network for University
Dr Mary Crowe General Manager
Mr Seamus Shaw Service & Support Manager

ARO - Internet Business Development
26 Upper Pembroke Street
Dublin 2
Phone: 01-6373994 Fax: 01-6620365
Email: eolas@aro.ie
Web: http://www.aro.ie
SIC: 72605 Employees: 25
Internet Services
Mr Alan Roe Manager

Breakaway Solutions
3015 Lake Drive
The National Digital Park
Dublin 24
Phone: 01-4038473 Fax: 01-4038472
Email: info@zartis.com
Web: http://www.breakaway.com
SIC: 72605 Employees: 60
Web Design
Mr John Dennehy Managing Director
Mr Tom Carroll Finance Manager
Ms Dervla Cunningham Sales Manager
Mr Keith Davey Chief Technical Officer

ClickandGoNow.com
Unit 56 Parkwest Enterprise Centre
Dublin 12
Phone: 01-6235111 Fax: 01-6238119
Email: info@clickandgonow.com
Web: http://www.clickandgonow.com
SIC: 72605 Employees: 25
Internet Hotel Reservations Site
Mr Finbarr Power Managing Director

CMS Marketing
Unit B2 Carmount Business Park
Ballymount
Dublin 12
Phone: 01-6265346 Fax: 01-4197068
Email: info@cmsmarketing.com
Web: http://www.cmsmarketing.com
SIC: 72605 Employees: 30
Internet Services
Mr Noel Kelly Proprietor
Mr David O'Rourke Sales Manager

Core Value Ltd
Block 3 Harcourt Centre
Harcourt Road
Dublin 2
Phone: 01-4182270 Fax: 01-4182223
Email: answers@corevalue.ie
Web: http://www.corevalue.ie
SIC: 72605 Employees: 25
Internet Services
Mr Francis Buggy Managing Director

Double Click Internet Advertising
East Point Business Centre
2nd Floor, Freeman House
Dublin 3
Phone: 01-2460400 Fax: 01-2460499
Web: http://www.doubleclick.net
SIC: 72605 Employees: 80
Internet advertising
Mr Angus Kelsall Financial Director
Ms Julie-Anne Yore Human Resources Director

Easyquote Ltd
Unit 31, Guinness Enterprise Centre
Taylors Lane (CRM)
Dublin 8
Phone: 01-4100612 Fax: 01-4100985
Email: info@eayquote.ie
Web: http://www.eayquote.ie
SIC: 72605 Employees: 28
Internet On-line Directory Service
Mr Barney Joyce Managing Director
Mr Paul Joyce IT Director

Eicon Technology Manufacturing
Unit 4034 City West Business Campus
Saggart
Dublin 24
Phone: 01-6309000 Fax: 01-6309099
Email: info@eicon.com
Web: http://www.eicon.com
SIC: 72605 Employees: 55
Internet Cards Manufacturer
Mr Noel Lappin General Manager
Ms Jennifer Coade Accounts Manager
Ms Adrienne Ryan Research & Development Officer

Eircom Multimedia
East Point Business Park
Fairview
Dublin 3
Phone: 01-7010108 Fax: 01-7010186
Email: coporatesupport@eircom.net
Web: http://www.eircom.ie
SIC: 72605 Employees: 300
Internet Service Provider
Mr Fintan Lawler General Manager
Mr Peter Reynolds Finance Manager
Ms Karen Casey Personnel Manager
Ms Fiona Finn Sales Manager
Mr James Carrol Computer Manager

ENBA Internet Bank
The Ocean Building
Grand Canal Street Lower
Dublin 4
Phone: 01-6306300 Fax: 01-6306999
Email: info@first-e.com
Web: http://www.first-e.com
SIC: 72605 Employees: 600
Internet Banking
Mr Gerard Huber Managing Director
Mr Kevin Anderson Financial Controller

Esat Net
Grand Canal Plaza
Upper Grand Canal Street
Dublin 4
Phone: 01-6768744 Fax: 01-2424001
Email: info@iol.ie
Web: http://www.iol.ie
SIC: 72605 Employees: 45
Internet Services
Ms Lisa Dillon Marketing Executive
Mr Owen McGovern Head of Finance
Mr Ciaran Coleman HR Director
Mr Mark Horgan-Gaul Sales Manager
Ms Edel Behen IT Manager

Escher Europe
9 -13 Blackhall Place
Blackhall House
Dublin 7
Phone: 01-6713185 Fax: 01-6713195
Email: reception@eschergroup.com
Web: http://www.eschergroup.com
SIC: 72605 Employees: 25
Internet Postage
Mr Lee Church Managing Director
Mr Gerard Gleeson Financial Controller
Mr Martin McAdam Sales & Marketing Manager
Mr Mark Robertson Computer Manager

Euro Commerce
Unit 3015 Lake Drive
City West Business Campus
Dublin 24
Phone: 01-4038456 Fax: 01-4038457
Email: info@eurocommerce.ie
Web: http://www.eurocommerce.ie
SIC: 72605 Employees: 30
E- Commerce
Mr Peter Allen Managing Director

Eware
Embassy House
Ballsbridge
Dublin 4
Phone: 01-6187800 Fax: 01-6187888
Email: info@eware.com
Web: http://www.eware.com
SIC: 72605 Employees: 70
Internet & Wireless Company
Mr Ivan MacDonald Chief Executive Officer
Mr Mike McGearty Finance Manager
Mr Greg Casey Sales Director

Formus Broadband Ireland
AIG Centre
North Wall Quay
Dublin 1
Phone: 01-8878200 Fax: 01-8878201
Email: sales@formus.ie
Web: http://www.formus.ie
SIC: 72605 Employees: 60
Internet Services
Mr Teri McNulty General Manager
Mr Brian Murphy Finance Manager
Mr John Sharp Sales Director

Indigo
Unit B2 Eastpoint Business Park
Fairview
Dublin 3
Phone: 01-6046901 Fax: 01-7010375
Email: info@indigo.ie
Web: http://www.indigo.ie
SIC: 72605 Employees: 130
Internet Service Provider
Mr Fintan Lawlor General Manager
Mr Peter McDumphy Finance Manager
Ms Marcie Kinahan Help Desk Manager
Mr Sean Moroney Sales & Marketing Manager

Interact
Manor House
Baile An Tsagairt, Spiddal
Galway Co. Galway
Phone: 091-553855 Fax: 091-553866
Email: info@interact.ie
Web: http://www.interact.ie
SIC: 72605 Employees: 55
Web Development & Consultancy
Mr Dermot Duignan Managing Director
Mr Dermot Lally Sales Manager

Internet Ireland
3050 Lake Drive
City West Digital Park
Dublin 24
Phone: 01-4112000 Fax: 01-4112245
Web: http://www.internetireland.ie
SIC: 72605 Employees: 30
Internet Services
Mr Barry Breslin Managing Director
Mr Mark Lawlor Operations Director

Kadius
19A Rosemount Business Park
Dublin 11
Phone: 01-8850300 Fax: 01-8211102
Email: info@kadius.com
Web: http://www.kadius.com
SIC: 72605 Employees: 44
Web content solutions
Mr David Murray CEO
Mr Nicholas Hodges IT Manager

Labyrinth Ltd
Styne House Upper Hatch Street
Dublin 2
Phone: 01-2402000 Fax: 01-2402015
Email: info@labyrinth.ie
Web: http://www.labyrinth.ie
SIC: 72605 Employees: 72
Internet Services
Mr Eddie Murphy Managing Director
Ms Dara Barrett Finance Manager
Mr Trevor Dagg Sales & Marketing Manager

Net Café
211 Lower Rathmines Road
Dublin 6
Phone: 01-4971605 Fax: 01-4971605
Web: http://www.netfcafe.ie
SIC: 72605 Employees: 40
Internet Cafes
Mr Nigel Burke General Manager

Net House
113 Lower Rathmines Road
Dublin 6
Phone: 01-4960261 Fax: 01-4960262
Email: info@nethousecafes.com
Web: http://www.nethousecafes.com
SIC: 72605 Employees: 30
Internet Services
Mr Dennis Neimand Partner
Mr Neil Sission Partner

New World Commerce
2nd Floor
16-20 South Cumberland Street
Dublin 2
Phone: 01-4334300 Fax: 01-4334301
Email: info@nwcgroup.com
Web: http://www.newworldcommerce.com
SIC: 72605 Employees: 35
Internet Marketing Company
Mr Donal Daly Chief Executive
Mr Mike Gannon Finance Manager
Mr Michael Leary Sales Manager

Oniva Media Productions
Warrington House
Mount Street Crescent
Dublin 2
Phone: 01-6609036 Fax: 01-6600988
Email: info@oniva.com
Web: http://www.oniva.com
SIC: 72605 Employees: 70
Web Site Design
Mr Wansa Managing Director
Mr Jacko Befhoff Financial Controller
Mr Ciaran Nelis Business Development Manager
Mr Cliff Rosney Operation Manager
Mr Chris Davey IT Officer

Online.ie
18 Fairview
Dublin 3
Phone: 01-8554321 Fax: 01-8170643
Email: info@online.ie
Web: http://www.online.ie
SIC: 72605 Employees: 50
Mr Colm Grealy Managing Director
Mr Denis Lally Fianacial Controller
Mr Frank Hannagan Sales Director
Mr Barry Flannagan Technical Director

Servecast
3A South Prince's Street
Dublin 2
Phone: 01-6796831 Fax: 01-4748003
Email: info@servecast.com
Web: http://www.servecast.com
SIC: 72605 Employees: 40
Internet Broadcasting
Mr David Hall Operations Director
Mr Mark Omeara Financial Controller
Mr David Marie Sales Director
Ms Jan Ulander IT Manager

Sourceskills Ltd
Unit 45 Southern Cross Business Park
Boghall Road
Bray Co. Wicklow
Phone: 086-8364252 Fax: 086-2765829
SIC: 72605 Employees: 25
E learning Training Course Wear
Ms Ann Marie Knight Manager

UTV Internet
64 Waterloo Road
Ballsbridge
Dublin 4
Phone: 01-6643494 Fax: 01-6643493
Email: info@utvinternet.com
Web: http://www.utvinternet.com
SIC: 72605 Employees: 50
Internet Service Provider
Ms Lisa Clarkin Managing Director
Mr Simon O'Rouke Sales Director

Via Networks
26 Upper Fitzwilliam Street
Dublin 2
Phone: 01-6623617 Fax: 01-6627674
Email: info@via-net-.ie
Web: http://www.vianet.ie
SIC: 72605 Employees: 30
Internet Service Provider
Mr Tony Meadley Managing Director

WBT Systems
Block 2, The Harcourt Centre
Harcourt
Dublin 2
Phone: 01-6704740 Fax: 01-4785544
Email: info@wbtsystems.com
Web: http://www.wbtsystems.com
SIC: 72605 Employees: 80
Web Based Training
Mr Scott Kadle Managing Director
Mr Paul Dooley Finance Manager
Ms Jacinta Duite Personnel Manager
Mr Barry Byrne Computer Manager

Webfactory
10 Upper Fitzwilliams Street
Dublin 2
Phone: 01-6789992 Fax: 01-6625970
Email: info@webfactory.ie
Web: http://www.webfactory.ie
SIC: 72605 Employees: 45
Web Design, Development & Consultancy
Mr John O'Shea Managing Director
Mr David Smyth Financial Controller
Mr Mark Henry Sales & Marketing Manager

World Port Communications Inc
Blanchardstown
Dublin 15
Phone: 01-2412400 Fax: 01-2412411
Email: info@wrcp.com
Web: http://www.wrcp.com
SIC: 72605 Employees: 100
Web Hosting
Mr Jim Martin Chief Executive Officer
Ms Charlotte Casagrand Finance Manager
Mr Justin McCabe Sales Manager

Xelector
2nd Floor ESB Building Fleet Street
Dublin 2
Phone: 01-6326140 Fax: 01-6710785
Email: info@xelector.com
Web: http://www.xelector.com
SIC: 72605 Employees: 60
Internet Company
Mr Xavier Azalbert Managing Director
Mr Kevin Duffy Finance Manager
Ms Helen Martin Human Resources Manager
Ms Aisling Carroll Sales & Marketing Manager

BPSL
25 Corrig Road
Sandyford Industrial Estate
Dublin 18
Phone: 01-2957827 Fax: 01-2959731
Email: info@bpsl.com
Web: http://www.bpsl.com
SIC: 72609 Employees: 23
Disaster recovery Firm (computers)
Mr Peter Monaghan Manager
Mr Eamon Connolly Manager

CNH Information Technology Centre
IDA Business Park
Navan Co. Meath
Phone: 046-77600 Fax: 046-77601
Email: info@cnh.ie
Web: http://www.cnh.ie
SIC: 72609 Employees: 68
Information Technology Centre
Mr Rob Stewart Managing Director
Mr Martin Capper Financial Controller
Ms Marie Lee Personnel Director
Ms Adrienne Duffy Systems Administrator

Computer Resources
Quantum House
Temple Road
Blackrock Co. Dublin
Phone: 01-6420800 Fax: 01-2832385
Web: http://www.payroll.com
SIC: 72609 Employees: 50
Computer Resources/Payroll Packaging
Mr Michael Toomey Managing Director
Mr Paul Gaggin Financial Controller
Mr Michael Algan Sales & Marketing Manager
Mr David Smow Computer Manager

CPL Solutions
83 Merrion Square
Dublin 2
Phone: 01-6146066 Fax: 01-6146011
SIC: 72609 Employees: 100
Computer Placement
Ms Anne Heraty Chief Executive
Ms Jill Kelly Sales Manager
Mr Greg Kennedy IT Manager

Dutec Ltd
5 - 6 Corcanree Business Park
Dock Road
Limerick Co. Limerick
Phone: 061-225677 Fax: 061-225681
Email: enquiries@dutec.ie
SIC: 72609 Employees: 25
Manufacturer & Duplicate Computer Disks
Mr Sean Conway Manager
Mr Kevin Ryan Financial Controller

Ebeon Ltd
Unit 4 Bracken Road
Sandyford Industrial Park
Dublin 18
Phone: 01-2061550 Fax: 01-2063444
Email: info@ebeon.com
Web: http://www.ebeon.com
SIC: 72609 Employees: 120
Computer/ E Commerce Activities
Mr Bill Donaghue Manager
Mr Pat Crawford Sales Manager

EDS Ireland Ltd
Treasury Building
Lower Canal Street
Dublin 2
Phone: 01-7039221 Fax: 01-7039040
Email: postmaster@eds.com
Web: http://www.eds.com
SIC: 72609 Employees: 415
Data System Provider
Mr Peter Donnelly Managing Director
Mr Fintan Brennan Finance Manager
Mr David Waters IT Manager

Hitachi Koki Imaging Solutions Europe
Clonshaugh Industrial Estate
Clonshaugh
Dublin 17
Phone: 01-8036504 Fax: 01-8036666
Email: info@hitachi-hkis.com
Web: http://www.hitachi-hkis.com
SIC: 72609 Employees: 245
Digital Document Solutions
Mr Gerard Hudson Director

International Computers Ltd
ICL House, Harcourt Centre
Harcourt Street
Dublin 2
Phone: 01-2076900 Fax: 01-4025184
Email: info@icl.co.uk
Web: http://www.icl.co.uk
SIC: 72609 Employees: 200
Computers Service
Mr John Clare Service Manager
Mr Ray Brown Finance Director
Mr Noel Dylan Sales Director

NETG Ireland
Hamilton House
National Technological Park
Limerick Co. Limerick
Phone: 061-331430 Fax: 061-201699
Web: http://www.netg.com
SIC: 72609 Employees: 180
Computer Based Training
Ms Geraldine Kelly Managing Director
Ms Elaine O'Hara Financial Controller
Ms Juliette Finlay Human Resources Manager
Mr Dermot O'Longaigh IT Manager

NUI Maynooth
Computer Centre
Maynooth Co. Kildare
Phone: 01-7083830 Fax: 01-6286249
Email: reception@may.ie
Web: http://www.may.ie
SIC: 72609 Employees: 30
University Computer Services Department
Mr John O'Connell Director Computer Centre

PCI
19-24 St Andrews Street
Dublin 2
Phone: 01-7057434 Fax: 01-7057800
Email: post@pci.ie
Web: http://www.anpost.ie
SIC: 72609 Employees: 80
Technology Group of An post
Mr John Cronin Managing Director
Ms Maureen Dunne Finance Manager
Mr John Glynn Sales Director
Mr Donal O'Sullivan MIS Manager

Record Data Ltd
Marina Commercial Park
Centre Park Road
Cork Co. Cork
Phone: 021-4310066 Fax: 021-4321255
Web: http://www.recorddata.com
SIC: 72609 Employees: 40
Document Storage
Mr Bill Kearney Managing Director
Mr Tim O'Brien Sales & Marketing Manager

Shinko Micro Electronics
Unit D Greenhills Centre
Greenhills
Dublin 24
Phone: 01-4520744 Fax: 01-4520539
Email: shinko.microelectronics@fme.ie
SIC: 72609 Employees: 400
Manufacture Microchips
Mr Hioaki Muraishi Managing Director
Mr Terry Kiely Financial Controller
Mr Roger Murphy Personnel Manager
Mr David Quirke Computer Manager

Research & Development

73 Research & Development
73000Research & Development/Laboratories

BHP Lab Ltd
Unit 4 Enterprise Centre, New Road
Thomondgate
Limerick Co. Limerick
Phone: 061-455399 Fax: 061-455447
SIC: 73000 Employees: 32
Laboratory Services
Mr Michael Boland Managing Director
Ms Marie Sherlock Accountant
Ms Christine Clifford Personnel Manager

Bio Research Ireland
Enterprise Ireland
Glasnevin
Dublin 9
Phone: 01-8370177 Fax: 01-8370176
Email: info@biores-irl.ie
Web: http://www.biores-irl.ie
SIC: 73000 Employees: 250
Bio Technology Organisation
Dr James Ryan Chief Executive
Ms Miriam O'Gorman Personnel Officer
Mr Seamus O'Hara Business Development Manager
Ms Mary Gillick Operations Manager

Biological Laboratories (Europe) Ltd
Carrentrila
Ballina Co. Mayo
Phone: 096-70355 Fax: 096-22517
Email: marketing@biolabs.ie
Web: http://www.biolabs.ie
SIC: 73000 Employees: 140
Laboratory
Ms Catherine Corfield Managing Director

Central Fisheries Board
Mobhi Boreen
Glasnevin
Dublin 9
Phone: 01-8379206 Fax: 01-8360060
Email: info@cfb.ie
Web: http://www.cfb.ie
SIC: 73000 Employees: 370
Research/Conservation/Development of Fisheries
Mr John O'Connor Chief Executive
Ms Nuala O'Byrne Director of Finance
Mr John McPhillips Director of Personnel
Ms Margaret Purltoll Administrative Manager
Mr Don McLave Director - Information Systems

CIMRU
Manufacturing Research Centre
Nuns Island NUI
Galway Co. Galway
Phone: 091-750414 Fax: 091-562894
Email: info@nuigalway.ie
Web: http://cimru.nuigalway.ie
SIC: 73000 Employees: 30
CIM Application Research Group/Consultancy
Prof Jim Browne Director
Ms Catherine Hayden Accounts Manager

Economic & Social Research Institute
4 Burlington Road
Dublin 4
Phone: 01-6671525 Fax: 01-6686231
Email: admin@esri.ie
Web: http://www.esri.ie
SIC: 73000 Employees: 100
Research Institute
Prof Brendan Whelan Director
Mr Charles O'Regan Head of Accounts
Ms Gillian Davidson Secretary
Ms June Ryan Computer Manager

Health Research Board
73 Lower Baggot Street
Dublin 2
Phone: 01-6761176 Fax: 01-6611856
Email: hrb@hrb.ie
Web: http://www.hrb.ie
SIC: 73000 Employees: 30
Health Research
Dr Ruth Barrington Chief Executive Officer
Ms Carol Cronin Accounts Secretary
Mr Philip Turley Computer Manager

Microchem Laboratories Ltd
Clogherane
Dungarvan Co. Waterford
Phone: 058-44440 Fax: 058-42855
Email: info@microchem.ie
Web: http://www.microchem.ie
SIC: 73000 Employees: 70
Contract Laboratory
Mr Ciaran Geoghegan Joint Managing Director
Ms Carol Murphy Accounts Supervisor
Ms Gail Carroll Sales Executive
Mr Hugh Marren IT Specilaist

National Food Centre
Dunsinea
Castleknock
Dublin 15
Phone: 01-8059500 Fax: 01-8059550
Email: info@teagasc.ie
Web: http://www.teagasc.ie
SIC: 73000 Employees: 100
Food Research/Food Training Courses
Dr Vivian Tarrant Director
Mr Con Breen Support Services Manager
Mr Frank Synnott Computer Manager

Public Analyst Laboratory
Sir Patrick Dunne
Lower Grand Canal Street
Dublin 2
Phone: 01-6612022 Fax: 01-6628532
Email: palabdub@indigo.ie
SIC: 73000 Employees: 40
Public Laboratory
Mr Kevin Moyles Public Analyst
Ms Suzanne Gregary Accounts Manager
Mr Michael O'Sullivan Computer Manager

Quintiles Ireland Ltd
Block N, East Point Business Park
Dublin 3
Phone: 01-8195100 Fax: 01-8195500
Email: info@quintiles.com
Web: http://www.quintiles.com
SIC: 73000 Employees: 350
Research pharmaceutical
Ms Marie Kenny Managing Director
Mr John Vaughan Financial Controller
Ms Anne Spring Director of Human Resources
Ms Susan Lennon Sales & Marketing Manager
Ms Siobhan Costello ITIT Operations Director

A & L Goodbody
IFSC Centre
North Wall Quay
Dublin 1
Phone: 01-6613311 Fax: 01-6492649
Email: law@algoodbody.ie
Web: http://www.algoodbody.ie
SIC: 74112 Employees: 450
Solicitors
Mr Frank O'Riordan Managing Partner
Mr Jim McSweeney Financial Controller
Ms Sharon Scally Personnel Director
Ms Aine Maguire Marketing Manager
Ms Denise Edwards Systems Manager

Business Activities

Arthur Cox
Earlsfort Terrace
Dublin 2
Phone: 01-6180000 Fax: 01-6180618
Email: mail@arthurcox.ie
Web: http://www.arthurcox.ie
SIC: 74112 Employees: 300
Solicitors
Mr James O'Dwyer Echairman & Senior Partner
Mr Joseph Fagan Finance Director
Ms Caroline Molloy Administration Manager

Arthur O'Hagan & Co
9 Harcourt Street
Dublin 2
Phone: 01-4758701 Fax: 01-4781583
Email: info@aohagan.ie
SIC: 74112 Employees: 24
Solicitors
Mr John Gleeson Manager

Barry Galvin and Sons
91 South Mall
Cork Co. Cork
Phone: 0214-271962 Fax: 0214-272835
Email: info@bcgalvin.ie
SIC: 74112 Employees: 40
Solicitors
Ms Brenda Cunningham Managing Partner

BCM Hanby Wallace Solicitors
St Michael Close, 1 High Street
Dublin 8
Phone: 01-6056900 Fax: 01-6056966
Email: info@bcmhanbywallace.com
Web: http://www.bcmhanbywallace.com
SIC: 74112 Employees: 115
Solicitors
Mr Brian Wallace Managing Partner
Mr John Burke Financial Controller
Ms Patricia Gallagher Personnel Manager

Beauchamps Solicitors
Dollard House
Wellington Quay
Dublin 2
Phone: 01-4180600 Fax: 01-4180699
Email: securemail@beauchamps.ie
Web: http://www.beauchamps.ie
SIC: 74112 Employees: 75
Solicitors
Mr Imelda Reynolds Managing Partner
Mr Bart Mooney Financial Controller
Mr Gary Rice Business Development Partner
Mr Joe Bowe Administration Partner
Mr George Campbell IT Manager

Brian J Chesser & Co
19 Catherine Street
Waterford Co. Waterford
Phone: 051-875233 Fax: 051-877045
SIC: 74112 Employees: 107
Solicitors
Mr Brian Chesser Proprietor

Conway Kelleher Tobin
29 South Mall
Cork Co. Cork
Phone: 021-4273192 Fax: 021-4270390
Email: ckt@ckt.ie
Web: http://www.ckt.ie
SIC: 74112 Employees: 30
Solicitors Firm
Mr Rory Conway Partner
Ms Breda Donegan Finance Manager
Ms Terri O'Brien Sales & Marketing Manager
Mr Dermot Conway Computer Manager

Deloitte & Touche
Deloitte & Touche House
Earlsfort Terrace
Dublin 2
Phone: 01-4172200 Fax: 01-4172300
Email: info@deloitte.ie
Web: http://www.deloitte.ie
SIC: 74112 Employees: 1500
Notaries
Mr Pat Kenny Manager
Mr Eanna McHugh Finance Manager
Mr Martin Smith Personnel Manager
Mr Michael Kearnan Production Manager
Ms Gretti McCormac IT Manager

Dermot G O'Donovan & Partners
Third Floor Millhouse
Henry Street
Limerick Co. Limerick
Phone: 061-314788 Fax: 061-310441
Email: solrs@dgodonanvan.ie
SIC: 74112 Employees: 35
Solicitors
Mr Dermot O'Donovan Senior Partner
Ms Margaret McMahon Accountant
Mr Michael Sherry Senior Partner

Dillon & Eustace
Grand Canal House
1 Upper Grand Canal Street
Dublin 4
Phone: 01-6670022 Fax: 01-6670042
Email: info@dilloneustace.ie
Web: http://www.dilloneustace.ie
SIC: 74112 Employees: 68
Solicitors
Mr David Dillon Managing Director
Ms Sharon McCarthy Financial Controller

Eugene F Collins
3 Burlington Road
Dublin 4
Phone: 01-6675111 Fax: 01-6675200
Email: lawyer@efc.ie
Web: http://www.efc.ie
SIC: 74112 Employees: 80
Solicitors
Mr Anthony Collins Senior Partner
Mr Gerry Lawlor Finance Manager
Mr Eric Dowdall Computer Manager

Business Services

Gore & Grimes
Cavendish House
Smithfield
Dublin 7
Phone: 01-8729299 Fax: 01-8729877
Email: sols@goregrimes.ie
SIC: 74112 Employees: 25
Solicitors Practices
Ms Denise Cullen Manager

Hayes & Sons
Lavery House
Earlsfort Terrace
Dublin 2
Phone: 01-6624747 Fax: 01-6612163
Email: law@hayesons.ie
Web: http://www.hayesons.ie
SIC: 74112 Employees: 47
Solicitors Practices
Mr Andrew O'Rorke Managing Partner
Mr Peter Harrison Finance Manager

Heather Lennon & Co
City Quay House
Dublin 2
Phone: 01-6703232 Fax: 01-6703434
Email: solrs@lennonheather.ie
Web: http://www.lennonheather.ie
SIC: 74112 Employees: 28
Solicitors
Ms Aine Lernihan Principal

Holmes O'Malley & Sexton Solictors
5 Pery Square
Limerick Co. Limerick
Phone: 061-313222 Fax: 061-310414
Email: info@homs.ie
Web: http://www.homs.ie
SIC: 74112 Employees: 60
Solicitors Firm
Mr John Hayes Senior Partner
Mr Gerard McNamara Financial Controller
Ms Audrey Healy IT Manager

Ivor Fitzpatrick & Co
44-45 St Stephens Green
Dublin 2
Phone: 01-6787000 Fax: 01-6787004
Email: ivorfitz@iol.ie
SIC: 74112 Employees: 80
Solicitors
Mr Ivor Fitzpatrick Partner

JW O'Donovan Solicitors
53 South Mall
Cork Co. Cork
Phone: 021-7300200 Fax: 021-4273704
Email: mail@jwod.ie
Web: http://www.jwod.ie
SIC: 74112 Employees: 23
Solicitors
Mr David Walsh Office Manager
Mr Cormac O'Hanlon Partner

Kennedy McGonagle Ballagh
20 Northumberland Road
Ballsbridge
Dublin 4
Phone: 01-6609799 Fax: 01-6609434
Email: info@kmb.ie
Web: http://www.kmb.ie
SIC: 74112 Employees: 30
Solictors Firm
Mr Rodger Ballagh Managing Director

Kenny Stephenson Chapman
Newtown
Waterford Co. Waterford
Phone: 051-877620 Fax: 051-877620
Email: waterford@ksc.ie
Web: http://www.ksc.ie
SIC: 74112 Employees: 26
Solicitors
Mr Charles Galloway Senior Partner
Ms Linda Fitzpatrick Computer Manager

Kilroys Solicitors
69 Lower Leeson Street
Dublin 2
Phone: 01-6614499 Fax: 01-4395602
Email: kilroys@kilroys.ie
Web: http://www.kilroys.ie
SIC: 74112 Employees: 38
Solicitors
Mr Kevin O'Brien Principal

Land Registry & Registry of Deeds
Chancery Street
Dublin 7
Phone: 01-6707500 Fax: 01-8048144
Web: http://www.irlgov.ie/la
SIC: 74112 Employees: 600
Department of Land Registry & Registry of Deeds
Ms Catherine Treacy Registrar
Mr Colm Ruane Financial Controller

Lavelle Coleman
51-52 Fitzwilliam Square
Dublin 2
Phone: 01-6619826 Fax: 01-6614581
Email: info@lavelco.ie
Web: http://www.lavelco.ie
SIC: 74112 Employees: 34
Solicitors
Mr David Coleman Partner
Ms Rose Sweeney Office Manager
Mr Michael Lavelle Partner

Mason Hayes and Curran
6 Fitzwilliam Square
Dublin 2
Phone: 01-6145000 Fax: 01-6145001
Email: mail@mhc.ie
Web: http://www.mhc.ie
SIC: 74112 Employees: 140
Solicitors
Mr Declan Moylan Manager
Ms Andrea Fuhapinkey Finance Director

McCann Fitzgerald
2 Harbourmaster Place
IFSC
Dublin 1
Phone: 01-8290000 Fax: 01-8290010
Email: postmaster@mccann-fitzgerald.ie
Web: http://www.mccann-fitzgerald.ie
SIC: 74112 Employees: 280
Solicitors Firm
Mr Ronan Maloney Partner
Mr Seamus Toomey Financial Controller
Ms Rosaleen Philpott Personnel Officer
Mr Paul Errity Computer Manager

McLoughlin & Donaldson
47 Merrion Square
Dublin 2
Phone: 01-6763465 Fax: 01-6612083
Email: mail@maclachlan.ie
SIC: 74112 Employees: 35
Solicitors Firm
Mr Norman MacLachlan Senior Partner
Ms Catherine Hallinen Financial Controller

Michael Houlihan & Partners
9-11 Bindon Street
Ennis Co. Clare
Phone: 065-6828706 Fax: 065-6821870
Email: info@mlhoulihan.securemail.ie
SIC: 74112 Employees: 30
Solicitors Firm
Mr Michael Houlihan Senior Partner

MJ O'Connor & Co
2 Lower George Street
Wexford Co. Wexford
Phone: 053-22555 Fax: 053-24365
Email: info@wexlaw.com
Web: http://www.wexlaw.com
SIC: 74112 Employees: 25
Solicitors Firm
Mr John O'Leary Partner

Noel Smyth & Partners
22 Fitzwilliam Square
Dublin 2
Phone: 01-6321000 Fax: 01-6613979
Email: solrs@nspartners.ie
SIC: 74112 Employees: 35
Solicitors
Mr Colman Bermingham Managing Partner
Ms Cathy Daniel Office Manager

Nolan Farrell & Goff
Newtown
Waterford Co. Waterford
Phone: 051-872934 Fax: 051-873804
Email: info@nfg.ie
SIC: 74112 Employees: 40
Solicitors
Mr James Mulhern Manager
Mr Martin Bulger Office Manager

O'Connor's Solicitors
8 Clare Street
Dublin 2
Phone: 01-6764488 Fax: 01-6766764
Email: mail@oconnorsolicitors.ie
Web: http://www.oconnorsolicitors.ie
SIC: 74112 Employees: 23
Solicitors Firm
Mr John O'Connor Manager

O'Donnell Sweeney
The Earlsfort Centre
The Earlsfort Terrace
Dublin 2
Phone: 01-6644200 Fax: 01-6644300
Email: r@odonnellsweeney.ie
Web: http://www.odonnellsweeney.ie
SIC: 74112 Employees: 90
Solicitors
Mr David O'Byrne Managing Partner
Ms Sally French Finance Manager
Ms Sharon Brady Computer Manager

O'Flynn Exhams
58 South Mall
Cork Co. Cork
Phone: 021-4277788 Fax: 021-4272117
Email: ofexcork@indigo.ie
SIC: 74112 Employees: 75
Solicitors
Mr Fachta O'Driscoll Senior Partner
Mr Michael Quinlan Financial Controller

O'Rourke Reid & Co Solicitors
Pepper Canister House
Mount Street Crescent
Dublin 2
Phone: 01-6614440 Fax: 01-6614443
Email: lex@oroukereidsolicitors.ie
SIC: 74112 Employees: 40
Solicitors
Mr Dermott O'Rourke Partner
Mr Joseph Mangon Financial Controller
Mr Eamon O'Reilly Personnel Director

Orpen Franks & Co
28/30 Burlington Road
Dublin 4
Phone: 01-6689622 Fax: 01-6689004
Email: law@orpenfranks.ie
SIC: 74112 Employees: 40
Solicitors
Mr John O'Donovan Manager
Mr Martin Callaghan Financial Controller

P J O'Driscoll
73 South Mall
Cork Co. Cork
Phone: 021-4271421 Fax: 021-4274709
Email: enquiries@pjodriscoll.ie
Web: http://www.pjodriscoll.ie
SIC: 74112 Employees: 40
Solicitors
Mr P J O'Driscoll Proprietor
Mr Brendan Hogan Office Manager

Business Services

Patrick O'Reilly & Co
9-10 Sth Great Georges Street
Dublin 2
Phone: 01-6793412 Fax: 01-6793421
SIC: 74112 Employees: 23
Solicitors Firm
Mr P J O'Reilly Managing Director

Peter Casey & Sons ltd
Circular Road
Roscommon Co. Roscommon
Phone: 090-326101 Fax: 090-325305
SIC: 74112 Employees: 60
Solicitors
Mr peter Casey Manager

PF O'Reilly & Co
9-10 South Great Georges Street
Dublin 2
Phone: 01-6793565 Fax: 01-6792812
Email: info@pforeilly.ie
Web: http://www.pforeilly.ie
SIC: 74112 Employees: 26
Solicitors
Mr Peter O'Reilly Partner

Ronan Daly Jermyn Solicitors
12 South Mall
Cork Co. Cork
Phone: 021-4272333 Fax: 021-4802790
Web: http://www.rdj.ie
SIC: 74112 Employees: 74
Solicitors
Mr John Buckley Managing Partner
Mr Michael Daly Financial Controller
Ms Marie McSweeney Personnel Manager

Seamus Maguire & Co
10 Main Street
Blanchardstown
Dublin 15
Phone: 01-8211288 Fax: 01-8211442
SIC: 74112 Employees: 25
Solicitors
Mr Seamus Maguire Managing Director

TP Robinson Solicitors
94 Merrion Square West
Dublin 2
Phone: 01-6764581 Fax: 01-6767110
Email: info@tprobinson.com
SIC: 74112 Employees: 25
Solicitors
Mr Ronan O'Brien Managing Partner
Mr Gearoid O' Byrne Finance Manager

Whitney Moore & Kelleher
Wilton Park House
Wilton Place
Dublin 2
Phone: 01-6760631 Fax: 01-6766462
Email: postmaster@wmk.ie
SIC: 74112 Employees: 50
Solicitors
Mr Paul Hayes Managing Director
Ms Anita Farrell Accounts Manager

William Fry
Fitzwilton House
Wilton Place
Dublin 2
Phone: 01-6625000 Fax: 01-6395333
Email: central.mail@williamfry.ie
Web: http://www.williamfry.ie
SIC: 74112 Employees: 145
Solicitors
Mr Owen O'Connell Managing Director
Mr Graham Dawson Accountant
Ms Niamh Mangan Human Resources Manager
Ms Karen O'Leary Marketing Manager

Business Services

Legal Aid Board
Stephens Green House
Earlsford Terrace
Dublin 2
Phone: 01-6615811 Fax: 01-6763426
Email: legalaid@eircom.net
SIC: 74119 Employees: 36
Legal Aid and Advice
Mr Frank Goodman Chief Executive
Mr Seamus Sisk Financial Controller
Mr Richard O'Reilly Personnel Manager

Rochford Brady Legal Services
Dollard House
65 Frances Street
Dublin 8
Phone: 01-6777250 Fax: 01-4532223
Email: rochford@lawsearch.ie
Web: http://www.rochford.ie
SIC: 74119 Employees: 50
Legal Agency
Mr Philip Grant Managing Director
Ms Ann McGlynn Personnel Director

The Bar Council of Ireland
The Law Library
The Four Courts
Dublin 7
Phone: 01-8174900 Fax: 01-8175150
Email: barcouncil@lawlibrary.ie
Web: http://www.lawlibrary.ie/barcouncil
SIC: 74119 Employees: 42
Legal Association
Mr Jerry Carroll Director

The Legal Aid Board
4th Floor Saint Stephens Green House
Earlsfort Terrace
Dublin 2
Phone: 01-2400900 Fax: 01-2400972
Email: info@legal-aid.ie
Web: http://www.legal-aid.ie
SIC: 74119 Employees: 100
Legal Aid
Mr Frank Counahan Manager

BDO Simpson Xavier
Simpson Xavier Court
20/23 Merchants Quay
Dublin 8
Phone: 01-6170100 Fax: 01-6790111
Email: info@bdosx.ie
Web: http://www.bdosx.ie
SIC: 74121 Employees: 340
Chartered Accountants
Mr Anthuan Xavier Managing Partner
Ms Laura Murphy Personnel Manager
Ms Rita O'Reilly Marketing Manager
Ms Mary McCabe Computer Manager

Brendan Murphy & Co
30 Upper Drumcondra Road
Dublin 9
Phone: 01-8379106 Fax: 01-8369305
Email: info@bmurphyandco.iol.ie
SIC: 74121 Employees: 25
Accountancy Practice
Mr Brendan Murphy Sole Practitioner

Brenson Lawlor
Argyle Square Morehampton Road
Donnybrook
Dublin 4
Phone: 01-6689760 Fax: 01-6689778
Email: info@brenson-lawlor.ie
Web: http://www.brenson-lawlor.ie
SIC: 74121 Employees: 40
Chartered Accountants
Mr Patrick Lawlor Managing Partner
Mr Henry Kinch Finance Manager
Mr Brendan Brophy Computer Manager

Butler Fitzpatrick Cavanagh Donnelly
1 Old Castlewood Avenue
Dublin 6
Phone: 01-4970935 Fax: 01-4960061
Email: bfcd@indigo.ie
SIC: 74121 Employees: 23
Chartered Accountants
Mr Frank Cavanagh Partner

CAG Chartered Accounts
Steamship House
Dock Street
Galway Co. Galway
Phone: 091-568788 Fax: 091-568801
Email: caggroup@eircom.net
SIC: 74121 Employees: 30
Chartered Accountants
Mr Tony McGrath Managing Partner

Chapman Flood & Mazars
Block 1
Christ Church Square
Dublin 8
Phone: 01-4534444 Fax: 01-4546788
Email: postmaster@mazars.ie
Web: http://www.chapmanfloodmazars.ie
SIC: 74121 Employees: 110
Chartered Accountants
Mr Brendan Watters Managing Partner
Mr Enda Gunnell Personnel Manager
Mr Simon Coyle Sales & Marketing Manager
Mr Eoin Baird Computer Manager

Cooney Carey
4/5 Dawson Street
Dublin 2
Phone: 01-6779000 Fax: 01-6779805
Email: info@cooneycarey.ie
Web: http://www.cooneycarey.ie
SIC: 74121 Employees: 40
Chartered Accountants & Taxation Advisors
Mr Anthony Carey Managing Partner
Ms Aine Mulligan Financial Controller
Ms Maire Keating Personnel Manager
Ms Mary Flanagan Computer Manager

Cronin & Co
1 Terenure Place
Terenure
Dublin 6w
Phone: 01-4901670 Fax: 01-4901184
Email: info@cronin-co.ie
SIC: 74121 Employees: 50
Accountants
Mr Micheal Cronin Manager
Ms Sinead Hoey Finance Director

Deacy Concannon
Woodquay Court
Galway Co. Galway
Phone: 091-565830 Fax: 091-564687
Email: info@deacy.ie
Web: http://www.deacy.ie
SIC: 74121 Employees: 35
Accountancy Firm
Mr Robert Deacy Senior Partner

Derek Quinlan & Associates
Clyde Road
Ballsbridge
Dublin 4
Phone: 01-6686276 Fax: 01-6686858
SIC: 74121 Employees: 25
Accountants
Mr Derek Quinlan Proprietor

Ernst & Young
Harcourt Centre
Harcourt Street
Dublin 2
Phone: 01-4750555 Fax: 01-4750599
Email: e-y.ireland@ie.eyi.com
Web: http://www.ey.com
SIC: 74121 Employees: 700
Accountants, Advisors & Consultants
Mr John Hogan Managing Partner
Mr Paul Redmond Finance Partner
Mr Paul Selfridge HR Director
Mr Greg Byrne Marketing Director
Mr William Cotter IT Director

Farrell Grant & Sparks Tax Consultants
Molyneux House
68-69 Bride Street
Dublin 8
Phone: 01-4758137 Fax: 01-4182044
Email: fgs@fgs.ie
Web: http://www.fgs.ie
SIC: 74121 Employees: 80
Chartered Accountants
Mr Pierce Farrell Managing Partner
Mr Andrew Watson Financial Controller
Ms Claire Small Sales Manager
Mr Andrew Johnson IT Manager

Fitzpatrick Morris Barrett
74 Pembroke Road
Ballsbridge
Dublin 4
Phone: 01-6609566 Fax: 01-6609484
Email: info@fmb.ie
Web: http://www.fmb.ie
SIC: 74121 Employees: 25
Chartered Accountants
Mr Tom Fitzpatrick Senior Partner
Mr John Kavanagh Financial Advisor/Partner
Mr John Morris Company Secretary
Mr David McArdle Sales & Marketing Manager

Frank Lynch & Company
Avoca House
28 Seatown Place
Dundalk Co. Louth
Phone: 042-9332273 Fax: 042-9334509
SIC: 74121 Employees: 35
Accountants
Mr Frank Lynch Senior Partner
Mr Tony McBride Partner

Gaule Bermingham & Co
61 O'Connell Street
Limerick Co. Limerick
Phone: 061-310555 Fax: 061-419147
Email: gauleber@iol.ie
SIC: 74121 Employees: 30
Accountants
Mr Nigel Gaule Managing Director

Gilroy Gannon & Company
25 Stephen Street
Sligo Co. Sligo
Phone: 071-61747 Fax: 071-43283
Email: info@gilroygannon.com
SIC: 74121 Employees: 50
Chartered Accountants
Mr Declan Gilroy Senior Partner
Mr Alan Palmer Financial Controller
Mr Joseph Gannon Senior Partner

Gorman AGN Inc
15 Herbert Street
Dublin 2
Phone: 01-6764120 Fax: 01-6621509
Email: postmaster@gorman.ie
Web: http://www.gorman.ie
SIC: 74121 Employees: 25
Chartered Accountants
Mr WJ Gorman Senior Partner

Business Services

Grant Thornton
Ashford House
Tara Street
Dublin 2
Phone: 01-6714677 Fax: 01-2888208
Web: http://www.johnwoods.ie
SIC: 74121 Employees: 72
Chartered Accountants
Mr James A Murphy Managing Partner
Mr John Woods Partner
Mr Aidan Connaughton Partner
Mr Dermot Hurley Computer Manager

Greene Chartered Accountants
5 St Andrews Terrace
Newtown
Waterford Co. Waterford
Phone: 051-875521 Fax: 051-877144
Email: info@greeneco.ie
Web: http://www.greeneco.ie
SIC: 74121 Employees: 33
Company Formation
Mr Tom Greene Manager

Hargaden Moor
Grand Canal House
1 Upper Grand Canal Street
Dublin 4
Phone: 01-2600500 Fax: 01-2600508
SIC: 74121 Employees: 27
Accountants
Mr David Hargaden Managing Director

Hayden Brown
Grafton Buildings
34 Grafton Street
Dublin 2
Phone: 01-6771951 Fax: 01-6771308
Email: hbrown@eircom.net
SIC: 74121 Employees: 28
Chartered Accountants
Mr Donal Hampson Managing Partner
Mr Stephen Brown Sales Manager

Hopkins O'Halloran Grant
14 Fitzwilliam Square
Dublin 2
Phone: 01-6762960 Fax: 01-6762946
SIC: 74121 Employees: 45
Accountants Practices
Mr Gerard Hopkins Proprietor

Horwath Bastow Charleton
Marine House
Clanwilliam Court
Dublin 2
Phone: 01-6760951 Fax: 01-6625105
Email: info@horbc.ie
SIC: 74121 Employees: 90
Chartered Accountants
Mr Brian Conroy Senior Partner
Mr Bob Nealon Financial Controller

Houlihan Cushnahan
1-4 Adelaide Road
Glasthule
Dun Laoghaire Co. Dublin
Phone: 01-2804311 Fax: 01-2843186
Email: houlcush@iol.ie
SIC: 74121 Employees: 25
Chartered Accountants
Mr Peter Houlihan Partner

IFAC Accountant Dublin
Irish Farm Centre
Bluebell
Dublin 12
Phone: 01-4551036 Fax: 01-4551053
Email: ifac@indigo.ie
SIC: 74121 Employees: 150
IFAC Accountant
Mr Peadar Murphy Chief Executive
Ms Una Burgess Accounts Manager
Mr Pat Donovan DP Manager

Kearney McArdle McEneaney & Ryan
12 Crowe Street
Dundalk Co. Louth
Phone: 042-9336811 Fax: 042-9333372
Web: http://www.kayserscomputing.com
SIC: 74121 Employees: 35
Certified Accountants
Mr Joe Kearney Senior Partner

KPMG
90 South Mall
Cork Co. Cork
Phone: 021-4254500 Fax: 021-4254525
Email: info@kpmg.ie
Web: http://www.kpmg.ie
SIC: 74121 Employees: 50
Accountancy Firm
Mr Colm Clifford Senior Partner

McDwyer Lennon & Co
Esker Place
Cathedral Road
Cavan Co. Cavan
Phone: 049-4331088 Fax: 049-4361276
Email: mdly@eircom.net
SIC: 74121 Employees: 30
Chartered Accountants
Mr Raymond McDwyer Managing Partner
Ms Carmel Gallagher Accounts Officer
Ms Lucilla O'Hanlon Administration Officer
Mr Eugene O'Callaghan Computer Manager

Millne O'Dwyer & Co
Beck House
Kilbride Street
Tullamore Co. Offaly
Phone: 0506-41161 Fax: 0506-21972
Email: info@millneodwyer.ie
Web: http://www.millneodwyer.ie
SIC: 74121 Employees: 23
Accountancy Firm
Ms Vanessa Kelly Manager

Moore Stephens & Co
16 Fitzwilliam Square
Dublin 2
Phone: 01-6765543 Fax: 01-6623284
Email: postmaster@moorestephens.com
Web: http://www.moorestephens.com
SIC: 74121 Employees: 30
Chartered Accountants
Mr Roger Kennedy Partner
Mr Tony Spollen Financial Controller

O'Connor Associates
1 Christchurch Square
Dublin 8
Phone: 01-4732445 Fax: 01-4546788
Email: postmaster@mazars.ie
Web: http://www.mazars.ie
SIC: 74121 Employees: 100
Accountants Practices
Mr Brendan Watters Manager
Mr Owen Baired IT Manager

O'Connor Leddy & Holmes
Century House
Harolds Cross Road
Dublin 6w
Phone: 01-4961444 Fax: 01-4961637
Email: oclh@iol.ie
SIC: 74121 Employees: 43
Accountants
Mr John Leddy Managing Director
Mr Mark Tully Financial Controller
Mr Liam Tobin Personnel Officer
Ms Kathleen Camon Computer Manager

O'Hare & Associates
27-30 Merchants House
Merchants Quay
Dublin 8
Phone: 01-6771003 Fax: 01-6771829
Email: info@oha.ie
Web: http://www.oha.ie
SIC: 74121 Employees: 50
Chartered Accountants
Mr Liam Twohig Managing Director
Mr William McElroy Financial Administrator
Mr Hugh O'Hare Consultant

O'Neill Foley
Patrick's Court
Patrick Street
Kilkenny
Phone: 056-21157 Fax: 056-63218
Email: accounts@onf.ie
SIC: 74121 Employees: 40
Chartered Accountants
Mr Tom O'Connor Partner
Mr David Walsh Partner
Mr Leslie Moynan Partner

Oliver Freaney & Co
43-45 Northumberland Road
Ballsbridge
Dublin 4
Phone: 01-6142500 Fax: 01-6142555
Email: info@ofc.ie
Web: http://www.ofc.ie
SIC: 74121 Employees: 80
Chartered Accountants
Mr Noel Fox Managing Partner
Mr Niall Garvey Financial Controller
Mr Paul Wyse Marketing Manager
Ms Patrica Freaney Computer Manager

Ormsby & Rhodes
9 Clare Street
Dublin 2
Phone: 01-6767244 Fax: 01-6768377
Email: mail@ormsby-rhodes.ie
Web: http://www.ormsby-rhodes.ie
SIC: 74121 Employees: 55
Chartered Accountants
Mr Tom Moore Partner

OSK
OSK House
29 Lower Baggot Street
Dublin 2
Phone: 01-6619256 Fax: 01-6614233
Email: info@osk.ie
Web: http://www.osk.ie
SIC: 74121 Employees: 55
Chartered Accountants
Mr Sean Fitzpatrick Managing Partner
Ms Orla Ruane Financial Controller

Patrick McNamara & Associates
Lee Biew House
11/12 South Terrace
Cork Co. Cork
Phone: 021-4965455 Fax: 021-4963941
Email: pmcncork@iol.ie
SIC: 74121 Employees: 38
Accountants
Mr Patrick McNamara Sole Practitioner

Peevers Slye & Partners
4 Greenview Terrace
Prince Street
Tralee Co. Kerry
Phone: 066-7126333 Fax: 066-7124540
Email: info@traleepartnership.ie
SIC: 74121 Employees: 25
Accountants
Mr John Slye

PricewaterhouseCoopers
Gardner House
Wilton Place
Dublin 2
Phone: 01-6789999 Fax: 01-6626200
Email: info@ie.pwcglobal.com
Web: http://www.pwcglobal.com/ie
SIC: 74121 Employees: 2000
Chartered Accountants
Mr Donal O'Connor Managing Partner
Mr Ronan Murphy Financial Controller
Ms Eileen Ryan Human Resources Director
Mr Ken Johnston Sales & Marketing Manager
Mr Seamus Fitzsimmons IT Manager

Russell Brennan & Keane
Irishtown
Athlone Co. Westmeath
Phone: 0902-80600 Fax: 0902-78083
Email: info@rbk.ie
Web: http://www.rbk.ie
SIC: 74121 Employees: 100
Accountants
Mr Jim Keane Senior Partner
Mr Liam Rattigan Personnel Manager

Ryan Glennon & Co
Trinity House, Charlesown Road
Ranelagh
Dublin 6
Phone: 01-4965388 Fax: 01-4965880
Email: info@ryanglennonn.com
Web: http://www.ryanglennon.com
SIC: 74121 Employees: 50
Chartered Accountants
Mr Liam Ryan Chartered Accountant

Institute of Legal Accountants
Wellfield House
Blessington Road
Naas Co. Kildare
Phone: 045-875640 Fax: 045-866766
SIC: 74124 Employees: 100
Institute of Legal Accountants
Mr John Tanigawa Chairman

MK Brazil & Co
Gladstone House, 50 The Quay
Waterford Co. Waterford
Phone: 051-877980 Fax: 051-874504
Email: mkbadmin@mkbrazil.com
SIC: 74124 Employees: 24
Accountants & Auditors
Mr Jim Grant Manager
Mr Joe Gelhunty Financial Controller
Mr John Foley Sales & Marketing Manager

AC Neilsen
Knockmaun House
42-47 Lower Mount Street
Dublin 2
Phone: 01-6765112 Fax: 01-6766621
Email: info@acneilsen.com
Web: http://www.acnielsen.com
SIC: 74130 Employees: 70
Market Research Company
Mr John Neilson Managing Director
Mr Liam Geraghty Finance Manager
Mr Connor Camtwell Country Manager
Mr Fred O'Connell Production Director

IDS Market Research Ltd
3 Sandyford Business Park
Blackthorn Avenue
Dublin 18
Phone: 01-2604818 Fax: 01-2104816
Email: info@idsmarketresearch.com
Web: http://www.idsmediagroup.com
SIC: 74141 Employees: 75
Marketing Research & Analysis
Mr Martin Crilly Managing Director

DataDirection
Ocuco House, Coolmine Business Park
Blanchardstown
Dublin 15
Phone: 01-8201588 Fax: 01-8226162
Email: info@datadirection.com
Web: http://www.datadirection.com
SIC: 74130 Employees: 50
Market Research Services
Mr Brian Cooney Manager
Mr Vincent Kelly Manager

Irish Marketing Surveys Ltd
20-21 Upper Pembroke Street
Dublin 2
Phone: 01-6761196 Fax: 01-6760877
Email: imsl@indigo.ie
Web: http://www.imsl.ie
SIC: 74130 Employees: 50
Market Research Firms
Mr Eamonn Williams Managing Director
Mr John Morgan Financial Controller
Ms Maura Walsh Research Director
Mr Alan Sheehy Director

Landsdowne Market Research
49 St Stephen's Green
Dublin 2
Phone: 01-6613483 Fax: 01-6613479
Email: landsdowne@iol.ie
SIC: 74130 Employees: 40
Market Research
Mr Roger Jupp Managing Director
Mr John Morgan Finance Manager
Mr Robin Addis Chairman
Ms Rosaleen Tarleton IT Director

Link Analysis
140 Terenure Road West
Kimmage Cross Roads
Dublin 6w
Phone: 01-4927640 Fax: 01-4927640
Email: linkanalysis@iol.ie
SIC: 74130 Employees: 29
Market Research Company
Mr Derek Quinn Managing Director

Morimrc Ireland Ltd
Unit 65, The Omni Centre
Santry
Dublin 9
Phone: 01-8621122 Fax: 01-8621117
Email: trc.reception@mrc.ie
Web: http://www.mrc.ie
SIC: 74130 Employees: 70
Market Research
Ms Lesley McClure Managing Director
Mr Peter McDowell Financial Controller

MRBI Ltd
Temple House
Blackrock Co. Dublin
Phone: 01-2781011 Fax: 01-2781022
Email: info@tnsofres.com
Web: http://www.tnsofres.com
SIC: 74130 Employees: 60
Market Research Company
Mr Jack Jones Chairman
Mr Neil Anderson Financial Controller
Ms Anne Kennedy Personnel Director
Mr Ian McShane Marketing Director
Ms Sandra Harrison Jones Production Director
Mr Julian Glavey Computer Manager

Drury Communications Ltd
1 Richview Office Park
Clonskeagh
Dublin 14
Phone: 01-2605000 Fax: 01-2605066
Email: drury@drurycom.com
Web: http://www.drurycom.com
SIC: 74141 Employees: 40
Public Relations Consultants
Mr Billy Murphy Managing Director
Ms Hilary Murray Financial Controller
Mr Tom Collins Public Affairs

Business Services

Edelman Worldwide
5th Floor Huguenot House
35/38 St Stephen's Green
Dublin 2
Phone: 01-6789333 Fax: 01-6614408
Email: info@edelman.com
Web: http://www.edelman.com
SIC: 74141 Employees: 25
Public Relations Consultants
Mr John Mahony Chairman
Ms Claire Kendlin Finance Manager
Mr Hugh Gillanders Joint Managing Director

Fleishman-Hillard Saunders
15 Fitzwilliam Quay
Dublin 4
Phone: 01-6188444 Fax: 01-6602244
Email: postmaster@fleishman.com
Web: http://www.fleishman.com
SIC: 74141 Employees: 60
Public Relations Consultants
Mr John Saunders Managing Director
Mr John McGoldrick Financial Controller
Ms Carla Glynn Personnel Manager

Murray Consultants
35 Upper Mount Street
Dublin 2
Phone: 01-6614666 Fax: 01-6326444
Email: murcon@iol.ie
SIC: 74141 Employees: 45
Public Relations Consultants
Mr Joseph Murray Managing Director
Mr Kevin O'Reilly Financial Controller
Ms Lorraine Daly Personnel Secretary
Mr Eddie Power Computer Manager

Accenture
1 Harbourmaster Place
IFSC
Dublin 1
Phone: 01-6462000 Fax: 01-6462020
Web: http://www.accenture.com
SIC: 74143 Employees: 650
Management Consultants
Mr Leo Blennerhassett Manager
Mr Ken Spain Finance Manager
Ms Alice Hiney Personnel Manager
Ms Joanne Cardiff Computer Manager

BSM
Calbro House
Tuam Road
Galway Co. Galway
Phone: 091-773270 Fax: 091-773276
Email: info@bsm.ie
Web: http://www.bsm.ie
SIC: 74143 Employees: 35
Management & Technology Consultants
Mr Brian O'Grady Managing Director
Ms Eithne McKernan Sales & Marketing Director

Colornet Ltd
32a Rosemount Buisness Drive
Dublin 15
Phone: 01-8219270 Fax: 01-8243385
Email: sales@cnet.ie
Web: http://www.cnet.ie
SIC: 74143 Employees: 50
Document Management
Mr Gerry Terry Managing Director

ETP
Moatstown House
Athy Co. Kildare
Phone: 0507-31989 Fax: 0507-31092
Email: info@etpint.com
Web: http://www.etpint.com
SIC: 74143 Employees: 30
Project Management
Mr Fergus O'Connell Chief Executive Officer
Ms Bernadette McHugh Financial Controller

Business Services

F & B Property Management
22 South William Street
Dublin 2
Phone: 01-6677002 Fax: 01-6677011
SIC: 74143 Employees: 30
Management of holiday home property
Mr Ciaran Dolan Co-ordinator

French & Associates
10-11Blanchardstown Corporate Park
Ballycoolin
Dublin 15
Phone: 01-4060600 Fax: 01-4969377
Email: enquiry@frenchassociates.com
Web: http://www.frenchassociates.com
SIC: 74143 Employees: 50
Credit Management Consultants
Mr Paul French Managing Director
Mr Stephen Waters Financial Controller
Mr Ivor Deane Sales Director

Guardian Group Ltd
Harbour House
Loughquay
Limerick Co. Limerick
Phone: 061-319077 Fax: 061-319078
Email: info@guardiangroup.ie
Web: http://www.guardiangroup.ie
SIC: 74143 Employees: 150
Security Management Consultant
Mr Gerry O'Shea Managing Director
Mr Noel McNarama Accounts Manager
Ms Geraldine Lynch Operations Manager
Ms Deidre Quilcy General Administrator

Leading Edge Ireland Ltd
Charter House
Cobh Co. Cork
Phone: 021-4813684 Fax: 021-4813785
Email: info@leadingedge.ie
Web: http://www.leadingedge.ie
SIC: 74143 Employees: 40
Management Consulting Agency
Mr Joe Aherne Managing Director
Ms Sheila Butler Operation Manager

LGM Tramtrax Ltd
Landscape House, Landscape Road
Churchtown
Dublin 14
Phone: 01-2157000 Fax: 01-2157070
Email: info@lgmtramtrax.ie
Web: http://www.lgmtramtrax.ie
SIC: 74143 Employees: 2500
Faculty Management & Engineering
Mr Paul Mellon Managing Director
Mr Brian Brown Financial Controller
Ms Clare Mulville Office Manager
Mr Pat Reynolds IT Manager

Merc Partners
12 Richview Office Park
Clonskeagh
Dublin 14
Phone: 01-2830144 Fax: 01-2830550
Email: postmaster@merc.ie
Web: http://www.merc.ie
SIC: 74143 Employees: 25
Management Consultants
Mr Bill Hennessy Managing Partner
Mr Kieron Delaney Financial Controller

OMT Group
Top Floor, 41 O'Connell Street
Limerick Co. Limerick
Phone: 061-411478 Fax: 061-417175
Email: info@omt.ie
Web: http://www.omt.ie
SIC: 74143 Employees: 25
Management Consultants
Ms Elaine O'Donovan Managing Director
Mr James Young Administration Manager
Ms Carol O'Reilly Director

Process Control & Automation Systems
Strawhall Industrial Estate
Carlow Co. Carlow
Phone: 0503-70040 Fax: 0503-42620
Email: info@pcas.ie
Web: http://www.pcas.ie
SIC: 74143 Employees: 40
Information Management Systems
Mr Aidan Lynch Managing Director
Ms Mary Yates Accounts Manager
Mr Tom Donagher Sales Manager
Mr Michael Phelan Engineering Manager
Mr Brian Maguire Computer Manager

Shannon Free Airport Development Co
Shannon Co. Clare
Phone: 061-361555 Fax: 061-361903
Email: info@shannondev.ie
Web: http://www.shannon-dev.ie
SIC: 74143 Employees: 200
Development of Shannon Region
Mr Kevin Thompson Acting Executive Officer
Ms Terese Ross Financial Controller
Ms Deirdre Hughes Human Resources Manager
Mr Michael Leydon Industry Division Manager
Mr David Hogan Corporate Services Manager

South Kerry Development Partnership
IDA Industrial Estate, Valentia Road
Cahirciveen
Killarney Co. Kerry
Phone: 066-9472925 Fax: 066-9472725
Email: skdp@iol.ie
Web: http://www.southkerry.net
SIC: 74143 Employees: 33
Development Partnership
Mr Bill Thorne General Manager
Ms Joan Enright Accounts Manager
Ms Sinead Whyte Leader Co-ordinator

Vector Workplace & Facility Mgm
Unit 47 Finglas Business Park
Jamestown Road
Dublin 11
Phone: 01-6150616 Fax: 01-8645290
Email: info@vector-fm.com
Web: http://www.vector-fm.com
SIC: 74143 Employees: 80
Facilities management
Mr Martin McMahon Managing Director
Ms Anita Ryan Financial Controller
Mr Tony Holmes IT Manager

CoI Consulting Ltd
46a Quarter Road, Camlough
Besbrook
Drogheda, Co Louth
Phone: 041-9454545 Fax: 041-9454543
Email: reception@consultant.com
SIC: 74402 Employees: 25
Consulting Company
Mr M Irwin Managing Director

Bruce Copeland Marketing
Ballycanew
Gorey Co. Wexford
Phone: 055-27291 Fax: 055-27398
Email: info@minotell.iol.ie
SIC: 74144 Employees: 103
Marketing Company
Mr Bruce Copeland Proprietor
Ms Patricia Bashir Accounts Manager
Mr John Jordan Sales Representative

Contract Personnel Marketing
33 Greenmount Office Park
Harolds Cross
Dublin 6w
Phone: 01-4544313 Fax: 01-4544410
Email: cpmire@iol.ie
SIC: 74144 Employees: 25
Marketing Company
Mr Joe Gavin Managing Director
Mr Desmond Power Finance Manager
Mr Stephen O'Reilly Personnel Manager
Mr David Dent Technical Manager

Creative Solutions Ltd
10 Terminus Mills
Clonskeagh
Dublin 6
Phone: 01-2838118 Fax: 01-2838115
SIC: 74144 Employees: 30
Sales Promotion, Direct Marketing & Marketing Communications
Mr James O'Connor Director
Ms Dympha McHugh Finance Manager
Ms Bernie Cryan Personnel Manager

Delaney Marketing
1 Clarinda Park North
Dun Laoghaire Co. Dublin
Phone: 01-2802641 Fax: 01-2805405
Email: info@dmc.ie
Web: http://www.dmc.ie
SIC: 74144 Employees: 30
Marketing & Events Consultants
Mr Patrick Delaney Proprietor

Enterprise IG
Distillery Building
Fumbally Court
Dublin 8
Phone: 01-4546377 Fax: 01-4546383
Email: infodublin@enterpriseig.com
Web: http://www.enterpriseig.com
SIC: 74144 Employees: 28
Marketing & Design
Mr Jim Dunne Director
Mr Alan Walsh Finance Manager
Mr Peter Kruseman Director
Mr Cathal McDonagh Production Manager

Initiative Media Dublin
Iveagh Court
6-8 Harcourt Road
Dublin 2
Phone: 01-4751895 Fax: 01-4785226
Email: postmaster@initiativemedia.com
Web: http://www.initiativemedia.com
SIC: 74144 Employees: 30
Media Specialist
Mr Dave Harland Managing Director
Ms Ann-Marie Simonidis Research Manager

Pharmacia Ireland Ltd
PO Box 1752
Boeing Road Airways Industrial
Dublin 17
Phone: 01-8428733 Fax: 01-8428936
Web: http://www.pnu.com
SIC: 74144 Employees: 40
Marketing
Mr Gerard McMorrough Managing Director
Mr David Higgins Financial Controller
Mr Michael Byrne General Pharmaceutical Manager

Energy Services International
Boghall Road
Bray Co. Wicklow
Phone: 01-2867792 Fax: 01-2867797
Email: info@solarturbines.com
SIC: 74145 Employees: 480
Provide Technical Services to Oil Industry
Mr Mark Fitzgerald General Manager
Mr John Hefferan Finance Manager
Mr John Curley Director of Business Develop
Mr Gerry McCarthy Regional Manager
Mr Bruce Carroll Computer Manager

Archaeological Development Services
Windsor House 11, Fairview Strand
Fairview
Dublin 3
Phone: 01-8531009 Fax: 01-8531036
Email: ads@iol.ie
SIC: 74146 Employees: 40
Archaeologists
Ms Katrina Stephens Administrator
Ms Katie Hyland Computer Manager

Business Services

Environmental Protection Agency
PO Box 3000 Johnstown
Castle Estate
Wexford Co. Wexford
Phone: 053-47120 Fax: 053-60699
Email: info@epa.ie
Web: http://www.epa.ie
SIC: 74146 Employees: 230
Promote Environmental Protection in Ireland
Mr Liam McCumiskey Director General
Mr Jim Hurley Personnel Manager
Ms Mary Kinsella Computer Manager

FLI International Lining Systems
Six Cross Roads Business Park
Carriganard
Waterford Co. Waterford
Phone: 051-353190 Fax: 051-353177
Email: info@fli.ie
Web: http://www.fli.ie
SIC: 74146 Employees: 40
Environmental Services
Mr Michael Flynn Managing Director
Mr JJ Doherty Finance Manager
Mr Paddy Coakley Sales Manager

Jones Environmental (Ireland) Ltd
Kingswood Drive
City West Business Campus
Dublin 24
Phone: 01-2697377 Fax: 01-4039301
Web: http://www.jeil.ie
SIC: 74146 Employees: 70
Environmental Services
Mr Chris Bateman Managing Director
Mr Barry Fenton Director
Mr Pat Phibbs Sales Manager

K.T Cullen & Co Ltd
Bracken Business Park
Sandyford Industrial Estate
Dublin 18
Phone: 01-2697222 Fax: 01-2941823
Email: info@ktcullan.ie
Web: http://www.ktcullan.ie
SIC: 74146 Employees: 40
Environmental Consultants
Mr Kevin Cullan Managing Director
Ms Anne Cullan Finance Manager
Mr Terri Hayes Personnel Manager
Ms Emer Wright Sales & Marketing Manager
Mr Richard Cantwell Computer Manager

Kevin T Cullen & Co Ltd
Bracken Road
Sandyford Industrial Estate
Dublin 18
Phone: 01-2941717 Fax: 01-2941823
Email: info@ktcullen.ie
Web: http://www.ktcullen.ie
SIC: 74146 Employees: 37
Geologists
Mr Kevin Cullen Proprietor

Margaret Gowen & Co Ltd
2 Killinery View Lower Albert Road
Glenageary
Dun Laoghaire Co. Dublin
Phone: 01-2300433 Fax: 01-2300865
Email: archaeology@mglarc.com
Web: http://www.mglarc.com
SIC: 74146 Employees: 35
Archaeological Consultants & Project Managers
Ms Margaret Gowen Managing Director
Ms Dolores Cotter Financial Controller
Ms Nessa Walsh Operations Manager

OMAC Laboratories Ltd
Athenry Road
Loughrea
Galway Co. Galway
Phone: 091-841741 Fax: 091-842146
Email: omac@eircom.net
SIC: 74146 Employees: 25
Geochemical & Assay Service
Mr Michael O'Neill Managing Director
Mr Finbar O'Shea Finance Manager

Philip Farrelly & Co
2 Kennedy Road
Navan Co. Meath
Phone: 046-71818 Fax: 046-28479
Email: info@pfarrelly.com
SIC: 74146 Employees: 35
Agricultural & Enviromental Consultants
Mr Philip Farrelly Proprietor
Mr Brendan Scully Manager

Electrolux Professional Ltd
Unit 8 Orchard Park
Finisklin Industrial Estate
Sligo Co. Sligo
Phone: 071-60056 Fax: 071-60098
Web: http://www.electrolux.ie
SIC: 74147 Employees: 35
Quality Monitoring Service
Mr Michael Lagan Area Manager

Finglas Cabra Partnership
Rosehill House, Finglas Road
Dublin 11
Phone: 01-8342022 Fax: 01-8640211
Email: info@fcp.ie
Web: http://www.fcp.ie
SIC: 74147 Employees: 37
Development Partnership
Mr Michael Bowl Chief Executive

Innovex Ireland
Quintiles Buildings
Fairview
Dublin 3
Phone: 01-8195499 Fax: 01-8195573
Email: info@qdub.quintiles.com
Web: http://www.innovexglobal.com
SIC: 74147 Employees: 50
Pharmaceutical Consultants
Mr John Kirnan Managing Director
Mr David Shanahan Accounts Manager
Ms Ann Spring Personnel Manager
Mr Pat Kerley Business Manager
Ms June Kelleher Business Manager

MV Technology Ltd
Unit 3&5 IDA Enterprise Centre
Pearse Street
Dublin 2
Phone: 01-6718177 Fax: 01-6718470
Email: info@mvt.ie
Web: http://www.mvt.ie
SIC: 74147 Employees: 120
Manufacturing Consultants
Mr Jay Davidson Managing Director
Mr David Varian Financial Controller
Ms Barbara Keating Sales Manager
Mr James Mahon Technical Director

NIFAST
Unit 46 Airways Industrial Estate
Santry
Dublin 17
Phone: 01-8424333 Fax: 01-8424461
Email: info@nifast.ie
Web: http://www.nifast.ie
SIC: 74147 Employees: 30
Health & Safety Consultants
Mr Clive Carroll Managing Director
Mr Joseph Sheeky Financial Controller

Buytel Ltd
17 Harcourt Street
Dublin 2
Phone: 01-6039505 Fax: 01-4754816
Email: admin@buytel.com
Web: http://www.buytel.com
SIC: 74148 Employees: 33
Voice Verification
Mr Patrick Keaney Managing Director

DMR Consulting & Amdahl Ireland
Airside Business Park
Swords Co. Dublin
Phone: 01-8403001 Fax: 01-8136100
Email: marketing_ireland@dmr.com
Web: http://www.dmr.ie
SIC: 74148 Employees: 270
Business Solutions Centre
Mr Frank Kennedy General Manager
Mr Philip Finane Recruitment Manager
Mr Tom Bowen District Sales Manager
Mr David Delaney IT Manager

Dundalk Regional Development Centre
Dublin Road
Dundalk Co. Louth
Phone: 042-9331161 Fax: 042-9331163
Email: admissions@dkit.ie
Web: http://www.dkit.ie
SIC: 74148 Employees: 47
Unit For Start Up Companies
Mr Gerry Caroll Manager

Northside Partnership
Coolock Development Centre
Bunratty Drive, Coolock
Dublin 17
Phone: 01-8485630 Fax: 01-8485661
Email: nsp@northsidepartnership.ie
Web: http://www.northsidepartnership.ie
SIC: 74148 Employees: 46
Enterprise Company
Ms Marian Vickers Manager
Ms Irvine Beare Accounts Manager
Ms Fiona Nolan Personnel Manager
Ms Rowena Newman Computer Manager

Repak Ltd
The Red Cow Interchange Estate
1 Ballymount Road, Clondalkin
Dublin 22
Phone: 01-6237747 Fax: 01-4670197
Email: info@repak.ie
Web: http://www.repak.ie
SIC: 74148 Employees: 35
Business Advice To Packaging Companies
Mr Andrew Heatherington Manager
Mr William Collins Financial Controller

CSA Group Ltd
CSA House, Unit 6/7 Dundrum Bus Park
Windy Arbour
Dublin 14
Phone: 01-2964667 Fax: 01-2964676
Email: vbyrne@csa.ie
Web: http://www.csa.ie
SIC: 74149 Employees: 40
Consultant Geologist
Ms Viv Byrne Managing Director
Mr Ray O'Dowd Accountant
Mr Eamonn Kelly IT Manager

Business Services

FR Kelly & Company
27 Clyde Road
Ballsbridge
Dublin 4
Phone: 01-6602111 Fax: 01-6682844
Email: post@frkelly.ie
Web: http://www.frkelly.ie
SIC: 74149 Employees: 65
Patent & Trade Marks
Mr Peter Kelly Partner
Ms Rosaleen Martin Finance Manager
Ms Jacqui McElhinney Personnel Manager
Mr Liam Birkett Sales & Marketing Manager
Mr Colm Carberry Computer Manager

News Extracts Ltd
7 Ely Place
Dublin 2
Phone: 01-6616966 Fax: 01-6615361
Email: newsext@indigo.ie
SIC: 74149 Employees: 35
Press Cuttings Agency
Mr Stephen Cousins Managing Director

Pearse Trust Ltd
7th Floor Hume House
Ballsbridge
Dublin 4
Phone: 01-6600664 Fax: 01-6600200
Email: info@pearse-trust.ie
Web: http://www.pearse-trust.ie
SIC: 74149 Employees: 42
Company Formations & Administration
Mr Joseph Hickey Managing Director
Ms Catherine Foley Accountant

Shannon Business Centre
Shannon Co. Clare
Phone: 061-362422 Fax: 061-362024
SIC: 74149 Employees: 30
Business Services
Ms Ann Magoufis General Manager

Tomkins & Co
5 Dartmouth Road
Leeson Park
Dublin 6
Phone: 01-6605033 Fax: 01-6606920
Email: postmaster@tomkins.ie
Web: http://www.tomkins.ie
SIC: 74149 Employees: 50
Patent & Trade Mark Agents
Mr Peter Short Managing Partner
Mr David Gardiner Financial Controller
Dr Christina Gates Partner

DCC Plc
DCC House, Brewery Road
Stillorgan
Blackrock Co. Dublin
Phone: 01-2831011 Fax: 01-2831017
Email: info@dcc.ie
Web: http://www.dcc.ie
SIC: 74150 Employees: 2000
Industrial/Financial Holding Company
Mr Jim Flavin Chief Executive
Mr Fergal O'Dwyer Financial Controller
Ms Anne Keenan Human Resources Manager
Mr Donal Murphy Head of IT

IWP International Plc
19 Fitzwilliam Square
Dublin 2
Phone: 01-6611958 Fax: 01-6611957
Email: info@iwp.ie
Web: http://www.iwp.ie
SIC: 74150 Employees: 1900
Industrial Holding Company
Mr Joe Moran Chief Executive
Mr Bernard Byrne Financial Director
Mr Tom Richardson Computer Manager

Killeen Investments Ireland
Lexus House
Killeen Road
Dublin 12
Phone: 01-4504966 Fax: 01-4504981
SIC: 74150 Employees: 100
Industrial Holding Company
Mr Paddy Barrett Chief Executive
Mr Barney Moran Financial Director
Mr Dave Weir Distribution Manager
Mr John Keane Computer Manager

Warnants Holding Ltd
Comsat House, UA1 Centrepoint Bus Park
Oak Road
Dublin 12
Phone: 01-4975784 Fax: 01-4500977
Email: comsaths@indigo.ie
SIC: 74150 Employees: 100
Holding Company
Mr Sean O'Mahony Director
Mr Patrick Brophy Financial Controller

A & D Wejchert
23 Lower Baggot Street
Dublin 2
Phone: 01-6610321 Fax: 01-6610203
Email: mail@wejchert.ie
SIC: 74201 Employees: 40
Architect Practice
Mr A Wejchert Partner
Ms Danuta Wejchert Partner

Anthony Reddy & Associates
The Malt House
North Block, Grand Canal Quay
Dublin 2
Phone: 01-6704800 Fax: 01-6704801
Email: arad2@iol.ie
Web: http://www.anthonyreddy.com
SIC: 74201 Employees: 30
Architects/Planning Consultants
Mr Anthony Reddy Director

Arthur Gibney & Partners
20 Harcourt Street
Dublin 2
Phone: 01-4784300 Fax: 01-4752092
Email: info@agparchitects.ie
Web: http://www.agparchitects.ie
SIC: 74201 Employees: 25
Architects/Interior Design
Mr David Harris Principal

Berke Kennedy Doyle
6/7 Harcourt Terrace
Dublin 2
Phone: 01-6610399 Fax: 01-6767385
Email: architecture@bkd.ie
Web: http://www.
SIC: 74201 Employees: 95
Architects
Mr Paul Berke Kennedy Proprietor
Ms Kay Colman Financial Controller
Ms Deirdre Hargaden Personnel Manager
Mr Seamus Rowan Computer Manager

Brady Shipman Martin Architects
26 Temple Road
Dartry
Dublin 6
Phone: 01-4979651 Fax: 01-4966651
Email: mail@bsmconsult.com
SIC: 74201 Employees: 30
Landscape Architects
Mr David Bagnell Senior Partner
Ms Nuala O'Connor Financial Controller

Brian O'Halloran & Associates
23 Herbert Place
Dublin 2
Phone: 01-6764017 Fax: 01-6762963
Email: mail@bohaa.ie
Web: http://www.bohaa.ie
SIC: 74201 Employees: 45
Architects/Project Managers
Mr Brian O'Halloran Senior Partner
Ms Helmi Keegan Financial Controller
Mr Peter Hanna Partner & Office Manager
Mr John Kelly Computer Manager

Building Consultancy Group
16 St Stephen's Green
Dublin 2
Phone: 01-7038256 Fax: 01-7038083
SIC: 74201 Employees: 38
Architects, Engineers & Surveyors
Mr Adrian Mitchell Managing Director

Burke Kennedy Doyle Architects
6/7 Harcourt Terrace
Dublin 2
Phone: 01-6182400 Fax: 01-6767385
Email: architecture@bkd.ie
Web: http://www.bkd.ie
SIC: 74201 Employees: 100
Architects Practices
Mr Paul Burke-Kennedy Partner
Ms Kay Coleman Financial Controller
Mr Seamus Rowan IT Manager

Connor Keogh & McUlcaire
Woodquay Court
Woodquay
Galway Co. Galway
Phone: 091-563191 Fax: 091-568683
Email: hgloc@iol.ie
SIC: 74201 Employees: 38
Architects & Consulting Engineers
Mr Frank McGrath Managing Director
Ms Josephine Noone Sales & Marketing Manager
Mr John Fitzmorris Computer Manager

DE Blacam and Meagher
29 Raglan Road
Dublin 4
Phone: 01-6681555 Fax: 01-6681075
Email: mail@debm.ie
SIC: 74201 Employees: 30
Architect Practices
Mr Shane Deblacan Partner
Ms Linda Ingrim Financial Controller
Mr John Meragh Partner

Douglas Wallace
25 Temple Lane
Dublin 2
Phone: 01-6777411 Fax: 01-6777876
Email: design@douglaswallace.ie
Web: http://www.douglaswallace.com
SIC: 74201 Employees: 75
Architects
Mr Hugh Wallace Director
Ms Emma Rice Financial Controller
Ms Vanessa Brady Marketing Manager

Fewer McGinley Associates
Wyse House
Adelphi Quay
Waterford Co. Waterford
Phone: 051-876991 Fax: 051-878676
Email: fma@iol.ie
SIC: 74201 Employees: 23
Architects Practice
Mr Nicholas Fewer Principal
Mr Tony Power Sales Manager

Business Services

Gilroy McMahon
The Mill Building
Unit 10 Greenmount Indust Est
Dublin 12
Phone: 01-4978516 Fax: 01-4970099
Email: gmcm@indigo.ie
SIC: 74201 Employees: 40
Architects
Mr Desmond McMahon Senior Partner
Mr Paul Keegan Finance Manager

Henry J Lyons & Partners
47/48 Pearse street
Dublin 2
Phone: 01-8883333 Fax: 01-8883322
Email: hjl@hjlyons.com
SIC: 74201 Employees: 87
Architects
Mr Maociosa O'Floinn Managing Director
Mr Kevin O'Dea Finance Director

Horan Keogan Ryan
Carnegie House
Library Road
Dun Laoghaire Co. Dublin
Phone: 01-6636400 Fax: 01-6636401
Email: architecture@hkr.ie
Web: http://www.hkr-architects.com
SIC: 74201 Employees: 50
Architectural Practice/Town Planning
Consultancy/Space Planning & Interior Desig
Mr Tony Horan Director
Mr Jerry Ryan Director
Ms A Harrington Personnel Manager
Mr John Keogan Director
Mr B Gallagher Computing Manager

John Duffy Design Group
24 The Crescent
Monkstown
Blackrock Co. Dublin
Phone: 01-2844455 Fax: 01-2807075
Email: info@johnduffydesign.ie
Web: http://www.jddg.ie
SIC: 74201 Employees: 27
Architects & Interior Designers
Mr John Duffy Managing Director
Ms Sheila Tuit Company Accountant
Mr Eunan Byrne Personnel Manager
Mr Tara McFadden Production Manager
Ms Sarah Kelly Computer Manager

Kennedy O'Sullivan
9 Clarinda Park North
Dun Laoghaire Co. Dublin
Phone: 01-2300923 Fax: 01-2843563
SIC: 74201 Employees: 23
Architects Practice
Mr Joe Kennedy Principal

KMD Architecture
4 Princes Street South
City Quay
Dublin 2
Phone: 01-6770077 Fax: 01-6771186
Email: info@kmd.ie
Web: http://www.kmd.ie
SIC: 74201 Employees: 65
Architects/Project Managers
Mr Eugene Dunne Managing Director
Mr Colm Reid Personnel Manager
Mr Mike Kinsella Marketing Manager
Mr Patrick Singleton Computer Manager

McNally Design Ltd
Warrington House
Mount Street Crescent
Dublin 2
Phone: 01-6611477 Fax: 01-6612755
Email: info@mcnallydesign.com
Web: http://www.irishpubcompany.com
SIC: 74201 Employees: 120
Architect & Design
Mr Mel McNally Managing Director
Ms Frances O'Shaughnessey Financial Controller
Mr Conor Kelly Sales Director
Mr Liam McNally IT Manager

Moloney O'Beirne & Architects
Northumberland Hall
Northumberland Avenue
Dun Laoghaire Co. Dublin
Phone: 01-2844684 Fax: 01-2844691
Email: mail@mob.ie
SIC: 74201 Employees: 30
Architects
Mr Bernard Moloney Director
Ms Kay Clooney Company Secretary
Ms Carole O'Riordain Computer Manager

Murray O'Laoire & Architects
Fumbally Court, Fumbally Lane
Dublin 8
Phone: 01-4537300 Fax: 01-4534062
Email: mail@dublin.murrayolaoire.com
Web: http://www.murrayolaoire.com
SIC: 74201 Employees: 100
Architects
Mr Sean O'Laoire Managing Partner
Mr Mike Foley Financial Controller
Mr Calbhac O'Carroll Manager Director
Mr Bryan Donnellan Sales & Marketing Manager

National Building Agency Ltd
Hatherton, Richmond Avenue South
Milltown
Dublin 6
Phone: 01-4979654 Fax: 01-4972540
Email: info@nba.ie
Web: http://www.nba.ie
SIC: 74201 Employees: 60
Architects & Surveyors
Mr Matt O'Connor Managing Director
Mr Michael Conway Financial Controller
Mr Paraic Donoghue Company Secretary
Mr Brian Farrell Computer Manager

O'Mahony Pike Architects
Milltown House
Mount St. Annes Milltown
Dublin 6
Phone: 01-2027400 Fax: 01-2830822
Email: admin@omp.ie
Web: http://www.omp.ie
SIC: 74201 Employees: 60
Architect Practice
Mr James Pike Director
Ms Penny Pike Accounts Manager
Mr David Smith Sales & Marketing Manager
Mr Martin O'Toole Computer Manager

O'Riordan Staehli Architects
Schoolhouse Studio, Carrigaline Road
Doulgas
Cork Co. Cork
Phone: 021-4362922 Fax: 021-4363048
Email: orsa@iol.ie
Web: http://www.orsa.ie
SIC: 74201 Employees: 40
Architect Firms
Mr Donagh O'Riordan Principal
Ms Annette Dunne Accountant
Mr Padraig Hyde Technical Associate

OMS Architechs
14-15 Sir John Rogersons Quay
Dublin 2
Phone: 01-6773490 Fax: 01-6774849
Email: architects@oms.ie
SIC: 74201 Employees: 28
Architects
Mr John Smyth Partner
Mr Toal O'Muire Partner

RKD Architects
59 Northumberland Road
Ballsbridge
Dublin 4
Phone: 01-6681055 Fax: 01-6683699
Email: mail@rkd.ie
Web: http://www.rkd.ie
SIC: 74201 Employees: 80
Architects/Interior Designers/Project
Managers/Masterplanners
Mr David Browne Partner
Ms Geraldine Dunne Finance Manager
Mr Sedick Abrahams IT Manager

Ryan Keogan Horan
40 Main Street
Blackrock Co. Dublin
Phone: 01-2834567 Fax: 01-2836278
Email: hkr@hkr.ie
Web: http://www.hkr.ie
SIC: 74201 Employees: 24
Architects Practices
Mr Tony Horan Senior Partner

Scott Tallon Walker Architects
19 Merrion Square
Dublin 2
Phone: 01-6760621 Fax: 01-6613300
Email: mail@stw.ie
Web: http://www.stw.ie
SIC: 74201 Employees: 104
Architects
Mr Michael Tallon Managing Partner
Ms Christina Lynch Company Secretary

Simon J Kelly & Partners
Corrib Castle
Waterside
Galway Co. Galway
Phone: 091-563459 Fax: 091-565427
Email: mail@sjk.ie
Web: http://www.sjk.ie
SIC: 74201 Employees: 30
Architect Firms
Mr Conor Kelly Managing Director

Costins Nursery
Portgloriam, Kilcock
Naas Co. Kildare
Phone: 01-6287237 Fax: 01-6287934
Email: costins@indigo.ie
SIC: 74202 Employees: 25
Landscape Gardeners & Contractors
Mr John Joe Costin Proprietor

P O'Brien & Sons (Landscaping) Ltd
Streamstown
Malahide Co. Dublin
Phone: 01-8452555 Fax: 01-8453281
Email: info@obrienlandscaping.com
SIC: 74202 Employees: 45
Landscape Contractors
Mr Peter O'Brien Managing Director

Redlough Landscapes Ltd
Belgree
Mulhuddart
Dublin 15
Phone: 01-8207033 Fax: 01-8207035
Email: redlough@iol.ie
Web: http://www.redlough-landscapes.20.com
SIC: 74202 Employees: 25
Landscape Gardeners & Contractors
Mr Liam Loghnane Managing Director

Business Services

Bruce-Shaw Partnership
28 Fitzwilliam Place
Dublin 2
Phone: 01-6614711 Fax: 01-6614722
Email: info@bspdub.ie
Web: http://www.bspdub.ie
SIC: 74203 Employees: 600
Quantity Surveyor
Mr Brendan O'Mara Chairman
Mr Paul Keogh Head of Accounts
Ms Ann Gallagher Company Secretary
Mr Sean Compton Department Manager

Lisney Surveyors
24 St Stephen's Green
Dublin 2
Phone: 01-6382700 Fax: 01-6615086
Email: dublin@lisney.com
Web: http://www.lisney.com
SIC: 74203 Employees: 350
Land Surveyors
Mr Peter Brown Managing Director
Mr Eanna Henderson Finance Manager

Mulcahy McDonagh & Partners
46-48 Pembroke Road
Ballsbridge
Dublin 4
Phone: 01-6689833 Fax: 01-6689003
Email: info@mmp.ie
Web: http://www.mmp.ie
SIC: 74203 Employees: 42
Quantity Surveyors
Mr Patrick O'Donohue Managing Director
Mr Vincent Crowley Financial Controller
Mr John Daly Sales & Marketing Manager

Nolan Ryan Partnership
Otteran House, Otteran Place
South Parade
Waterford Co. Waterford
Phone: 051-878918 Fax: 051-874453
Email: waterford@nolanryan.ie
Web: www.nolanryan.ie
SIC: 74203 Employees: 50
Surveyors -Quantity
Mr Paul Nolan Senior Partner

Atkins McCarthy
Villa Franca
Douglas Road
Cork Co. Cork
Phone: 021-4294993 Fax: 021-4293527
Email: cork@mccarthy.iol.ie
SIC: 74204 Employees: 30
Consulting Engineers
Mr Jack Sheehan Managing Director

Callaghan Engineering Ltd
Wentworth House 19-20 Hogan Place
Lower Grand Canal Street
Dublin 2
Phone: 01-6620484 Fax: 01-6614424
Email: mail@calleng.ie
Web: http://www.calleng.ie
SIC: 74204 Employees: 50
Engineering Consultants
Mr Dolan O'Callaghan Managing Director
Ms Helena Gleeson Finance Manager
Ms Miriam O'Callaghan Sales & Marketing Manager
Mr Declan Maguire Computer Manager

DBFL
22/23 Holles Street
Dublin 2
Phone: 01-6766343 Fax: 01-6610825
Email: dbfl@iol.ie
SIC: 74204 Employees: 60
Consultant Engineer Practice
Mr Jim Lawlor Partner
Mr Ron Battye Partner
Mr Paul Ford Partner
Mr Patrick Darling Partner

DPS Engineering & Construction Ltd
Landscape House, Baldonnell Business Park
Baldonnell
Dublin 22
Phone: 01-2961844 Fax: 01-2961850
Email: info@dps.ie
Web: http://www.dps.ie
SIC: 74204 Employees: 30
Consulting Engineers
Mr Frank Keogh Manager

EG Pettit & Company
Springville House, Blackrock Road
Cork Co. Cork
Phone: 021-4966400 Fax: 021-4966153
Email: dcc@egpettit.ie
Web: http://www.egpettit.ie
SIC: 74204 Employees: 100
Consultant Engineer Practice
Mr Ger O'Sullivan Managing Director
Mr Declan Horgan Finance Manager
Ms Stella O'Sullivan Personnel Manager
Mr John Healy Computer Manager

Homan O'Brien
5 Marine Terrace
Dun Laoghaire Co. Dublin
Phone: 01-2805666 Fax: 01-2842617
Email: hoba@indigo.ie
Web: http://www.homanobrien.ie
SIC: 74204 Employees: 50
Consulting Engineers
Mr Seamus Homan Managing Director
Ms Gillian O'Loughlin Accounts Manager
Mr James Cosgrove Sales & Marketing Manager

Hugh Munro & Co Ltd
Tramway House
36 Dartry Road
Dublin 6
Phone: 01-4975716 Fax: 01-4975886
SIC: 74204 Employees: 125
Consultant Engineer Practice
Mr Brendan Sheehan Joint Chief Executive

Jacobs Engineering Inc
Merrion House, Merrion Road
Dublin 4
Phone: 01-2695666 Fax: 01-2695497
Email: postmaster@jacobs.com
Web: http://www.jacobs.com
SIC: 74204 Employees: 550
Engineering Consultants
Mr Fred Barry Chief Executive
Mr Tony Comerford Financial Controller
Ms Dympna Moran Personnel Manager
Mr Martin McCarthy Sales Manager
Mr John Hewitt Network Manager

Jennings O'Donovan & Partners
Finisklin Industrial Estate
Sligo Co. Sligo
Phone: 071-61416 Fax: 071-61080
Email: info@jodirl.com
Web: http://www.jodirl.com
SIC: 74204 Employees: 30
Consulting Engineers
Mr Frank McAleenan Joint Managing Director
Ms Rose Davis Financial Controller
Mr Rory McLaughlin Joint Managing Director

JV Tierney & Company Ltd
Marleigh House
13 Leinster Road West
Dublin 6
Phone: 01-4976761 Fax: 01-4976909
Email: mail@jvtierney.ie
SIC: 74204 Employees: 50
Consultant Engineer Practice
Mr Tom Keating Managing Director
Mr Michael Callan Director
Mr Finn Ahern Computer Manager

M C O'Sullivan & Company Ltd
Ashurst, Mount Merrion Avenue
Blackrock Co. Dublin
Phone: 01-2884499 Fax: 01-2835676
Email: info@dublin.mcos.ie
Web: http://www.dublin.mcos.ie
SIC: 74204 Employees: 310
Consulting Engineers
Mr KJ O'Sullivan Managing Director
Ms Patricia O'Shea Accounts Manager
Mr Jerry Grant Human Resources Director
Mr PJ Rudden Director of Business Dev
Mr Donagh McGrath Computer Manager

MacArdle McSweeney Associates
11-12 Warrington Place
Dublin 2
Phone: 01-6618122 Fax: 01-6785105
Email: info@mma.ie
Web: http://www.mma.ie
SIC: 74204 Employees: 71
Consulting Engineering Practice
Mr Michael McSweeney Managing Director
Mr David Wilkinson Finance Manager
Mr William Bennett Computer Manager

Malachy Walsh & Partners
Boreenmanna Road
Cork Co. Cork
Phone: 021-4962866 Fax: 021-4962929
Email: admin@mwpcork.iol.ie
SIC: 74204 Employees: 65
Engineering Consultants
Mr Anthony Moloney Managing Director
Mr John Kenny Finance Manager

Materials Ireland
Enterprise Ireland
Glasnevin
Dublin 9
Phone: 01-8082418 Fax: 01-8367028
Email: materials-ireland@mat-irl.ie
Web: http://www.mat-irl.ie
SIC: 74204 Employees: 50
Materials Technology Consultancy
Mr Jim Lawler Director

MC O'Sullivan & Co Ltd
Inishmore
Ballincollig
Cork Co. Cork
Phone: 021-4870200 Fax: 021-4873742
Email: info@cork.mcos.ie
Web: http://www.cork.mcos.ie
SIC: 74204 Employees: 65
Consulting Engineers
Mr Brendan O'Halloran Director
Ms Rita O'Sullivan Administrator

McKenna Engineering Services Ltd
Riverview Business Park
Dublin 12
Phone: 01-4197744 Fax: 01-4197755
Email: info@mesl.com
Web: http://www.mesl.com
SIC: 74204 Employees: 85
Consulting Engineering
Mr Bob McKenna Managing Director
Mr Philip Stroughair Financial Controller
Mr Kieran Timmons Computer Manager

Michael Punch & Assiosiates
NIB Building, Stephen Street
Sligo Co. Sligo
Phone: 071-50551 Fax: 071-50788
Email: sligo@mpp.ie
SIC: 74204 Employees: 130
Consulting Engineers
Mr Pat Hanley Managing Director

Mott MacDonald EPO
8 Fitzwilliam Place
Dublin 2
Phone: 01-6768222 Fax: 01-6623290
Email: engineers@mmepo.ie
Web: http://www.mottmacepo.co.uk
SIC: 74204 Employees: 90
Consulting Engineers
Mr Tom O'Connor Managing Director

National Environmental Sciences Ltd
Kylemore Road
Dublin 12
Phone: 01-4504922 Fax: 01-4504929
SIC: 74204 Employees: 23
Acoustic Engineers
Mr Terry Donnelly Manager

Nicholas O'Dwyer & Co
Carrick House
Dundrum Centre
Dublin 14
Phone: 01-2984499 Fax: 01-2984957
Email: nodwyer@nicholasodwyer.com
Web: http://www.nicholasodwyer.com
SIC: 74204 Employees: 55
Consulting Engineers
Mr Richard Crowe Managing Director

O'Connor Sutton Cronin
9 Prussia Street
Dublin 7
Phone: 01-6618677 Fax: 01-8682100
Email: ocsc@ocsc.ie
Web: http://www.ocsc.ie
SIC: 74204 Employees: 80
Consulting Engineers - Civil & Structural
Mr John O'Connor Joint Managing Director
Mr James Barrett Company Secretary
Mr Kevin Cronin Joint Managing Director
Mr Joe Johnson Computer Manager

Project Management Group
Loughmahon Technology Park
Blackrock
Cork Co. Cork
Phone: 021-4358922 Fax: 021-4358933
Email: info@pmc.pmg.ie
Web: http://www.pmg.ie
SIC: 74204 Employees: 1000
Engineering Consultancy
Mr Pat McGrath Managing Director
Mr Larry Westman Finance Director
Mr Jim O'Dwyer Director of Human Resources
Mr Billy O'Neill Marketing Manager
Mr Charlie Campbell Operation Director
Mr Niall Twoney Head of Automation

Ryan Hanley Consulting Engineers
The Villa, The Crescent
Galway Co. Galway
Phone: 091-587116 Fax: 091-587110
Email: rhc@ryanhanley.ie
SIC: 74204 Employees: 50
Consulting Engineers
Mr Michael Gannon Managing Director
Ms Mary Cathal Finance Director

Shanahan Engineering Ltd
65 Monkstown Road
Blackrock Co. Dublin
Phone: 01-2809888 Fax: 01-2800952
Email: shanahan@shanahaneng.ie
Web: http://www.shanahaneng.ie
SIC: 74204 Employees: 60
Engineering Services
Mr Liam Shanahan Managing Director
Ms Una O'Keefe Financial Controller
Mr Paul Bauress Manager of Operations
Mr James Greaney International Project Manager

Thomas Garland & Partners
28-30 Rathmines Park
Dublin 6
Phone: 01-4964322 Fax: 01-4964725
Email: mail@tgp.ie
Web: http://www.tgp.ie
SIC: 74204 Employees: 42
Consultant Engineer Practice
Mr Frank Cavanagh Managing Director
Mr John Coakley Financial Controller
Mr Dominic O'Moore IT Manager

Tractech (Ireland) Ltd
Finisklin Industrial Estate
Sligo Co. Sligo
Phone: 071-62388 Fax: 071-62668
Email: info@tractech.com
Web: http://www.tractech.com
SIC: 74204 Employees: 90
Manufacturing Engineering
Mr Denis O'Connell Director of Operations
Mr Des Bree Financial Controller
Mr Arthur Gent Human Resources Manager
Mr Rob Aitchison Sales & Marketing Manager
Mr Michael Merrick Product Manager
Ms Collette Hamilton IT Specialist

Value Engineering Ltd
Courtstown Industrial Estate
Little Island
Cork Co. Cork
Phone: 021-4353222 Fax: 021-4354266
Email: info@valueengineering.ie
Web: http://www.valueengineering.ie
SIC: 74204 Employees: 25
Consulting Engineers
Mr Tim O'Riordan Manager

PS Patton Interiors Ltd
115 Lagan Road
Dublin Industrial Est, Glasnevin
Dublin 11
Phone: 01-8305009 Fax: 01-8305024
Email: pattoninteriors@tinet.ie
Web: http://www.pattoninteriors.com
SIC: 74208 Employees: 40
Interior Designers
Mr Dermot Patton Managing Director
Mr Liam Loughlin Finance Manager
Mr Marc Patton Sales Director

Stratus Technologies Ireland Ltd
College Business & Technology Park
Blanchardstown Road North
Dublin 15
Phone: 01-8096000 Fax: 01-8242586
Web: http://www.stratus.com
SIC: 74208 Employees: 85
Design & Development of Hardware
Mr Michael O'Keefe Managing Director
Ms Hilda Stafford Financial Controller
Mr Eugene McGinley Personnel Manager

Abbey Plc
1 Setanta Place
Dublin 2
Phone: 01-6703033 Fax: 01-6703010
Email: info@kingscroft.ie
Web: http://www.abbeydev.co.uk
SIC: 74209 Employees: 350
Property Developers
Mr Richard Shortt Managing Director
Mr David Dawson Financial Controller(UK)
Mr Nick Collins Personnel Manager

Business Services

Chadwick Building Services
Greenhills Industrial Estate
Grennhills Road, Walkinstown
Dublin 12
Phone: 01-4602888 Fax: 01-4501075
Email: reception@chadwick.ie
SIC: 74209 Employees: 60
Building Consultants
Mr Berty Treacy Managing Director
Mr Frank Brown Finance Manager
Mr John Lowe Personnel Manager
Mr Ed Gogerty Marketing Manager
Mr Michael Fox IT Manager

Anderson Spratt Group
Tower 1 Fumbally Court
Fumbally Lane
Dublin 8
Phone: 01-4731344 Fax: 01-4732118
Email: recruit@andersonspratt.ie
Web: http://www.andersonspratt.ie
SIC: 74402 Employees: 70
Advertising Agency
Ms Deborah Brannelly Director
Ms Mary Nagle Director

Bates Ireland Ltd
9 Upper Pembroke Street
Dublin 2
Phone: 01-6760221 Fax: 01-6765201
Email: adv@batesireland.ie
Web: http://www.batesireland.ie
SIC: 74402 Employees: 23
Advertising Agency
Mr Joe Clancy Chief Executive
Mr Barry Kennedy Accounts Director
Mr Ian Doherty Creative Director
Mr Brendan Diggin Production Manager
Ms Mary Keegan Financial Director

Cawley Nea Ltd
41A Blackberry Lane
Rathmines
Dublin 6
Phone: 01-4966920 Fax: 01-4966923
Email: post@cawleynea.ie
Web: http://www.cawleynea.ie
SIC: 74402 Employees: 30
Advertising Agencies
Mr Chris Cawley Managing Director
Mr Eamonn Burke Financial Controller
Mr Brian Swords Deputy Managing Director
Mr Richard Harris Production Manager

CDP Associates Advertising Ltd
46 Wellington Road
Ballsbridge
Dublin 4
Phone: 01-6689627 Fax: 01-6681341
Email: info@cdpassociates.ie
Web: http://www.cdpassociates.ie
SIC: 74402 Employees: 29
Advertising Agency
Mr Peter O'Keeffe Managing Director
Ms Claire Cluskey Financial Director
Mr Peter O'Donnell Director
Mr David Woods Production Manager
Mr Ronan O'Loughlin Media Director

Dan Advertising
22 Penrose Wharf
Penrose Quay
Cork Co. Cork
Phone: 021-4271060 Fax: 021-4274745
Email: danad@indigo.ie
SIC: 74402 Employees: 50
Advertising Company
Mr Jim McCoy Managing Director
Ms Pamela Barrett Advertising Manager
Mr Michael Flemming Sales & Marketing Manager

Business Services

DDFH & B Advertising Ltd
3 Christ Church Square
Dublin 8
Phone: 01-4106666 Fax: 01-4106699
Email: info@ddfhb.ie
Web: http://www.ddfhb.ie
SIC: 74402 Employees: 100
Advertising Agency
Mr Jim Donnelly Managing Director
Mr Brendan Gainey Financial Controller
Mr Padraig Doyle Personnel Manager
Mr Sean Whitaker Director of Planning
Mr Derek Lawlor Production Manager
Mr Michael O'Reilly Financial Director

Des O'Meara & Partners
23 Fitzwilliam Place
Dublin 2
Phone: 01-5000600 Fax: 01-5000660
Email: info@desomeara.ie
Web: http://www.desomeara.ie
SIC: 74402 Employees: 35
Advertising Agency
Mr Liam O'Donohoe Chief Executive
Mr Andrew Kennedy Financial Director
Mr Des O'Meara Executive Chairman
Ms Eimear O'Reilly Production Manager
Mr Ciaran O'Reilly Director

Doherty-Padbury Advertising
105 Lower Baggot Street
Dublin 2
Phone: 01-6764008 Fax: 01-6767072
Email: info@doherty.ie
Web: http://www.doherty.ie
SIC: 74402 Employees: 53
Advertising Agency
Mr Mark Beggs Managing Director
Mr Enda Maloney Financial Controller
Ms Trish O'Siullivan Human Resources Manager
Mr Pascal Taggart Chairman
Mr William Byrne Production Manager
Mr Andrew O'Donoghue Information Systems

Euro RSCG
Harcourt Centre
50-53 Harcourt Street
Dublin 2
Phone: 01-4757981 Fax: 01-4781724
Email: info@eurorscg.ie
Web: http://www.eurorscg.ie
SIC: 74402 Employees: 60
Advertising & Marketing Company
Mr Gerard Nagle Chief Executive
Mr Martin Ryan Financial Controller
Ms Laura White Media Manager
Mr Tim Ivers Deputy Managing Director
Mr Paul Cullen Media Manager

IDS Media Group Ltd
3 Sandyford Business Park
Blackthorn Avenue
Dublin 18
Phone: 01-2604818 Fax: 01-2104816
Email: info@idsmarketresearch.com
Web: http://www.idsmediagroup.com
SIC: 74402 Employees: 75
Advertising Services Company
Mr Martin Crilly Managing Director

Irish International Group
17 Gilford Road
Sandymount
Dublin 4
Phone: 01-2602000 Fax: 01-2602111
Email: email@irish-international.ie
Web: http://www.irish-international.ie
SIC: 74402 Employees: 100
Advertising Agency
Mr Ian Young Managing Director
Mr William Nolan Finance Manager
Mr David McLoughlin Sales & Marketing Manager
Mr Eamon Clarkin Director

Lopex Ireland
3 Leeson Close
Dublin 2
Phone: 01-6766911 Fax: 01-6611992
Email: advertising@young-ad.ie
SIC: 74402 Employees: 50
Advertising Company
Mr Sean O'Meara Managing Director
Mr Peter O'Brien Financial Controller
Mr Conor Murphy Media Executive

McCann Erickson
Hambleden House
19-26 Lower Pembroke Street
Dublin 2
Phone: 01-6766366 Fax: 01-6767077
Email: info@europe.mccann.com
Web: http://www.mccann.com
SIC: 74402 Employees: 67
Advertising Agency
Mr Brian Sparks Managing Director
Ms Kathryn O'Moore Financial Controller
Ms Linda Brown Office Manager
Mr Bill McDonagh Traffic Manager
Mr David Egan Computer Manager

McConnell Group
18 Charlemont Place
Dublin 2
Phone: 01-4781544 Fax: 01-4780544
Email: info@mcconnells.ie
Web: http://www.mcconnells.ie
SIC: 74402 Employees: 125
Advertising Agency
Mr Jarlath Jennings Managing Director
Mr Pat Hurley Financial Controller
Mr Jim Murray Company Secretary
Mr Peter Kieran Print Manager
Mr Chris Hussey Computer Manager

More Group Ireland Ltd
Beech House
Beech Hill Road
Dublin 4
Phone: 01-4784500 Fax: 01-4784582
Email: edel.mccabe@moregroup.com
Web: http://www.moregroup.com
SIC: 74402 Employees: 65
Outdoor Advertising Agency - Posters
Mr Terry Buckley Managing Director
Ms Edel McCabe Sales Manager

O'Connor O'Sullivan Partnership
52 Northumberland Road
Dublin 4
Phone: 01-6682833 Fax: 01-6603711
Email: info@ocos.ie
Web: http://www.ocos.ie
SIC: 74402 Employees: 24
Advertising Company
Mr Owen O'Connor Chairman
Mr Paul Doyle Finance Manager
Ms Annette O'Callaghan Media Manager

Ogilvy & Mather
8/9 Appian Way
Dublin 6
Phone: 01-6609300 Fax: 01-6605363
Email: info@ogilvy.com
Web: http://www.ogilvy.ie
SIC: 74402 Employees: 120
Advertising Agency
Mr Michael Welsford Chairman
Mr David Haugh Finance Manager
Mr Eamon Medlar Computer Project Manager

Rainbow Displays Ltd
Dublin Industrial Estate
Glasnevin
Dublin 11
Phone: 01-8303666 Fax: 01-8306730
Email: raindist@indigo.ie
SIC: 74402 Employees: 25
Promotional Advertising
Mr Colin Murray Manager
Mr Terry Ryan Sales Manager

TDI Metro Ltd
26 Fitzwilliam Square South
Dublin 2
Phone: 01-6614155 Fax: 01-6785559
Email: info@tdi.ie
Web: http://www.tdi.ie
SIC: 74402 Employees: 50
Outdoor Advertising Contractors
Mr John Tachell Managing Director
Mr John Hyde Financial Controller
Mr Philip Brown Sales Director

Young Advertising Ltd
64 Lower Leeson Street
Dublin 2
Phone: 01-6615599 Fax: 01-6611992
Email: advertising@young-ad.ie
Web: http://www.young-ad.ie
SIC: 74402 Employees: 50
Advertising
Mr Brian Hayes Managing Director
Ms Florence Small Company Accountant
Mr Conor Murphy Technical Manager

Brandwell Ireland Ltd
Unit 12, North West Business Park
Ballycoolin
Dublin 15
Phone: 01-8348444 Fax: 01-8342688
Email: info@brandwell.ie
SIC: 74403 Employees: 45
Promotional Merchandise/Leathergoods/Luggage & Hosiery
Mr Sean Mahon Managing Director
Mr Robert Barter Financial Director
Mr Jeff Mahon Sales & Marketing Director
Ms Deirdre Smith Operation Manager

Innisfree Promotions
Innisfree House
Strandhill Road
Sligo Co. Sligo
Phone: 071-62630 Fax: 071-50300
SIC: 74403 Employees: 104
Promotional Consultants
Ms Helena McMahon Director
Mr Barry McMahon Sales Director

Irish Goodwill Products Ltd
5 Walkinstown Road
Dublin 12
Phone: 01-4506586 Fax: 01-4501323
Email: sales@irishgoodwill.iol.ie
SIC: 74403 Employees: 25
Advertising, Promotional Items, Plastic Products Manufacture
Mr Jim Warrington Managing Director
Mr William Bell Sales Manager

John O'Carroll
Unit G 537 North Circular Road
Dublin 1
Phone: 01-8558222 Fax: 01-8558140
Email: info@bright.ie
Web: http://www.brightprint.ie
SIC: 74403 Employees: 35
Corporate Gifts & Printed T-shirts
Mr Ian Redmond Managing Director
Ms Mary Young Accounts
Mr Mark Redmond Sales & Marketing Manager

Link Display
Expo House
Prussia Street
Dublin 7
Phone: 01-8380973 Fax: 01-8689108
Email: linkdis@iol.ie
SIC: 74403 Employees: 24
Exhibition Stands Shopfitting Props & Decorations
Mr Don Reynold Director
Mr Donal Smith Sales Manager

Business Services

Mace Promotions
Valetta House
York Road
Dun Laoghaire Co. Dublin
Phone: 01-2802909 Fax: 01-2809487
Email: thestudio@eircom.net
Web: http://www.mace.ie
SIC: 74403 Employees: 30
Sales Promotions Company
Ms Suzanne Gogarty Chief Executive

MDM Group
22 Cookstown Industrial Estate
Tallaght
Dublin 24
Phone: 01-4510711 Fax: 01-4510721
Email: info@movex.ie
SIC: 74403 Employees: 50
Promotion Company
Mr Michael Kiely Managing Director
Ms Audrey Cleary Financial Controller
Mr David Cullen Sales & Marketing Manager

National Pen Ltd
Finnabair Industrial Park
Dundalk Co. Louth
Phone: 042-9388500 Fax: 042-9388586
Email: postmaster@pens.com
Web: http://www.penseurope.com
SIC: 74403 Employees: 200
Promotional Products - Pens
Mr Peter Donnelly Vice President
Ms Richella McEntee Financial Controller
Ms Clodagh Sands Human Resources Manager
Ms Pauline McCabe Sales
Mr John Kavanagh Production Manager
Mr Rory McCabe IT Manager

Pareto Marketing
Belmount Church Galloping Green
Stillorgan Road
Dublin
Phone: 01-2888099 Fax: 01-2888291
Email: info@paretomarketing.com
Web: http://www.paretomarketing.com
SIC: 74403 Employees: 500
Promotional Consultants
Mr David Whelan Chairman
Mr David Connor Business Development Director

Professional Merchandising & Marketing Services
Pearse House, Pearse Road
Sligo Co. Sligo
Phone: 071-44700 Fax: 071-44100
Email: info@pmms.ie
Web: http://www.pmms.ie
SIC: 74403 Employees: 30
Promotional Consultants
Ms Paula Lawlor Managing Director
Ms Karen Elliott Human Resources Director
Ms Gillian Owens Account Manager
Mr Austin Connolly Production Manager

Shamrock Rosettes
Unit 7 Clonshaugh Industrial Estate
Coolock
Dublin 17
Phone: 01-8672774 Fax: 01-8671727
SIC: 74403 Employees: 30
Manufacture Rosettes & Promotional Packing
Mr Kevin O'Toole General Manager
Mr Gerard Martin Sales Director

Bright Marketing Promotions Print
Unit G
537 North Circular Road
Dublin 1
Phone: 01-8558222 Fax: 01-8558140
Email: ian@brightprint.ie
Web: http://www.brightprint.ie
SIC: 74404 Employees: 24
Advertising Materials
Mr Ian Redmond Managing Director
Ms Mary Young Accounts Manager

Everbrite Europe
Cloverhill Industrial Estate
Clondakin
Dublin 22
Phone: 01-4576088 Fax: 01-4576085
Email: ireland@everbrite.com
Web: http://www.everbrite.com
SIC: 74404 Employees: 40
Manufacture Neon Signs
Mr Terry Egan Managing Director
Ms Tara McEntee Finance Manager

Irish Prestige Signs Ltd
Unit 123, Western Industrial Estate
Chestnut Road
Dublin 12
Phone: 01-4565855 Fax: 01-4504043
Email: sales@ipsltd.ie
SIC: 74404 Employees: 55
Sign Manufacturers
Mr Paddy Waldron Managing Director
Mr Pearse Joyce Finance Manager
Mr Brendan Kilcline Sales Manager
Ms Claire McMahon Administration Director

Nameplate Services Ltd
1 Jamestown Industrial Centre
Inchicore
Dublin 8
Phone: 01-4532659 Fax: 01-4531154
SIC: 74404 Employees: 30
Sign Manufacturers
Mr John Dalton Manager

Rennicks Group
Kilbride
Mulhuddart
Dublin 15
Phone: 01-8204333 Fax: 01-8859210
Email: sales@rennicks.com
Web: http://www.rennicks.com
SIC: 74404 Employees: 600
Manufacturing Signs
Mr Michael Flanagan Managing Director
Mr Bill Fitzgerald Finance Manager
Mr Frank Murphy Sales Manager
Ms Kathleen Synnott Computer Manager

Dafil
16 Parkmore Industrial Estate
Long Mile Road
Dublin 12
Phone: 01-4508006 Fax: 01-4507391
SIC: 74405 Employees: 30
Direct Marketing
Mr Pearse Maher Managing Director
Mr Francis Higgins Sales & Marketing Manager
Mr Kevin Thair Computer Manager

IDS Media Group (2002) Plc
3 Sandyford Business Park
Blackthorn Avenue
Dublin 18
Phone: 01-2604818 Fax: 01-2104816
Email: info@idsmediagroup.com
Web: http://www.idsmediagroup.com
SIC: 74405 Employees: 75
Telemarketing, Direct Marketing, Direct Mail, Marketing Research & Analysis
Mr Martin Crilly Managing Director
Ms Shirley Ennis Office Manager
Ms Liz McGivern Personnel Officer
Mr Raymond Brown Sales Director
Ms Una McGivern CC Manager
Mr Gareth McLoughlin IT Manager

Independent Communications
3050 Lake Drive, Citywest Bus Prk
Dublin 24
Phone: 01-4112000 Fax: 01-4112001
Email: info@independent.ie
Web: http://www.independent.com
SIC: 74405 Employees: 200
Independent Directory
Mr Paul Staunton Managing Director

Lyrico
Unit 41 Parkwest Industrial Estate
Dublin 12
Phone: 01-4541722 Fax: 01-4537028
Email: ray.sisson@lyrico.com
Web: http://www.lyrico.ie
SIC: 74405 Employees: 100
Direct Mail Stationery Company
Mr David Phillips Proprietor

Magazine Mailing Services Ltd
Unit 4 Portside Business Centre
East Wall Road
Dublin 3
Phone: 01-8364832 Fax: 01-8365183
Email: tonyl@indigo.ie
SIC: 74405 Employees: 23
Mailing Company
Mr Tony Lynch Managing Director
Mr John Lacken Sales Manager
Ms Anita Cervi Computer Manager

Mail Marketing (Dublin) Ltd
Unit 117-118 Bann Road
Dublin Industrial Estate
Dublin 11
Phone: 01-8680577 Fax: 01-8680594
Email: mailmktg@iol.ie
Web: http://www.mailmarketing.ie
SIC: 74405 Employees: 40
Printing & Fulfilment House
Mr Scott Lindsay Managing Director
Ms Ann Browne Finance Manager
Mr Eddie Sharpe Sales & Marketing Manager
Ms Lea Wilkinson Computer Manager

Marketing Network
16 Earlsfort Terrace
Dublin 2
Phone: 01-6627111 Fax: 01-6627122
Email: info@marketingnetwork.ie
Web: http://www.marketingnetwork.ie
SIC: 74405 Employees: 30
Direct Marketing & Sales Promotion
Mr Kieran Killeen Managing Director
Mr Noel Comerford Financial Director
Mr Neil Harvey Commercial Director

PHS (Ireland) Ltd
Unit, M50 Business Park
Ballymount
Dublin 12
Phone: 01-4784509 Fax: 01-4092701
Email: info@responsegroup.ie
Web: http://www.responsegroup.ie
SIC: 74405 Employees: 120
Response Handling
Mr John Keane Managing Director
Mr Hugh Raftery Financial Controller
Mr Harry Boland Company Secretary
Mr Lesley Carter Computer Manager

Templeogue Enterprises
St Michael's House,
Templeogue Road
Dublin 6
Phone: 01-4902223 Fax: 01-4903063
SIC: 74405 Employees: 80
Direct Mail
Mr Steven Henessey Managing Director
Mr Jim McKeown Financial Controller
Mr Nesson Rickard Human Resources Manager
Mr Kevin Gregory Computer Manager

Best Western International
3rd Floor
20-22 Lower Hatch Street
Dublin 2
Phone: 01-7038500 Fax: 01-6766016
Email: dubcro@bestwestern.com
Web: http://www.bestwestern.com
SIC: 74406 Employees: 70
European Reservations & Call Centre
Ms Suzy McDonald V P Of International Operation
Ms Elizabeth Nunan Human Resources Manager
Mr Marcel Knowls International Manager

Business Services

Clientlogic
Unit 2 Swords Business Campus
Balheary Road
Swords Co. Dublin
Phone: 01-8576000 Fax: 01-8903235
Web: http://www.clientlogic.com
SIC: 74406 Employees: 270
Call Centre
Mr Donal McGarry Managing Director
Mr Ken Duncan Finance Director

DER Ireland Ltd
IDA Business Park
Newcastle
Galway Co. Galway
Phone: 091-583222 Fax: 091-583225
Email: derireland@eircom.net
SIC: 74406 Employees: 32
German Travel Service Company (Call Centre)
Mr Kevin Keogh Manager
Ms Kirsten Miedermueller Supervisor

Ebookers.com
First Floor, Block 6-7
Irish Life Centre Lower Abbey St
Dublin 1
Phone: 01-8783135 Fax: 01-8783099
Email: info@ebookers.com
Web: http://www.ebookers.com
SIC: 74406 Employees: 60
Call Centre
Ms Rose Kervick General Manager
Ms Christine Turley Personnel Manager
Ms Caroline McNicholas Sales Manager
Mr Drew Duggan Production Manager
Mr Larry O'Brien Computer Manager

Fora na Gaeilge
7 Merrion Square
Dublin 2
Phone: 01-6763222 Fax: 01-6398401
Email: eolas@forasnagaeilge.ie
Web: http://www.forasnagaeilge.ie
SIC: 74406 Employees: 40
Promoting Irish Language
Mr Micheal De Hai Chief Executive

Lufthansa Global Telesales
East Point Business Park
Dublin 3
Phone: 01-8191056 Fax: 01-8191169
Email: info@globaltelesales.ie
Web: http://www.lufthansa.ie
SIC: 74406 Employees: 250
Call Centre
Mr Volper Lorenz Executive Director
Ms Natalie Laplasse General Manager

Merchants Group
Cork Business & Technology Park
Model Farm Road
Cork Co. Cork
Phone: 021-4868686 Fax: 021-4868787
Email: info@merchants.co.uk
Web: http://www.merchants.co.uk
SIC: 74406 Employees: 200
European Outsourcing Bureau/Call Centre
Mr John Drury Business Development Manager
Mr Anthony Fenton Finance Manager
Ms Michelle Whitty Human Resources Manager

Redison Hotels International
4 Richview Office Park
Clonskeagh
Dublin 14
Phone: 01-7060200 Fax: 01-7060225
Web: http://www.radisson.com
SIC: 74406 Employees: 58
Call Centre for Radisson Hotel
Ms Jennifer McQuaid General Manager
Ms Helle Karlstev Personnel Manager

Sitel TMS
Block 8, Park West Business Park
Nangor Road
Dublin 12
Phone: 01-6300300 Fax: 01-6300333
Email: info@sitel.com
Web: http://www.sitel.com
SIC: 74406 Employees: 300
Call Centre
Mr Nick Wheeler Managing Director
Ms Mairead Donohoe Financial Accountant
Mr Alan Naughton Sales Manager
Ms Kerry Brine IT Manager

United Airlines
Block T East Point Business Park
Clontarf
Dublin 3
Phone: 01-8191761 Fax: 01-8191504
SIC: 74406 Employees: 432
Call Centre
Ms Sharon Kennedy Reservations Manager

UPS (United Parcel Services)
Block 5 Tallaght Retail Centre
Tallaght
Dublin 24
Phone: 01-4002000 Fax: 01-4004444
Web: http://www.ups.com
SIC: 74406 Employees: 400
Parcel Delivery Service
Mr Robb Birr General Manager
Ms Deirdre Carney Human Resources Manager
Mr Juan Ramon Garcia Lopez IT Manager

Adecco
Regional Office
33 Upper Merrion Street
Dublin 2
Phone: 01-4596464 Fax: 01-4596486
Email: info@adecco.ie
Web: http://www.adecco.ie
SIC: 74500 Employees: 650
Recruitment Agency
Mr Richard McMillan Chief Executive

Ard Meats Ltd
10 Roden Place
Dundalk Co. Louth
Phone: 042-9326655 Fax: 042-9336529
SIC: 74500 Employees: 100
Supply Workers For Meat Factories- Line Labour
Mr Michael McArdle Proprietor

Atlanco Ltd
221-223 Lower Rathmines Road
Dublin 6
Phone: 01-4910555 Fax: 01-4910424
Email: atlanco@atlanco.ie
Web: http://www.atlanco.ie
SIC: 74500 Employees: 28
Recruitment Consultants
Mr Michael O'Shea Managing Director
Mr Michael Wann Financial Controller
Ms Patrice Murphy Sales Manager
Mr Declan Murphy Commercial Manager

Ballymun Job Centre
Ballymun Shopping Centre
Ballymun
Dublin 11
Phone: 01-8425722 Fax: 01-8420134
Email: bmunjob@indigo.ie
SIC: 74500 Employees: 30
Job Centre
Mr Mick Creedon Manager
Ms Mary Callaghan Personnel Director

Computer Placement Ltd
83 Merrion Square
Dublin 2
Phone: 01-6146000 Fax: 01-6146011
Email: info@cpl.ie
Web: http://www.cpl.ie
SIC: 74500 Employees: 80
Recruitment Company & IT Training Consultants
Ms Anne Heraty Chief Executive
Ms Josephine Tierney FinanceDirector
Mr Paul Carroll Business Development Director
Mr Greg Kennedy Chief Technology Officer

Dorset College
66 Lower Dorset Street
Dublin 1
Phone: 01-8603776 Fax: 01-8308079
SIC: 74500 Employees: 50
Recruitment
Ms Helen Hughes Managing Director

Eden Recruitment
125 Lower Baggot Street
Dublin 2
Phone: 01-6616744 Fax: 01-6616767
Email: info@edenrecruitment.ie
Web: http://www.edenrecruitment.ie
SIC: 74500 Employees: 37
Employment Agency
Mr Ken Lee Managing Director

Facilities Management.ie
Greenmount Industrial Estate
Harolds Cross
Dublin 12
Phone: 01-4542281 Fax: 01-4541360
Email: info@faclitiesmanagement.ie
Web: http://www.facilitiesmanagment.ie
SIC: 74500 Employees: 130
Recruitment Agency
Ms Jackie Montgomery Managing Director
Ms Caroline Murphy Administration Manager
Mr Colin Donnery Personnel Manager
Ms Carol Thuillier Sales Manager
Ms Therese Cullen General Computer Manager

Hays Accountants Personnell
6 Dawson Street
Dublin 2
Phone: 01-6790788 Fax: 01-6704738
Email: haysap@eircom.net
SIC: 74500 Employees: 60
Recruitment
Ms Lorraine Darcey General Manager
Mr Mark Sheldon Personnel Manager

Hays Montrose
62 Lower Baggot Street
Dublin 2
Phone: 01-6612772 Fax: 01-6612265
Email: dublin@hays-montrose.ie
Web: http://www.hays-montrose.ie
SIC: 74500 Employees: 25
Employment Agencies
Mr Rowan O'Grady Managing Director
Mr Richard Urdley Director

Head Hunt International
68 Harcourt Street
Dublin 2
Phone: 01-4188188 Fax: 01-4781663
Email: info@headhunt.ie
Web: http://www.headhunt.ie
SIC: 74500 Employees: 30
Recruitment Agency
Ms Sylvia Harrison Managing Director
Mr Mark O'Brien Head of IT

Jigsaw Employment
19-22 Dane Street
Dublin 1
Phone: 01-6622663 Fax: 01-6623191
SIC: 74500 Employees: 40
Recruitment
Mr Jim Dwan Managing Director

Business Services

Marlborough Group
Marlborough House
111-113 Grafton Street
Dublin 2
Phone: 01-6173800 Fax: 01-6777546
Email: info@marlborough.ie
Web: http://www.marlborough.ie
SIC: 74500 Employees: 600
Recruitment Agency
Mr David McKenna Chief Executive
Mr Gerard Kelly Financial Director
Ms Tina Mulhearne Human Resources Manager
Mr David Lynch Systems Administrator

Noel Recruitment
St Johns House, High Street
Tallaght
Dublin 24
Phone: 01-4782100 Fax: 01-4610870
Web: http://www.noelrecruit.ie
SIC: 74500 Employees: 70
Employment Agencies
Mr Mark Staunton Director
Ms Catherine Brandon Personnel Manager
Mr John Halpin Sales Manager

Parc Group
St Johns Court Swords Road
Santry
Dublin 9
Phone: 01-8161777 Fax: 01-8161766
Email: info@parc-group.com
Web: http://www.parcaviation.com
SIC: 74500 Employees: 60
Recruitment Agency
Mr Peter Keenan Chief Executive
Mr Richard Belton Finance Manager
Mr Richie Wall Marketing Manager
Mr Brian Finnegan Computer Manager

Portoron Contract Boners Ltd
Ballybay
Castleblayney Co. Monaghan
Phone: 042-9748118 Fax: 042-9748119
SIC: 74500 Employees: 51
Service Companies to the Meat Trade
Mr John Connolly Manager
Mr John Hamilton Sales Manager

Premier Recruitment
85/89 South Main Street
Cork Co. Cork
Phone: 021-2300300 Fax: 021-2300303
Email: cork@premierjob.ie
Web: http://www.premierjobs.ie
SIC: 74500 Employees: 85
Employment Agencies
Mr Patrick Fitzgerald Managing Director
Mr Finbar McCarthy IT Director

Richmond House
Merchants House, Merchants Quay
Dublin 8
Phone: 01-6612138 Fax: 01-6796442
Email: jobs@richmond.ie
Web: http://www.richmond.ie
SIC: 74500 Employees: 55
Recruitment Agency
Mr Richard Moulton Chairman
Ms Rachel Walsh Accounts Manager
Ms Rachel Bowe Commercial Manager
Mr Robert Parg Sales Manager
Ms Caroline Kelly IT Manager

Tallaght Local Employment Services
Unit 4, The Village Square
Tallaght
Dublin 24
Phone: 01-4622747 Fax: 01-4621002
Email: info@tallaghtles.com
SIC: 74500 Employees: 30
Employment Agencies
Ms Jackie Johnson Co-ordinator

Tech Source Ltd
Kilbarry Industrial Estate
Dublin Hill
Cork Co. Cork
Phone: 021-4393002 Fax: 021-4398449
Email: tsource@indigo.ie
Web: http://www.techsource.ie
SIC: 74500 Employees: 50
Employment Out-Sourcing
Mr Pat Kenny Managing Director

TMP Worldwide
10 Lower Mount Street
Dublin 2
Phone: 01-6765078 Fax: 01-6765111
Email: info@tmpw.co.uk
Web: http://www.ie.eresourcing.tmp.com
SIC: 74500 Employees: 25
Recruitment
Ms Ursula Hannon Managing Director
Mr James Maley Sales Consultant
Mr Colin Ashmore Computer Manager

A1 Alarms Ltd
76-77 Kilmainham Road
Dublin 8
Phone: 01-4538513 Fax: 01-4542869
SIC: 74602 Employees: 25
Security Supplies
Mr Allan Crinion Managing Director

Action Security Systems
15 Main Street
Dundrum
Dublin 14
Phone: 01-2988699 Fax: 01-2989222
Email: sales@actionsecurity.ie
SIC: 74602 Employees: 30
Security Systems
Mr Derek Mooney Joint Managing Director
Mr Paul Daly Commercial Manager

ADT Fire & Security
ADT House, Crossguns Bridge
Phibsboro
Dublin 7
Phone: 01-8305888 Fax: 01-8305998
Email: info@adt.ie
Web: http://www.adt.ie
SIC: 74602 Employees: 155
Security Company
Mr Kevin McGrath Managing Director
Mr Malcolm Wilson Financial Controller
Mr Pat O'Sullivan Sales Manager
Mr Ray Shimmins Services Manager

At Risk Security
Unit 3 Belmont Complex
15 Naas Road
Dublin 22
Phone: 01-4640073 Fax: 01-4640093
SIC: 74602 Employees: 50
Security Equipment
Mr Hugh Downes Managing Director
Mr Des Connolly Financial Controller

Bell Communications Ltd
Collins Avenue East
Killester
Dublin 5
Phone: 01-8328354 Fax: 01-8317174
Email: cpbell@cpbell.com
Web: http://www.cpbell.com
SIC: 74602 Employees: 112
Security Company-Installation of Alarms
Mr Michael Fenton Managing Director
Mr Lee McMahon Finance Manager
Ms Catherine McCormack Personnel Manager
Mr Peter Kelly Marketing Manager
Mr Patrick Guilfoyle Computer Manager

Bell Security
Unit 6 The Westway Centre
Ballymount Avenue
Dublin 12
Phone: 01-4564544 Fax: 01-4564550
Email: bellsec@indigo.ie
Web: http://www.bellsec.com
SIC: 74602 Employees: 35
Security Company
Mr Willy Tighe Managing Director
Mr Darragh Murphy Finance Manager
Mr Owen Welsh (Snr) Director
Mr Owen Welsh (Jnr) Engineering Sales Surveyor

Burgolarm Security Ltd
Commercial Centre
Kinsale Road
Cork Co. Cork
Phone: 021-4964874 Fax: 021-4964780
SIC: 74602 Employees: 30
Security Company
Mr Neil Buckley General Manager
Ms Anne O'Connor Accountant

Carisle Security Services
High Street
Tallaght
Dublin 24
Phone: 01-4517641 Fax: 01-4624707
Email: platinum2@eircom.net
SIC: 74602 Employees: 500
Security Services
Mr Richard Mulvany Managing Director
Mr Shane McCann Human Resources Manager
Mr John Walsh Sales & Marketing Manager

Chubb Ireland Ltd
2 Stillorgan Industrial Park
Blackrock Co. Dublin
Phone: 01-2953333 Fax: 01-2955779
Email: chubb@connect.ie
Web: http://www.chubb.ie
SIC: 74602 Employees: 980
Security Equipment
Mr David Burns Managing Director
Mr Seamus Storn Personnel Manager
Mr Paul Eastwood Operation Manager
Mr John Cleary Computer Manager

CP Security-Bell Communications
63 Collins Avenue East
Killester
Dublin 5
Phone: 01-8317100 Fax: 01-8317174
Email: cpbell@cpbell.com
SIC: 74602 Employees: 100
Security Services
Mr Michael Fenton Managing Director
Mr Liam McMahon Finance Manager
Ms Catherine McCormack Personnel Manager
Mr Peter Kelly Sales Manager
Mr Patrick Guilfoyle Computer Manager

Directlink Security
Unit 3b, Huntstown Shopping Centre
Dublin 15
Phone: 01-8209334 Fax: 01-8209324
SIC: 74602 Employees: 50
Direct Link Security Services
Mr John Caffery Managing Director
Mr Gerry Byrne Personnel Manager

Eircom Phone Watch
Unit 4 Sandyford Park, Burton Hall
Sandyford
Dublin 18
Phone: 01-2956900 Fax: 01-2958199
Email: rkeating@phonewatch.ie
Web: http://www.eircom.ie
SIC: 74602 Employees: 45
Security Systems
Mr Nick Quigley General Manager
Ms Rose Keating Sales Manager

Elite Security
Riverlodge, Mourneabbey
Mallow Co. Cork
Phone: 022-29994 Fax: 022-29995
SIC: 74602 Employees: 35
Security Service
Mr Paul Kane Proprietor
Ms Carol Cronin Finance Manager

Enkel Security Co
80 Rockwood Park
Cahermoneen
Tralee Co. Kerry
Phone: 066-7125265 Fax: 066-7120065
SIC: 74602 Employees: 30
Security Companies
Mr Nigel Kelleher Managing Director

Express Security Group
Millfield Business Park
Mallow Road
Cork Co. Cork
Phone: 021-4211111 Fax: 021-4211888
Email: express@eircom.net
Web: http://www.indigo.ie/express
SIC: 74602 Employees: 80
Security Personnel,Car Park Manager & Clamping
Mr Ken O'Reilly Managing Director
Ms Edna Levis Financial Controller
Mr Derry Hurley Personnel Officer
Mr Sean Cullinane Sales Manager
Mr Brian Scanlon Production Director

FBH Security
Coolmine Industrial Estate
Clonsilla
Dublin 15
Phone: 01-8216611 Fax: 01-8216164
Email: fbh@fimark_group.ie
SIC: 74602 Employees: 30
Safes & Fireproof Products
Mr Andrew Mackin Managing Director
Mr Sandy Wilson Finance Manager
Mr Matt Harris Personnel Manager
Mr Peter Coogan Computer Manager

Federal Security Ltd
Pier 19, Ushers Island
Dublin 8
Phone: 01-6776188 Fax: 01-6776934
Email: federalsecurity@eircom.net
Web:
http://www.homepage.tinet.ie/~federalsecurity
SIC: 74602 Employees: 220
Security Company
Mr William Hennesey Managing Director
Mr Gerry Molloy Financial Controller
Ms Gay Duke Secretary

GMS Services Ltd
149 Lower Drumcondra Road
Dublin 9
Phone: 01-8369051 Fax: 01-8369051
SIC: 74602 Employees: 30
Security Services
Ms Patricia Moore Managing Director

Group 4 Securitas Ireland
51 Bracken Road
Sandyford Industrial Estate
Dublin 18
Phone: 01-8732211 Fax: 01-2179114
Email: info@group4securitas.com
Web: http://www.group4securitas.com
SIC: 74602 Employees: 350
Security Protection Equipment
Mr Eammon Hudson Managing Director
Mr Frank Young Personnel Manager
Mr Brain Walsh Marketing Manager
Mr Rory Brady Operations Manager
Mr Martin Farrell Computer Manager

Hi Tech Services Ltd
Crufty, Beamore
Drogheda Co. Louth
Phone: 041-9842273 Fax: 041-9842273
SIC: 74602 Employees: 35
Security Services
Mr Joe Dunne Partner
Mr Martin Dunne Partner

Highway Safety Developments Ltd
Knocktopher
Co. Kilkenny
Phone: 056-68702 Fax: 056-68854
Email: hsd@eircom.net
Web: http://www.hsd.ie
SIC: 74602 Employees: 34
Manuf, Distributors & Installers of Signage, Barrier Systems & Safety Products
Mr Michael Farrell Managing Director
Mr Eamon Teehan C P A
Mr Jim Deneefe Sales Director

Jaebrade Security Services
Unit 1/3, 1st Floor, Park Shopping Centre
Prussia Street
Dublin 7
Phone: 01-4501455 Fax: 01-8686122
Email: jaebrade@indigo.ie
SIC: 74602 Employees: 150
Security Firm
Mr Richard Foy Manager
Mr Willie McKinley Contracts Manager
Ms Patricia Foy Sales & Marketing Manager
Mr Noel O'Gorman IT Manager

JN Cummins & Co Ltd
Mayfield
Cashel Co. Tipperary
Phone: 062-62214 Fax: 062-62947
Email: info@jncfence.com
Web: http://www.jncfence.com
SIC: 74602 Employees: 35
Security Fencing Company
Mr James Cummins Managing Director
Mr John Cummins Financial Controller
Mr Barry Fitzpatrick Contracts Manager

Magnum Security
Unit 2, Logan Industrial Park
Blackrock
Dublin 6w
Phone: 01-4900856 Fax: 01-4900291
Email: info@chubb.ie
Web: http://www.chubb.ie
SIC: 74602 Employees: 150
Security Company
Mr Tim Cummins Managing Director
Mr Alan Owens Financial Controller

MCM Security Ltd
40 Leitrim Street
Cork Co. Cork
Phone: 021-4503222 Fax: 021-4508732
Email: mcmsecurity@eircom.net
SIC: 74602 Employees: 2000
Security Company
Mr Bill Smyth Managing Director
Mr Derek Daly Financial Controller
Ms Moira O'Leary Director of Administration
Mr Robert Scannell Sales Director

MSI Ltd
Baldoyle Industrial Estate
Dublin 13
Phone: 01-8391425 Fax: 01-8391998
Email: msi@indigo.ie
Web: http://www.biocycle.ie
SIC: 74602 Employees: 30
Civil & Mechanical Engineers
Mr Frank Cavanagh Manager Director
Ms Sandra Elmes Finance Manager
Mr Brian McGonigle Production Manager

Business Services

Night Owl
Security House
Ballyboughal Co. Dublin
Phone: 01-8407553 Fax: 01-8433652
Email: sales@nightowl.ie
Web: http://www.nightowl.ie
SIC: 74602 Employees: 35
Security
Mr Martin Holles Managing Director

Oscar Security
Oscar House
309a Galtymore Road
Dublin 12
Phone: 01-4556488 Fax: 01-4551957
SIC: 74602 Employees: 85
Security Company
Mr Donal O'Brien Managing Director
Mr Tony Whelan Operation Manager

Paragon Security Services Ltd
14 Belvedere Place
Dublin 1
Phone: 01-8364506 Fax: 01-8556502
Email: paragonsecurity@eircom.net
SIC: 74602 Employees: 80
Security Company
Mr Kevin Malone Manager
Ms Annette Malone Finance Manager
Mr Terry Doyle Personnel Manager
Mr Kevin Malone Jnr IT Manager

Park West Security Ltd
Unit 23, The Maltings Business Park
54/55 Marrowbone Lane
Dublin 8
Phone: 01-4546900 Fax: 01-4733041
SIC: 74602 Employees: 80
Security Services
Mr Brian Behan Managing Director
Mr Kieron Byrne Personnel Manager

Private Security Ireland Ltd
7a Jamestown Road
Dublin 8
Phone: 01-4534720 Fax: 01-4531477
Email: info@privatesecurity.ie
Web: http://www.privatesecurity.ie
SIC: 74602 Employees: 35
Security Services
Mr Patrick McKenna Manager
Mr James Smith Finance Director

Provincial Security Ltd
Cutlery Road
Newbridge Co. Kildare
Phone: 045-431015 Fax: 045-434188
SIC: 74602 Employees: 50
Security Company
Mr Carl Dunleavy Manager
Mr Stephen McDermot Sales Manager
Mr Jim Brady Operation Manager

Screen Guard
White Swan Business Park
Greenville Avenue
Dublin 8
Phone: 01-4545330 Fax: 01-4545424
Email: sales@screenguard.com
Web: http://www.screenguard.com
SIC: 74602 Employees: 25
Security Systems
Mr Paul Colton Managing Director
Mr Rodger McClure Sales Director
Mr Paul Colton IT Manager

Securicor Security Services Ireland Ltd
Herberton Road
Rialto
Dublin 12
Phone: 01-4743800 Fax: 01-4540450
Email: sales@securicor.ie
Web: http://www.securicor.co.uk
SIC: 74602 Employees: 800
Security Services
Mr Bernard Smith Managing Director
Mr Michael Lavelle Finance Director
Mr Grahame Pickett Human Resources Director
Mr Larry Maguire Sales & Marketing Manager
Mr Gerry Savage Cash Services Manager
Mr James Plunkett IT Manager

Securiforce & Chubb Ltd
Unit 2, Stillorgan Industrial Park
Stillorgan
Blackrock Co. Dublin
Phone: 01-2163400 Fax: 01-2955779
Email: general.info@chubb.ie
Web: http://www.chubb.ie
SIC: 74602 Employees: 3000
Manned Security Service
Mr David Byrne Managing Director
Ms Connie Kelleher Finance Manager
Ms Barbara Hopkins Personnel Manager
Ms Sinead Horgan Sales & Marketing Manager
Mr Michael Devitt Computer Manager

Security Plus Ltd
Whiteswan Business Centre
Greenville Avenue
Dublin 8
Phone: 01-4532733 Fax: 01-4530631
Email: securityplus@iol.ie
SIC: 74602 Employees: 150
Security Services
Mr Tim O'Shea Managing Director
Ms Jacinta Kerri Financial Controller
Mr Rory O'Connor Sales Manager
Mr Noel Farrell Operation Manager

Shepherd Security
84 Main Street
Bray Co. Wicklow
Phone: 01-2862570 Fax: 01-2862883
SIC: 74602 Employees: 30
Security Company
Mr William Atkinson Managing Director
Mr Russell Atkinson IT Manager

Specialist Security Services
U63a Cherry Orchard Industrial Estate
Dublin 10
Phone: 01-6260269 Fax: 01-6234781
Email: specsec@indigo.ie
SIC: 74602 Employees: 26
Security Services & Maintenance
Mr John Henry Managing Director
Mr Paddy McBerthy Accountant

Top Security Ltd
Westgate House, Westgate Business Pk
Ballymount
Dublin 24
Phone: 01-4900333 Fax: 01-4967713
Email: customerservice@topsecurity.iol.ie
SIC: 74602 Employees: 80
Security Services
Mr Emmet O'Rafferty Managing Director
Mr Colm Dunne Financial Controller
Mr Robert Brown IT Manager

Unitec Security Ltd
Ticroghan West
Kinnegad
Mullingar Co. Westmeath
Phone: 044-75649 Fax: 044-75649
SIC: 74602 Employees: 30
Security Services
Mr Pat Lynch Managing Director
Ms Nuala Lynch Director

Ailsbury Contract Cleaning Ltd
15 Priory Hall
Stillorgan
Blackrock Co. Dublin
Phone: 01-2835266 Fax: 01-2835269
Email: info@ailsbury.com
Web: http://www.ailsbury.com
SIC: 74701 Employees: 850
Cleaning Services & Maintenance
Ms Stella O'Connell Proprietor
Ms Geraldine Brown Operations Director
Mr George O'Connell Sales Executive

Cannon Hygienic Products
Unit 2, Richmond Industrial Estate
8 North Richmond Street
Dublin 1
Phone: 01-8556791 Fax: 01-8556594
Email: info@cannon.iol.ie
SIC: 74701 Employees: 90
Sanitary Disposal & Cleaning Supplies
Ms Eileen Finn Managing Director
Ms Amanda O'Reilly Finance Manager
Ms Shirley Higgs Sales Manager

Clean Habit Ltd
9 Ballycasey House
Shannon Co. Clare
Phone: 061-361461 Fax: 061-361461
SIC: 74701 Employees: 80
Cleaning
Mr PJ Quirke Managing Director

Cleanwell Industrial Products
Smithstown Industrial Estate
Shannon Co. Clare
Phone: 061-360191 Fax: 061-363762
Email: info@cleanwell.com
Web: http://www.cleanwell.com
SIC: 74701 Employees: 25
Supply of Cleaning Equipment & Materials
Mr Tom O'Brien Managing Director
Ms Siobhan Boyd Finance Manager
Ms Fiona O'Brien IT Manager

Corporate Cleaning Services
Unit 7C Crossagalla Industrial Estate
Ballysimon Road
Limerick Co. Limerick
Phone: 061-318177 Fax: 061-318232
Email: corpcs@iol.ie
SIC: 74701 Employees: 80
Cleaning Services
Mr Killian Slattery Managing Director

CPS Cleaning Services
Unit 5, Donore Industrial Estate
Drogheda Co. Louth
Phone: 041-9841100 Fax: 041-9835992
Email: info@cps.ie
SIC: 74701 Employees: 160
Contract Cleaning Services
Mr Paul Maguire Managing Director

Dyno Rod
56-58 Townsend Street
Dublin 2
Phone: 01-6704477 Fax: 01-6704484
Email: dublin@dynorod.ie
Web: http://www.dynorod.ie
SIC: 74701 Employees: 90
Drain & Sewer Cleaning
Mr Colin Lynam Managing Director
Mr Kieran Crowley Finance Manager
Mr Donal Lynam Personnel Manager

FM Cleaning Services
11 Hillview Grove, Lismonaghan
Letterkenny Co. Donegal
Phone: 074-28202 Fax: 074-27583
Email: fmcleaning@eircom.net
SIC: 74701 Employees: 40
Contract Cleaners
Mr Fintan Houston Managing Director
Ms Annette Houston Sales & Marketing Manager

Business Services

Glan Ltd
78 O'Connell Street
Limerick Co. Limerick
Phone: 061-410060 Fax: 061-311199
SIC: 74701 Employees: 30
Cleaning Services
Mr John Bernard Managing Director

Grosvenor Cleaning Services Ltd
64 Heather Road
Sandyford Industrial Estate
Dublin 18
Phone: 01-2954866 Fax: 01-2954301
Email: ireland@gcs.iol.ie
Web: http://www.grosvenorbuildingservices.com
SIC: 74701 Employees: 4000
Contract Cleaning
Mr Bernard McCauley Managing Director
Ms Rose Lyons Personnel Manager
Ms Helen Kennedy Sales & Marketing Manager
Ms Marie Cunningham Operations Director

ISS Ireland Ltd
11-13 Maltas Street
Dublin 8
Phone: 01-4537711 Fax: 01-4537870
Email: cmacnamara.irl@iss.euro.geis.com
Web: http://www.iss.euro.geis.com
SIC: 74701 Employees: 2300
Contract Cleaners
Mr David Healy Managing Director
Mr Michael Madsen Finance Manager
Ms Pauline Hayden Office Manager
Mr Cecil McNamara Marketing Director
Ms Kay Daly Operations Manager

Mercury Cleaning Services Ltd
19 Holybrook Road
Clontarf
Dublin 3
Phone: 01-4785299 Fax: 01-4785297
SIC: 74701 Employees: 40
Cleaning & Maintenance Service
Mr Pat Jackson Manager
Ms Paula Judge Administration

Moore Enterprise Ltd
Unit T7, Maple Avenue
Stillorgan
Blackrock Co. Dublin
Phone: 01-2953901 Fax: 01-2953905
Email: info@mooreenterpriseltd.ie
SIC: 74701 Employees: 300
Contract Cleaners
Mr Greg Moore Managing Director
Ms Michelle Kinsella Accounts Manager
Ms Michelle Moore Director

NCH Ireland
Bracetown Business Park
Clonee
Navan Co. Meath
Phone: 01-8014021 Fax: 01-8014077
Email: info@europe01.nch.com
SIC: 74701 Employees: 100
Cleaning Products
Mr Mario Kelly General Manager

Noble Waste Disposal
Fassaroe
Bray Co. Wicklow
Phone: 01-2829610 Fax: 01-2050774
Email: noblewaste@eircom.net
SIC: 74701 Employees: 58
Waste Disposal Services
Mr Michael Noble Managing Director
Mr Stewart Ferguson Finance Manager

Business Services

Noonan Cleaning Ltd
Hilton House, Ardee Road
Rathmines
Dublin 6
Phone: 01-4967700 Fax: 01-4967487
Email: service@noonanservices.ie
Web: http://www.noonanservices.ie
SIC: 74701 Employees: 3500
Cleaning Services & Maintenance
Mr Noel Noonan Chief Executive
Mr Bernard Lawlor Finance Manager
Mr John O'Donoghue Personnel Manager
Mr Peter Holt Sales Director
Ms Sandra Abbott IT Manager

Office & Industrial Cleaners Ltd
Unit 8 Grand Canal Business Centre
Dublin 8
Phone: 01-4548880 Fax: 01-4548884
SIC: 74701 Employees: 30
Cleaning Services & Maintenance
Mr Frank McEwen Proprietor

OMC Scientific Ltd
Ballysimon Road
Limerick Co. Limerick
Phone: 061-208182 Fax: 061-419980
Email: contact@omcsci.iol.ie
SIC: 74701 Employees: 25
Parts Cleaning & Surface Treatment Company
Mr Pat Dillon Manager
Mr Tom Griffin Finance Director
Mr Sean O'Grady IT Manager

Puresafe Ltd
55 Cromwells Fort Road
Walkinstown
Dublin 12
Phone: 01-4509105 Fax: 01-4503907
SIC: 74701 Employees: 150
Contract Cleaning
Mr James Reid Manager

Retail Petroleum Solutions
Gurteens
Ballina Co. Mayo
Phone: 096-21244 Fax: 096-71313
Email: info@rps.ie
Web: http://www.rps.ie
SIC: 74701 Employees: 50
Petrol Pump Maintenance
Mr Tom Melvin Proprietor

Service Master
6 Fairview Strand
Dublin 3
Phone: 01-8559555 Fax: 01-8559558
Email: servicemastersean@eircom.net
SIC: 74701 Employees: 100
Cleaning Services & Maintenance
Mr Sean Harte Proprietor

Staunton Contract Cleaning
16 Beach Court
Grattan Road
Galway Co. Galway
Phone: 091-584755 Fax: 091-589109
Email: staunton@esatclear.ie
SIC: 74701 Employees: 100
Contract Cleaning
Ms Margaret Kearns Manager

Castle Hygiene Equipment Ltd
Quarry Road
Cabra
Dublin 7
Phone: 01-8380511 Fax: 01-8382588
Email: info@castlemh.ie
Web: http://www.castlemh.ie
SIC: 74703 Employees: 40
Cleaning Equipment & Supplies
Mr Val Murray Managing Director
Mr Dermott Kane Financial Controller
Mr Damian Murray Sales Manager
Mr Ken Murray Operation Manager

Henkel-Ecolab Ltd
Beachwood Close, Boghall Road
Bray Co. Wicklow
Phone: 01-2868225 Fax: 01-2869298
Email: info@henkel-ecolab.com
Web: http://www.henkel-ecolab.com
SIC: 74703 Employees: 60
Cleaning Equipment & Supplies
Mr Declan McAteer Managing Director
Mr James Phelan Finance Manager
Mr Derek George Sales Director

Micronclean Ireland Ltd
Spiddal Industrial Estate
Spiddal
Galway Co. Galway
Phone: 091-553066 Fax: 091-553068
Email: micronclean@eircom.net
SIC: 74703 Employees: 40
Cleanrooms - Equipment & Supplies
Mr Clement Higgins Director
Ms Evelyn Higgins Personnel Manager
Mr Raymond Heffernan Sales Manager
Ms Kirstin Pauquet IT Co-Ordinator

McSharry's Pharmacy
Donegal Town Shopping Centre
The Glebe
Donegal Co. Donegal
Phone: 073-21112 Fax: 073-21560
SIC: 74812 Employees: 79
Photographic Processing, Printing & Enlarging
Mr Tom Murray Manager

O'Flaherty Pharmacy
37 Cecil Street
Limerick Co. Limerick
Phone: 061-310055 Fax: 061-312030
Email: cecilstp@indigogofree.ie
Web: http://www.oflahertypharmacy.ie
SIC: 74812 Employees: 79
Photographic Processing, Printing & Enlarging
Mr Richard O'Flaherty Manager
Ms Sinead Finucane Supervisor

Photoworld
Parnell Street
Ennis Co. Clare
Phone: 065-6829344 Fax: 065-6823484
SIC: 74812 Employees: 79
Photographic Processing, Printing & Enlarging
Ms Pat Kelly Managing Director

Spectra Photo
Unit 1D Stillorgan Park Ind Estate
Stillorgan Dublin 18
Blackrock Co. Dublin
Phone: 01-2954224 Fax: 01-2956333
Email: mkt@spectra.ie
Web: http://www.spectra.ie
SIC: 74812 Employees: 35
Development of Photographs
Mr John Cathal Manager
Ms Siobhan Mc Loughlin Finance Director
Ms Amelda Markey Personnel Manager
Mr Adian McGegney Sales & Marketing Manager

Trucolor Laboratories
Rathealy Road
Fermoy Co. Cork
Phone: 025-31888 Fax: 025-32414
Email: digital@trucolor.ie
Web: http://www.trucolor.ie
SIC: 74812 Employees: 40
Photographic Processing Laboratory
Mr Patrick Frawley Managing Director
Mr Declan Rushe General Manager

Gestetner Ltd
Dublin Industrial Estate
127 Slaney Road
Dublin 11
Phone: 01-8301388 Fax: 01-8300540
Web: http://www.gestetner.com
SIC: 74813 Employees: 55
Photographic Services
Mr John Milne Managing Director
Mr David Heffernan Financial Controller
Ms Cilla O'Brien Marketing Manager

Hodgers Laboratories Ltd
4E Avonbeg Estate
Longmile Road
Dublin 22
Phone: 01-4509141 Fax: 01-4509707
SIC: 74813 Employees: 40
Photographic Services
Ms Louise Ryan Managing Director
Ms Bridget McDonnell Company Accountant
Mr Noel Duffy Personnel Director

Photo Me Ireland Ltd
33 Weatherwell Industrial Estate
Clondalkin
Dublin 22
Phone: 01-4572121 Fax: 01-4572275
SIC: 74813 Employees: 27
Supply Photo Booths
Mr Christy O'Malley Managing Director
Ms Barabra Hopkins Finance Manager

Quirke labortories
Quirke Laboratories
41 Rathmines Road Lower
Dublin 6
Phone: 01-4964666 Fax: 01-4964942
SIC: 74813 Employees: 30
Photographic Company
Mr Noel Quirke Managing Director
Ms Audrey McKenna Finance Manager
Mr Peter Byrne General Manager

Ashbourne Meat Processors Ltd
Naas Industrial Estate
Naas Co. Kildare
Phone: 045-875400 Fax: 045-897755
SIC: 74820 Employees: 80
Meat Packaging & Export
Mr Daniel Houlihan Managing Director
Mr Noel McCrumlish Finance Manager
Mr Peter McMahon Sales Manager
Mr Tommy Drogmam Production Manager
Mr Dermot Sweeney Office Manager

Barlo Packaging Ltd
Newbridge Business Park
Newbridge Co. Kildare
Phone: 045-437900 Fax: 045-437902
SIC: 74820 Employees: 100
Packaging
Mr Christopher Haward Managing Director

Enviro Paper Bags Ltd
Unit 24 Marahoe Road Ind Park
Malahide Road
Dublin 17
Phone: 01-8482864 Fax: 01-8477727
Email: info@ept.ie
Web: http://www.ept.ie
SIC: 74820 Employees: 25
Paper Bags,Checkout Bags,Paper Products
Mr David Booker Manager

Irish Casing Company Ltd
Spollanstown
Tullamore Co. Offaly
Phone: 0506-21714 Fax: 0506-51306
Email: irecasco@eircom.net
SIC: 74820 Employees: 200
Meat Casing
Mr Trevor Brown Managing Director
Mr Dermot Minnock Financial Controller

Business Services

ITW Hi-Cone
Quartertown Industrial Estate
Mallow Co. Cork
Phone: 022-43111 Fax: 022-43115
Email: info@hi-cone.com
Web: http://www.hi-cone.com
SIC: 74820 Employees: 35
Multi Packaging of Cans & Bottles
Mr Brian Colgan Plant Manager
Mr Bob Gardiner General Manager

Jefferson Smurfit Group
Beech Hill
Clonskeagh
Dublin 4
Phone: 01-2696622 Fax: 01-2694481
Email:
SIC: 74820 Employees: 6000
Print & Packaging
Mr Michael Smurfit Chief Executive
Mr G A Egan Group Financial Controller
Mr Gary McGann Chief Operations Officer

Mid Cork Pallets & Packaging
Clondrohid
Macroom Co. Cork
Phone: 026-41311 Fax: 026-42278
Email: mcpp@iol.ie
SIC: 74820 Employees: 85
Packaging Materials
Mr Sean Lehane Manager

Packaging Professionals
Unit 1a Santry Avenue
Industrial Estate
Dublin 9
Phone: 01-8427777 Fax: 01-8427788
Email: packingprofessionals@eircom.net
SIC: 74820 Employees: 50
Packaging Service
Mr Christopher Creamer Manager

Steripack Ltd
Kilbeggan Road
Clara
Tullamore Co. Offaly
Phone: 0506-31888 Fax: 0506-31887
Email: sales@steripack.ie
Web: http://www.steripack.ie
SIC: 74820 Employees: 50
Medical Packaging
Mr Gary Moore Manager
Mr Aidan O'Brien Finance Manager
Mr Pat McCormick Operations Manager

Synthetic Packaging
Ballycumber Road
Clara
Tullamore Co. Offaly
Phone: 0506-31282 Fax: 0506-31224
Email: synpkg@iol.ie
SIC: 74820 Employees: 100
Synthetics Packaging
Mr Tony McCormick Managing Director
Mr Kevin McGivern Finance Manager
Ms Ann Buckley Personnel Manager
Ms Marian Holmes Accounts Manager

Tec-Pak Ltd
Gurteen
Askeaton
Limerick Co. Limerick
Phone: 061-392661 Fax: 061-393677
Email: tecpacltd@eircom.net
SIC: 74820 Employees: 28
Packaging Materials
Mr Brian Edwards Proprietor

Terra Ltd
Institute Road
Bailieboro
Cavan Co. Cavan
Phone: 042-9665222 Fax: 042-9665519
SIC: 74820 Employees: 30
Packaging Service
Mr Patrick McKevitt Managing Director
Mr Niall McQuillan Accountant

Watershed Label Centre Ltd
18 Canal Turn
Clondalkin Industrial Estate
Dublin 22
Phone: 01-4570001 Fax: 01-4572250
Email: label@indigo.ie
SIC: 74820 Employees: 25
Adhesive Labels & Packaging
Mr Tom Waters Managing Director
Ms Mary Maher Finance Manager
Mr Frank Donnelly Sales & Marketing Manager

Euro Translations
18 Mary Street
Cork Co. Cork
Phone: 021-4311800 Fax: 021-4311671
SIC: 74830 Employees: 100
Translation Services
Ms Francoise Letellier Managing Director

SDL International
The Boulevard Quinsboro Road
Bray Co. Wicklow
Phone: 01-2050200 Fax: 01-2828395
Email: info@sdlintl.com
Web: http://www.sdlintl.com
SIC: 74830 Employees: 250
Translations For Software Packaging
Mr Mark Lancaster Managing Director
Mr Paul McManus Sales & Marketing Manager
Mr Terry McGoff Research Manager

Baseline Creative Studies
Bloom House
15 Mountjoy Square
Dublin 1
Phone: 01-8557133 Fax: 01-8557626
SIC: 74840 Employees: 28
Graphic Design
Mr Alec Drew Manager

Strategic Designs
Westland Square, Pearse Street
Dublin 2
Phone: 01-6718844 Fax: 01-6718045
Email: info@bfk.ie
Web: http://www.bfk.ie
SIC: 74840 Employees: 40
Graphic Design
Mr Kevin Barry Managing Director
Mr Howard Kent Director
Ms Fiona Martin Creative Director

Ray Murray Ltd
53-55 McCurtain Street
Cork Co. Cork
Phone: 021-4504555 Fax: 021-4504921
Email: raymurry@iol.ie
SIC: 74841 Employees: 120
Credit Facilities
Mr Liam O'Leary Managing Director
Mr Raymond Murray Sales & Marketing Manager
Mr John Brennan IT Manager

Jack Restan Displays
Walkinstown Avenue
Dublin 12
Phone: 01-4566987 Fax: 01-4503815
Email: info@jrdisplays.ie
Web: http://www.jrdisplays.ie
SIC: 74843 Employees: 30
Exhibition Displays
Mr Jack Restan Proprietor

MDA Exhibitions Ltd
Exhibition House, Landy Ind Estate
Knocklyon Road
Dublin 16
Phone: 01-4938555 Fax: 01-4938556
Email: info@mda.ie
Web: http://www.mda.ie
SIC: 74843 Employees: 55
Exhibition Organisers
Mr Ronald Petrie Managing Director
Mr Gerald Petrie Sales Manager

University College Cork
Western Road
Silverdale Estate Ballinlough
Cork Co. Cork
Phone: 021-4276871 Fax: 021-4270271
Email: info@ucc.ie
Web: http://www.ucc.ie
SIC: 74843 Employees: 1000
Conference centre operators
Dr G Wrixon President

Public Administration & Service

Department of the Taoiseach
Government Buildings
Upper Merrion Street
Dublin 2
Phone: 01-6624888 Fax: 01-6789791
Email: webmaster@taoiseach.irlgov.ie
Web: http://www.irlgov.ie/taoiseach
SIC: 75100 Employees: 298
Department of the Taoiseach
Mr Dermot McCarthy Secretary General

European Commission
18 Dawson Street
Dublin 2
Phone: 01-6625113 Fax: 01-6341112
Email: info@euireland.ie
Web: http://www.euireland.ie
SIC: 75100 Employees: 25
European Commission
Mr Philip Ryan Press Officer
Ms Sarah Barnes Personnel Manager
Mr Peter Doyle Director

Government Supplies Agency
4/5 Harcourt Road
Dublin 2
Phone: 01-6613111 Fax: 01-4753189
Email: opq@ie
Web: http://www.opw.ie
SIC: 75100 Employees: 70
Government Purchasing/Supplies
Mr Jim Ryan Assistant Director
Mr Pat Granhan Assistant Director

Health & Safety Authority
10 Hogan Place
Dublin 2
Phone: 01-6147000 Fax: 01-6147020
Email: information@hsa.ie
Web: http://www.hsa.ie
SIC: 75100 Employees: 600
Health & Safety Advisors
Mr Tom Walsh Chairperson

National Roads Authority
St Martins House
Waterloo Road
Dublin 4
Phone: 01-6602511 Fax: 01-6680009
Email: info@nra.ie
Web: http://www.epa.ie
SIC: 75100 Employees: 75
Road Improvement/Maintenance
Mr Michael Tobin Chief Executive
Mr John Maher Accountant
Mr Cyril Sullivan Head of Internal Support
Mr Ronan Quinn IT Manager

Office of Director/Consumer Affairs
4 Harcourt Road
Dublin 2
Phone: 01-4025500 Fax: 01-4025501
Email: odca@entent.ie
Web: http://www.odca.ie
SIC: 75100 Employees: 65
Government Department - Consumer Advice
Ms Carmel Foley Director
Ms Anne Gale Accounts Manager
Ms Katherine Lennahan Personnel Manager
Mr David Campbell IT Manager

Office of Public Works
51 St Stephens Green
Dublin 2
Phone: 01-6476000 Fax: 01-6610747
Email: opw@iol.ie
Web: http://www.opw.ie
SIC: 75100 Employees: 750
Office of Public Works
Mr Barry Murphy Chairman
Ms Linda Henley Press & Information Officer

Office of the Ombudsman
18 Lower Leeson Street
Dublin 2
Phone: 01-6785222 Fax: 01-6610570
Email: ombudsman@ombudsman.irlgov.ie
Web: http://www.irlgov.ie/ombudsman/
SIC: 75100 Employees: 60
Office of the Ombudsman
Mr Kevin Murphy Commissioner
Mr Patrick Whelan Director

Ordnance Survey Ireland
Phoenix Park
Dublin 8
Phone: 01-8205300 Fax: 01-8204156
Email: custserv@osi.ie
Web: http://www.irltob.ie/osi
SIC: 75100 Employees: 1960
State Mapping Agency
Mr Richard Kirwin Managing Director
Ms Jennifer Conroy Financial Controller
Mr Gregory Whelan Personnel Manager
Mr Steven Curran Development Manager
Mr Cormac Clancey IT Manager

President's Establishment
Phoenix Park
Dublin 8
Phone: 01-6171000 Fax: 01-6171001
SIC: 75100 Employees: 60
President of Ireland
Mr Brian McCarthy Secretary to President

Government

Carlow County Council
County Offices
Athy Road
Carlow Co. Carlow
Phone: 0503-70300 Fax: 0503-41503
Email: secretar@carlowcoco.ie
Web: http://www.carlowcountycouncil.ie
SIC: 75111 Employees: 340
County Council
Mr Tom Dowling County Manager
Mr Pat Delaney Finance Officer
Mr Gerry O'Brien Personnel Officer
Mr Jim Kearney County Secretary
Mr O O'Riordan County Engineer
Mr John Forde IT Officer

Donegal County Council
County House
Lifford Co. Donegal
Phone: 074-72222 Fax: 074-41205
Email: info@donegal.ie
Web: http://www.donegal.ie
SIC: 75111 Employees: 700
County Councils
Mr Micheal McCloone County Manager

Fingal County Council
46-49 Upper O'Connell Street
Dublin 1
Phone: 01-8727777 Fax: 01-8725782
Email: info@fingalcoco.ie
Web: http://www.fingalcoco.ie
SIC: 75111 Employees: 1000
County Council
Mr William Soffe County Manager
Mr Pat Keane Finance Manager
Mr Jim Cunningham Personnel Manager
Mr Gerry Duane Head of IT

Laois County Council
County Hall
Portlaoise Co. Laois
Phone: 0502-64000 Fax: 0502-22313
Email: secretar@laoiscoco.ie
Web: http://www.laois.ie
SIC: 75111 Employees: 400
County Council & Corporations
Mr Michael Malone County Manager
Mr Peter Scully Head of Finance

Leitrim County Council
Court House
Carrick On Shannon Co. Leitrim
Phone: 078-20005 Fax: 078-22205
Email: secretar@leitrimcoco.ie
Web: http://www.leitrimcoco.ie
SIC: 75111 Employees: 200
County Council
Mr John Tiernan County Manager
Mr Seamus Martin Finance Manager
Mr Martin Dolan Acting County Secretary
Mr Joe Lowe County Development Officer
Mr Kevin Clancy Computer Manager

Longford County Council
Aras an Chontae
Great Water Street
Longford Co. Longford
Phone: 043-46231 Fax: 043-41233
Email: secretar@longfordcoco.ie
Web: http://www.longford.ie
SIC: 75111 Employees: 280
County Council
Mr Michael Killeen County Manager
Mr Tommy McDonald Finance Officer
Mr Frank Sheridan Director of Enterprise

Roscommon County Council
Court House
Roscommon Co. Roscommon
Phone: 0903-37100 Fax: 0903-37108
Email: secretar@roscommoncoco.ie
Web: http://www.roscommoncoco.ie
SIC: 75111 Employees: 600
County Council
Mr Derry O'Donnell County Manager
Mr Larry Doyle Head of Finance
Ms Mary Lindsay Personnel Officer
Mr Martin Finan Head of IT

Sligo County Council
Council Offices
Sligo Co. Sligo
Phone: 071-56666 Fax: 071-41119
Email: secretar@sligococo.ie
SIC: 75111 Employees: 400
County Council
Mr Hugo Kearns County Manager
Mr A McConnell Finance Officer

South Dublin County Council
County Hall, Town Centre
Tallaght
Dublin 24
Phone: 01-4149000 Fax: 01-4149111
Email: council@sdcc.ie
Web: http://www.sdcc.ie
SIC: 75111 Employees: 900
County Council
Mr Frank Kavanagh County Manager
Mr Hugh Hogan Corporate Services

Waterford County Council
Waterford County Civic Offices
Davitt's Quay
Dungarvan Co. Waterford
Phone: 058-22000 Fax: 058-42911
Email: info@waterfordcoco.ie
Web: http://www.waterfordcoco.ie
SIC: 75111 Employees: 500
County Council
Mr Donal Connolly County Manager
Mr Paul Clerkin Finance Manager

Wexford County Council
County Hall
Spawell Road
Wexford Co. Wexford
Phone: 053-65000 Fax: 053-43406
Email: postmaster@wexfordcoco.ie
Web: http://www.wexford.ie
SIC: 75111 Employees: 450
County Council
Mr Seamus Dooley County Manager
Ms Annette O'Neill Head of Finance
Mr Adrian Doyle Planning & Econ Development
Mr Tony Larkin Director of Comm Enterprise

Clonmel Corporation
Town Hall
Clonmel Co. Tipperary
Phone: 052-22100 Fax: 052-22216
Email: tclerk@clonmelcorp.ie
Web: http://www.clonmel.ie
SIC: 75112 Employees: 100
Corporation
Mr Ned Gleeson County Manager
Mr John Doyle Accountant
Ms Clare Curley Administration Officer
Ms Geraldine Tobin IT Officer

Drogheda Corporation
Corporation Offices
Fair Street
Drogheda Co. Louth
Phone: 041-9833511 Fax: 041-9839306
Email: tclerk@droghedacorp.ie
Web: http://www.droghedacorp.ie
SIC: 75112 Employees: 186
Corporation
Mr Des Foley Town Clerk
Mr Micheal Cooney Administrative Officer
Ms Bronagh O'Reilly Senior Staff Officer

Food Safety Authority of Ireland
Block E, Abbey Court
Lower Abbey Street
Dublin 1
Phone: 01-8171300 Fax: 01-8171301
Email: info@fsai.ie
Web: http://www.fsai.ie
SIC: 75112 Employees: 75
Food Safety Authority
Mr Patrick Wall Chief Executive
Mr Ray Dolan Financial Controller
Ms Colette Carroll Human Resources Manager
Ms Sinead Brennan Rec/Admin Assist
Mr Tom O'Regan IT Manager

Galway Corporation
City Hall
College Road
Galway Co. Galway
Phone: 091-536400 Fax: 091-567493
Email: info@galwaycity.ie
Web: http://www.galwaycity.ie
SIC: 75112 Employees: 500
Borough Council
Mr John Tierney City Manager
Mr PJ McGovern Head of Finance
Ms Martina Moloney Director of Enterprise
Mr Robert Curley IT Manager

Irish Aviation Authority
Huntstown
Cloghran
Swords Co. Dublin
Phone: 01-8144670 Fax: 01-8445374
Email: info@iaa.ie
Web: http://www.iaa.ie
SIC: 75112 Employees: 150
Semi-Government Office - Aviation Authority
Mr Matt Bergen Managing Director

Kilkenny Corporation
City Hall
High Street
Kilkenny Co. Kilkenny
Phone: 056-65457 Fax: 056-63422
SIC: 75112 Employees: 75
Borough Council/Corporation
Mr Donal O'Brien Town Clerk
Mr Brian Tyrrell Administrative Officer

Limerick Corporation
City Hall
Limerick Co. Limerick
Phone: 061-415799 Fax: 061-415266
SIC: 75112 Employees: 600
Borough Council/Corporation
Mr Brendan Keating City Manager
Mr Ger Dillon Acting Head of Finance

Sligo Corporation
Town Hall
Sligo Co. Sligo
Phone: 071-42141 Fax: 071-41056
Email: tclerk@sligocorp.ie
SIC: 75112 Employees: 100
Corporation
Mr Hubert Kearns County Manager
Ms Anna Jones Finance Manager
Mr John McNabola Town Clerk

The Competition Authority
Parnell House
14 Parnell Square
Dublin 1
Phone: 01-8045400 Fax: 01-8045401
Email: info@ca.ie
Web: http://www.pca.ie
SIC: 75112 Employees: 25
Enforcement of Competition Law
Dr John Fingleton Chairman
Mr Ciaran Quigley Secretary to The Authority

Waterford Corporation
City Hall
Waterford Co. Waterford
Phone: 051-309900 Fax: 051-879124
Email: tclerk@waterfordcorp.ie
Web: http://www.waterfordcorp.ie
SIC: 75112 Employees: 300
Borough Council/Corporation
Mr Eddie Breen City Manager
Mr John Murphy Finance Manager
Ms Colette Byrne Director of Community & Enterp

Wexford Corporation
Municipal Buildings
Wexford Co. Wexford
Phone: 053-42611 Fax: 053-45947
Email: wexfordcorporation@wexfordcorp.ie
Web: http://www.wexfordcorp.ie
SIC: 75112 Employees: 90
Corporation
Mr Pat Collins Town Clerk
Ms Louise O'Rourke Finance Officer

Athlone UDC
Town Hall
Athlone Co. Westmeath
Phone: 0902-72107 Fax: 0902-72100
Email: tclerk@athloneudc.ie
Web: http://www.athloneudc.ie
SIC: 75113 Employees: 60
Urban District Council
Mr John Walsh Town Clerk
Mr Aidan Vass Finance Manager
Mr Michael Connolly Town Engineer

Ballina UDC
Tone Street
Ballina Co. Mayo
Phone: 096-21399 Fax: 096-22819
Email: info@bnaudc.mayococo.ie
Web: http://www.bnaudc.mayococo.ie
SIC: 75113 Employees: 40
Urban District Council
Mr Paul Benson Town Clerk
Mr Eddie Munnelly Town Engineer

Ballinasloe UDC
Civic Offices
Ballinasloe Co. Galway
Phone: 0905-42263 Fax: 0905-42689
Email: info@ballinasloeudc.ie
Web: http://www.ballinasloeudc.ie
SIC: 75113 Employees: 41
Urban District Council
Ms Mary Molloy Acting Town Clerk
Mr Michael Sheil Town Engineer

Birr UDC
Town Hall
Birr Co. Offaly
Phone: 0509-20187 Fax: 0509-20187
SIC: 75113 Employees: 25
Urban District Council
Ms Edel O'Brien Town Clerk
Mr Tom Shanahan Town Engineer

Dundalk UDC
Town Hall
Dundalk Co. Louth
Phone: 042-9332276 Fax: 042-9336761
Email: info@dundalkudc.ie
Web: http://www.louthcoco.ie/dundalkudc
SIC: 75113 Employees: 200
Urban District Council
Mr Frank Pentony Town Clerk
Ms Joan Smith Human Resources Director
Mr Michael Duffy IT Manager

Government

Ennis UDC
Waterpark House
Drumbiggle
Ennis Co. Clare
Phone: 065-6828040 Fax: 065-6828182
Email: admin@ennisudc.ie
Web: http://www.ennisudc.ie
SIC: 75113 Employees: 76
Urban District Council
Mr Thomas Ryan Town Clerk
Ms Josephine Cotter-Coughlan Administrative Officer
Mr Michael Corley Chairperson
Mr Tom Tiernan Executive Engineer
Mr Michael Hannon IT Manager

Enniscorthy UDC
Market Square
Enniscorthy Co. Wexford
Phone: 054-33540 Fax: 054-35115
SIC: 75113 Employees: 40
Urban District Council
Mr Donal Minnock Town Clerk

Fermoy UDC
Council Offices
Fermoy Co. Cork
Phone: 025-31201 Fax: 025-32331
SIC: 75113 Employees: 80
Urban District Council
Mr Maurice Manning Town Clerk

Mallow UDC
Town Hall
Main Street
Mallow Co. Cork
Phone: 022-21542 Fax: 022-43201
Email: admin@mallow.ie
Web: http://www.mallow.ie
SIC: 75113 Employees: 45
Urban District Council
Ms Theresa Whyte County Manager
Mr N O'Connor Chairperson
Ms Sharon Corcoran Town Clerk

Monaghan UDC
Town Hall
1 Dublin Street
Monaghan Co. Monaghan
Phone: 047-82079 Fax: 047-84549
SIC: 75113 Employees: 45
Urban District Council
Mr Declan Nelson County Manager

Thurles UDC
Slievenamon Road
Thurles Co. Tipperary
Phone: 0504-21433 Fax: 0504-21045
Email: info@thurlesudc.ie
Web: http://www.thurlesudc.ie
SIC: 75113 Employees: 30
Urban District Council
Mr Michael Ryan Town Clerk
Mr Terry O'Niadh County Manager

East Coast Area Health Board
Southern Cross House
Southern Cross Business Park
Bray Co. Wicklow
Phone: 01-2014200 Fax: 01-2014201
SIC: 75120 Employees: 2640
East Coast Area Health Board
Mr Michael Lyons Chief Executive Officer

Eastern Regional Health Authority
Canal House, Canal Road
Dublin 6
Phone: 01-6201600 Fax: 01-4065601
SIC: 75120 Employees: 14000
Local Health Authority
Mr Kieran Hickey Chief Executive Officer
Mr Liam Woods Finance Manager
Ms Mary Kelly Personnel Officer
Mr Matt O'Connor Senior Administrative Officer
Mr Gerry Brennan Technical Services Officer

Mid Western Health Board
31-33 Catherine Street
Limerick Co. Limerick
Phone: 061-316655 Fax: 061-483350
Email: eolas@mwhb.ie
Web: http://www.mwhb.ie
SIC: 75120 Employees: 6500
Health Board
Mr Stiofan DeBurca Chief Executive Officer
Mr Paddy McDonald Finance Manager
Ms Maria Corcoran Personnel Officer
Mr Gerry McNamara Technical Services Officer
Mr Richard McMahon Assist Chief Executive Officer

Midland Health Board
Central Offices
Arden Road
Tullamore Co. Offaly
Phone: 0506-21868 Fax: 0506-51760
Email: info@mhb.ie
Web: http://www.mhb.ie
SIC: 75120 Employees: 4300
Local Health Authority
Mr Denis Doherty Chief Executive Officer
Mr Diarmuid Collins Finance Manager
Mr Larry Bane Personnel Officer
Mr Brendan Colleary Technical Services Officer
Mr Tom Carty Management Services Officer

North Eastern Health Board
Navan Road
Kells Co. Meath
Phone: 046-40341 Fax: 046-41459
SIC: 75120 Employees: 5085
Health Board Services
Mr Paul Robinson Chief Executive Officer

North Western Health Board
Manorhamilton Co. Leitrim
Phone: 072-20400 Fax: 072-20431
Email: info@nwhb.ie
Web: http://www.nwhb.ie
SIC: 75120 Employees: 5050
Health Board
Mr Pat Harvey Chief Executive Officer
Mr Anthony Travers Finance Manager
Mr William Murphy Personnel Manager
Mr Anton Murphy Regional Materials Manager
Mr Gerard Hanley Technical Services Manager

Western Health Board
Merlin Park Headquarters
Galway Co. Galway
Phone: 091-751131 Fax: 091-752644
Email: ceowhb@bsi.ie
SIC: 75120 Employees: 7500
Health Board
Dr Sheelah Ryan Chief Executive
Mr Liam Minihan Director of Finance
Ms Brid Kelly Director of Human Resources
Dr Sean Conroy Corporate & Public Affairs Man
Ms Grainne Cahill Technical Services Officer

Companies Registration Office
Parnell House, 14 Parnell Square
Dublin 1
Phone: 01-8045200 Fax: 01-8045222
Email: moylan@entenp.ie
Web: http://www.cro.ie
SIC: 75131 Employees: 110
Companies Registration Office
Mr Paul Farrell Chief Registrar
Mr Brendan Moylan Assistant Registrar
Mr Donagh Kelly Computer Manager

Cork City Partnership Ltd
Sunbeam Industrial Park
Millfield, Mallow Road
Cork Co. Cork
Phone: 021-4302310 Fax: 021-4302081
Email: partnershipcork@eircom.net
SIC: 75131 Employees: 50
Regional & Social Development for Cork City
Mr Jim O'Flynn Chief Executive Officer
Ms Heather Underwood Office Administrator

Department of Enterprise, Trade & Employment
23 Kildare Street
Dublin 2
Phone: 01-6312121 Fax: 01-6762654
Email: webmaster@entemp.ie
Web: http://www.entemp.ie
SIC: 75131 Employees: 1000
Department of Enterprise, Trade & Employment
Mr Paul Haran Secretary General
Mr Ronnie Sheehan Principal Officer
Mr Padraig Cullinane Personnel Officer
Mr Eamon Laird Principal Officer

Department of Public Enterprise
25 Clare Street
Dublin 2
Phone: 01-6707444 Fax: 01-6041538
Email: info@dpe.ie
Web: http://www.irl.gov.ie
SIC: 75131 Employees: 2540
Department of Public Enterprise
Mr Brendan Tuohy Secretary General
Mr Austin McGarry Personnel Manager
Ms Mary Sheerin Information Officer

National Standards Authority of Ireland
Glasnevin
Dublin 9
Phone: 01-8073800 Fax: 01-8073838
Email: nsai@nsai.ie
Web: http://www.nsai.ie
SIC: 75131 Employees: 80
Standards Authority
Mr Simon Kelly Chief Executive

IDA Ireland
Wilton Park House, Wilton Place
Dublin 2
Phone: 01-6034000 Fax: 01-6034000
Email: info@ida.ie
Web: http://www.ida.ie
SIC: 75133 Employees: 400
Industrial Development
Mr Sean Dorgan Chief Executive
Mr Martin Burbridge Finance Manager
Mr Dennis Fitzpatrick Personnel Officer
Mr Brendan Halpin Sales & Marketing Executive

Board for Employment of the Blind
Davitt Road
Goldenbridge
Dublin 12
Phone: 01-4559570 Fax: 01-4557941
SIC: 75134 Employees: 35
Board for Employment of the Blind
Mr Seamus Miller Chief Executive

Enterprise Trade & Employment
Kildare Street
Dublin 2
Phone: 01-6614444 Fax: 01-6312827
Email: webmaster@entenp.ie
Web: http://www.entenp.ie
SIC: 75134 Employees: 1000
Government Department
Mr Billy Hawkes Principal Officer
Mr Padraig Cullinane Personnel Manager
Mr Eamon Laird Sales Manager

Government

FAS
27-33 Upper Baggot Street
Dublin 4
Phone: 01-6070500 Fax: 01-6070600
Email: info@fas.ie
Web: http://www.fas.ie
SIC: 75134 Employees: 2500
FAS -Training & Employment Services
Dr Roddy Malloy Director General
Mr Donal Sands Finance Manager
Mr Gregory Craig Public Relations Manager
Mr Brendan Murphy IT Director

Balbriggan Enterprise Centre
13 Drogheda Street
Balbriggan Co. Dublin
Phone: 01-8415141 Fax: 01-8411010
Email: dedg@club.ie
SIC: 75135 Employees: 40
Enterprise House
Mr Adrian Brown Manager

Enterprise Ireland
Glasnevin
Dublin 9
Phone: 01-8082000 Fax: 01-8082020
Email: client.service@enterprise-ireland.com
Web: http://www.enterprise-ireland.com
SIC: 75135 Employees: 700
Service to Industry (Semi-State Body)
Mr Dan Flinter Chief Executive
Mr Jim Daly Finance Manager
Mr Liam O'Donohue Personnel Manager
Ms Deirdre McDonough Computer Manager

National Patent Office
Government Buildings
Hebron Road
Kilkenny Co. Kilkenny
Phone: 056-20111 Fax: 056-20100
Web: http://www.patentsoffice.ie
SIC: 75136 Employees: 72
Government - National Patent Office
Mr Sean Fitzpatrick Controller

Udaras Na Gaeltachta
Na Forbacha
Galway Co. Galway
Phone: 091-503100 Fax: 091-503101
Email: eolas@udaras.ie
Web: http://www.udaras.ie
SIC: 75136 Employees: 112
Business Development Organisation
Mr Ruan O'Bric Chief Executive
Mr Antoin O'Hioruaidh Accounts Manager
Mr Caoimhin O'Fliathmhin Head of Personnel
Mr Seosamh MacAnPhearsuin Sales & Marketing Manager
Mr Padraig O'hAolain Information Manager
Mr Sean O'Raighna Computer Manager

Department of Arts, Heritage, Gaeltacht & Islands
43-49 Mespil Road
Dublin 4
Phone: 01-6473000 Fax: 01-6473051
Email: eolas@ealga.ie
Web: http://www.irlgov.ie/ealga
SIC: 75141 Employees: 2000
Department of Arts, Heritage, Gaeltacht & the Islands
Mr Philip Furlong Secretary General
Mr Michael Conroy Principal Officer

Chief Inspector of Taxes Head Office
Setanta Centre
Nassau Street
Dublin 2
Phone: 01-6716777 Fax: 01-6798821
SIC: 75142 Employees: 2862
Office of the Revenue Commissioners
Mr Christopher Clayton Chief Inspector
Mr Art O'Connor Principal Inspector

Office of the Revenue Commissioners
Dublin Castle
Dublin 2
Phone: 01-6792777 Fax: 01-6715011
Email: info@revenue.ie
Web: http://www.revenue.ie
SIC: 75142 Employees: 6000
Office of the Revenue Commissioners
Mr Dermot Quigley Chairman
Ms Josephine Feehily Commissioner
Mr Frank Daly Commissioner

Department Of Finance
Government Buildings
Upper Merrion Street
Dublin 2
Phone: 01-6767571 Fax: 01-6789936
Email: info@finance.irlgov.ie
Web: http://www.irlgov.ie/finance
SIC: 75143 Employees: 556
Department of Finance
Mr John Hurley Secretary General
Ms Patricia Coleman Principal Officer

General Registery Office
Joyce House
8 Lombard Street East
Dublin 2
Phone: 01-6711000 Fax: 01-6354440
Email: info@groireland.ie
Web: http://www.groireland.ie
SIC: 75143 Employees: 500
Births Deaths & Marriages
Mr Jim Clearey General Manager
Mr Noel Usher Chief Environmental Officer
Mr Kevin Hanlon Computer Manager

Office of the Civil Service Commission
1 Lower Grand Canal Street
Dublin 2
Phone: 01-6615611 Fax: 01-6616534
Email: info@csclac.irlgov.ie
Web: http://www.irlgov.ie/csclac
SIC: 75143 Employees: 200
Recruitment of Civil Service Personnel
Mr Bryan Andrews Chief Executive Officer
Mr Val McBride Higher Executive Officer
Mr Padraig Love Assistant Chief Executive
Mr Brian McKeown Assistant Principal
Mr Liam Hurley Assistant Principal Officer

Office of the Comptroller & Auditor General
Treasury Building Lower Yard
Dublin Castle
Dublin 2
Phone: 01-6793122 Fax: 01-6031010
Email: webmaster@audgen.irlgov.ie
Web: http://www.irlgov.ie/audgen
SIC: 75143 Employees: 130
Government Appointed Auditors
Mr John Purcell Comptroller/Auditor General
Mr John Buckley Secretary General
Mr Michael Buckley Deputy Director
Mr John Kerr IT Manager

Animal Health And Welfare Division
Deparment of Agriculture and Food
Kildare Street
Dublin 2
Phone: 01-6072436 Fax: 01-6619031
Web: http://www.daff.irlgov.ie
SIC: 75161 Employees: 2500
Animal Health & Welfare Division
Mr Aidan Murray Principal Officer (Veterinary)

Department of Agriculture Food & Rural Development
Agriculture House
Kildare Street
Dublin 2
Phone: 01-6789011 Fax: 01-6616263
Web: http://www.irlgov.ie/daff
SIC: 75161 Employees: 4880
Department of Agriculture,Food & Rural Development
Mr John Malone Secretary General
Ms Marian Byrne Principal Officer
Mr Joe Shortall Personnel Director
Mr Martin Heraghty Press Secretary
Mr John McCarthy IT Section

Department of the Marine & Natural Resources
Leeson Lane
Dublin 2
Phone: 01-6199200 Fax: 01-6618214
Web: http://www.marine.gov.ie
SIC: 75161 Employees: 440
Department of the Marine & Natural Resources
Ms Julie O'Neill Secretary General

Irish Food Board
Clanwilliam Court
Lower Mount Street
Dublin 2
Phone: 01-6685155 Fax: 01-6687521
Email: info@bordbia.ie
Web: http://www.bordbia.ie
SIC: 75161 Employees: 60
Market Division of Food
Mr Michael Duffy Chief Executive
Mr Gerry Bailey Financial Controller
Mr Seamus Kenny Company Secretary
Mr John McGrath Marketing Manager
Mr Julian Smith IT Manager

Irish Sea Fisheries Board
Crofton Road
Dun Laoghaire Co. Dublin
Phone: 01-2841544 Fax: 01-2841123
Email: info@bim.ie
Web: http://www.bim.ie
SIC: 75161 Employees: 120
Advisory Service to Sea Fish Industries
Mr Pat Keogh Chief Executive
Mr Frank Flannagan Accountant
Mr Des Kerley Personnel Manager
Ms Helen Brophy Marketing Manager
Mr Eamon Robins Computer Manager

Marine Institute
80 Harcourt Street
Dublin 2
Phone: 01-4766500 Fax: 01-4784988
Email: info@marine.ie
Web: http://www.marine.ie
SIC: 75161 Employees: 130
Promoting & Funding Marine Research & Development
Dr Peter Heffernan Chief Executive
Mr Niall Gibbons Finance Manager
Ms Cathy Quigley Personnel Manager
Mr Jerry McCarthy Computer Manager

North Western Regional Fisheries
Abbey Street
Ballina Co. Mayo
Phone: 096-22788 Fax: 096-70543
Email: nwrfb@iol.ie
SIC: 75161 Employees: 55
Regional Fisheries Board
Mr Vincent Roche Chief Officer
Mr John Coneely Assistant Manager

South Western Regional Fisheries
1 Nevilles Terrace
Masseytown
Macroom Co. Cork
Phone: 026-41221 Fax: 026-41223
Email: buck@swrfb.ie
Web: http://www.swrfb.ie
SIC: 75161 Employees: 30
Regional Fisheries Board
Mr Aidan Barry Manager
Ms Ann Hogan Accounts
Mr Patrick Buck Assistant Manager

Vet Livestock & Farm Development
St Munchin's House
Dock Road
Limerick Co. Limerick
Phone: 061-317555 Fax: 061-318089
SIC: 75161 Employees: 280
Department of Agriculture
Mr Pat O'Malley Regional Officer

Western Regional Fisheries Board
Wier Lodge, Earls Island
Galway Co. Galway
Phone: 091-563118 Fax: 091-566335
Email: wrfb@iol.ie
SIC: 75161 Employees: 150
Development & Protection of Fisheries
Mr Michael Kennedy Chief Executive Officer

State Laboratory
Abbotstown
Dublin 15
Phone: 01-8217700 Fax: 01-8217320
Email: info@statelab.ie
Web: http://www.statelab.ie
SIC: 75164 Employees: 85
Government Laboratory
Dr Maire Walsh State Chemist
Ms Maureen Dunne Higher Executive Officer
Mr Conor Murphy Senior Chemist

Department of Education & Science
Marlborough Street
Dublin 1
Phone: 01-8734700 Fax: 01-8729553
Email: master@educ.irlgov.ie
Web: http://www.irlgov.ie/educ
SIC: 75171 Employees: 1200
Department of Education & Science
Mr John Dennehy Secretary General
Mr Paddy McDonagh Assistant Secretary General
Ms Pauline Gildea Personnel Officer
Mr Seamus McLoughlin Principal Officer

FETAC
Marino Instituite of Education
Griffith Avenue
Dublin 9
Phone: 01-8531910 Fax: 01-8372481
Email: info@fetac.ie
Web: http://www.fetac.ie
SIC: 75171 Employees: 40
Awards Council
Mr Stan McHugh Chief Executive

Higher Education Authority
Floor 3 Marine House
Clanwilliam Court
Dublin 2
Phone: 01-6612748 Fax: 01-6610492
Email: info@hea.ie
Web: http://www.hea.ie
SIC: 75171 Employees: 30
Educational Funders & Advisors
Mr John Hayden Secretary/Chief Executive
Ms Mary Kerr Deputy Secretary
Mr Padraic Mollett Head of Administration

Longford Vocational Education Committee
Battery Road
Longford Co. Longford
Phone: 043-46384 Fax: 043-45360
SIC: 75171 Employees: 82
Vocational Education Committee
Ms Josephine O'Donnell Chief Executive Officer

National Council for Education Awards
26 Mountjoy Square
Dublin 1
Phone: 01-8556526 Fax: 01-8554250
Web: http://www.ncea.ie
SIC: 75172 Employees: 40
Monitor of Educational Standards
Mr Seamus Purcell Acting Director
Mr Tom Cullivan Assistant Registrar
Ms Renee Scully Personnel Officer

Department Of the Environment & Local Government
Custom House
Dublin 1
Phone: 01-8882000 Fax: 01-8882888
Email: press_office@eviron.irlgov.ie
Web: http://www.eviron.ie
SIC: 75181 Employees: 800
Department of the Environment
Mr Niall Callan Secretary General
Mr Tom O'Mahony Corporate Services

Met Eireann
Glasnevin Hill
Dublin 9
Phone: 01-8064255 Fax: 01-8064275
Email: meteireann@met.ie
SIC: 75181 Employees: 250
Weather Forecast
Mr Declan Murphy Director
Mr Colm Faherty Finance Manager
Mr Liam Campbell Sales Manager

Radiological Protection Institute
3 Clonskeagh Square
Dublin 14
Phone: 01-2697766 Fax: 01-2697437
Email: info@rpii.ie
Web: http://www.rpii.ie
SIC: 75181 Employees: 70
Environmental Radiation
Mr Thomas O'Flaherty Chief Executive
Ms Teresa Grant Accounts Manager
Mr Paul Fitzgerald Computer Manager

Traffic Offices
Civic Offices
Fishamble Street
Dublin 2
Phone: 01-6722592 Fax: 01-6796463
SIC: 75181 Employees: 82
Government Department - Traffic Offices
Mr John Fitzgerald City Director

Valuation Office
Irish Life Centre
Abbey Street Lower
Dublin 1
Phone: 01-8171000 Fax: 01-8171180
Email: info@valoff.ie
Web: http://www.valoff.ie
SIC: 75181 Employees: 145
Property Valuation Agency
Mr James Rogers Commissioner

Housing Maintenance Depots
U10 Clondalkin Industrial Estate
Dublin 12
Phone: 01-4570099 Fax: -
SIC: 75183 Employees: 23
County Council
Mr Peter Clinton Clerk Of Works

Department of Foreign Affairs
80 St Stephens Green
Dublin 2
Phone: 01-4780822 Fax: 01-4785924
Web: http://www.irlgov.ie/iveagh
SIC: 75210 Employees: 1300
Department of Foreign Affairs
Mr Dermot Gallagher Secretary General
Mr Liam MacGabhann Head of Finance

Air Corps
Casement Aerodrome
Baldonnell
Dublin 22
Phone: 01-8046561 Fax: 01-4591036
Email: webmaster@defence.irlgov.ie
Web: http://www.irlgov.ie/defence
SIC: 75221 Employees: 800
Air Corps
Brig John O'Brien Commanding Officer

Army Command Headquarters
Curragh
Kildare Co. Kildare
Phone: 045-445000 Fax: 045-441626
Email: webmaster@defence.irlgov.ie
Web: http://www.irlgov.ie/defence
SIC: 75221 Employees: 9500
Defence Forces
Brig Saunderson General Officer Commanding

Department of Defence
Parkgate
Infirmary Road
Dublin 7
Phone: 01-8379911 Fax: 01-6703399
Email: info@defence.irlgov.ie
Web: http://www.irlgov.ie/defence
SIC: 75221 Employees: 450
Department of Defence
Mr David O'Callaghan Secretary General
Mr Patrick Hogan Finance Manager
Mr John Nolan Press Officer
Mr Greg McNamee IT Manager

Naval Service
Haulbowline
Cobh Co. Cork
Phone: 021-4378777 Fax: 021-4378108
Email: haul@iol.ie
Web: http://www.irlgov.ie/defence
SIC: 75221 Employees: 1000
Defence Forces
Cmdr John Kavanagh Flag Officer-Naval Services
Capt Frank Lynch OC Naval Operations
Capt Paul Keaney OC Naval Support

Chief State Solicitor's Office
Osmond House
Little Ship Street
Dublin 8
Phone: 01-4176100 Fax: 01-4176299
SIC: 75230 Employees: 200
Chief State Solicitor's Office
Mr David O'Hagan Chief State Solicitor
Mr Seamus Crowe Head of Administration

Department of Justice, Equality Law & Reform
72-76 St Stephen's Green
Dublin 2
Phone: 01-6028202 Fax: 01-6615461
Email: info@justice.ie
Web: http://www.irlgov.ie/justice
SIC: 75230 Employees: 1000
Department of Justice Equality Law & Reform
Mr Tim Dalton Secretary General
Mr Ken Bruton Finance Officer

Director of Public Prosecutions
14-16 Merrion Street
Dublin 2
Phone: 01-6789222 Fax: 01-6610915
Email: prosecut@indigo.ie
Web: http://www.dppireland.ie
SIC: 75230 Employees: 40
Director of Public Prosecutions
Mr James Hamilton Director
Mr Joe Mulligan Finance Manager
Mr Barry Donoghue Deputy Director

National Assessment & Remand Unit
Kildonan Road
Finglas West
Dublin 11
Phone: 01-8343422 Fax: 01-8362967
SIC: 75230 Employees: 60
Young Offenders Assessment Centre
Mr Danny Lynch Deputy Director

Office of the Attorney General
Government Buildings
Upper Merrion Street
Dublin 2
Phone: 01-6616944 Fax: 01-6761806
Email: info@ag.irlgov.ie
Web: http://www.irlgov.ie/ag
SIC: 75230 Employees: 130
Office of the Attorney General
Mr Michael McDowell Attorney General
Ms Finola Flanagan Director General

Probation & Welfare Service
Smithfield Chambers
Smithfield
Dublin 7
Phone: 01-8733722 Fax: 01-8722737
SIC: 75230 Employees: 200
Department of Justice Equality & Law Reform
Mr Martin Tansey Principal Probation Officer
Ms Grace Grant IT Manager

Garda College
Templemore
Thurles Co. Tipperary
Phone: 0504-31217 Fax: 0504-32235
SIC: 75241 Employees: 80
Training College
Supt Eamonn Keatings Superintendent

Garda Síochána
Phoenix Park
Dublin 8
Phone: 01-6660000 Fax: 01-6662013
Email: info@garda.ie
Web: http://www.garda.ie
SIC: 75241 Employees: 9500
Police Headquarters
Mr Patrick Byrne Commissioner
Mr Dan Walsh Finance Manager
Mr M Murphy Human Resources Manager
Mr Eddie Cussen Computer Manager

Arbour Hill Prison
Arbour Hill
Dublin 7
Phone: 01-6719333 Fax: 01-6799518
SIC: 75242 Employees: 150
Prison
Mr Patrick Dunne Governor

Cork Prison
Rathmore Road
Cork Co. Cork
Phone: 021-4503277 Fax: 021-4518860
SIC: 75242 Employees: 200
Prison
Mr Frank McCarthy Governor
Mr James O'Sullivan Assistant Governor
Mr Liam Metclaffe Deputy Governor

Combat Poverty Agency
The Bridgewater Centre
Conyngham Road Islandbridge
Dublin 8
Phone: 01-6706746 Fax: 01-6706760
Email: info@cpa.ie
Web: http://www.cpa.ie
SIC: 75301 Employees: 30
Government Agency- Combat Poverty
Ms Helen Johnston Director
Ms Maria O'Neill Finance Officer
Mr Sean Misteil Head of Organisational Management & Development

Personnel Management & Development Unit
Hawkins House
Poolbeg Street
Dublin 2
Phone: 01-6714711 Fax: 01-6354001
Email: queries@health.irlgov.ie
Web: http://www.doh.ie
SIC: 75301 Employees: 400
Department of Health
Mr Michael Kelly Director
Mr Dermot Morgan Finance Manager

University College Hospital
Newcastle Road
Galway Co. Galway
Phone: 091-524222 Fax: 091-526588
Email: mgt@srv.vsi.ie
Web: http://www.srv.vsi.ie
SIC: 75301 Employees: 1750
Hospital / Health Service
Ms Bridget Howley General Manager
Mr Tony Baynes Finance Manager
Mr Christy O'Hara Personnel Officer
Mr Kevin Clancy Deputy General Manager
Mr Martin Molloy IT Manager

Department of Social, Community & Family Affairs
Aras Mhic Dhiarmada
Store Street
Dublin 1
Phone: 01-8748444 Fax: 01-7043801
Web: http://www.welfare.ie
SIC: 75302 Employees: 4700
Department of Social, Community & Family Affairs
Mr Edmund Sullivan Secretary General

Education

80 Education
80101 Crèche/Nursery Schools
80102 Primary Schools
80103 Special Schools
80211 Secondary (Intermediate) Schools
80212 Secondary (Grammar) Schools
80220 Further Education/VEC
80301 Agricultural Colleges
80302 University & University Faculties
80400 Government Training Centres
80410 Driving Schools
80421 Training Companies
80422 Language Schools
80429 Education (Other)

Athlone Institute of Technology
Dublin Road
Athlone Co. Westmeath
Phone: 0902-24400 Fax: 0902-24417
Web: http://www.ait.ie
SIC: 80220 Employees: 350
Further Education/VEC
Prof Ciaran O'Cathain Director
Mr John McKenna Finance Manager
Ms Alison Sheridan Human Resource Manager
Mr Pearse Murphy IT Manager

Ballsbridge College of Further Education
Shelbourne Road
Ballsbridge
Dublin 4
Phone: 01-6684806 Fax: 01-6682361
Email: info@ballsbridge.cdvec.ie
Web: http://www.ballsbridgecollege.com
SIC: 80220 Employees: 40
College of Further Education
Mr Evan Buckley Principal
Ms Gay O'Callaghan Head of Computers

Ballyfermot College of Further Education
Ballyfermot Road
Dublin 10
Phone: 01-6269421 Fax: 01-6266754
Email: info@bcfe.cdvec.ie
Web: http://www.bcfe.ie
SIC: 80220 Employees: 160
Further Education
Ms Maureen Conway Principal
Mr Diarmuid O'Brien Deputy Principal
Ms Rita Clifford Deputy Principal
Mr Peter Burke IT Teacher

Bridgetown Vocational College
Bridgetown
Wexford Co. Wexford
Phone: 053-35257 Fax: 053-35155
Web: http://homepage.eircom.net/~btownvc
SIC: 80220 Employees: 60
Vocational College
Mr Tony Power Principal
Mr Maurice Tracey Head of Computers

Bruce College
Audley House
St Patricks Hill
Cork Co. Cork
Phone: 021-4504122 Fax: 021-4509048
Email: info@brucecollege.ie
Web: http://www.brucecollege.ie
SIC: 80220 Employees: 30
College
Mr Mehall Landers Principal

Education

Bruce College
65 O'Connell Street
Limerick Co. Limerick
Phone: 061-416811 Fax: 061-410780
Email: postmaster@brucecollege.ie
Web: http://www.brucecollege.ie
SIC: 80220 Employees: 25
College
Mr Liam O'Hurra Director
Mr Chris Murcy Finance Manager

Carnew Community College
Carnew
Arklow Co. Wicklow
Phone: 055-26318 Fax: 055-26311
SIC: 80220 Employees: 42
Vocational College
Mr Martin Phillips Principal
Mr Ken Sweeney Computer Teacher

Cavan VEC
Keadue
Cavan Co. Cavan
Phone: 049-4331044 Fax: 049-4331467
SIC: 80220 Employees: 43
Further Education/VEC
Mr John McKay Chief Executive Officer
Ms Bernadette Power Assistant Staff Officer
Mr Rory Moore Personnel Manager

Central Technical Institute
Parnell Street
Waterford Co. Waterford
Phone: 051-874053 Fax: 051-870136
Email: centechw@iol.ie
Web: http://www.cti-clonmel.ie
SIC: 80220 Employees: 40
Post Leaving Certificate College
Mr Paudie Geary Principal
Mr Harry Beaver Head of Computers

City of Cork VEC
Emmet Place
Cork Co. Cork
Phone: 021-4273377 Fax: 021-4275680
Email: ceo@corkvec.ie
Web: http://www.corkcec.ie
SIC: 80220 Employees: 1400
Further Education/VEC
Mr Richard Langford Chief Executive Officer
Ms Ursula Fitzgerald Finance Manager
Mr John O'Regan Personnel Officer
Mr Pat Maguire DP Manager

City of Dublin VEC
Town Hall
Ballsbridge
Dublin 4
Phone: 01-6680614 Fax: 01-6680710
SIC: 80220 Employees: 1350
Further Education College
Mr William Arundel Chief Executive Officer
Mr Anthony Dawson Finance Manager
Ms Lill Thomas Acting Head of Personnel
Mr John McGrath Principal Officer

Clare VEC
Station Road
Ennis Co. Clare
Phone: 065-6828107 Fax: 065-6824928
Email: coclarevec@eircom.net
Web: http://homepage.tinet.ie/~coclarevec
SIC: 80220 Employees: 120
Vocational Education Committee
Mr Seamus O'Laithain Chief Executive Officer
Mr Gerard Lyons Accounts Manager
Mr Stephen Flaherty Administration Manager
Mr Gerard Lyons Accounts Manager

College Of Marketing & Design
41 Mountjoy Square
Dublin 1
Phone: 01-8363044 Fax: 01-8559842
SIC: 80220 Employees: 1500
Dublin Institute Of Technology
Ms V Byrne Manager

Cork Institute of Technology
Rossa Avenue
Bishopstown
Cork Co. Cork
Phone: 021-4326100 Fax: 021-4545343
Email: info@cit.ie
Web: http://www.cit.ie
SIC: 80220 Employees: 1000
Further Education/VEC
Mr Patrick Kelleher Director
Ms Claire Sinnott Finance Manager
Mr Eamonn O'Connor Head of Admissions
Dr Brendan Murphy Head of Computing

County Wicklow VEC
Wentworth Place
Wicklow Co. Wicklow
Phone: 0404-67338 Fax: 0404-62556
SIC: 80220 Employees: 30
VEC Head Office
Mr Seamus Reynolds Chief Executive Officer
Ms Carmel Whelan Senior Staff Officer

Crumlin College
Crumlin Road
Dublin 12
Phone: 01-4540662 Fax: 01-4538855
SIC: 80220 Employees: 40
School
Mr Phillip Galvin Principal

Deele College
Raphoe
Lifford Co. Donegal
Phone: 074-45493 Fax: 074-45493
SIC: 80220 Employees: 30
College
Mr PJ McGowan Principal
Mrs Sadie Kelly Secretary
Mr Daniel Coghan Deputy
Ms Marita Bonner IT Co-ordinator

Drogheda College of Further Education
King Street
Drogheda Co. Louth
Phone: 041-9837105 Fax: 041-9841653
Email: recept@slcc.ie
Web: http://www.slcc.ie
SIC: 80220 Employees: 35
Further Education College
Mr Michael Dowd Principal
Dr John McDonald Head of Computers

Dublin Business School
13-14 Aungier Street
Dublin 2
Phone: 01-4177500 Fax: 01-4177543
Email: admissions@dbs.edu
Web: http://www.dbs.edu
SIC: 80220 Employees: 110
Arts & Business School
Mr Gerry Muldowney Director
Mr Donal Quill Finance Manager
Ms Olivia Meagher Director of Marketing
Mr David Richard Head of IT

Dublin County VEC
Main Road
Tallaght
Dublin 24
Phone: 01-4515666 Fax: 01-4515196
SIC: 80220 Employees: 54
Further Education/VEC
Mr Pat O'Connor Chief Executive Officer
Ms Debbie Howlett Finance Manager
Ms June Fitzpatrick Personnel Manager
Mr Paul McEvoy Assistant Principal Officer

Dublin Insitute of Technology
30 Upper Pembroke Street
Dublin 2
Phone: 01-6611133 Fax: 01-4023399
Email: info@dit.ie
Web: http://www.dit.ie
SIC: 80220 Employees: 1000
Education
Dr Brendan Goldsmith President
Mr Craig Larner Finance Manager
Mr David Spring Personnel Manager
Mr Conor Cahill Director of Computer Services

Dun Laoghaire College of Further Education
17 Cumberland Street
Dun Laoghaire Co. Dublin
Phone: 01-2809676 Fax: 01-2843767
Email: info@dlcfe.ie
Web: http://www.dlcfe.ie
SIC: 80220 Employees: 60
Post Leaving Certificate College
Mr John Howe Principal
Mr Eugene Fitzgerald Head of Computers

Dun Laoghaire Institute of Art Design & Technology
Carraiglea Park
Kill Avenue
Dun Laoghaire Co. Dublin
Phone: 01-2144600 Fax: 01-2144700
Email: info@iadt-dl.ie
Web: http://www.iadt-dl.ie
SIC: 80220 Employees: 60
Further Education/VEC
Ms Roisin Hogan Director
Mr Donal Keane Economics
Mr Kevin Browne Personnel Officer
Mr Barry McIntire Business Manager
Mr Colin Hennessy Computer Manager

Dundalk Institute Of Technology
Dublin Road
Dundalk Co. Louth
Phone: 042-9370200 Fax: 042-9333505
Email: reception@dkit.ie
Web: http://www.dkit.ie
SIC: 80220 Employees: 400
Further Education/VEC
Mr Tom Collins Director
Mr Peter McGrath Finance Manager
Mr Gerald O'Driscoll Personnel Officer
Mr Peter Fuller Head of Business Dept
Mr Dennis Cummins Head of Computers

Franciscan College of Agriculture & Horticulture
Multyfarnham
Mullingar Co. Westmeath
Phone: 044-71137 Fax: 044-71387
SIC: 80220 Employees: 30
Further Education - Agricultural
Fr Bernard Jones Rector

Froebel College of Education
Sion Hill
Blackrock Co. Dublin
Phone: 01-2888520 Fax: 01-2880618
Email: admin@froebel.ie
Web: http://www.froebel.ie
SIC: 80220 Employees: 43
Further Education/VEC
Sr Darina Hosey Principal
Sr Breda Hourigan Bursar
Ms Elizabeth O'Ladhain Head of Computers

Education

Galway & Mayo Institute of Technology
Castlebar
West Port Road
Castlebar Co. Mayo
Phone: 094-25700 Fax: 094-25757
Email: info@gmit.ie
Web: http://www.gmit.ie
SIC: 80220 Employees: 100
Further Education
Mr Richard Thorn Head of Centre
Mr Jim Fennell Financial Controller
Ms Ann Donnelly Personnel Manager
Mr Gerry Agnew Computer Manager

Galway City VEC
Island House
Cathedral Square
Galway Co. Galway
Phone: 091-562292 Fax: 091-562358
Email: info@cgvec.ie
Web: http://www.cgvec.ie
SIC: 80220 Employees: 185
Further Education/VEC
Mr Pat Ryan Chief Executive Officer
Mr John McNamara Financial Administrator
Mr John McNamara Administrative Officer

Good Counsel College
New Ross Co. Wexford
Phone: 051-421182 Fax: 051-421909
Email: jhennebry.ias@eircom.net
SIC: 80220 Employees: 69
College
Fr John Hennebry Principal

Hewitt College
Thompson House
MacCurtain Street
Cork Co. Cork
Phone: 021-4550430 Fax: 021-4550431
SIC: 80220 Employees: 30
College
Ms Ethna Cronin Secretary

Institute Of Education (6th Form)
82-85 Lower Leeson Street
Dublin 2
Phone: 01-6613511 Fax: 01-6619050
Email: info@ioe.ie
Web: http://www.portobello.ie
SIC: 80220 Employees: 75
Educational Institute
Mr Raymond Kearns Director
Mr Peter Kearns IT Manager

Institute of Technology Carlow
Kilkenny Road
Carlow Co. Carlow
Phone: 0503-70400 Fax: 0503-70500
Email: info@itcarlow.ie
Web: http://www.itcarlow.ie
SIC: 80220 Employees: 300
Further Education/VEC
Mr John Gallagher Director
Ms Mary Jordan Administration Officer
Mr Jim McEntee Industrial Liaison Officer
Mr Mike Baker Head of Computers

Institute of Technology Galway - Mayo
Dublin Road
Galway Co. Galway
Phone: 091-753161 Fax: 091-751107
Web: http://www.gmit.ie
SIC: 80220 Employees: 650
Further Education
Mr Larry Elwood Head of Business
Ms Marion Coy Business Studies

Institute of Technology Letterkenny
Port Road
Letterkenny Co. Donegal
Phone: 074-64100 Fax: 074-64111
Web: http://www.lyit.ie
SIC: 80220 Employees: 300
Further Education
Mr Paul Hannigan Director
Mr Vincent Murphy Computer Science

Institute of Technology Limerick
Moylish Park
Limerick Co. Limerick
Phone: 061-208208 Fax: 061-208209
Email: information@lit.ie
Web: http://www.lit.ie
SIC: 80220 Employees: 430
Further Education
Mr James MacDonagh Director
Mr Jimmy Brown Finance Officer

Institute of Technology Tallaght
Tallaght
Dublin 24
Phone: 01-4042000 Fax: 01-4042700
Email: queries@it-tallaght.ie
Web: http://www.it-tallaght.ie
SIC: 80220 Employees: 280
Further Education
Dr Colum Collins Director
Mr Paul Caffrey Financial Controller
Mr Michael Quinlan Personnel Manager
Mr Damien Roche Business Manager
Mr Brian Looney Computer Manager

Irish Management Institute
National Management Centre
Sandyford Road, Sandyford
Dublin 18
Phone: 01-2078400 Fax: 01-2955150
Email: reception@imi.ie
Web: http://www.imi.ie
SIC: 80220 Employees: 74
Further Education
Mr Barry Kenny Chairman
Mr Tim McCormick Economics Manager
Mr Gus Liston IT Manager

Jobstown Community College
Jobstown
Tallaght
Dublin 24
Phone: 01-4525788 Fax: 01-4525712
Email: jobstowncc@eircom.net
SIC: 80220 Employees: 59
Secondary College
Mr Ronan Connolly Principal
Mr Stan Love Head of Computers

Kildare VEC
Limerick Road
Naas Co. Kildare
Phone: 045-897358 Fax: 045-879916
SIC: 80220 Employees: 879
Further Education/VEC
Mr Colm O'Ceannabhain Chief Executive Officer
Ms Patricia Dunning Assistant Staff Officer
Mr Michael Malone Lecturer

Kilkenny VEC
Butler Court
Patrick Street
Kilkenny Co. Kilkenny
Phone: 056-70966 Fax: 056-65281
Email: cbarron.ias@tinet.ie
SIC: 80220 Employees: 23
Further Education/VEC
Mr Roger Curran Chief Executive Officer
Ms Patricia Burke Senior Staff Officer

Kylemore College
Kylemore Road
Ballyfermot
Dublin 10
Phone: 01-6265901 Fax: 01-6234780
Email: info@kylemore.cdvec.ie
Web: http://www.kylemore.cdvec.ie
SIC: 80220 Employees: 51
Senior College
Mr Declan MacDaid Principal
Ms Deirdre Nolan Vice Principal
Ms Brid Canavan Computer Teacher

Laois VEC
Ridge Road
Portlaoise Co. Laois
Phone: 0502-21352 Fax: 0502-21877
Email: laoisvec@eircom.net
SIC: 80220 Employees: 160
Admission Offices For VEC
Mr Ronan Rice Chief Executive Officer
Ms Janet Molloy Accounts Manager
Ms Margaret Corcoran Senior Staff Officer

Leitrim VEC
St Georges Terrace
Carrick On Shannon Co. Leitrim
Phone: 078-20024 Fax: 078-21362
SIC: 80220 Employees: 140
Vocational Education Committee
Mr John Blunnie Chief Executive Officer
Mr Robert McNabb Senior Staff Officer

Limerick County VEC
Lower Mallow Street
Limerick Co. Limerick
Phone: 061-314612 Fax: 061-414671
Email: colvec@tinet.ie
SIC: 80220 Employees: 24
Further Education/VEC
Mr Sean Burke Chief Executive Officer
Ms Anne Kelly Senior Staff Officer

Louth VEC
Chapel Street
Dundalk Co. Louth
Phone: 042-9334047 Fax: 042-9339412
Email: colouthvec@tinet.ie
SIC: 80220 Employees: 400
VEC
Dr Peter Connolly Chief Executive Officer
Mr Cathal Byrne Administrative Officer
Ms Mary Sloane Manager

Meath VEC
Old Vocational School
Abbey Road
Navan Co. Meath
Phone: 046-21447 Fax: 046-29821
Email: meath.vec@edunet.ie
Web: http://www.edunet.ie
SIC: 80220 Employees: 300
Further Education/VEC
Mr Peter Kierans Chief Executive Officer
Ms Marie Heaney Accounts Manager
Ms Anne Keane Personnel Manager
Ms Joan Regan Computer Manager

National College of Art & Design
100 Thomas Street
Dublin 8
Phone: 01-6364200 Fax: 01-6364207
Email: info@ncad.ie
Web: http://www.ncad.ie
SIC: 80220 Employees: 100
Further Education/VEC
Prof Noel Sheridan Director
Mr Ken Langan Registrar
Mr Mark Lawless Head of Business
Mr Kevin Atherton Media Manager

National College of Ireland
PO Box 8316
IFSC Mayor Street
Dublin 1
Phone: 01-4060500 Fax: 01-4972200
Email: info@ncirl.ie
Web: http://www.ncirl.ie
SIC: 80220 Employees: 85
College
Ms Joyce O'Connor President
Mr John McGarrigle Registrar
Mr Dennis O'Brien Governing Body
Mr Padraig McDonagh Director of Marketing & Commun

Networking Dublin 15
Buzzardstown House
Buzzardstown Lane, Mulhuddart
Dublin 15
Phone: 01-8200759 Fax: 01-8200310
SIC: 80220 Employees: 25
Computer Training
Ms Bernie Calley Manager

Our Lady's Bower
Retreat Road
Athlone Co. Westmeath
Phone: 0902-74777 Fax: 0902-74853
Email: bower@iol.ie
SIC: 80220 Employees: 100
Secondary School
Sr Denise O'Brien Principal
Ms Anne-Marie Lough School Secretary
Mr Roderick O'Duinnin IT Co-ordinator

Portobello College Dublin
South Richmond Street
Dublin 2
Phone: 01-4755811 Fax: 01-4755817
Email: admin@portobello.ie
Web: http://www.portbello.ie
SIC: 80220 Employees: 70
Further Education/VEC
Mr Raymond Kearns President
Ms Nina Carthy Economics
Ms Frances Baker Administrator
Mr Rory O'Donnell Head of IT

Roscommon VEC
Lanesboro Street
Roscommon Co. Roscommon
Phone: 0903-26151 Fax: 0903-26537
SIC: 80220 Employees: 70
Vocational Education Committee
Mr Larry O'Farrelly Chief Executive Officer
Ms Marian Conway Clerical Officer
Ms Dolores Flynn Senior Staff Officer

Saint Columba's College
Stranorlar
Lifford Co. Donegal
Phone: 074-31246 Fax: 074-32528
SIC: 80220 Employees: 70
Secondary College
Mr Gerard Bennett Principal
Ms Bernie Rowan Secretary
Mr Micheal O'Boyle Vice Principal
Mr Jimmy Phair Computer Teacher

Sallynoggin College of Further Education
Pearse Street
Sallynoggin
Dun Laoghaire Co. Dublin
Phone: 01-2852985 Fax: 01-2848437
Email: reception@scs.dife.ie
Web: http://www.scs.dife.ie
SIC: 80220 Employees: 40
Further Education College
Mr Fred Meaney Principal

Senior College
Elbana Avenue
Dun Laoghaire Co. Dublin
Phone: 01-2800385 Fax: 01-2800386
Email: info@scd.ie
Web: http://www.scd.ie
SIC: 80220 Employees: 30
Vocational School
Mr Jack Griffin Principal
Mr Barry O'Callaghan Vice Principal
Ms Breda Billis Public Relations Officer

Skerrys College
9-11 Wellington House
Patricks Hill
Cork Co. Cork
Phone: 021-4507027 Fax: 021-4507659
Email: info@skerrys.ie
Web: http://www.skerrys.ie
SIC: 80220 Employees: 35
Business College
Ms Audrey McCarthy President
Ms Noreen O'Keeffe Administration Manager
Mr Gerard O'Donovan Head of Computers

Sligo County VEC
Riverside
Sligo Co. Sligo
Phone: 071-61511 Fax: 071-43093
Email: sligovec@iol.ie
SIC: 80220 Employees: 90
Vocational Education Committee
Mr Loman Conway Chief Executive Officer
Mr Martin Farrell Senior Staff Officer
Mr Martin Farrell Sales Manager

Sligo VEC
Quay Street
Sligo Co. Sligo
Phone: 071-42438 Fax: 071-44121
Email: sligovec@eircom.net
SIC: 80220 Employees: 34
Further Education/VEC
Mr James Sproule Chief Executive Officer
Mr Jack Lynch Finance Manager

St Angela's College
Loughgill
Sligo Co. Sligo
Phone: 071-41406 Fax: 071-44585
SIC: 80220 Employees: 40
College of Home Economics
Sr Maryanne O'Connor President

St Moges College
Bawboy
Cavan Co. Cavan
Phone: 049-9523156 Fax: 049-9523156
SIC: 80220 Employees: 30
College
Mr Aidan Rudden Manager

Summerhill College
Sligo Co. Sligo
Phone: 071-60311 Fax: 071 62048
Email: shc@iol.ie
SIC: 80220 Employees: 60
College
Mr Michael Murphy Headmaster
Mrs Marie Ward Secretary
Mr Michael Kilcoyne Vice Principal
Mr David Harding IT Co-ordinator

Tipperary (SR) VEC
The Mall
Clonmel Co. Tipperary
Phone: 052-23067 Fax: 052-25951
SIC: 80220 Employees: 400
Admissions Office for VEC
Mr Pat Mooney Chief Executive Officer
Mr Pat Hegarty Senior Staff Officer

Tralee Institute of Technology
Clash
Tralee Co. Kerry
Phone: 066-7145600 Fax: 066-7125711
Email: postmaster@ittralee.ie
Web: http://www.ittralee.ie
SIC: 80220 Employees: 375
Further Education College
Dr Sean McBride Director
Mr Donal Fitzgibbon Financial Controller
Mr Paul O'Dea Personnel Officer
Ms Deirdre Lillis Computer Manager

Tralee VEC
Main Street
Tralee Co. Kerry
Phone: 066-7121488 Fax: 066-7121531
Email: info@cokerryed.ie
Web: http://www.cokerryed.ie
SIC: 80220 Employees: 27
Further Education / VEC
Dr Barney O'Reilly Chief Executive Officer
Ms Brigid Fitzmaurice Administrator

University of Dublin Trinity College
Dublin 2
Phone: 01-6687988 Fax: 01-6772694
Web: http://www.tcd.ie
SIC: 80220 Employees: 1950
Further Education
Mr John Murray Business Manager
Mr Antoin Murphy Economics

University Of Limerick
Limerick Co. Limerick
Phone: 061-202700 Fax: 061-330316
Web: http://www.ul.ie
SIC: 80220 Employees: 200
Schools & Colleges - Third level (Universities)
Prof Noel Whelan Vice President
Mr Donal Dineen Head Department of Economic
Mr Donncha O'Maidin Head of CSI

Waterford City Vocational Education
30 The Mall
Waterford Co. Waterford
Phone: 051-874007 Fax: 051-872822
SIC: 80220 Employees: 100
Further Education & Vocational Education
Mr Kieran Lyons Chief Executive Officer
Mr Pat Purcell Finance Manager
Mr Paul Walsh Head of Computers

Waterford Institute of Technology
Cork Road
Waterford Co. Waterford
Phone: 051-302000 Fax: 051-378292
Email: info@wit.ie
Web: http://www.wit.ie
SIC: 80220 Employees: 600
Institute of Technology
Dr Martin Venie Acting Principal
Mr Tony McFeely Financial Controller
Mr Aidan McGrath Computer Services Manager

Westmeath VEC
Bridge House
Bellevue Road
Mullingar Co. Westmeath
Phone: 044-48389 Fax: 044-43533
SIC: 80220 Employees: 400
Further Education/VEC
Mr Gearoid O'Bradaigh Chief Executive Officer
Mr William Reynolds Finance Manager
Ms Marie Brazil Marketing Manager

Wexford County VEC
St Iberius House
Common Quay Street
Wexford Co. Wexford
Phone: 053-23896 Fax: 053-24109
SIC: 80220 Employees: 23
Further Education/VEC
Mr James Dunne Chief Executive Officer
Mr Michael Long Senior Staff Officer

Education

Ballyhaise Agricultural College
Ballyhaise
Cavan Co. Cavan
Phone: 049-4338108 Fax: 049-4338540
Email: college@ballyhaise.teagasc.ie
Web: http://www.ballyhaise.teagasc.ie
SIC: 80301 Employees: 30
Agricultural College
Mr Felix McCabe Principal

Gurteen Agricultural College
Ballingarry
Roscrea Co. Tipperary
Phone: 067-21282 Fax: 067-21290
Email: info@gurteencollege.ie
Web: http://www.gurteencollege.ie
SIC: 80301 Employees: 30
Agricultural College
Mr Mike Pearson Principal

Kildalton College (Teagasc)
Piltown
Carrick On Suir Co. Tipperary
Phone: 051-643105 Fax: 051-643797
Email: reception@killdalton.teagasc.ie
SIC: 80301 Employees: 80
Agricultural College
Mr Micheal Connlen Managing Director

Teagasc
19 Sandymount Avenue
Ballsbridge
Dublin 4
Phone: 01-6376000 Fax: 01-6688023
Email: reception@hq.teagasc.ie
Web: http://www.teagasc.ie
SIC: 80301 Employees: 1500
Agriculture & Food Development Authority
Dr Liam Downey Director
Mr Denis Bates Finance Manager
Mr Bill Barry Personnel Manager
Mr Michael Miley Public Relations Manager

Biotechnology Centre
University College Dublin
Belfield
Dublin 4
Phone: 01-7062264 Fax: 01-2692016
SIC: 80302 Employees: 28
University
Prof Eamonn Duke Head of Department

Centre for Soft Condensed Matter
Faculty of Science
UCD Belfield
Dublin 4
Phone: 01-7062355 Fax: 01-7062127
Email: science@ucd.ie
Web: http://www.ucd.ie
SIC: 80302 Employees: 160
University
Prof Michael Kennedy Dean of Science

Department of Computer Science
O'Reilly Institute
Trinity College
Dublin 2
Phone: 01-6081033 Fax: 01-6772204
SIC: 80302 Employees: 132
University
Prof John Byrne Head of Department

Dublin City University
Innovation & Business Relations Dept
Dublin City University
Dublin 9
Phone: 01-7005000 Fax: 01-7045505
SIC: 80302 Employees: 2000
University
Dr Tony Glynn Head Of Department
Mr Alan Smeaton Head of Computer Science

Faculty of Food Science
National Food Biotechnology Centre
University College
Cork Co. Cork
Phone: 021-4273803 Fax: 021-4276318
Email: nfbc@ucc.ie
Web: http://www.ucc.ie
SIC: 80302 Employees: 70
Food Biotechnology Centre
Prof Gerald Fitzgerald Head of Food Science
Ms Mary Hough Administration Manager

IS Services
Trinity College
Dublin 2
Phone: 01-6081762 Fax: 01-6711181
Email: info@tcd.ie
Web: http://www.tcd.ie
SIC: 80302 Employees: 60
University
Mr Michael Nolan Director
Ms Grace Dempsey Head of Finance
Mr Brian Thornburgh Personnel Manager
Mr John Murphy Computer Systems Manager

Mater Dei Institute of Education
Clonliffe Road
Dublin 3
Phone: 01-8376027 Fax: 01-8370776
Email: info@materdei.ie
Web: http://www.materdei.ie
SIC: 80302 Employees: 30
University Faculty
Fr Dermot Lane President
Ms Mary Roche Bursar
Mr Colm Sharkey Business Manager
Mr Andrew McGrady Education Department

Michael Smurfit School of Business
UCD
Carysfort Avenue
Blackrock Co. Dublin
Phone: 01-7068934 Fax: 01-2831911
Web: http://www.ucd.ie/jsb
SIC: 80302 Employees: 40
University
Ms Mary Lambkin Dean
Ms Niamh Boyle Director of Marketing

Milltown Institute of Theology & Philosophy
Milltown Park, Sanford Road
Ranelagh
Dublin 6
Phone: 01-2698388 Fax: 01-2692528
Email: info@milltown-institute.ie
Web: http://www.milltown-institute.ie
SIC: 80302 Employees: 70
Third Level College
Rev Brian Grogan President
Ms Amanda Corrigan Head of Computers

National University of Ireland (Galway)
University Road
Galway Co. Galway
Phone: 091-524411 Fax: 091-525700
Web: http://www.nuigalway.ie
SIC: 80302 Employees: 1150
University
Mr Iognaid O'Muircheartigh President
Ms Mary Dooley Bursar
Mr Chris McNairney Human Resources Director

The Chemistry Department
N U I
Galway Co. Galway
Phone: 091-750315 Fax: 091-525700
SIC: 80302 Employees: 40
Chemistry
Prof Butler

Trinity College Computer Laboratory
Trinity College
Dublin 2
Phone: 01-6772941 Fax: 01-6772694
Email: info@tcd.ie
Web: http://www.tcd.ie
SIC: 80302 Employees: 400
Computer Department of University
Mr John Heggarty Chief Executive
Ms Grace Dempsey Financial Controller
Ms Patricia Daly Establishment Officer
Mr Mike Nolan Director of IT Services

National Training & Development Institute
Roslyn Park, Beech Road
Sandymount
Dublin 4
Phone: 01-2057200 Fax: 01-2057211
Web: http://www.rehab.ie
SIC: 80400 Employees: 600
Job Training
Mr Frank Flannery Chief Executive
Mr Tim Walsh Finance Manager
Ms Dorothy Gunne Personnel Director
Ms Aisling Balbirnie Head Of Marketing
Mr Gary Merrigan IT Manager

Paul Partnership
Unit 25 Tait Business Centre
Dominic Street
Limerick Co. Limerick
Phone: 061-419388 Fax: 061-418098
Email: info@paulpartnership.ie
SIC: 80400 Employees: 50
Local Development Partnership
Ms Anne Kavanagh Manager
Mr Declan Maher Financial Administrator

St Andrews Resource Centre
114-116 Pearse Street
Dublin 2
Phone: 01-6771589 Fax: 01-6715734
Email: stand@connect.ie
SIC: 80400 Employees: 200
Training Centre / Community Resource Centre
Mr John Fitzsimmons Administrator
Ms Eileen Ryan Finance Manager
Ms Elaine Boland Supervisor

Irish School of Motoring
96 Ranelagh Road
Ranelagh
Dublin 6
Phone: 01-2805690 Fax: 01-4972646
SIC: 80410 Employees: 80
Driving Schools
Mr Pat Walsh Manager

Assidian
17 Carysfort Avenue
Blackrock Co. Dublin
Phone: 01-2787111 Fax: 01-2787136
Email: info@assidian.com
SIC: 80421 Employees: 25
On Line Training for Telecoms
Mr Enda O'Doherty Managing Director
Mr Donald Hickey Personnel Manager
Mr Rupert Bowen Sales Manager

CATT-Centre For Advanced Technology Training
Fitzwilliam Court
Leeson Close
Dublin 2
Phone: 01-2162800 Fax: 01-2162077
Email: catt.dublin@siemens.ie
Web: http://www.catt.ie
SIC: 80421 Employees: 30
Computer Training
Ms Deirdre Duignan
Ms Suzanne Brierty Sales Manager

Education

CERT
Amiens Street
Dublin 1
Phone: 01-8847700 Fax: 01-8556821
Email: info@cert.ie
Web: http://www.cert.ie
SIC: 80421 Employees: 180
Training Hotel Skills
Mr Shaun Quinn Chief Executive
Mr Jack Hickey Accounts Manager
Ms Mary White Personnel Manager
Mr Simon Fullam Press/Information Officer
Mr Kevin Moriarty Specialist Services Manager

Clondalkin Job Initiative
Unit 3 Oakfield Industrial Estate
Clondalkin
Dublin 22
Phone: 01-4030847 Fax: 01-4579522
SIC: 80421 Employees: 71
Training & Employment Agency
Mr Ken Clarke Co-Ordinator

Computer Network Institute/CNI/CATT
Leeson Close
Fitzwilliam Court
Dublin 2
Phone: 01-2162816 Fax: 01-2162077
Email: catt.dublin@siemens.ie
Web: http://www.catt.ie
SIC: 80421 Employees: 50
Computer Training
Mr Derek Wilson General Manager
Ms Renne Synott Sales Manager

Conhairle
44 North Great Georges Street
Dublin 1
Phone: 01-8747503 Fax: 01-8747490
SIC: 80421 Employees: 30
Provide Services for People With Disabilities
Ms Josette Cuthbert Regional Manager

Flexible Learning Ireland
Nicholas House
Cove Street
Cork Co. Cork
Phone: 021-4317435 Fax: 021-4313936
Email: administration@flexiblelearning.ie
Web: http://www.flexiblelearning.ie
SIC: 80421 Employees: 40
Flexible Learning
Mr Connor O'Brien Managing Director
Ms Hilary Madden Accounts Manager

Internet Certification Institute
Mary Ross Centre
Holland Road
Limerick Co. Limerick
Phone: 061-333300 Fax: 061-333301
Web: http://www.prosofttraining.com
SIC: 80421 Employees: 100
Internet Training
Mr John McNamara Director

Irish Social Firms Initiative
Parnell Business Centre
10a Parnell Square
Dublin 1
Phone: 01-8746911 Fax: 01-8735066
Email: isfi@iol.ie
SIC: 80421 Employees: 38
Training Services
Mr Mick Coughlan Director
Ms Geraldine Carroll Training Officer

Liberty Risk Services
46 Airways Industrial Estate
Santry
Dublin 9
Phone: 01-8424161 Fax: 01-8424461
Email: enq@nifast.ie
SIC: 80421 Employees: 30
Employee Training
Mr Clive Carroll Managing Director

Macra na Feirme
Irish Farm Centre
Bluebell
Dublin 12
Phone: 01-4508000 Fax: 01-4514908
Email: macra@macra.ie
Web: http://www.indigo.ie/~macra
SIC: 80421 Employees: 30
Rural Training/Education
Mr T J Maher President
Mr Mark Fagan Accounts Manager
Mr Terry Cooke Administration Manager
Mr Damian McDonald Chief Executive

Moorehaven Centre (Tipperary) Ltd
O'Brien Street
Tipperary Co. Tipperary
Phone: 062-52437 Fax: 062-33566
Email: moorehavenblk@eircom.net
SIC: 80421 Employees: 30
Training Centre & Sheltered Workshop
Ms Marie Blake Manager

Prime Learning Group
Lonsdale Road
National Technology Park
Limerick Co. Limerick
Phone: 061-720000 Fax: 061-720001
Email: info@primelearning.com
Web: http://www.primelearning.com
SIC: 80421 Employees: 60
On Line Learning Company
Mr Terry O'Brien Chief Executive Officer
Mr Ronan McMahon Finance Manager
Mr Kevin Bolger IT Manager

Roslyn Park College
Beach Road
Sandymount
Dublin 4
Phone: 01-2057205 Fax: 01-2057217
SIC: 80421 Employees: 48
Training & Development Company
Ms Dorothy O'Leary Chief Executive
Mr Frank Kennedy Finance Manager
Mr Ken O'Brien Personnel Manager
Mr Frank Sweeney Marketing Director

Trade Development Institute of Ireland Ltd
Ferryhouse
48 Lower Mount Street
Dublin 2
Phone: 01-6611903 Fax: 01-6614991
Email: tdi@tdigroup.ie
Web: http://www.tdigroup.ie
SIC: 80421 Employees: 170
International Consultants & Training
Mr Michael Boyd Managing Director
Mr John Tobin Financial Controller
Ms Gillian Davidson Personnel Manager
Ms Paula Dawson IT Manager

Ulster Bank Training & Development
Group Centre
Georges Quay
Dublin 2
Phone: 01-6084000 Fax: 01-6084888
Web: http://www.ulsterbank.com
SIC: 80421 Employees: 1000
Learning & Development
Mr Paddy McMahon Chief Executive
Mr Don Williams Head of Finance & Central Serv
Ms Nicola Kearney Human Resources Manager
Mr Colum Lyons Head of Central IT

Alliance Francaise
1 Kildare Street
Dublin 2
Phone: 01-6761732 Fax: 01-6764077
Email: info@alliance-francaise.ie
Web: http://www.alliance-francaise.ie
SIC: 80422 Employees: 38
French Language/Culture Promotion
Mr Francois Chambroud Director
Ms Elizabeth Gilligan Administrator

Language Centre Of Ireland (L.C.I.)
45 Kildare Street
Dublin 2
Phone: 01-6716266 Fax: 01-6716430
Email: info@lci.ie
Web: http://www.lci.ie
SIC: 80422 Employees: 67
Language Training
Mr Tom Doyle Managing Director
Ms Siobhan Moore Financial Controller
Ms Katie Jennings Computer Manager

Sundai Ireland International
Curragh Grange Green Road
Curragh
Kildare Co. Kildare
Phone: 045-441888 Fax: 045-441306
SIC: 80422 Employees: 25
Japanese School
Mr Hugh Graham General Manager

American College Dublin
2-3 Merrion Square
Dublin 2
Phone: 01-6768939 Fax: 01-6768941
Email: degree@amcd.ie
Web: http://www.amcd.ie
SIC: 80429 Employees: 97
Private 3rd Level College
Dr Donald Ross President
Ms Bridget O'Connor Dean of Administration
Mr Graham Glanville IT Manager

An Grianan Adult Education College
An Grianan
Termonfeckin
Drogheda Co. Louth
Phone: 041-9822119 Fax: 041-9822690
SIC: 80429 Employees: 30
Adult Education & self catering cottages
Ms Anne Flanagan Manager

Athlone Education Center
Moydrum Road
Athlone Co. Westmeath
Phone: 0902-76500 Fax: 0902-76500
SIC: 80429 Employees: 30
Education Centre
Ms G Murphy Director

City of Limerick VEC
Presentation Court
Sexton Street
Limerick Co. Limerick
Phone: 061-400333 Fax: 061-418248
Email: adulted@clvec.iol.ie
Web: http://www.lvec.org
SIC: 80429 Employees: 200
Adult Education
Ms Mary Hamilton Adult Education Officer
Ms Maura Roach Computer Manager

College of Music
Chatham Row
Dublin 2
Phone: 01-6778820 Fax: 01-6778404
SIC: 80429 Employees: 34
Education (Other)
Dr Ita Beausang Principal
Mr Ed Delaney Bursar

Cork VEC
Floor 9 County Hall
Cork Co. Cork
Phone: 021-4285465 Fax: 021-4273465
SIC: 80429 Employees: 1000
Education
Mr Barra O'Brien Chief Executive Officer

Crawford College of Art & Design
Sharman Crawford Street
Cork Co. Cork
Phone: 021-4966777 Fax: 021-4962267
Email: gsscott@cit.ie
Web: http://www.cit.ie
SIC: 80429 Employees: 23
Education (Other)
Mr Geoff Steiner-Scott Principal

Curriculum Development Unit
Sundrive Road
Crumlin
Dublin 12
Phone: 01-4535487 Fax: 01-4537659
Email: info@cdu.cdvec.ie
Web: http://www.cdu.cdvec.ie
SIC: 80429 Employees: 40
Education Development
Mr Aidan Clifford Deputy Director
Ms Alisia Prado Finance Manager
Ms Clodagh Kennedy Personnel Manager

Dun Laoghaire VEC
Pearse Street
Sallynoggin
Dun Laoghaire Co. Dublin
Phone: 01-2850666 Fax: 01-2850920
Email: dunlaoghaireguiry@drvec.ie
Web: http://www.drvec.ie
SIC: 80429 Employees: 500
Education Authority
Mr John Ryan

Institiuid Teangeolaiochta Eireann
31 Plas Mhic Liam
Dublin 2
Phone: 01-6765489 Fax: 01-6610004
Email: ite@ite.ie
Web: http://www.ite.ie
SIC: 80429 Employees: 30
Education Research
Mr Owen MacEogain Director
Ms Maire Seoighthe Secretary
Mr Donnagh O'Croinin IT Manager

Institute of Public Administration
57-61 Lansdowne Road
Dublin 4
Phone: 01-2403600 Fax: 01-6689138
Email: sales@ipa.ie
Web: http://www.ipa.ie
SIC: 80429 Employees: 120
Educational Courses/Training/Research/Publishing
Mr Patrick Hall Director General
Mr Cyril Sullivan Finance Manager
Ms Mary Rose Tobin Personnel Manager
Mr Tony McNamara Marketing Manager

Irish School of Ecumenics
Bea House
Milltown Park
Dublin 6
Phone: 01-2601144 Fax: 01-2601158
Email: ise@iol.ie
Web: http://www.teo.ie/ise
SIC: 80429 Employees: 30
Educational Institution
Rev Kenneth Kearn Director
Mr Pat Carroll Development Manager
Ms Alison Woods Administration

Leinster School of Music
GCD, South Circular Road
Dublin 8
Phone: 01-4751532 Fax: 01-4549265
Email: leinster.school@gcd.ie
Web: http://www.gcd.ie
SIC: 80429 Employees: 30
Music School
Ms Sheila Murphy Manager
Mr Gary Deaton Computer Manager

Marino Institute of Education
Griffith Avenue
Dublin 9
Phone: 01-8057700 Fax: 01-8335290
Email: info@mie.ie
Web: http://www.mie.ie
SIC: 80429 Employees: 50
Primary Teacher Training
Br Donal Leader Director
Mr Mark O'Donnell Finance Manager
Ms Sile Boylan Facilities Manager
Br Rory Geoghegan Head of IT

Mayo VEC
Newtown
Castlebar Co. Mayo
Phone: 094-24188 Fax: 094-24187
Email: vec@tinet.ie
SIC: 80429 Employees: 245
Education (Other)
Mr Joseph Langan Chief Executive Officer
Ms Marion McHale Accounts Officer
Mr Pat Leyden Administrative Officer

Royal College of Physicians of Ireland
6 Kildare Street
Dublin 2
Phone: 01-6616677 Fax: 01-6763989
Email: information@rcpi.ie
Web: http://www.rcpi.ie
SIC: 80429 Employees: 42
Medical Association
Mr Jonathan W Bailey Chief Executive Officer

Royal Irish Academy of Music
36 Westland Row
Dublin 2
Phone: 01-6764412 Fax: 01-6622798
Email: riam@indigo.ie
Web: http://www.riam.ie
SIC: 80429 Employees: 100
Music Academy
Dr John O'Connor Director
Mr Tony Maddigan Registrar
Ms Clare O'Callaghan Assistant Staff Officer

School of Cosmic Physics
(Geophysics & Astrophysics Depts)
5 Merrion Square
Dublin 2
Phone: 01-6621333 Fax: 01-6621477
Email: postmaster@cp.dias.ie
Web: http://www.cp.dias.ie
SIC: 80429 Employees: 50
School of Cosmic Physics
Mr Brian Jacob Geophysics Professor
Mr Luke Drury Astrophysics Professor
Mr John Walsh Experimental Officer

Sonairte
The National Ecology Centre
Laytown
Drogheda Co. Louth
Phone: 041-9827572 Fax: 041-9828130
Email: sonairte@drogheda.edunet.ie
Web: http://www.drogheda.ie
SIC: 80429 Employees: 54
Education Visitor Centre
Mr Sean McCabe Chief Executive

Waltons New School of Music
69 South Great Georges Street
Dublin 2
Phone: 01-4781884 Fax: 01-4751346
Email: waltons@indigo.ie
SIC: 80429 Employees: 55
Music School
Mr John Mardirosian Director

Health & Social Work

85 Health & Social Work
85111 Hospitals (Public Sector)
85112 Hospitals (Private)
85113 Nursing Homes
85116 Hospitals (Geriatric)
85117 Hospitals (Mental)
85118 NHS Trusts
85119 Childminders/Day Nurseries
85121 Health Centres/Clinics
85122 Medical Institutions (Other)
85123 Day Care Centres
85124 Doctors (GP)
85130 Dentists
85141 Opticians
85142 Chiropodists
85143 Nurses/Midwives
85144 Physiotherapists
85145 Psychologists
85149 Other Human Health Activities
85200 Veterinary Surgeons
85201 Veterinary Clinics
85313 Care Homes (Childrens)
85314 Care Homes (Hostel/Shelter/Residential)
85320 Social Welfare
85321 Charities
85322 Citizens Advice Bureau

The National Children's Hospital
Tallaght
Dublin 24
Phone: 01-4142000 Fax: 01-4142896
Email: info@amnch.ie
Web: http://www.amnch.ie
SIC: 85111 Employees: 2150
Hospital
Mr Michael Lyons Chief Executive Officer
Mr Gerry Lynch Finance Manager
Ms Mairead Shields Human Resources Director
Mr Brendan Carr IT Director

Athlone District Hospital (St Vincents)
North Gate Street
Athlone Co. Westmeath
Phone: 0902-75301 Fax: 0902-83154
SIC: 85111 Employees: 100
General Hospital
Mr Joe Martin Hospital Administrator

Aut Even Hospital
Freshford Road
Kilkenny Co. Kilkenny
Phone: 056-75275 Fax: 056-62149
Web: http://www.auteven.org
SIC: 85111 Employees: 110
Private Hospital
Sr Anna Corcoran Head of Administration
Ms Bridget Kirwan Personnel Manager
Mr Gerard McMorrow Hospital Manager
Ms Margaret Lennon IT Manager

Beaumont Hospital
Beaumont Road
Dublin 9
Phone: 01-8377755 Fax: 01-8376982
Email: beaumont@iol.ie
Web: http://www.iol.ie/~beaumont/
SIC: 85111 Employees: 2350
General Hospital
Mr Pat Lyons Chief Executive
Ms Evelyn Hempenstall Financial Controller
Ms Francis Milner Acting Personnel Officer
Mr Tony Kenny Computer Manager

Health & Social

Bon Secours Hospital
Glasnevin
Dublin 9
Phone: 01-8367101 Fax: 01-8375896
Email: info@bonsecours.iol.ie
Web: http://www.bonsecours.iol.ie
SIC: 85111 Employees: 300
Private Hospital
Mr Gareth Jones Chief Executive Officer
Ms Mary Stenson Accountant
Ms Sheila O'Leary Personnel Manager
Sr Mary Gleeson IT Manager

Cappagh National Orthopaedic Hospital
Cappagh
Finglas
Dublin 11
Phone: 01-8341211 Fax: 01-8140327
Email: capmaine@eircom.net
Web: http://www.cappagh.ie
SIC: 85111 Employees: 315
Orthopaedic Hospital
Mr Aidan Gleeson Manager/Secretary
Mr Danny Dunne Finance Manager
Ms Emer Agnew Personnel Officer

Carlow Hospital
Sacred Heart
Carlow Co. Carlow
Phone: 0503-30054 Fax: 0503-36461
SIC: 85111 Employees: 98
Hospitals
Ms Mary O'Hanlon Administrator

Castlecomer District Hospital
Castlecomer
Kilkenny Co. Kilkenny
Phone: 056-41246 Fax: 056-41927
SIC: 85111 Employees: 29
District Hospital
Ms Geraldine Phelan Matron
Ms Tammy Philips Clerical Officer
Ms Maureen Lawlor Sales & Marketing Manager

Cherry Orchard Hospital
Cherry Orchard
Ballyfermot
Dublin 10
Phone: 01-6264702 Fax: 01-6265864
SIC: 85111 Employees: 290
Hospitals
Ms Cora Bolger Hospital Manager

Children's Hospital
Temple Street
Dublin 1
Phone: 01-8748763 Fax: 01-8748355
SIC: 85111 Employees: 700
Children's Hospital
Mr Paul Cunniffe Secretary/Manager
Mr John Kennedy Accountant
Ms Mona Baker Personnel Manager
Ms Helen Cosgrave Development Officer

Clane General Hospital
Prosperous Road
Clane
Naas Co. Kildare
Phone: 045-868004 Fax: 045-868814
SIC: 85111 Employees: 55
General Hospital
Mr Sean Leyden Chief Executive
Ms Gladys Leyden Matron

Community Hospital
Skibbereen Co. Cork
Phone: 028-21677 Fax: 028-22583
SIC: 85111 Employees: 50
General Hospital
Ms Patricia O'Mahony Matron

Cork Sisters Of Mercy
Grenville Place
Cork Co. Cork
Phone: 021-4271971 Fax: 021-4276341
Email: mercy@mercy-hosp-cork.ie
Web: http://www.mercy-hosp-cork.ie
SIC: 85111 Employees: 1000
Hospitals
Mr John A Murphy Secretary/Manager
Mr John O'Shea Human Resources Director

Dungloe Hospital
Dungloe
Letterkenny Co. Donegal
Phone: 075-21044 Fax: 075-21687
SIC: 85111 Employees: 77
Hospital
Sr Ann Brady Matron

Ely Hospital
Ferrybank
Wexford Co. Wexford
Phone: 053-23433 Fax: 053-23638
SIC: 85111 Employees: 60
Hospital
Sr Joan Berney Acting Matron
Ms Breda O'Reilly Accounts Manager

Ennis General Hospital
Ennis Co. Clare
Phone: 065-6824464 Fax: 065-6820476
SIC: 85111 Employees: 250
Hospital
Ms Geraldine Crowe Acting Hospital Administrator
Ms Maria Fox Accounts Manager

Erinville Hospital
Western Road
Cork Co. Cork
Phone: 021-4275211 Fax: 021-4275502
SIC: 85111 Employees: 180
Maternity Hospital
Sr Mary O'Brien Matron
Ms Kathleen Bowen Administrator

General Hospital Tullamore
Ardan Road
Tullamore Co. Offaly
Phone: 0506-46227 Fax: 0506-46146
SIC: 85111 Employees: 600
Hospital
Mr Peter Waters Manager

Gorey District Hospital
Gorey Co. Wexford
Phone: 055-21102 Fax: 055-21479
SIC: 85111 Employees: 30
District Hospital
Ms Ann Coakley Matron

Highfield Hospital Group
Swords Road
Whitehall
Dublin 9
Phone: 01-8374444 Fax: 01-8379013
Email: highfieldhospital@eircom.net
SIC: 85111 Employees: 150
Private Hospital
Mr Michael Eustace Chief Executive
Ms Feena Hosford Financial Controller

Hospital Of The Assumption
Leugh Road
Thurles Co. Tipperary
Phone: 0504-21055 Fax: 0504-22549
SIC: 85111 Employees: 100
Hospital
Ms Patricia O'Neill Hospital Administrator

Hume Street Hospital
Hume Street
Dublin 2
Phone: 01-6766935 Fax: 01-6762967
SIC: 85111 Employees: 50
Hospital
Mr Robert Martin Chief Executive

James Connolly Memorial Hospital
Blanchardstown
Dublin 15
Phone: 01-8213844 Fax: 01-8203565
SIC: 85111 Employees: 800
General Hospital
Mr Tom Gorey Hospital Manager
Mr Shane Brennan Personnel Manager

Leopardstown Park Hospital
Foxrock
Dublin 18
Phone: 01-2955055 Fax: 01-2955957
SIC: 85111 Employees: 140
Hospital
Mr Pat Smyth Chief Executive
Mr Nick Kelly Finance Manager
Ms Marie-Ann Byrne Personnel Manager

Longford/Westmeath General Hospital
Mullingar Co. Westmeath
Phone: 044-40221 Fax: 044-43155
SIC: 85111 Employees: 500
General Hospital
Mr Joe Martin Administrator

Lourdes Orthopaedic Hospital
Ballycallan Road
Kilcreene
Kilkenny Co. Kilkenny
Phone: 056-52465 Fax: 056-51402
SIC: 85111 Employees: 54
Orthopaedic Hospital
Mr Richard Dooley Manager
Mr Joe Clohessey Finance Manager

Louth County Hospital
Dublin Road
Dundalk Co. Louth
Phone: 042-9334701 Fax: 042-9331343
SIC: 85111 Employees: 300
General Hospital
Mr Barney McNeany Managing Director
Ms Deirdre Dineen Hospital Administrator
Ms Julie Dellew Computer Manager

Mayo General Hospital
Castlebar Co. Mayo
Phone: 094-21733 Fax: 094-21454
SIC: 85111 Employees: 600
General Hospital
Ms Jo Byrne Acting Hospital Administrator
Ms Clodagh Gerrity Personnel Manager

Monaghan General Hospital
Monaghan Co. Monaghan
Phone: 047-81811 Fax: 047-84437
SIC: 85111 Employees: 300
General Hospital
Mr Tommy Coyle Senior Administrator

Naas General Hospital
Naas Co. Kildare
Phone: 045-897221 Fax: 045-874492
SIC: 85111 Employees: 420
General Hospital
Mr Michael Knowles Hospital Manager

National Rehabilitation Hospital
Rochestown Avenue
Dun Laoghaire Co. Dublin
Phone: 01-2854777 Fax: 01-2851053
SIC: 85111 Employees: 300
Hospital
Mr Derek Green Chief Executive Officer
Mr Pat Gribben Financial Controller
Ms Colette Walsh Personnel Manager

Health & Social

Nenagh General Hospital
Tyone
Nenagh Co. Tipperary
Phone: 067-31492 Fax: 067-33440
SIC: 85111 Employees: 170
General Hospital
Mr Martin Quigley Hospital Administrator
Mr PJ Cleary Matron

North West Hospice
P O Box 294
G P O
Sligo Co. Sligo
Phone: 071-43317 Fax: 071-43255
Email: nwhosp@iol.ie
Web: http://www.iol.ie/nwhospice
SIC: 85111 Employees: 28
Hospice
Ms Noreen McGloin Chairperson
Dr Peter Boles Medical Director

Our Lady of Lourdes Hospital
Drogheda Co. Louth
Phone: 041-9837601 Fax: 041-9833868
Email: personnel@eircom.net
SIC: 85111 Employees: 1300
Hospital
Mr Declan Collins Acting General Manager
Mr Blayne Cowan Finance Manager
Ms Deirdre Dineen Acting Personnel Manager
Ms Frances Smith Computer Manager

Our Lady's Hospital
Navan Co. Meath
Phone: 046-21210 Fax: 046-28387
Email: navlib@indigo.ie
SIC: 85111 Employees: 400
General Hospital
Ms Aileen Maguire Director of Nursing
Ms Linda Davis Finance Director
Mr Seamus O'Shea Hospital Administrator

Our Lady's Surgical Hospital
The Green
Cashel Co. Tipperary
Phone: 062-61022 Fax: 062-61549
SIC: 85111 Employees: 170
Hospital
Ms Breda Kavanagh Hospital Manager
Ms Mary Ryan Accounts Manager

Portiuncula Hospital
Ballinasloe Co. Galway
Phone: 0905-42140 Fax: 0905-42916
Email: portiunculastaff@tinet.ie
SIC: 85111 Employees: 450
General Hospital
Ms Bridgette McHugh General Manager
Ms Edel Gilmore Financial Controller
Mr Colm Kavanagh Personnel Officer
Ms Anita Carey DP Manager

Portlaoise General Hospital
Dublin Road
Portlaoise Co. Laois
Phone: 0502-21364 Fax: 0502-22986
SIC: 85111 Employees: 400
General Hospital
Mr Kieran Madden Administrator
Ms Josephine Lowry Acting Deputy Administrator
Ms Mary Fitzpatrick Acting Deputy Administrator

Raheen District Hospital
Tuamgraney
Scarriff
Ennis Co. Clare
Phone: 061-923007 Fax: 061-923084
SIC: 85111 Employees: 38
District Hospital
Mr Seamus McAnulty Administrator
Ms Pauline McNamara Matron

Rotunda Hospital
Parnell Square West
Dublin 1
Phone: 01-8730700 Fax: 01-8726523
Web: http://www.rotunda.ie
SIC: 85111 Employees: 525
Maternity Hospital
Mr Noel Nelson Chief Secretary
Mr Paul Burke Personnel Manager
Mr Noel Carbury Head of IT/Patient Services

Royal Victoria Eye & Ear Hospital
Adelaide Road
Dublin 2
Phone: 01-6785500 Fax: 01-6761858
SIC: 85111 Employees: 240
Eye & Ear Hospital
Ms Aida Whyte Registrar/Secretary
Mr Joseph McKeown Accountant
Ms Majella Byrne Personnel Officer

Saint Colmcille's Hospital
Loughlinstown
Dublin 18
Phone: 01-2825800 Fax: 01-2825686
SIC: 85111 Employees: 350
Hospital
Mr Tom Mernagh Administrator
Mr Ray Madden Accounts Manager
Mr Shay Torsey Personnel Manager

Saint John's Hospital
Saint John's Square
Limerick Co. Limerick
Phone: 061-415822 Fax: 061-415231
SIC: 85111 Employees: 157
Hospital
Mr Tim Kennelly Manager

Saint Joseph's Hospital
Springdale Road
Raheny
Dublin 5
Phone: 01-8478433 Fax: 01-8478220
SIC: 85111 Employees: 100
Hospital
Ms Teresa Ayres General Manager
Ms Catherine Groves Finance Officer
Ms Madge Harford Matron

Saint Loman's Hospital
Ballyowen
Palmerstown
Dublin 20
Phone: 01-6264561 Fax: 01-6262224
SIC: 85111 Employees: 100
Hospital
Ms Anna-Marie Keys Area Manager

Saint Luke's General Hospital
Freshford Road
Kilkenny Co. Kilkenny
Phone: 056-51133 Fax: 056-21149
SIC: 85111 Employees: 800
General Hospital
Mr Dan McCarthy Managing Director
Mr Joe Clonossey Finance Manager
Ms Mary Mooney Personnel Officer

Sligo General Hospital
The Mall
Sligo Co. Sligo
Phone: 071-71111 Fax: 071-74645
SIC: 85111 Employees: 1000
Hospital
Ms Frances Rogers General Manager
Ms Mary Coleman Finance Manager
Mr Donal McLoughlin Personnel Manager
Mr Phelan O'Rourke MIS Manager

St Canices Hospital
Sion Road
Kilkenny Co. Kilkenny
Phone: 056-52341 Fax: 056-21812
SIC: 85111 Employees: 150
Hospital
Ms Mary O'Hanlon Administrator
Ms Breda McDonald Personnel Manager

St Finbarr's Hospital
Douglas Road
Cork Co. Cork
Phone: 021-4966555 Fax: 021-4966563
SIC: 85111 Employees: 450
Hospital
Ms Margaret Garvey Hospital Manager
Ms Clare MacGabhann Acting Director of Nursing

St Francis Hospice
Station Road
Raheny
Dublin 5
Phone: 01-8327535 Fax: 01-8327635
Email: info@sfh.ie
SIC: 85111 Employees: 110
Hospice
Ms Ethel McKenna Chief Executive Officer
Ms Mary Farrell Administrator
Sr Margaret Cashman Director of Nursing
Ms Alison Banker Information Officer

St James Hospital
IMS Department
1 James Street
Dublin 8
Phone: 01-4162572 Fax: 01-4545609
Web: http://www.iol.ie/~deskenny/acbi.html
SIC: 85111 Employees: 2300
Association of Clinical Biochemists
Ms Nuala McCarroll Honorary Secretary

St Joseph's Hospital
Clonsilla
Dublin 15
Phone: 01-8217120 Fax: 01-8214684
SIC: 85111 Employees: 200
Hospitals
Ms Zoe Killeen Director General

St Joseph's Hospital
Trim
Navan Co. Meath
Phone: 046-31229 Fax: 046-37454
SIC: 85111 Employees: 100
Hospitals
Sr Mary Cannon Matron

St Joseph's Hospital (Bantry)
Bantry Co. Cork
Phone: 027-50133 Fax: 027-51209
SIC: 85111 Employees: 46
Hospital
Ms Breda Cronin Matron

St Luke's Hospital
Highfield Road
Rathgar
Dublin 6
Phone: 01-4065000 Fax: 01-4972941
SIC: 85111 Employees: 450
Cancer Hospital
Mr Lorcan Birthist Chief Executive Officer
Ms Anne McMahon Accountant
Ms Josephine Fitzmaurice Personnel Manager
Mr William Corkery Services Manager

St Luke's Home Mahon Ltd
Castle Road
Mahon
Cork Co. Cork
Phone: 021-4359444 Fax: 021-4359450
Email: info@stlukes.ie
Web: http://www.stlukes.ie
SIC: 85111 Employees: 98
Hospitals
Ms Clodagh Drennan Manager

St Mary's Orthopaedic Hospital
Gurranabraher
Cork Co. Cork
Phone: 021-4303264 Fax: 021-4303527
SIC: 85111 Employees: 98
Hospitals
Ms Margaret Rider Matron
Mr Donal Murphy Administrator

St Michael's Hospital
Lower Georges Street
Dun Laoghaire Co. Dublin
Phone: 01-2806901 Fax: 01-2844651
Email: tur@smhos.iol.ie
Web: http://www.smhos.iol.ie
SIC: 85111 Employees: 230
General Hospital
Mr Kevin O'Connor Secretary/Manager
Mr Seamus Murtagh Accountant

St Nessan's Orthopaedic Hospital
Croom
Kilmallock Co. Limerick
Phone: 061-397276 Fax: 061-397392
SIC: 85111 Employees: 146
Hospital
Mr John Hennessey General Manager
Ms Marie Giltenane Head of Nursing
Ms Ann Fitzpatrick Administration Officer

St Vincents Hospital
Dungarvan Co. Waterford
Phone: 058-41125 Fax: 058-44485
SIC: 85111 Employees: 200
Hospitals
Ms Bridget Burke Matron

Swinford District Hospital
Dublin Road
Swinford
Claremorris Co. Mayo
Phone: 094-51102 Fax: 094-52679
SIC: 85111 Employees: 45
District Hospital
Mr Michael Fahey Administrator
Ms Nora Murtagh Accountant
Ms Gertrude Morris Matron

Tralee General Hospital
Rathass
Tralee Co. Kerry
Phone: 066-7126222 Fax: 066-7126241
Email: tgh@indigo.ie
SIC: 85111 Employees: 700
General Hospital
Mr Jimmy O'Connor Senior Executive Officer
Mr Pat O'Driscoll Computer Operations Manager

Waterford Regional Hospital
Dunmore Road
Waterford Co. Waterford
Phone: 051-848000 Fax: 051-848572
SIC: 85111 Employees: 1500
Hospital
Mr Richard Dooley General Manager
Ms Des O'Herlihy Finance Manager
Ms Theo Neijenhuizen Deputy Manager - Personnel
Mr Pat Tyrrell Personnel Manager
Mr William McGrath Team Services Manager
Mr Eamon Gavin Information System Officer

Wexford General Hospital
Newtown Road
Wexford Co. Wexford
Phone: 053-42233 Fax: 053-41910
SIC: 85111 Employees: 700
General Hospital
Ms Teresa Hanrahan Hospital Manager
Mr Michael Kehoe Finance Manager

Blackrock Clinic
Rock Road
Blackrock Co. Dublin
Phone: 01-2832222 Fax: 01-2064374
Email: admin@blackrock-clinic.com
Web: http://www.blackrock-clinic.com
SIC: 85112 Employees: 425
Private Hospital
Mr Bryan Harty Hospital Director
Mr Brian Scollard Chief Accountant
Ms Susan Pinkster Personnel Director
Ms Evelyn Sheehan Marketing Director
Mr Michael McGowan Director Information Systems

Mater Private Hospital
Eccles Street
Dublin 7
Phone: 01-8858888 Fax: 01-8858541
Email: info@materprivate.ie
Web: http://www.materprivate.ie
SIC: 85112 Employees: 450
Private Hospital
Mr Mark Moran Chief Executive
Mr John Mooney Financial Controller
Ms Angela Hogan Human Resources Manager
Mr JJ Cummins Production Manager
Mr Michael Power IT Manager

Saint Ita's Hospital
Portrane
Donabate
Swords Co. Dublin
Phone: 01-8436337 Fax: 01-8436377
SIC: 85112 Employees: 650
Psychiatric Hospital
Mr Martin Connor Director of Nursing
Mr Seamus Murphy General Manager

Saint Mary's Hospital
Main Street
Baldoyle
Dublin 13
Phone: 01-8323056 Fax: 01-8393718
SIC: 85112 Employees: 65
Hospital for Handicapped Children
Ms Lorraine Robinson Chief Executive
Sr Maureen Mulhern Nursing Director

St Joseph's Geriatric Hospital
Dungarvan Co. Waterford
Phone: 058-20900 Fax: 058-44485
SIC: 85112 Employees: 90
Hospitals
Ms Bridget Burke Matron

St Joseph's Private Clinic
Springdale Road
Raheny
Dublin 5
Phone: 01-8478187 Fax: 01-8478174
SIC: 85112 Employees: 42
Private Clinic
Ms Teresa Ayres Hospital Manager
Ms Catherine Groves Finance Officer

St Joseph's Private Hospital
Garden Hill
Sligo Co. Sligo
Phone: 071-62649 Fax: 071-71255
SIC: 85112 Employees: 70
Private Hospital
Mr Kieran Egan Manager
Sr Desmond Carroll Matron

Stewarts Special Hospital
Palmerstown
Dublin 20
Phone: 01-6264444 Fax: 01-6261707
SIC: 85112 Employees: 650
Hospital - Special Needs
Ms Maura Donovan Chief Executive

Bushy Park Nursing Home
Nenagh Co. Tipperary
Phone: 067-27442 Fax: 067-31547
SIC: 85113 Employees: 35
Nursing Homes
Mr Vincent Kinsella Manager

Carrigoran House
Newmarket On Fergus
Ennis Co. Clare
Phone: 061-368100 Fax: 061-368170
Email: carrigoranhse@oceanfree.net
SIC: 85113 Employees: 130
Private Nursing Homes
Sr Rachel O'Keeffe Administrator

La Verna Nursing Home
30 Haddon Road
Clontarf
Dublin 3
Phone: 01-8339879 Fax: 01-8329839
SIC: 85113 Employees: 30
Nursing Homes
Ms Aileen Tevlin Director of Nursing

Lakeland Nursing Home Ltd
Mount Pleasant
Loughrea
Galway Co. Galway
Phone: 091-842240 Fax: 091-847124
SIC: 85113 Employees: 35
Nursing Home
Mr Joe Kenny Proprietor

Moyglare Nursing Home
Moyglare Road
Maynooth Co. Kildare
Phone: 01-6289022 Fax: 01-6293904
SIC: 85113 Employees: 43
Nursing Home
Ms Nuala Doyle Proprietor

Sancta Maria Nursing Homes
Enniscrone
Sligo Co. Sligo
Phone: 096-36239 Fax: 096-36774
Email: sanctamaria@eircom.net
SIC: 85113 Employees: 36
Nursing Homes
Mr Terry Cauley Proprietor

St Francis Private Hospital
Ballinderry
Mullingar Co. Westmeath
Phone: 044-41500 Fax: 044-41330
SIC: 85113 Employees: 130
Homes - Nursing
Sr Pauline O'Sullivan Administrator
Mr Liam Staines Financial Controller
Mr Padraig Bergra Chief Executive

Tara Private Nursing Home
5-6 Putland Road
Bray Co. Wicklow
Phone: 01-2863931 Fax: 01-2760220
Email: niaocan@eircom.net
SIC: 85113 Employees: 50
Nursing Homes
Mr Paul Costello General Manager
Ms Ann Costello Matron

Tara Winthrop Private Clinic
Nevinstown Lane
Pinnock Hill
Swords Co. Dublin
Phone: 01-8079631 Fax: 01-8902384
SIC: 85113 Employees: 70
Long and short term medical care for the elderly and terminally ill
Ms Rena Galvin Proprietor

Health & Social

Bloomfield Hospital
Bloomfield Avenue, Morehampton Road
Donnybrook
Dublin 4
Phone: 01-6683815 Fax: 01-6687693
SIC: 85116 Employees: 60
Private Psycho-geriatric Hospital
Mr Derek Pullen Secretary

Cobh General Hospital
Cobh Co. Cork
Phone: 021-4811345 Fax: 021-4811686
SIC: 85116 Employees: 35
Geriatric Hospital
Ms Maureen Condon General Manager

Ennistymon District Hospital
Ennistymon
Ennis Co. Clare
Phone: 065-7071622 Fax: 065-7071845
SIC: 85116 Employees: 28
Community Hospital
Ms Maureen Griffin Matron
Mr Seamus McNulty Financial Controller
Mr Pascal Moynahan Administrator

Heatherside Hospital
Buttevant
Cork Co. Cork
Phone: 022-24377 Fax: 022-24739
SIC: 85116 Employees: 75
Psychiatric & Geriatric Hospital
Ms Anne O'Connell Matron

Royal Hospital
Donnybrook
Dublin 4
Phone: 01-4972844 Fax: 01-4972682
Email: management@rhd.ie
SIC: 85116 Employees: 350
Geriatric Hospital
Mr John Kennedy Manager
Mr Keith Blackmore Accountant
Ms Anne Holly Personnel Officer

St Mary's Hospital
Dublin Road
Drogheda Co. Louth
Phone: 041-9838680 Fax: 041-9844970
SIC: 85116 Employees: 300
Geriatric Hospital
Sr Bernadette Murphy Acting Ward Sister
Mr Aidan McGuinness Administrator

Aras Naomh Chaolain
Knock Road
Castlerea Co. Roscommon
Phone: 0907-20016 Fax: 0907-20320
SIC: 85117 Employees: 175
Psychiatric & Geriatric Hospital
Mr Eamon Hannan Manager Support Services

Community Mental Health
Summerhill
Wexford Co. Wexford
Phone: 053-23899 Fax: 053-23899
SIC: 85117 Employees: 80
Mental Health Service
Ms Bridget Morran Manager

Dawn House
Wexford Co. Wexford
Phone: 053-45351 Fax: 053-45351
SIC: 85117 Employees: 30
Centre for Learning Disabilities
Ms Mary Black Manager

Mental Health Services
Ballytivnan
Sligo Co. Sligo
Phone: 071-42111 Fax: 071-43593
SIC: 85117 Employees: 38
Psychiatric Hospital/School
Mr Denis Moynihan Administrator

Saint Brigid's Hospital
Ballinasloe Co. Galway
Phone: 0905-42117 Fax: 0905-42660
Email: stbrigid@eircom.net
SIC: 85117 Employees: 300
Psychiatric Hospital
Mr Adrian Ahern Director
Ms Mary Feeney Head of Accounts
Ms Mona Eanes Personnel Manager

Saint Finan's Hospital
Killarney Co. Kerry
Phone: 064-31022 Fax: 064-35019
SIC: 85117 Employees: 250
Psychiatric Hospital
Mr Tom Walsh Chief Administrator
Mr Pat McCarthy Finance Manager

Saint Michael's House
Clinic & Administration Builiding
Ballymun
Dublin 9
Phone: 01-8840200 Fax: 01-8840211
Email: info@smh.ie
Web: http://www.smh.ie
SIC: 85117 Employees: 420
Services to Mentally Handicapped
Mr Paul Ledwidge Chief Executive Officer
Mr James McKeown Finance Manager
Mr Nessan Rickard Human Resources Manager
Mr Kevin Gregory Computer Manager

St Brendan's Hospital
Rathdown Road
Dublin 7
Phone: 01-8385844 Fax: 01-8680020
SIC: 85117 Employees: 450
Psychiatric Hospital
Dr Angela Mohan Clinical Director
Ms Teresa Ayres Administrator

St John of God Hospital
Stillorgan
Blackrock Co. Dublin
Phone: 01-2881781 Fax: 01-2881034
SIC: 85117 Employees: 200
Psychiatric Hospital
Mr Ray Leonard General Manager
Ms Monica Mooney Manager

St Joseph's Hospital
Mulgrave Street
Limerick Co. Limerick
Phone: 061-416166 Fax: 061-416774
SIC: 85117 Employees: 200
Psychiatric Hospital
Mr Michael McMahon Senior Hospital Administrator
Mr Padraic Gilliagan Chief Nurse

St Lomans Hospital
Devin Road
Mullingar Co. Westmeath
Phone: 044-40191 Fax: 044-43022
SIC: 85117 Employees: 350
Psychiatric Hospital
Mr Richard Walsh General Manager

St Mary's Hospital
Westport Road
Castlebar Co. Mayo
Phone: 094-21333 Fax: 094-26671
Email: mmhs@eircom.net
SIC: 85117 Employees: 350
Psychiatric Hospital
Mr Tony O'Boyle Hospital Administrator

Ambulance Station
James Street
Dublin 8
Phone: 01-4540545 Fax: 01-4540546
SIC: 85118 Employees: 46
Health Board Services
Mr Larry Doran Managing Director

Child Care Services
Park House
North Circular Road
Dublin 7
Phone: 01-8387122 Fax: 01-8387488
SIC: 85118 Employees: 30
Health Board Services Community Welfare
Mr John Fennell Senior Executive

Dublin Well Woman Centre
67 Pembroke Road
Ballsbridge
Dublin 4
Phone: 01-6609860 Fax: 01-6603062
Email: info@wellwomancentre.ie
Web: http://www.wellwomancentre.ie
SIC: 85118 Employees: 50
Health Care Service For Women
Ms Alison Begas Chief Executive
Ms Angela Kenny Manager

Northern Area Health Board
Community Care Area 7
193 Richmond Road
Dublin 3
Phone: 01-8575400 Fax: 01-8575401
SIC: 85118 Employees: 4000
Health Board Services
Ms Anne Halpin Manageress

Northwestern Health Board (Community Services)
Lower Main Street
Ballybofey
Lifford Co. Donegal
Phone: 074-31391 Fax: 074-31982
SIC: 85118 Employees: 43
Health Board
Mr Kieran Doherty General Manager
Mr John Toye Head of Finance
Ms Paula Quinn Office Manager

South Western Area Health Board
Unit 1 Millenium Park
Nace
Kildare Co. Kildare
Phone: 045-880400 Fax: 045-880493
SIC: 85118 Employees: 4500
Health Services
Mr Pat Donnelly Chief Executive Officer
Mr Declan Lyons Director of Finance
Mr Tony McMahon Human Resources Manager
Mr Seamus O' Brein Manager of Special Projects
Ms Brid Clarke Operation Manager
Mr Pat Bennett Planning & Development Manager

Barrington's Medical Centre
Georges Quay
Limerick Co. Limerick
Phone: 061-313334 Fax: 061-312939
SIC: 85121 Employees: 28
Private Medical Centre
Mr Chris Jones Administrator

Cliff Beirne
The North Brook Clinic
59 North Brook Road Ranelagh
Dublin 6
Phone: 01-4068180 Fax: 01-4967100
SIC: 85121 Employees: 25
Clinic
Mr John Ludder Manager

Dublin Medical Centre
352 South Circular Road
Dublin 8
Phone: 01-4533030 Fax: 01-4539301
SIC: 85121 Employees: 27
Private Medical Centre
Dr Pierce Phelan Medical Director

Health & Social

Kilbarrack Health Centre
Foxfield Crescent
Raheny
Dublin 5
Phone: 01-8326533 Fax: 01-8322111
SIC: 85121 Employees: 45
Health Centre
Ms Anne O'Neill Dental Manager

Tropical Medical Bureau
5 Northumberland Avenue
Dun Laoghaire Co. Dublin
Phone: 01-2804996 Fax: 01-2805603
Email: tropical@iol.ie
Web: http://www.tmb.ie
SIC: 85121 Employees: 25
Vaccinations/Pre Departure Medicals
Dr Graham Fry Medical Director
Ms Miriam Edge Administration Manager
Mr Richard Boyd Development Manager

Ambulance Centre
Mauldlings Industrial Estate
Naas Co. Kildare
Phone: 045-879610 Fax: 045-871009
SIC: 85122 Employees: 50
Ambulance Service
Mr Martin Dunne Area Manager

Bio Medical Research Ltd
BMR House
Parkmore Business Park West
Galway Co. Galway
Phone: 091-774300 Fax: 091-774301
Web: http://www.siendertone.ie
SIC: 85122 Employees: 200
Medical Research
Mr Kevin McDonnell Managing Director
Mr Phillip Moschetta Finance Manager
Ms Irene Kavanagh Personnel Director
Mr Colin Lawlor International Sales Manager

Central Remedial Clinic
Vernon Avenue
Clontarf
Dublin 3
Phone: 01-8057400 Fax: 01-8335496
Email: tdcrc@iol.ie
Web: http://www.crc.ie
SIC: 85122 Employees: 180
Remedial Clinic
Mr Paul Kiely Chief Executive
Mr Tony Kett Administrator
Mr Pat O'Grady Chairman

Cheeverstown House Ltd
Kilvere
Templeogue
Dublin 6
Phone: 01-4904681 Fax: 01-4905753
Email: cheevers@iol.ie
SIC: 85122 Employees: 220
Services for the Disabled
Mr Brendan Sutton Chief Executive Officer
Mr Brian Gallagher Human Resources Manager
Ms Sheila Brady Public Relations Manager
Mr William Shorten Director of Services

Drug Treatment Centre Board
Trinity Court
30-31 Pearse Street
Dublin 2
Phone: 01-6771122 Fax: 01-6779080
SIC: 85122 Employees: 70
Drug Treatment Board
Ms Sheila Heffernan General Manager
Ms Lucy Woolmington Accounts Manager
Ms Grainne Coulson Personnel Director

Dublin Dental Hospital
Lincoln Place
Dublin 2
Phone: 01-6127200 Fax: 01-6711255
Email: info@dental.tcd.ie
Web: http://www.tcd.ie/dental_school
SIC: 85122 Employees: 300
Dental Teaching Hospital
Mr Brian Murray Chief Executive Officer
Mr Paul Walters Financial Controller
Mr Lauri Cryan HR Administrator
Mr James Swan Facilities Manager
Mr Luke Feeney IT Manager

Franciscan Social Justice Initiatives
4 Merchants Quay
Dublin 8
Phone: 01-6790044 Fax: 01-6713738
Email: info@nqp.ie
SIC: 85122 Employees: 100
Drugs & HIV Service
Mr Tony Geoghan Director
Mr Basil Cronin Finance Manager
Ms Gabriel Kinahan IT Manager

Irish Blood Transfusion Service
National Blood Centre
James Street
Dublin 4
Phone: 01-4322800 Fax: 01-4322930
Email: info@ibts.ie
Web: http://www.ibts.ie
SIC: 85122 Employees: 220
Blood Transfusion Services
Dr William Murphy National Medical Director
Mr Michael Burbridge Finance Manager
Ms Mairead Nelsey Personnel Manager

Irish Institute For Brain Injured
Kilnacourt House
Portarlington
Portlaoise Co. Laois
Phone: 0502-23139 Fax: 0502-23267
SIC: 85122 Employees: 23
Treatment Centre
Ms Michelle McCormack Secretary

Medical Council
Lynn House, Portobello Court
Lower Rathmines Road
Dublin 6
Phone: 01-4965588 Fax: 01-4965972
Email: secretary@mcirl.ie
SIC: 85122 Employees: 25
Registration of Medical Practices
Mr Brian Lea Registrar

Newcastle Hospital
Greystones Co. Wicklow
Phone: 01-2819001 Fax: 01-2819325
Email: PGBnew@eircom.net
SIC: 85122 Employees: 150
Psychiatric Hospital
Mr Pat Byrne Acting Area Manager
Ms Maeve Litton Acting Administrator

Our Lady's Hospice
Harold's Cross
Dublin 6w
Phone: 01-4972101 Fax: 01-4972714
SIC: 85122 Employees: 450
Hospice
Mr Michael Murphy Chief Executive Officer
Ms Peggy Toomey Finance Director
Ms Breda Flynn Human Resources Director

Peamount Hospital
Newcastle
Clonmel Co. Tipperary
Phone: 052-6280685 Fax: 052-6282306
Email: peamount@iol.ie
SIC: 85122 Employees: 450
Chest Disease/Mental Handicapped
Mr Raymond Gallagher Manager
Mr Kevin MacNamee Accountant
Ms Barbara Fitzgerald Director of Nursing

Saint Vincent's Hospital
Convent Avenue, Richmond Road
Fairview
Dublin 3
Phone: 01-8375101 Fax: 01-8370801
SIC: 85122 Employees: 220
Psychiatric Hospital
Mr Edward Byrne Chief Executive
Mr Tom Houlihan Personnel Manager

St Luke's Cancer Research Fund
Oakland, Highfield Road
Rathgar
Dublin 6
Phone: 01-4976491 Fax: 01-4972941
SIC: 85122 Employees: 400
Cancer Hospital
Mr Lorcan Birthistle Chief Executive
Ms Anne McMahon Accounts Manager
Ms Josephine Cox Human Resources Director

St Mary's Peamount Hospital
Newcastle Road
Newcastle
Dublin 22 Co. Dublin
Phone: 01-6010348 Fax: 01-6282306
SIC: 85122 Employees: 32
Medical Practise
Ms Barbra Fitzgerald Managing Director

St Vincents University Hospital
Elm Park
Dublin 4
Phone: 01-2694533 Fax: 01-2696018
SIC: 85122 Employees: 2500
Hospital
Mr Nicholas Germyn CCO

Barnardos
C/o Millbrook Lawns Health Centre
St Dominic's Road, Tallaght
Dublin 24
Phone: 01-4525090 Fax: 01-4621368
Email: info@barnardos.tallaght.ie
Web: http://www.barnardos.tallaght.ie
SIC: 85123 Employees: 25
Child Care
Ms Breda Kennedy Project Leader

Coolock Health Centre
Cromcastle Road
Dublin 5
Phone: 01-8476617 Fax: 01-8479944
Email: info@ehb.ie
SIC: 85124 Employees: 26
GP Surgery
Dr James Kirby GP
Dr John Dunlop GP
Dr Margaret Hughes GP

Specsavers Opticians
13a Cruise Street
Limerick Co. Limerick
Phone: 061-312811 Fax: 061-316363
Web: http://www.specsavers.com
SIC: 85141 Employees: 40
Opticians
Mr Paul Smyth Manager
Mr Niamh Coleman Computer Manager

Vision Express
204 The Square
Blessington Road, Tallaght
Dublin 24
Phone: 01-4598722 Fax: 01-4598723
SIC: 85141 Employees: 30
Opticians
Ms Siobhan McGolderick Manager

Cluain Mhuire Family Centre
Newtownpark Avenue
Blackrock Co. Dublin
Phone: 01-2833766 Fax: 01-2833886
SIC: 85145 Employees: 47
Psychology
Ms Monica Mooney Director

Health & Social

St Davnet's Hospital
Monaghan Co. Monaghan
Phone: 047-81822 Fax: 047-81527
Email: cmmhs@internet.ie
SIC: 85145 Employees: 490
Psychiatric Hospital
Mr Eugene Caulfield Administrator
Ms Elaine Evans Assistant Administrator

Chief Ambulance Officer
Western Health Board
Castlebar Co. Mayo
Phone: 094-21698 Fax: 094-21921
SIC: 85149 Employees: 104
Ambulance officer
Mr Ray Bonar Manager

National Association For Deaf People
35 North Frederick Street
Dublin 1
Phone: 01-8723800 Fax: 01-8723816
Email: nad@iol.ie
Web: http://www.iol/~nad
SIC: 85149 Employees: 25
Services for the Deaf
Mr Niall Keane Chief Executive

National Council for Blind
Whitworth Road
Dublin 9
Phone: 01-8307033 Fax: 01-8307787
Email: info@ncbi.ie
Web: http://www.ncbi.ie
SIC: 85149 Employees: 85
Social Services Organisation
Mr Desmond Kenny Chief Executive
Mr John Russell Financial Controller
Ms Helen Shanahan Personnel Manager
Ms Sarah Gahan Public Relations Officer
Mr Collyn Kenny IT Manager

Prosper Fingal Ltd
Strand Street
Skerries Co. Dublin
Phone: 01-8490915 Fax: 01-8494314
Email: info@prosperfingal.org
SIC: 85149 Employees: 50
Services for the Disabled
Mr Pat Reen Director of Services

St John of God Brothers
Administration Centre
Granada Stillorgan
Blackrock Co. Dublin
Phone: 01-2882200 Fax: 01-2831274
Email: director@sjog.ie
Web: http://www.sjog.ie
SIC: 85149 Employees: 2100
Treatment of Disturbed Children
Br Ronan Lennon Provincial Manager
Mr Michael Murphy Financial Controller
Mr John Pepper Human Resource Manager
Ms Anne Freeman Technical Services Manager
Mr I.D Hamilton Data Processing Manager

Tabor Lodge
Ballindeasig
Belgooly
Kinsale Co. Cork
Phone: 021-4887110 Fax: 021-4887377
SIC: 85149 Employees: 25
Treatment Centre for Gambling/Alcohol
Sr Margaret Kiely Programme Director

Waverley Ambulance Service Ltd
175 James Street
Dublin 8
Phone: 01-6772661 Fax: 01-6772283
Email: wav@indigo.ie
SIC: 85149 Employees: 60
Private Ambulance Service
Mr Gerard Farrell Director

Intervet Ireland Ltd
Cookstown Industrial Estate
Tallaght
Dublin 24
Phone: 01-4511544 Fax: 01-4511906
SIC: 85201 Employees: 35
Veterinary & Industry Suppliers
Mr Matt Browne Managing Director
Mr Ciaran Glynn Finance Manager

Myross Development Co
Unit 3 Knockalisheen Road
Myross
Limerick Co. Limerick
Phone: 061-325696 Fax: 061-328346
SIC: 85313 Employees: 27
Cater for Children at Risk at Home
Mr Tom Dunne Managing Director

Brabazon Trust
2 Gilford Road
Sandymount
Dublin 4
Phone: 01-2691677 Fax: 01-2839508
Email: manager@brabazontrust.ie
Web: http://www.brabazontrust.ie
SIC: 85314 Employees: 39
Shelter Home for the Elderly
Mr Graham Farrell Manager
Ms Daphne Morgan Matron

Iveagh Hostel
Bride Road
Dublin 8
Phone: 01-4540182 Fax: 01-4536316
SIC: 85314 Employees: 30
Shelter For Homeless Men
Mr Frederick Stephenson Manager

RCCN Ballyhoura Ltd
Health Centre
Hospital
Kilmallock Co. Limerick
Phone: 061-383644 Fax: 061-383148
Email: rccn@gofree.indigo.ie
SIC: 85314 Employees: 34
Provide caring services for the elderly & children
Ms Cecelia Deasy Managing Director

Western Care Associates
Fr Mulhern Cresent
Belmullet
Ballina Co. Mayo
Phone: 097-81353 Fax: 097-81353
SIC: 85314 Employees: 500
Care Associates
Mr James Rock General Manager

Adoption Board
Shelbourne House, Shelbourne Road
Ballsbridge
Dublin 4
Phone: 01-6671392 Fax: 01-6671438
Email: info@adoptionboard.ie
Web: http://www.adoptionboard.ie
SIC: 85320 Employees: 25
Adoption Board
Mr David Woolfe Registrar

An Bord Pleanala
Floor 3 Block 6 Irish Life Centre
Lower Abbey Street
Dublin 1
Phone: 01-8728011 Fax: 01-8722684
Email: bord@pleanala.ie
Web: http://www.pleanala.ie
SIC: 85320 Employees: 120
Appeals Processing Board
Mr Paul Mullally Chief Officer
Mr Dermot Collins Secretary
Mr David Curran Personnel Officer

Carers Association Ltd National Office
Metropole Centre, James Street
Kilkenny Co. Kilkenny
Phone: 056-21424 Fax: 056-21466
Email: nationalcareline@carersireland.com
Web: http://www.carersireland.com
SIC: 85320 Employees: 200
Support For Carers
Mr Eddie Collins-Hughes Director

Community Welfare
Rathdown Road
Grangegorman
Dublin 7
Phone: 01-8680444 Fax: 01-8682383
SIC: 85320 Employees: 150
Social Welfare
Mr Noel Mulvihill General Manager

Hodgkins United Group
Irish Cancer Society
5 Northumberland Road
Dublin 4
Phone: 01-6681233 Fax: 01-6687599
Email: admin@irishcancer.ie
SIC: 85320 Employees: 30
Support Group
Mr Barry Dempsey Chief Executive
Mr John McCormick Finance Manager
Ms Helen Gelletlie Marketing Director

Social Welfare Local Office
Hanover Street
Cork Co. Cork
Phone: 021-4270055 Fax: 021-4273770
Web: http://www.welfare.ie
SIC: 85320 Employees: 130
Social Welfare Office
Mr Pat Corcoran Manager
Ms Mary Fennessy Finance Manager

Barretstown Gang Camp
Barretstown Castle
Ballymore Eustace
Naas Co. Kildare
Phone: 045-864115 Fax: 045-864197
Email: info@barretstowngc.ie
Web: http://www.barretstowngc.ie
SIC: 85321 Employees: 27
Charity
Mr David Strahan Chief Executive

Capuchin Day Centre
29 Bow Street
Dublin 7
Phone: 01-8720770 Fax: 01-8724565
SIC: 85321 Employees: 36
Charity Organisation
Br Kevin Crowley General Manager

Catholic Lay Apostolate Ltd
D18 Edward Centre
Edward Street
Tralee Co. Kerry
Phone: 066-7124972 Fax: 066-7120566
SIC: 85321 Employees: 28
Charity Group
Mr Brendan Walsh Manager

Cerebral Palsy Ireland
Marino Centre
Church Road
Bray Co. Wicklow
Phone: 01-2867543 Fax: 01-2866803
Email: cpimarino@oceanfree.net
Web: http://www.cpi.ie
SIC: 85321 Employees: 25
Medical Institution
Mr Germaine Gammell Administrator

Concern Worldwide
52-55 Lower Camden Street
Dublin 2
Phone: 01-4177777 Fax: 01-4757362
Email: info@concern.ie
Web: http://www.concern.ie
SIC: 85321 Employees: 73
Aid to Underdeveloped Countries
Mr David Begg Chief Executive
Mr Ray McElroy Financial Controller
Ms Geraldine Holden Head of Personnel Division
Ms Sally Anne Kinahan Sales & Marketing Manager

CRC- RTB Promotions Ltd
10 Parnell Square East
Dublin 1
Phone: 01-8748626 Fax: 01-8740051
SIC: 85321 Employees: 100
Charity Fundraising
Dr Senan Mullins Chief Executive Officer
Mr Phillip McCabe Finance Manager
Mr Robin Bailey Sales & Marketing Manager
Mr Liam Hynes Administration Manager

Dublin Central Mission
Mount Tabor
Sandymount Green
Dublin 4
Phone: 01-2605766 Fax: 01-2605786
Email: dcmiss@iol.ie
SIC: 85321 Employees: 145
Charity
Rev John Stephens Superintendent
Mr David Lee Finance Manager

Dublin Simon Community
Night Shelter
Ushers Island
Dublin 8
Phone: 01-6792391 Fax: -
SIC: 85321 Employees: 23
Charities
Ms Susan O'Neill Project Leader
Ms Caroline Maher Assistant Project Leader

Enable Ireland
Sandymount Avenue
Dublin 4
Phone: 01-2695355 Fax: 01-2601478
Email: info@enableireland.ie
Web: http://www.enableireland.ie
SIC: 85321 Employees: 450
Charity
Mr Michael Cummins Chief Executive
Mr Ray Jordan Financial Controller
Ms Clare Dennehy Personnel Manager
Ms Fiona McLoughlin Marketing Manager
Mr Donal Cashman Chairman

Irish Cancer Society
5 Northumberland Road
Dublin 4
Phone: 01-6681855 Fax: 01-6687599
Email: admin@cancer.ie
Web: http://www.cancer.ie
SIC: 85321 Employees: 100
Funding for Cancer Research & Information
Mr Barry Dempsey Chief Executive
Mr John McCormack Treasurer
Ms Olwyn Ryan Office Administrator
Mr James Cassidy Fundraising Co-Ordinator

Irish Guide Dogs for the Blind
Model Farm Road
Cork Co. Cork
Phone: 021-4870929 Fax: 021-4874152
Email: igda@iol.ie
SIC: 85321 Employees: 28
Train Irish Guide Dogs for the Blind
Mr Sean Walsh Chief Executive
Ms Sharon Russell Secretary

Irish Red Cross
16 Merrion Square
Dublin 2
Phone: 01-6765135 Fax: 01-6614461
Email: redcross@iol.ie
Web: http://www.redcross.ie
SIC: 85321 Employees: 100
Ambulance - Red Cross
Ms Carmel Dunn Secretary General
Mr Desmond Kavanagh Treasurer
Ms Maureen O'Sullivan Honorary Secretary

ISPCC
20 Molesworth Street
Dublin 2
Phone: 01-6794944 Fax: 01-6791746
Email: ispcc@ispcc.ie
Web: http://www.ispcc.ie
SIC: 85321 Employees: 50
Prevention of Cruelty to Children
Mr Paul Gilligan Chief Executive
Mr Michael Sheridan Manager

National Lottery
Lower Abbey Street
Dublin 1
Phone: 01-8364444 Fax: 01-8366034
Email: webmaster@lottery.ie
Web: http://www.lotto.ie
SIC: 85321 Employees: 78
Operation of National Lottery
Mr Ray Bates Director
Mr Noel Browne Chief Accountant
Mr Brendan McGenra Personnel Manager
Mr Malachy Moynihan Sales & Marketing Manager
Mr Cathal McNally Operations Manager
Ms Mary Daly Acting IT Manager

Parental Equality
54 Middle Abbey Street
Dublin 1
Phone: 01-8740163 Fax: 01-8725392
Email: info@parentalequality.ie
Web: http://www.parentalequality.ie
SIC: 85321 Employees: 40
Charities
Mr Alan Beirne Project Manager

Rape Crisis Centre
70 Lower Leeson Street
Dublin 2
Phone: 01-6614911 Fax: 01-6610873
Email: rcc@indigo.ie
Web: http://www.drcc.ie
SIC: 85321 Employees: 25
Charities
Ms Breda Allen Chairperson
Ms Naomi Patton Accountant

Respond Voluntary Housing Association
Airmount
Dominic Place
Waterford Co. Waterford
Phone: 051-357901 Fax: 051-304007
Email: respondwfd@esatclear.ie
SIC: 85321 Employees: 50
Registered Charity - Housing
Mr Pat Cogan Executive Director
Mr Tomas English Financial Controller
Mr Rod Young IT Co ordinator

SOS
Callan Road
Kilkenny Co. Kilkenny
Phone: 056-64000 Fax: 056-61212
Email: soskilk@iol.ie
SIC: 85321 Employees: 110
Voluntary Organisation to Help Mentally Handicapped
Mr Tom Shanahan Manager
Ms Bridget Keating Accounts Manager

Trocaire
169 Booterstown Avenue
Blackrock Co. Dublin
Phone: 01-2885385 Fax: 01-2883577
Email: info@trocaire.ie
Web: http://www.trocaire.org
SIC: 85321 Employees: 150
Third World Aid
Mr Justin Kilcullen Director
Ms Eileen Ryan Financial Controller
Mr Brendan Schutte Human Resources Manager
Ms Phyllis Divilly Donor Leader
Mr Brian Lowes Head of IT

Victim Support
32 Arran Quay
Dublin 7
Phone: 01-8780870 Fax: 01-8780944
Email: info@victimsupport.ie
Web: http://www.victimsupport.ie
SIC: 85321 Employees: 40
Charity
Ms Lillian McGovern Chief Executive Officer
Ms Rachel Shevlin Personnel Manager
Ms Teresa O'Donoghue Computer Manager

Sewage, Refuse & Sanitation

90 Sewage, Refuse & Sanitation
90001 Sewage Disposal
90002 Refuse Disposal Fumigation
90004 Skip Hire

Axxon Waste
Greenview, Greenhills Road
Walkinstown
Dublin 12
Phone: 01-4508055 Fax: 01-4564585
SIC: 90002 Employees: 190
Waste Disposal
Mr Sam Stears Managing Director
Mr William Campbell Finance Manager
Mr Derek Melvin Sales Manager

Blanchardstown Finglas Waste Disposal
Blanchardstown
Dublin 15
Phone: 01-6620177 Fax: 01-4514166
SIC: 90002 Employees: 38
Waste Disposal
Mr Gerry Burns Managing Director

IPODEC
Ballymount Cross
Tallaght
Dublin 24
Phone: 01-4136500 Fax: 01-4136501
SIC: 90002 Employees: 90
Waste Management/Disposal/Recycling
Ms Florence Mahony Managing Director
Mr Pat Fennell Financial Controller
Mr Maurice Walsh Area Manager
Mr Tom O'Mahony Operations Manager

Manvik Plant
Unit A Weatherwell Business Park
Clondalkin
Dublin 22
Phone: 01-4670699 Fax: 01-4670645
Email: manvikplant@netscape.net
SIC: 90002 Employees: 30
Refuse Compacting
Mr Alan Kershaw Managing Director
Mr John Byrne Finance Manager
Mr Willie Green Sales Manager
Mr Michael Grey Production Manager
Mr Keith Miller Computer Consultant

National Waste Management
41 3rd Avenue, Cookstown Ind Estate
Tallaght
Dublin 24
Phone: 01-4515555 Fax: 01-4514166
Email: info@nationalwaste.ie
SIC: 90002 Employees: 45
Waste Management
Mr Gerry Bryne Manager
Mr Martin Ryan Sales & Marketing Manager

O'Hagan Waste Disposal
Bawnogues
Straffan
Naas Co. Kildare
Phone: 01-6288420 Fax: 01-6275073
SIC: 90002 Employees: 25
Waste Disposal
Ms Helen O'Hagan Proprietor

Rentokil Initial Ltd
47 Terenure Road East
Dublin 6
Phone: 01-4902788 Fax: 01-4920861
Email: info@rentokil-initial.ie
Web: http://www.rentokil-initial.ie
SIC: 90002 Employees: 100
Pest Control
Mr Fergus Reynolds Chief Executive
Mr Micheal O'Mahoney Sales & Marketing Manager

Shannon Environmental Services
Smiths Town Industrial Estate
Shannon Co. Clare
Phone: 061-708699 Fax: 061-708647
Email: info@chemisloc.ie
SIC: 90002 Employees: 50
Chemical Waste Disposal
Ms Hilary Lawless Managing Director
Mr Tony O'Sullivan Accountant

Wheel Bin Services Ltd
3 Williamsons Place
Dundalk Co. Louth
Phone: 042-9330789 Fax: 042-9330730
Web: http://www.oxigen.ie
SIC: 90002 Employees: 60
Waste Collection Services
Mr Sean Doyle Managing Director
Ms Leontia Lord Financial Controller

ID Sterile Technologies Ltd
3a Sandyford Office Park
Blackthorn Avenue
Dublin 18
Phone: 01-2604818 Fax: 01-2604818
SIC: 90003 Employees: 30
Waste Disposal - Healthcare
Mr Andrew McCann General Manager

Sterile Technologies Ireland Ltd
430 Beech Road
Western Industrial Estate
Dublin 12
Phone: 01-4565796 Fax: 01-4565295
Email: sti@iol.ie
SIC: 90003 Employees: 30
Waste Disposal - Healthcare
Mr Des Rogers Partner
Mr Tony Fall Partner

Membership Organisations

91 Membership Organisations
91111 Business Chamber/Trade Federations
91112 Business Clubs
91120 Professional Associations
91200 Trade Unions/Employee Groups
91310 Religious/Similar Groups
91311 Presbyteries
91312 Presbyterian Religion
91313 Church of Ireland Religion
91315 Methodist Religion
91317 Baptist Religion
91318 Pentecostal Religion
91319 Places of Worship (Other)
91320 Political Parties/Groups
91331 Clubs & Associations – Governing Bodies
91332 Clubs & Associations
91333 Housing Associations
91334 Youth Centres/Clubs
91335 Community Services/Centres/Groups

Ballybeg CDP Ltd Co
Project Office
Ballybeg
Waterford Co. Waterford
Phone: 051-350100 Fax: 051-357917
Email: cdp.ballybeg@oceanfree.net
SIC: 91111 Employees: 50
Community Developement Organisation
Ms Briege Dowling Managing Director

Area Development Management Ltd
Holbrook House
Holles Street
Dublin 2
Phone: 01-2400700 Fax: 01-6610411
Email: enquiries@adm.ie
Web: http://www.adm.ie
SIC: 91120 Employees: 50
Local Economic Development Association
Dr Tony Crooks Chief Executive Officer
Mr Kevin McCambridge Financial Controller
Mr David Brennan Company Secretary
Mr Scott Thompson Computer Manager

Comhairle
7th Floor Hume House
Ballsbridge
Dublin 4
Phone: 01-6059000 Fax: 01-6059099
Email: comhairle@comhairle.ie
Web: http://www.comhairle.ie
SIC: 91120 Employees: 55
Public Information Body
Ms Leonie Lunny Chief Executive
Ms Mary Fitzgerald Administrator
Mr Brendan O'Dea Training Officer
Mr Tony McQuinn Senior Manager

County & City Finance Officers Assoc
Dublin Corporation Block 1 Floor 5
Civic Offices Fishamble Street
Dublin 8
Phone: 01-6722173 Fax: 01-6779050
Email: info@dublincorp.ie
SIC: 91120 Employees: 34
Local Authority - Finance
Mr John Sheridan Deputy Finance Officer
Mr Micheal Redmond Finance Manager

Director of Consumer Affairs Office
4 Harcourt Road
Dublin 2
Phone: 01-4025555 Fax: 01-4025501
SIC: 91120 Employees: 45
Consumer Pricing Observers
Mr William Fagan Director
Mr Bernard O'Kelly Assistant Principal
Mr Colin Baird Information Officer

GSM Association
Blackrock Co. Dublin
Phone: 01-2695922 Fax: 01-2695958
Web: http://www.gsmworld.com
SIC: 91120 Employees: 30
Membership Organisation for GSM
Ms Margaret Keegan Manager
Ms Liz Crawley Finance Director
Ms Marie King Sales Director
Mr Oliver Lebaf IT Manager

Inst. of Chartered Secretaries & Administrators
PO Box 7568
Foxrock
Dublin 18
Phone: 01-2832451 Fax: 01-2832452
Email: irishoffice@icsa.co.uk
Web: http://www.icsa.org.uk
SIC: 91120 Employees: 151
Professional & Training Institute
Mr Tony O'Dwyer President

Institute of Engineers
22 Clyde Road
Ballsbridge
Dublin 4
Phone: 01-6684341 Fax: 01-6685508
Email: info@iei.ie
Web: http://www.iei.ie
SIC: 91120 Employees: 25
Professional Body
Dr Jane Grimson President
Mr Sean Connolly PR Officer

Irish Horse Racing Authority
Leopardstown Racecourse
Foxrock
Dublin 18
Phone: 01-2892888 Fax: 01-2892019
Email: info@irishracing.iha.ie
Web: http://www.iha.ie
SIC: 91120 Employees: 65
Authority for Horse Racing in Ireland
Mr Martin Moore Chief Executive
Mr Ben Daley Administration Manager
Ms Betty O'Connell Marketing/Promotions Dept
Mr Kieran O'Sullivan Technical Manager

Irish Industrial Explosives
87-89 Waterloo Road
Dublin 4
Phone: 01-6685193 Fax: 01-6685248
SIC: 91120 Employees: 105
Professional Association
Mr Karl Strecker Managing Director
Mr Brendan Piggott Financial Controller
Mr Bill Cashman Engineer
Mr Declan Murphy Group Accountant

Irish Music Rights Organisation Ltd
Copyright House, Pembroke Row
Lower Baggot Street
Dublin 2
Phone: 01-6614844 Fax: 01-6763125
Email: info@imro.ie
Web: http://www.imro.ie
SIC: 91120 Employees: 45
Arts/Cultural Bodies
Mr Adrian Gaffney Chief Executive
Ms Carmel Ryan Company Secretary
Mr Owen Colley IT Manager

Irish Nurses Organisation
11 Fitzwilliam Place
Dublin 2
Phone: 01-6760137 Fax: 01-6610466
Email: ino@ino.ie
Web: http://www.ino.ie
SIC: 91120 Employees: 65
Professional Body/Union for Nurses
Mr Liam Doran Chief Executive Officer
Ms Una O'Brien Accounting Officer
Ms Lenore Mrkwicka Deputy General Secretary
Ms Louise Brown Computer Manager

Law Society of Ireland
Blackhall Place
Dublin 7
Phone: 01-6710711 Fax: 01-6710704
Email: lawsociety@iol.ie
Web: http://www.lawsociety.ie
SIC: 91120 Employees: 130
Regulatory & Educational Body
Mr Ken Murphy Director General
Mr Killian MacDomhnaill Financial Director
Ms Maureen Seabrook Personnel Officer
Mr Conal O'Boyle Editor
Mr Tom Blennerhasset Computer Manager

Registry Office of The Turf Club
The Curragh
Kildare Co. Kildare
Phone: 045-445600 Fax: 045-445699
SIC: 91120 Employees: 35
Professional Organisation
Mr Brian Kavanagh Chief Executive
Mr Denis Egan Financial Controller

Civil and Public Service Union
19/20 Adele Road
Dublin 2
Phone: 01-6765394 Fax: 01-6762918
Email: headoffice@cpsu.ie
Web: http://www.cpsu.ie
SIC: 91200 Employees: 23
Trade Union for Civil Servants
Mr Blair Horan General Secretary
Ms Ursula Nolan Financial Secretary

Communication Worker's Union
575 North Circular Road
Dublin 1
Phone: 01-8366388 Fax: 01-8365582
Email: info@cwu.ie
Web: http://www.cwu.ie
SIC: 91200 Employees: 25
Trade Union
Mr Con Scanlon General Secretary
Mr Joe Maher Deputy General Secretary

Impact Union
Nerney's Court
Dublin 1
Phone: 01-8171500 Fax: 01-8171501
Web: http://www.iol.ie/arena/impact
SIC: 91200 Employees: 55
Trade Union
Mr Peter McLoone General Secretary
Ms Anna Leonard Accounts Manager
Ms Vera Smyth Administration Officer
Mr Bernard Harbour Information Officer
Ms Valerie West Computer Manager

Irish Congress of Trade Unions
31-32 Parnell Square
Dublin 1
Phone: 01-8897777 Fax: 01-8872012
Email: congress@ictu.ie
Web: http://www.ictu.ie
SIC: 91200 Employees: 35
Trade Union Organisation
Mr David Begg General Secretary
Mr Tommy Coleman Finance Manager
Mr Oliver Donohoe Press/Information Officer

Irish National Teachers Organisation
35 Parnell Square
Dublin 1
Phone: 01-8722533 Fax: 01-8722462
Email: editor@into.ie
Web: http://www.into.ie
SIC: 91200 Employees: 31
Union & Intouch Magazine
Mr Joe O'Toole General Manager
Ms Cecelia Power Sales Manager

Mandate
9 Cavendish Row
Dublin 1
Phone: 01-8746321 Fax: 01-8729581
Email: mandate@mandate.ie
SIC: 91200 Employees: 43
Trade Associatons & Trade Unions
Mr Owen Nulty General Secretary
Mr Brendan Archibald Personnel Director
Ms Margie O'Rourke Technical Manager

SIPTU Headquarters
Liberty Hall
Eden Quay
Dublin 1
Phone: 01-8749731 Fax: 01-8749368
Email: info@siptu.ie
Web: http://www.siptu.ie
SIC: 91200 Employees: 160
Trade Union
Mr John McDonald General Secretary
Mr John Fay Head of Finance/Administration
Mr Seamus Shields Head of Publications
Mr Tony Hughes Head of Systems Department

Salvation Army
York House
York Street
Dublin 2
Phone: 01-4785623 Fax: 01-4785623
SIC: 91310 Employees: 24
Religious Group - Salvation Army - Mens Hostel
Maj William Richmond Officer in Charge

YMCA
Aungier Street Complex
Aungier Street
Dublin 2
Phone: 01-4782607 Fax: 01-4781896
Email: info@ymca.ie
Web: http://www.ymca.ie
SIC: 91310 Employees: 25
Christian Organistation
Mr David Barry Chief Executive
Ms Hazel Jeffers Finance Manager
Ms Mary Seery Kearney Deputy Chief Executive

Central Office of Church of Ireland
Church of Ireland House, Church Avenue
Rathmines
Dublin 6
Phone: 01-4978422 Fax: 01-4978821
Email: office@rcbdub.org
Web: http://www.ireland.anglican.org
SIC: 91313 Employees: 40
Administration Headquarters Church of Ireland
Mr Robert Sherwood Chief Officer & Secretary
Mr Dennis Riordan Finance Manager
Ms Valerie Beatty Head of G&S Services
Mr Ken Cinnamond IT Manager

Irish Rugby Football Union
62 Lansdowne Road
Ballsbridge
Dublin 4
Phone: 01-6473800 Fax: 01-6473801
Email: info@irfu.ie
Web: http://www.irfu.ie
SIC: 91331 Employees: 300
Irish Rugby Promotion
Mr Philip Browne Chief Executive
Mr John Lyons Treasurer
Mr Ray Loughead President
Mr Martin Murphy Operations Director

Bohemian Football Club
Dalymount Park
Dublin 7
Phone: 01-8680923 Fax: 01-8686460
Email: bohemians@eircom.net
SIC: 91332 Employees: 30
Sports Clubs & Assocaitions
Mr Gerry Cuffe Honorary Secretary
Mr Alan Williams Commerical Manager
Mr Dale O'Reilly President

Brainwave (Irish Epilepsy Association)
249 Crumlin Road
Dublin 12
Phone: 01-4557500 Fax: 01-4557013
Email: info@epilepsy.ie
Web: http://www.epilepsy.ie
SIC: 91332 Employees: 29
Epilepsy Association
Mr Mike Glynn Chief Executive
Ms Elizabeth Ryan Accounts Manager
Ms Marion Wilkinson Director of Services

Construction Industry Federation
Construction House
Canal Road
Dublin 6
Phone: 01-4977487 Fax: 01-4966953
Email: cif@cif.ie
Web: http://www.cif.ie
SIC: 91332 Employees: 70
Construction Federation
Mr Liam Kelleher Director General
Mr Eugene O'Neill Secretary/Financial Controller
Ms Renee McManus Personnel Manager
Mr Peter McCabe Director Business Development

Irish Wheelchair Association
Saint Georges Terrace
Carrick On Shannon Co. Leitrim
Phone: 078-20811 Fax: 078-20569
Email: drclm@iwa.ie
Web: http://www.iwa.ie
SIC: 91332 Employees: 265
Associations & Institutes
Ms Imelda Gaffey Community Manager

The Watergarden
Ladywell Street
Thomastown
Kilkenny Co. Kilkenny
Phone: 05-624690 Fax: 056-54766
SIC: 91332 Employees: 40
Working With People That Have Special Needs
Mr Merlin Brockette Manager

TPN Ireland Ltd
3 Naas Road Industrial Park
Dublin 12
Phone: 01-4569632 Fax: 01-4553115
SIC: 91332 Employees: 36
Parental Nutrition
Mr Paul Mullaly Manager

Housing Institute of Ireland
57-61 Lansdowne Road
Dublin 4
Phone: 01-6686233 Fax: 01-6689135
Email: info@ipa.ie
SIC: 91333 Employees: 100
Housing Education & Research Body
Mr John Gallagher Director General
Mr Cyril Sullivan Financial Controller
Ms Eileen Kelly Sales & Marketing Manager
Mr Tom Fuller Computer Manager

Catholic Youth Care
Arran Quay
Dublin 7
Phone: 01-8725055 Fax: 01-8725010
Email: info@cyc.ie
Web: http://www.cyc.ie
SIC: 91334 Employees: 100
Diocesan Youth Agency
Rev Jim Caffrey Director
Mr Edmond O'Connor Finance Manager
Sr Uainin Clarke Chairperson
Ms Maire Ni Chionnaiin Head Of Youth Work Services

National Youth Federation
20 Lower Dominic Street
Dublin 1
Phone: 01-8729933 Fax: 01-8724183
Email: info@nyf.ie
Web: http://www.nyf.ie
SIC: 91334 Employees: 23
Youth Training & Social Work
Mr Tony Murphy Chief Executive
Mr Sean Moriarty Treasurer
Ms Siobhan Cotter President

An Cosan
Kiltelown Village Centre, Jobstown
Tallaght
Dublin 24
Phone: 01-4628488 Fax: 01-4628496
Email: info@ancosan.com
SIC: 91335 Employees: 27
Community Enterprise & Educational Childcare
Ms Rosemarie McGill Chief Executive

County Wexford Community Workshop Ltd
Bellefield
Enniscorthy Co. Wexford
Phone: 054-33069 Fax: 054-34788
Email: info@cwcwe.ie
Web: http://www.cwcwe.ie
SIC: 91335 Employees: 30
Rehabilitation Workshops
Mr Trevor Jacob Manager
Mr Colin Levington Finance Manager
Ms Marie Plummer Personnel Manager

Drimangh Development Group
Mother McCauley Centre
Curlew Road
Dublin 12
Phone: 01-4552771 Fax: 01-4552771
SIC: 91335 Employees: 41
Community Employment
Ms Pat Clarke
Ms Anette Gannon

Old Youghal Road Project
Old Youghal Road
Mayfield
Cork Co. Cork
Phone: 021-4551586 Fax: 021-4551586
SIC: 91335 Employees: 30
Community Centre
Ms Rosella Sheehan Manager

Ringsend District Community Centre
Thorncastle Street
Ringsend
Dublin 4
Phone: 01-6604789 Fax: 01-6672351
SIC: 91335 Employees: 25
Community Centre
Ms Orla Murphy Assistant supervisor

Seanphara Community Unit
St Cancices Road
Glasnevin
Dublin 11
Phone: 01-8373722 Fax: 01-8272720
SIC: 91335 Employees: 45
Community Services
Ms Kay Gilmore Manager

Recreational, Cultural & Sporting

92 Recreational, Cultural & Sporting
92110 Film Production/Distribution
92130 Cinemas
92201 Radio Stations
92202 Television Stations
92311 Theatre
92312 Music Composers
92320 Art Galleries/Museums
92330 Fair & Amusement Park Activities
92349 Entertainment (Other)
92400 News Agency Activities
92510 Libraries
92521 Museums
92530 Zoos, Gardens & Nature Reserves
92610 Sports Arenas & Stadiums
92611 Ice Rinks & Roller Skating Rinks
92612 Bowling Alleys
92614 Horse Riding Stables/Schools
92615 Golf Courses
92616 Leisure Swimming & Sport Centres
92617 Outdoor Education/Pursuits Centres
92620 Sport/Recreational Services
92622 Horse Trainers
92623 Horse Jockeys
92710 Betting Shops
92720 Amusement Arcades

Agtel
37 Fitzwilliam Square
Dublin 2
Phone: 01-6053737 Fax: 01-6766137
Email: info@agtel.ie
Web: http://www.agtel.ie
SIC: 92110 Employees: 50
TV & Video Production
Mr John Cummins Managing Director
Mr Vernon Crowley Financial Controller

Mint Productions
1 Kengar Mews
Rathgar Avenue
Dublin 6
Phone: 01-4913333 Fax: 01-4913334
SIC: 92110 Employees: 40
Broadcasting & Corporate Productions
Mr Steve Carson Proprietor

Screen Scene Ltd
41 Upper Mount Street
Dublin 2
Phone: 01-6611501 Fax: 01-6610491
Email: info@screenscene.ie
Web: http://www.screenscene.ie
SIC: 92110 Employees: 52
Post Production
Mr Eamonn Maloney Director
Ms Maura O'Byrne Financial Controller
Mr Jim Duggan Sales Director
Mr Alan Byrne Director

The Yard
20 Upper Sheriff Street
Dublin 1
Phone: 01-8553545 Fax: 01-8553565
Email: info@theyard.ie
Web: http://www.theyard.ie
SIC: 92110 Employees: 35
Post Production/Editing & Transmission
Mr Lawrence Fee Managing Director
Mr Peter O'Hara Financial Controller
Ms Liz MacDonnell Sales & Marketing Manager

Gate Multiplex
North Main Street
Cork Co. Cork
Phone: 021-4279595 Fax: 021-4279891
SIC: 92130 Employees: 40
Cinema
Ms Margaret Green Manager
Mr Andrew Beasley Finance Manager

Reel Picture
Time Square
Ballincollig
Cork Co. Cork
Phone: 021-4876300 Fax: 021-4876302
SIC: 92130 Employees: 30
Cinemas & Bowling Alleys
Mr Jim O'Leary Manager

Sheridan IMAX
Parnell Centre
Parnell Street
Dublin 1
Phone: 01-8174200 Fax: 01-8174230
Email: info@dublinimax.ie
Web: http://www.dublinimax.ie
SIC: 92130 Employees: 35
Cinemas & Bowling Alleys
Mr Francis Murray Manager

Sterndale Holdings Ltd
Ormonde Centre
Victoria Road
Greystones Co. Wicklow
Phone: 01-2872554 Fax: 01-2010736
Email: grahams@eircom.net
Web: http://www.slaneyplaza.net
SIC: 92130 Employees: 45
Cinema Company
Mr Graham Spurling Managing Director

Carlow Kildare Radio
Lismard House Tullow Street
Carlow Co. Carlow
Phone: 0503-41048 Fax: 0503-41047
Email: info@ckrfm.com
Web: http://www.ckrfm.com
SIC: 92201 Employees: 70
Radio Station
Ms Deborah O'Neill Chief Executive
Mr Seamus Reddy Finance Manager
Mr Ronan Sirr Production Manager

CRC FM
Market Square
Castlebar Co. Mayo
Phone: 094-25555 Fax: 094-25989
Email: crcfm@eircom.net
Web: http://www.castlebar.ie/crcfm
SIC: 92201 Employees: 35
Community Radio Station
Mr Peter Killeen Station Manager
Ms Colette Ford Sales Manager

FM 104
Hume House, Pembroke Road
Ballsbridge
Dublin 4
Phone: 01-6689689 Fax: 01-6689401
Email: mail@fm104.ie
Web: http://www.fm104.ie
SIC: 92201 Employees: 45
Radio Station
Mr Dermot Hanrahan General Manager
Mr Tim Fenn Financial Controller
Ms Helena Kelly Personnel Manager
Ms Margaret Nelson Sales Director
Mr Andy Matthews Production Manager

FM Shannonside
Minard House
Sligo Road
Longford Co. Longford
Phone: 043-48555 Fax: 043-48384
Email: sales@shannonside.tinet.ie
Web: http://www.shannonside.tinet.ie
SIC: 92201 Employees: 50
Radio Broadcast
Mr Richard Devlin Chief Executive
Mr Mel O'Brien Credit Controller
Ms Kathy Rodgers Personnel Director
Ms Kathy Casey Sales Co-Ordinator

Limericks Live 95fm
PO Box 295, Radio House
Richmond Court, Dock Road
Limerick Co. Limerick
Phone: 061-400195 Fax: 061-419595
Email: mail@live95fm.ie
Web: http://www.live95fm.ie
SIC: 92201 Employees: 35
Radio Station
Mr Joe Nash General Manager
Ms Edel Ryan Madigan Finance Manager
Mr Gerry Long Sales Manager
Mr James Hyland Production Manager
Mr Ronan O'Connor Computer Manager

LMFM
The Broadcasting Centre
Rathmullen Road
Drogheda Co. Louth
Phone: 041-9832000 Fax: 041-9832957
Email: info@lmfm.ie
SIC: 92201 Employees: 40
Radio Station
Mr Michael Crawley Managing Director
Ms Eileen Duggan Promotions Manager
Mr Eddie Cafferty Technical Advisor

Lyric Fm
Cornmarket Building
Cornmarket
Limerick Co. Limerick
Phone: 061-207300 Fax: 061-207390
Email: lyric@rte.ie
Web: http://www.lyricfm.ie
SIC: 92201 Employees: 40
Radio Stations
Mr Seamus Crimmins Chief Executive
Ms Mary O'Mahoney Sales & Marketing Director
Mr Ian Smith IT Manager

Midlands Radio 3 FM
The Mall
William Street
Tullamore Co. Offaly
Phone: 0506-51333 Fax: 0506-52546
Email: goodcompany@midlandsradio.fm
SIC: 92201 Employees: 60
Radio Stations
Mr Joe Yerkes Managing Director
Ms Anne Conroy Accountant
Mr Albert Fitzgerald Sales Director
Mr Michael Reid Programming Director

NEAR FM
CDC Bunratty Drive
Dublin 17
Phone: 01-8671016 Fax: 01-8486111
Email: nearfm@iol.ie
Web: http://www.nearfm.ie
SIC: 92201 Employees: 30
Radio Station
Mr Jack Byrne Chairman
Ms Sally Galiana Office Manager
Mr Ciaran Murray Office Manager
Mr Vincent Teeling Computer Manager

Radio County Sounds Ltd 103 Fm
The Majestic
Gouldhill
Mallow Co. Cork
Phone: 022-22961 Fax: 022-42488
Email: info@103fm.ie
Web: http://www.103fm.ie
SIC: 92201 Employees: 25
Radio Stations
Mr Michael Brett Studio Manager

Radio Kerry Teoranta
Main Street
Tralee Co. Kerry
Phone: 066-7123600 Fax: 066-7129887
Email: sales@radiokerry.ie
Web: http://www.radiokerry.ie
SIC: 92201 Employees: 50
Radio Station
Mr Paul Sheehan General Manager
Ms Marie Sweeney Finance Manager

Radio Kilkenny
Hebron Road
Hebron Industrial Estate
Kilkenny Co. Kilkenny
Phone: 056-62777 Fax: 056-63586
Email: onair@radiokilkenny.com
SIC: 92201 Employees: 30
Radio Station
Mr Dermot Healy Chief Executive
Mr Paddy Horohan Sales & Marketing Manager

Radio Limerick 95FM
17 Patrick Street
Limerick Co. Limerick
Phone: 061-319595 Fax: 061-419890
Email: rlotv@netscape.net
Web: http://www.rlo105.com
SIC: 92201 Employees: 25
Radio/ Satellite Services
Mr Gerard Madden Chief Executive
Ms Carmel Burke Advertising Sales Manager

Radio Na Gaeltachta
Casla
Connemara
Galway Co. Galway
Phone: 091-506677 Fax: 091-506688
Email: rng@rte.ie
Web: http://www.rte.ie
SIC: 92201 Employees: 64
Radio Broadcast
Mr Tomas Mac Con Iiomair Managing Director
Mr Seosamh O'Braonain Finance Manager

RTE
Donnybrook
Dublin 4
Phone: 01-2083111 Fax: 01-2083080
Email: rte@iol.ie
Web: http://www.rte.ie/
SIC: 92201 Employees: 2000
Broadcasting
Mr Bob Collins Director General
Mr Gerard O'Brien Finance Manager
Mr Vincent Bradley Director of Personnel
Mr Liam Miller Head of Programming
Mr Michael Gallagher Head of IT

RTE Cork
Father Matthew Street
Cork Co. Cork
Phone: 021-4805805 Fax: 021-4273829
Web: http://www.rte.ie/tv
SIC: 92201 Employees: 60
Radio Stations
Mr Colm Crowley Head of Production
Mr Brian O'Dwyer IT Manager

Shannonside Northern Sound Radio
Minard House
Sligo Road
Longford Co. Longford
Phone: 043-47777 Fax: 043-46591
Email: shannonside@eircom.net
SIC: 92201 Employees: 30
Radio Station
Mr Richard Devlin Chief Executive Officer
Ms Cathy Casey Sales Manager

South East Radio
Custom House Quay
Wexford Co. Wexford
Phone: 053-45200 Fax: 053-45295
Email: info@southeastradio.ie
Web: http://www.southeastradio.ie
SIC: 92201 Employees: 25
Radio Broadcast
Mr Eamon Butler Managing Director
Mr Liam Dwyer General Manager

Tipp FM
Davis Road
Clonmel Co. Tipperary
Phone: 052-26222 Fax: 052-25447
Email: reception@tippfm.com
Web: http://www.tippfm.com
SIC: 92201 Employees: 40
Radio Station
Mr Paul Byrne Chief Executive
Ms Veronica Wise Finance Manager
Ms Eleanor Lahart Sales Manager
Ms Sarah McCormack Production Manager
Mr Arron Burchall IT Manager

Waterford Local Radio FM
Radio Centre Georges Street
Waterford Co. Waterford
Phone: 051-877592 Fax: 051-877420
Email: info@wlrfm.com
Web: http://www.wlrfm.com
SIC: 92201 Employees: 23
Advertising Companies
Mr Des Whelan Manager
Ms Sharon Hogan Administration Manager
Mr Jonathan Earl Sales Manager

WLR FM
The Radio Centre Georges Street
Waterford Co. Waterford
Phone: 051-872248 Fax: 051-877420
Email: sales@wlrfm.com
Web: http://www.wlr.ie
SIC: 92201 Employees: 35
Radio Station
Mr Des Whelan Managing Director
Mr Jonathan Earl Advertising Manager
Mr Paul Byrne Computer Manager

Coco Television Productions Ltd
19 Creighton Street
Dublin 2
Phone: 01-6170480 Fax: 01-6170481
Email: info@cocotelevision.ie
Web: http://www.cocotelevision.ie
SIC: 92202 Employees: 25
Television Production
Mr Stuart Switzer Managing Director

Dermot McCabe
Annex 8
RTE Donnybrook
Dublin 4
Phone: 045-522079 Fax: 01-2083109
Email: mccabed@rte.ie
Web: http://www.rte.ie
SIC: 92202 Employees: 30
Head of Broadcast Systems Engineering
Mr Dermot McCabe

Independent Pictures
37/39 Fitzwilliam Square
Dublin 2
Phone: 01-6053700 Fax: 01-6766137
SIC: 92202 Employees: 100
Television Production
Mr John Cummins Managing Director
Mr Vernon Crowley Financial Controller

Multi-Channel TV Cork
5 Georges Quay
Abbey Court House
Cork Co. Cork
Phone: 021-4311111 Fax: 021-4311481
SIC: 92202 Employees: 70
Cable TV Station
Mr Neill McNally Operations Manager
Ms Mary Horgan Accounts Manager
Ms Helen Maloney Personnel Manager
Mr Stephen O'Mahony Sales & Marketing Manager

Telegael Ltd
Spiddal
Galway Co. Galway
Phone: 091-553460 Fax: 091-553464
Email: eolas@telegael.com
Web: http://www.telegael.com
SIC: 92202 Employees: 35
Television Facilities Company
Mr Paul Cummins Managing Director
Ms Maeve Joyce Development Manager
Mr Enda Bonner Sales Manager
Ms Siobhan Gabhra Productions Manager

TV3
Westgate Business Park
Ballymount
Dublin 24
Phone: 01-4193333 Fax: 01-4193322
Email: info@tv3.ie
Web: http://www.tv3.ie
SIC: 92202 Employees: 150
Television Network
Mr Rick Hedderington Director
Mr Michael Cahill Personnel Manager
Mr Pat Kylie Sales Manager

Tyrone Productions Ltd
23 Little Mary Street
Dublin 7
Phone: 01-8894900 Fax: 01-8894993
Email: tyrone@tyroneproductions.ie
SIC: 92202 Employees: 30
Television Production
Ms Joan Egan Managing Director
Mr Siun Ni Raghallaigh Accountant
Ms Patrica Carroll General Manager

Windmill Lane Pictures Ltd
4 Windmill Lane
Dublin 2
Phone: 01-6713444 Fax: 01-6718413
Email: info@windmilllane.com
Web: http://www.windmilllane.com
SIC: 92202 Employees: 70
Television Production
Mr John Ingram Managing Director
Mr Jim Collins Finance Manager
Mr Dave Quinn Personnel Manager
Mr Kevin Galligan Sales & Marketing Manager
Mr Declan Hogan Computer Manager

Abbey Theatre
National Theatre Society
26 Lower Abbey Street
Dublin 1
Phone: 01-8748741 Fax: 01-8729177
Email: press@abbeytheatre.ie
Web: http://www.abbeytheatre.ie
SIC: 92311 Employees: 120
Theatre
Mr Richard Wakely Managing Director
Mr Martin Fahy General Manager
Ms Grainne Howe Secretary
Mr Tony Wakefield Technical Director
Ms Katherine Brownridge Computer Manager

Cork Opera House
The Box Office
Emmet Place
Cork Co. Cork
Phone: 021-4270022 Fax: 021-4272504
Email: halfmoontheatre@eircom.net
Web: http://www.corkoperahouse.ie
SIC: 92311 Employees: 60
Theatre
Mr Gerry Burns Managing Director
Ms Aileen Sweeney Finance Manager
Ms Sandra Hourihan Box Office Manager

National Concert Hall
Earlsfort Terrace
Dublin 2
Phone: 01-4170077 Fax: 01-4170078
Email: info@nch.ie
Web: http://www.nch.ie
SIC: 92311 Employees: 80
Concert Hall
Ms Judith Woodworth Director
Mr John Nolan Finance Manager
Ms Jacqueline Mahon Marketing Manager
Mr Barry Walsh Events & Operations Manager

Point Exhibition Co Ltd
East Link Bridge
Dublin 1
Phone: 01-8366777 Fax: 01-8366422
Email: admin@thepoint.ie
Web: http://www.thepoint.ie
SIC: 92311 Employees: 25
Theatre & Exhibition Hall
Mr Michael Adamson Chief Executive
Mr Kieran Spillane Financial Controller
Mr Cormac Rennick General Manager

Irish Museum of Modern Art
Military Road
Kilmainham
Dublin 8
Phone: 01-6129900 Fax: 01-6129999
Email: info@modernart.ie
Web: http://www.modernart.ie
SIC: 92320 Employees: 100
Irish Museum Modern Art
Mr Colm Ronan Banquet Manager
Mr Frank Brennan Finance Manager
Ms Jean Stanley Personnel Manager
Ms Catherine O'Byrne Sales Banquet Co-Ordindator
Ms Rowena Neville Assistant Press Officer

National Gallery of Ireland
Merrion Square West
Dublin 2
Phone: 01-6615133 Fax: 01-6615372
Email: argal@eircom.net
Web: http://www.nationalgallery.ie
SIC: 92320 Employees: 80
Art Gallery
Mr Raymond Keaveney Director
Mr Gerry D'Arcy Finance Manager
Ms Marie Fitzgerald Shop Manager

National Museum of Ireland
Kildare Street
Dublin 2
Phone: 01-6777444 Fax: 01-6766116
Email: natmuscb@indigo.ie
SIC: 92320 Employees: 150
Art Museum
Dr Patrick Wallace Director
Mr Ciaran Butler Administrator
Ms Sylvia Frawley IT Manager

Unique Entertainment
4D Rosemount Park Drive
Ballycoolin
Dublin 11
Phone: 01-8226600 Fax: 01-8226611
Email: sales@unique-ent.ie
Web: http://www.unique-ent.ie
SIC: 92349 Employees: 30
Entertainment agencies
Mr Clive Jackson Managing Director
Ms Ingrid Murray Finance Manager
Mr Padraig Kelly Sales & Marketing Manager

Donegal County Library
Rosemount
Letterkenny Co. Donegal
Phone: 074-21968 Fax: 074-21740
Email: dglcolib@iol.ie
Web: http://www.donegal.ie
SIC: 92510 Employees: 35
Public Library
Mr Liam Ronayne County Librarian

National Library of Ireland
Kildare Street
Dublin 2
Phone: 01-6030200 Fax: 01-6766690
Email: info@nli.ie
Web: http://www.nli.ie
SIC: 92510 Employees: 80
National Library of Ireland
Mr Brendan O'Donoghue Director
Ms Sandra McDermott Sales Director

The Law Library
Distillery Building
Church Street
Dublin 7
Phone: 01-8174593 Fax: 01-8174901
SIC: 92510 Employees: 320
Law Library
Mr Barry O'Donnell Proprietor

Blarney Castle Estate
Blarney
Cork Co. Cork
Phone: 021-4385252 Fax: 021-4381518
Email: tornstill@eircom.net
SIC: 92521 Employees: 25
Castle
Mr Mervyn Johnston Managing Director

Greyhound Racing Stadium
Youghal Co. Cork
Phone: 024-92305 Fax: 024-92305
SIC: 92610 Employees: 24
Greyhound Racing Stadium
Mr Finbar Coleman Manager

Bray Bowl
Quinsboro Road
Bray Co. Wicklow
Phone: 01-2864455 Fax: 01-2864460
SIC: 92612 Employees: 30
Bowling Centres
Mr Fintan Quinn Proprietor
Mr Adrian Quinn Finance Manager

Druid's Glen Golf Club
Newtownmountkennedy
Greystones Co. Wicklow
Phone: 01-2873600 Fax: 01-2873699
Email: druids@indigo.ie
Web: http://www.druidsglen.ie
SIC: 92615 Employees: 60
Golf Club
Mr Dennis Kane General Manager
Ms Geraldine Dunne Financial Controller

Recreation

Fota Island Co Ltd
Fota Golf Club, Fota Island
Carrigtwohill
Cork Co. Cork
Phone: 021-4883700 Fax: 021-4883713
Email: reservations@fotaisland.ie
Web: http://www.fotaisland.ie
SIC: 92615 Employees: 30
Golf Club
Mr Eoin Cotter Managing Director
Mr Colin Donovan Finance Manager
Mr Kevin Mulcahay General Manager

Harbour Point Golf Club
Clash Road
Little Island
Cork Co. Cork
Phone: 021-4353094 Fax: 021-4354408
Email: hpoint@iol.ie
SIC: 92615 Employees: 25
Golf Club
Mr Sean O'Connell Proprietor
Ms Niamh O'Connell Manager

Hermitage Golf Club
Lucan Co. Dublin
Phone: 01-6264781 Fax: 01-6264781
SIC: 92615 Employees: 60
Golf Clubs & Courses
Mr Paddy Maguire General Manager

Luttrellstown Castle Country Club
Castleknock
Dublin 15
Phone: 01-8089900 Fax: 01-8089989
Email: enquiries@luttrellstown.ie
Web: http://www.luttrellstown.ie
SIC: 92615 Employees: 85
Golf Club & Exclusive Castle Accommodation
Mr John Flavin General Manager
Mr Brendan Donnellan Finance Manager
Ms Linda Halpin Personnel Manager
Ms Adrienne Clarke Sales & Marketing Manager
Ms Fiona Teehan Castle Operations Manager

Saint Helen's Bay Golf & Country Club
Kilrane
Rosslare Harbour
Wexford Co. Wexford
Phone: 053-33234 Fax: 053-33803
Email: sthelens@iol.ie
Web: http://www.sthelensbay.com
SIC: 92615 Employees: 40
Golf Club
Mr Larry Byrne Manager
Ms Louise Johnston Finance Manager
Mr Barry Brennan Sales & Marketing Manager

Tralee Golf Club - Bar & Restaurant
West Barrow
Ardfert
Tralee Co. Kerry
Phone: 066-7136379 Fax: 066-7136008
Email: info@tralee-golf.com
Web: http://www.tralee-golf.com
SIC: 92615 Employees: 45
Golf Club
Mr Patrick Nugent Manager

Athlone Leisure World
Diskin Enterprise Centre
Grace Road
Athlone Co. Westmeath
Phone: 0902-94766 Fax: 0902-94762
SIC: 92616 Employees: 35
Leisure Centre
Mr Turlough O'Brien Manager

Clondalkin Sports & Leisure Centre
Nangor Road
Clondalkin
Dublin 22
Phone: 01-4574858 Fax: 01-4576058
Email: scdls@eircom.net
Web: http://www.clondalkin.com/cslc
SIC: 92616 Employees: 70
Sports & Leisure Centre
Mr Richard Williams Managing Director
Ms Eithne O'Reilly Accounts Manager

Fermoy Leisure Centre
Town Park
Fermoy Co. Cork
Phone: 025-33272 Fax: 025-33232
SIC: 92616 Employees: 30
Leisure Centre
Ms Caroline Casey Manager

LeisurePlex
Malahide Road
Coolock
Dublin 17
Phone: 01-8485722 Fax: 01-8485729
SIC: 92616 Employees: 80
Leisure Centre
Ms Mairead Murphy Manager

Lucan Sports & Leisure Centre
Esker
Grissen Valley Park
Lucan Co. Dublin
Phone: 01-6241930 Fax: 01-6214128
SIC: 92616 Employees: 30
Sports & Leisure Centre
Mr Richie Williams Proprietor
Ms Norah Finn Senior Duty Manager

Splash World
Railway Square
Tramore
Waterford Co. Waterford
Phone: 051-390176 Fax: 051-390214
Email: info@splashworld.ie
Web: http://www.splashworld.ie
SIC: 92616 Employees: 30
Leisure Centre
Mr Bob Breen General Manager

Sports Link Ltd
Furry Park, Swords Road
Santry
Dublin 9
Phone: 01-8621200 Fax: 01-8621162
Email: info@sportslink.com
Web: http://www.sportslink.com
SIC: 92616 Employees: 50
Lesiure/Social Centre
Ms Orla Scott Manager

Tralee Regional Sports & Leisure Centre
Clounalour, Oakpark
Tralee Co. Kerry
Phone: 066-7126442 Fax: 066-7128160
Email: lboh@iol.ie
Web: http://www.traleesportscentre.com
SIC: 92616 Employees: 25
Leisure Sport Centre
Mr Liam Bohan Managing Director

Blessington Lakes Leisure Centre
Burgage
Blessington
Naas Co. Kildare
Phone: 045-865092 Fax: 045-865024
Email: blesslws@eircom.net
SIC: 92617 Employees: 31
Outdoor Adventure Centre
Mr Paul Ashmore Managing Director

Cavan Centre
Residential Centre for Outdoor Educ
Ballyjamesduff
Cavan Co. Cavan
Phone: 049-8544436 Fax: 049-8544436
SIC: 92617 Employees: 23
Outdoor Education
Mr Pat Carthy Director

Lough Muckno Activities Centre
Loughmuckno Leisure Park
Castleblayney Co. Monaghan
Phone: 042-9746356 Fax: 042-9746610
SIC: 92617 Employees: 25
Outdoor Adventure Centre
Ms Joan Langan Park Manager

Powerscourt Springs
Coolakay
Enniskerry
Bray Co. Wicklow
Phone: 01-2761000 Fax: 01-2761626
Email: info@powerscourtsprings.iol.ie
Web: http://www.powerscourtsprings.iol.ie
SIC: 92620 Employees: 50
Health Farm
Ms Catherine Harrington Manager
Ms Anne Murphy Finance Manager

Stewart's Sports Centre
Waterstown Avenue
Palmerstown
Dublin 20
Phone: 01-6269879 Fax: 01-6235759
SIC: 92620 Employees: 30
Sports Complex
Mr Eddie Ince Manager

Tallaght Sports Complex
Balrothery
Tallaght
Dublin 24
Phone: 01-4515105 Fax: 01-4515744
Email: padraic@indigo.ie
SIC: 92620 Employees: 40
Sports Complex
Mr Padraig Kenny Manager
Mr John Beattie Accountant
Mr Lorcan Shelley Duty Manager

Thurles Stadium Ltd
Townspark
Thurles Co. Tipperary
Phone: 0504-21003 Fax: 0504-26009
SIC: 92620 Employees: 25
Sport/Recreational Services
Mr Brian Collins Racing Manager

Friarstown Stables
Friarstown
Naas Co. Kildare
Phone: 045-521387 Fax: 045-522264
Email: prendergastkp@eircom.net
SIC: 92622 Employees: 30
Race Horse Trainer
Mr Kevin Prendergast Trainer
Ms Frances Doyle Accountant

JS Bolger
Glebe House
Culcullen
Carlow Co. Carlow
Phone: 056-43150 Fax: 056-43256
Email: jsb@iol.ie
SIC: 92622 Employees: 60
Horse Trainer
Mr Jim Bolger Proprietor

Boyle Bookmakers (Head Office)
31 Shop Street
Drogheda Co. Louth
Phone: 041-9834344 Fax: 041-9834258
SIC: 92710 Employees: 230
Betting Shop
Mr John Maguire General Manager
Ms Aileen McGinn Finance Manager
Ms Heather Glenn Operation Manager
Mr Feargal French IT Manager

Hackett Bookmakers
79 Dame Street
Dublin 2
Phone: 01-6775101 Fax: 01-6777938
Email: helpdesk@hackettbet.com
Web: http://www.hackettbet.com
SIC: 92710 Employees: 100
Bookmakers
Ms Monica Hackett Managing Director
Mr Paul Hackett Finance Manager
Mr John Hackett Sales & Marketing Manager
Mr Joe Creigton Technical Manager

Mulholland Bookmakers
Cuirt na Tra
Salthill
Galway Co. Galway
Phone: 091-523739 Fax: 091-526629
SIC: 92710 Employees: 30
Bookmakers
Ms Margaret Mulholland Proprietor

Power Leisure
Block 2, The Village Green
Tallaght
Dublin 24
Phone: 01-4045900 Fax: 01-4045901
Email: info@paddypower.com
Web: http://www.paddypower.com
SIC: 92710 Employees: 700
Bookmakers (Head Office)
Mr Stewart Kenny Chief Executive
Mr Charlie Kelly Company Secretary
Ms Tara Fullam HR Manager
Mr Jimmy Mangan Operations Manager
Mr Ben Traynor IT Manager

William Hill Call Centre
Unit 1 Advanced Factory
Dublin Road
Athlone Co. Westmeath
Phone: 0902-33003 Fax: 0902-33031
SIC: 92710 Employees: 200
Call Centre for Off-Shore Betting
Mr William Hill

Dawsons Family Fun
Strand Road
Bray Co. Wicklow
Phone: 01-2860974 Fax: 01-2865307
SIC: 92720 Employees: 45
Amusement Centres
Mr Fergal Fogarty Proprietor
Ms Suzanne Lenihan Financial Controller

Service Activities Other

93 Service Activities Other
93011 Dry Cleaning/Allied Services
93012 Launderette
93013 Laundries
93021 Hairdressers (Ladies)
93022 Hairdressers (Mixed)
93023 Hairdressers (Mens)
93024 Beauty Salons
93030 Funeral Parlours/Directors
93041 Health Studios/Gyms
93049 Personal Services (Other)
93051 Domestic Services
93052 Wedding Services

Prescotts Cleaners Ltd
56 St Brigids Road
Artane
Dublin 5
Phone: 01-8311100 Fax: 01-8311443
SIC: 93011 Employees: 100
Dry Cleaners
Mr Herbert Scarry Director

Clane Cleaners Ltd
Newbridge Industrial Estate
Newbridge
Naas Co. Kildare
Phone: 045-435455 Fax: 045-435456
SIC: 93012 Employees: 44
Laundry Services
Mr Pat Kelly Managing Director
Ms Sharon Clarke Company Secretary

Sovereign Launderies
Commons Road
Dromiskin
Dundalk Co. Louth
Phone: 042-9382550 Fax: 042-9382981
SIC: 93012 Employees: 26
Laundrette
Mr Jim Creaney Manager

Sak's Hair Stylists
15 Sackville Place
Dublin 1
Phone: 01-8786344 Fax: -
SIC: 93021 Employees: 23
Hairdressers
Ms Ann O'Reilly Proprietor

Sundrelle Accessories Ltd
U9 Ashbourne Business Park
Ashbourne
Navan Co. Meath
Phone: 01-8351199 Fax: 01-8352960
Email: sundrell@iol.ie
SIC: 93021 Employees: 29
Hairdressers
Mr Frank O'Gorman Managing Director

Peter Mark
The Plaza
15 Ely Place
Dublin 2
Phone: 01-6614888 Fax: 01-6613673
Email: info@petermark.ie
Web: http://www.petermark.ie
SIC: 93022 Employees: 1500
Hairdressing
Mr Mark Keaveney Joint Managing Director
Mr Paul Keaveney Financial Controller
Ms Jacqui Walpola Personnel Manager
Ms Jenny McDermot Marketing Manager

Robert Chambers
69 Grafton Street
Dublin 2
Phone: 01-6771323 Fax: 01-6712275
SIC: 93022 Employees: 40
Hairdressing Salon & School
Mr Robert Chambers Proprietor
Ms Fiona Hopwood Manager

Toni & Guy
44 Claredon Street
Dublin 2
Phone: 01-6714401 Fax: 01-6710211
SIC: 93022 Employees: 50
Hairdressers Unisex
Mr Alan Boyce Proprietor
Ms Helen Murray Assistant Manager

Finlays Funeral Home
Tierney Street
Ardee Co. Louth
Phone: 041-6853603 Fax: 041-6856353
Email: info@finlaysnet.com
Web: http://www.finlaysnet.com
SIC: 93030 Employees: 23
Funeral Director
Mr John Finlay Managing Director
Mr John Henessy Finance Manager

Leeside Leisure Centre
St Patricks Quay
Cork Co. Cork
Phone: 021-4551444 Fax: 021-4551445
Email: leisure@metropoleh.com
Web: http://www.metropole.com
SIC: 93041 Employees: 25
Health Clubs
Ms Niamh Harrington Manager

St Endas Sports Complex
Kilmallock Road
Limerick Co. Limerick
Phone: 061-410416 Fax: 061-319950
Email: stendasleisure@eircom.net
SIC: 93041 Employees: 30
Health Studios/Gyms
Ms Breda Deedigan Manager

Total Fitness
River Road
Castleknock
Dublin 15
Phone: 01-8221646 Fax: 01-8221636
SIC: 93041 Employees: 40
Health Club
Mr Callan Davidson Manager
Mr Patrick Herring Finance Manager
Ms Amy Keenan Sales Manager

Westpoint Health & Fitness Centre
Blanchardstown Centre
Blanchardstown
Dublin 15
Phone: 01-8221103 Fax: 01-8221946
SIC: 93041 Employees: 50
Health Club
Mr Denis McCoy Manager
Ms Anne Stack Personnel Officer

Waters Technology
Wexford Business Park
Drinagh
Wexford Co. Wexford
Phone: 053-21592 Fax: 053-21681
Web: http://www.waters.com
SIC: 93049 Employees: 80
Chromatography
Mr Terry Shortt Managing Director

Embassy of Australia
Fitzwilton House
Wilton Terrace
Dublin 2
Phone: 01-6761517 Fax: 01-6623566
Email: info@australianembasy.ie
Web: http://www.australianembasy.ie
SIC: 99000 Employees: 24
Embassy
Mr Robert Halverson Ambassador
Mr Peter Hurtitch First Secretary Admin
Ms Meave Counihan Personnel Director
Mr Michael Roche IT Officer

Embassy of France
36 Ailesbury Road
Ballsbridge
Dublin 4
Phone: 01-6680777 Fax: 01-2830178
Email: tresse@ambasrance.ie
Web: http://www.ambasfrance.ie
SIC: 99000 Employees: 45
Embassy of France
Mr Henri De Coignac Ambassador
Mr Ghirry Terrier First Secretary

Embassy of People's Republic of China
40 Ailesbury Road
Dublin 4
Phone: 01-2691707 Fax: 01-2839938
SIC: 99000 Employees: 24
Embassy
Mr Jinjiong Zheng Ambassador

Embassy of the Russian Federation
186 Orwell Road
Rathgar
Dublin 14
Phone: 01-4922048 Fax: 01-4923225
SIC: 99000 Employees: 24
Embassy of Russia
Mr Evguemi Mikhailov Ambassador

Embassy of the United Kingdom
29 Merrion Road
Dublin 4
Phone: 01-2053700 Fax: 01-2053885
Email: trade.dublin@fco.gov.uk
Web: http://www.britishembassy.ie
SIC: 99000 Employees: 50
Embassy
Sir Ivor Roberts Ambassador
Mr Martin McIntosh Commercial Counsellor
Ms Sarah Tiffin First Secretary (Economic)

Embassy of the United States of America
42 Elgin Road
Ballsbridge
Dublin 4
Phone: 01-6687122 Fax: 01-6689946
Email: info@usembassy.ie
Web: http://www.usembassy.ie
SIC: 99000 Employees: 40
Embassy
Mr Michael Sullivan Ambassador
Mr William Crawford Commercial Attache

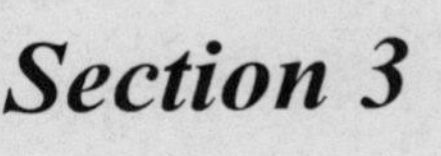

Section 3

Alphabetical Index of Companies

Alpabetical Index

Index

Company Credentials

Ireland's Leader in Databases, Telemarketing and Business Intelligence

Established in 1994, The **IDS Media Group** is one of the leading International Customer Relationship Management Services companies.

The company exists to; *Satisfy our client's need to build, develop and exploit profitable relationships with customers, throughout the world.*

We do this proving International Customer Relationship Management (CRM) Services, using advanced Data Manipulation and Contact Management tools. This enables us to manage the communication with selected customers using various direct media packages, optimising their long-term value. We do this using highly trained staff from a Multilingual, Multi-Channel, Web Enabled Customer Contact Centre

Business Intelligence from Data
The company has developed a package of Data Manipulation services which build and enhance the quality of databases. Services range from basic data entry to cleaning and profiling data. These services allow companies to save on their data management and processing costs, as well as gain useful marketing knowledge through the manipulation, data warehousing, data mining and profiling of their own databases.

Business Information – UK and Ireland
IDS owns and distributes the largest single source of business intelligence on all 275,000 businesses in Ireland as well as the UK Business Universe, a database of over 3 million UK firms.

Business Information – UK, Europe, Austral-Asia and the Americas
IDS distributes marketing information on businesses and consumers world-wide.

Telephone Marketing
IDS currently provides telemarketing solutions to companies across the world, serving the b2b and b2c markets. Our success has been achieved by consistently investing in high quality personnel and sophisticated call handling technology. These resources are employed to suit any project large or small, ensuring the client only pays for the resources they require.

Direct Marketing and Call Centre Consultancy
IDS has many years of experience in building databases, telemarketing and in the building and operation of call centres. Specific assignments recently have included building a world wide marketing database, script writing for telemarketing projects and recruitment of operators into a client service call centre.

Market Research
The company provides both quantitative and qualitative Market Research. Using Computer Aided Telephone Interview (CATI) software, IDS can conduct 1000s of telephone interviews with businesses and consumers world wide. Past studies involve customer retention, customer satisfaction, buyer behaviour, communications research and market testing of new products.

Business Directories
IDS also publishes a range of national and local directories as well as specialist reports covering both business to business topics and specialist industry sectors. The directories are available on hard copy and CD.

The Cream of

Irish Industry Commerce & Government

€ Euro Order Form

A Directory of 5000 of the Largest Businesses in the Republic of Ireland

The Cream of Irish Industry Directory is the most comprehensive and current collection of business information on the Republic of Ireland's largest companies, organisations and government bodies. It is the essential marketing tool and reference guide to the Republic of Ireland Market. It provides full contact details and information on the cream of Irish manufacturing, services and government sectors. As well as 5000 of the Top Company's business records, 14,000+ senior managers and directors, company web sites and email addresses, the directory also provides a 23 page alphabetical index plus a business sector and geographical market profile of the Republic of Ireland.

Each business entry in the directory contains the following information;

- The name of the most senior manager or director in the company and their job title
- The names and job title of the manager/director responsible for finance, sales, personnel, production and IT
- The company phone, fax, Company e-mail and web address (where available)
- The number of staff employed within the organisation
- The business activity of the company with the corresponding Classification code (SIC)

The directory is sorted on business sector. Entry into the directory was based on selecting Ireland's top employers (based on staff numbers employed). The information was sourced from the Irish Business Masterfile, a comprehensive marketing database of over 275,000 businesses and organisations on the Island of Ireland, as well as over 80,000 professionals. This database holds details on every type and size of business, as well as 120 fields of in-depth demographic and marketing information on each record.

To receive a copy of the directory, please complete and return (by post or fax) the order form below.

✂-- ORDER FORM --

Please supply the following;

Published 275 Page Directory	***Qty***	***Total***
The Cream of Irish Industry Commerce & Government (ISBN 1861800304) @ €149	____	______
The Cream of Northern Ireland's Industry Commerce & Government (1861800290) €149	____	______
Mailing Address Labels (Primary Contact Name)	***Qty***	***Total***
Republic of Ireland – Top 5000 @ €650	____	______
Northern Ireland – Top 5000 @ €650	____	______
Electronic Marketing Databases – All Data (No Credits or Usage Restrictions)	***Qty***	***Total***
Republic of Ireland – Top 5000 @ €950	____	______
Northern Ireland – Top 5000 @ €950	____	______
Republic of Ireland – The next 5000 largest companies @ €950	____	______
Northern Ireland – The next 5000 largest companies @ €950	____	______

Required electronic formats: Access 97 [ ] Excel 97 [ ] Dbase [ ] ASCII/CSV [ ]

Subject to Terms and Conditions. All Prices are in Euro

Sub Total	______
Delivery	€6.95
Vat @ 20%	______
Total (Inc VAT)	______

(a) I enclose a cheque made payable to IDS Media Group for €............

(b) Please debit €........... from my Credit Card .... ***Exp:*** .... /..... ***Type:*** MC/Visa/Amex

Signed: .... Name: .... Phone No: ....

Delivery Name & Address ....

....

Post to; IDS, 3 Sandyford Office Park, Blackthorn Ave, Dublin 18 ☎1800 927222 (01-2604816) **Fax** 01-2604818
Email: publishing@IDSMediaGroup.com **Home Page:** http://www.IDSMediaGroup.com

IDS Media Group
3 Sandyford Office Park
Blackthorn Avenue
Dublin 18
Ph: 01-2604818
Fx: 01-2604816

r Sirs

date Your Details

u company details are missing or are incorrect, please fill in the page below and fax it back.

pany: :
ress: :
:

:
ne: :
: :
il: :
: :
loyees: :
duct: :

ior Management & Areas of Responsibility

mary Manager: :
ance: :
es: :
keting: :
puting/IT: :
sonnel/HR: :
ining: :
duction/Ops: :
chasing: :
tionary: :
lth & Safety: :

se enter your Name ____________________

ards

ica Allen
or

FAX BACK NUMBER 01-2604818